ANNUAL REVIEW OF PHYSIOLOGY

PREFACE

The *Annual Review of Physiology* is about to have a new Editor as age termines my services. My successor is Dr. Julius Comroe, who is well known to the physiological world, particularly for his work in the field of respiration. But he is much more than an investigator: he was chosen to lead the first Teaching Workshop of the Association of American Medical Colleges which dealt with Physiology, Biochemistry, and Pharmacology; he has been for many years Director of the Cardiovascular Research Institute of the University of California, San Francisco; and of special significance to his new task, he served until very recently as Editor of *Circulation Research,* bringing new energy and efficiency to this journal's administration. We may confidently expect that under his direction, the *Annual Review of Physiology* will undergo a similar rejuvenation.

Looking back over the thirty-two challenging and enjoyable years of my work with the *Annual Review,* I am impressed by the continuity of its policies, format, and procedures. Indeed the plans which we have followed remain substantially as they were formulated by Dr. James Murray Luck, to whom the *Annual Reviews* owe a great debt of gratitude as their founder. However stable the general plan, there remain many degrees of freedom for improvement of which Dr. Comroe will make good use. He has our sympathy and encouragement.

The *Annual Review of Physiology* is losing the immediate editorial care that Joann Huddleston has given it for years, which has made the work of the editors relatively easy. She is assuming increasing supervisory duty as Assistant to the Editor-in-Chief as the family of *Annual Reviews* grows larger. Barbara Murphy has undertaken the grave task of replacing her.

Finally we again acknowledge the fine work which our printer George Banta Company has done for all these years.

VICTOR E. HALL

ERRATA

Volume 32 (1970)—Reproduction, by David T. Armstrong

page 454 line 3 : 88 *should read* 30
page 460 line 8 : concluded *should read* inferred

CONTENTS

REPRINTS

The conspicuous number (1055 to 1070) aligned in the margin with the title of each review in this volume is a key for use in the ordering of reprints.

The sale of reprints from all *Annual Reviews* volumes was initiated in July 1970. Reprints of most articles published in the *Annual Reviews of Physiology and Microbiology* from 1968 to 1970 and the *Annual Reviews of Biochemistry and Psychology* from 1961 to 1970 are now maintained in inventory.

Available reprints are priced at the uniform rate of $1 each postpaid. Payment must accompany orders less than $10. The following discounts will be given for large orders: $5–9, 10 percent; $10–$24, 20 percent; $25 and over, 30 percent. All remittances are to be made payable to Annual Reviews Inc. in US dollars. California orders are subject to sales tax. One-day service is given on items in stock.

For orders of 100 or more, any *Annual Reviews* article will be specially printed and shipped within 6 weeks. Reprints that are out of stock may also be purchased from the Institute for Scientific Information, 325 Chestnut Street, Philadelphia, Pa. 19106. Direct inquiries to the Annual Reviews Inc. reprint department.

The sale of reprints of articles published in the *Reviews* has been expanded in the belief that reprints as individual copies, as sets covering stated topics, and in quantity for classroom use will have a special appeal to students and teachers.

CATECHOLAMINE FUNCTIONS[1]

J. AXELSSON

Department of Physiology, University of Iceland
Reykjavik, Iceland

The author was invited to focus upon such aspects of his subject as particularly interested him. These must now be delimited. The term catecholamine refers to sympathomimetic amines "possessing the catechol nucleus and includes noradrenaline, adrenaline and isoprenaline" (1). The present review will be limited to the three latter. Further, the author is particularly interested in muscles, preferably unstriated ones. As for the functions of the three amines, two of them, besides being used as drugs, act as natural transmitters of information in the living control systems. A dictionary will define function as special activity or purpose. In these pages purposes will be passed over in silence. Thus the discussion will be limited to special activities of the three amines. Established functions or special activities of the catecholamines (CA) are legion, but they will be discussed only with respect to their possible effects on the mechanical activity of smooth muscles.

To offset to some degree the narrow scope of the present article, some recent reviews and monographs on several aspects of CA functions may be referred to. Reviews concerning most of these functions are to be found in the *Second Symposium on Catecholamines* (2) and the *New York Academy of Science Annual on New Adrenergic Blocking Drugs* (3). Several chapters of the latest edition of *Recent Advances in Pharmacology* (4) either are entirely devoted to CAs or contain references to important aspects of their function. A review by Himms-Hagen (5), based on no less than 806 papers, covers the function of the CAs as regulators of metabolism. Cavallito's review (6) is devoted to structure-activity relationships, Kopin's (7) to false adrenergic transmitters and Ahlquist's to "the adrenergic receptor" and "agents which block adrenergic receptors" (8, 9). The review by Bloom & Giarman is written with special reference to the central nervous system (10). So is a more recent one by Anden, Carlsson & Häggendal (11) on localization and function, storage and release of the monoamines. The effects of sympathomimetic amines on skeletal muscle are thoroughly re-

[1] Abbreviations used in this article are: CA (catecholamine); E (epinephrine); NE (norepinephrine); IP (isoproterenol); MP (membrane potential); AP (action potential); EJP (excitatory junction potential); SJP (spontaneous junction potential); ACh (acetylcholine).

viewed by Bowman & Nott (12). In my opinion, the review by Jewell & Blinks (13) on Drugs and The Mechanical Properties of Heart Muscle has a message to everyone concerned with drugs in spite of its spare treatment of the CAs themselves. The mechanism of transmission of excitation from sympathetic nerves to smooth muscle was reviewed by Burnstock & Holman (14), and several aspects of CA function in various types of smooth muscle were discussed by Somlyo & Somlyo (15, 16), Holz (17), Lundholm, Mohme-Lundholm & Svedmyr (18), and Miller & Lewis (19). A monograph by Iversen (20) is primarily concerned with the fate of norepinephrine (NE) after its release, and a review by Robison, Butcher & Sutherland (21) summarizes what is known about the effects of CAs on the intracellular levels of cyclic AMP in various tissues. Both give a lucid description of some of the most interesting developments in the CA field during the period under review. These references may satisfy the reader's curiosity where I fail to do so.

ADRENERGIC RECEPTORS

The concept of adrenergic receptors figures in everything that is said and thought about functions of the CAs. It affects the questions asked and then changes as a result of the answers obtained. In 1968 Ahlquist wrote: "By definition, the adrenergic receptor is that part of certain effector cells that allows them to detect and respond to epinephrine and related compounds. The receptor can be described only in terms of effector response to drug application" (9). Since every measured biochemical and biophysical change initiated by a drug in an effector can be considered a response of the effector to the drug in question, the choice of response is simply determined by the recording technique mastered by the investigator. The responses chosen by Ahlquist (9) and most pharmacologists to "describe" their "receptors" are, with the exception of the cardiac chronotropic effect, mechanical end responses, i.e. changes in length or tension.

Mechanical responses usually come at the end of chains of measurable biophysical events that may be independently affected in various ways by the CAs. Such a chain measured simultaneously in one and the same piece of tissue might consist, for instance, of the following: a change in membrane resistance towards ions would alter the membrane potential (MP). This in turn would change the frequency of discharge (and possibly the configuration) of action potentials (AP), and the final result would be a change of tension. The direction of the MP changes associated with the resistance changes allows some inferences about the ions involved. If, for example, an increase in MP follows a decrease in membrane resistance, it is interpreted as an increase in membrane conductance for potassium (K). Similarly, a decrease in MP recorded simultaneously with decreased resistance is often taken to indicate increased membrane conductance for sodium (Na) and possibly chloride (Cl), depending on the resting potential and Cl equilibrium potential of the tissue. The introduction of the method of simultaneous measurements of resistance and other biophysical phenomena and its successful application by Bülbring & Tomita (22–25) and Brading, Bülbring & Tomita (26, 27) has greatly advanced our understanding of CA functions in smooth muscle.

It was stated above that the mechanical response comes at the end of a long chain of biophysical events, each of which may be affected by CAs. There is also some evidence that the mechanical activity of many smooth muscles may be affected by CAs independently of this chain (28–38). Generally one may say that the CAs affect the mechanical activity of smooth muscles by changing either the pattern of electrical activity or the existing relationship between electrical and mechanical activity. Frequently the final response is determined in both ways (38). Further complications arise from the fact that the mechanical properties of smooth muscles are extremely ill defined (37, 39). Also, remember that the above interpretation of the relation between MP and ion permeabilities and other arguments of this kind used in this review are all based on the classical membrane theory, and that alternative interpretations might be offered by means of other models, e.g. the association-induction hypothesis (see Ling 40–42, and Jones 43).

These considerations suffice to make us aware of the obscurity of Ahlquist's concept of adrenergic receptors. Similar considerations have led Moran (44, 45) to introduce the concept of an operational receptor which includes all the unknown steps in the reaction from the initial interaction of drug and tissue to the final mechanical response. As our knowledge of single steps increases, the operational receptor shrinks, until it becomes equivalent to the "true receptor". The obscurity has not been diminished by the introduction of the Greek alphabet into the discussion of CA functions. The distinction between two different adrenergic receptors was primarily based on differences in potency (9, 46–48). The groups of blocking agents, usually referred to as α-adrenergic blockers and β-adrenergic blockers (45, 49–52), are also used to "classify" the effects of CAs. According to Moran (45) "the classification of adrenergic receptors in terms of responses is based upon rank orders of potency of agonists as well as selective blockade." Ahlquist (48) explains that "the terms alpha and beta were selected only because *excitatory* and *inhibitory* did not properly describe these receptors." This is true enough, indeed it is something of an understatement. Whenever the present reviewer refers to an α effect or a β effect, or otherwise appeals to the Greek alphabet, this only means that the responses in question have been so described by reputable authors.

At the receptor end of postulated causal chains, biochemists have discovered enzymic reactions initiated by CAs and have gone on from there. From the other end biophysicists are tracing the events backwards with steadily improving technique. Excellent work has been done at both ends. It is in the middle that confusion arises. Attempts at tying up the ends are still at their best only interesting speculations. Interpretations of experiments as having established or refuted causal relationships between certain biochemical and biophysical events are common, both among the experimenters themselves and among those reviewing their results. They are usually unjustified.

NOREPINEPHRINE AS A NEURAL TRANSMITTER

In their function as natural transmitters of information the CAs may be characterized as either blood-borne or neural transmitters. Even from a functional point of view this distinction appears justified, since the same CA may induce different effects depending on whether it is released from sympathetic nerve endings or reaches the effector by the blood stream. Some differences between the action of blood-borne NE and the effects of adrenergic stimulation [and most authors are now satisfied that the transmitter is NE (53)] have been demonstrated, e.g. in the human forearm vessels (54, 55) and in the splanchnic vessels and the vascular bed of hindlimb skeletal muscle of dogs (56). These have been attributed to different distribution of the two receptor types in the effector.

Our knowledge of the functions of NE as a neural transmitter has been greatly increased in extent as well as detail by the introduction and continuing development and refinement of various experimental techniques, such as the fluorescent histochemical method for demonstrating monoamines (57–67). The methodologically minded reader is referred to the monograph by Iversen (20) and the recent critical review by Gershon (53) on the development of methods for identification of neurotransmitters to smooth muscles. The fluorescence method reveals the overall distribution and density of the innervations (68–73). Its successful application to all kinds of smooth muscle is extensively reviewed by Burnstock (74), while Speden (75) restricts his account of NE innervation to blood vessels. Electronmicroscopic studies (76–82) have revealed the details of the nerve muscle relationship, and development of the histochemical methods for localization of CAs at electronmicroscopic level (83, 84) has still further improved the picture. A recent review by Geffen & Livett (85) discusses the origin, functions, and fate of vesicles in sympathetic neurons. Combination of these methods with the estimation of the quantities of NE present in tissues and released from nerves (86–91) has given information on the NE content, distribution, and transport in sympathetically innervated organs. Finally, employment of electrophysiological technique has provided information about some of the biophysical changes initiated by the transmitter in the postsynaptic membrane of various types of smooth muscle (92–120), and their relation to the mechanical end effects (11, 75, 109, 114).

Release and uptake.—The mechanism of release of CAs will be discussed very briefly.

Two suggestions have been put forward by De Robertis & Vaz Ferreira (121). According to one, the CAs would pass out of the vesicles to the cytoplasm and leave the nerve by diffusion; the vesicle membrane would be left behind. The other suggestion is that the chromaffin granule would move through the cytoplasm to the plasma membrane where it would extrude its contents by exocytosis.

Recently, immunological techniques have been used to show that two protein components of the noradrenergic vesicles (chromogranin A and dopamine β-hydroxylase) accompany the release of NE from perfused spleen during nerve stimulation (122, 123). This finding provides evidence that release of the vesicle contents does indeed occur by a process of exocytosis.

Burn & Rand (124) have suggested that acetylcholine (ACh) is essential for the release of NE from adrenergic fibers. This so-called cholinergic-link hypothesis has been critically reviewed (125) and it is not proposed to discuss it fully. However, the writer would like to call attention to the following recent papers. Burn & Malik showed that the response of the rat mesenteric arteries to sympathetic stimulation is greatly increased in the presence of physostigmine, neostigmine, or DEP when the frequency of stimulation is as low as 1/sec. The increase becomes less as the frequency rises and no increase is seen at a frequency of 6/sec (126). Botulinum toxin, which is known to prevent release of ACh from cholinergic terminals, blocks the response to postganglionic sympathetic stimulation in a number of tissues (127). Nerve impulses are not an essential feature of the action of ACh in releasing NE, since twice as much NE is released by a concentration of ACh which completely depolarizes the nerve as is released by a lower concentration which causes continuous antidromic firing. Moreover tetrodotoxin (10^{-8} M) abolishes the asynchronous discharges caused by ACh but does not affect the release of NE by ACh (128).

Almost 40 years ago, Burn (129, 130) suggested that CAs from the blood might be taken up by sympathetic endings in blood vessels. Brown & Gillespie (131) measured transmitter overflows from the spleen and showed that enzymic degradation was apparently not the means of physiological inactivation. Later, Macmillan (132) and Paton (133) suggested that NE released by the nerves might be reincorporated. Direct evidence for neural uptake of exogenous NE was obtained by the fluorescent histochemical method, by radioautography, and by a combination of both (134). The uptake of CAs into postganglionic sympathetic neurons is an active process that can occur against concentration gradients as high as 10,000:1 (20). Blakeley, Brown & Geffen (135) have shown that the reuptake of NE is of physiological importance. Reuptake appears to be the principal mechanism of transmitter inactivation, as well as being essential for the maintenance of NE stores. This reuptake process is probably identical with Iversen's "uptake₁" (20). The active uptake mechanisms must interfere with the actions of the blood-borne CAs. All estimations of the effects or potency of directly applied CAs must be affected by uptake, unless precautions are taken to inhibit active uptake (20). Another uptake mechanism (uptake₂) operating in sympathetically innervated tissue was distinguished by Iversen (136). Avakian & Gillespie (137) used histochemical methods to prove that it represented an uptake of NE into muscle. Iversen & Langer (138) have discussed the role of uptake$_2$ in the extraneuronal metabolism of CAs. They have suggested that uptake$_2$ may be a major mechanism for CA inactivation in sparsely innervated tissues such as vascular smooth muscle.

Many of the substances which block adrenergic receptors also block CA uptake (139). Consequently a blocking agent may also increase the amount of transmitter available at the receptors. Such processes can lead to difficulties in interpreting experimental results. Langer (140) has investigated the metabolism of ^{3}H-NE released by nerves and has discussed how this is modified by the blocking of receptors which interferes with neuronal and extraneuronal uptake processes. The emergence of extraneuronal uptake into muscle cells as a process of physiological important raises the possibility that we may have to consider intracellular as well as surface receptors for CAs.

Effects on the vas deferens.—The adrenergic innervation of the vas deferens is dense. It is even suggested that every cell may receive individual innervation. There are, however, considerable differences between species in this respect (74, 82, 141). In the vas deferens, the width of the synaptic cleft is only of the order of 200 Å. Transmitter release causes graded depolarizations, i.e. excitatory junctions potentials (EJPs), and these may be recorded in every cell. The tissue is therefore highly suitable for investigation of the postsynaptic effects of adrenergic nerve stimulation, and it has been more extensively studied in that respect than any other smooth muscle.

Spontaneously occurring junction potentials (SJPs) have been recorded from the vas deferens of guinea pig, rat, and mouse (98). Their amplitude varies from 20 mV to less than 1 mV (98), and Holman (106) is satisfied that, by analogy with skeletal neuromuscular junctions, the "excitatory SJPs are due to the spontaneous release of transmitter from axon varicosities in a packaged manner." In cells with low resting potential, SJPs may occasionally initiate action potentials (APs) and contraction (106). However, EJPs of an amplitude around 30 mV are usually needed to initiate APs. Such EJPs are obtained by nerve stimulation. In the mouse and rat single stimuli may be sufficient; in the guinea pig repeated stimulation with summation and facilitation may be required.

α-Adrenergic blockers abolish the excitatory responses of the vas deferens to nerve stimulation only in very high concentrations. This has raised doubts about NE being the transmitter. All other methods for identifying the transmitter however indicate that it is NE, and Holman (106) points out that the high density of synapses in this tissue might for short periods allow local concentration of NE too high to be overcome by the inhibitor. Assuming that the excitatory effects of nerve stimulation are mediated by α-receptors, the underlying ionic mechanisms remain to be revealed. Although it is generally believed that the α-excitatory effects in different tissues involve increased conductance for cations, the only evidence known to the author is in fact obtained from the vas deferens. It indicates that the action of the transmitter is similar to that of ACh at the skeletal neuromuscular junction (106, 117).

Effects on intestinal motility.—Our ideas about the adrenergic innervation of the gastrointestinal tract are changing. The old belief that sympathetic nerves terminate on the intestinal muscle layers and that the inhibitory function of neuronal NE is mediated by a direct action of the transmitter on the muscle cells is now questioned. Studies with the fluorescent histochemical method (142–146) indicate that the adrenergic innervation of the intestines may largely be confined to NE terminals impinging on ganglion cells in both Auerbach's and Meissner's plexuses. Thus the inhibitory effects of adrenergic nerves on intestinal motility may to a great extent occur via the myenteric ganglia and postganglionic cholinergic fibers (147–149). The hypothesis that parasympathetic nervous activity is under sympathetic control gained support from the findings of Paton & Vizi (150) and Kosterlitz, Lydon & Watt (151) that NE as well as E greatly reduces the ACh release from the myenteric plexus of the guinea pig ileum. The recent experiments of Crowcroft, Holman & Szurszewski (152) have shown that repetitive stimulation of the extrinsic nerves of the guinea pig distal colon reduces or temporarily abolishes the continuous electrical activity of enteric ganglion cells. This might be due to interference with either conduction in or release of transmitter from cholinergic nerves (149, 153).

The function of the CAs as inhibitory modulators of ganglionic transmission is thought to be mediated by α receptors situated on the cholinergic neurons (149, 152, 154, 155). However, a deeper understanding of the mechanisms involved is still missing. The acceptance of control of cholinergic nerves as one function of CAs in the intestine does not exclude the possibility that neuronal NE has also a direct inhibitory action on intestinal smooth muscle cells. The transmitter may reach the adjoining muscle by diffusion from nerve endings in the myenteric plexus (156).

Electrophysiological studies of the effects of sympathetic nerve stimulation on intestinal smooth muscle show that single stimuli do not cause hyperpolarization (101, 112). Further, the membrane potential only increases by 10–20 mV, no matter how intense and prolonged the stimulation. This contrasts with the effects of stimulation of unknown inhibitory neurons. Single stimuli hyperpolarize the muscle by as much as 50 mV. This response is unaffected by sympathetic blocking drugs (157–159). During adrenergic nerve stimulation Bennett et al (112) detected hyperpolarization in pacemaker cells only and concluded that abolition of action potentials in "driven regions" is due to suppression of spontaneous spike discharge in "pacemaker" regions. Holman (106) argues that since the effects of adrenergic nerve stimulation on the guinea pig taenia coli are similar to the inhibitory action of exogenous NE, it is "reasonable to expect that both sources of norepinephrine might have the same effect on membrane properties." Bülbring & Tomita (22, 24) showed that those effects of exogenous NE that were blocked by α-adrenergic blockers in taenia coli were probably due to increased conductance towards both K and Cl. In view of the relatively small hyperpolarization caused by adrenergic nerve stimulation in the taenia coli, Holman suggests that it too might be the consequence of increased conductance for both K and Cl. The argument rests on the fact that while the K equilibrium potential for the taenia coli is about 90 mV, the equilibrium potential for Cl is low and probably less than the resting MP (160). Thus, under the influence of NE released from the nerve terminals, the membrane potential might be "clamped somewhere between E_K and E_{Cl}". In view of this argument the hyperpolarization in response to sympathetic nerve stimulation might be classified as an α effect.

Effects on vascular smooth muscles.—In vascular musculature there is great variation in innervation, from the umbilical artery and vein apparently without innervation, to the arteries in rabbit ear and mesentery possessing a dense nerve plexus (74). A feature common to most vascular smooth muscle is, however, that innervation is confined to the outside of the media (70, 71). Exceptions where nerves are present within the media are sheep carotid artery (114), cutaneous veins (161), and renal vein and artery (74). Further, in most blood vessels the closest contacts between nerve and muscle membranes are of the order of 1000 Å; Devine (162) found that the width of the synaptic cleft in small mesenteric arteries and intestinal arterioles varied from 1000 to 10,000 Å.

Thus the pattern of vascular innervation is very different from that of the vas deferens. Structural differences have functional consequences. For example, diffusion distances for the neural transmitter must be long. Many factors besides distance influence the diffusion and thus the effectiveness of the released transmitter in depolarizing the effector cell membranes. Physical factors, such as the volume of diffusion, the diffusion coefficient of NE in vascular tissue, and the cross-sectional area of diffusion, are not known (75). The concentration gradient is determined by the quantity of transmitter released and also by the amount taken up by the nerve terminals or inactivated by other means (20, 163, 164). These considerations have raised doubts about the effectiveness of the adrenergic innervation of vascular smooth muscle. Histochemical methods, however, have revealed that NE may diffuse through the media during repetitive stimulation (165). No SJPs have been observed, but in four types of artery a single stimulus to an adrenergic nerve initiated discrete depolarizations in the outermost cells (108, 109). Speden (75) argues that if the criterion of an effective transmission is that a single nerve stimulus should produce a discrete depolarization of a single cell membrane, then even the most distant cells in these arteries are effectively innervated.

Steedman (115) found that the frequency of slow potential fluctuations and of APs in mesenteric arteries increased during adrenergic nerve stimulation, and Keatinge (114) made a similar observation in the common carotid artery of sheep. There are arteries, however, in which nerve stimulation appears to mediate contraction either without any potential changes or with EJPs of small amplitude that do not initiate APs (109, 111, 166, 167). In one and the same artery the MP at the time of nerve stimulation may determine the mode of activation (75). Speden (108, 109) found that EJPs in various arteries in response to repetitive nerve stimulation summate if the frequency of stimulation is 2/sec or faster. The normal physiological discharge rate in vasoconstrictor nerves appears to be similar (75, 168). Thus summation of transmitter action seems likely to occur during maintenance of normal blood pressure (75). In veins adrenergic nerve stimulation increases tension. This effect is mediated by α receptors (169). Holman et al (120) detected no depolarization in response to single stimuli, but during repetitive stimulation the frequency of spike discharge increased with increasing frequency of stimulation. The effect outlasted the duration of stimulation. It appears therefore that stimulation may initiate vasoconstriction whether accompanied by potential changes or not. There is no direct evidence on the ionic mechanisms involved.

Effects on uterine smooth muscle.—More than 60 years ago Dale (170) found that stimulation of the hypogastric nerve of the cat relaxed the virgin uterus, contracted the early pregnant uterus, and had a diphasic effect on the late pregnant uterus. Nevertheless, Vogt (171) assures us that the transmitter liberated remains the same throughout pregnancy. In the nonpregnant (estrogen-dominated) rabbit, however, stimulation of the hypogastric nerve causes contraction, and there is no indication that the response is not mediated by NE (172, 173). Miller & Marshall (174) confirmed and extended these results, and found that in the progesterone-dominated rat uterus, nerve stimulation inhibited spontaneous contractions. The contractions of the estrogen-dominated uterus were abolished by an α blocker, the relaxations in the progesterone-dominated one by a β blocker. Thus it appears that in the uterus the α and β receptors come and go according to the hormonal state of the animal. Further, if each receptor type is taken to mediate the same end effect in all species, the "dominance" of α and β, depending on hormonal state, varies from species to species.

Catecholamines as Circulating Hormones and Drugs

Effects on the vas deferens.—Holman (105) found that exogenous NE contracts the vas deferens, but only in high concentration. The vas deferens is densely innervated (80, 141); the effect on it of exogenous NE is potentiated and prolonged by drugs that inhibit the uptake mechanism (105). Holman (106) has therefore put forward the hypothesis "that the sensitivity of a smooth muscle to exogenous transmitter is inversely related to the density of its innervation." In the same article Holman (106) refers to a paper by Holman & Jowett (107) suggesting the existence of inhibitory β receptors in the vas deferens. The β receptors would mediate "stabilization of the cell membrane" and thus explain the depression of transmission caused by NE in low concentrations. The relative insensitivity of the vas deferens towards directly applied NE may account for the paucity of literature on the effects of exogenous CAs on this muscle. There is no evidence on the ionic mechanisms involved, other than that already mentioned on the EJPs.

Effects on intestinal smooth muscle.—According to Ahlquist's criteria both α and β receptors mediate inhibition in the rabbit and canine ileum (175–177) and in human and guinea pig taenia coli (22, 24, 178–181). Jenkinson & Morton (180) suggested that intestinal smooth muscle was "probably unique in that activation of both alpha and beta receptors cause the same end effect, which is relaxation." This is doubtful. For example, Maengwyn-Davis (cited by Hornbrook 182) has reported that cat bronchial muscle relaxes after both alpha and beta stimulation. Further, α receptors in the intestinal sphincters behave inconsistently, and in the terminal ileum they mediate excitation (170, 183). The same holds for the esophagus and stomach (184–186). In other parts of the ileum, α receptors are "involved in the inhibition of the myogenic pendular movements whether by sympathetic nerve stimulation or by administered catecholamines" (149). This inhibition in the circular muscle is mediated primarily by α receptors and in the longitudinal muscle by β receptors (149). Thus inhibition of intestinal motility by exogenous CAs is mediated by β receptors as well as some α receptors.

Recently Bülbring & Tomita (22, 24) have shown that the α-inhibitory effect in normally polarized taenia coli of the guinea pig was due to a block of spontaneous AP discharge caused by hyperpolarization of the cell membrane; the hyperpolarization in turn is the consequence of decreased membrane resistance towards both K and Cl. Some years earlier Jenkinson & Morton (180, 181, 187, 188) employed a tracer technique to show that CAs cause increase in K permeability in the depolarized taenia coli. This effect is mediated by α receptors. It thus appears that in the taenia coli, the α receptor may initiate different chains of events, depending on the MP or the external concentration of K.

In a previous volume of the *Annual Review of Physiology* Rothstein (189), reviewing membrane phenomena, refers to these experiments of Jenkinson & Morton (180) as having shown that "the electrical effects of norepinephrine but not the effects on tension, can be explained by the increased passive permeability to potassium". However, Jenkinson & Morton (180, 187) performed their experiments on a depolarized muscle and no electrical activity was observed. In a normally polarized muscle (in which an effect on electrical activity could have been observed) an increase in K permeability would certainly have explained both "the electrical effects" and "the effects on tension". In the depolarized taenia coli, however, Jenkinson & Morton found an additional effect of CAs, a relaxation of the contracture tension, which was unrelated to the increase in K conductance. This effect is mediated by β receptors.

In the normally polarized taenia coli, a combination of CAs with β receptors results in suppression of generator potentials without detectable change in MP or membrane resistance (24). If, by analogy with heart muscle, the diastolic or pacemaker potential is caused by a spontaneous decrease in K conductance, it would be effectively suppressed by an increase in K conductance. A working hypothesis of Brading, Bülbring & Tomita (26) postulates that in the taenia coli, calcium (Ca), strategically situated at inner and outer membrane sites, independently controls membrane conductance towards K and Na respectively. Increased Ca at inner sites increases K conductance. Decreased Ca at outer sites increases Na conductance (190). The presence of Ca in the bathing solution is essential for the action of the CAs (25, 191), and the effects of raising the external concentration of Ca on MP and membrane resistance strongly resemble those of E (22, 25, 27, 192).

We now apprehend the outline of what might be called the Ca hypothesis of CA action. It postulates that both α and β stimulation cause increased Ca binding to inner membrane sites, but to very different degrees. The β-receptor stimulation is just sufficient to maintain the resting state since no increase in membrane conductance or potential is recorded, while α stimulation causes marked increase in both. Accordingly, the β effect in normally polarized taenia coli is observed when the spontaneous decrease in K conductance, underlying the generator potential, is opposed in the presence of CA because of a delayed dissociation of Ca from K conductance controlling inner sites (25, 193).

In the depolarized muscle, changes in K conductance are without effect on the contracture tension (181). It is possible, however, that the causal chains initiated by the β receptors, resulting in relaxation of depolarized as well as polarized muscle, may be identical up to a point. By analogy with striated muscle, but without direct evidence, it is assumed that relaxation in smooth muscle depends on an active transport of activator Ca away from the contractile elements. Because of shortage of intracellular structures paralleling those of striated muscle, this process, if accelerated as a consequence of a β-receptor stimulation, might result in sufficient accumulation of Ca at the plasma membrane to prevent the spontaneous decrease in K conductance and thereby the development of generator potentials. Relaxation would result from the lowering of the Ca concentration at the actin-myosin complex. The last common step in the β action in polarized and depolarized taenia coli would thus be a redistribution of Ca between cell compartments.

In the course of time many hypotheses have been put forward to explain the hyperpolarization and cessation of AP discharge caused by CAs in intestinal smooth muscle: stimulation of an electrogenic Na pump (194, 195), accumulation of indiffusible inorganic anions (196), increase in lactic acid production (197), reduction in Na conductance (198, 199), a selective increase in K conductance (187), to mention a few. In normal solution the effects of CAs on K efflux are variable and unconvincing (200, 201). Setekleiv (202) presents data showing that the changes in K efflux in response to E may be in either direction and are apparently related to the external concentration of K. In the normally polarized taenia coli direct demonstration of increased K efflux is hampered by its own consequences, i.e. changes in the frequency of discharge of AP and in MP. Setekleiv (203) argues that the rise in MP may oppose and obscure the eventual increase in K efflux produced by E in normal solution and the consequent reduction in the frequency of APs would tend to do the same (180). Jenkinson & Morton (180) demonstrated that the increase in K efflux in response to E in normal solution was more obvious when spontaneous activity had been abolished by lowering the temperature than when the muscles were spontaneously active before drug application.

Bülbring & Kuriyama (191, 204) concluded that the low MP of taenia coli was due to high Na permeability resulting from poor Ca fixation at the cell membrane. Epinephrine might act by increasing Ca fixation, thus reducing Na permeability and stabilizing the membrane. In spite of the recent evidence on changes in K and Cl conductance, Holman (106) still retains a feeling for the old suggestion that the inhibitory effects of the CAs might involve a stimulation of an ionic pump. She argues that "if Ca as well as Na ions were handled by such a pump, an increase in its activity could lead to membrane stabilization as the result of an increase in the Ca concentration immediately outside the cell membrane." She thus combines the ideas of pump stimulation and decreased Na conductance. According to the recent ideas of Bülbring and her associates, an increase in intracellular Ca would be expected to increase K conductance and thereby the MP. It is thus suggested that opposite effects on the amount of intracellular Ca might serve the same end: abolition of AP discharge and consequent relaxation. Here considerable flexibility of thought is called for.

Setekleiv (202), reviewing experiments designed to determine the effect of CAs on Na permeability, finds all results obtained so far inconclusive. To establish conductance changes towards K and Cl is certainly not the last word. Their causes have to be traced and there some of the older hypotheses, in a modified form, may prove useful. Different mechanisms may operate in parallel and contribute to the final effect in different degrees, depending on the experimental conditions.

Effects on vascular smooth muscle.—Deviations from the classical picture of mechanical activation are as prominent in the response to exogenous CAs as during nerve stimulation. Contractions of arteries in response to E and NE may be accompanied by an increase in electrical activity, by a slow sustained depolarization, or by a hyperpolarization, or may occur without any potential change (111, 115, 205–207). There are great differences in the electrical responses of isolated and intact arteries to CAs. In isolated arteries high concentrations are usually needed to produce depolarization. Depolarized arteries contract in response to CAs without a detectable change in MP (29, 167, 205, 208). Keatinge found that E in the presence of an α blocker relaxed the contracture tension of depolarized arteries (206). In general, depolarized arteries appear to maintain their normal specificity and sensitivity to vasoactive agents (75).

In the rat and rabbit portal vein and the rabbit anterior mesenteric vein, NE causes depolarization and increases the frequency of discharge of APs and consequently tension (32–34, 118, 120). Further, in normally polarized veins NE causes a change in the relationship between the electrical and mechanical activity (32–34, 37, 209). In the presence of NE, an AP of a given size and shape appears to initiate greater tension than would be expected from the recordings of the electrical activity as potential changes. This has recently been quantitatively established (38). In the same veins, depolarized by high K solutions, NE causes an increase in tension without a change in MP (32–34). This effect is mediated by α receptors. In these veins E, too, causes depolarization and increases the frequency of AP discharge (210, 211).

In the portal vein isoproterenol (IP) increases the frequency of the bursts of APs but simultaneously reduces the number of APs within a burst and consequently decreases tension. IP also changes the relationship between electrical and mechanical activity, but in the opposite way to NE. In the presence of IP, an AP of a given size and shape gives less tension than would be predicted from the potential change recordings. IP relaxes the contracture tension maintained by the depolarized vein and this effect might, according to Ahlquist's criteria, be characterized as a β effect. There is a striking similarity between all the described effects of IP and the effects of reducing the concentration of extracellular Ca (33, 34).

Considerable information is available on changes in MP, in the pattern of electrical activity, and in the relationship between electrical and mechanical activity constituting the response of vascular smooth muscle to CAs. The underlying ionic mechanisms, however, are still to be revealed. The α-excitatory effect is assumed, without evidence, to involve increased conductance for cations. The suggestion has been ventured that here also the CA effects may be explained by an interference with the various functions of Ca (38). In the portal vein Axelsson et al (33, 209) showed that NE restores discharge of APs and tension for a short while when both are abolished in Ca-free solution. Additional evidence indicates that NE stimulates the release of intracellularly stored Ca, but in Ca-deficient solution this Ca is soon lost (38). If we assume that NE occupies extracellular binding sites for Ca and releases inactive or bound Ca from intracellular stores, then depolarization and increased frequency of discharge would occur as a consequence of the increased Na conductance; at the same time there would be a gradual increase in K conductance as Ca accumulated at inner membrane sites because of increasing intracellular Ca. This process would tend to counteract the electrical excitation. On the other hand the relationship between electrical and mechanical activity would be expected to continue to change in favor of the mechanical. This response pattern was revealed by the quantitative analysis of the electrical and mechanical responses of the rat portal vein to NE (38).

Possibly the Ca hypothesis contains a clue to the nature of automaticity and its different patterns in different tissues. The writer of the next review on this subject will, no doubt, be happy to inform you how unfounded this optimism was. Thus, in vascular smooth muscle the α receptors may mediate increase in tension independently of potential changes and regardless of the MP at the time of drug application. This may be achieved by increasing intracellular free Ca. An increase in tension simultaneous with hyperpolarization, as observed by Shibata & Briggs (207), could be explained by this hypothesis if it was assumed that occupation of extracellular Ca sites did not occur.

Effects on uterine muscle.—The effects of exogenous CAs on this tissue are no less of a puzzle than those of adrenergic nerve stimulation. It used to be assumed that E relaxed the rat uterus independently of its hormonal state. However, in the presence of β blockers E may cause a contraction and this effect is abolished by α blockers (184, 212–214). Further studies by Marshall (215) revealed that the effects of exogenous NE in the rat depended on the hormonal state of the uterus. Uteri from ovariectomized rats which had been treated with estrogen responded to NE by contraction which was converted to relaxation by an α blocker. If the rats were treated with a combination of estrogen and progesterone the response to NE was relaxation; in the presence of a β blocker the relaxation was converted to contraction. Similarly during early and midpregnancy NE generally caused relaxation. On the basis of these experiments, Marshall (215) suggested that in the rat estrogen increases the sensitivity of α receptors to CAs. This means that intrinsic properties of receptors may change with experimental conditions. However, in some other species, where α receptors mediate the same end effect as in the rat, estrogen would appear to have just the opposite effects on receptor sensitivity.

The MP of the nonpregnant uterus is low (35–40 mV). During pregnancy it increases (60–65 mV) and approaches the calculated K-equilibrium potential (70–80 mV). As the ionic content of the uterus of various species remains constant throughout pregnancy (except in the cat where the intracellular Cl content is increased), the increase in MP is probably caused by an increase in the K conductance (216–218). As described above, Bülbring & Tomita (22) showed that the α-inhibitory effect of E on the guinea pig taenia coli was due to increased K and Cl conductances. If a similar mechanism operates in cat uterine muscle, one might expect the increase in K conductance to determine the MP change in the virgin uterus, and hyperpolarization would result. In the pregnant uterus, however, the K conductance is already high, and the effect on Cl conductance might therefore predominate and result in depolarization (219). Different end effects would be obtained with E, although the receptor and several of the initial steps were the same. This argument rests on the assumption that in the pregnant cat uterus the Cl equilibrium potential is lower than the resting potential.

But Adam was not to stay in paradise. In the uterus there are two types of adrenergic receptors, "one for uterine stimulation and one for inhibition" (220). Miller (220) has accumulated evidence that is "consistent with the hypotheses that uterine stimulation is mediated by the alpha receptor, and inhibition by the beta receptor." Unfortunately, for the line of thought developed above, he reports that the two effects of E on the cat uterus are blocked by different blocking agents.

The depolarized uterine muscle is relaxed by CAs (28, 30, 32, 221). The effect is mediated by β receptors, and Schild (30, 31) suggests that the mechanism behind it involves prevention of the entry of external Ca, activation of a Ca-accumulating mechanism, or a combination of both. Schild supposes that the same mechanism operates to relax the normally polarized uterus. An accumulation of intracellular Ca at the cell membrane would, according to the Ca hypothesis of CA action, lead to hyperpolarization and relaxation. It is assumed by Marshall (222) and Abe (219) that the inhibitory effects of E in polarized uterine muscle involve increased Ca binding at the membrane.

Effects on other types of muscle.—Besides the effects described, CAs cause retraction of the third eyelid and contraction of dilator muscle of the pupil, seminal vesicles, and splenic smooth muscle. These effects are associated with the α-adrenergic receptor (9, 18). The β receptor is associated with relaxation of bronchial and tracheal smooth muscle and coronary vessels, with increased frequency of APs in the heart, and with increased myocardial force developed per AP (9, 18).

A short summary.—Stimulation of α receptors induces depolarization, increased frequency of APs, and contraction, but also hyperpolarization, decreased frequency of discharge, and relaxation. Within the same tissue α receptors may mediate all these effects. In one piece of tissue they may mediate different permeability changes, depending on MP and other factors. In polarized muscles α stimulation may increase the force developed per AP, and in depolarized muscles either leave tension unaffected or increase it.

Stimulation of β receptors may, in polarized muscles, induce decrease or

increase in the frequency of AP discharge with following mechanical consequences. The same receptors mediate both a decrease and an increase in the
force developed per AP. In depolarized muscles they mediate relaxation.

Ahlquist (48) was certainly justified when he wrote that "excitatory and
inhibitory did not properly describe these receptors."

This annoying complexity has led some authors to postulate an increased
number of receptor types. According to Robison, Butcher & Sutherland
(21) one has now come to the recognition "that alpha receptors and beta
receptors must each constitute a class or family of receptors." This is probably what is tactfully referred to by Paton & Payne (1) as "a further
though somewhat unprofitable multiplication of postulated receptors." The
author has no delusions that extensive use of the Greek alphabet will promote understanding of CA functions. Speaking of the use and abuse of
Greek, one is reminded of Moran's (45) warning against "the circular reasoning in which we indulge". Moran substantiates his warning by the following example: "We now characterize an effect which is blocked by a beta
adrenergic blocking drug as one subserved by the beta adrenergic receptor
because it is blocked, and we classify a new drug as a beta adrenergic blocking drug because it blocks an effect we have a priori called a beta effect,
perhaps on the basis of being blocked by an older established beta adrenergic blocking drug".

Impressed by the lack of consistency in the end responses induced by a
given receptor type in different tissues of the same species as well as in the
same tissues between species, and even within the same tissue and species,
some authors have concluded that "the properties of these receptors may
change" (21). Although the mechanical end responses may change, the necessity of postulating change in the receptor is doubtful. Marshall & Vaughan
Williams (223) observed that ACh initiated contractions in atria that
had ceased to beat at low temperature. It is well known that ACh normally
slows the heart rate by increasing K conductance (224). Marshall (225)
explains the paradox by showing that cooling lowered the MP until APs
were no longer propagated. ACh then restored activity by repolarizing. The
same mechanism, presumably initiated by the same receptor, may thus produce entirely different end effects. Similar observations have been made
with E during exposure of taenia coli to glucose-free solution (226). Under
the same circumstances E may increase the tension development at the same
time as it decreases the frequency of discharge (227).

The chains of events initiated by the contact with the same receptor may
be several, even opposing each other. For example, increased free intracellular Ca might primarily increase tension development, but could also abolish spike discharge and thereby tension by binding at membrane sites. Increased supply of metabolic energy might increase mechanical force, but
could also be utilized to stabilize the membrane and thus abolish spike discharge and tension. Different experimental variables may interfere at vari-

ous stages and thus change the impact of the various processes on the end response.

We should follow Ahlquist's (48) advice and "keep in mind that invoking a receptor mechanism does not explain the real nature of the interaction between a tissue and a drug." Ahlquist continues: "When better knowledge of a receptor is obtained, for example, the exact identification of the enzyme or enzyme system involved, the need for receptor vanishes" (48). Many laboratories are now working towards the elimination of that need.

Enzymes replacing Greek letters.—At the "receptor end" biochemists have not only revealed several enzymic reactions that may be steps in causal chains initiated by CAs, but have also contributed constructively to the discussion about CA functions by offering us an enzyme for a Greek letter.

Since their discovery of adenosine 3′,5′-monophosphate (cyclic AMP) (228) Sutherland and his fellow workers have accumulated impressive evidence about the role played by this nucleotide in the response of various tissues to CAs. Many other workers have made valuable contributions and it appears that wherever one has troubled to look, CAs interfere with the level of intracellular cyclic AMP (21). This was confirmed for smooth muscle by Bueding et al (229), Szego & Davis (230), and Dopps & Robison (231).

Sutherland, Rall & Menon (232) showed that cyclic AMP is formed from adenosine triphosphate (ATP) in a reaction which requires magnesium (Mg), and the enzyme or enzyme system that catalyzes this reaction was named adenyl cyclase. Increased levels of intracellular cyclic AMP are believed to result from β-receptor stimulation. The argument rests on the classical criteria of agonist potency and selective blockade; Robison, Butcher & Sutherland (233) confirm that the effects of CAs on cyclic AMP accumulation are inhibited by β blockers and that the order of potency for stimulation agrees with the definition of a β effect. In 1967 the same authors, summarizing the results of previous studies, found it "likely that in most and perhaps all tissues the beta receptor and adenyl cyclase are the same". At the time, the claim of having "identified the beta adrenergic receptor as adenyl cyclase" (234) met with some criticism. Nickerson (cited by Cotton 234) pointed out that what had been shown was only "a correlation between changes in adenyl cyclase activity and the actions of various agonists and antagonists on beta receptors".

In 1970 Robison et al (21) maintained their view that "many and perhaps all of the effects associated with adrenergic β receptors are mediated by an increase in the intracellular level of cyclic AMP". They conclude that "there is every reason to believe that the adrenergic β receptor is an integral part of the adenyl cyclase system". They assure us that "most of the available evidence supports this hypothesis, and there is no evidence which is incompatible with it". Observations compatible with their claim are that in skeletal muscle and in mammalian heart muscle of all species studied,

CAs increase the level of cyclic AMP by an interaction with β receptors (21, 235–237). Incidentally, these authors (21) suggest that E and glucagon stimulate "the same adenyl cyclase" in heart but "by way of a different set of receptors". This implies either that the claimed identification of the β receptor with adenyl cyclase is abandoned, or else that other receptors stimulating β receptors are now postulated. But the question of identity is in this case semantic.

Robison, Butcher & Sutherland (21) are not satisfied with having unmasked the β receptors but propose that "all α-receptor effects are mediated by a decrease in the intracellular level of cyclic AMP" (238). The idea is based on the considerable overlap between effects associated with a fall in cyclic AMP and those mediated by α receptors (21). The α and β receptors might then represent separate sites on the adenyl cyclase system mediating respectively inhibition and stimulation of that enzyme. Robison, Butcher & Sutherland (21) find it "attractive to suppose that all of the physiologically important effects of the CAs result from either an increase or a decrease in the level of cyclic AMP in one or more cellular compartments". I find the idea attractive enough but as yet unsubstantiated.

Other candidates for the α receptor have been nominated. At an early stage Belleau (239) proposed that ATP might form an integral part of the adrenergic receptor surface and Bloom & Goldman (240) conceived the formation of a CA-ATP complex, whereby "an ATPase-like activity would be catalysed at the alpha receptor level" (241). Belleau's (241) candidate is the Na-activated transport ATPase system of the cell membrane, and while the adenyl cyclase is Mg-dependent, the α-receptor membrane ATPase requires Ca. The attempts to integrate Ca into the primary receptor site are most interesting. α-Receptor activation by CAs could be cocatalytic with that of Ca. This would explain why their effects are additive. Activation of the α receptor is supposed to increase free intracellular Ca, which in turn catalyzes a number of actions. The general ideas of the linkage of CAs and Ca put forward by Belleau (241) are supported by later findings (242).

There is still another suggestion as to the chemical nature of an adrenergic receptor. Honig & Stam (243) advanced the idea that the "adrenergic inotropic receptor" in the heart is intracellular, the actomyosin system itself. The receptor mediating this positive inotropic effect (a change in the normal relationship between the electrical and mechanical activity in that muscle) is normally thought to be a β receptor. Recently, however, Govier (244) claimed that a part of these effects was mediated by α receptors. Honig & Stam (243) performed their experiments on isolated myofibrils and found that CAs stimulated ATPase activity and the contractile responses of the cardiac actomyosin. They proposed that the rate of utilization of ATP by actomyosin is increased by CAs.

Dresel (245) discussed the ideas put forward by Belleau and concluded that Belleau's attempts to assign a chemical structure to a receptor "should not be dismissed as premature". He continues: "it shows the pharmacologist that sooner or later he will have to face up to the chemical basis of this nebulous concept of a receptor". There is no doubt that Belleau's "attempts" have reached maturity (246–249). The stereochemical models which have been offered represent the closest approach yet towards the materialization of α and β receptors (240, 241, 250, 251).

The concept of receptor is changing. Moran's (45) operational receptor referred to earlier may, ignorance permitting, include all steps of the reaction from the first interaction of drug and tissue to the mechanical end effect. This has consequences for our interpretation of the action of adrenergic α and β blockers. By definition, their site of blockade is the operational receptor which may, in the present state of our knowledge, include the entire sequences of reaction steps (45). A receptor has been recently defined as "a pattern of forces" interacting with another pattern of forces represented by the CA molecule. The interaction of hormone with receptor leads to "some kind of conformational perturbation" (241, 252) resulting in an alteration in the catalytic activity of adenyl cyclase (238).

It may be questioned whether we are much better off with adenyl cyclase instead of the letter β, and how much information is conveyed by the statement that increased levels of intracellular cyclic AMP "mediate" all the different effects associated with adrenergic β receptors.

Probably the best known function of cyclic AMP is the stimulation of phosphorylase activation in skeletal muscle (253). This involves a stimulation of a protein kinase (253–255) which in the presence of ATP and Mg catalyzes the activation of phosphorylase b kinase. The active form then catalyzes the conversion of phosphorylase b to active phosphorylase a, which in turn catalyzes the breakdown of glycogen. The phosphorylase b kinase reaction requires Ca in addition to ATP and Mg. In at least some smooth muscles the effects of cyclic AMP include phosphorylase activation and increased rate of lactic acid production (256, 257). But this is only one of the reaction chains catalyzed by this nucleotide. There is evidence that cyclic AMP is "capable of triggering a wide variety of otherwise unrelated cellular functions" (21). It has been shown to act as a "second messenger" for a great many hormones (235, 238, 258, 259). Calcium has figured in various ways in connection with cyclic AMP (260–262). As already mentioned, it may be needed for some actions of the nucleotide, or cyclic AMP may have effects on the metabolism or translocation of Ca (263, 264). It is even considered possible that conversion of ATP to cyclic AMP might cause a significant release of Ca (238, 265). The information content in the claim that all β effects are mediated by increased levels of cyclic AMP is indeed limited. However, the complexity of the causal chains catalyzed by cyclic AMP holds some promise for the future. Gradually the various biochemical steps in these chains will be determined. Then, and only then, from all the reactions that constitute the interaction between tissue and drug, shall we be able to sort out the causal chains which determine the mechanical end responses.

ACKNOWLEDGMENTS

The author is greatly indebted to Mr. Gylfason and many members of the University Department of Pharmacology, Oxford, for their helpful suggestions and criticisms and to the Swedish Natural Science Research Council for financial support.

LITERATURE CITED

1. Paton, W. D. M., Payne, J. P. 1968. *Pharmacological Principles and Practice*. London: Churchill. 417 pp.
2. *Second Symposium on Catecholamines*. 1966. ed. G. H. Acheson. *Pharmacol. Rev.* 18:1–803
3. 1967. New Adrenergic Blocking Drugs: Their Pharmacological, Biochemical and Clinical Actions. *Ann. N.Y. Acad. Sci.* 139:541–1009
4. *Recent Advances in Pharmacology*. 1968, ed. J. M. Robson, R. S. Stacey. London: Churchill. 557 pp.
5. Himms-Hagen, J. 1967. Sympathetic regulation of metabolism. *Pharmacol. Rev.* 19:367–461
6. Cavallito, C. J. 1968. Some relationships between chemical structure and pharmacological activities. *Ann. Rev. Pharmacol.* 8:39–66
7. Kopin, I. J. 1968. False adrenergic transmitters. *Ann. Rev. Pharmacol.* 8:377–94
8. Ahlquist, R. P. 1966. The adrenergic receptor. *J. Pharm. Sci.* 55:359–67
9. Ahlquist, R. P. 1968. Agents which block adrenergic β-receptors. *Ann. Rev. Pharmacol.* 8:259–72
10. Bloom, F. E., Giarman, N. J. 1968. Physiologic and pharmacologic considerations of biogenic amines in the nervous system. *Ann. Rev. Pharmacol.* 8:229–58
11. Anden, N. E., Carlsson, A., Häggendal, J. 1969. Adrenergic mechanisms. *Ann. Rev. Pharmacol.* 9:119–34
12. Bowman, W. C., Nott, M. W. 1969. Actions of sympathomimetic amines and their antagonists on skeletal muscle. *Pharmacol. Rev.* 21:27–72
13. Jewell, B. R., Blinks, J. R. 1968. Drugs and the mechanical properties of the heart muscle. *Ann. Rev. Pharmacol.* 8:113–30
14. Burnstock, G., Holman, M. E. 1963. Smooth muscle: autonomic nerve transmission. *Ann. Rev. Physiol.* 25:61–90
15. Somlyo, A. P., Somlyo, A. V. 1968. Vascular smooth muscle. I. Normal structure, pathology, biochemistry and biophysics. *Pharmacol. Rev.* 20:197–272
16. Somlyo, A. P., Somlyo, A. V. 1968. Electromechanical and pharmacomechanical coupling in vascular smooth muscle. *J. Pharmacol. Exp. Ther.* 159:129–45
17. Holz, S. 1968. Drug action on digestive system. *Ann. Rev. Pharmacol.* 8:171–86
18. Lundholm, L., Mohme-Lundholm, E., Svedmyr, N. 1968. Metabolic effects of catecholamines. *Biological Basis of Medicine* 2:102–30. London: Academic
19. Miller, J. W., Lewis, J. E. 1969. Drugs affecting smooth muscle. *Ann. Rev. Pharmacol.* 9:147–72
20. Iversen, L. L. 1967. *The Uptake and Storage of Noradrenaline in Sympathetic Nerves*. Cambridge Univ. Press
21. Robison, G. A., Butcher, R. W., Sutherland, E. W. 1970. The Catecholamines. *Biochemical Actions of Hormones*, ed. G. Litwack, New York: Academic. 2nd ed. In press
22. Bülbring, E., Tomita, T. 1968. The effect of catecholamines on the membrane resistance and spike generation, in the smooth muscle of the guinea-pig taenia coli. *J. Physiol. London* 194:74–6P
23. Bülbring, E., Tomita, T. 1969. Increase of membrane conductance by adrenaline in the smooth muscle of guinea-pig taenia coli. *Proc. Roy. Soc. B* 172:89–102
24. Bülbring, E., Tomita, T. 1969. Suppression of spontaneous spike generation by catecholamines in the smooth muscle of the guinea-pig taenia coli. *Proc. Roy. Soc. B* 172:103–19
25. Bülbring, E., Tomita, T. 1969. Effect of calcium, barium and manganese on the action of adrenaline in the

smooth muscle of the guinea-pig taenia coli. *Proc. Roy. Soc. B* 172: 121–36

26. Brading, A. F., Bülbring, E., Tomita, T. 1969. The effect of temperature on the membrane conductance of the smooth muscle of the guinea-pig taenia coli. *J. Physiol. London* 200:621–35

27. Brading, A. F., Bülbring, E., Tomita, T. 1969. The effect of sodium and calcium on the action potential of the smooth muscle of the guinea-pig taenia coli. *J. Physiol. London* 200:637–54

28. Edman, K. A. P., Schild, H. O. 1961. Interactions of acetylcholine, adrenaline and magnesium with calcium in the contraction of depolarized rat uterus. *J. Physiol. London* 155:10–11P

29. Waugh, W. H. 1962. Adrenergic stimulation of depolarized arterial muscle. *Circ. Res.* 11:264–76

30. Schild, H. O. 1964. Calcium and the effects of drugs on depolarized smooth muscle. *Pharmacology of Smooth Muscle*, ed. E. Bülbring, 95–104. Oxford: Pergamon

31. Schild, H. O. 1966. Calcium and the relaxant effect of isoproterenol in the depolarized rat uterus. *Pharmacol. Rev.* 18:495–501

32. Cuthbert, A. W., Sutter, M. C. 1965. The effects of drugs on the relation between the action potential discharge and tension in a mammalian vein. *Brit. J. Pharmacol.* 25:592–601

33. Axelsson, J., Johansson, B., Jonsson, O., Wahlström, B. 1966. The effects of adrenergic drugs on electrical and mechanical activity of the portal vein. *Symp. Elec. Activ. Innerv. Blood Vessels Cambridge. Bibl. Anat.* 8:16–20

34. Johansson, B., Jonsson, O., Axelsson, J., Wahlström, B. 1967. Electrical and mechanical characteristics of vascular smooth muscle response to norepinephrine and isoproterenol. *Circ. Res.* 21:619–33

35. Matthews, E. K., Sutter, M. C. 1967. Ouabain-induced changes in the contractile and electrical activity, potassium content, and response to drugs of smooth muscle cells. *Can. J. Physiol. Pharmacol.* 45:509–20

36. Axelsson, J., Gudmundsson, G., Wahlström, B. 1968. Quantitative analysis of the correlation between electrical and mechanical activity in smooth muscle. *Acta Physiol. Scand.* 73:c. 23

37. Axelsson, J. 1970. Mechanical properties of smooth muscle, and the relationship between mechanical and electrical activity. *Smooth Muscle*, ed. E. Bülbring, A. F. Brading, A. W. Jones, T. Tomita, 289–315. London: Arnold. 676 pp.

38. Axelsson, J., Gudmundsson, G., Wahlström, B. Quantitative analysis of the electrical and mechanical activity of the rat portal vein. In press

39. Aberg, A. K. G., Axelsson, J. 1965. Some mechanical aspects of an intestinal smooth muscle. *Acta Physiol. Scand.* 64:15–27

40. Ling, G. N. 1962. *A Physical Theory of the Living State: The Association-Induction Hypothesis.* New York: Blaisdell

41. Ling, G. N. 1965. The membrane theory and other views for soluble permeability, distribution, and transport in living cells. *Perspect. Biol. Med.* 9:87–106

42. Ling, G. N. 1965. The physical state of water in living cell and model systems. *Ann. N.Y. Acad. Sci.* 125:401–17

43. Jones, A. W. 1970. Application of the 'Association-Induction Hypothesis' to ion accumulation and permeability of smooth muscle. *Smooth Muscle.* See Ref. 37, 122–50

44. Moran, N. C. 1966. Pharmacological characterization of adrenergic receptors. *Pharmacol. Rev.* 18:503

45. Moran, N. C. 1967. Aims of the Conference. *Ann. N.Y. Acad. Sci.* 139:545–48

46. Ahlquist, R. P. 1948. A study of the adrenotropic receptors. *Am. J. Physiol.* 153:586–600

47. Ahlquist, R. P. 1965. Effects of the autonomic drugs on the circulatory system. *Handbook of Physiology.* Sec. II. *Circulation*, ed. W. F. Hamilton, P. Dow, 3:2457–75. Bethesda: Am. Physiol. Soc.

48. Ahlquist, R. P. 1967. Development of the concept of alpha and beta adrenotropic receptors. *Ann. N.Y. Acad. Sci.* 139:549–52

49. Moran, N. C., Perkins, M. E. 1958. Adrenergic blockade of the mammalian heart by a dichloro analogue of isoproterenol. *J. Pharmacol.* 124:223–37

50. Moran, N. C., Perkins, M. E. 1961. An evaluation of adrenergic blockade of the mammalian heart. *J. Pharmacol. Exp. Ther.* 133 :192–201

51. Ghouri, M. S. K., Haley, T. J. 1969. Structure-activity relationships in the adrenergic-blocking agents. *J. Pharm. Sci.*, 58 :511–38

52. Biel, J. H., Lum, B. K. B. 1966. The β-adrenergic blocking agents, pharmacology and structure-activity relationships. *Progr. Drug Res.* 10 :46

53. Gershon, M. D. The identification of neurotransmitters to smooth muscle. *Smooth Muscle.* See Ref. 37, 496–524

54. Brick, I., Hutchinson, K. J., Roddie, I. C. 1967. The vasodilator properties of noradrenaline in the human forearm. *Brit. J. Pharmacol.* 30 :561–67

55. Brick, I., Hutchinson, K. J., Roddie, I. C. 1967. A comparison of the effects of circulating noradrenaline and vasoconstrictor nerve stimulation on forearm bloodvessels. *J. Physiol. London* 189 :27–28P

56. Glick, G., Epstein, S. E., Wechsler, A. S., Braunwald, E. 1967. Physiological differences between the effects of neuronally released and blood borne norepinephrine on beta adrenergic receptors in the arterial bed of the dog. *Circ. Res.* 21 :217–27

57. Eränkö, O. 1955. Distribution of fluorescing islets, adrenaline and noradrenaline in the adrenal medulla of the hamster. *Acta Endocrinol. Copenhagen* 18 :174–79

58. Eränkö, O. 1967. The practical histochemical demonstration of catecholamines by formaldehyde-induced fluorescence. *J. Roy. Microsc. Soc.* 87 :258–76

59. Barter, R., Pearse, A. G. E. 1953. Detection of 5-hydroxytryptamine in mammalian enterochromaffin cells. *Nature* 172 :810

60. Barter, R., Pearse, A. G. E. 1955. Mammalian enterochromaffin cells as the source of serotonin (5-hydroxytryptamine) *J. Pathol. Bacteriol.* 69 :25–31

61. Carlsson, A., Falck, B., Hillarp, N. Å. 1962. Cellular localisation of brain monoamines. *Acta Physiol. Scand.* 56 : *Suppl. 196*, 1–28

62. Falck, B. 1962. Observations on the possibilities of the cellular localisation of monoamines by a fluorescence method. *Acta Physiol. Scand.* 56 : *Suppl. 197*, 1–25

63. Falck, B., Hillarp, N. Å., Thieme, G., Torp, A. 1962. Fluorescence of catecholamines and related compounds condensed with formaldehyde. *J. Histochem. Cytochem.* 10 : 348–54

64. Corrodi, H., Hillarp, N. Å. 1963. Fluoreszenzmethoden zur histochemischen Sichtbarmachung von Monoaminen. 1. Identifizierung der fluoreszierenden Produkte aus Modellversuchen mit 6,7-Dimethoxyisochinolinderivaten und Formaldehyd. *Helv. Chim. Acta* 46 : 2425–30

65. Corrodi, H., Hillarp, N. Å. 1964. Fluoreszenzmethoden zur histochemischen Sichtbarmachung von Monoaminen. 2. Identifizierung des fluoreszierenden Produktes aus Dopamin und Formaldehyd. *Helv. Chim. Acta* 47 :911–18

66. Dahlström, A., Fuxe, K. 1964. A method for the demonstration of monoamine-containing nerve fibres in the central nervous system. *Acta Physiol. Scand.* 60 :293–94

67. Jonsson, G. 1967. *The formaldehyde fluorescence method for the histochemical demonstration of biogenic monoamines.* Thesis. Stockholm

68. Norberg, K.-A., Hamberger, B. 1964. The sympathetic adrenergic neuron. Some characteristics revealed by histochemical studies on the intraneuronal distribution of the transmitter. *Acta Physiol. Scand.* 63 : *Suppl. 238*, 1–42

69. Malmfors, T. 1965. Studies on adrenergic nerves. The use of rat and mouse iris for direct observations on their physiology and pharmacology at cellular and subcellular levels. *Acta Physiol. Scand.* 64 : *Suppl. 248*, 1–93

70. McLean, J. R., Burnstock, G. 1966. Histochemical localisation of catecholamines in the urinary bladder of the toad (*Bufo marinus*). *J. Histochem. Cytochem.* 14 :538–48

71. McLean, J. R., Burnstock, G. 1967. Innervation of the urinary bladder of the sleepy lizard (*Trachysaurus rugosus*). 1. Fluorescent histochemical localisation of catecholamines. *Comp. Biochem. Physiol.* 20 :667–73

72. McLean, J. R., Burnstock, G. 1967. Innervation of the lungs of the toad (*Bufo marinus*). II. Fluorescent histochemistry of catecholamines. *Comp. Biochem. Physiol.* 22:767–73

73. McLean, J. R., Burnstock, G. 1967. Innervation of the lungs of the sleepy lizard (*Trachysaurus rugosus*). I. Fluorescent histochemistry of catecholamines. *Comp. Biochem. Physiol.* 22:809–13

74. Burnstock, G. 1970. Structure of smooth muscle and its innervation. *Smooth Muscle.* See Ref. 37, 1–69

75. Speden, R. N. 1970. Excitation of vascular smooth muscle. *Smooth Muscle.* See Ref. 37, 558–88

76. Caesar, R., Edwards, G. A., Ruska, H. 1957. Architecture and nerve supply of mammalian smooth muscle tissue. *J. Biophys. Biochem. Cytol.* 3:867–78

77. Taxi, J. 1965. Contribution à l'étude des connexions des neurones moteurs du systeme nerveux autonome. *Natur. Zool.* 7:413–674

78. Thaemert, J. C. 1963. The ultrastructure and disposition of vesiculated nerve processes in smooth muscle. *J. Cell Biol.* 16:361–77

79. Thaemert, J. C. 1966. Ultrastructural interrelationships of nerve processes and smooth muscle cells in three dimensions. *J. Cell Biol.* 28:37–49

80. Nagasawa, J., Suzuki, T. 1967. Electron miscroscopic observations on the innervation of the smooth muscle. *Tohoku J. Exp. Med.* 91:299–313

81. Bennett, M. R., Rogers, D. C. 1967. A study of the innervation of the taenia coli *J. Cell Biol.* 33:573–96

82. Merrillees, N. C. R. 1968. The nervous environment of individual smooth muscle cells of the guinea-pig vas deferens. *J. Cell Biol.* 37:794–817

83. Bloom, F. E., Barrnett, R. J. 1966. Fine structural localisation of noradrenaline in vesicles of autonomic nerve endings. *Nature* 210:599–601

84. Lewis, P. R., Shute, C. C. D. 1967. The simultaneous demonstration of catecholamines and cholinesterase with the electronmicroscope. *J. Physiol. London* 186:53–55P

85. Geffen, L. B., Livett, B. G. 1970. Origin, functions and fate of synaptic vesicles in sympathetic neurons. *Physiol. Rev.* In press

86. Dahlström, A., Häggendal, J. 1966. Some quantitative studies of the noradrenaline content in the cell bodies and terminals of a sympathetic adrenergic neuron system. *Acta Physiol. Scand.* 67:271–77

87. Dahlström, A., Häggendal, J., Hökfelt, T. 1966. The noradrenaline content of the varicosities of sympathetic adrenergic nerve terminals in the rat. *Acta Physiol. Scand.* 67:289–94

88. Ritzen, M. 1967. Cytochemical identification and quantitation of biogenic amines — A microspectrophotometric and autoradiographic study. MD thesis. Stockholm

89. Livett, B. G., Geffen, L. B. 1967. Transport of C¹⁴-noradrenaline down sympathetic nerves. Presented to *Aust. Soc. Clin. Exp. Pharmacol.* Nov. 29–30th

90. Dearnaley, D. P., Geffen, L. B. 1966. Effect of nerve stimulation on the noradrenaline content of the spleen. *Proc. Roy. Soc. B* 166:303–15

91. Brown, L., Dearnaley, D. P., Geffen, L. B. 1967. Noradrenaline storage and release in the decentralized spleen. *Proc. Roy. Soc. B* 168:48–56

92. Eccles, J. C., Magladery, J. W. 1937. The excitation and response of smooth muscle. *J. Physiol. London* 90:31–67

93. Eccles, J. C., Magladery, J. W. 1937. Rhythmic responses of smooth muscle. *J. Physiol. London* 90:68–99

94. Burnstock, G., Holman, M. E. 1961. The transmission of excitation from autonomic nerve to smooth muscle. *J. Physiol. London* 155:115–33

95. Burnstock, G., Holman, M. E. 1962. Spontaneous potentials at sympathetic nerve endings in smooth muscle. *J. Physiol. London* 160:446–60

96. Burnstock, G., Holman, M. E. 1962. Effect of denervation and of reserpine treatment on transmission at sympathetic nerve endings. *J. Physiol. London* 160:461–69

97. Burnstock, G., Holman, M. E. 1964. An electrophysiological investigation of the actions of some autonomic blocking drugs on transmis-

sion in the guinea-pig vas deferens. *Brit. J. Pharmacol.* 23 :600–12

98. Burnstock, G., Holman, M. E. 1966. Junction potentials at adrenergic synapses. *Pharmacol. Rev.* 18 :481–93

99. Orlov, R. S. 1962. On impulse transmission from motor sympathetic nerve to smooth muscle. *Fiziol. Zh. SSSR* 48 :342–48

100. Orlov, R. S. 1963. Spontaneous electrical activity of smooth muscle cells before and after denervation. *Fiziol. Zh. SSSR* 49 :115–21

101. Gillespie, J. S. 1962. Spontaneous electrical and mechanical activity of stretched and unstretched intestinal smooth muscle cells and their response to sympathetic nerve stimulation. *J. Physiol. London* 162 :54–75

102. Kuriyama, H. 1963. Electrophysiological observations on the motor innervation of the smooth muscle cells in the guinea-pig vas deferens. *J. Physiol. London* 169 :213–28

103. Burnstock, G., Holman, M. E., Kuriyama, H. 1964. Facilitation of transmission from autonomic nerve to smooth muscle of guinea-pig vas deferens. *J. Physiol. London* 172 :31–49

104. Holman, M. E. 1964. Electrophysiological effects of adrenergic nerve stimulation. *Pharmacology of Smooth Muscle.* See Ref. 30, 19–35

105. Holman, M. E. 1967. Some electrophysiological aspects of transmission from noradrenergic nerves to smooth muscle. *Circ. Res.* 21: *Suppl. 3,* 71–82

106. Holman, M. E. 1970. Junction potentials in smooth muscle. *Smooth Muscle.* See Ref. 37, 244–88

107. Holman, M. E., Jowett, A. 1964. Some actions of catecholamines on the smooth muscle of the guinea-pig vas deferenes. *Aust. J. Exp. Biol. Med. Sci.* 42 :40–53

108. Speden, R. N. 1964. Electrical activity of single smooth muscle cells of the mesenteric artery produced by splanchnic nerve stimulation of the guinea-pig. *Nature* 202 :193–94

109. Speden, R. N. 1967. Adrenergic transmission in small arteries. *Nature* 216 :289–90

110. Takeda, H., Nakanishi, H. 1965. Electrical and mechanical activity of the guinea-pig vas deferens in

situ. *Ann. Rep. Shionogi Res. Lab.* 15 :163–66

111. Su, C., Bevan, J. A., Ursillo, R. C. 1964. Electrical quiescence of pulmonary artery smooth muscle during sympathomimetic stimulation. *Circ. Res.* 15 :20–27

112. Bennett, M. R., Burnstock, G., Holman, M. E. 1966. Transmission from perivascular inhibitory nerves to the smooth muscle of the guinea-pig taenia coli. *J. Physiol. London* 182 :527–40

113. Hashimoto, Y., Holman, M. E., Tille, J. 1966. Electrical properties of the smooth muscle membrane of the guinea-pig vas deferens. *J. Physiol. London* 186 :27–41

114. Keatinge, W. R. 1966. Electrical and mechanical response of arteries to stimulation of sympathetic nerves. *J. Physiol. London* 185 : 701–15

115. Steedman, W. M. 1966. Micro-electrode studies on mammalian vascular muscle. *J. Physiol. London* 186 : 382–400

116. Bennett, M. R. 1967. The effect of intracellular current pulses in smooth muscle cells of the guinea-pig vas deferens at rest and during transmission. *J. Gen. Physiol.* 50 : 2459–75

117. Dorward, P., Holman, M. E. 1967. Excitatory action of noradrenaline on smooth muscle. *Aust. J. Exp. Biol. Med. Sci.* 45 :48P

118. Holman, M. E., Kasby, C. B., Suthers, M. B. 1967. Electrical activity of rabbit portal vein. *Aust. J. Exp. Biol. Med. Sci.* 45 :50P

119. Tomita, T. 1967. Current spread in the smooth muscle of the guinea-pig vas deferens. *J. Physiol. London* 189 :163–76

120. Holman, M. E., Kasby, C. B., Suthers, M. B., Wilson, J. A. F. 1968. Some properties of the smooth muscle of rabbit portal vein. *J. Physiol. London* 196 :111–32

121. De Robertis, E., Vaz Ferreira, A. 1957. Electron microscope study of the excretion of catechol-containing droplets in the adrenal medulla. *Exp. Cell Res.* 12 :568–74

122. Geffen, L. B., Livett, B. G., Rush, R. A. 1970. Immunological localization of chromogranins in sheep sympathetic neurones and their release by nerve impulses. *J. Physiol. London* 204 :58–59P

123. De Potter, W. P., De Schaepdryver, A. F., Moerman, E. J., Smith, A. D. 1969. Evidence for the release of vesicle proteins together with noradrenaline upon stimulation of the splenic nerve. *J. Physiol. London* 204:102–4P

124. Burn, J. H., Rand, M. J. 1959. Sympathetic postganglionic mechanism. *Nature* 184:163–65

125. Ferry, C. B. 1966. Cholinergic link hypothesis in adrenergic neuroeffector transmission. *Physiol. Rev.* 46:420–56

126. Burn, J. H., Malik, K. U. 1970. Effects of anticholinesterase on the response to stimulation of adrenergic fibres. *J. Physiol.* 208:82P

127. Rand, M. J., Whaler, B. C. 1965. Impairment of sympathetic transmission by botulinum toxin. *Nature* 206:588–91

128. Haeusler, G., Thoenen, H., Haefely, W., Hurlimann, A. 1968. Electrical events in cardiac adrenergic nerves and noradrenaline release from the heart induced by acetylcholine and KCl. *Arch. Pharmakol. Exp. Pathol.* 261:389–411

129. Burn, J. H. 1932. On vasodilator fibres in the sympathetic, and on the effect of circulating adrenaline in augmenting the vascular response to sympathetic stimulation *J. Physiol. London* 75:144–59

130. Burn, J. H. 1933. A pharmacological approach to the cause of asthma. *Proc. Roy. Soc. Med. London* 27:31

131. Brown, G. L., Gillespie, J. S. 1957. The output of sympathetic transmitter from the spleen of the cat. *J. Physiol. London* 138:81–102

132. MacMillan, W. H. 1959. A hypothesis concerning the effect of cocaine on the action of sympathomimetic amines. *Brit. J. Pharmacol.* 14:385–91

133. Paton, W. D. M. 1960. *Adrenergic Mech. Ciba Found. Symp.* 124–27

134. Gillespie, J. S., Kirpekar, S. M. 1965. The inactivation of infused noradrenaline by the cat spleen. *J. Physiol. London* 176:205–27

135. Blakeley, A. G. H., Brown, L., Geffen, L. B. 1969. Uptake and re-use of sympathetic transmitter in the cat's spleen. *Proc. Roy. Soc. B* 174:51–68

136. Iversen, L. L. 1965. The uptake of catecholamines at high perfusion concentrations in the rat isolated heart: a novel catecholamine uptake process. *Brit. J. Pharmacol.* 25:18–33

137. Avakian, O. V., Gillespie, J. S. 1968. Uptake of noradrenaline by adrenergic nerves, smooth muscle and connective tissue in isolated perfused arteries and its correlation with the vasoconstrictor response. *Brit. J. Pharmacol.* 32:168–84

138. Iversen, L. L., Langer, S. Z. 1969. Effects of phenoxybenzamine on the uptake and metabolism of noradrenaline in the rat heart and vas deferens. *Brit. J. Pharmacol.* 37:627–37

139. Gillespie, J. S., Hamilton, D. N. H., Hosie, R. J. A. 1970. The extraneuronal uptake and localization of noradrenaline in the cat spleen and the effects on this of some drugs, of cold and of denervation. *J. Physiol. London* 206:563–90

140. Langer, S. Z. 1970. The metabolism of [³H] noradrenaline released by electrical stimulation from the isolated nictitating membrane of the cat and from the vas deferens of the rat. *J. Physiol. London* 208:515–46

141. Yamauchi, A., Burnstock, G. 1969. Post-natal development of the innervation of the mouse vas deferens. A fine structural study. *J. Anat.* 104:1–15

142. Jacobowitz, D. 1965. Histochemical studies of the autonomic innervation of the gut. *J. Pharmacol. Exp. Ther.* 149:358–64

143. Hollands, B. C. S., Vanov, S. 1965. Localization of catecholamines in visceral organs and ganglia of the rat, guinea-pig and rabbit. *Brit. J. Pharmacol.* 25:307–16

144. Gabella, G., Costa, M. 1967. Le fibre adrenergiche nel canale alimentare. *Giorn. Accad. Med. Torino* 130: fasc. 1–6

145. Campbell, G., Burnstock, G. 1968. Comparative physiology of gastrointestinal motility. *Handbook of Physiology.* Sec. IV. *Alimentary Canal.* Washington: Am. Physiol. Soc.

146. Read, J. B., Burnstock, G. 1968. Comparative histochemical studies of adrenergic nerves in the enteric plexuses of vertebrate large intestine. *Comp. Biochem. Physiol.* 27:505–17

147. Kosterlitz, H. W., Watt, A. J. 1965. Adrenergic receptors in the guinea-pig ileum. *J. Physiol. London* 177: 11P

148. Lum, B. K. B., Kermani, M. H., Heilman, R. D. 1966. Intestinal relaxation produced by sympathomimetic amines in the isolated rabbit jejunum: selective inhibition by adrenergic blocking agents and by cold storage. *J. Pharmacol. Exp. Ther.* 154:463–71

149. Lee, C. Y. 1970. Adrenergic receptors in the intestine. *Smooth Muscle.* See Ref. 37, 549–57

150. Paton, W. D. M., Vizi, E. S. 1969. The inhibitory action of noradrenaline and adrenaline on acetylcholine output by guinea-pig ileum longitudinal muscle strip. *Brit. J. Pharmacol.* 35:10–28

151. Kosterlitz, H. W., Lydon, R. J., Watt, A. J. 1970. The effects of adrenaline, noradrenaline and isoprenaline on inhibitory alpha and beta adrenoreceptors in the longitudinal muscle of the guinea-pig ileum. *Brit. J. Pharmacol.* 39:398–413

152. Crowcroft, P. G., Holman, M. E., Szurszewski, J. H. 1970. Excitatory input from the colon to the inferior mesenteric ganglion. *J. Physiol. London* 208:19P

153. Schaumann, W. 1958. Zusammenhänge zwischen der Wirkung der Analgetica und Sympathicomimetica auf den Meerschweinchen Dünndarm. *Arch. Exp. Pathol. Pharmakol.* 233:112–24

154. McIsaac, R. J. 1966. Ganglionic blocking properties of epinephrine and related amines *Int. J. Neuropharmacol.* 5:15–26

155. Lee, C. Y., Tseng, L. F. 1966. A further study on the adrenergic inhibition of the peristaltic reflex of the gut. *Abstr. 3rd Int. Pharmacol. Congr. Sao Paulo,* 117

156. Gershon, M. D. 1967. Inhibition of gastrointestinal movement by sympathetic nerve stimulation: The site of action. *J. Physiol. London* 189: 317–27

157. Bennett, M. R., Burnstock, G., Holman, M. E. 1966. Transmission from intramural inhibitory nerves to the smooth muscle of the guinea-pig taenia coli. *J. Physiol. London* 182:541–58

158. Bülbring, E., Tomita, T. 1967. Properties of the inhibitory potential of smooth muscle as observed in the response to field stimulation of the guinea-pig taenia coli. *J. Physiol. London* 189:299–315

159. Kuriyama, H., Osa, T., Toida, N. 1967. Nervous factors influencing the membrane activity of intestinal smooth muscle. *J. Physiol. London* 191:257–70

160. Casteels, R., Kuriyama, H. 1966. Membrane potential and ion content in the smooth muscle of the guinea-pig's taenia coli at different external potassium concentrations. *J. Physiol. London* 184:120–30

161. Ehinger, B., Falck, B., Sporrong, B. 1966. Adrenergic fibres to the heart and to peripheral vessels. *Bibl. Anat.* 8:35–45

162. Devine, C. E. 1966. Neuromuscular relationships in rat intestinal and mesenteric blood vessels. *Proc. Univ. Otago Med. Sch.* 44:9–11

163. Brown, G. L. 1965. The release and fate of the transmitter liberated by adrenergic nerves. *Proc. Roy. Soc. B* 162:1–19

164. Kopin, I. J. 1966. Biochemical aspects of release of norepinephrine and other amines from sympathetic nerve endings. *Pharmacol. Rev.* 18:513–23

165. Gerova, M., Gero, J., Dolezel, S. 1967. Mechanisms of sympathetic regulation of arterial smooth muscle. *Experientia* 23:639–40

166. Su, C., Bevan, J. A. 1965. The electrical response of pulmonary artery muscle to acetylcholine, histamine and serotonin. *Life Sci.* 4:1025–29

167. Su, C., Bevan, J. A. 1966. Electrical and mechanical responses of pulmonary artery muscle to neural and chemical stimulation. *Bibl. Anat.* 8:30–34

168. Folkow, B. 1952. Impulse frequency in sympathetic vasomotor fibres correlated to the release and elimination of the transmitter. *Acta Physiol. Scand.* 25:49–76

169. Johansson, B., Ljung, B. 1967. Sympathetic control of rhythmically active vascular smooth muscle as studied by a nerve-muscle preparation of portal vein. *Acta Physiol. Scand.* 70:299–311

170. Dale, H. H. 1906. On some physiological actions of ergot. *J. Physiol. London* 34:163–206

171. Vogt, M. 1965. Transmitter released in cat uterus by stimulation of the hypogastric nerves. *J. Physiol. London* 179 :163–71

172. Schofield, B. M. 1952. The innervation of the cervix and cornu uteri in the rabbit. *J. Physiol. London* 117 :317–28

173. Setekleiv, J. 1964. Uterine motility of the estrogenized rabbit. I. Isotonic and isometric recording *in vivo*. Influence of anaesthesia and temperature. *Acta Physiol. Scand.* 62 :68–78

174. Miller, M. D., Marshall, J. M. 1965. Uterine response to nerve stimulation; relation to hormonal status and catechol amines. *Am. J. Physiol.* 209 :859–65

175. Furchgott, R. F. 1960. Receptors for sympathomimetic amines. *Adrenergic Mech. Ciba Found. Symp.* 246–52

176. Ahlquist, R. P., Levy, B. 1959. Adrenergic receptive mechanism of canine ileum. *J. Pharmacol. Exp. Ther.* 127 :146–49

177. Levy, B., Ahlquist, R. P. 1967. Adrenergic receptors in intestinal smooth muscle. *Ann. N.Y. Acad. Sci.* 139 :781–87

178. Bucknell, A., Whitney, B. 1964. A preliminary investigation of the pharmacology of the human isolated taenia coli preparation. *Brit. J. Pharmacol.* 23 :164–75

179. Brody, T. M., Diamond, J. 1967. Blockade of the biochemical correlates of contraction and relaxation in uterine and intestinal smooth muscle. *Ann. N.Y. Acad. Sci.* 139 :772–80

180. Jenkinson, D. H., Morton, I. K. M. 1967. Adrenergic blocking drugs as tools in the study of the actions of catecholamines on the smooth muscle membrane. *Ann. N.Y. Acad. Sci.* 139 :762–71

181. Jenkinson, D. H., Morton, I. K. M. 1967. The role of α and β-adrenergic receptors in some actions of catecholamines on intestinal smooth muscle. *J. Physiol. London* 188 :387–402

182. Hornbrook, K. R. 1967. Report on the discussion of Session III : Physiological and biochemical aspects of adrenergic blockade. II. *Ann. N.Y. Acad. Sci.* 139 :821–25

183. Munro, A. F. 1951. The effect of adrenaline on the guinea-pig intestine. *J. Physiol. London* 112 : 84–94

184. Burnstock, G. 1960. Membrane potential changes associated with stimulation of smooth muscle by adrenaline. *Nature* 186 :727–28

185. Bailey, D. M. 1965. The action of sympathomimetic amines on circular and longitudinal smooth muscle from the isolated oesophagus of the guinea-pig. *J. Pharm. Pharmacol.* 17 :782–87

186. Furchgott, R. F. 1967. The pharmacological differentiation of adrenergic receptors. *Ann. N.Y. Acad. Sci.* 139 :553–70

187. Jenkinson, D. H., Morton, I. K. M. 1965. Effects of noradrenaline and isoprenaline on the permeability of depolarized intestinal smooth muscle to inorganic ions. *Nature* 205 :505–6

188. Jenkinson, D. H., Morton, I. K. M. 1967. The effect of noradrenaline on the permeability of depolarized intestinal smooth muscle to inorganic ions. *J. Physiol. London* 188 :373–86

189. Rothstein, A. 1968. Membrane phenomena. *Ann. Rev. Physiol.* 30 : 15–72

190. Tomita, T. 1970. Electrical properties of mammalian smooth muscle. *Smooth Muscle.* See. Ref. 37, 197–243

191. Bülbring, E., Kuriyama, H. 1963. Effects of changes in ionic environment on the action of acetylcholine and adrenaline on the smooth muscle cells of guinea-pig taenia coli. *J. Physiol. London* 166 : 59–74

192. Bülbring, E., Tomita, T. 1968. The effects of Ba^{2+} and Mn^{2+} on the smooth muscle of guinea-pig taenia coli. *J. Physiol. London* 196 :137–39P

193. Kuriyama, H. 1970. Effects of ions and drugs on the electrical activity of smooth muscle. *Smooth Muscle.* See Ref. 37, 366–98

194. Burnstock, G. 1958. The action of adrenaline on excitability and membrane potential in the taenia coli of the guinea-pig and the effect of DNP on this action and on the actions of acetylcholine. *J. Physiol. London* 143 :183–94

195. Bülbring, E. 1960. Biophysical changes produced by adrenaline and nor-

adrenaline. *Adrenergic Mech. Ciba Found. Symp.*, 275–87

196. Shanes, A. M. 1958. Electrochemical aspects of physiological action in excitable cells. *Pharmacol. Rev.* 10:59–164

197. Lundholm, L., Mohme-Lundholm, E. 1960. The action of adrenaline on carbohydrate metabolism in relation to some of its pharmacodynamic effects. *Adrenergic Mech. Ciba Found. Symp.* 305–21

198. Bülbring, E. 1962. Electrical activity in intestinal smooth muscle. *Physiol. Rev.* 42: *Suppl.* 5:160–74

199. Bueding, E., Bülbring, E. 1964. The inhibitory action of adrenaline. Biochemical and biophysical observations. *Pharmacology of Smooth Muscle*. See Ref. 37, 37–54

200. Born, G. V. R., Bülbring, E. 1956. The movement of potassium between smooth muscle and the surrounding fluid. *J. Physiol. London* 131:690–703

201. Bülbring, E., Goodford, P. J., Setekleiv, J. 1966. The action of adrenaline on the ionic content and on sodium and potassium movements in the smooth muscle of the guinea-pig taenia coli. *Brit. J. Pharmacol.* 28:296–307

202. Setekleiv, J. 1970. Effects of drugs on ion distribution and flux in smooth muscle. *Smooth Muscle*. See Ref. 37, 343–65

203. Setekleiv, J. 1967. Factors influencing the ^{42}K efflux from the smooth muscle of guinea-pig taenia coli. *J. Physiol. London* 188:39–40P

204. Bülbring, E., Kuriyama, H. 1963. Effects of changes in the external sodium and calcium concentrations on spontaneous electrical activity in smooth muscle of guinea-pig taenia coli. *J. Physiol. London* 166:29–58

205. Keatinge, W. R. 1964. Mechanism of adrenergic stimulation of mammalian arteries and its failure at low temperatures. *J. Physiol. London* 174:184–205

206. Keatinge, W. R. 1966. Electrical mechanical responses of vascular smooth muscle to vasodilator agents and vasoactive polypeptides. *Circ. Res.* 18:641–49

207. Shibata, S., Briggs, A. H. 1966. The relationships between electrical and mechanical events in rabbit aortic strips. *J. Pharmacol. Exp. Ther.* 153:466–70

208. de la Lande, I. S., Cannell, V. A., Waterson, J. G. 1966. The interaction of serotonin and noradrenaline on the perfused artery. *Brit. J. Pharmacol.* 28:255–72

209. Axelsson, J., Wahlström, B., Johansson, B., Jonsson, O. 1967. Influence of the ionic environment on spontaneous electrical and mechanical activity of the rat portal vein. *Circ. Res.* 21:609–19

210. Funaki, S., Bohr, D. F. 1964. Electrical and mechanical activity of isolated vascular smooth muscle of the rat. *Nature* 203:192–94

211. Nakajima, A., Horn, L. 1967. Electrical activity of single vascular smooth muscle fibres. *Am. J. Physiol.* 213:25–30

212. Jensen, K. B., Vennerød, A. M. 1961. Reversal of the inhibitory action of adrenaline and histamine on rat uterus. *Acta Pharmacol. Toxicol.* 18:298–306

213. Brooks, J. R., Schaeppi, U., Pincus, G. 1965. Evidence for the presence of alpha adrenergic excitatory receptors in the rat uterus. *Life Sci.* 4:1817–21

214. Diamond, J., Brody, T. M. 1966. Hormonal alteration of the response of the rat uterus to catecholamines. *Life Sci.* 5:2187–93

215. Marshall, J. M. 1967. Comparative aspects of the pharmacology of smooth muscle. *Fed. Proc.* 26:1104–10

216. Casteels, R., Kuriyama, H. 1965. Membrane potential and ionic content in pregnant and non-pregnant rat myometrium. *J. Physiol. London* 177:263–87

217. Jones, A. W. 1968. Influence of oestrogen and progesterone on the electrolyte accumulation in the rabbit myometrium. *J. Physiol. London* 197:19–20P

218. Bülbring, E., Casteels, R., Kuriyama, H. 1968. Membrane potential and ion content in cat and guinea-pig myometrium and the response to adrenaline and noradrenaline. *Brit. J. Pharmacol.* 34:388–407

219. Abe, Y. 1970. The hormonal control and the effects of drugs and ions on the electrical and mechanical activity of the uterus. *Smooth Muscle*. See Ref. 37, 396–417

220. Miller, J. W. 1967. Adrenergic re-

ceptors in the myometrium. *Ann. N.Y. Acad. Sci.* 139:788–98

221. Edman, K. A. P., Schild, H. O. 1963. Calcium and the stimulant and inhibitory effects of adrenaline in depolarized smooth muscle. *J. Physiol. London* 169:404–11

222. Marshall, J. M. 1968. Relation between the ionic environment and the action of drugs on the myometrium. *Fed. Proc.* 27:115–19

223. Marshall, J. M., Vaughan Williams, E. M. 1956. Pacemaker potentials. The excitation of isolated rabbit auricles by acetylcholine at low temperatures. *J. Physiol. London* 131:186–99

224. Harris, E. J., Hutter, O. F. 1956. The action of acetylcholine on the movement of potassium ions in the sinus venosus of the heart. *J. Physiol. London* 133:58P

225. Marshall, J. M. 1957. Effects of low temperature on transmembrane potentials of single fibers of the rabbit atrium. *Circ. Res.* 5:664–69

226. Axelsson, J., Högberg, S. G. R., Timms, A. R. 1965. The effect of removing and readmitting glucose on the electrical and mechanical activity and glucose and glycogen content of the intestinal smooth muscle from the taenia coli of the guinea-pig. *Acta Physiol. Scand.* 64:28–42

227. Axelsson, J., Bueding, E., Bülbring, E. 1961. The inhibitory action of adrenaline on intestinal smooth muscle in relation to its action on phosphorylase activity. *J. Physiol. London* 156:357–74

228. Sutherland, E. W., Rall, T. W. 1958. Fractionation and characterization of a cyclic adenine ribonucleotide formed by tissue particles. *J. Biol. Chem.* 232:1077

229. Bueding, E., Butcher, R. W., Hawkins, J. T., Timms, A. R., Sutherland, E. W., Jr. 1966. Effect of epinephrine on cyclic adenosine 3′,5′-phosphate and hexose phosphates in intestinal smooth muscle. *Biochim. Biophys. Acta* 115:173–78

230. Szego, C. M., Davis, J. S. 1967. Adenosine 3′,5′-monophosphate in rat uterus: Acute elevation by estrogen. *Proc. Nat. Acad. Sci. USA* 58:1711–18

231. Dobbs, J. W., Robison, G. A. 1968. Functional biochemistry of beta receptors in the uterus. *Fed. Proc.* 27:352

232. Sutherland, E. W., Rall, T. W., Menon, T. 1962. Adenyl cyclase. I. Distribution, preparation, and properties. *J. Biol. Chem.* 237:1220

233. Robison, G. A., Butcher, R. W., Sutherland, E. W. 1970. Adenyl cyclase as an adrenergic receptor. *Ann. N.Y. Acad. Sci.* 139:703–23

234. Cotten, M.deV. 1970. Report on the discussion of session II: Physiological and biochemical aspects of adrenergic blockade. *Ann. N.Y. Acad. Sci.* 139:754–57

235. Sutherland, E. W., Robison, G. A., Butcher, R. W. 1968. Some aspects of the biological role of adenosine 3′,5′-monophosphate (cyclic AMP). *Circ. Res.* 37:279–306

236. Murad, F., Vaughan, M. 1969. Effects of glucagon on rat heart adenyl cyclase. *Biochem. Pharmacol.* 18:1053–59

237. Levey, G. S., Epstein, S. E. 1969. Activation of adenyl cyclase by glucagon in cat and human heart. *Circ. Res.* 24:151–56

238. Robison, G. A., Butcher, R. W., Sutherland, E. W. 1970. On the relation of hormone receptors to adenyl cyclase. *Fundamental Concepts in Drug-Receptor Interactions*, 59–91. New York: Academic

239. Belleau, B. 1960. *Adrenergic Mech. Ciba Found. Symp.*, 223

240. Bloom, B. M., Goldman, I. M. 1966. *Advan. Drug Res.* 3:121

241. Belleau, B. 1967. Stereochemistry of adrenergic receptors: newer concepts on the molecular mechanism of action of catecholamines and antiadrenergic drugs at the receptor level. *Ann. N.Y. Acad. Sci.* 139:580–605

243. Honig, C. R., Stam, A. C. 1967. The influence of adrenergic mediators and their structural analogs on cardiac actomyosin systems. *Ann. N.Y. Acad. Sci.* 139:724–40

244. Govier, W. C. 1968. Myocardial alpha adrenergic receptors and their role in the production of a positive inotropic effect by sympathomimetic agents. *J. Pharmacol. Exp. Ther.* 159:82–90

245. Dresel, P. E. 1967. Report on the discussion of session I: General concepts of receptors. *Ann. N.Y. Acad. Sci.* 139:645–48

246. Belleau, B. 1968. *Physico-chemical Aspects of Drug Action*, ed. E. J. Ariens, 207. Oxford: Pergamon

247. Belleau, B., Tani, H. 1969. Selective irreversible blockade of the catecholamine alpha receptor by a leptocurare-like bis-alkylating agent. *Can. J. Pharm. Sci.* 4:14–16

248. Belleau, B., Ditullio, V., Godin, D. 1969. The mechanism of irreversible adrenergic blockade by N-carbethoxydihydroquinolines. Model studies with typical serine hydrolases. *Biochem. Pharmacol.* 18: 1039–44

249. Martel, R. R., Berman, R., Belleau, B. 1969. Pharmacology of EEDQ (N-ethoxycarbonyl-2-ethoxy-1,2-dihydroquinoline). *Can. J. Physiol. Pharmacol.* 47:909–12

250. Belleau, B. 1958. The mechanism of drug action at receptor surfaces. *Can. J. Biochem. Physiol.* 36:731–53

251. Belleau, B. 1966. Steric effects in catecholamine interactions with enzymes and receptors. *Pharmacol. Rev.* 18:131–140

252. Belleau, B. 1965. Conformational pertubation in relation to the regulation of enzyme and receptor behaviour. *Advan. Drug Res.* 2:89–126

253. Krebs, E. G., DeLange, R. J., Kemp, R. G., Riley, W. D. 1966. Activation of skeletal muscle phosphorylase. *Pharmacol. Rev.* 18:163

254. DeLange, R. J., Kemp, R. G., Riley, W. D., Cooper, R. A., Krebs, E. G. 1968. Activation of skeletal muscle phosphorylase kinase by adenosine triphosphate and adenosine 3′,5′-monophosphate. *J. Biol. Chem.* 243:2200–8

255. Walsh, D. A., Perkins, J. P., Krebs, E. G. 1968. *Fed. Proc.* 27:339

256. Mohme-Lundholm, E. 1963. Smooth muscle phosphorylase and enzymes affecting its activity. *Acta Physiol. Scand.* 59:74–84

257. Lundholm, L., Mohme-Lundholm, E., Svedmyr, N. 1966. Second Symposium on catecholamines. Physiological interrelationships. *Pharmacol. Rev.* 18:255–72

258. Butcher, R. W., Robison, G. A., Hardman, J. G., Sutherland, E. W. 1968. The role of cyclic AMP in hormone actions. *Advan. Enzyme Regul.* 6:357–89

259. Robison, G. A., Butcher, R. W., Sutherland, E. W. 1969. *Cyclic AMP*. New York: Academic

260. Kukovetz, W. R., Pöch, G. 1967. The action of imidazole on the effects of methylxanthines and catecholamines on cardiac contraction and phosphorylase activity. *J. Pharmacol. Exp. Ther.* 156:514–21

261. Nayler, W. G. 1967. Calcium exchange in cardiac muscle: A basic mechanism of drug action. *Am. Heart J.* 73:379–94

262. Williamson, J. R. 1966. Kinetic studies of epinephrine effects in the perfused rat heart. *Pharmacol. Rev.* 18:205–10

263. Chase, L. R., Aurbach, G. D. 1968. Renal adenyl cyclase: anatomically separate sites for parathyroid hormone and vasopressin. *Science* 159: 545–47

264. Wells, H., Lloyd, W. 1968. Inhibition of the hypocalcemic action of thyrocalcitonin by theophylline and isoproterenol. *Endocrinology* 82: 468–74

265. Rasmussen, H., Tenenhouse, A. 1968. Cyclic adenosine monophosphate, CA^{++}, and membranes. *Proc. Nat. Acad. Sci. USA* 59:1364–70

ACTIONS OF VERTEBRATE SEX HORMONES 1056

H. G. WILLIAMS-ASHMAN and A. H. REDDI

The Ben May Laboratory for Cancer Research and Department of Biochemistry
University of Chicago, Chicago, Illinois

INTRACELLULAR PROTEIDS BINDING SEX HORMONES AND THEIR METABOLITES

An almost daily growing literature deals with proteids in nuclei and cytoplasm of responsive cells that exhibit a high and stereospecific affinity for sex hormones or some of their metabolites. Although these macromolecules appear to be intimately involved in the selective uptake and retention of these hormones by various reproductive organs, their relationship to the biochemical mechanisms by which sex hormones influence tissue size and functions remains very far from clear. Wurtman (1) has rightly pointed out that the all too common designation of these entities as receptors is ambiguous, considering the mechanistic implications of this term as often used by physiologists and pharmacologists. Wurtman (1) proposes that noncommittal names like estrogen (hormone)-binding proteins may be more appropriate until the precise functions of these substances are elucidated. There is much to be said for this, or the more laconic terms estrophile and androphile, recently introduced by Jensen (2) and Liao & Fang (3) respectively. However, the latter type of epithet could almost as well apply to a variety of other unrelated marcromolecules, as, for example, certain proteins in blood serum that interact with sex and adrenocortical hormones with varying degrees of avidity and specificity, or the host of enzymes catalyzing metabolic transformations of gonadal steroids. In our current state of profound ignorance as to the molecular basis of sex hormone action, further discussion of these terminologies is likely to degenerate into nothing but a dispute about words.

Estrogen uptake by intact normal cells.—The pioneer studies of Jensen & Jacobson (4, 5) revealed that relatively large amounts of radioisotope persisted in certain female reproductive organs following injection of immature rats with physiological doses of tritiated 17β-estradiol of very high specific radioactivity. Comparable findings were first obtained by Glascock & Hoekstra (6) in regard to the fate of the synthetic estrogen hexestrol in young sheep and goats. Reviews from the laboratories of Jensen (7–15) and Gorski (16, 17) discuss their early investigations on the selective uptake and retention of labeled estrogens by various tissues as studied either

31

in living animals, or with intact cell preparations such as uterine horns or tissue slices incubated with the hormones in buffered Ringer solutions. The following general picture emerged, which was corroborated and amplified by experiments of Stone, Martin, Baggett, Axelrod, Eisenfeld, King, Terenius, Michael, Talwar, Lisk, Attramadal, Mobbs, Villee, Mahesh, and others documented in the aforementioned review articles (7–17):

Organs such as uterus, vagina, and anterior pituitary show a strong affinity for many estrogens, e.g., 17β-estradiol, 17α-methylestradiol, 17α-ethinylestradiol, and hexestrol. The uptake of these estrogens is blocked both in vivo and in vitro by antiuterotropic drugs like ethamoxytriphetol (MER-25), nafoxidine (Upjohn-11,100), clomiphene, and Parke-Davis CI-628. Depression of uterine growth by various doses of nafoxidine paralleled reduction of estradiol uptake. On the contrary, inhibitors of RNA and protein synthesis like actinomycin D and puromycin or cycloheximide, which are well known to counteract estrogen-induced uterine growth and many early biochemical concomitants of this process, hardly interfere with uterine binding of 17β-estradiol. The incorporation of 17β-estradiol by uteri involves two distinct phenomena: an uptake process which is not saturable even with hyperphysiological levels of administered hormone, and a retention process of many hours duration, which is saturated by physiological doses of 17β-estradiol. As might be expected, the precise characteristics of 17β-estradiol uptake and retention by estrogen-sensitive cells depend critically, among other things, on the route and vehicle of steroid administration. 17β-Estradiol, 17α-ethinylestradiol, hexestrol, and some other estrogens can definitely initiate uterine growth without undergoing chemical change, at least under some biological circumstances. Other estrogens, such as estrone and mestranol, bind only poorly to female reproductive tissues; there is evidence compatible with the view that the estrogenicity of the latter two substances is due to their conversion in the organism to 17β-estradiol and 17α-ethinylestradiol respectively. "Impeded" estrogens (18) like estriol show a certain degree of affinity for rat uterus where they are taken up without being changed chemically, but their retention is of shorter duration than that of 17β-estradiol. Retention of 17β-estradiol by isolated rat uterine horns is abolished by addition of sulfhydryl reagents (iodoacetamide, N-ethylmaleimide, p-hydroxymercuribenzoate) to the incubation medium.

These observations have served as a starting point for many recent investigations. It has become apparent that 17β-estradiol may actually be converted into estrone by certain estrogen-responsive tissues, even though this transformation is not detectable in immature rat uterus (4, 5), calf uterus (19), anterior pituitary, and some other organs. Breuer (20, 21) perfused rat inner female genital organs (vagina, uterus, and ovary) with ^{14}C-labeled estrone and 17β-estradiol and demonstrated considerable interconversion of both steroid substrates. Sweat et al (22) reported that 17β-estradiol was oxidized to estrone by human endometrium and myometrium, the latter tissue being the less active. A 17β-hydroxysteroid dehydrogenase oxidizing 17β-

estradiol that utilizes NAD or NADP was purified to a high degree from rabbit myometrium by Jütting and co-workers (23). The activity of the enzyme in crude extracts depended on the physiological state of the uterus, being increased immensely by pregnancy or estrogen administration. Using a clever double isotope diffusion technique, Gurpide & Welch (24) observed extensive interconversion of 17β-estradiol and estrone by human endometrial slices. A thorough study by Pack (25) using uterine slices indicated that oxidation of 17β-estradiol to estrone occurs readily with preparations from adult, but not immature, rats. Since Jensen (4, 5) found that radioisotope from injected estrone is largely in the form of 17β-estradiol in immature rat uterus, and making the unproven assumption that oxidation of 17β-estradiol and reduction of estrone are catalyzed by the same uterine 17β-hydroxysteroid dehydrogenase, the lack of extensive transformation of 17β-estradiol to estrone in immature uterus might not reflect only low activity of any appropriate functional enzyme, but rather might involve other factors, such as unfavorable ambient concentrations of the oxidized and reduced forms of NAD and NADP. For it is well established that, at physiological pH values, the equilibrium constant for interconversion of 17β-estradiol and estrone by pyridine nucleotides permits facile reversibility of the reaction (26). We shall allude to the point later in our discussion of estrogen-mediated pyridine nucleotide transhydrogenase reactions. But it may be appropriate to mention here the technique developed by Wenzel (27) for estimation of the oxidation of the 17β-hydroxyl group of steroids. Substances like 17β-estradiol and testosterone are labeled with tritium in the 17α position, so that their oxidation by hydroxysteroid dehydrogenases results in the formation of reduced pyridine nucleotides containing tritium at carbon 4 of the nicotinamide moiety. Oxidation of NAD-^{3}H or NADP-^{3}H so produced by mitochondrial respiratory chains forms tritiated water which can be determined very simply. Using this technique, Wenzel & Kraus (28) concluded that oxidation of 17β-estradiol and testosterone in intact rats does not seem to be limited solely by the activity of 17β-hydroxysteroid dehydrogenases. Wenzel & Pollow (29) observed that tritium from the 17α position of 17β-estradiol was extensively transferred to androstenedione when the steroids were incubated with rat liver slices, suggesting some sort of compartmentalization of pyridine nucleotide pools within the cells. These reactions are catalyzed by cytoplasmic hydroxysteroid dehydrogenases (30). The nature of the tritiated reduced products of androstenedione varied with the sex of the animals and was altered in the female direction after treatment of male rats with cyproterone acetate (31). Wenzel & Pollow (29) could obtain no evidence for oxidation of 17α-^{3}H-labeled 17β-estradiol by immature rat uterus, in confirmation of an earlier report from Jensen's laboratory (11).

There have appeared a number of reports on autoradiographic localization of the tritiated estrogens taken up by responsive tissues. An authoritative review by Stumpf (32) discusses technical aspects of these researches, with special reference to the problem of redistribution artefacts; dry mounting of freeze-dried sections seems to be the best available procedure. A pronounced concentration in cell nuclei of ^{3}H-17β-estradiol was found in epithelial, connective tissue, and muscle cells of uterus (33–36), in acidophiles, basophiles, and chromophobes of anterior pituitary (37–39), and in certain neurons in the hypothalamus (38, 40, 41). No preferential localization of radioactivity was demonstrable in cell nuclei of tissues such as liver and adrenal, or other areas of the brain.

Binding of estrogens by various regions of the hypothalamus continues to receive attention. Earlier studies on this topic from a number of laboratories are summarized by Everett (42) and McGuire & Lisk (43). The latter authors injected rats with a single trace dose of tritiated 17β-estradiol, and then at various intervals separated blocks of tissue from different parts of the hypothalamus and adjacent structures; preferential accumulation of radioactivity was observed in the preoptic area and arcuate nucleus, whereas no hormone retention occurred in regions either anterior to the preoptic area or posterior to the mammillary region, nor in the thalamus, and binding of 17β-estradiol by the mammillary region itself was of borderline significance (43). These findings are in general agreement with studies by others involving autoradiography (38, 40, 41) or uptake of radioactivity from injected labeled estrogens by hypothalamic tissues in vivo (42, 44). Experiments by McGuire & Lisk (45) involving administration of ^{3}H-17β-estradiol to normal or ovariectomized rats suggested similarities in the uptake and retention of radioisotope in uterus, anterior pituitary, and hypothalamus; the radioactivity levels in these tissues appeared to be more or less inversely related to the presumed concentrations of circulating estrogens, since they were high at diestrus and low during estrus. These observations would fit in with earlier (8, 9, 46) and more recent (47, 48) demonstrations that uptake of labeled 17β-estradiol by hypothalamus, hypophysis, and hypothalamus is reduced by concomitant administration of the unlabeled hormone, or estrogen antagonists.

Whalen & Maurer (49), on the contrary, reported that accumulation of injected ^{3}H-17β-estradiol by hypothalamus did not fluctuate with endogenous estrogen levels during the estrus cycles of intact female rats. Yet when Kato (50) incubated rat anterior hypothalamic tissue in vitro with labeled 17β-estradiol, uptake was somewhat greater with preparations from animals in diestrus as compared with estrus or proestrus. Disputes (cf 45, 49) as to effects of estrogens on the amounts of "receptors" for these hormones in responsive tissues such as uterus and hypothalamus, which relate solely to published measurements of uptake of labeled estrogens in vivo (see also 51–54), are hard to adjudge at the moment. This is because such experiments may be complicated by a variety of factors which were not fully evaluated under the same conditions, such as the degree of binding of various estrogens to plasma proteins vis-a-vis the circulating levels of "free" 17β-estradiol, the variety of endogenous estrogenic or other substances which can be taken up by tissues, possible blood-brain barriers to estrogens operating at various times of the host's existence, and especially the multiplicity of intracellular estrogen-binding macromolecules in various responsive tissues which we shall discuss shortly.

Some interesting recent investigations have been prompted by the well-established fact that treatment of neonatal female rats with androgens or estrogens interferes with the normal postnatal differentiation of the preoptic-anterior hypothalamic area, so that it fails to exercise control of cyclic output of gonadotropins by the anterior pituitary, and modes of sexual behavior, after puberty. McGuire & Lisk (55) administered testosterone propionate or 17β-estradiol benzoate in large doses to female rats just after birth; 90 days later the animals, which exhibited little or no mating behavior, were oöphorectomized, and uptake of tritium into various regions of the hypothalamus and anterior pituitary was determined over a period of several hours following injection of ^{3}H-17β-estradiol. Estrogen treatment of newborns resulted in profound disruption of 17β-estradiol retention by the hypophysis, and the anterior, middle, and posterior areas of the hypothalamus. Androgen administration to the neonates, on the contrary, caused a large decrease in hormone uptake by the anterior pituitary but not to any great extent in any of the hypothalamic tissues. In intact (56) and ovariectomized (57) female rats that were subject to androgen sterilization at birth, Flerko and his colleagues found a decreased uptake of injected radioactive 17β-estradiol by uterus, anterior pituitary, and anterior hypothalamus, but not in the posterior hypothalamus. Similar findings were obtained by Vertes & King (58). These conclusions have been questioned by Green, Luttge & Whalen (59) who believe that body weight differences, rather than a blockade of estrogen "receptor" sites, by neonatal androgenization are responsible for the results obtained. According to Anderson & Greenwald (38), when rats that had been treated at 5 days of age with a large amount of testosterone propionate were injected in adulthood with labeled 17β-estradiol, there were fewer labeled cells in the preoptic area and ventral medial-arcuate nuclei as compared with controls that were not androgensterilized (grain counts in the pars distalis were essentially normal in the latter animals). Interpretation of such experiments on permanent changes in various rodent tissues induced by fetal or neonatal testosterone should take into account that neonatal androgen administration evokes profound changes in steroid-transforming enzymes in rat liver from the 30th day of life onwards (60). Moreover, exposure of newborn rats to their own testicular secretions can influence the levels of a specific testosterone metabolite (3β,17α-dihydroxy-5-α-androstane-3-sulfate) in blood serum of adult castrate males (61). Extensive pertinent investigations on sexual differences in steroid metabolism in adult mammals are considered in excellent reviews by Schriefers (62, 63).

Presl et al (64) measured the accumulation of tritiated 17β-estradiol by various parts of the brain, pituitary, uterus and striated muscle in tissues of female rats varying between 5 and 50 days of age. Marked accumulation of radioactivity at 5 and 10 days of age was common to all the organs examined. A sharp decrease in incorporation was found around 10 days after birth, the values remaining low and stable thereafter in all tissues except uterus and pituitary. These workers discuss age differences in the uptake of hormone by the median eminence and anterior hypothalamus as compared with other districts of the brain. Additional data on the uptake of ^{3}H-β-estradiol by anterior hypophysis and hypothalamus are provided by Attramadal & Aakvaag (65).

Terenius (66) has reported further studies on blockade by sulfhydryl agents on entry of 17β-estradiol into immature mouse uterine halves incubated in Ringer phosphate solutions. N-ethylmaleimide and p-chloromercuribenzoate inhibited both uptake and retention of 17β-estradiol, whereas uptake but not retention of the hormone was depressed by iodoacetate. N-ethylmaleimide also blocked uterine uptake and retention of the synthetic estrogen $meso$-hexestrol, but not of the less estrogenic stereoisomer $racemic$-hexestrol. In another contribution, Terenius (67) found that the unnatural ($-$) optical antipode of the natural ($+$) 17β-estradiol was a potent inhibitor of the uptake of tritiated 17β-estradiol by mouse uterus and vagina. The unnatural ($-$) antipode proved to be only very feebly active as an estrogen. But as the experiments on its inhibition of uterine uptake of the radioactive ($+$) antipode suggested, the ($-$) antipode indeed proved to be an anti-estrogen in the sense that it inhibited uterine growth evoked by the natural ($+$) antipode. Similar studies on optical antipodes of the synthetic estrogens doisynoestrol and methallenestril were documented (67).

Phenomenological studies on selective uptake and retention of labeled estrogens by the chick oviduct (68–70) and other avian tissues (68) have been published.

Uptake of estrogens by mammary gland, and by mammary and other tumors.—Sander (71) and Lemon (72) have reviewed the fate of estrogens in normal and malignant breast tissue. Greater accumulation of radioactivity from injected 17β-estradiol was found in normal rodent mammary gland as compared with fat or skeletal muscle, although the uptake of hormone was not as pronounced as in uterus (73, 74). Ovariectomy (73) but not hypophysectomy (75) increased incorporation of 17β-estradiol by normal rat breast tissue, where most of the radioisotope was retained in epithelial cells rather than in the stroma (76). Tritiated 17β-estradiol was also progressively taken up by rat mammary gland slices incubated in Krebs-Ringer phosphate buffer; addition of glucose to the medium did not influence the results (77). Rat mammary carcinomas induced by 7, 12-dimethylbenz[a] anthracene (DMBA) were found by Sander (71, 78), Terenius (79), Mobbs (80–82), King et al (83), and Jensen et al (10) to concentrate estrogens both in vivo and in vitro. The nuclear localization of radioactivity from the injected estrogens was striking. Huggins (84) had previously established that some rat DMBA-induced mammary cancers are hormone dependent—in the sense that they regress after ovariectomy—whereas other members of the same class of tumors, even in the same animal, can be classed as hormone independent, as their growth is not retarded by excision of the ovaries. There is evidence that the capacity of hormone-dependent rat DMBA-induced mammary cancers to bind and retain 17β-estradiol is greater than that of corresponding neoplasms of the hormone-independent variety (10, 71, 79, 82, 85).

Uptake of labeled estrogens by human mammary cancers and their metastases, with particular reference to objective clinical responses to endocrine ablative surgery, is the subject of increasingly active investigation (10, 71, 72, 85–91a). If it could be substantiated, the claim of Adams & Wong (92) that "paraendocrine" behavior can be ascribed to certain human breast cancers (inasmuch as they appear to aromatize testosterone to estriol via 16 α-hydroxytestosterone) could be an important factor determining the diminished ability of hormone-independent mammary tumors to bind labeled estrogens. However, although Jones et al (93) observed a definite albeit minuscule conversion of androstenedione and dehydroepiandrosterone to 16α-hydroxytestosterone by chopped human breast cancer tissue, no evidence was obtained for formation of estriol (a minute amount of estrone did, however, seem to be produced).

Williams & MacLeod (94) state that the presence of growing pituitary 7315α tumors (which secrete prolactin and ACTH) in ovariectomized and adrenalectomized mice had but little influence on the uptake of tritiated 17β-estradiol by the pituitary, hypothalamus, and uterus of the host animals. Nevertheless the plasma levels of the hormone were somewhat lower in the tumor-bearing creatures, apparently as a result of considerable uptake of radioactivity by the tumor cells.

Stereospecific estrogen-binding proteids in responsive tissues.—The earliest studies on localization of radioactivity in cell-free extracts of uteri from immature or spayed rats injected with labeled 17β-estradiol were made by Jensen et al (7), Noteboom & Gorski (95), King et al (33, 96), Talwar et al (97), and Baulieu's group (98, 99). There was consensus that when uteri which had been excised 15 min to 6 hr after injection of the tritiated hormone were homogenized in sucrose or hypotonic salt solutions, and then subjected to differential centrifugation, the majority of the total tritium was associated with the easily sedimentable nuclear-myofibrillar fraction; the rest of the hormone resided mainly in the cytosol fraction, which remained in solution after removal of all cytoplasmic particulate material. The 17β-estradiol in both of the latter fractions was largely bound noncovalently to macromolecules. The hormone in firm combination with nuclear macromolecules was originally found by Jensen et al (8, 9, 14, 15) to be extractable with 0.3 M KCl at pH 7.4. More recently, Puca & Bresciani (100) showed that 0.4 M KCl at pH 8.5 was a more efficient extraction medium for this nuclear material.

When rat uterine horns were incubated at 37° with very low concentrations (10^{-10} M) of ^{3}H-17β-estradiol in vitro, the distribution of radioisotope in centrifugal fractions of tissue homogenates prepared at the end of the experiments was similar to that found when the hormone was administered in vivo (8, 9, 14, 15). However, if the test tube incubations were performed at 2°, much less radioactivity became associated with the cell nuclei, and most of the hormone was left in the cytosol fraction. Yet on subsequent warming to 37° after preliminary incubations at low temperatures, increased entry of tritium into the nuclei occurred (101). These observations, confirmed by Gorski et al (16) and by Rochefort & Baulieu (102), indicated that labeled 17β-estradiol can bind tenaciously to macromolecules in uterine cytosol at 2°, and may then become associated with nuclear macromolecules by a temperature-dependent process.

Talwar et al (97) were the first to demonstrate that 17β-estradiol bound to macromolecules in uterine cytosol was not dissociated by passage through Sephadex G-100. More recent investigations by Talwar's group (103) and others (15, 100) using gel-filtration techniques showed that the cytosol of various estrogen-responsive tissues contains stereospecific proteids that firmly bind certain estrogens (but not other steroids such as cortisol and testosterone), the binding process being optimal in the range of pH 7—8.5 and at 37°, even though it is readily demonstrable at lower temperatures. A signal technical advance was made by Toft & Gorski (104, 105), who applied uterine cytosol preparations from animals injected with labeled 17β-estradiol to sucrose density gradients, and examined the radioactivity profiles after ultracentrifugation. They observed that the bound radioisotope sedimented as a discrete peak, whose sedimentation coefficient was reckoned to be about 9.5S. It has, however, become clear from the recent work of Jensen et al (14, 15, 101), Erdos (106, 107), and Rochefort & Baulieu (108) that estrogen-binding macromolecules in cytosol fractions from both calf and rat uterus have sedimentation coefficients closer to 8S.

The tight binding between labeled 17β-estradiol and the uterine cytoplasmic 8S macromolecule is disrupted by proteolytic enzymes but not by DNase or RNase (15, 16, 104–106) which suggest it is a proteid rather than a polynucleotide. The 8S proteid-17β-estradiol complex tends, especially in the unrefined state, to form heavier aggregates. This aggregation occurs rather slowly on standing and is hastened by addition of ammonium sulfate, or passage of crude soluble tissue extracts through Sephadex G-200 (8, 106); after purification by preparative density gradient centrifugation the 8S complex no longer aggregates (15). In the presence of 0.3–0.4 M KCl, the cytoplasmic 8S proteid-estrogen complex dissociates into subunits of sedimentation coefficient around 4S (14–16, 106, 109). De Sombre, Puca & Jensen (110, 111) have purified this cytosol estrogen-binding proteid 4S subunit more than 5000-fold from calf uterus, using a procedure involving ammonium sulfate precipitation, gel filtration, and chromatography on DEAE-cellulose, after treatment of crude starting material with Ca^{++}, which prevents reversion to the 8S form or larger aggregates. The isoelectric points of the 8S and 4S proteids in combination with 17β-estradiol appear to be 5.8 and 6.4 respectively; molecular weights of 75,000 (4S) and 200,000 (8S) were computed from their behavior on gel filtration (111).

The spontaneous formation of the cytosol 8S estrogen-receptor complex even at 2° enables the total 8S proteid binding capacity of soluble ultracentrifuged extracts of various tissues to be determined very easily, simply by adding increasing amounts of labeled 17β-estradiol until the 8S peak obtained on sucrose density gradient ultracentrifugation no longer increases. By this method, it was found (14, 15, 101) that if the 8S proteid capacity of rat uterus is taken as 100, then the capacity of vagina is about 50 and of pituitary (in males and females) is about 30. Testis, ovary, adrenal, and seminal vesicle gave values of about 2–3, whilst other tissues examined (diaphragm, muscle, liver, ventral prostate, and kidney) in the rat exhibited a very low but experimentally significant capacity, with values in the range of 0.3–0.6. The 8S proteid therefore appears to be widely distributed among various tissues, but is present only in large amounts in classical "target organs" which are highly responsive to estrogens. Eisenfeld (112) concluded that cytosol preparations from rat hypothalamus contain macromolecules that bind 17β-estradiol, as indicated by experiments in which the latter tritiated steroid was mixed with ultracentrifuged hypothalamic extracts, and the material then passed through Bio-Gel P-10 to remove free hormone. Binding of 17β-estradiol was inhibited by the cold steroid both in vivo and in vitro, and by treatment with chymotrypsin or p-chloromercuriphenylsulfonate, but not by in vitro addition of progesterone, testosterone, or DNase or RNase. Even hyperphysiological doses (0.5 μg) of 17β-estradiol in vivo do not saturate the cytoplasmic 8S binding proteid in rat uterus; this reserve capacity of the 8S macromolecule suggests that it is responsible for the nonsaturable uptake process of estrogens by uterus in vivo (101). A rapid and progressive fall in the total 8S proteid capacity of uterine cytosol preparations is seen over the first 4 hr after injection of a physiological amount of estrogen. After this time, the 8S proteid capacity rises slowly, but not if the animals are treated with cycloheximide 30 min before giving the labeled hormone, which suggests synthesis of new 8S proteid (14, 15, 101).

The binding of various estrogenic substances to uterine 8S cytosol proteids continues to be examined. Generally speaking, only substances with "true" estrogenic activity or various estrogen antagonists associate tightly to the proteid, as evidenced by competition with labeled 17β-estradiol for the binding sites (13–16, 47, 48, 79, 95, 99, 113–116). Affinity constants for 17β-estradiol with the 8S proteid determined between 0° and 4° have been variously reported as 2.8×10^{10} M^{-1} (113), 7×10^{11} M^{-1} (52), and 1.4×10^9 M^{-1} (105) for rat uterus, and as 1.3×10^{11} M^{-1} (109) for rabbit uterine cytosol. A mean value for the association constant of close to 1×10^{10} M^{-1} enables the free energy of association to be computed as -12.7 kcal per mole (113). These affinities of 17β-estradiol for uterine cytosol binding proteids are orders of magnitude greater than the affinity of this steroid for an estrogen-binding β-globulin (probably testosterone-binding globulin) of blood plasma (K_a approximately 1×10^8 M^{-1}) (117, 118), or serum albumin (K_a around 1×10^5 M^{-1}) (119). Thermodynamic and kinetic aspects of the interaction of estrogens with the soluble uterine binding proteids are discussed fully in a penetrating review by Ellis & Ringold (113), who also consider environmental factors influencing the binding process, such as ionic strength (113), divalent metal ions (120, 121), and denaturing agents like urea and guanidium chloride (113).

There exist minor variations in the properties of uterine cytosol 8S estrogen-binding proteids among various species (15, 109, 122). These macromolecules can be exploited as the basis of specific competitive radioligand binding assays for various estrogens (113, 114, 123, 124).

Some years ago, Jensen and Jungblut and their co-workers (8–10) developed an ingenious method to adsorb the soluble uterine estrogen-binding proteid to chromatographic columns of an adsorbent containing 17β-estradiol joined through its phenolic A ring to diazotized p-aminobenzylcellulose. Vonderhaar & Mueller (125) have repeated these experiments with the additional use of columns in which the hormone is bound through a 17α side chain to polyvinyl-(N-phenylenemaleimide). Cuatrecasas (125a) has mentioned that estradiol-Sepharose derivatives can be easily prepared and may be used for separation of specific estradiol-binding proteins by affinity chromatography.

Muldoon & Warren (126), continuing their interesting studies on 4-mercuri-17β-estradiol, have shown that the latter compound interacts with the soluble estrogen-binding proteid of rat uterus, a process which is inhibited by prior treatment of the preparations with 17β-estradiol. This reaction appears to involve formation of a covalent mercaptide linkage between sulfhydryl groups of the estrogen-binding proteid and 4-mercuri-17β-estradiol, whereas the tight combination of 17β-estradiol itself with the protein clearly involves only noncovalent forces. They obtained evidence that 4-mercuri-17β-estradiol does not suffer cleavage of the mercury-carbon bond in vivo. The latter compound and its mercaptide with 2-mercaptoethanol [i.e. 4-(2-hydroxyethylmercapto) mercuri-17β-estradiol] increased glucose 6-phosphate and 6-phosphogluconate dehydrogenase activities when applied intraluminally to ovariectomized rat uteri; these effects could not be ascribed to contamination by free 17β-estradiol and were not mimicked by p-chloromercuribenzoate or its mercaptide with 2-mercaptoethanol. When administered in vivo, 4-mercuri-17β-estradiol causes uterine hyperemia and water imbibition and proliferation of endometrial epithelial cells.

Brökelmann (127) reports that addition of hydrogen peroxide to the incubation medium tremendously increases the binding of tritiated 17β-estradiol to proteins in ultracentrifuged uterine extracts. However, this almost certainly involves covalent binding of 17β-estradiol through ring A to macromolecules. It is well known that peroxidases in uterus and other tissues catalyze oxidation of various phenolic hormones, including 17β-estradiol, to phenoxy free radicals which are very reactive substances that undergo all sort of secondary interactions, including addition to proteins. This subject was reviewed some years ago by Williams-Ashman (128, 129). New data on analagous covalent binding of phenolic estrogen degradation products to proteins by liver microsomal-reduced pyridine nucleotide systems are presented by Marks & Hecker (130). Recently, Brökelmann & Fawcett (131), in an electronmicroscopic histochemical staining study, have shown that uterine peroxidase is present not only in erythrocytes and tissue eosinophiles but also in the endoplasmic reticulum and nuclear envelope of the epithelial cells. The gigantic increases in uterine peroxidases evoked by estrogens in vivo (cf 128) were prevented by administration of acetoxycycloheximide, which suggests that new enzyme synthesis was involved (131).

Nuclei isolated from uterine cells that have been exposed to 17β-estradiol, either in vivo or in vitro, contain radioactivity that is largely bound to a proteid extractable with 0.3–0.4 M KCl. This 5S nuclear estrogen-binding proteid is clearly separable by sucrose density gradient ultracentrifugation from the 4S subunit of the cytoplasmic 8S proteid discussed above (14, 15, 101) despite some reports to the contrary (109). Direct addition of labeled 17β-estradiol to isolated cell nuclei or nuclear extracts does not yield significant quantities of radioactive 5S proteid after extraction with 0.4 M KCl, although some hormone is sequestered by intact nuclei. The tight association of hormone with nuclear 5S proteid is demonstrable, however, in whole homogenates incubated at 37°, or when cell nuclei are incubated with cytosol preparations containing the cytoplasmic 8S estrogen-binding proteid. These facts have led to the formulation by Jensen et al (15, 101) of a two-step mechanism of interaction of estrogens in uterus, confirmed and extended by Shyamala & Gorski (132) and Brecher & Wotiz (133). This hypothesis states that estradiol first combines with the 8S cytoplasmic proteid, which then enters cell nuclei by a temperature-dependent process to give rise to the nuclear 5S proteid-estrogen complex, in which form the hormone is largely retained in the tissue for considerable periods of time. There are indications that in the absence of 17β-estradiol, the cytosol 8S proteid will not enter nuclei, even at 37°. Under certain experimental conditions, a significant quantity of 4S proteid as well as 5S proteid in combination with radioactive 17β-estradiol can be extracted from nuclei. It appears that, in some instances, more 8S proteid-estrogen complex can be taken up by nuclear preparations than can be converted to 5S proteid complex, so that the excess 8S complex is extracted with 0.4 M KCl as the 4S subunit. It is not known whether the uptake of cytoplasmic 8S proteid-estrogen complex by nuclei involves a transfer of hormone to some pre-existing nuclear proteid, or whether the 8S material undergoes transformation to the nuclear 5S complex. In the latter instance, it can be imagined (15) that the 5S complex represents the 4S subunit in union with estrogen which has either (a) suffered a change in conformation, or (b) lost some buoyant (lipid?) moiety, or (c) become associated with some additional substances of nuclear origin. Jensen et al (15) favor the latter notion.

A very recent preliminary communication by Brecher et al (134) hints that formation of the rat uterine 5S protein-17β-estradiol complex may also occur under certain circumstances in the complete absence of cell nuclei. They state that a temperature-dependent conversion of the 4S subunit of the cytosol 8S proteid to a 5S proteid-17β-estradiol complex occurs when uterine cytosol preparations are heated to 25° in the presence of 17β-estradiol, but not of estrone. This transformation is demonstrable in the absence or presence of added KCl (0.15–0.4 M), is retarded somewhat by Ca^{++}, Mg^{++}, or Mn^{++} and more strongly by EDTA, and is enhanced by raising the pH over the range of 6.9 to 8.5. Passage of the cytosol extracts through Sephadex G-25 abolishes this conversion to the cytoplasmic 5S proteid, which can be restored by adding cytosol preparations which have been heated to 45° so as to destroy all 4S estrogen-binding proteid. Clark & Gorski (135) made the interesting observation that binding of ^{3}H-17β-estradiol to uterine cytosol proteins enables radioactivity subsequently to be bound not only to isolated cell nuclei, but also to inert insoluble material, e.g., glass pellets. In this study (135) no evidence was obtained, contrary to reports of others (136) that a specific nuclear factor was necessary for binding of 17β-estradiol already complexed with cytosol proteids to isolated cell nuclei. Another knotty facet of the whole problem is the finding of Giannopoulos & Gorski (137) that when intact rat uteri are incubated with labeled 17β-estradiol under conditions where most of the hormone remains in the cytoplasm, and are then homogenized in media containing 0.4 M KCl, the tritium present in soluble ultracentrifuged extracts is bound mainly to a macromolecule with a sedimentation coefficient of 6.3S rather than of 4S or 5S. The same 6.3S estrogen-binding proteid was also present in ultracentrifuged extracts of homogenates made in 0.4 M KCl of uteri which contained large amounts of the hormone in the nuclear fraction. The significance of this putative 6.3S form of the cytoplasmic uterine estrogen-binding proteid remains to be clarified.

Various problems posed by the existence of different types of cytoplasmic and nuclear estrogen-binding proteids in responsive cells are considered by King (138) and Baulieu (139). The ability of calf uterus nuclear preparations to associate firmly with 17β-estradiol was found by Puca & Bresciani (140) to be depressed by prior iodination with iodine in KI; it was concluded that tyrosyl and histidyl residues participate in the binding of estrogens. Stereochemical aspects of the combination of various estrogenic molecules with uterine nuclear proteids were examined by Brecher & Wotiz (141) and Puca & Bresciani (142). Association constants for interaction of 17β-estradiol and uterine 5S nuclear proteids have been estimated as 1.5 × 10⁹ M^{-1} at 4° (142) and 1.1 × 10⁹ M^{-1} at 0° (132) near neutral pH.

There are reports that much of the radioactivity in cell nuclei isolated from responsive tissues of rats injected with ³H-17β-estradiol remains together with euchromatin and heterochromatin fractions during preparation of these nucleoproteins (19, 143, 144), and that the hormone is extractable therefrom by solutions of high ionic strength. King and his colleagues (143–145) provided evidence that nuclear estrogen-binding macromolecules from rat uterus or DMBA-induced mammary carcinoma are acidic proteins that can be precipitated (together with bound 17β-estradiol) by protamine sulfate (145a).

We shall reserve further consideration of the possible physiological importance of the participation of cytoplasmic estrogen-binding proteids in the transfer of this class of hormone to cell nuclei until we have discussed the nature of various intracellular macromolecules responsible for binding of androgens or gestagens by certain higher animal cells.

Uptake of androgens by animal cells and formation of 5α-androstane and other derivatives.—The recent availability of tritium-labeled testosterone and other androgenic steroids of very high specific radioactivity has permitted considerable progress in regard to the disposition of these hormones among various animal tissues. Aspects of this topic are considered in reviews by Ofner (146), Stumpf (32), Liao & Fang (3), Grant (147), Wilson & Gloyna (148), Williams-Ashman (149), Williams-Ashman & Reddi (150), and Baulieu & Robel (151).

After injection of labeled testosterone or androstenedione there occurs a definite selective uptake of these hormones by many androgen-sensitive organs such as the prostate gland (152–169) and seminal vesicles (152, 167, 170, 171) of mammals, and the uropygial (preen) gland of ducks (148). A localization of radioisotope in the nuclei of epithelial cells of prostate and seminal vesicle was observed 0.5–3 hr after injection of tritiated testosterone in autoradiographic experiments (32, 172–174). No such selective labeling was demonstrable in liver or diaphragm, or in fibromuscular cells of prostate or seminal vesicle. Smear autoradiograms of cell nuclei isolated after incubation of minced rat ventral prostate with ³H-testosterone disclosed concentration of radioactivity in cell nuclei in experiments conducted at 37°, but not at 2° (172). The failure of Mosebach et al (175) to demonstrate any selective accumulation of testosterone in seminal vesicles of immature rats may possibly be ascribed to their use of relatively large doses of hormone of low specific radioactivity, as Tveter & Attramadal (169) point out. Uptake of radioisotope from administered ³H-testosterone by the hypothalamus and pituitary has been documented (176–178). Certain male heterosexual remnant tissues in females, such as the preputial gland, also concentrate testosterone in vivo (148, 152). No selective uptake of labeled androgens by male muscle tissues—including very sensitive structures such as the levator ani—has been demonstrable (148, 152). When minced prostatic tissue is incubated in vitro with labeled testosterone, more hormone is taken up in comparison with a number of other tissues less responsive to androgens, and a significant proportion of the intracellular radioactivity is associated with nuclei (3, 153, 157).

The entry of tritium from ^{3}H-testosterone into male accessory reproductive glands in vivo, and also glans penis (178), is depressed by administration of nonradioactive androgens like androstenedione and 17α-methyltestosterone as well as by progesterone and corticosterone (155), and also by androgen antagonists such as 17α-methyl-β-nortestosterone (155) and cyproterone acetate (178) or cyproterone (171), although one group found the latter free alcohol to be ineffective (155). Whalen et al (178) reported that cyproterone acetate, under conditions where it inhibited uptake and retention of testosterone by seminal vesicle and glans penis, had no influence on radioactivity levels in hypothalamus or the preoptic-diagonal band of the brain. Although this observation seems to fit in with reports that systemic administration of cyproterone acetate does not depress mating behavior in mature male rats (179 and other references cited in 178), it is still uncertain whether, in adult animals, antiandrogens of this type can cross the blood-brain barrier (178).

Bruchovsky & Wilson (152) found that 5α-dihydrotestosterone (17β-hydroxy-5α-androstane-3-one) was a major metabolite produced from administered ^{3}H-testosterone in rat ventral prostate cytoplasm within minutes after injection of the hormone. The prostatic cytoplasm contained in addition 5α-androstane-3α,17β-diol, androsterone, and residual testosterone, whereas only 5α-dihydrotestosterone together with smaller amounts of testosterone were recovered from prostatic cell nuclei for periods as long as 2 hr. *Free* labeled 5α-dihydrotestosterone was detected only in prostate, seminal vesicale, preputial gland, kidney, and, to a minute extent, in blood plasma. Note that no accumulation of 5α-dihydrotestosterone could be demonstrated in the androgen-sensitive levator ani muscle or other muscular tissues. These findings of extensive formation of 5α-dihydrotestosterone in male genital glands in vivo have been confirmed by other groups (146, 153, 166, 167, 171, 180–182a). The epididymis of rats (180), the comb, wattles, and coccygeal gland of chicks (148, 180), and the preputial glands of both male and female rodents (180) are other androgen-responsive tissues which readily transform testosterone into 5α-dihydrotestosterone. The latter reaction also proceeds in liver, but in this organ, 5α-dihydrotestosterone or other metabolic derivatives thereof are quickly conjugated to yield very polar metabolites, and free 5α-dihydrotestosterone is not retained by liver cell nuclei (148).

Gomez & Hsia (183) and Wilson & Walker (184) reported that slices of human skin actively convert testosterone into 5α-dihydrotestosterone, a finding confirmed by others (185, 186). As in most other extrahepatic tissues (cf 62, 63), no reduction of testosterone to form 5β-dihydro derivatives was observed. The rates of conversion were especially high with skin specimens taken from perineal areas (scrotum, prepuce, labia majora, clitoris). 5α-Dihydrotestosterone formation by prepuce increased over the first 3 months of postnatal life and then fell progressively thereafter, so that in adult men, the activity was almost as low as that found in slices of nonperineal skin from all age groups (184).

Comparative studies on transformation of testosterone to 5α-dihydrotestosterone by slice preparations of prostates from various mammalian species were carried out by Gloyna & Wilson (180). The activity of rat ventral prostate was highest, followed by that of man, baboon, dog, and lion, all of which exhibited values of greater than 100 pmoles of steroid transformed per hour per 100 mg of tissue. Much lower rates were seen with prostate slices from mice, guinea pigs, cats, and bobcats, and in two species (bull and rabbit) the conversion was minuscule. In comparison with the rates observed with prostate slices of immature animals, 5α-dihydrotestosterone production increased with age in dogs, markedly declined with age in bulls, and remained at about the same level in both immature and adult cats (180).

These findings have led Wilson (148, 180) to suggest that "dihydrotestosterone may be involved in prostatic growth" (meaning elaboration of new cells), which at first sight might fit in with the previously mentioned observation (184) of a decline in 5α-dihydrotestosterone formation with increasing age in human foreskin. A very recent preliminary note by Siiteri & Wilson (187) announces that the ratio of concentration of 5α-dihydrotestosterone to that of testosterone is nearly fivefold greater in the prostates of patients with benign hypertrophy of the gland in comparison with normal individuals. The concentrations of testosterone and of androst-4-ene-3,17-dione did not vary significantly between the periurethral and outer zones of the prostate, whereas the level of 5α-dihydrotestosterone in the periurethral zones was two- to threefold greater than that found in the outer zones of normal or hypertrophic glands. There was no significant difference in the ability of normal or benign hypertrophic prostatic tissue to convert testosterone into 5α-dihydrotestosterone in vitro. An interesting series of investigations were conducted by Morfin et al (188) on the fate of labeled testosterone infused into the common arterial supply of the canine prostate and urinary bladder, two tissues of common embryological origin which nevertheless differ profoundly in their responsivity to androgens. In the dog prostate, there was extensive metabolism of testosterone to yield almost exclusively 5α-reduced products, mainly 5α-dihydrotestosterone and 5α-androstane-3β,17β-diol. On the contrary, the metabolism of testosterone by urinary bladder was both more limited and more oxidative, with androst-4-ene-3,17-dione as the major and 5α-androstane-3,17-dione as the minor products. Comparable experiments by Weiner et al (189) on infusion of dog submaxillary gland with radioactive testosterone revealed that in this tissue also, most of the transformed testosterone was in the form of the oxidized product androst-4-ene-3,17-dione. These workers (189) point out that the well-known sexual dimorphism of the submandibular glands of certain rodents is not exhibited by canine salivary glands.

Anderson & Liao (153) examined the fate of tritiated testosterone after its incubation at 37° with minces of rat ventral prostate suspended in buffered saline media. If the cell nuclei of such preparations were isolated at the end of the incubations, they retained considerable amounts of radio-isotope, most of which was in the form of 5α-dihydrotestosterone together with lesser quantities of the unchanged steroid, all the steroids being ex-tractable with methylene chloride. The cytoplasmic fraction contained these substances as well as at least five other unconjugated metabolites. The selec-tive retention of radioactivity largely in the form of 5α-dihydrotestosterone by nuclei of minced prostate in vitro was not observed with minces of thy-mus, liver, brain, and diaphragm. Incubation of rat and bovine brain homog-enates with ^{14}C testosterone and a NADPH-generating system is said, how-ever, to result in formation of 5α-dihydrotestosterone and androst-4-ene-3,17-dione (190); and rat (although not bovine) brain apparently also cata-lyzes the production of 5α-androstane-3α,17β-diol and smaller amounts of 5β-androstane-3α,17β-diol (191, see also 191a).

Bruchovsky & Wilson (152), and Liao and his colleagues (3, 153, 167) discovered a chromatin-bound steroid 5α-reductase in prostatic cell nuclei that catalyzes a NADPH-dependent reduction of the double bond in ring A of testosterone to give 5α-dihydrotestosterone. Earlier experiments on this transformation by the groups of Ofner, Farnsworth, Shimazaki and others are reviewed in detail by Ofner (146); it was demonstrated that cyto-plasmic microsomes from male genital glands also possessed such steroid 5α-reductase activity. Recently Shimazaki et al (192) reported that reduction of testosterone in the 5α position decreased with age in the ventral prostates of postpubertal rats, whereas oxidation of the steroid at C-17 did not dimin-ish concomitantly. Orchiectomy resulted in a decrease in 5α-reductase activ-ity, which could be restored by administration of testosterone propionate. The nature, multiplicity, and subcellular distribution of enzymes, in andro-gen-responsive and other tissues, that catalyze the conversion of testoste-rone to 5α-dihydrotestosterone need to be examined much more thoroughly. [The enzymology of hepatic steroid 5α- and 5β-reductase is considered ex-tensively by Schriefers (62, 63).] For this might, among other things, ena-ble development of specific inhibitors of the enzymic conversion of testos-terone to 5α-dihydrotestosterone in various tissues. Such substances could conceivably exhibit interesting antiandrogenic properties. Farnsworth (193), apparently unaware of similar earlier studies by Shimazaki et al (194), found that fairly high levels of 17β-estradiol, estrone, and diethyl-stilbestrol (but not of 2-methoxyesterone or 17α-estradiol) inhibit the re-duction of testosterone to 5α-dihydrotestosterone by human prostate in vi-tro. Farnsworth's (193) data are puzzling, because his protocols indicate that increasing the concentration of the active estrogens often diminished their inhibitory effects. Nonestrogenic antiandrogens like cyproterone acetate appear to have little influence on the conversion of testosterone to 5α-dihydrotestosterone in androgen-sensitive tissues (3, 166, 171).

Formation of 5α-dihydrotestosterone from testosterone by explants of rodent prostates grown in organ culture has been reported (195, 196).

All of these findings, taken together with the demonstration that in many bioassay systems 5α-dihydrotestosterone possesses an androgenic potency equal to or even greater than that of testosterone (3), raise the possibility that in at least some androgen-sensitive tissues, 5α-dihydrotestosterone serves as an "active form" of the principal circulating androgens of testicular origin. Further aspects of this hypothesis are considered below.

5α-Dihydrotestosterone-binding proteids.—Bruchovsky & Wilson (197) isolated prostatic cell nuclei from rats treated with ³H-testosterone and extracted them with buffered 0.6 M NaCl. After gel filtration, an acidic protein fraction was obtained to which considerable amounts of radioactivity were firmly bound, largely in the form of 5α-dihydrotestosterone. The binding of the steroid to this macromolecule was destroyed by treatment with proteolytic enzymes, but not with DNase or RNase. This was in contrast to a previous report by Mangan et al (160) which suggested that radioactivity from administered testosterone was associated with prostatic nuclear DNA. Mainwaring (168) also provided evidence that radioisotope predominantly in the form of 5α-dihydrotestosterone was bound strongly but noncovalently to acidic nuclear proteins in rat ventral prostate, and that the binding proteid was closely associated with chromatin in the nuclei. Unhjem et al (182) noticed in both in vivo and in vitro experiments that 5α-dihydrotestosterone associated firmly with two major cytoplasmic macromolecules in rat prostate; one of these was reported to have a sedimentation coefficient of 9.3S and seemed to be the same as a specific binding proteid indicated by gel-filtration studies, whilst the other macromolecule (sedimentation coefficient about 4.5S) appeared to be serum albumin. Association of labeled 5α-dihydrotestosterone with specific cytoplasmic proteids in male genital glands was also found by Parsons, Mangan & Neal (198), Mainwaring (181), Stern & Eisenfeld (171), Baulieu & Jung (199), and Unhjem & Tveter (200).

A comprehensive investigation by Fang et al (3, 167) disclosed that an apparently specific 5α-dihydrotestosterone-binding proteid can be extracted from prostate cell nuclei with the aid of buffered 0.4 M KCl. Sucrose density gradient centrifugations of this material indicated a sedimentation coefficient of about 3S. Fang et al (167) state that prostate cytosol also contains a similar binding proteid with a sedimentation coefficient (3.5S) slightly higher than that of its nuclear counterpart. This does not agree with a value of 8S reported by Mainwaring (181) for a cytoplasmic proteid with a high affinity for 5α-dihydrotestosterone isolated from the same tissue. Fang et al (167) found that when isolated prostatic cell nuclei were incubated with tritiated testosterone or 5α-dihydrotestosterone, there was little or no retention of radioisotope by nuclear macromolecules. Addition of a cytosol fraction to the nuclear system, however, permitted extensive retention of 5α-dihydrotestosterone in the form of an intranuclear 3S proteid complex. Evidence was put forward (cf 200a) in support of a two-step mechanism whereby 5α-dihydrotestosterone first combines with a cytosol 3.5S proteid, and in that form can then enter nuclei so as to be retained there as a complex with a 3S proteid which is extractable from the nuclei with solutions of high ionic strength. The cytosol and the nuclear forms of the specific 5α-dihydrotestosterone-binding proteid exhibit different sensitivities to temperature, according to Fang et al (167). Neither testosterone nor cortisol interacted strongly with the prostatic cytosol 3.5S binding macromolecule, which appeared, however, to bind progesterone and 17β-estradiol to some extent (167).

Remarkably low concentrations of the antiandrogens cyproterone and cyproterone acetate depress the formation of complexes between 5α-dihydrotestosterone and specific binding proteids demonstrable in cytoplasmic (171, 199) and nuclear (201) fractions of homogenates of male accessory reproductive glands.

Disposition of progesterone in various tissues.—O'Malley et al (202) have examined the fate of labeled progesterone in the chick oviduct, a tissue in which progesterone can specifically induce synthesis of the protein avidin, but not of other proteins like ovalbumin whose biosynthesis in this organ is under estrogenic control. The oviduct did not concentrate progesterone from blood. The radioactivity in the oviduct derived from circulating progesterone was associated with both nuclear and soluble fractions of homogenates of the tissue. Incubation of oviduct minces with ^{3}H-progesterone allowed fairly extensive metabolism of the steroid to unidentified products. There were indications that the cytosol fraction contained macromolecules that firmly bound progesterone in the unchanged form; progesterone was released by exposure to proteolytic enzymes but not by DNase or RNase. In vivo studies by Falk & Bardin (203) showed longer retention of tritiated progesterone in uterus as compared with heart or diaphragm of oöphorectomized guinea pigs. Most of the radioactivity taken up by the uterus was in the form of unchanged progesterone. Uterine uptake of progesterone was not blocked by cortisol, 17β-estradiol, or testosterone, which suggested that the retention of progesterone was selective. Other purely descriptive studies on the uptake of labeled progesterone by pituitary, brain, and genital tissues have been published (204–206). Frost et al (206a) examined the metabolism of ^{14}C-labeled progesterone by minces of human skin and vaginal mucosa. A variety of products were obtained which involved reduction of the 20-ketone to a 20α-ol, reduction of the 3-ketone to 3α-ol and 3β-ol, and saturation of the double bond in ring A to yield 5α-pregnane derivatives. No 5βhydrogenated metabolites were detected. Armstrong & King (207) state in a preliminary communication that rat uterine slices and homogenates readily convert progesterone to 3α-hydroxy-5α-pregnane-20-one, this reaction being increased by treatment of castrates with estrogen. The reduction of the double bond in ring A of progesterone to yield 5α-pregnane-3,20-dione was demonstrated with isolated uterine cell nuclei, and it appears that further reduction of the 3-ketone groups occurs at extranuclear sites. Here it may be mentioned that Wenzel et al (208) obtained a direct transfer of tritium from the 17α position of 17β-estradiol to progesterone (yielding 20α-hydroxy-Δ^4-pregnen-3-one-20β-³H) when the steroids were incubated with slices of female rate liver or ovaries; they concluded that 17β-estradiol may regulate progesterone metabolism in these organs. The nature, distribution, and multiplicity of enzymes in various mammalian tissues which catalyze transformations of progesterone is in urgent need of clarification.

Karsznia et al (209) observed that soluble extracts of rat prostate contain large molecules which bind pregnenolone and progesterone, but not testosterone, 17β-estradiol. deoxycorticosterone, or corticosterone. A similar protein could not be detected in liver. The significance of these findings is obscure, considering that the prostate is rather insensitive to progesterone, although extremely high doses of this hormone have been reported to exhibit some androgenlike activity in castrated rodents (210).

A progesterone-binding protein from the uterus of castrated rats was studied by Milgrom & Baulieu (211). It could not be distinguished from plasma corticosteroid-binding globulin by a variety of criteria, including sedimentation and electrophoretic behavior, thermolability, and gel-filtration characteristics, even though a simple contamination of the uterine preparations by plasma was excluded. Leymaire & Gueriguian (212) have described a soluble macromolecule in the corpus luteum of the pregnant cow which binds progesterone.

It is evident that our understanding of specific intracellular macromolecules that may bind progesterone or its metabolites remains very rudimentary.

General remarks on intracellular sex hormone-binding proteids.—The discovery of specific intracellular proteids that bind estrogens, 5α-dihydrotestosterone etc is unquestionably a significant advance which has much potential bearing on the problem of the competence of different vertebrate tissues to respond to various types of sex hormones. These fascinating new findings, however, raise many more questions than they answer, a few of which will now be considered.

The aforementioned evidence that intracellular macromolecules may function as parts of a two-step mechanism for uptake and retention by cell nuclei of estrogens or 5α-dihydrotestosterone in female and male reproductive organs makes it easy to imagine some functional relationships, which might be put as follows. First, this machinery might simply represent a device to transport sex hormones or their metabolites into the nucleus, where the steroids could then directly influence nuclear biochemical events, e.g., the formation of RNA molecules, the penetration of molecules in and out of the nuclear membrane etc (see below). Secondly, it is conceivable that sex hormones or their metabolites in union with specific proteids represent the true "active forms" of the hormones; if this proved to be the case, then it might be fruitless to attempt to influence certain biochemical processes in cell-free systems by direct addition of substances like 17β-estradiol or 5α-dihydrotestosterone in the free form, rather than as their complexes with cytoplasmic or nuclear forms of the binding proteins. At this juncture we may mention that Seshadri & Warren (213) claim that estrone (but not 17β-estradiol) directly augments incorporation of guanine, guanosine, and uracil (but not $5'$-GMP, GTP, or UTP) into RNA of cell nuclei isolated from rat uterus, but not from rat lung. The authors hint that cytoplasmic contaminants of the uterine nuclear preparations may be involved in this somewhat paradoxically specific effect of estrone, which is in contrast to an earlier report of Barker & Warren (214) that 17β-estradiol directly increases the template capacity of uterine chromatin for RNA synthesis. The effects of temperature and inhibitors of protein byosynthesis on RNA polymerase activity of nuclei isolated from rat uteri incubated in vitro, following treatment of the animals with estrogens, that are described by Nicolette, Lemahieu & Mueller (215) are hardly germane to the aforementioned in vitro effects of estrogens on uterine nuclear RNA biosynthesis. The latter studies hint that uninterrupted protein biosynthesis is necessary for maintenance of uterine RNA polymerase activity under the stated conditions.

Raynaud-Jammet & Baulieu (216) made the interesting observation that enhancement of uterine nuclear RNA synthesis with labeled CTP as precursor by very low concentrations of 17β-estradiol required the presence of a cytoplasmic factor. In the absence of cytoplasmic components, Bashirelahi et al (217, 218) found that direct addition of 5α-dihydrotestosterone increased the entry of labeled cytidine into RNA of nuclei from the prostates of androgen-deficient rats. Experimental confirmation and extension of all of these findings of enhancement of nuclear biosynthetic processes by sex hormones in vitro will be awaited with great interest.

A third possibility would be that it is not so much the function of these proteids to transport the hormones into the nucleus, but rather the other way round, that is, by combination with cytoplasmic forms of the specific macromolecules, the hormones might in some way change their properties (conformation?), so that the proteids can get into and be retained by cell nuclei. This would mean that the hormones might act in a permissive fashion so as to influence only the intracellular translocation of specific proteids which might themselves serve controlling functions in the absence of steroids. These speculations are likely to be put to experimental test over the new few years.

Perhaps too much stress is being put on the cell nucleus as the ultimate destination of estrogens or active forms of androgens; even though a major fraction of these hormones may be found in nuclei of responsive cells in vivo, this does not necessarily imply that the nucleus is the sole or even major site of the basic regulatory influences of the hormones. Furthermore, the often employed designation of these specific intracellular sex hormone binding proteids known today as "*the* receptors" for estrogens or androgens may have conscious or unconscious implications of unitary mechanisms of hormone action which may turn out to appear too simplistic.

It is regrettable that a number of recently published studies with cell-free preparations dealing with the role of specific cytoplasmic-binding proteids in the capture of sex hormones by isolated cell nuclei have given little attention to energy-yielding enzymic reactions whose products may conceivably influence nuclear retention of the hormones. It is easy to imagine, for example, that ATP generation by nuclear glycolytic reactions could be of importance in this respect. This matter is reminiscent of some of the pioneer investigations on passage of small molecules, such as L-amino acids, through the membranes of isolated cells or organelles in which due regard was not given to energy-dependent transport processes, so that the in vitro experiments did not mirror correctly all of the events operative in the living organism.

The evidence that 5α-dihydrotestosterone may represent an "active form" of testosterone in certain androgen-sensitive tissues presents semantic difficulties. If such considerations are substantiated, can one then regard circulating testosterone as a "hormone" rather than as a sort of "pro-hormone"? Here it must be remembered that other metabolic transformation products of testosterone or androst-4-ene-3,17-dione are formed in androgen-sensitive tissues, notably various 5α-androstanediols. Conceivably the latter substances, even though they do not appear to be retained by cell nuclei, themselves act as regulators, as has already been hypothesized (146, 195, 196).

One can argue that the functions of various intracellular sex hormone-binding proteids will be difficult to fathom until these macromolecules are purified to a state of homogeneity, so that their properties and composition (especially with respect to possible subunits) can be defined. Current experimentation along these lines has concentrated very heavily on use of sucrose density gradient centrifugations and gel-filtration techniques as markers for these proteids. In almost every instance, the presence of these macromolecules has been inferred from measurements of the radioactivity of the bound low molecular weight ligand (hormone). Although the binding constants for association of the steroids with these proteids are very large under certain specified experimental conditions, the possibility that certain purification procedures could enrich these proteids but actually remove the bound hormone should not be ignored. It might be enlightening to find means of stabilizing these proteids in the absence of sex hormones, and to attempt to isolate them in this state.

Proteids are not the only class of intracellular macromolecules with which sex hormones can associate. Attention continues to be given to quantitative aspects of the binding of steroids to highly purified ribo- and deoxyribopolynucleotides (219–220a). The physiological significance of these relatively weak noncovalent interactions is debatable.

TESTICULAR FEMINIZATION SYNDROME

The use of organisms in which there are genetically determined blocks of specific metabolic processes to elucidate the biosynthesis or functions of small molecules is a commonplace of physiological chemistry. The rare condition often called testicular feminization syndrome, which Money and his co-workers (221) have now more aptly rechristened the androgen-insensitivity syndrome, holds promise of providing considerable insight into the action of androgenic hormones. In its full-blown human form (which appears to have a genetic basis), the patients have abdominal testes, no ovaries, an uncomplicated XY sex karotype, a strikingly female external phenotypic appearance after the age of puberty (although pubic and axillary hair may be sparse or absent), and a short vagina but no real uterus. These patients appear to be refractory to various androgenic steroids applied locally or administered systemically. A good recent review of the clinical picture is provided by Ionesco (222).

The metabolism of radioactive testosterone in patients with the androgen-insensitivity syndrome has been further investigated by Mauvais-Jarvis et al (223). In normal men, the yields of urinary 5α-androstane-3α,17β-diol derived from testosterone given by either the intravenous or the percutaneous route were respectively 3 and 6 times greater than those obtained when testosterone was given orally, which permits the hormone to enter the liver directly via the portal vein. Thus it appears that in normal males, reduction of testosterone to yield 5α-metabolites occurs extensively outside the liver. Patients with the androgen-insensitivity syndrome, on the other hand, showed similar rates of formation of the 5α-androstanediol, regardless of the mode of injection of the labeled testosterone, indicating little extrahepatic 5α-hydrogenation. These metabolic abnormalities found in patients with the androgen-insensitivity syndrome could be mimicked to some extent by treatment of normal males with estrogens. It appeared that subjects exhibiting the symptoms of testicular feminization are about ten times more sensitive to exogenous estrogens than normal males, as indicated by the fall in urinary 5α-dihydrotestosterone and the 5α-androstanediol and by increases in the level of plasma proteins that bind testosterone. The conclusion reached was that the apparent defect in extrahepatic 5α reduction of testosterone in patients with the androgen-insensitivity syndrome may not necessarily reflect any enzymic impairment, but rather may be due to an estrogen-induced rise of plasma proteins that bind testosterone, so that an abnormally low concentration of unbound circulating testosterone may be available to peripheral tissues that are normally androgen-responsive. Effects of sex and of estrogen treatment on the excretion of urinary metabolites of testosterone, with particular reference to products reduced in ring A of the steroid, are discussed in other contributions by Mauvais-Jarvis and his colleagues (224, 225).

A markedly diminished conversion of testosterone to 5α-dihydrotestosterone by skin slices from patients with the androgen-insensitivity syndrome has been reported by two groups (185, 186). However, that the picture is not altogether simple is evident from an exhaustive study on this conversion in skin from various human anatomical sites by Wilson & Walker (184). In patients with the androgen-insensitivity syndrome, formation of 5α-dihydrotestosterone by specimens of labia majora was indeed lower than in normal females, whereas no difference between the two groups was noticed when skin was excised from the mons veneris (which forms 5α-dihydrotestosterone at slower rates than labial skin in normal women). Unequivocal measurements of testosterone 5α-reductase activity in cell-free skin preparations would be desirable in this context. Furthermore, Strickland & French (226) showed that 5α-dihydrotestosterone like testosterone when administered parenterally did not evoke nitrogen retention or any other signs of androgenicity in patients with the androgen-insensitivity syndrome. Thus it appears that failure of 5α-dihydrotestosterone production cannot be the only lesion in this disorder. It would be interesting to examine tissues from patients with this syndrome to see whether they contain specific intracellular proteids that bind 5α-dihydrotestosterone and are involved in nuclear retention of this steroid.

Bardin et al (227, 228) have recently studied the formation, metabolism, and physiological effects of testosterone in a strain of male pseudohermaphroditic rats originally developed by Stanley and Gumbreck. These creatures, which may provide an experimental model for the human androgen-insensitivity syndrome, contain inguinal testes, but other normal male structures are absent, such as scrotum, seminal vesicles, prostate gland, and vas deferens. The defect is hereditary, passed by normal females to half of the male progeny, although the precise genetics remain poorly understood. The phenotype of these pseudohermaphroditic rats is very female, with tiny phallus, short vagina, and well-developed nipple lines. Bardin et al (227) found that these animals secrete about 25% as much testosterone as normal males. However, other studies (228) revealed that treatment of the rats with testosterone failed to induce a significant increase in the weights of the preputial glands, as is observed in castrated males or normal females. In addition, exogenous testosterone failed to alter the hexobarbital sleeping times in the pseudohermaphroditic rats, whilst androgen decreases the time of sleep induced by hexobarbital in both females and orchiectomized males. Moreover, conversion of testosterone to 5α-dihydrotestosterone by minces of preputial glands in the presence of an NADPH-generating system was the same in both normal and Stanley-Gumbreck rats. This hints that the insensitivity of end organs to testosterone could not be explained by a defect in the conversion of testosterone to 5α-dihydrotestosterone, a conclusion borne out by the finding (228) that administration of 5α-dihydrotestosterone also failed to increase preputial gland weights in these animals. Wilson & Gloyna (148), however, report a small albeit abnormally low increase in preputial gland weight following treatment of Stanley-Gumbreck rats with large doses of 5α-dihydrotesterone.

Outstanding contributions by Money, Ehrhardt and their colleagues (221, 229) consider the role of physiological, psychological, and sociological factors in the development of gender identity and behavior of patients with the androgen-insensitivity syndrome.

EFFECTS OF SEX HORMONES ON ORGAN CULTURES, WITH COMMENTS ON DNA SYNTHESIS AND CELL DIVISION IN RELATION TO GENITAL TISSUE GROWTH

Baulieu, Lasnitzki & Robel (195, 196) added various 19-carbon steroids to explants of rat ventral prostate in organ cultures, using a synthetic medium supplemented with blood serum. Under their experimental conditions, radioactive testosterone was metabolized to 5α-dihydrotestosterone and another, unidentified nonpolar substance; about 90% of the radioisotope appeared to stay in the cytoplasm. Addition of high concentrations (3×10^{-5} M) of testosterone maintained cell height and secretory activity and had a moderate effect on the number of cells in mitosis. Various 5β-androstane derivatives tested were inert. Large amounts of 5α-dihydrotestosterone stimulated "cell proliferation" to a greater extent than testosterone, but had little or no influence on cell height or secretory activity. Baulieu et al (195, 196) concluded that 5α-dihydrotestosterone may be "especially concerned with cell division". Assessment of this revolutionary hypothesis of a specialized action of a major metabolite of testosterone must await full publication of the details of these experiments, especially in regard to the histological changes.

Lasnitzki (230) reports that 3-methylcholanthrene also induces "epithelial hyperplasia" in rat ventral prostate organ cultures; however, examination of her illustrations shows a bizarre piling up of several rows of small crowded cells of a type never seen in the normal gland in vivo. The absence of added insulin from the culture media employed by Baulieu et al (195, 196) is another stumbling block to interpretation of their experiments, because Lostroh (231) has shown quite clearly that under many circumstances, insulin is necessary for augmentation of both citrate formation and incorporation of tritiated leucine into proteins by addition of testosterone or 5α-dihydrotestosterone to prostate organ cultures; possibly sufficient insulin was present in the sera added to the media of Baulieu et al (195, 196).

The extent to which DNA synthesis and cell multiplication contribute to the sex hormone-induced growth of various tissues in gonadectomized adult mammals varies greatly from one particular organ to another. Some organs, e.g. mouse levator ani muscles, increase in size in response to androgens almost entirely as a result of hypertrophy of cells. A thorough ultrastructural analysis of effects of testosterone on the levator ani muscle of castrated adult rats was undertaken by Gori, Pellegrino & Pollera (232), who review the older literature on this topic. Other organs in adult orchiectomized animals, such as the ventral prostate and seminal vesicles, grow in response to androgens by a process which involves considerable cell hyperplasia, in addition to hypertrophy of epithelial cells, formation of secretory products and their retention in the glandular acini, and elaboration of new blood vessels. The onset of increased DNA synthesis and enhancement of mitosis in these organs is a relatively late event, and clearly occurs after prior demonstrable increases in RNA synthesis etc (see below). Kosto et al (233) and Coffey et al (234) studied the incorporation of labeled formate and thymidine into DNA by tissue minces, and DNA polymerase activity, during various phases of the growth of regressed rat ventral prostates induced by daily doses of large amounts of testosterone propionate. Orchiectomy resulted in only a modest fall in the low DNA polymerase activity of normal prostate. Following daily injections of androgen, little change was observed over the first 24 hr in DNA synthesis or polymerase levels. By 48 hr, the DNA polymerase activities rose manyfold, reaching a maximum increase of as much as 30-fold at 3–5 days after commencement of the hormone treatments. Despite continued injection of androgen, the prostatic DNA polymerase activities subsequently declined, pari passu with a plateauing of ventral prostate size (234). Essentially the same picture was seen in hypophysectomized rats (233). These findings are comparable with observations made on many other mammalian cells suggesting that large quantities of enzymes involved in DNA replication are elaborated and retained only during periods close to the S phase of the cell cycle. The factors which determine the ultimate restrictions on the total number of cells in sex hormone-dependent organs in mature mammals, regardless of the intensity or duration of the gonadal hormone stimulus, remain very poorly understood. And nothing is known about the relationship of cell division to the "organizational" effects of androgens on the initial embryonic differentiation of many structures that in later life are androgen-dependent.

Synergistic effects of prolactin and other pituitary hormones on the androgen-induced growth of certain male genital tissues, recently reviewed by Reddi (235), will have to be taken into account in any comprehensive consideration of the extent to which male reproductive organs can grow in the absence of frank neoplasia. The complexities of this problem are highlighted by recent experiments of Whalen (236) on penile dimensions in adult rats which had been subject to certain hormonal manipulations just after birth. Neonatally castrated animals exhibited reduced penile development even when injected with testosterone in infancy. Treatment of these creatures with testosterone in adulthood caused an increase in shaft and glans length and in total weight of the phallus. This enhancement of penile growth by administration of androgen to adults was much greater in the rats which had received a single dose of androgen on the first or fourth day of life, and after neonatal castration. Evidently the penis passes through a critical period of differentiation around the time of birth which has a profound influence on the degree to which the size of the penis can be influenced hormonally in adult rodents. Here we can point out that clinical observations by Laron & Sarel (237) hint that growth hormone as well as androgen is an important determinant of human penis and testicular size.

Hormone-induced differentiation of some types of cells in organ cultures may require cell multiplication so that new gene products are synthesized only in daughter cells. This appears to be the case, for example, of mammary glands grown in organ culture, whose undifferentiated epithelial cells can be stimulated to divide and differentiate by addition of insulin plus adrenal cortical hormones plus prolactin, so as to produce secretary alveolar cells which synthesize casein and lactose. Recent advances in this field are reviewed by Turkington (238, 239). Inhibitors of DNA synthesis and also various androgenic hormones added in vitro prevent the mammary gland cells from entering the S phase of the cell cycle and any appearance of casein synthesis or lactose synthetase; however, these inhibitors do not completely abolish the action of prolactin in inducing milk proteins in cultures of postmitotic cells, which had been treated with insulin and hydrocortisone. Estrogens are, of course, of paramount importance for mammary gland growth in vivo. But in organ cultures of normal or neoplastic mouse mammary tissue insulin-mediated cell proliferation is reported to be inhibited 70–80% by extremely low levels (10^{-12} M) of 17β-estradiol. If the concentration of 17β-estradiol is increased to 10^{-10} M, maximal increases in DNA synthesis in response to insulin are observed, according to Turkington (238–240), and even higher concentrations (10^{-8} M) of 17β-estradiol exert a diphasic inhibitory action. These effects apparently result from modification of the rate at which the cells enter the DNA synthetic phase, and are shared qualitatively by estrone, estriol, and diethylstilbestrol. How far they are pertinent to the estrogenic enhancement of mammary growth in vivo is not clear.

ESTROGEN-MEDIATED PYRIDINE NUCLEOTIDE TRANSHYDROGENASE REACTIONS

A long-standing controversy (241, 242) as to whether a 17β-estradiol dehydrogenase from human placenta, which reacts almost equally well with NAD and NADP, is really capable of catalyzing hydrogen transfers between NADPH and NAD in the presence of minute concentrations of 17β-estradiol or other of its steroid substrates now appears to have been finally settled in the affirmative (243, 244). With highly refined preparations of this enzyme, Karavolas, Orr & Engel (243) confirmed the original finding of Talalay & Williams-Ashman (241) that when 17β-estradiol was added in catalytic quantities as a mediator for transhydrogenations between NADPH and NAD, the steroid was converted to estrone and the latter again reduced, a determinable steady-state ratio of 17β-estradiol/estrone being quickly attained. Other evidence for the oxidation-reduction hypothesis has been published (243, 244). As was shown earlier (241), and is only to be expected, Karavolas et al (243) now report that estrogens which do not contain an oxidizable steroidal 17β-hydroxyl group (e.g. 17α-methylestradiol or diethylstilbestrol) cannot serve as mediators for pyridine nucleotide transhydrogenase reactions promoted by this human placental 17β-hydroxysteroid dehydrogenase. Jarabak & Sack (245) have undertaken a thorough analysis of the steroid specificity of the latter cold-sensitive enzyme, and its inhibition by certain antiestrogenic compounds.

Further studies by Karavolas, Orr & Engel (243) have suggested that soluble extracts of human placenta contain an additional protein which catalyzes estrogen-mediated pyridine nucleotide transhydrogenations. This enzyme appears to be quite distinct from the 17β-estradiol dehydrogenase, and does not involve a mechanism whereby the hormonal cofactors undergo oxidoreduction. The enzyme is stated to be activated by 17β-estradiol and by diethylstilbestrol, but not by either estrone or 17α-methylestradiol. When this enzyme catalyzes hydrogen transfer from NADPH to NAD in the presence of 17β-estradiol, no estrone is apparently formed; its activity is enhanced by high concentrations of NaCl, whereas the transhydrogenase function of the 17β-hydroxysteroid dehydrogenase is depressed at high ionic strengths.

The physiological significance of pyridine nucleotide transhydrogenase reactions catalyzed by either of the aforementioned human placental enzymes remains uncertain. Although these reactions may indeed be related to some of the actions of estrogens on human placental preparations in vitro (129, 241, 242), the total activity of both enzymes in human placental extracts is rather feeble (241, 243), and there is no evidence for widespread occurrence of enzymes of this class among estrogen-sensitive tissues (129).

INTRACELLULAR "SECOND MESSENGERS" AND SEX HORMONE ACTION

Cyclic nucleotides.—It is a commonplace that adenosine-3′,5′-cyclic monophosphate (cyclic AMP) serves as an intracellular "second messenger" to mediate many if not all actions of a number of different hormones, including catecholamines, glucagon, ACTH, vasopressin, and certain gonadotropins. An up-to-date review by Butcher, Robison & Sutherland (246) discusses this topic and points out that the recent discovery of other cyclic ribonucleoside monophosphates (such as cyclic GMP) in tissues raises the possibility that a variety of small molecules of this class would function as intracellular mediators for various hormones. Whether cyclic AMP or any other low molecular weight substances serve as second messengers for the actions of estrogens, gestagens, or androgens, however, remains a moot point.

Szego & Davis (247) have continued their studies of the very quick increases in cyclic AMP concentrations in uteri of ovariectomized rats following intravenous administration of 17β-estradiol. This effect was blocked by the β-adrenergic antagonists propanolol and dichloroisoproterenol. Bilat-

eral adrenalectomy virtually nullified the inhibitory effect of dichloroisoproterenol but only interfered slightly with the action of propanolol. The α-adrenergic blocking agents phentolamine and dibenzyline were essentially inert. Talwar and his colleagues (248, 249) have followed up older observations of Hechter's group (see 248 for references) that cyclic AMP and
other cyclic nucleotides can stimulate a number of biosynthetic reactions in
isolated uterine preparations. Sharma & Talwar (248) report that cyclic
AMP in concentrations of 0.1 mM, or the dibutyryl derivative in concentrations of 0.001 mM, stimulate uptake of tritiated uridine and leucine and
their respective incorporation into RNA and proteins by uterine horns from
oöphorectomized rats. The effect of cyclic AMP was rapid, and was not
mimicked in short-term experiments by 5'-AMP or 5'-GMP, although in experiments of 2 hr duration the latter nucleotides exerted actions similar to
those of cyclic AMP, but of smaller magnitude. Sharma & Talwar (248)
concluded that the first effects of cyclic AMP were on the penetration of
uridine and leucine into uterine cells, but that at later intervals in these in
vitro experiments (60–120 min) a true increase in RNA synthesis was facilitated by the cyclic nucleotide, whose actions at all periods were not depressed by inhibitors of protein biosynthesis. It was pointed out that an unequivocal relationship of cyclic AMP to estrogen-induced proliferation of
rat uterus remains to be demonstrated. Effects of cyclic AMP on uterine
contractility have been investigated (250, 251).

Two publications from O'Malley's laboratory (252, 253) concern the response of adenyl cyclase in chick oviduct to steroid hormones. Neither adenyl cyclase activity nor cyclic AMP levels in this organ were enhanced by
administration of diethylstilbestrol. The latter estrogen did, however,
acutely increase adenyl cyclase activity in uteri of castrated rats; but since
the effect was prevented by administration of DL-propanolol, it was apparently mediated by catecholamines. Progesterone, on the other hand, evoked a
significant albeit delayed enhancement of oviduct adenyl cyclase activity
which was manifest at 3–6 hr after injection of the hormone, and reached
250% of that of control animals by 24 hr; no such changes were observed in
liver or lung. The relation of increases in oviduct adenyl cyclase activity to
the induction of avidin synthesis is equivocal, in the view of Kissel et al (253).

No effect of testosterone administration on the adenyl cyclase activity of
the ventral prostates of hypophysectomized rats could be detected by Rosenfeld & O'Malley (250). However, Singhal, Vijayvargiya & Ling (254)
found that injection of cyclic AMP together with theophylline at two 12 hr
intervals resulted in twofold or greater increases in the activity of hexokinase, phosphofructokinase, pyruvate kinase, and glucose 6-phosphate dehydrogenase in the seminal vesicles of either orchiectomized or immature rats.
Even larger enhancements of these seminal vesicle enzyme activities were
observed following administration of the dibutyryl analog of cyclic AMP
plus theophylline. Both the cyclic nucleotides plus theophylline also increased the fresh weight of the seminal vesicles by more than 30%. Concur-

rent administration of actinomycin D or cycloheximide diminished the increases in organ weight and enzyme activities due to cyclic AMP plus theophylline. Singhal et al (254) believe that these results hint that cyclic AMP may play a role as a "second messenger" in the action of androgens on rat seminal vesicle, although they state, citing a review on male accessory reproductive glands (210) that "since adrenalcortical hormones may exert androgen-like effects on accessory sexual tissues, it is not possible, at present, to rule out the involvement of the adrenal cortex in the observed stimulation of various seminal vesicular enzymes induced by cyclic AMP". This statement as written could be subject to misinterpretation, because although androgens of adrenal origin indeed stimulate the growth and functions of male genital glands (210), many mineralocorticoid and glucocorticoid hormones (whose output by the adrenal cortex might be increased by cyclic AMP administration) exert no such androgenic actions in reasonable doses. Considering the failure of others to demonstrate any effects of testosterone on male accessory gland adenyl cyclase activity, whether cyclic AMP is an important intermediary in the actions of androgens on these organs must remain an open question.

Evidence has been obtained recently (255–257) that cylic AMP-stimulable protein phosphokinase reactions involving histone and other protein substrates (including certain enzymes) may play a central role in the amplification of effects of hormones on cyclic AMP levels in tissues. Reddi, Ewing & Williams-Ashman (258) found that the activity of soluble histone phosphokinases in rat uterus and ventral prostate was not greatly influenced as a result of castration or the respective administration of estrogens or androgens. In their immature state, these secondary sexual organs are replete with histone phosphokinases that are susceptible to activation by cyclic AMP. In a preliminary communication, King & Gordon (259) note that extracts of rat uterine nuclei made with 0.3 M NaCl contained, in addition to a 17β-estradiol-binding proteid considered above, a protein phosphokinase that utilizes dephosphorylated phosvitin, but not histones, as a substrate. This phosphokinase activity was decreased after ovariectomy and enhanced by 17β-estradiol treatment. The protein phosphokinase could be separated from the 17β-estradiol-binding protein by sucrose density gradient centrifugation, but the two proteins may be associated with the chromatin of uterine nuclei. King & Gordon (259) suggested that "protein phosphokinase activation may represent an early step in cell activation by this hormone."

Polyamines.—The polyamines spermidine and spermine are ubiquitous constituents of nucleated vertebrate cells. The ability of these substances to complex with, and to influence the enzymic synthesis and degradation of DNA and RNA and to interact with ribosomes has led to many speculations that they may serve as intracellular regulators of macromolecular biosynthetic processes in animal tissues (260). The rat ventral prostate is exceptionally rich in polyamines, large amounts of spermidine and spermine being secreted by this gland in sexually mature animals. Moulton & Leonard (261) found changes in tissue concentrations of spermidine in rat uterus, prostate, and seminal vesicles after gonadectomy and sex hormone treatments which led them to postulate that "steroid induced changes in spermidine levels may play an important role in the synthesis of certain types of RNA, formation of ribosomes, and synthesis of proteins in accessory sex organs."

Caldarera et al (262) reported that the RNA polymerase activity (measured at both high and low ionic strengths) of nuclear preparations from the ventral prostate of castrated rats was increased by addition of spermine to values comparable to those exhibited by prostatic nuclei from normal animals (no data on effects of spermine or spermidine on RNA polymerase activity of normal prostatic cell nuclei were provided). From these observations and the finding of a decline in prostatic spermidine and spermine levels after orchidectomy which could be prevented by androgen treatment, Caldarera et al (262) postulated that changes in polyamine concentrations may be causally related to the enhanced nuclear RNA synthesis which occurs in the prostate of castrates after androgen administration. A detailed study of spermine and spermidine concentrations and of enzymes involved in polyamine biosynthesis in rat ventral prostate by Pegg et al (263) did not support this contention. The high levels of polyamines in this tissue indeed fall dramatically after removal of the testes. And after injection of testosterone into the castrates, marked increases in two key enzymes of polyamine biosynthesis (L-ornithine decarboxylase, and a putrescine-activated S-adenosylmethionine decarboxylase which synthesizes spermidine) are observed within 6 hr after administration of the hormone. A significant rise in tissue spermidine levels did not occur for at least 24 hr (before which time marked increases in RNA synthesis have been reported under similar conditions), and spermine levels did not become elevated until about 5 days after commencement of daily testosterone injection. Pegg et al (263) concluded that during the early phases of androgen-induced prostatic growth there is some degree of coupling between spermidine synthesis and the production of new RNA (largely ribosomal RNA) molecules.

A high concentration of spermidine and spermine is not characteristic of all lobes of the rat prostate, despite their common embryological origin from the fetal urogenital sinus. Thus in adult rats, the anterior prostate (coagulating) gland contains very much less spermidine and spermine than the ventral lobe. Brasel et al (264) showed that changes in RNA/DNA ratio and also DNA polymerase activity during the androgen-dependent growth of the anterior prostate of castrated rats were similar in quantity and chronology to that found in the ventral prostate, despite the large differences in the polyamine content of the two lobes of the gland in sexually mature males.

A comprehensive discussion of the role of polyamines in reproductive physiology and sex hormone actions is given by Williams-Ashman & Lockwood (265).

PHYSIOLOGICAL ACTIONS OF 5β-HYDROGENATED STEROID METABOLITES AND EFFECTS OF SEX HORMONES ON ERYTHROPOIESIS

Granick & Kappas (266) made the important observation that a number of 5β-androstane and 5β-pregnane compounds, some of which are known to be metabolic transformation products of testosterone and progesterone respectively, are potent inducers of porphyrin synthesis in chicken embryo liver cell cultures. The glucuronide derivatives of even the most active 5β-hydrogenated steroid inducers were devoid of activity. Compounds such as 17α-hydroxy-5β-pregnane-3,20-dione   and   5β-pregnane-3α,17α-diol-20-one were active in the concentration range of 10^{-6} to 10^{-8} M; they stimulated heme formation in chick blastoderm erythroid cells as well as in embryonic liver preparation. Kappas & Granick (267) showed that inhibitors of nucleic acid and proteins biosynthesis (e.g. actinomycin D, mitomycin C, puromycin, and acetoxycycloheximide) inhibited the porphyrin-inducing effect of the steroids, and it was suggested that the latter process involved the formation of δ-aminolevulinic acid synthetase, the rate-limiting enzyme in heme biosynthesis. Addition of UDP-glucuronic acid depressed the increased porphyrin production due to the steroids, possibly as a result of glucuronidation of the active steroid inducers. These findings were strengthened by direct measurements of δ-aminolevulinic acid synthetase in the livers of developing chick embryos by Kappas et al (268), who found that 5β-hydrogenated steroids were very active in this in vivo assay as well as in the tissue culture experiments.

Kappas & Granick (267) were led by their investigations to consider whether endogenously derived steroid metabolites of the 5β-androstane and 5β-pregnane series might be the physiological agents which account for periodic, spontaneous (i.e. not drug related) exacerbations of hepatic porphyria in patients exhibiting the genetic lesion of this disorder. Kappas et al (269) have indeed detected, in the plasma of several patients with acute intermittent porphyria, a substance(s) which strongly enhances porphyrin synthesis in chick embryo liver cells growing in primary culture. Inducing properties were not found in the plasma of normal subjects or of porphyric patients in remission; they were detected, however, in plasma of normal women ingesting contraceptive steroids. Rifkind et al (270) have examined the ability of various oral contraceptive steroids to induce hepatic δ-aminolevulinic acid synthetase in vitro. It is well established that the activity of hepatic δ-aminolevulinic acid synthetase is elevated in patients with acute intermittent porphyria. Now Gillette et al (271) find that patients with this disease generate abnormal amounts of a 5β-H-metabolite (etiocholanolone) as compared with a 5α-H-metabolite (androsterone) of testosterone. These results hint that in acute intermittent porphyria there may be a deficiency in hepatic steroid Δ^4-5α-reductase activity.

The stimulatory effects of androgens on erythropoiesis were reviewed by Gordon et al (272) and Piliero et al (273). Fried & Gurney (274) found that the stimulatory effect of androgens on erythropoiesis in normal and polycythemic female mice was abolished by nephrectomy, which suggests that the kidney may be involved. Gordon et al (272, 275) have considered three mechanisms by which steroids can regulate erythropoiesis in mammals. First, steroids may stimulate the production of erythropoietin, perhaps in some instances via an action on the formation and release of the renal erythropoietic factor (erythrogenin). Secondly, androgens may potentiate the effects of erythropoietin (276, 277). And a third possibility is that androgens influence the bone marrow directly (278). Mirand et al (279) concluded that the antiandrogenic steroid cyproterone acetate had no effect per se on erythropoiesis, but inhibited the effects of testosterone and of erythropoietin. In the light of the aforementioned findings of the potent actions of 5β-hydrogenated steroid metabolites on porphyrin biosynthesis, it is interesting that Gorshein & Gardner (280) observed increased ^{59}Fe incorporation into circulating erythrocytes by several steroids with the 5β-H configuration while those with a 5α-H configuration were inactive; the most active substance was 5β-pregnane-3,20-dione. Similar studies by Gordon et al (275) showed that 11-ketopregnenolone was very potent in stimulating ^{59}Fe incorporation. In the same investigation, administration of an antiserum to human urinary erythropoietin markedly depressed the erythropoietic actions of testosterone, but not those exerted by 11-ketopregnenolone. Moreover, examination of the blood plasma of rats treated with testosterone propionate or 11-ketopregnenolone, using an assay involving transfusion-induced plethoric mice, disclosed that testosterone but not 11-ketopregnenolone enhanced the production of erythropoietin. These important studies indicate a dissociation of the erythropoietic effects of testosterone (acting via erythropoietin) and of 5β-hydrogenated steroids like 11-ketopregnenolone (acting directly). In line with this conclusion is the report of Necheles & Rai (281) that the 5β-hydrogenated steroid etiocholanolone directly stimulates heme formation by human bone marrow cells in vitro.

Comprehensive reviews by Kappas and his colleagues (282–285) deal with these erythropoietic as well as other aspects of the pharmacology of gonadal hormones and their metabolites, including impairment by estrogens of hepatic excretory activity, actions of steroids on the reticuloendothelial system, the nausea and vomiting of pregnancy, and the pyrogenic effects of steroids such as progesterone and etiocholanolone (cf 286). In the latter connection, Freeman et al (287) have recently studied the thermogenic actions of progesterone in thyroidectomized and in ovariectomized-hypophysectomized rats. Progesterone-induced temperature elevations were observed in animals lacking the thyroid, and appear to be mediated via the central nervous system, although the precise mechanism is obscure.

The findings that 5α-hydrogenated metabolites may be involved in the androgenic regulation of male secondary sexual organ function (see above) and that 5β-hydrogenated metabolites may influence erythropoiesis and other physiological events throw an entirely new light on the importance of metabolic transformations of testosterone. Remember that 5α-hydrogenated metabolic products are formed in male genital glands, whereas the production of 5β-hydrogenated metabolites does not occur there and is confined largely if not exclusively to the liver (cf 62, 63). Here it may be germane to mention the important studies of Conney and his co-workers on the increased metabolism by the liver of estrogens (288, 289) and androgens (289, 290) caused by administration of drugs such as phenobarbital and chlorinated insecticides like DDT and chlordane. Levin, Welch & Conney (291) made the interesting observation that treatment of immature rats with phenobarbital or chlordane for several days prior to injection of testosterone or testosterone propionate markedly depressed the growth-promoting effects of these steroids on the seminal vesicles, presumably as a result of increased metabolic inactivation of the androgens by the liver. Similar experiments by Levin et al (292) showed that prior treatment of rats with phenobarbital decreased the uterotropic actions of some oral contraceptive steroids. Such findings and many other considerations underscore that caution should be exercised in the interpretation of relative differences of the activity of parenterally administered steroids vis-a-vis related end organ responses, such as are used, for example, for assay of so-called anabolic steroids. The latter are considered in encylopedic volumes by Vida (293) and Krüskemper (294).

INFLUENCES OF SEX HORMONES ON STRUCTURE, METABOLISM, AND FUNCTIONS OF REPRODUCTIVE ORGANS

There continue to appear very many publications describing morphological, functional, and biochemical changes in various reproductive organs resulting from administration or deprival of gonadal hormones. This vast literature includes many accounts of isolated phenomena which are not immediately related to any definitive hypotheses or their testing. For this reason, and because of limitations of space, no exhaustive coverage is attempted here. Hopefully the following discussion of only a small fraction of recent contributions may provide some flavor of the breadth of current researches. Regretfully it does not always seem to be appreciated that many of the more biochemically oriented studies purporting to deal with "mechanism of action" of sex hormones actually recount modulations by sex hormones of metabolic process patterns that are utterly dependent, in any particular organ in a given species, on restrictions for potential expression of large sections of the total genome which are firmly imposed much earlier in their developmental history. Moreover, many measurements made with isolated tissue preparations, in which various degrees of the original cellular organization may have been preserved, are sometimes interpreted solely in terms of intracellular reactions without due regard for interplays between different cell types which may be crucial for the development of the organ in the living animal, e.g., epithelial-mesenchymal interactions of the nature so thoroughly studied in pancreatic cytodifferentiation (295).

There is a wealth of evidence that androgenic hormones elaborated during fetal and early neonatal life of certain mammals are essential for the initial development of certain organs of the male reproductive tract, as well as for the differentiation of neural structures which in later life control male modes of gonadotropin output and sexual behavior (149, 150, 221, 236, 296, 297, 297a). Such "organizational" or "morphogenetic" actions of androgens which are manifest irreversibly only during restricted, critical periods of early development are often contrasted with the classical "activational" ("excitatory") or "inhibitory" (e.g. feedback inhibitions of hypothalamico-hypophyseal mechanisms regulating gonadotropin secretions) actions demonstrable throughout later life. The biochemical proceedings which underlie such "organizational" effects of androgens on responsive tissues (see above) may very well differ profoundly in detail from those which occur when, for example, the same organs in an adult castrate are induced to grow by testosterone. This obviously does not imply, however, any hard and fast difference in the basic molecular interactions by which these processes are set in motion by androgenic hormones. This situation is somewhat comparable to the difficulties in understanding relationships between the mechanisms by which thyroid hormones influence metabolic rate, etc, in adult animals on the one hand, and, on the other, initiate entirely new processes of growth and differentiation, as in the metamorphosis of some amphibians; Tata (298) considers this problem in depth.

Ribonucleic acid and protein synthesis.—New reviews (3, 147, 149, 150, 202, 249, 299–306a) detail sex hormonal influences on intermediary reactions in nuclear RNA synthesis (transcription), the intracellular translocation of ribonucleic acids, and the utilization of different species of polyribonucleotide in cytoplasmic ribosomal protein synthesis (translation). It remains to be established, however, whether the swift and pronounced enhancement of RNA and protein biosynthetic reactions can account for all of the physiological actions of gonadal steroids on genital tissues. The excitement and importance of recent studies on biochemical mechanisms related to gene expression as influenced by sex hormones has tended to overshadow studies in less fashionable areas. For example, there are clear-cut effects of estrogens on uterine blood flow (307). Again, Tata (308) has shown that accumulation of new cytoplasmic ribosomes induced by a number of growth-promoting hormones (including androgens) is closely coordinated with synthesis of new endoplasmic reticulum membrane phospholipids in a manner which perhaps cannot be explained solely in terms of alterations in the activity of the necessary biosynthetic enzymes.

Marked and in some circumstances very rapid increases in incorporation of radioactive nucleosides into female genital tissue ribonucleic acids resulting from estrogen treatment (305) have been confirmed in various reports, some of which include consideration of the development of uterus during early pregnancy with respect to implantation versus nonimplantation sites (309–315). Under certain biological conditions entry of tritiated uridine into uterine RNA is apparently influenced by insulin and growth hormone, especially when the process is stimulated by 17β-estradiol (316). Early estrogen-induced increases in the incorporation of precursors into uterine ribosomal RNA, followed by enhancement of tRNA formation and the synthesis of DNA-like RNA (cf 305) have been confirmed (313), although methodological problems in the extraction and fractionation of uterine RNA cannot be ignored (317). Billing, Barbiroli & Smellie (314, 315) have carefully examined the uptake of labeled RNA precursors in immature rat uterus at various periods over the first day following injection of 17β-estradiol. Over the first 5 hr there was a close correlation between uptake of precursors and their incorporation into RNA. Even when RNA synthesis was inhibited 80% or more by actinomycin D, the uptake of tritiated ribonucleosides into both acid-soluble and RNA fractions was still increased nearly threefold at 2 hr after estrogen administration. It was concluded that one of the primary early effects of estrogen under the stated conditions was to increase the transport of RNA precursors into the uterus, a process which reaches a maximum (2–3 hr after estrogen injection) at a time corresponding to maximum uterine water imbibition (314). When the effect of 17β-estradiol on transport of these precursors into uterus was taken into account, there appeared to be no increase in the amount of labeled nucleosides incorporated into RNA until at least 5 hr after giving the estrogen (315).

Using ovariectomized rabbits, Church & McCarthy (318) corroborated previous experiments in other species (cf 19, 305, 319) that within a short period after injection of 17β-estradiol into ovariectomized animals there was a significant increase in the capacity of uterine chromatin preparations to prime RNA synthesis. These workers also hybridized pulse-labeled RNA formed from labeled uridine in various tissues with rabbit spleen DNA. The experiments indicated differences in the population of DNA-like RNA molecules in both uterus and liver after estrogen treatment; no change was detected in lung RNA. The hormone-stimulated RNA species in liver and uterus did not appear to be completely homologous. Both the normal and estrogen-treated tissues clearly contained some RNA molecules which were restricted to the nucleus and did not reach the cytoplasm. Some RNAs confined to the nucleus in normal liver entered the cytoplasm of hormone-treated cells. The spectrum of RNA molecules restricted to uterine nuclei before estrogen administration was much more dramatic. Church & McCarthy (318) concluded that estrogens can induce changes in RNA transcription that are at least partially organ specific, and additionally exercise a selective control over the transport of certain nuclear RNA molecules into the cytoplasm.

O'Malley and his colleagues (202, 320–322) and Gorbman's group (323, 324) carried out DNA-RNA hybridization studies with pulse-labeled RNAs formed in chick oviduct after estrogen or progesterone administration. Estrogen treatment over a period of several days resulted in the gradual appearance of new species of hybridizable RNA molecules which appeared to correlate with synthesis of the specific proteins ovalbumin and lysozyme (202). However, in the absence of ancillary evidence, these techniques certainly do not permit identification of new forms of hybridizable RNA with any particular messenger ribonucleic acids, the only unequivocal test for the latter being a direct demonstration of their direction of production of a well-defined protein by isolated polyribosomes. Portions of the hybridizable material may well represent heterogenous RNAs that never escape from the cell nucleus. Progesterone stimulation of chick oviduct causes the formation of additional new species of hybridizable RNA molecules (202), some of which conceivably are involved in the specific induction of avidin synthesis in oviduct by this hormone (202). Effects of ovarian hormones on formation of hybridizable RNA during vitellogenesis in *Uta stansburiana* were examined (324).

Note that estrogens increase quantitatively and qualitatively the tRNA-methylase activity of uterus (325) and chick oviduct (326). The enzymic acetylation of histones, reactions which could be germane to the regulation of RNA transcription, is said by Libby (327) to be directly enhanced by low concentrations of 17β-estradiol in cell-free preparations from rat uterus.

Estrogens initiate the differentiation of tubular glands in the magnum region of the immature chick oviduct and stimulate the elaboration of the cell-specific egg white proteins, ovalbumin and lysozyme. Morphological and ultrastructural studies on this differentiation process have been carried out by O'Malley and his colleagues (202) and by Oka & Schimke (328, 329). Concomitant treatment with progesterone from the beginning of estrogen treatment prevents the appearance of glands and synthesis of cell-specific proteins (328). But once the glands have been formed, then progesterone not only ceases to depress lysozyme synthesis but also substitutes for estrogen (328, 329). Ovalbumin-secreting glands begin to develop about 4 days after commencement of estrogen injections, and ciliated cells (concerned with motility) appear on day 6. By 9 days of estrogen treatment there appear goblet cells, which can synthesize avidin when stimulated by progesterone (202). An important paper by Palmiter, Christensen & Schimke (330) describes studies in which chicks were treated for 10 days with 17β-estradiol (primary stimulation) and the hormone treatment then terminated. This led to a decrease in oviduct size and protein content, and a reduction in protein and RNA synthesis. When 17β-estradiol or progesterone were administered again (secondary stimulation), protein and RNA synthesis were reestablished within a day, during which time the rate of ovalbumin synthesis rose several hundredfold in the absence of any cell division. The biochemical responses during secondary stimulation by either 17β-estradiol or progesterone were similar over the first 18 hr, whereas at later times the rate of protein synthesis continued to rise with estrogen but not progesterone. Electronmicroscopic and biochemical studies by Palmiter et al (330) indicated that enhanced protein synthesis during the secondary stimulation is associated with organization of ribosomes into polysomes within gland cells. During the early stages of secondary stimulation the polysomes appear to be assembled largely from preexisting monosomes and only later do newly formed ribosomes enter the polysomes. Contrary to Tata's (303) conclusion from experiments on other systems that biosynthetic responses to hormones may depend heavily on newly generated ribosomes, in the oviduct system of Palmiter et al (330) both old and new ribosomes seem to mix in the same pool.

Continued studies on enhancement of RNA polymerase reactions in isolated nuclear preparations, as affected by in vivo treatment with estrogens (202, 215, 331–333) and androgens (3, 302, 334) in appropriate tissues, have become harder to assess in the light of new evidence (335, 336) that there probably exist at least two separate DNA-dependent RNA polymerases in mammalian cell nuclei. Speichinger & Barker (337) noted small changes in the melting curve (heat denaturation) of double-stranded human uterine DNA due to addition of very high concentrations of 17β-estradiol which were abolished by equimolar amounts of 17α-estradiol; it is difficult to see how these observations relate to the control of uterine nuclear RNA formation by active estrogens. Trachewsky & Segal (338) confirmed Liao's (3) finding that estrogens alter the nearest-neighbor base frequency of RNA synthesized by isolated uterine nuclei to give a product more resembling ribosomal RNA insofar as it manifests a higher content of guanosine and cytidine. The same situation is known to pertain to the action of androgens on rat prostate (300). Liao & Stumpf (339) now provide autoradiographic support for a selective increase by testosterone of nucleolar RNA synthesis in this organ. Other aspects of the influence of androgens on RNA formation in male genital glands (340–342) and in kidney (302, 343, 344) have been published. Shimada & Gorbman (345) found long-lasting changes in ribonucleic acid synthesis in the forebrains of female rats that had been injected with testosterone just after birth. Similarly, Clayton et al (346) observed that after treatment of newborn female rats with androgen, the entry of tritiated uridine into RNA in two regions of the amygdala and anterior hypothalamus is altered quite differently from that seen in the brain as a whole. The latter two investigations represent pioneer attempts to study biochemical correlates of androgen-induced sexual differentiation of the brain. Kobayashi & Gorski (347) have studied effects on the latter process of antibiotics that inhibit macromolecular biosynthetic reactions.

The well-known uterotrophic actions of androgens prompted an interesting study by Yudaev & Prokovsky (348) on the in vivo incorporation of labeled adenine into uterine RNA of spayed immature rats as influenced by either 17β-estradiol or testosterone phenylpropionate. The specific radioactivity of uterine nuclear RNA was increased by the androgen and actually diminished following injection of 17β-estradiol under their experimental conditions (pool sizes of proximate RNA precursor nucleotides do not appear to have been determined). A fraction of the rapidly labeled RNA synthesized as a result of androgen treatment appeared to be restricted to the nucleus and did not enter the cytoplasm.

Measurement of the DNA and RNA content of reproductive organs in relation to the age of rats (349) and of effects of ovarian hormones on RNA base ratios in different regions of rabbit brain (350) have been recorded.

The alterations in the synthesis of various proteins by cytoplasmic polyribosomal systems induced in genital tissues by sex hormones in many instances seem to occur after prior enhancement of nuclear RNA synthesis. However, at least one protein, separable by starch-gel electrophoresis, is known to be formed very rapidly in immature rat uterus after a single injection of estrogen (350a). Barnea & Gorski (351) have shown that this involves de novo synthesis of the protein, which begins 40 min after injection of 17β-estradiol, reaches a maximum by about 2 hr, and then declines markedly. That hormone-induced synthesis of many other proteins occurs later does not, however, necessarily imply that gonadal steroids function in this context solely by influencing transcriptional events. Recent studies by Tomkins and his co-workers (see 352 for references) indicate that adrenal cortical hormones may influence enzyme synthesis in cultured mammalian cells primarily by influencing the formation and functions of a putative posttranscriptional repressor substance, which seems to exert its actions at a translational level.

Few contemporary studies on sex hormonal regulation of protein biosynthesis deal unequivocally with the formation (as opposed to biological activity) of specific proteins, such as has been accomplished in regard to control by progesterone of avidin production in chick oviduct (202, 306, 353). Florini (354) attempted to determine whether testosterone treatment altered protein synthesis in rat soleus muscle in a qualitative as well as quantitive fashion by comparing radioactivity profiles of various proteins which had been labeled with leucine, using the techniques of disc electrophoresis and isoelectric focusing on polyacrylamide gels. Although androgen administration increased labeling of the total muscle proteins by 50–70%, no qualitative changes in the labeling of the different protein bands could be detected.

There are many recent accounts of changes in the activity of various enzymes in female reproductive organs due to estrogen administration (355–363) or as correlates of female sexual cycles or pregnancy (364–368). Descriptions of androgen-dependent changes in various enzymes in male genital (369–377a) and other (378–380) tissues became available.

Mainwaring (381, 382) has considered the influence of androgens on mac-romolecular synthetic processes in prostate in relation to age of mice. And aspects of amino acid incorporation by cell-free mouse kidney preparations as affected by testosterone are considered by Kochakian et al (383, 384). Changes in the activity of various liver enzymes resulting from sex hor-mone treatments (385–389) were recently documented. In no instance has any really definitive insight been gained into the mechanisms by which sex hormones influence these enzymic activities in vivo, which in some instances may depend on alterations in the rate of protein degradation rather than synthesis. Caveats that fundamental differences exist in gene expression mechanisms in eucaryotes versus procaryotes, that our present understand-ing of the biochemistry let alone the regulation of RNA and protein synthe-sis in mammalian cells is full of gaps, and that experiments in which inhibi-tors of RNA and protein synthesis are used in attempts to dissect the inter-mediary processes affected by hormones are subject to all sorts of limita-tions have all been voiced so frequently that their reiteration in the more recent endocrinological literature will not be catalogued here.

Ribonucleic acid preparations and genital tissue growth.—Fujii & Villee (390) have continued their studies on seminal vesicle growth induced by instillation into the lumen of this organ of RNA preparations isolated from rat tissues by the phenol-sodium dodecyl sulfate procedure. Active RNAs were obtained from seminal vesicle, prostate, liver, and kidney of mature but not immature male rats. Fractionation of these crude RNA mixtures by sucrose density gradient centrifugation gave material with a sedimentation coefficient around 18S which caused a 22% increase in seminal vesicle weight; other RNA fractions from these separations as well as liver soluble RNA were ineffective. Although these findings might be construed to mean that RNA obtained from seminal vesicle or some other adult male rat tis-sues contains expressible information for protein biosynthesis, it seems equally possible that the active ribonucleic acids could somehow trigger off various macromolecular synthetic processes within seminal vesicle cells without serving a true messenger RNA function.

Androgens and cation-activated ATPase reactions.—Farnsworth (391) reported that the direct addition of very low concentrations of testosterone increases the $Mg^{++} + Na^+ + K^+$-stimulated ATPase activity of rat ventral prostate microsomal preparations. This observation is of considerable inter-est in view of the androgenic regulation of secretory processes in this organ (210) and also because within an hour after injection of testosterone into orchiectomized rats the total concentration of ATP in ventral prostate falls dramatically (392). However, Ahmed & Williams-Ashman (393) were unable to corroborate this in vitro effect of testosterone on the cation-acti-vated ATPase of prostate microsomes or membrane preparations obtained therefrom by flotation in high-density sucrose solutions; 5α-dihydrotestos-

terone was similarly inert. Nonetheless, large decreases in the activity of prostatic microsomal Na^+-K^+-activated ATPase occurred as a result of castration (393); these changes were reversed by androgen administration.

Uptake of glucose and glycogen synthesis.—Bergamini et al (394)
showed that glycogen levels in rat levator ani muscles fall rapidly after orchiectomy. After an irreducible time lag of 6 hr following injection of testosterone, the glycogen concentration began to rise. This was accompanied
by increases in 2-deoxyglucose penetration and phosphorylation, and in the
entry of xylose into the cells. Increases in hexokinase and glucose 6-phos-
phate-independent glycogen synthetase activities were also observed within
12 hr of androgen administration. Concurrent treatment with actinomycin
D or puromycin abolished the testosterone-induced glycogen synthesis. Bergamini (395) reported additive effects of insulin and testosterone on glycogen content and 2-deoxyglucose phosphorylation (but not on xylose uptake)
in levator ani muscles, in which tissue Turner & Leonard (396) studied
effects of testosterone on glycogen phosphorylase. Under different experimental conditions, Mills & Spazziani (397) could not find any increase in
penetration of 2-deoxyglucose into levator ani muscles as a result of androgenic stimulation. Effects of estrogens on glucose uptake and glycogen formation in uterus have been reported (398–400), some of which seem to
depend on new protein synthesis.

Mitochondrial reactions.—Pegg & Williams-Ashman (401) showed that
castration reduced amino acid incorporation by isolated prostate mitochondria, a process which unlike cytoplasmic polyribosomal protein synthesis is
insensitive to cycloheximide but is depressed by chloramphenicol. The activity could be restored by treatment with testosterone, but only after a lag
period of about 24 hr, which is much longer than the time required to demonstrate pronounced effects of androgen on nuclear RNA biosynthesis in
this organ. These experiments were conducted under conditions where externally supplied ATP was used to support mitochondrial protein synthesis,
so that the results were not complicated by possible hormonal-induced alterations in energy transductions by the mitochondrial electron transport
chain. The rather sluggish response of the prostatic mitochondrial protein-
synthesizing apparatus to testosterone hints that the effects of androgen
might be indirect, and mediated via secondary alterations in the cytoplasmic
environment of the particles in vivo. Doeg (402, 403) found that androgens
increase lipid biosynthesis by mitochondria from male genital glands. Here
it can be mentioned that testosterone treatment of female mice alters the
glycosphingolipid composition of kidney in the direction of that normally
seen in male animals (404).

Gonadal hormones and sebaceous glands.—The well-known stimulatory
effects of androgens on holocrine sebaceous glands have received further at-

tention; the subject is reviewed by Straus & Pochi (405). Effects of pituitary hormones on the response of sebaceous and preputial glands to testosterone (406) and progesterone (407) were reexamined. Krähenbühl & Desaulles (408) made the important observation that in castrated female rats, a dose of progesterone which evokes only a marginal increase in preputial gland weight induced very large growth of the organ when α-melanocyte-stimulating hormone was also injected. α-MSH alone had little effect and its potentiation of progesterone action was more pronounced than with testosterone. It is known that androgens influence the synthesis of preputial gland lipids, whose chemistry is considered in two recent papers (409, 410). Systematic studies on effects of sex and pituitary hormones on sebum production in young rats were carried out by Nikkari & Valavaara (411).

Miscellanea.—Breuer and his colleagues (412, 413) found that in vitro addition of some 2-hydroxylated steroidal estrogens to liver cytosol preparations inhibits reactions catalyzed by the S-adenosylmethionine-catechol-O-methyltransferase in the preparations. Inhibitory effects of diethylstilbestrol and its congeners on human prostatic DNA polymerase were recorded by Harper et al (414). Hormonal influences on the development of reproductive organs of fetal guinea pigs studied in organ culture considered in the light of genetic expression are discussed by Price, Zaaijer & Ortiz (415).

A remarkable contribution (416) concerns an effect of androgens on protein biosynthesis which has been recognized since antiquity. The investigator spent periods of several weeks on a remote island in comparative isolation, and noticed a decrease in his beard growth, which increased again, however, on the day before he left the island only to become intensive during the first day or so on the mainland. Quantitative measurements of increase in growth of facial hair seemed to correlate with the anticipation, as well as the initial resumption of heterosexual congress, although if coital activity was maintained for a week or more the beard growth declined to normal within 4–6 days. Tension, anxiety, nervousness, excessive mental fatigue, and alcoholic beverages were stated to increase beard growth whereas excessive physical exercise and high temperatures had the opposite effect. Author and collaborator(s) remain anonymous.

Medieval Chinese Protoendocrinology

"There can be little doubt that between the +11th and the +17th century the Chinese iatro-chemists were producing preparations of androgens and estrogens which were probably quite effective in the quasi-empirical therapy of the time. This must surely be considered an extraordinary achievement for any type of scientific medicine before the age of modern science." So ends a thorough assembly of textual evidence by Needham & Lu Gwei-Djen (417) which, together with a companion paper (418), indicates that medieval Chinese alchemists, knowing nothing of steroid chemistry, developed ingenious procedures involving evaporations, precipitations with soap-bean saponins and powdered calcium sulfate, and clever sublimatories enabling them to isolate from hundreds of gallons of urine "white, crystalline, glistening, lustrous material like translucent jade or pearls" which almost certainly was rich in mixtures of androgens and estrogens, together with cholesterol and other substances. The historical researches of Needham & Lu, admirably summarized in a recent short exposé (419), open an exciting new chapter in the history of endocrinology. Presumably these publications represent drafts for a section of one of the forthcoming volumes of Needham's *Science and Civilisation in China* (420), one of the great wonders of scholarship of all times. The epoch-making discovery of the presence of large amounts of sex hormones in pregnancy urine by Ascheim and Zondek in 1927, and the isolation soon thereafter of pure steroid sex hormones from urine by Doisy, Butenandt, Marrian, and others, are events usually considered to represent the birth of the modern era of sex endocrinology. Now Needham & Lu have shown us that the Chinese adumbrated by many hundreds of years the achievements of the master sex steroid chemists of the second and third decade of our century. Anyone interested in an overview of the classic papers on sex hormone isolation should consult a fine illustrated memoir by Raspé (421).

LITERATURE CITED

1. Wurtman, R. J. 1968. *Science* 159: 1261
2. Jensen, E. V. 1968. *Science* 159:1261
3. Liao, S., Fang, S. 1970. *Vitam. Horm.* 27:17–90
4. Jensen, E. V., Jacobson, H. I. 1960. In *Biological Activities of Steroids in Relation to Cancer*, ed. G. Pincus, E. P. Vollmer, 161–78. New York: Academic
5. Jensen, E. V., Jacobson, H. I. 1962. *Recent Progr. Horm. Res.* 18:387–414
6. Glascock, R. F., Hoekstra, W. G. 1959. *Biochem. J.* 72:673–82
7. Jensen, E. V. 1964. *Excerpta Med. Int. Congr. Ser. No. 83*, 420–33
8. Jensen, E. V., De Sombre, E. R., Hurst, D. J., Kawashima, T., Jungblut, P. W. 1967. *Arch. Anat. Microscop. Morphol. Exp.* 56:547–69
9. Jungblut, P. W., Hätzel, I., De Sombre, E. R., Jensen, E. V. 1967. *18. Colloq. Ges. Physiol. Chem.* 58–86
10. Jensen, E. V., De Sombre, E. R., Jungblut, P. W. 1967. In *Endogenous factors influencing host-tumor balance*, ed. R. W. Wissler, T. Dao, S. Wood, Jr., 15–30. Chicago, Ill: Univ. Chicago Press
11. Jensen, E. V. et al 1966. In *Steroid Dynamics*, ed. T. Nakao, G. Pincus, J. Tait, 133–57. New York: Academic
12. Jensen, E. V., De Sombre, E. R., Jungblut, P. W. 1967. In *Horm. Steroids*, ed. L. Martini, 492–500. Amsterdam: Excerpta Med. Found.
13. Jungblut, P. W. 1969. In *Advances in the Biosciences*, ed. G. Raspé, 2: 157–81. Oxford: Pergamon, and Braunschweig: Vieweg
14. Jensen, E. V., Suzuki, T., Numata, M., Smith, S., De Sombre, E. R. 1969. *Steroids* 13:417–27
15. Jensen, E. V., Numata, M., Smith, S., Suzuki, T., De Sombre, E. R. 1969. *Develop. Biol. Suppl. 3*, 151
16. Gorski, J., Toft, D., Shyamala, G., Smith, D., Notides, A. 1968. *Recent Progr. Horm. Res.* 24:45–80
17. Gorski, J., Notides, A., Toft, D., Smith, D. E. 1967. *Clin. Obstet. Gynecol.* 10:17–28
18. Huggins, C., Jensen, E. V. 1955. *J. Exp. Med.* 102:335–46

19. Maurer, H. R., Chalkley, G. R. 1967. *J. Mol. Biol.* 27:431–41
20. Breuer, H., Breuer, J., Dahmn, K., Knuppen, R., Lehmann, W. D. 1969. *Advances in the Biosciences,* ed. G. Raspé, 2:113–42. Oxford: Pergamon and Braunschweig: Vieweg
21. Lehmann, W. D., Breuer, H. 1968. *Naturwissenschaftan* 55:182–83
22. Sweat, M. L., Bryon, M. J., Young, R. B. 1967. *Endocrinology* 81:167–72
23. Jütting, G., Thun, K. J., Kuss, E. 1967. *Eur. J. Biochem.* 2:146–51
24. Gurpide, E., Welch, M. 1969. *J. Biol. Chem.* 244:5159–69
25. Pack, B. A. 1969. *Metabolism of estrogens and their sulfates in rat uterine slices*. MS thesis. Wayne State Univ., Detroit, Mich.
26. Talalay, P. 1957. *Rec. Chem. Progr.* 18:31–49
27. Wenzel, M., Blum, K. U. 1967. *Z. Klin. Chem. Klin. Biochem.* 5: 202–5
28. Wenzel, M., Kraus, E. 1967. *Acta Endocrinol.* 56:385–90
29. Wenzel, M., Pollow, K. 1967. *Z. Physiol. Chem.* 348:1667–76
30. Wenzel, M., Wolf, S. 1969. *Z. Physiol. Chem.* 350:1203–12
31. Wenzel, M., Pollow-Hanisch, B., Pollow, K. 1969. *Z. Physiol. Chem.* 350:791–92
32. Stumpf, W. E. 1970. *J. Histochem. Cytochem.* 18:21–29
33. King, R. J. B., Gordon, J., Inman, D. R. 1965. *J. Endocrinol.* 32:9–15
34. Stumpf, W. E. 1968. *Endocrinology* 83:777–82
35. Stumpf, W. E. 1969. *Endocrinology* 85:31–37
36. Mobbs, B. G. 1968. *J. Endocrinol.* 41:69–74
37. Stumpf, W. E. 1968. *Z. Zellforsch. Mikrosk. Anat.* 92:23–33
38. Anderson, C. H., Greenwald, G. S. 1969. *Endocrinology* 85:1160–65
39. Attramadal, A. 1970. *Z. Zellforsch. Mikrosk. Anat.* 104:597–614
40. Stumpf, W. E. 1968. *Science* 162: 1001–3
41. Attramadal, A. 1970. *Z. Zellforsch. Mikrosk. Anat.* 104:572–81
42. Everett, J. W. 1969. *Ann. Rev. Physiol.,* 31:383–416

43. McGuire, J. L., Lisk, R. D. 1969. *Neuroendocrinology* 4:289–95
44. Eisenfeld, A. J. 1967. *Biochim. Biophys. Acta* 136:498–507
45. McGuire, J. L., Lisk, R. D. 1968. *Proc. Nat. Acad. Sci.* 61:497–503
46. Kato, J., Villee, C. A. 1967. *Endocrinology* 80:1133–38
47. Callantine, M. R., Clemens, L. E., Shih, Y. 1968. *Proc. Soc. Exp. Biol. Med.* 128:382–86
48. Terenius, L. 1969. *Acta Pharmacol. Toxicol.* 27:120–28
49. Whalen, R. E., Maurer, R. A. 1969. *Proc. Nat. Acad. Sci.* 63:681–85
50. Kato, J. 1970. *Acta Endocrinol.* 63: 577–84
51. Psychoyos, M. A., Alberga, A., Baulieu, E.-E. 1968. *Compt. Rend. Acad. Sci.* D 266:1407–9
52. Alberga, A., Baulieu, E.-E. 1968. *Mol. Pharmacol.* 4:311–23
53. Kato, J., Inaba, M., Kobayashi, T. 1969. *Acta Endocrinol.* 61:585–91
54. Kraay, R. J., Black, L. J. 1970. *Proc. Soc. Exp. Biol. Med.* 133:376
55. McGuire, J. L., Lisk, R. D. 1969 *Nature* 221:1068–69
56. Flerkó, B., Mess, B. 1968. *Acta Physiol. Acad. Sci. Hung.* 33:111–13
57. Flerkó, B., Mess, B., Illei-Donhoffer, A. 1969. *Neuroendocrinology* 4: 164–69
58. Vertes, M., King, R. J. B. 1969. *J. Endocrinol.* 45:29–30
59. Green, R., Luttge, W. G., Whalen, R. E. 1969. *Endocrinology* 85:373–78
60. Denef, C., De Moor, P. 1969. *Endocrinology* 85:259–69
61. Kraulis, I., Clayton, R. B. 1968. *J. Biol. Chem.* 243:3546–47
62. Schriefers, H. 1967. *Vitam. Horm.* 25:271–314
63. Schriefers, H. 1969. *Advances in the Biosciences* 2:69–102. See Ref. 20
64. Presl, J., Röhling, S., Horský, J., Herzmann, J. 1970. *Endocrinology* 86:899–902
65. Attramadal, A., Aakvaag, A. 1970. *Z. Zellforsch. Mikrosk. Anat.* 104: 582–96
66. Terenius, L. 1967. *Mol. Pharmacol.* 3:423–28
67. Terenius, L. 1968. *Mol. Pharmacol.* 4:301–10
68. Hawkins, R. A., Heald, P. J., Swain, M., Taylor, P. D. 1970. *Acta Endocrinol.* 63:253–64
69. Cecil, H. C., Bitman, J., Shaffner,

C. S. 1970. *Acta Endocrinol.* 63: 265–74
70. Terenius, L. 1969. *Acta Endocrinol.* 60:79–90
71. Sander, S. 1969. The uptake of oestradiol in normal breast tissue and in induced breast cancer of the rat, 1–23. Oslo: Universitetsforlaget
72. Lemon, H. M. 1970. *Cancer* 25:423–35
73. Sander, S. 1968. *Acta Endocrinol.* 58:49–56
74. Puca, G. A., Bresciani, F. 1969. *Endocrinology* 85:1
75. Sander, S. 1968. *Acta Endocrinol.* 59:235–38
76. Sander, S., Attramadal, A. 1968. *Acta Endocrinol.* 58:235–42
77. Sander, S. 1968. *Acta Pathol. Microbiol. Scand.* 73:29–36
78. Sander, S., Attramadal, A. 1968. *Acta Pathol. Microbiol. Scand.* 74:169–78
79. Terenius, L. 1968. *Cancer Res.* 28: 328-37
80. Mobbs, B. G. 1966. *J. Endocrinol.* 36: 409–14
81. Mobbs, B. G. 1968. *J. Endocrinol.* 41:339–44
82. Mobbs, B. G. 1969. *J. Endocrinol.* 44: 463–64
83. King, R. J. B., Cowan, D. M., Inman, D. R. 1965. *J. Endocrinol.* 32:83–90
84. Huggins, C. 1965. *Cancer Res.* 25: 1163–67
85. King, R. J. B. 1968. In *Prognostic Factors in Breast Cancer,* ed. A. P. M. Forrest, P. B. Kunkler, 354–62. London: Livingston
86. Sander, S. 1968. *Acta Pathol. Microbiol. Scand.* 74:301–02
87. Braunsberg, H., Irvine, W. T., James, V. H. T. 1968. In *Prognostic factors in breast cancer,* ed. A. P. M. Forrest, P. B. Kunkler, 363–67. London: Livingston
88. Deshpande, N., Jensen, V., Bulbrook, R. D., Berne, T., Ellis, F. 1967. *Steroids* 10:219–32
89. Korenman, S. G. 1970. *J. Clin. Endocrinol.* 30:639–45
90. Pearlman, W. H., DeHertogh, R., Laumas, K. R., Pearlman, M. R. J. 1969. *J. Clin. Endocrinol.* 29:714–20
91. Jensen, E. V. Personal communication
91a. Johansson, H., Terenius, L., Thoren, L. 1970. *Cancer Res.* 30:692–98
92. Adams, J. B., Wong, M. S. F. 1968.

J. Endocrinol. 41:41–52
93. Jones, D., Cameron, E. H. D., Griffiths, K., Gleave, E. N., Forrest, A. P. M. 1970. *Biochem. J.* 116:919–21
94. Williams, T. E., MacLeod, R. M. 1970. *J. Nat. Cancer Inst.* 44:349
95. Noteboom, W. D., Gorski, J. 1965. *Arch. Biochem. Biophys.* 111:559–68
96. King, R. J. B., Gordon, J. 1966. *J. Endocrinol.* 34:431–37
97. Talwar, G. P., Segal, S. J., Evans, A., Davidson, O. W. 1964. *Proc. Nat. Acad. Sci.* 52:1059–66
98. Baulieu, E.-E., Alberga, A., Jung, I. 1967. *Compt. Rend. Acad. Sci.* 265:354–57
99. Baulieu, E.-E. 1967. *Rev. Fr. Hematol.* 7:589–600
100. Puca, G. A., Bresciani, F. 1968. *Nature* 218:967–69
101. Jensen, E. V., Suzuki, T., Kawashima, T., Stumpf, W. E., Jungblut, P. W., De Sombre, E. R. 1968. *Proc. Nat. Acad. Sci.* 59:632–38
102. Rochefort, H., Baulieu, E.-E. 1969. *Endocrinology* 84:108–16
103. Talwar, G. P., Sopori, M. L., Biswas, D. K., Segal, S. J. 1966. *Biochem. J.* 107:765–74
104. Toft, D., Gorski, J. 1966. *Proc. Nat. Acad. Sci.* 55:1574–81
105. Toft, D., Shyamala, G., Gorski, J. 1967. *Proc. Nat. Acad. Sci.* 57:1740–43
106. Erdos, T. 1968. *Biochem. Biophys. Res. Commun.* 32:338–43
107. Erdos, T., Gospodarowicz, D., Bessada, R., Fries, J. 1968. *Compt. Rend. Acad. Sci. D* 266:2164–67
108. Rochefort, H., Baulieu, E.-E. 1968. *Compt. Rend. Acad. Sci.* 267:662–65
109. Korenman, S. G., Rao, C. R. 1968. *Proc. Nat. Acad. Sci.* 61:1028–33
110. De Sombre, E. R., Puca, G. A., Jensen, E. V. 1969. *Biochem. J.* 115:47
111. De Sombre, E. R., Puca, G. A., Jensen, E. V. 1969. *Proc. Nat. Acad. Sci.* 64:148–54
112. Eisenfeld, A. J. 1969. *Nature* 224:1202–3
113. Ellis, D. J., Ringold, H. J. 1971. In *Biochemical endocrinology: III. The sex steroids: Molecular mechanisms,* ed. K. W. McKerns. New York: Appleton-Century-Crofts
114. Korenman, S. G. 1968. *J. Clin. Endocrinol.* 28:127
115. Korenman, S. G., Perrin, L. E., McCallum, T. P. 1969. *J. Clin. Endocrinol.* 29:879
116. Korenman, S. G. 1969. *Steroids* 13:163–77
117. Rosner, W., Christy, W. P., Kelly, W. G. 1969. *Biochemistry* 8:3100–8
118. Mercier-Bodard, C., Baulieu, E.-E. 1968. *Compt. Rend. Acad. Sci. D* 267:804–7
119. Sandberg, A. A., Slaunwhite, W. R., Jr., Antoniades, H. N. 1957. *Recent Progr. Horm. Res.,* 13:209–67
120. Brecher, P., Pasquina, A., Wotiz, H. H. 1969. *Endocrinology* 85:612–14
121. Emanuel, M. B., Oakey, R. E. 1969. *Nature* 223:66–67
122. Wyss, R. H., Heinrichs, W. L., 1968. *J. Clin. Endocrinol. Metab.* 28:1227–30
123. Baulieu, E.-E., Alberga, A., Jung, I. 1967. *Compt. Rend. Acad. Sci.* 265:501–4
124. Milgrom, E., Baulieu, E.-E. 1969. *Biochim. Biophys. Acta* 194:602–5
125. Vonderhaar, B., Mueller, G. C. 1969. *Biochim. Biophys. Acta* 176:626–31
125a. Cuatrecasas, P. 1970. *J. Biol. Chem.* 245:3059–65
126. Muldoon, T. G., Warren, J. C. 1969. *J. Biol. Chem.* 244:5430–35
127. Brökelmann, J. 1969. *J. Histochem. Cytochem.* 17:394–407
128. Williams-Ashman, H. G., Liao, S. 1964. In *Actions of Hormones on Molecular Processes,* ed. D. Kritchevsky, G. Litwak, 482–508. New York: Wiley
129. Williams-Ashman, H. G. 1965. *Cancer Res.* 25:1096–120
130. Marks, F., Hecker, F. 1969. *Biochim. Biophys. Acta* 187:250–65
131. Brökelmann, J., Fawcett, D. W. 1969. *Biol. Reprod.* 1:59–71
132. Shyamala, G., Gorski, J. 1969. *J. Biol. Chem.* 244:1097–103
133. Brecher, P. I., Wotiz, H. H. 1969. *Endocrinology* 84:718–26
134. Brecher, P. I., Numata, M., De-Sombre, E. R., Jensen, E. V. 1970. *Fed. Proc.* 29:249 (Abstr. 14)
135. Clark, J. H., Gorski, J. 1969. *Biochim. Biophys. Acta* 192:508–15
136. Brecher, P. I., Vigersky, R., Wotiz, H. S., Wotiz, H. H. 1967. *Steroids* 10:635–51

137. Giannopoulos, G., Gorski, J. 1970. Fed. Proc. 29 :469 (Abstr. 1263)
138. King, R. J. B. 1969. Biochem. J. 115 : 29–30P
139. Baulieu, E.-E. 1969. Abh. Deut. Akad. Wiss. Berlin, Kl. Med. No. 2 :148–54
140. Puca, G. A., Bresciani, F. 1970. Nature 225 :1251–52
141. Brecher, P. I., Wotiz, H. H. 1968. Proc. Soc. Exp. Biol. Med. 128 : 470–73
142. Puca, G. A., Bresciani, F. 1969. Nature 223 :745–47
143. King, R. J. B., Gordon, J., Steggles, A. W. 1969. Biochem. J. 114 :649–57
144. Pooley, A. S., King, R. J. B. 1969. Biochem. J. 115 :48P
145. Steggles, A. W., Vertes, M., King, R. J. B. 1969. Biochem. J. 115 : 48P–49P
145a. Steggles, A. W., King, R. J. B. 1970. Biochem. J. 118 :695–701
146. Ofner, P. 1969. Vitam. Horm. 26 : 237–84
147. Grant, J. K. 1969. In Essays in Biochemistry, ed. P. N. Campbell, G. D. Greville 5 :2–58. New York : Academic
148. Wilson, J. D., Gloyna, R. E. 1970. Recent Progr. Horm. Res. 26 :309–36. In press
149. Williams-Ashman, H. G. 1970. In The Androgens of the Testis, ed. K. B. Eik-Nes, 117–43. New York : Dekker
150. Williams-Ashman, H. G., Reddi, A. H. 1971. In Biochemical Actions of Hormones, ed. G. Litwak, Vol. 2. New York : Academic. In press
151. Baulieu, E.-E., Robel, P. 1970. In The Androgens of the Testis, 49–71. See Ref. 149
152. Bruchovsky, N., Wilson, J. D. 1968. J. Biol. Chem. 243 :2012–21
153. Anderson, K. M., Liao, S. 1968. Nature 219 :277–79
154. Tveter, K. J. 1969. Endocrinology 85 : 597–600
155. Tveter, K. J., Aakvaag, A. 1969. Endocrinology 85 :683–89
156. Tveter, K. J. 1969. Acta Endocrinol. 60 :60–8
157. Tveter, K. J. 1969. Acta Endocrinol. Suppl. 128, 44
158. Tveter, K. J. 1970. Acta Endocrinol. 63 :489–98
159. Tveter, K. J. 1967. Acta Pathol. Microbiol. Scand. Suppl. 187, 110
160. Mangan, F. R., Neal, G. E., Williams,

D. C. 1968. Arch. Biochem. Biophys. 124 :27–40
161. Roy, S. K., Laumas, K. R. 1969. Acta Endocrinol. 61 :629–40
162. Appelgren, L. E. 1969. Acta Endocrinol. 62 :505–12
163. Thomas, J. A., Knych, E. T., Jr., Mawhinney, M. G. 1970. Eur. J. Pharmacol. 8 :361–63
164. Thomas, J. A., Smith, C. G., Mawhinney, M. G., Knych, E. T., Jr. 1970. Acta Endocrinol. 63 : 505–11
165. Geller, J., Van Damme, O., Garabieta, G., Loh, A., Rettura, J., Seifter, E. 1969. Endocrinology 84 :1330–35
166. Belham, J. E., Neal, G. E., Williams, D. C. 1969. Biochim. Biophys. Acta 187 :159–62
167. Fang, S., Anderson, K. M., Liao, S. 1969. J. Biol. Chem. 244 :6584–95
168. Mainwaring, W. I. P. 1969. J. Endocrinol. 44 :323–33
169. Tveter, K. J., Attramadal, A. 1968. Acta Endocrinol. 59 :218–26
170. Tveter, K. J., Unhjem, O. 1969. Endocrinology 84 :963–66
171. Stern, J. M., Eisenfeld, A. J. 1969. Science 166 :233–35
172. Sar, M., Liao, S., Stumpf, W. E. 1970. Endocrinology 86 :1008–111
173. Tveter, K. J., Attramadal, A. 1969. Endocrinology 85 :350–54
174. Tveter, K. J. 1970. Acta Endocrinol. 63 :207–15
175. Mosebach, K.-O., Jühe, H., Dirscherl, W. 1967. Acta Endocrinol. 54 :557–67
176. Rinkens, D., Mosebach, K.-O. 1968. 13 Symp. Deut. Ges. Endokrinol., 134–37
177. Resko, J. A., Goy, R. W., Phoenix, C. H. 1967. Endocrinology 80 :490–98
178. Whalen, R. E., Luttge, W. G., Green, R. 1969. Endocrinology 84 :217–22
179. Whalen, R. E., Edwards, D. A. 1969. Endocrinology 84 :155–56
180. Gloyna, R. E., Wilson, J. D. 1969. J. Clin. Endocrinol. 29 :970–77
181. Mainwaring, W. I. P. 1969. J. Endocrinol. 45 :333–414
182. Unhjem, O., Tveter, K. J., Aakvaag, A. 1969. Acta Endocrinol. 69 :153–64
182a. Kowarski, A., Shalf, J., Migeon, C. 1969. J. Biol. Chem. 244 :5269–72
183. Gomez, E. C., Hsia, S. L. 1968. Biochemistry 7 :24–32

184. Wilson, J. D., Walker, J. D. 1969. *J. Clin. Invest.* 48 :371–79
185. Mauvais-Jarvis, P., Bercovici, J. P., Gauthier, F. 1969. *J. Clin. Endocrinol. Metab.* 29 :417–21
186. Northcutt, R. C., Island, D. P., Liddle, G. W. 1969. *J. Clin. Endocrinol. Metab.* 29 :422–24
187. Siiteri, P. K., Wilson, J. D. 1970. *Proc. Endocrine. Soc.* Abstr. 78
188. Morfin, R. F., Aliapoulios, M. A., Chamberlain, J., Ofner, P. 1970. *Endocrinology* 87 :394–405
189. Weiner, A. L., Ofner, P., Sweeney, E. A. 1970. *Endocrinology* 87 : 406–9
190. Sholiton, L. J., Werk, E. E. 1969. *Acta Endocrinol.* 61 :641–48
191. Sholiton, L. J., Hall, I. L., Werk, E. E. 1970. *Acta Endocrinol.* 63 : 512–18
191a. Jaffe, R. B. 1969. *Steroids* 14 :483– 98
192. Shimazaki, J., Matsushita, I,. Furuya, N., Yamanaka, H., Shida, K. 1969. *Endocrinol. Jap.* 16 :453–58
193. Farnsworth, W. E. 1969. *Invest. Urol.* 6 :423–27
194. Shimazaki, J., Kurihara, H., Ito, Y., Shida, K. 1965. *Gunma J. Med. Sci.* 14 :312–25
195. Baulieu, E. E., Lasnitzki, I., Robel, P. 1968. *Biochem. Biophys. Res. Commun.* 32 :575–77
196. Baulieu, E. E., Lasnitzki, I., Robel, P. 1968. *Nature* 219 :1155–56
197. Bruchovsky, N., Wilson, J. D. 1968. *J. Biol. Chem.* 243 :5953–60
198. Parsons, I. C., Mangan, F. R., Neal, G. E. 1970. *Biochem. J.* 117 :425– 30
199. Baulieu, E. E., Jung, I. 1970. *Biochem. Biophys. Res. Commun.* 38 : 599–602
200. Unhjem, O., Tveter, K. J. 1969. *Acta Endocrinol.* 60 :571–78
200a. Fang, S., Liao, S. 1969. *Fed. Proc.* 28 :846 (Abstr. 3288)
201. Fang, S., Liao, S. 1969. *Mol. Pharmacol.* 5 :420–31
202. O'Malley, B. W., McGuire, W. L., Kohler, P. O., Korenman, S. G. 1969. *Recent Progr. Horm. Res.* 25 :105–60
203. Falk, R. J., Bardin, C. W. 1970. *Endocrinology* 86 :1059–63
204. Laumas, K. R., Farooq, A. 1966. *J. Endocrinol.* 36 :95–96
205. Laumas, K. R. 1969. *Abh. Deut. Akad. Wiss. Berlin, Kl. Med.* No. 2 :155–63

206. Seiki, K., Miyamoto, M., Tamashita, A., Kotani, M. 1969. *J. Endocrinol.* 43 :129–30
206a. Frost, P., Gomez, E. C., Weinstein, G. D., Lamas, J., Hsia, S. L. 1969. *Biochemistry* 8 :948–52
207. Armstrong, D. T., King, E. E. 1970. *Fed. Proc.* 29 :250 (Abstr. 22)
208. Wenzel, M., Langold, M., Hallac, P. 1969. *J. Biol. Chem.* 244 :4523–25
209. Karsznia, R., Wyss, R. H., Heinrichs, W. L., Herrmann, W. L. 1967. *Endocrinology* 84 :1238–46
210. Price, D., Williams-Ashman, H. G. 1961. In *Sex and Internal Secretions,* ed. W. C. Young, Chap. 6, 366–488. Baltimore: Williams & Wilkins. 3rd ed.
211. Milgrom, E., Baulieu, E. E. 1968. *Compt. Rend. Acad. Sci. D* 267 : 2005–7
212. Leymaire, P., Gueriguian, J. L. 1969. *Compt. Rend. Acad. Sci. D* 268 : 1342
213. Seshadri, B., Warren, J. C. 1969. *Biochim. Biophys. Acta* 195 :566– 68
214. Barker, K. L., Warren, J. C. 1967. *Endocrinology* 80 :536–39
215. Nicolette, J .A., Lemahieu, M. A., Mueller, G. C. 1968. *Biochim. Biophys. Acta* 166 :403–9
216. Raynaud-Jammet, C., Baulieu, E. E. 1969. *Compt. Rend. Acad. Sci. Paris D* 268 :3211–14
217. Bashirelahi, N., Chader, G. J., Villee, C. A. 1969. *Biochem. Biophys. Res. Commun.* 37 :976–81
218. Bashirelahi, N., Villee, C. A. 1970. *Biochim. Biophys. Acta* 202 :192– 94
219. Cohen, P., Kidson, C. 1969. *Proc. Nat. Acad. Sci.* 63 :458–64
220. Kidson, C., Thomas, A., Cohen, C. 1970. *Biochemistry* 9 :1571–76
220a. Cohen, P., Chin, R. C., Kidson, C. 1969. *Biochemistry* 8 :3603
221. Masica, D. N., Money, J., Ehrhardt, A. A., Lewis, V. G. 1969. *Johns Hopkins Med. J.* 124 :34–43
222. Ionesco, B. 1969. *Rev. Roum. Endocrinol.* 6 :191–203
223. Mauvais-Jarvis, P., Bercovici, J. P., Crepy, O., Gauthier, F. 1970. *J. Clin. Invest.* 49 :31–40
224. Mauvais-Jarvis, P., Floch, H. H., Bercovici, J. P. 1968. *J. Clin. Endocrinol. Metab.* 28 :460
225. Mauvais-Jarvis, P., Bercovici, J. P., Floch, H. H. 1969. *Rev. Fr. Etud. Clin. Biol.* 14 :159

226. Strickland, A., French, F. S. 1969. *J. Clin. Endocrinol. Metab.* 29 : 1284–86
227. Bardin, C. W., Allison, J. E., Stanley, A. J., Gumbreck, L. G. 1969. *Endocrinology* 84 :435–36
228. Bardin, C. W., Bullock, L., Schneider, G., Allison, J. E., Stanley, A. J. 1970. *Science* 167 :1136–38
229. Money, J., Ehrhardt, A. A., Masica, D. N. 1968. *Johns Hopkins Med. J.* 123 :105–14
230. Lasnitzki, I. 1969. *Cancer Res.* 29 : 318–26
231. Lostroh, A. J. 1968. *Proc. Nat. Acad. Sci.* 60 :1312–18
232. Gori, Z., Pellegrino, C., Pollera, M. 1969. *Exp. Mol. Pathol.* 10 :199–218
233. Kosto, B., Calvin, H. I., Williams-Ashman, H. G. 1967. *Advan. Enzyme Regul.* 5 :25–37
234. Coffey, D. S., Shimazaki, J., Williams-Ashman, H. G. 1968. *Arch. Biochem. Biophys.* 124 :184–98
235. Reddi, A. H. 1969. *Gen. Comp. Endocrinol. Suppl. 2,* 81–85
236. Whalen, R. E. 1968. In *Perspectives in reproduction and sexual behavior,* ed. M. Diamond, 303–40. Bloomington : Indiana Univ. Press
237. Laron, Z., Sarel, R. 1970. *Acta Endocrinol.* 63 :625–33
238. Turkington, R. W. 1970. In *Biochemical Endocrinology: III. The Sex Steroids: Molecular Mechanisms,* ed. K. W. McKerns. New York : Appleton-Crofts
239. Turkington, R. W. 1969. *NY State J. Med.* 69 :2649–55
240. Turkington, R. W., Hilf, R. 1968. *Science* 160 :1457–59
241. Talalay, P., Williams-Ashman, H. G. 1960. *Recent Progr. Horm. Res.* 16 :1–47
242. Villee, C. A., Hagerman, D. D., Joel, P. B. 1960. *Recent Progr. Horm. Res.* 16 :49–77
243. Karavolas, H. J., Orr, J. C., Engel, L. L. 1969. *J. Biol. Chem.* 244 : 4413–21
244. Hagerman, D. D. 1969. *Arch. Biochem. Biophys.* 134 :196–206
245. Jarabak, J., Sack, G. H., Jr. 1969. *Biochemistry* 8 :2203–12
246. Butcher, R. W., Robison, G. A., Sutherland, E. W. 1970. In *Control Processes in Multicellular Organisms,* ed. G. E. W. Wolstenholme, J. Knight, 64–84. London : Churchill
247. Szego, C. M., Davis, J. S. 1969. *Mol. Pharmacol.* 5 :470–80
248. Sharma, S. K., Talwar, G. P. 1970. *J. Biol. Chem.* 245 :1513–19
249. Talwar, G. P. et al 1970. In *Control Processes in Multicellular Organisms,* 108–30. See Ref. 246
250. Mitznegg, P., Heim, F., Meythaler, B. 1970. *Life Sci.* 9 :121
251. Triner, L., Overweg, N. A., Nahas, G. G. 1970. *Nature* 225 :282–83
252. Rosenfeld, M. G., O'Malley, B. W. 1970. *Science* 168 :253–55
253. Kissel, J. H., Rosenfeld, M. G., Chase, L. R., O'Malley, B. W. 1970. *Endocrinology* 86 :1019–24
254. Singhal, R. L., Vijayvargiya, R., Ling, G. M. 1970. *Science* 168 : 261–63
255. Miyamoto, E., Kuo, J. F., Greengard, P. 1969. *J. Biol. Chem.* 244 :6395
256. Langan, T. A. 1969. *J. Biol. Chem.* 244 :5763
257. Meyer, S. E., Krebs, E. G. 1970. *J. Biol. Chem.* 245 :3153–60
258. Reddi, A .H., Ewing, L. L., Williams-Ashman, H. G. 1970. *Fed. Proc.* 29 :730 (Abstr. 2740)
259. King, R. J. B., Gordon, J. 1969. *Biochem. J.* 114 :59–60
260. Williams-Ashman, H. G., Pegg, A. E., Lockwood, D. H. 1969. *Advan. Enzyme Regul.* 7 :291–323
261. Moulton, B. C., Leonard, S. L. 1969. *Endocrinology* 84 :1461–65
262. Caldarera, C. M., Moruzzi, M. S., Barbiroli, B., Moruzzi, G. 1968. *Biochim. Biophys. Res. Commun.* 33 :266–71
263. Pegg, A. E., Lockwood, D. H., Williams-Ashman, H. G. 1970. *Biochem. J.* 117 :17–31
264. Brasel, J. A., Coffey, D. S., Williams-Ashman, H. G. 1968. *Med. Exp.* 18 :321–26
265. Williams-Ashman, H. G., Lockwood, D. H. 1970. *Ann. NY Acad. Sci.* 171 :882
266. Granick, S., Kappas, A. 1967. *J. Biol. Chem.* 242 :4587–93
267. Kappas, A., Granick, S. 1968. *J. Biol. Chem.* 243 :346–51
268. Kappas, A., Song, C. S., Levere, R. D., Sachson, R. A., Granick, S. 1968. *Proc. Nat. Acad. Sci.* 61 : 509–13
269. Kappas, A., Song, C. S., Sassa, S., Levere, R. D., Granick, S. 1969. *Proc. Nat. Acad. Sci.* 64 :557–64
270. Rifkind, A. B., Gillette, P. N., Song,

C. S., Kappas, A. 1970. *J. Clin. Endocrinol.* 30 :330–35

271. Gillette, P. N., Bradler, H. L., Gallagher, T. F., Kappas, A. 1970. *J. Clin. Invest.* 49. In press

272. Gordon, A. S., Mirand, E. A., Wenig, J., Katz, R., Zajani, E. D. 1968. *Ann. NY Acad. Sci.* 149 :318–35

273. Piliero, S. J., Medici, P. T., Haber, C. 1968. *Ann. N.Y. Acad. Sci.* 149 :336–55

274. Fried, W., Gurney, C. W. 1968. *Ann. NY Acad. Sci.* 149 :356–65

275. Gordon, A. S., Zajani, E. D., Levere, R. D., Kappas, A. 1970. *Proc. Nat. Acad. Sci.* 65 :919–24

276. Naets, J. P., Wittek, M. 1968. *Ann. NY Acad. Sci.* 149 :366–76

277. Meineke, H. A., Crafts, R. C. 1968. *Ann. NY Acad. Sci.* 149 :298–307

278. Jacobson, W., Sidman, R. L., Diamond, L. K. 1968. *Ann. NY Acad. Sci.* 159 :389–405

279. Mirand, E. A., Groenewald, J. H. Kenny, G. M., Murphy, G. P. 1969. *Experientia* 25 :1104

280. Gorshein, D., Gardner, F. H. 1970. *Proc. Nat. Acad. Sci.* 65 :564–68

281. Necheles, T. F., Rai, U. S. 1969. *Blood* 34 :380–84

282. Kappas, A., Granick, S. 1968. *Ann. NY Acad. Sci.* 151 :842–49

283. Song, C. S., Rifkind, A. B., Gillette, P. N., Kappas, A. 1969. *Am. J. Obstet. Gynecol.* 105 :813–47

284. Kappas, A. 1968. *N. Engl. J. Med.* 278 :378–84

285. Kappas, A., Levere, R. D., Granick, S. 1968. *Sem. Hematol.* 5 :323–34

286. Kappas, A., Palmer, R. H. 1963. *Pharmacol. Rev.* 15 :123–67

287. Freeman, M. E., Crissman, J. K., Jr., Louw, G. N., Butcher, R. L., Inskeep, E. K. 1970. *Endocrinology* 86 :717–20

288. Welch, R. M., Levin, W., Conney, A. H. 1968. *J. Pharmacol. Exp. Ther.* 160 :171–78

289. Kuntzman, R., Welch, R., Conney, A. H. 1966. *Advan. Enzyme Regul.* 4 :149–60

290. Conney, A. H. 1967. *Pharmacol. Rev.* 19 :317–66

291. Levin, W., Welch, R. M., Conney, A. H. 1968. *J. Pharmacol. Exp. Ther.* 169 :362–71

292. Levin, W., Welch, R. M., Conney, A. H. 1969. *Endocrinology* 83 : 149–56

293. Vida, J. A. 1969. *Androgens and Anabolic Agents: Chemistry and Pharmacology,* 1–326. New York : Academic

294. Krüskemper, H.-Z. 1968. *Anabolic Steroids,* 1–236. New York : Academic

295. Rutter, W. J. et al 1968. *Regulation of specific protein synthesis in cytodifferentiation. J. Cell. Physiol. Suppl.* 1 72 :1–18

296. Phoenix, C. H., Goy, R. W., Resko, J. A. 1968. In *Perspectives in Reproduction and Sexual Behavior,* ed. M. Diamond, 33–49. Bloomington : Indiana Univ. Press

297. Lisk, R. D. 1968. In *Perspectives in Reproduction and Sexual Behavior,* 287–302. See Ref. 296

297a. Neumann, F., Elger, W., Steinbeck, H., von Berswordt-Wallrabe, R. 1968. *13 Symp. Deut. Ges. Endokrinol.,* 78–101

298. Tata, J. R. 1970. In *Control Processes in Multicellular Organisms,* ed. G. E. W. Wolstenholme, J. Knight, 131–57. London : Churchill

299. Karlson, P. 1968. *Humangenetik* 6 : 99–109

300. Liao, S. 1968. *Am. Zool.* 8 :233–42

301. Villee, C. A. 1968. In *Perspectives in Reproduction and Sexual Behavior,* 231–39. See Ref. 296

302. Kochakian, C. D. 1969. *Gen. Comp. Endocrinol.* 13 :146–50

303. Tata, J. R. 1968. *Nature* 219 :331–37

304. McKerns, K. W. 1969. In *The Gonads,* ed. K. W. McKerns, 71–113. New York : Appleton-Century-Crofts

305. Hamilton, T. H. 1968. *Science* 161 : 649–60

306. O'Malley, B. W. 1969 *Trans. NY Acad. Sci.* 31 :578

306a. Koide, S. S. 1969. *N.Y. State J. Med.* 69 :542–47

307. Huckabee, W. E., Crenshaw, C., Cesset, L. B., Mann, L., Barron, D. H. 1970. *Quart. J. Exp. Physiol.* 55 :16

308. Tata, J. R. 1970. *Biochem. J.* 116 : 617–30

309. Prasad, M. R. N., Dass, C. M. S., Mohla, S. 1968. *J. Reprod. Fert.* 16 :97–104

310. Miller, B. G., Owen, W. H., Emmens, C. W. 1968. *J. Endocrinol.* 41 : 189–95

311. Miller, B. G., Emmens, C. W. 1969. *J. Endocrinol.* 43 :427–36

312. Heald, P. J., O'Grady, J. E. 1970. *Biochem. J.* 117 :65–71

313. Billing, R. J., Barbiroli, B., Smellie,

R. M. S. 1969. *Biochem. J.* 112 : 563–69

314. Billing, R. J., Barbiroli, B., Smellie, R. M. S. 1969. *Biochim. Biophys. Acta* 190 :52–59

315. Billing, R. J., Barbiroli, B., Smellie, R. M. S. 1969. *Biochim. Biophys. Acta* 190 :60–65

316. Miura, S., Koide, S. S. 1970. *Proc. Soc. Exp. Biol. Med.* 133 :882–85

317. Joel, P. B., Hagerman, D. D. 1969. *Biochim. Biophys. Acta* 195 :328–39

318. Church, R. B., McCarthy, B. J. 1970. *Biochim. Biophys. Acta* 199 :103–14

319. Teng, C.-S., Hamilton, T. H. 1968. *Proc. Nat. Acad. Sci.* 60 :1416

320. O'Malley, B. W., McGuire, W. L. 1968. *Proc. Nat. Acad. Sci.* 60 : 1527

321. O'Malley, B. W., McGuire, W. L., Middleton, P. A. 1968. *Nature* 218 :1249–51

322. Dingman, C. W., Aronow, A., Bunting, S. L., Peacock, A. C., O'Malley, B. W. 1969. *Biochemistry* 8 :489–95

323. Hahn, W. E., Church, R. B., Gorbman, A., Wilmat, L. 1968. *Gen. Comp. Endocrinol.* 10 :438–42

324. Hahn, W. E., Church, R. B., Gorbman, A. 1969. *Endocrinology* 84 : 738–45

325. Lipschitz-Wiesner, R., Srinivasan, P. R., Borek, E. 1970. *Fed. Proc.* 29 :46a (Abstr. 1262)

326. Hacker, B. 1969. *Biochim. Biophys. Acta* 186 :214–16

327. Libby, P. R. 1968. *Biochem. Biophys. Res. Commun.* 31 :59–65

328. Oka, T., Schimke, R. T. 1969. *J. Cell Biol.* 41 :816–31

329. Oka, T., Schimke, R. T. 1969. *J. Cell Biol.* 43 :123–37

330. Palmiter, R. D., Christensen, A. K., Schimke, R. T. 1970. *J. Biol. Chem.* 245 :833–45

331. McGuire, W. L., O'Malley, B. W. 1968. *Biochim. Biophys. Acta* 157 : 187–94

332. Nicolette, J. A. 1969. *Arch. Biochem. Biophys.* 135 :253–58

333. Hamilton, T. H., Widnell, C. C., Tata, J. R. 1968. *J. Biol. Chem.* 243 :408–17

334. Avdalovic, N., Kochakian, C. D. 1969. *Biochim. Biophys. Acta* 182 :382–93

335. Liao, S., Sagher, D., Lin, A. H., Fang, S. 1969. *Nature* 223 :297–98

336. Roeder, R. G., Rutter, W. J. 1970. *Proc. Nat. Acad. Sci.* 65 :675–82

337. Speichinger, J. P., Barker, K. L. 1969. *Steroids* 14 :132–43

338. Trachewsky, D., Segal, S. J. 1969. *Eur. J. Biochem.* 4 :279–85

339. Liao, S., Stumpf, W. E. 1968. *Endocrinology* 82 :629–32

340. Fujii, T., Villee, C. A. 1968. *Endocrinology* 82 :453–62

341. Fujii, T., Villee, C. A. 1968. *Endocrinology* 82 :463–67

342. Fujii, T., Villee, C. 1969. *Acta Endocrinol.* 60 :527–36

343. Yamanaka, H., Furuya, N., Shimazaki, J., Shida, K. 1969. *Endocrinol. Jap.* 16 :29–36

344. Kochakian, C. D., Nishida, M., Hirone, T. 1969. *Am. J. Physiol.* 217 :383–91

345. Shimada, H., Gorbman, A. 1970. *Biochem. Biophys. Res. Commun.* 38 :423–30

346. Clayton, R. B., Kogura, J., Kraemer, H. C. 1970. *Nature* 226 :810–12

347. Kobayashi, F., Gorski, R. A. 1970. *Endocrinology* 86 :285–89

348. Yudaev, N. A., Prokovsky, B. V. 1970. *Biokhimiya* 35 :72–78

349. Desjardins, C., MacMillan, K. L., Hafs, H. D. 1968. *Anat. Rec.* 161 : 17–22

350. Eleftheriou, B. E., Desjardins, C., Pattison, M. L. 1970. *J. Endocrinol.* 46 :331–40

350a. Gorski, J., Notides, A. 1969. In *Biochemistry of Cell Division*, ed. R. Baserga, 57–76. Indianapolis : Thomas

351. Barnea, A., Gorski, J. 1970. *Biochemistry* 9 :1899–904

352. Gelehrter, T. D., Tomkins, G. M. 1970. *Proc. Nat. Acad. Sci.* 66 : 390–97

353. Korenman, S. G., O'Malley, B. W. 1968. *Endocrinology* 83 :11–17

354. Florini, J. R. 1970. *Biochemistry* 9 : 909–12

355. Murdoch, R. N., White, I. G. 1968. *J. Endocrinol.* 42 :187–92

356. Murdoch, R. N., White, I. G. 1969. *J. Endocrinol.* 43 :167–74

357. Lea, M. A., Singhal, R. L., Valadares, J. R. E. 1970. *Biochem. Pharmacol.* 19 :113–24

358. Schwark, W. S., Singhal, R. L., Ling, G. M. 1969. *Biochim. Biophys. Acta* 192 :106–17

359. Singhal, R. L., Valadares, J. R. E. 1970. *Am. J. Physiol.* 218 :321

360. De Asua, L. F., Rozengurt, E., Car-

minatti, H. 1968. *Biochim. Biophys. Acta* 170:254–62

361. Dugan, F. A., Radhakrishnamurthy, B., Rudman, R. A., Berenson, G. S. 1968. *J. Endocrinol.* 42:261–66

362. Wilson, E. W. 1969. *J. Endocrinol.* 44:63–68

363. Hooper, K. C., Hopkinson, P. 1969. *Acta Endocrinol.* 61:378–84

364. Nishigori, H., Aizawa, Y. 1968. *Endocrinol. Jap.* 15:209

365. Noack, V. I., Schmidt, H. 1968. *Endokrinologie* 53:292–321

366. Mohla, S., Prasad, M. R. N. 1969. *Acta Endocrinol.* 62:489–97

367. Schmidt, H., Berle, P., Voigt, K. D. 1969. *Acta Endocrinol.* 61:729–36

368. Naidoo, S. S., Baitera, B. 1970. *Endocrinology* 86:835–42

369. Sirakov, L. M., Kochakian, C. D. 1970. *Biochim. Biophys. Acta* 204:364–70

370. Robinson, D., Stirling, J. L. 1968. *Biochim. Biophys. Acta* 170:420–21

371. Shimazaki, J., Furuya, N., Yamanaka, H., Shida, K. 1969. *Endocrinol. Jap.* 16:163–69

372. Toth, M., Manyai, S. 1968. *Acta Biochim. Biophys. Acad. Sci. Hung.* 3:337–52

373. Rao, S. S., Sheth, A. R., Gunaga, K. P. 1969. *Indian J. Exp. Biol.* 7:20–2

374. Gunaga, K. P., Sheth, A. R., Rao, S. 1969. *Indian J. Med. Res.* 57:84–8

375. Singhal, R. L., Valadares, J. R. E. 1968. *Biochem. J.* 110:703–11

376. Fishman, W. H., Ide, H., Rufo, R. 1969. *Histochemie* 20:287

377. Frieden, E. H., Fishel, S. S. 1968. *Biochem. Biophys. Res. Commun.*, 31:515–21

377a. Toth, M., Machovich, M. 1969. *Acta Biochim. Biophys. Acad. Sci. Hung.* 4:339–48

378. Kato, K., Ide, H., Shirahama, T., Fishman, W. H. 1970. *Biochem. J.* 117:161

379. Riekkinen, P. J., Niemi, M. 1968. *Endocrinology* 83:1224–31

380. Calissano, P., Angeletti, P. U. 1968. *Biochem. Biophys. Acta* 156:51–58

381. Mainwaring, W. I. P. 1968. *Biochem. J.* 110:79–86

382. Mainwaring, W. I. P. 1968. *Gerontologia* 14:133–41

383. Kochakian, C. D., Hama, T. 1969. *Acta Endocrinol.* 62:328–38

384. Kochakian, C. D. 1969. *Steroids* 14:77–90

385. Rose, D. P., Brown, R. R. 1969. *Biochim. Biophys. Acta* 184:412–19

386. Mowat, A. P. 1968. *J. Endocrinol.* 42:579–83

387. Lyman, R. L., Hopkins, S. M., Sheehan, G., Tinoco, J. 1968. *Biochim. Biophys. Acta* 152:197–207

388. Huff, S. D., Chaykin, S. 1968. *Endocrinology* 83:1259–67

389. Herzfeld, A., Knox, W. E. 1968. *J. Biol. Chem.* 243:3327–32

390. Fujii, T., Villee, C. A. 1969. *Proc. Nat. Acad. Sci.* 62:836–43

391. Farnsworth, W. E. 1968. *Biochim. Biophys. Acta* 150:446–51

392. Coffey, D. S., Ichinose, R. R., Shimazaki, J., Williams-Ashman, H. G. 1968. *Mol. Pharmacol.* 4:580–90

393. Ahmed, K., Williams-Ashman, H. G. 1969. *Biochem. J.* 113:829–36

394. Bergamini, E., Bombara, G., Pellegrino, C. 1969. *Biochim. Biophys. Acta* 177:220–34

395. Bergamini, E. 1969. *Biochim. Biophys. Acta* 177:235–40

396. Turner, J. W., Jr., Leonard, S. L. 1969. *Endocrinology* 84:589–94

397. Mills, T. M., Spazziani, E. 1968. *Biochim, Biophys. Acta* 150:435–45

398. Smith, D. E., Gorski, J. 1968. *J. Biol. Chem.* 243:4169–74

399. Gregoire, A. T., Guinness, B. J. 1968. *J. Reprod. Fert.* 17:427–32

400. Cecil, H. C., Bitman, J. 1968. *J. Endocrinol.* 42:65–77

401. Pegg, A. E., Williams-Ashman, H. G. 1968. *Endocrinology* 82:603–10

402. Doeg, K. A. 1968. *Endocrinology* 82:535–39

403. Doeg, K. A. 1969. *Endocrinology* 85:974–76

404. Hay, J. B., Gray, G. M. 1970. *Biochim. Biophys. Acta* 202:563–66

405. Strauss, J. P., Pochi, P. E. 1968. In *Clinical Endocrinology*, ed. E. B. Ashwood, C. E. Cassidy, 2:806. New York: Grune and Stratton

406. Ebling, F. J., Ebling, E., Skinner, J. 1969. *J. Endocrinol.* 45:245–56

407. Ebling, F. J., Ebling, E., Skinner, J. 1969. *J. Endocrinol.* 45:257–63

408. Krähenbühl, C., Desaulles, P. A. 1969. *Experientia* 25:1193–95

409. Spener, F., Mangold, H. K., Sansone, G. L., Hamilton, J. G. 1969. *Biochim. Biophys. Acta* 192:516–21

410. Sansone, G. L., Swartzendruber, D. C.,

Snyder, F. 1970. *Biochim. Biophys. Acta* 201:401–9

411. Nikkari, T., Valavaara, M. 1969. *J. Endocrinol.* 43:113–18
412. Knuppen, R., Lubrich, W., Haupt, O., Ammerlaln, V., Breuer, H. 1969. *Z. Physiol. Chem.* 350:1067–75
413. Breuer, H., Knuppen, R., Haupt, O. 1970. *Biochem. J.* 118. In press
414. Harper, M. E., Fahmy, A. R., Pierrepoint, C. G., Griffiths, K. 1970. *Steroids* 15:89–103
415. Price, D., Zaaijer, J. J. P., Ortiz, E. 1969. *Proc. Kon. Ned. Akad. Wetensch. C* 72:370

416. Anonymous. 1970. *Nature* 226:869–70
417. Needham, J., Lu, G. D. 1966. *Jap. Stud. Hist. Sci.* 5:150–71
418. Lu, G. D., Needham, J. 1964. *Med. Hist.* 8:101–21
419. Needham, J., Lu, G. D. 1968. *Endeavour* 27:130–32
420. Needham, J. 1954 onwards. *Science and Civilization in China*. Cambridge. In 7 volumes
421. Raspé, G. 1968. *Advances in the Biosciences*, ed. G. Raspé, 1:1–13. Oxford: Pergamon and Braunschweig: Vieweg

KIDNEY

Jack Orloff and Maurice Burg

Laboratory of Kidney and Electrolyte Metabolism, National Heart and Lung Institute, National Institutes of Health, Bethesda, Maryland

Introduction

We have made no attempt to cover the infinitely expanding literature relating to renal physiology of the past 2 years. This is virtually impossible if a critical analysis of the papers is to be attempted. Rather we have selected certain aspects of renal physiology of particular interest to us and have attempted to the best of our ability to evaluate their significance. We have thus restricted our attention largely to water and electrolyte transport in the proximal tubule, emphasizing contributions based on current micropuncture techniques. In addition we have sought to examine the defects and limitations as well as the advantages of the methods employed. For sentimental reasons we have summarized some of the current views regarding the mode and regulation of ammonia excretion. Other aspects of renal physiology have been extensively and critically reviewed in (1–15). Finally, should some of the numerous investigators whose important contributions have been neglected in the review feel slighted, this is unintentional and in some instances they may conceivably consider themselves fortunate. To those uncited and neither complimented nor inadvertently insulted we beg forgiveness. We had intended to leave few stones unturned.

Methods

Considerable effort has been directed to elucidate the mechanism of sodium transport in the proximal nephron, that of so-called glomerulotubular balance, and the role of the kidney, more specifically the proximal segment, in the regulation of extracellular fluid volume. The three problems though interrelated have been treated separately in most communications. Much of the evidence obtained in different laboratories, particularly with respect to glomerulotubular balance and fluid volume regulation, is conflicting and at this juncture no clear picture has evolved. Critical evaluation of the studies requires an appreciation of the methods used for the measurement of the pertinent variables, glomerular filtration rate and proximal tubular reabsorptive rate, and recognition of their limitations. Particularly in micropuncture studies has lack of recognition of the limitations led to conflicting interpretations of otherwise similar studies.

The earliest estimate of single nephron GFR (V_o) and net fluid absorption (C) was that of Walker and associates (16, 17). The method, since refined, simply requires systemic infusion of a glomerular marker such as inulin, blockade of the distal portion of the nephron with oil, and a timed collection of tubular fluid in a micropipet. It is essential 1. that the oil block prevent any leak of nonreabsorbed filtrate beyond the block, as well as reflux back into the proximal segment, and 2. that all of the filtrate be collected at the puncture site. V_0 can then be calculated from the relationship

$$V_0 = \frac{TF}{P_{inulin}} (V_L) \qquad\qquad 1$$

where V_L is rate of flow of tubular fluid at the collection site, and TF/P_{inulin}, the concentration ratio of inulin in tubular fluid and plasma at this point. Net absorption, C, in volume per unit time per unit tubule length is derived from

$$C = \frac{V_0}{L} \left(1 - \frac{P}{TF_{inulin}} \right) \qquad\qquad 2$$

where L is the length of the tubule from glomerulus to the puncture site. Though the point is rarely discussed, the measurement of L is not as precise as one would like. It is done on tubules microdissected from a macerated kidney, a procedure which, arguments to the contrary, must alter the architecture, elasticity, etc of the segment. Admittedly errors may be reproducible in a single laboratory and probably do not significantly affect the interpretations. The most critical datum is V_L and its absolute determinant the ability to collect *all* of the nonabsorbed glomerular filtrate formed per unit time which arrives at the puncture site proximal to the oil block without disturbing the dynamics of the system. Even if one ignores the possibility that the introduction of the oil block and manipulation of the micropipet may of itself alter intraluminal pressure and thereby affect filtration pressure, such that the relationship between V_0 and C is changed from that existing in the physiologic state, precise collection of all the filtered fluid is not insured. Gottschalk & Leyssac (18) and Schnermann et al (19) have discussed this problem in detail. Ideally the oil must serve two functions:

1. It must act as a *tight seal,* preventing both leakage of fluid beyond the block into the distal nephron and reflux from below. Leakage will result in an underestimate of V_L, reflux an overestimate of V_L and the ratio TF/P.

2. The "tight" seal must be "mobile" to permit detection of pressure-induced shifts in its location.

The latter is essential if movement of the oil block is to serve as an index of excessively rapid or slow collection. Thus if the rate of aspiration of fluid into the pipet exceeds the rate of flow of nonabsorbed filtrate down the lumen this, in theory, should be signaled by deflection of the oil drop upstream and vice versa. The two requirements, that of a *tight seal* which is at the same time *mobile,* are obviously conflicting (18) and may make the method somewhat impractical. Gottschalk & Leyssac (18) noted frequent undulation of the drop in their studies and interpreted this as indicative of leakage of fluid around the seal. Furthermore under other circumstances tubule collapse during aspiration in consequence of excessively rapid removal of nonabsorbed filtrate was not attended, as it should have been, by a proximal shift of the oil block. These observations led the authors to reject the use of the distal oil-drop method in their studies. They prefer instead to remove fluid slowly (at approximately 10–15% of the rate of volume flow within the tubule itself) from an unobstructed proximal segment and to measure only TF/P_{inulin} and L. It is their belief that a slow and gentle collection avoids experimentally induced disturbances in flow and permits a precise estimate of TF/P_{inulin} at the collection site. Though this may be a correct conclusion, only fractional reabsorption of fluid as a function of length can be determined directly in this fashion rather than the more important variables, V_o and C. C can be estimated indirectly from measurements of transit time (v.i.), the TF/P_{inulin} and the tubule radius if one assumes the latter to be constant (v.i.).

Schnermann et al (19) systematically investigated the use of the oil-block method in studies in which they measured transit time and intraluminal pressure during collection periods, in addition to V_L and TF/P_{inulin}. In their studies aspiration of fluid in the conventional manner decreased transit time and intraluminal pressure without necessarily displacing the oil block. The maneuver thereby increased V_o of itself and as in (18) the oil block did not provide independent evidence of excessively rapid aspiration. In contrast, no change in transit time or intraluminal pressure transpired if fluid was allowed to flow spontaneously into a pipet, whose resistance was "equal" to that of the remaining tubule in free flow. Their modification, though in theory reasonable, is technically difficult. In principle it requires two operators, one for the monitoring of pressure and transit time, the other for the collection procedure. Although the authors indicate that precise standardization of the procedure with fabrication of pipets of the correct resistance to flow should eliminate the need to measure pressure and transit time, this is difficult to accept, particularly since resistance may not be the same in all animals and in control and experimental periods. Of interest is their implied criticism of the "recollection technique". This technique entails reaspiration of fluid from the same site in the nephron following an experimental manipulation. An oil block is introduced prior to collection in both periods. The authors noted a "spontaneous" rise in intraluminal pressure following the control period in the absence of any experimental maneuver in a number of studies. They ascribe this to incomplete "disappearance" of the first oil block with resultant partial blockade of the distal nephron beyond the visual field. They suggest that results obtained in the recollection period are not readily interpretable unless special care is taken to make certain that the oil block has passed completely through the nephron, a condition which could only be detected by a recording of intraluminal pressure.

Gertz et al (20) provided a theoretical basis for the determination of C without the use either of an oil block or of timed collections. Two methods were proposed:

The first, the split-drop technique, involves measurement of the half-time for disappearance (reabsorption) of a saline droplet inserted between two oil columns which isolate the droplet from bordering luminal fluid. The oil is said not to produce histological damage on electronmicroscopic examination (21). The volume of the drop decreases exponentially with time, and if the assumption that the radius of the saline drop is constant is correct, the rate of approach of the two opposing oil columns is an adequate measure of the rate of decrease in volume of the drop. C is calculated from the relationship

$$C = \frac{\pi r^2 0.693}{t_{\frac{1}{2}}}$$

3.

where r is the internal radius of the tubule. The method, though in principle simple, is subject to observer bias which may influence the results (22, 23) and more importantly it requires precise measurement of r in order to compare C with that obtained with the conventional techniques. Difficulties in the selection of the proper tubule borders for measurement of r have been discussed (24) and have not in our opinion been resolved. Furthermore the assumption that the tubule is perfectly cylindrical even over short distances of several mm may be invalid. Gertz et al (20) and Brunner et al (25), recognizing the problem of accurate estimates of r, limited their original studies to calculation of the ratio $C/\pi r^2$ which requires only measurement of the half-time. This obviously is not a direct estimate of the reabsorptive rate and though assigned the eponym "intrinsic reabsorptive capacity" has fallen into disrepute (v.i.). As will be repeatedly emphasized, it is impossible to interpret changes in the ratio without precise estimates of r.

The second Gertz method requires measurement of the lissamine green transit time (T) developed by Steinhausen (26). The dye is injected into a peripheral vein and the elapsed time between the green flush of the kidney and the appearance of the front of the colored column of tubule fluid in the last proximal convolution recorded as the proximal transit time. C is calculated from the relationship

$$C = \frac{\pi r^2 \ln TF/P_{\text{inulin}}}{T}$$

4.

where TF/P is the inulin ratio at the point of the transit-time measurement. As with the split-drop technique the measurement of r is critical and again the ratio $C/\pi r^2$ has been substituted.

Early equivalence of the ratio $C/\pi r^2$ determined from the two methods, despite apparent differences in tubule diameter in the two situations, led to the view now generally believed to be erroneous (27), that C is directly dependent on r^2 or tubule volume. The equivalence noted above may therefore have been fortuitous (v.i.). C calculated from the three methods discussed above has been compared (28–30). In most cases C differed according to the method used. Though as implied above, a difference between that derived from the split-drop and transit-time studies was to be expected from the hypothesis that r^2 determined reabsorptive rate, this is no longer a tenable explanation. Furthermore C derived from free-flow and half-time studies (30) are approximately equal. There seems little virtue in or possibility of explaining the discrepant results logically. The compounding of systematic errors in one or more of the determinants is undoubtedly a factor, the most likely errors being the estimation of r (24, 29, 31) and acceptance of the assumption that the proximal convoluted tubule is a uniform cylinder throughout its length. Though recognizing the brilliance of the Gertz derivations, one must conclude, as have others (32, that many of the interpretations of observed changes in $C/\pi r^2$ or calculated C may be erroneous.

The occlusion-time techniques of Leyssac (33) has also been used to measure fluid absorption. The renal artery is clamped and the time for complete collapse of the proximal tubule (OT) recorded.

$$C = \frac{\pi r^2}{OT} \qquad\qquad 5.$$

Once again C depends on the measurement of r and is subject to the same criticisms. In Leysacc's view, however, r is constant in an individual tubule under the conditions of the studies and in fact doesn't vary appreciably in the same species. Because of this the reciprocal, $1/OT$, has been employed as an estimate of reabsorption. Any retrograde flow of fluid from below during the period of tubule collapse will affect the occlusion-time measurement. Though this is acknowledged (24) it is not considered an insurmountable problem by the authors and, in their view, appropriate corrections can be made.

Baines et al (34, 35) have employed the Hanssen technique (36–38) to measure relative single nephron filtration rate (V_o), relative intraluminal flow velocity (v), and fractional water reabsorption in proximal tubules attached to superficial and deep glomeruli. ^{14}C-labeled ferrocyanide, a glomerular marker, is injected as a bolus into the jugular vein of the animal and the kidney frozen at a precise time several seconds later. The ferrocyanide is converted to Prussian blue and the tubules removed by microdissection from macerated tissue. The mean velocity of flow of tubule fluid (v) is calculated from the distance from the glomerulus the wavefront of Prussian blue had traversed in the time period between the injection and the freezing of the kidney, with an appropriate correction for the transit time from the jugular vein to the glomerulus. V_o is assumed to be proportional to the ^{14}C content of the individual tubule, a reasonable hypothesis. Their data are sufficient to provide information about the relative flows and single nephron filtration rates of different tubule populations. The authors however also calculated the absolute value of V_o in the different populations of tubules from the mean radioactivity of the tubules and estimates of the number of glomeruli in each group and the whole kidney inulin clearance. They concluded that the V_o of the deeper nephrons exceeds that of the superficial. The mean value of V_o estimated in this fashion is similar to that obtained in free-flow micropuncture studies in vivo. This is a remarkable result in view of the multiplicity of assumptions, arithmetic manipulations, and SE of each of the measurements. *Quoi qu'il en soit*, it is doubtful whether the technique is of value other than to approximate differences between the relative filtration rates of deep and superficial nephrons. Fractional fluid reabsorption ($\%R$) was estimated from the relationship

$$\%R = 1 - \frac{\pi r^2 v}{V_o} \qquad 6.$$

where r again is tubule radius, which once again detracts from the validity of the calculation.

More recently the method has been refined by de Rouffignac et al (39). ^{14}C sodium ferrocyanide is injected, in this case, at a constant rate. At equilibrium a short pulse of nonradioactive ferrocyanide is injected as a bolus. The portion of each tubule containing the nonradioactive ferrocyanide (previously converted to Prussian blue) is analyzed for radioactivity. V_o is calculated from the total radioactivity per unit time divided by the plasma radioactivity. The method is certainly unique and affords an opportunity to measure V_o in otherwise inaccessible nephrons. Estimations of reabsorption using the above method are subject to the same drawbacks as are all other methods dependent on the measurement of tubular radius. The problem is compounded in this case since r is measured in macerated preparations. Though r is purported to be *similar* to that noted in vivo, in sections from tissue frozen or fixed in vivo and in functioning isolated perfused tubules of rabbits, according to Baines et al (34), it requires stretching of one's credulity to accept the necessary inference that r is the *same* in all.

Direct estimates of C which do not require a measurement of r can be obtained by microperfusing an isolated segment of the proximal tubule in vivo (40). A segment of tubule is isolated from surrounding intraluminal fluid with two oil blocks, one proximal to prevent glomerular filtrate from entering the portion under study and one distal. Artificial fluid containing a marker such as inulin is perfused at a constant rate and the nonabsorbed remainder recollected "completely" in a second more distal pipet. Absolute reabsorption can be estimated from the perfusion rate and the ratio of the inulin concentrations in collected and perfused fluid. The method has been used by Morgan & Berliner (41) in studies of the intrinsic reabsorptive capacity of the proximal nephron. It is of value in "excluding" the influence of the glomerulus itself on net reabsorption. Both Bojesen & Leyssac (24) and Morgan & Berliner (41) have pointed out the difficulty of insuring against leakage in this technique. The latter authors also emphasized potential errors in interpretation attendant upon the difficulty in selecting the proper osmolality of the artificial perfusing solution since it must in principle coincide with that of the glomerular ultrafiltrate in each specific animal.

C can also be determined directly in a somewhat similar fashion in isolated perfused rabbit tubules (30). The tubule is perfused at a constant rate through one end and the nonabsorbed fluid collected in a pipet attached to the distal end. Inulin or labeled albumin can be used as markers for fluid absorption and net absorption calculated as in the microperfusion method above. The method has none of the disadvantages attendant upon oil blockade and it is relatively simple to insure complete collection. Furthermore since the tubule may be bathed with normal serum and perfused with an ultrafiltrate of the same serum, selection of the proper osmolality is not a problem as in the in vivo microperfusion method. But its major advantage is at the same time its major disadvantage. One certainly may examine the effect of modifications in the bathing solution, of changes in intraluminal pressure or flow, of drugs, etc on intrinsic reabsorptive capacity. But it is not possible to relate the changes to the in vivo situation with certainty since the tubule is totally divorced from unknown and known extratubular influences, e.g. interstitial pressure, changes in blood flow, and feedback mechanisms, any one of which may be of prime importance in regulating reabsorption in vivo.

Gertz et al (42) have recently compared the results of single nephron GFR measurements using Walker et al (17) technique with those obtained with a new modification ("controlled suction") introduced by the authors. Results were accepted using the Walker method only if r and transit time remained constant during the procedure. Filtration rate estimated in this fashion was approximately 35 nl per min. Following the first determination the tubule was repunctured through the same hole with an oil-filled pipet. Fluid was drawn into the pipet and the intratubular pressure estimated as that counter pressure necessary to immobilize the oil water interface in the pipet. The oil was then injected into the tubule to form a long immobile distal block. Proximal fluid was then collected by suction at a pressure equal to the original "immobilization pressure" minus several centimeters of water to compensate for the resistance of the pipet to fluid movement. Filtration rate using the modified technique was approximately 18 nl per min. The authors consider this lower value correct and attribute the higher rates obtained with the usual methods to an abnormal increase in effective filtration pressure induced by excessive suction. The latter problem has been discussed and recognized, as noted above, by many authors. The magnitude of the effect in our view is still uncertain. The lower value of single nephron

GFR reported by Gertz et al (42) would if multiplied by the appropriate number of glumeruli yield a total kidney filtration rate considerably less than is observed in vivo.

We are convinced that none of the methods for the measurement of GFR in which a distal oil block is employed is completely satisfactory since the rate of filtration will necessarily be determined in part by the rate of fluid removal. It is conceivable that a closer approximation would be obtained if an indicator dilution technique were successfully developed. In principle, a flow marker such as labeled albumin could be injected into the proximal tubule at a constant slow rate (considerably less than that of tubular flow). Fluid could be collected in a second more distal pipet at a sufficiently slow rate to avoid significant alterations in the dynamics of the system. From the concentration of albumin at the distal point and the known rate of infusion one can calculate V_L from the relationship

$$V_L = \frac{\text{amount of albumin injected per unit time}}{\text{concentration of albumin at the puncture site}} \qquad 7.$$

If inulin were also administered to the animal intravenously, the inulin TF/P ratio at that point in the tubule can also be determined and V_o calculated in the usual manner.

The possibility that there is a difference between the glomerular filtration rates of superficial and deep nephrons was originally suggested by Walker & Oliver (16). They noted that the single nephron GFR in the superficial glomeruli in the guinea pig was 30% lower than that estimated from the creatinine clearance of the kidney and the estimated number of glomeruli. They suggested, as a possibility to account for the discrepancy, that the filtration rate of superficial nephrons might be less than that of the deeper nephrons. More convincing evidence of a difference between filtration rate of superficial and deep nephrons was provided by Horster & Thurau (43). Using the classical technique they found the mean single nephron GFR in the superficial nephrons of rats on a low salt diet to be 23 nl per min per g of kidney weight whereas that of the deeper nephrons was 38. Although a high Na diet in the rat did not alter the total GFR of the kidney, the single nephron GFR of the superficial nephrons increased to 58 whereas that of the deeper nephrons fell to 16. On the basis of appropriate calculations they concluded that the relative numbers of the superficial and deep nephrons were unchanged. This basic result has been confirmed by Jamison (44) and Stumpe, Lowitz & Ochwadt (45) who also found that the superficial nephron filtration rate on a low or "normal" salt diet in the rat is lower than the deep nephron filtration rate. Baines & de Rouffignac (35), using the Hansen technique referred to earlier, confirmed in large part these observations. More recently de Rouffignac & Bonvalet (46), though confirming Horster & Thurau's original observations on low salt diets, observed that a high salt diet increased the filtration rate in both populations of nephrons.

GLOMERULOTUBULAR BALANCE

It is a truism that the mammalian kidney is largely responsible for the maintenance and regulation of the volume and composition of the extracellular fluid compartment of the body. Precise regulation occurs in the face of variations both in the intake of salt and water and of glomerular filtration. Smith in 1951 (47) referred to this as glomerulotubular balance. He recognized that both glomerular and tubular activities were variable and that maintenance of salt and water balance required "appropriate compensatory changes" in reabsorption over a "wide range of activities in either component". It is of interest that he focused attention on the distal portions of the nephron as primarily involved in fine control and the site of the major compensatory changes, since in his view the proximal nephron virtually was maximally engaged at all times.

In recent years glomerulotubular balance has been redefined (and the credit incorrectly assigned to Smith), as that phenomenon which results in relative constancy of fractional reabsorption of salt and water in the proximal segment. This in essence is a description of an observation originally reported by Walker et al (17) and since repeatedly confirmed, that the TF/P_{inulin} ratio is virtually constant at a given point in the tubule despite spontaneously and experimentally induced changes in glomerular filtration rate (28, 32, 48–50). The definition overemphasizes the role of the proximal tubule in the regulation of salt and water balance which, though quantitatively of greatest significance for reconstitution of the size of the extracellular compartment, ignores the importance of the more distal segments in the final regulatory process.

Brenner et al (51), with prescience, deemed absolute constancy of TF/P_{inulin} as "ideal" glomerulotubular balance and implied that an increase or decrease in TF/P_{inulin}, which may occur when GFR is artificially altered (18, 27, 32, 52, 53), is therefore "nonideal". The term is unfortunate. It focuses undue attention on the deviation from a "hypothetical ideal" which may be a myth. In certain cases "significant deviations" were artifactual owing to methodological limitations. It is very difficult at present to conceive of a mechanism whereby an isotonic transport system always reabsorbs a constant fraction of its load when the latter varies. Though this may be the case, until more information is available, we prefer to consider proximal glomerulotubular balance as the parallelism and relative proportionality between glomerular filtration rate and proximal reabsorption (27, 29, 32, 54), recognizing that other tubule segments are also of importance and must act in concert to stabilize extracellular volume and composition. Aware of the danger of teleology we can reasonably view the proximal tubule as a buffer segment in which absolute reabsorption varies directly with load as the latter changes in order to minimize marked variations in delivery of fluid to the distal nephron. This concept depends on the assumption that load is the determinant and changes in tubular reabsorption the response, which though accepted by most investigators may be incorrect. Alternatively, as Bojesen (55) and Leyssac (56) believe, reabsorption may be the independent variable. Alterations in reabsorption, in their view, induce hydrodynamic changes in the tubule and thereby effect proportional changes in filtration rate.

A number of theories have been proposed to account for the parallelism between filtration rate and the reabsorptive rate in the proximal segment. That originally proposed by Gertz et al (20), subsequently adopted and expanded upon by Rector and his group (25, 57), and ultimately retracted by the latter (32) has received considerable attention. These authors believed that the rate of reabsorption in the proximal tubule was directly proportional to tubule volume and thereby the square of the tubule radius (r^2). Balance was achieved since an increase in filtration rate distended the tubule appropriately and vice versa. Thus r^2 was necessarily proportional to V_0. Much of the evidence has been challenged on methodological grounds and is no longer accepted. In the first place, tubule radius does not necessarily change in response to spontaneous or experimentally induced alterations in GFR under conditions when so-called glomerulotubular balance occurs. Baines et al (31) and Arrizurieta-Muchnik et al (27) observed no significant change in radius either during spontaneoeous variations in GFR or 30 min after GFR was lowered by arterial clamping, although an initial decrease had been observed in the latter study. Wahl et al (58) in Schnermann's laboratory also found no direct correlation between tubule radius and GFR during arterial clamping but initially discounted the observation as not pertinent to the physiological state since they had earlier reported (28) parallel changes in radius and filtration rate when the latter varied spontaneously. Most recently they too have acknowledged the error of their ways (59).

Limitations of the method of estimating radius with precision have been discussed (24, 29, 32).

Bojesen & Leyssac (24) have proposed a new basis for the measurement of r and dismiss earlier measurements by others as inaccurate. It is apparent however that qualitatively there is no necessary correlation between filtration rate and tubule radius. Indirect estimates of the relationship between r^2 and C during glomerulotubular balance by the use of the ratio $C/\pi r^2$ have also been made. GFR was altered by arterial clamping (27, 32, 58), renal vein constriction (32), and ureteral obstruction (32). In all the ratio changed when GFR was altered indicative of independence of the two variables C and r^2.

Finally the effect of changes in tubular radius induced by increasing outflow pressure on the absolute reabsorptive rate was studied in isolated perfused tubules of the rabbit by Burg & Orloff (30) and in rat proximal tubules microperfused in vivo by Morgan & Berliner (41). In both studies large increases in tubule volume were accompanied by little change in absolute reabsorption, nor was the reabsorptive rate altered by changes in perfusion rate. Since no evidence of perfusion-tubular balance was obtained in these pump-perfused tubules, the authors concluded not only that the Gertz thesis was incorrect but also that glomerulotubular balance is not an intrinsic property of the renal tubule epithelium. Rather it may be that changes in reabsorption are primary as believed by Leyssac (56), or that an attached glomerulus directly or indirectly provides the necessary signal, or that interstitial factors consequent to alteration of GFR are the determinants of the tubule response (54), or most likely, that ignorance reigns.

Schnermann et al (59) came to somewhat similar conclusions as did Burg & Orloff (30) and Morgan & Berliner (41) regarding the influence of tubule distention on reabsorption in studies in which indirect measurements of C were made during free flow in the rat. In their studies the "reabsorptive rate" actually decreased when filtration rate fell despite tubule distention, indicative of glomerulotubular balance independent of radius.

Revealing summaries of the background of the Gertz thesis and the nature of the possible artifacts which led to its earlier acceptance have been presented (27, 32). As mentioned earlier the calculation of C from transit time, TF/P_{inulin}, and $t_{1/2}$, though in theory possible, also requires precise estimates of r which at this juncture limits its use. Substitution of the ratio $C/\pi r^2$ (reabsorptive rate per unit volume) to obviate this difficulty would only be a virtue were C a direct function of r^2. Since it is not, the observed equivalance of the ratio under varying experimental conditions is likely to have been fortuitous (32). It is our belief that the ratio should be discarded, if for no other reason than to preserve the equanimity of subsequent reviewers.

Leyssac (56) has led a vocal minority who, in contrast to the views of the now silent majority in the Gertz camp, believe that changes in GFR are secondary to alterations in proximal reabsorptive rate. A primary increase in reabsorption is thought to reduce intraluminal pressure, permitting greater filtration until glomerulotubular balance is achieved. Glomerulotubular balance is thus a mechanism for stabilizing proximal intraluminal pressure and thereby flow to the more distal nephrons. Though irreverently referred to as the *Aubsaugen* hypothesis by some, the idea is interesting and bears serious consideration. It is difficult to account for the effects of specific changes in glomerular pressure per se on reabsorption within the context of the model, however. Interpretation of the studies depends in large part on the assumption that the reciprocal of the occlusion time (OT) (the time for complete collapse of the proximal tubule following acute interruption of filtration) is a direct measure of C which further requires that the tubule radius prior to clamping be equal in all of the animals. Bojesen & Leyssac (24) and Leyssac (60) have marshaled the evidence for this assumption in a reasonably convincing manner. It has been found (18, 24) that $1/OT$ (proportional to C) varies directly with the filtration rate measured immediately before interruption of filtration over a reasonable range of filtration rates. Since filtration is not occurring during the occlusion-time measurement, they conclude that tubular reabsorption is the independent variable which determined the antecedent filtration rate. Initially it was proposed that angiotensin inhibits proximal reabsorption and that it may be the messenger in a feedback system regulating intraluminal pressure. Others have noted no effect of angiotensin on the ratio $C/\pi r^2$ when added either to luminal fluid or to the peritubular capillary bed (61), nor was an effect on absolute reabsorptive rate noted in the isolated perfused rabbit tubule (30).

The fundamental idea of Leyssac that C determines GFR is attractive but the experimental results, even if one accepts the assumption on which the reciprocal $1/OT$ *is equated* with C, do not exclude an alternative interpretation. Variations in GFR may be accompanied by changes in filtration fraction, the volume and composition of the peritubular space, peritubular pressure changes, etc, which may directly affect reabsorption as others believe (v.i.). If this is correct there is no a priori reason to reject the possibility that these factors influenced by changes in GFR are still operative on the proximal tubule during the period of the occlusion-time estimate. Despite this, C-induced alterations in intraluminal pressure must be considered in evaluating studies of glomerulotubular balance.

Thurau & Schnermann (62) have postulated that angiotensin released in response to changes in the composition of the fluid in the distal nephron affects the glomerular afferent arteriole and alters GFR. Their view of autoregulation and glomerulotubular balance was based on the observation that complete collapse of the proximal tubule followed retrograde injection of isotonic or hypertonic saline into the distal convolution of a decapsulated kidney. Gottschalk & Leyssac (18), who were unable to confirm the results of the microperfusion studies, have rejected the theory and ascribe the earlier findings to artifact.

Emphasis on the role of the peritubular environment in the genesis of glomerulotubular balance has recently become fashionable. It has been postulated that physical changes in the tissue surrounding the proximal tubule which accompany alterations in GFR are primary determinants of reabsorption (54, 64, 65). These factors include the Starling forces across the peritubular capillary wall (that is the difference between net hydrostatic pressure and net colloid osmotic pressure) and interstitial volume. Since with few exceptions (66) no one seriously believes that the oncotic pressure gradient across the tubule wall can influence net absorption significantly (63), the proponents of the thesis have suggested that alterations in the net uptake of transported tubule fluid from the interstitial space into the peritubular capillary in some fashion affect proximal reabsorption. Of the mechanisms which may be involved, possible alterations in the net flux of fluid through potential intercellular spaces in the tubule wall have been discussed by Windhager et al (65). The concept is necessarily and appropriately vague. A change in glomerular pressure insofar as it modifies the filtration fraction will alter both the colloid osmotic and hydrostatic pressures within the peritubular capillary. Either of these changes in theory might affect the net transfer of fluid into the capillary-venous system. This assumes however that the change in capillary hydrostatic and oncotic pressure reflects similar changes in the pressure differences across the capillary wall, which has not yet been established.

Evidence for the role of peritubular factors has been presented by many investigators. Daugharty et al (67), following previous work of Earley and his collaborators (68), reported that subsequent to drug-induced renal vasodilatation, an increase in blood pressure decreases fluid reabsorption (presumably in the proximal nephron) in the intact animal. The decrease in absorption was reversed by an infusion of 30% albumin. They concluded that an elevation in intravascular capillary pressure decreases net tubular reabsorption whereas an increase in oncotic pressure has the opposite effect. Koch et al (69) on the basis of split-drop studies in hypertensive rats concluded that decreased proximal "reabsorption" may be induced by an increase in intravascular pressure or interstitial volume. In addition Vereerstraeten & Toussaint (66) observed that Na excretion (interpreted as reflecting a change in proximal reabsorption) falls when dogs are made hypoproteinemic by plasmapharesis without a significant change in renal blood flow. Windhager, Lewy & Spitzer (65) noted that the $t_{1/2}$ for split-drop disappearance in the rat was inversely related to the filtration fraction in control animals. The assumption was that the higher filtration fraction resulted in an increase in the colloid osmotic pressure of the capillary bed and consequently more rapid reabsorption of transported tubular fluid.

Brenner et al (70) concurred with the view that peritubular capillary oncotic pressure is at least one important determinant of proximal reabsorption. Within 20 sec of injection of solutions of differing protein concentration into the renal artery of the rat, they noted that fluid absorption was directly proportional to the measured protein concentration of the peritubular capillary. Spitzer & Windhager (71) estimated proximal reabsorption in the rat as a function of the colloid osmotic pressure of the capillary bed surrounding the tubule under investigation. They perfused a capillary directly with solutions of differing oncotic pressure and found a direct relationship both in free-flow and in split-drop studies between C determined from the ratio $C/\pi r^2$ and the calculated capillary oncotic pressure. The half-time in control studies was 10 sec, when Ringer's was perfused into the capillary 18 sec and with 8% dextran 10 sec. On the other hand Lowitz, Stumpe & Ochwadt (61), in the course of investigating the effect of angiotensin on the split-drop reabsorptive rate, reported half-times of approximately 10 sec in control studies with normal blood flow in the capillaries and 11 during perfusion of colloid-free Krebs Henseleit solution. Similar negative results were also reported recently by Baldamus et al (72). Confusion regarding the role of the peritubular oncotic pressure was also generated by the report that the filtration fraction is not altered when arterial clamping is used to reduce GFR despite maintenance of glomerulotubular balance (27). This result is inconsistent with the Windhager thesis though the authors for reasons not immediately apparent draw the opposite conclusion. Schnermann, Horster & Levine (19) reported that an increase in intraluminal pressure consequent to slow aspiration of an oil-blocked tubule reduces both GFR and C in a parallel fashion. Unless Steinhausen (73) is correct and each nephron is supplied by its own efferent capillary without significant anastomosis, it is difficult to conceive of a change in peritubular oncotic pressure so restricted as to influence only the immediately adjacent tubule. One would expect any significant gradient of oncotic pressure to be dissipated rapidly by flow from confluent vessels.

REGULATION OF SODIUM EXCRETION

Attempts to elucidate the renal mechanisms involved in the regulation of salt and water balance in the mammal have occupied renal physiologists for decades. Both the osmotic pressure and the volume of the fluid compartments of the body are maintained virtually constant despite wide variations in the intake of salt and water. Appropriate changes in water excretion by the kidney are responsible for the maintenance of osmotic pressure and of salt excretion for the maintenance of volume. The former process and the role of antidiuretic hormone in effecting changes in reabsorption of water in the distal nephron are understood; not so the regulation of salt excretion and thereby of volume. The latter problem has been on the "verge" of solution intermittently but no clear picture has evolved. We are unable to formulate a cohesive thesis to account for all of the observations and are impressed by the multiplicity of factors which may alter sodium excretion, none of which of itself is sufficient to explain volume regulation.

It is generally accepted, largely because of the experiments of de Wardener and his co-workers (see 63 for review), that changes in filtration rate and aldosterone activity do not explain the increase in salt excretion which follows saline-induced expansion of the extracellular compartment of an experimental animal. These workers have also excluded the role of the renal nerves and of many other factors. They favor the view that expansion of the extracellular compartment stimulates secretion of an unidentified hormone from an unknown site which acts in some unknown fashion in some portion or portions of the nephron (not the glomerulus) to promote excretion of the excess salt administered. The evidence for their thesis has been marshaled in an admirable review by de Wardener (63) which is recommended for its clarity of exposition and optimistic approach. They may be correct. The position is reasonable and by analogy with the control of water excretion, a hypothetical natriuretic hormone, probably not of renal origin (63, 74), may prove to be the elusive third factor. The latter term was coined to connote that factor other than filtration rate and aldosterone activity that is responsible for homeostasis.

The major deficiencies of the thesis are 1. that many factors can alter sodium excretion and since, despite rigorous control, attendant changes in known and unknown variables which may affect sodium excretion cannot be excluded with certainty, the 3rd factor might better be termed 3....n factors; and 2. that cross transfer of the hypothetical hormone from an experimental donor animal to a recipient results in only a small, albeit statistically significant, increase in Na excretion in the recipient (63). The recipient animal is not expanded in the best of the studies so that it is responding (if it is) only to residual hormone transferred from the donor and to none of its own, and in addition by the nature of the experimental design the 4th, 5th, etc factors which may be the important determinants of sodium excretion are not altered by the procedure. Depending upon the color of one's glasses, a minimum of three interpretations of the cross-transfusion data is possible: 1. There is no hormone since the diuresis in the recipient is small in comparison to the elicited by saline infusion into the donor. 2. A hormone is transferred which sensitizes the kidney or facilitates its response to the innumerable other "direct" renal factors (e.g. changes in filtration rate, physical alterations in the peritubular environment) which together may account for the regulation of volume in the intact animal. 3. The hormone has a short half-life and is dissipated in the transfer process; this interpretation is favored by de Wardener. In view of the uncertainties we can only summarize some of the recent studies directed at unraveling the "third factors".

The model generally selected for study of volume regulation is an initially normal animal whose extracellular or blood compartment is expanded by administration of an appropriate solution. The cause of the resultant increase in salt excretion is the physiologic mechanism under study. Arguments to the contrary, it is fair to state that no one had ever seriously believed that an increase in filtration rate alone, without changes in tubular reabsorption, accounted for the diuresis. It is unfortunate that de Wardener's unique contribution, in which he demonstrated unequivocally that diuresis following saline expansion occurs even when GFR is artificially fixed or lowered, has been interpreted as indicating that filtration rate is not an important factor in the regulation of salt excretion. It certainly must be in the intact animal, particularly if glomerulotubular balance is involved in the response. Alterations in the peritubular environment which may affect net absorption in the attached tubule segments may be determined in part by filtration.

Morgan & Berliner's (75) study in which an intravenous infusion of saline decreased net absorption in an isolated pump-perfused proximal segment in vivo, in which normal filtration in that nephron was eliminated, has been cited as evidence excluding participation of the glomerulus in the tubular response. This is not necessarily a correct conclusion since changes in the peritubular environment consequent to alterations in filtration rate of neighboring glomeruli cannot be excluded as participating in the genesis of the isolated tubules' response.

Garella, Chazan & Cohen (76) have resurrected the view that filtration rate is an important determinant of Na excretion insofar as it results in appropriate changes in net proximal reabsorption. They presume that the reduction in Na excretion which follows either thoracic vena cava constriction or volume depletion [both of which increase fractional reabsorption of fluid in the proximal nephron (77, 78)] is the converse of the depression in fractional reabsorption which attends saline infusion (50). They noted that both manipulations in dogs whose distal tubules were "blocked" by a combination of chlorathiazide and ethacrynic acid increased fractional reabsorption in association with a decrease in GFR. In other studies comparable falls in filtration rate were associated with comparable increases in fractional reabsorption, from which they concluded the obvious. The studies merely show once again that changes in GFR do influence sodium excretion, but only if the attached tubule responds appropriately, and cannot be cited as evidence against the studies of de Wardener and his associates (63) which eliminated an exclusive role of changes in GFR in the response to saline.

Changes in the Na concentration of the extracellular fluid also affect Na excretion which is not altogether surprising. Schrier et al (79) observed that despite comparable hemodynamic changes in the kidney, dextran in saline elicits a greater diuresis than dextran alone. Although differences in the changes in the relative sizes of the interstitial and vascular compartments produced by the two manipulations were considered as a possible explanation, in a later study Schrier and co-workers (80) observed a greater diuresis from isotonic and hypertonic saline free of colloid than from hypotonic saline alone. They concluded that a decrease in the sodium concentration of the extracellular fluid is antinatriuretic in that it increases net sodium reabsorption.

Andersson, Dallman & Olsson (81) believe that renal Na excretion may be under hypothalamic control in the goat. Infusion of hypertonic saline, but not hypertonic NH_4Cl, into the third ventrical of the goat increases both filtration rate and Na excretion. Analogous results without a measured change in filtration rate have been reported by Dorn et al (82) in the dog. The studies once again illustrate the multiplicity of known and unknown factors which may influence salt excretion. De Wardener (63), recognizing the difficulty of interpreting these studies, considers Andersson, Dallman & Olsson's studies provocative and perhaps evidence that the elusive hormone is of cranial origin.

Variations in aldosterone activity have as noted earlier been repeatedly excluded as an important determinant of the increase in Na excretion which follows intravenous saline. This is not to say that aldosterone has no effect on tubular transport of Na somewhere in the nephron or that a permissive effect, if the term is acceptable in this revolutionary age, is not essential. Keck, Brechtelsbauer & Kramer (83) attribute the slower rate of excretion of administered saline in animals depleted of Na by peritoneal dialysis than in nondepleted "Na-rich" animals to enhanced aldosterone activity in the former.

The importance of renal nerve activity in the regulation of volume is discounted by both de Wardener (63) and Berliner (84). Both cite as evidence that the transplanted and denervated kidney responds to a saline infusion in a manner not fundamentally different from that of a normal innervated kidney. Nevertheless the observation that Na excretion is greater in a denervated than in an innervated kidney still stimulates interest and enthusiasm. Changes can be demonstrated unequivocally only in the anesthetized animal and had previously been attributed by Berne (85) to an anesthesia-induced decrease in filtered Na load in the innervated kidney only. Blake & Jurf (86) and Bonjour, Churchill & Malvin (87) have reinvestigated denervation diuresis (in their studies a fall in Na excretion without a measurable change in filtration rate or blood flow on the innervated side) is a tubular phenomenon brought about by a redistribution in blood flow in the denervated kidney. No data are presented to counter or support the hypothesis. It is consonant however with Pomeranz, Birtch & Barger's (88) report that electrical stimulation of the renal nerves causes a redistribution of blood in the kidney. They interpret their kinetic data as indicating a decrease in perfusion of the outer cortex and an increase in the perfusion of the medulla. No measurements of Na excretion are reported. Bonjour, Churchill & Malvin (87) controlled filtration rate with appropriate manipulations and concluded that denervation specifically affects tubular Na reabsorption though not necessarily by a direct influence on the transport processes themselves.

Gill (89) in a recent review presents evidence for his belief that sympathetic activity exerts an important effect on tubular reabsorption of Na by inducing local renal vascular change. Heidenreich, Fülgraff, Laaff & Balshüsemann (90) report that beta sympathicomimetic drugs decrease Na excretion and filtration rate and that the effect is prevented by beta blockade. Gilmore & Michaelis (91, 92) have continued their investigation of the attenuating effect of cardiac denervation on the diuresis induced by dextran and saline in the dog. Their findings have been confirmed by Knox, Davis & Berliner (93) with saline as well, though the changes were quantitatively not very impressive and by McDonald et al (94). These papers are of intrinsic interest but at this stage the results are difficult to incorporate into any reasonable thesis with regard to volume control.

Similar considerations apply to the studies of Waugh & Kubo (95, 96) and of Dies et al (97) who have directed their attention to the role of the energy supply of the Na transport system in the tubule in the response to saline. Waugh & Kubo (95) originally proposed that dilution of substrates for Na transport, such as lactate, pyruvate, and α-ketoglutarate produced by a saline infusion, may reduce reabsorption and account for the diuresis.

Measurements of plasma levels caused them to reject this view and they now imply that a "third" factor may reduce the availability or utilization of energy sources for transport (96). The conclusions are based on changes in plasma free fatty acid concentration and Na excretion following injection of putative specific mobilizers of free fatty acids. Thus a drug-induced rise in free fatty acid concentration in plasma is attended by increased reabsorption of Na in the intact animal and a blunting of saline diuresis. Dies et al (97) observed a direct correlation between lactate and free fatty acid uptake and tubular Na reabsorption in the intact dog reminiscent of the relationship between O_2 consumption and tubular Na reabsorption as GFR was altered experimentally. No differences in the relationship were noted however if saline was infused. We would agree with Dies et al that it is unlikely that substrate is rate limiting in the response to saline but certainly cannot exclude the thesis on the basis of our value judgment alone. Waugh & Kubo (96) unfortunately did not study the effect on Na excretion in the nonsaline-loaded animal of the pharmacologic agents which are purported only to mobilize free fatty acid, which would conceivably be revealing.

As implied earlier, changes in the composition of the blood induced by saline, independent of changes in blood volume, may alter sodium excretion. These are certainly contributory factors but cannot be of fundamental concern until more is understood about the mechanism of fluid absorption itself. In any event Bahlman et al in de Wardener's laboratory (98, 99) conclusively excluded this as a factor in cross-circulation studies. Blood, whose composition was altered by exchange with a reservoir containing 2.5% albumin and saline, was equilibrated with that of a recipient dog. Injection of the equilibrated blood into the recipient did not alter Na excretion unless blood volume was also expanded. This ingenious study was repeated by Knox et al (100) and the data confirmed. In their study, although the inulin TF/P ratio in the proximal tubule fell as it does after saline infusion, Na excretion rose only slightly, albeit significantly, and the magnitude of the response was considerably less than that which follows saline. They point out that saline induces alterations in the composition of the blood which must contribute to the diuretic response. In our prejudiced view pure blood volume expansion probably is not the ideal model either for the study of the regulation of extracellular fluid volume or for the localization of the unknown volume sensor in the body, if we assume, which may be incorrect, that this is extrarenal. The latter problem, which involves the relationship between volume changes in the various fluid compartments of the body and the resultant diuresis, has been discussed by Shrier et al (79) most recently. Certainly, as has been repeatedly observed, natriuresis following infusion of whole blood is considerably less than that due to a comparable volume of saline (101). It is of some interest that saline will induce a diuresis in the face of the deteriorating effect of hemorrhage and hypotension on renal function as reported by Coelho & Bradley (102).

That the kidney is a remarkably intelligent organ which has repeatedly defied the rhetoric and ingenuity of otherwise reasonable investigators is attested to by its recently uncovered "ability" to alter the presumed active absorption of substances other than saline, when challenged with intravenous NaCl. Expansion of the extracellular compartment depresses the reabsorption of bicarbonate in man (103), rat (104), and dog (105) according to Slatopolsky et al, Purkerson et al, and Kurtzman respectively. The "effete physiologist" had previously adhered to the concept that a bicarbonate Tm exists (presumably in the proximal tubule). The investigators referred to above have demonstrated that the apparent Tm was a consequence of the experimental design of the titration studies, which routinely involved expansion of the extracellular compartment. If expansion is avoided, no tubular maximum can be demonstrated over a reasonable range of plasma bicarbonate concentration. Similarly Suki et al (106) have shown that phosphate excretion is augmented by a saline infusion independent of a change in GFR, and further that constriction of the thoracic vena cava which blunts the response to saline has an analogous effect on phosphate excretion. Blythe, Gitelman & Welt (107) have reported somewhat similar findings with respect to calcium excretion and lastly Robson, Srivastava & Bricker (108) noted that the glucose Tm is decreased in the rat when saline is administered. The latter studies did not exclude an additional effect of filtration rate which rose. The relevance of these findings either to the response to saline or to the glomerulotubular balance, if the two processes are truly separable, is an intriguing question.

Earley and co-workers (64, 68, 109) have led the flock who consider that physical changes in the peritubular environment, particularly as influenced by renal capillary hydrostatic pressure, are responsible for appropriate changes in net tubular reabsorption of salt and water in the maintenance of salt balance. Some of these studies have been discussed earlier since the acute response to changes in pressure, etc, may be involved in the compensatory alterations in the relationship between filtration rate and net absorption (so-called glomerulotubular balance) rather than in the response to saline. The latter appears to be a more sluggish response if one can deduce this from the temporal relationships observed in such studies. De Wardener implies that this may be his view as well (63).

Martino & Earley (109) consider renal perfusion pressure (in the peritubular capillary bed) the fundamental modulator of tubular Na reabsorption. Acetylcholine in their view induces a salt diuresis (which they consider the same as that produced by saline expansion) by increasing peritubular capillary pressure. Deep renal venous pressure was measured in the intact animal as an index of renal capillary pressure. It rose after the administration of acetylcholine and after the administration of saline, and rose even further when blood pressure was increased by administration of angiotensin to acetylcholine-treated animals. In all, Na excretion also rose. An infusion of hyperoncotic albumin decreased both intrarenal pressure and sodium excretion though not to control levels. An increase in capillary pressure is thought to reduce the capillary uptake from the interstitial space of transported tubular fluid. This is said to alter the intercellular channels in some nebulous fashion in the proximal tubule and reduce net Na transport. Earley and his co-workers borrow heavily in their arguments from the Curran & MacIntosh (110) and Diamond (111) model of intercellular transport as does de Wardener (63).

There are many problems in adapting this model to the kidney. In the first place the model was developed to account for isotonic transport across an epithelial structure in the absence of a measurable though necessary osmotic gradient. Diamond (111) proposed that the inaccessible hypertonic environment develops in the intercellular channel (in the gallbladder) in consequence of active sodium transport. These channels distend during the transport process as would be expected. The dimensions and permeability characteristics of the channel, alluded to repeatedly by the renal physiologist, were analyzed in his model only with respect to the ultimate development of *isotonicity* of the transported fluid—not net transfer. The dimensions of the proximal intercellular "spaces", if they exist, are considerably smaller than in the gallbladder and although Caulfield & Trump (112) report that they distend after saline infusion in the rat, this has not been confirmed. Changes in dimensions induced by an increase in pressure at the basal surface of the tissue or a change in pressure or interstitial volume per se might conceivably alter active Na transport, increase the diffusional permeability to sodium, change the concentration gradient for Na^+ across the tubule wall, etc, which might reduce net transport. No evidence as yet exists that this is the case, however.

Martino & Earley's (109) discussion of the problem is sufficiently guarded to be entirely acceptable both to those who agree and to those who do not. Both Bank et al (113) in the rat and Bentzel, Anagnostopoulos & Pandit (114) in *Necturus,* on the basis of indirect estimates of reabsorption (split-drop etc studies) and luminal or capillary hydrostatic pressure measurements, also concur with Earley that capillary hydrostatic pressure is important in regulating salt excretion. We do not deny the possibility but do not understand the theory. Sealey, Kirshman & Laragh (115), who apparently do understand it, consider that an appropriate change in capillary pressure is additive to the effect of "natriuretic hormone" (see below). Both Vereerstraeten & Toussaint (116) and Nizet et al (117, 118) believe that a fall in peritubular capillary oncotic pressure may be responsible for some of the decrease in Na reabsorption attendant upon saline infusion, in the first case in the intact animal (116) and in the second in the isolated perfused kidney (117, 118).

With respect to the vascular effects of acetylcholine and other analogous compounds, May & Carter (119) and Parmelee & Carter (120) present evidence that these drugs may alter transport independently of hemodynamic changes in the chicken at least, whereas Hayslett et al (121) (in the rat) agree in part with Earley that acetylcholine diuresis is mediated by pressure changes in the capillary bed. Willis et al (122) in contrast ascribes the diuresis resulting from bradykinin in the dog to changes in filtration rate and renal blood flow since clamping of the aorta eliminates the response.

The nature and existence of a natriuretic hormone has been the subject of much controversy. Even Homer Smith believed that the kidney, much as he admired its independent spirit, required a messenger, a natriuretic substance, to inform it of the state of the volume of surrounding otherwise ignorant milieu. De Wardener (63) in recent years has promoted this view most poignantly. Initially Mills et al (123), although tentatively committed to the belief that there was a natriuretic hormone, interpreted the miniscule diuresis induced by cross transfusion of blood from an expanded donor into a recipient dog as inconclusive evidence for its existence, whereas Johnston & Davis (124) on the basis of identical results concluded the reverse. De Wardener now believes that the evidence is reasonably strong for a hormone as do Pearce et al (125) but that the blunted diuresis in the recipient is a consequence of the short half-life of the hypothetical substance.

The hormone hypothesis is attractive and evidence in its favor though not overwhelming is certainly suggestive. Many of the assays for the factor are questionable, however. In our view an effect of a substance extracted from plasma on the inulin TF/P ratio in the proximal tubule, on short-circuit current in frog skin or toad bladder, or on PAH uptake of a cortical slice of the kidney, though conceivably valid, cannot be accepted unless it also elicits an appropriate diuresis in an intact animal that is unequivocally inexplicable on the basis of changes in filtration rate, etc. In general, blood of an "expanded animal" is used as a source of the "hormone" and the response of a test model, frog skin, or kidney to it and to similarly extracted blood obtained from a nondiuresing hydropenic animal is compared. Rector and co-workers (126) found such a substance. It increased the split-drop reabsorptive time in the proximal tubule of the rat, an observation subsequently not confirmed either by Wright et al (22) or by Hayslett et al (23). The deficiency of the method for estimation of intrinsic reabsorptive capacity has been discussed earlier. Wright et al (22) in addition found no effect of plasma of test animals on inulin TF/P ratio in the proximal tubule of test animals, though the ratio is uniformly depressed when saline is administered.

Buckalew, Martinez & Green (127) report a consistent "specific" decrease in the short-circuit current of toad bladder with a preparation of plasma from saline-expanded dogs. That obtained from jugular plasma is more potent than that from peripheral plasma. They report an approximate molecular weight of 3000. Bricker et al (128) had previously noted that the PAH Tm is reduced in dogs expanded with saline. An "active principle" from blood of such dogs and volume-expanded cows consistently depressed PAH uptake of rabbit cortical kidney slices. Nutbourne, with an assist from de Wardener (cited in 63), conceived the remarkable idea of perfusing a chamber containing an isolated frog skin with blood from an attached donor dog. Expansion of the dog with equilibrated blood to exclude changes in composition resulted in the expected increase in Na excretion in the dog and a simultaneous decrease in the short-circuit current of the frog skin. Clarkson et al in the same laboratory have, as reported by de Wardener in (63), confirmed Bricker's results with PAH in suspensions of tubular fragments from rabbits but also report a significant decrease in the K content and an increase in the Na content of the inhibited fragments. A natriuretic hormone obtained from jugular blood of cats following carotid occlusion has also been reported by Cort and his group (129). The test procedure is an appropriate effect on short-circuit current in frog skin and analysis of the "tubular Na rejection fraction" of cat and rat kidney. Buckalew, Martinez & Green (127), de Wardener (63), and Sealey, Kirshman & Laragh (115) have effectively criticized the results and attach little credence to the conclusions. An extract of plasma which satisfies some of the criteria for a natriuretic substance insofar as it promotes Na excretion in an intact animal has recently been reported by Sealey, Kirshman & Laragh (115). They have extracted plasma from salt-depleted and salt-loaded man and sheep. They have estimated its natriuretic effect in rats with "congenital diabetes insipidus maintained in salt and water balance". There is no question that the extract increases Na excretion in responsive animals and that control extracts from the blood of nonsalt-loaded subjects do not.

In contrast to Buckalew, Martinez & Green's (127) hormone, that of Sealey et al has an estimated molecular weight of between 5000 and 70,000. Furthermore the half-life of the hormone, in contrast to that of de Wardener's transfer substance, is reasonably long (several hours) and the hormone does not induce an immediate increase in Na excretion. Buckalew's substance on the other hand elicits an immediate decrease in short-circuit current and the effect disappears promptly when it is removed. Other differences in the properties of the two factors must be interpreted as indicating that they are not the same. We conclude that a final answer is not yet available but that a hormone may indeed be involved in the natriuresis induced by saline.

A search for the locus of action of the "hormone" in the kidney would seem a somewhat premature gambit. On the other hand, whatever the basis of volume regulation, if one accepts that the saline-expanded or blood volume-expanded animal in which Na excretion is elevated is the correct model for studying volume control, then the search for the site or sites of the obvious depression in Na reabsorption is reasonable. Dirks, Cirksena & Berliner (50) reported some time ago an unequivocal depression in fractional Na reabsorption in the proximal segment of saline-expanded dogs. This clearly could not account for the urinary effects of saline expansion since the magnitude of the latter was less than would be expected were the distal tubule inert. This has been discussed by Berliner (84) and his group. Howards et al (130) from that laboratory noted that blood volume expansion with hyperoncotic albumin or dextran depresses fractional reabsorption in the proximal segment to a similar degree as does saline, without an appreciable change in Na excretion. On the basis of clearance studies, Leeber, Murdaugh & David (131) concluded as did Berliner's group that the distal nephron must also be engaged in the process and alter its reabsorptive capacity to account for the diuresis. Brenner et al (78) arrived at a similar conclusion. They noted that although fractional reabsorption in the proximal tubule varied inversely with extracellular fluid volume, increasing with volume depletion and decreasing with expansion, Na excretion rose only when expansion was maximal.

Morgan & Berliner (75) measured Na reabsorption in microperfused loops of Henle and distal segments of the rat during extracellular volume expansion. No change in absorption in the distal segments was induced by the saline infusion though proximal reabsorption fell. They concluded that the adjustment necessary for induction of Na diuresis must occur in the collecting tubule or duct. It is of some interest that Sealey, Kirshman & Laragh (115) tentatively conclude that their hormone blocks Na reabsorption in the distal nephron. The problem is obviously unsettled. One fact is certain. The kidney knows how to regulate sodium excretion and we do not.

MECHANISM OF SODIUM AND WATER TRANSPORT

The mechanism of water and electrolyte transport across the tubule epithelium has generally been viewed as analogous to that in simpler epithelial tissues such as toad bladder and frog skin. The Ussing model of passive entry of Na across one face and active Na and K exchange at the other face of the cell, with modifications, has been applied with limited success to the proximal nephron. From both micropuncture and clearance studies, net Na transport is assumed to be an active process (at the peritubular surface) which generates a potential difference (negative within the lumen) sufficient to account for electrically coupled passive chloride movement. Water moves passively along an osmotic gradient created in an inaccessible microenvironment at or near the basal surface by active Na transport. In this view a coupled Na-K pump (or an electrogenic K-dependent Na pump with passive distribution of K between cell interior and extracellular space) is sufficient to account for maintenance of intracellular cation composition and net transfer of fluid from lumen to blood. The simple model has been questioned in recent years, largely because of uncertainty of the presence of a potential difference in the rat proximal tubule, "discrepant" tubule fluid to plasma chloride ratios at "equilibrium", and otherwise inexplicable changes in cell volume of leached swollen cortical slices which appear to be capable of shrinking back towards their normal volume under circumstances when active K-dependent transport of Na is inhibited. These problems will be discussed separately.

The existence of a spontaneous transepithelial potential difference of approximately 20 mV (lumen negative) was initially observed in rat and *Necturus* proximal tubules (132). The finding in the rat was challenged by Frömter & Hegel (133) who concluded that there was no spontaneous potential difference in the proximal tubule and that all earlier findings were artifactual. So convincing was their argument that many investigators rapidly followed suit and concurred (134). Maude (135) has recently re-evaluated the problem in the proximal tubule of rat cortical slices which he had previously shown to reabsorb fluid in a supposedly normal fashion (136). The tubule lumen was first filled with oil and a microelectrode tip inserted. If a high resistance (greater than 10 MΩ) was observed, the pipet tip was assumed to be in the intraluminal oil. Displacement of the oil with physiological saline solutions reduced the resistance to within 1 MΩ of that of the pipet tip itself. The latter finding was interpreted as further evidence that the tip was positioned correctly within the saline drop in the lumen. If it had been in the cell interior no change in resistance would have been noted following displacement of the oil. When these criteria were satisfied oil was injected to seal off the end of the perfusion pipet and the transepithelial potential difference measured. No potential difference was observed. Substitution of sulfate or ferrocyanide for chloride in the intraluminal droplet resulted in a small bionic potential equal to the liquid junction potential between the perfusion solution and the bathing medium.

More recently Burg & Orloff (137) have re-evaluated the problem in isolated perfused proximal tubules of the rabbit. Originally, in association with Isaacson & Grantham (134), these authors had reported no measurable potential difference in the proximal tubule. In their current studies a potential difference of approximately −4 mV (lumen negative) was uniformly obtained. The authors attribute their earlier failure to observe a potential to inadequate insulation of the broken ends of the tubule and damage to the epithelial cells incurred in advancing the microelectrode pipet into the lumen. The "convincing" arguments and findings of Frömter & Hegel (133) had an indeterminate effect on their interpretation. In the present studies the earlier experimental difficulties were avoided. The spontaneous potential was uniformly eliminated by the addition of ouabain, indicative of dependence of the potential on active Na transport. Malnic & Aires (138) have also reported the presence of a spontaneous potential of greater than 10 mV in the proximal tubule of rats in free flow. Although the present reviewers, on the basis of poetic license as well as confidence in their own results, are convinced that a transepithelial potential difference, albeit small, is present in the proximal tubule, at least in the rabbit, they concede that the problem is not settled.

As indicated above, coupled passive reabsorption of Cl along an electrical gradient created by active Na transport was generally accepted as the mechanism of Cl transport. The early findings (17) that the chloride TF/P ratio was greater than 1 was assumed to be a consequence of more rapid abstraction of sodium bicarbonate and water than of Cl during the reabsorptive process. Frömter & Hegel (133) and Maude's (135) finding of no electrical driving force to account for Cl movement was disconcerting, although

Ullrich (139) pointed out that the Cl chemical gradient consequent to fluid absorption was probably sufficient to effect passive movement of the anion. Danielson, Persson & Ulfendahl (140) and Trautner & Wieth (141), on the basis of micropuncture studies in the rat and clearance studies in man respectively, have also concluded that Cl movement in the proximal segment is passive.

Maude (135) and Malnic et al (138, 142) remain unconvinced. The former considers that Cl is transported on a neutral NaCl pump as in the gallbladder (143, 144). He bases his conclusion on 1. the absence of a potential difference in the proximal tubule of cortical slices and 2. a notable reduction in net reabsorption estimated by the Gertz shrinking-drop technique when sulfate is substituted for Cl in both the droplet (perfusate) and bathing solution, which occurs without the development of a potential difference—a finding analogous to that reported in gallbladder (145, 146). The decrease in the transport rate is thought to indicate a low affinity of the NaCl carrier system for Na sulfate. Obviously the conclusion depends on the validity of the estimate of the transepithelial potential. Maude concedes that the low electrical resistance of the tubule and thereby high Cl permeability may be sufficient to permit passive Cl movement along a very small potential difference (-4 mV in our tentative view) which conceivably may be missed, though he dismisses the argument.

Whatever the truth may be, a neutral pump, passive Cl movement along a small electrical gradient, or that "last refuge of the intellectually bankrupt, pinocytosis" (147), other more disconcerting problems with respect to Cl still are unsolved. Several years ago Kashgarian et al (148) observed, at a time when a 20 mV potential was fashionable, that the "equilibrium concentration" of chloride in a split drop in the proximal tubule was approximately equal to that in the plasma. He suggested logically that this indicated net secretion of Cl into the tubule lumen since otherwise the Cl concentration in tubule fluid would have been less than in plasma. Malnic et al (138, 142) have recently reinvestigated the problem in two separate studies. In the first, the chloride TF/P ratio and potential difference were determined in rats during free flow under a variety of experimental conditions. No ratios of less than 1 were observed. Furthermore, infusion of acetazolamide or Na bicarbonate caused the chloride TF/P ratio to fall below that of control animals, of animals made acidotic with ammonium chloride, or of animals infused with Na sulfate. They concluded that the distribution of Cl between tubule fluid and plasma was dependent on acidification of the proximal urine and that their results were inconsistent with passive behavior of the anion. In a later study Malnic & Aires (138) studied Cl transport using the split-drop and the stationary microperfusion techniques. Isotonic Na bicarbonate and Na sulfate were instilled in blocked portions of proximal tubule and analyzed for Cl concentration at varying periods of time in the presence and absence of acetazolamide. Chloride concentration rose in the perfusate in all and reached a steady state within 30–40 sec. The steady-state ratio was 1.39 with bicarbonate and 1.08 with sulfate. In the presence of acetezo-lamide the respective ratios were 1.07 and 1.01. The $t_{1/2}$ for disappearance of droplets of similar solutions was also measured using the Gertz tech-nique. In contrast to results with saline in which the volume of the drop de-creases exponentially from zero time, an initial increase in volume of ap-proximately 10 sec duration was observed with isotonic bicarbonate and Na sulfate, following which droplet size decreased at a rate comparable to that of saline. From comparisons of the rate of decrease in volume from 10–30 sec after institution of the experiment and the simultaneous rate of the Cl concentration rise, they concluded that the increase in the concentration of Cl in the perfusate was not a consequence of fluid absorption but rather of net secretion of Cl into the tubule lumen. The observations are obviously contrary to the hypothesis that the chloride TF/P ratios greater than 1 are a consequence of more rapid bicarbonate and water absorption as assumed by Walker et al (17). These authors cautiously considered a variety of hy-potheses but tend to favor that of Kashgarian et al (148) who postulated that hydrochloric acid conceivably is secreted in the process of proximal fluid acidification. Malnic & Aires (142) also re-examined the thesis origi-nally proposed by Rector & Clapp (149) that Cl is actively reabsorbed in the distal nephron. In contrast to the results of Rector & Clapp, the chloride TF/P ratio in the distal nephron in the more recent studies was never less than that predicted by the potential difference and the Nernst equation so that no requirement for active Cl reabsorption was necessary to account for the observations. The discrepant findings of the two laboratories are not readily explicable.

Several monkeywrenches have also been tossed at those who unwittingly have subscribed for at least a decade to the attractive and simple view of NaCl transport based on the frog skin model alluded to earlier. The icono-clasts, who have virtue on their side, include Kleinzeller & Knotkova (150), Maude (135, 151), Whittembury and associates (152, 153), MacKnight (154, 155, 156, 157), and perhaps Willis (158). Their studies, sufficiently complicated to preclude ready summary, are based on the original finding of Kleinzeller & Knotkova (150). They observed that the volume of cortical slices, first swollen and leached of K in K-free media at zero° C, returns towards normal (loses NaCl and water) when reincubated at 25° in either K-free media or in the presence of ouabain, without a measurable uptake of potassium. Since the classical Na-K exchange pump must be inoperative un-der these conditions, NaCl and water extrusion must occur by another mechanism. Kleinzeller & Knotkova (150) considered that this may be via a contractile system which squeezes or filters a NaCl solution out of the swol-len cell.

The other authors in general consider that a parallel NaCl pump, K and ouabain insensitive, is responsible for volume regulation, the electrogenic or Na-K exchange pump being relegated only to the maintenance of selective cation concentrations. Willis (158), on the basis of O_2 consumption studies and cation composition under numerous circumstances, considers that a "cryptic" Na-K pump which responds to an immeasurable microenvironment of K maintained by outward diffusion of cation from the cell may still be operative to account for the findings. Ouabain in his view is somehow excluded from the "cryptic pump" site. None of the other investigators cited above agrees. Whittembury & Proverbio (153) also observed that active K uptake in exchange for Na occurs in the cold since leached slices maintained in the cold take up K from the medium and lose Na [as Burg & Orloff (159) noted several years ago] but that shrinkage (net NaCl and water extrusion) does not occur. Potassium uptake is inhibited by ouabain. Ethacrynic acid on the other hand inhibits the restitution of volume of leached slices in K-free media at 25°C.

This two-pump hypothesis borrows in part from the work of Hoffman & Kregenow (160) who observed in red cells an ethacrynic acid-sensitive, ouabain-insensitive, moiety of "active" Na transport. MacKnight (157), in contrast, although he considers two pumps likely, discounts the ethacrynic acid inhibition of NaCl extrusion as a nonspecific effect of the agent on the viability or metabolism of the tissue.

Maude (151) has carried the story somewhat further by comparing the $t_{1/2}$ for split-drop disappearance in slices and the cell cation and water content of nonperfused slices under similar circumstances when reabsorption is inhibited either by ouabain or by the removal of K from the bathing medium. No correlation was observed between the degree of $t_{1/2}$ prolongation and the elevation in cell Na content. He concluded that this indicated two pumps, one responsible for net NaCl absorption in vivo, the other for the maintenance of the intracellular Na and K concentrations. This is based on the assumption that were the two processes (NaCl reabsorption and Na-K exchange) linked as in the Ussing hypothesis, an inverse correlation between net flux inhibition and cell Na concentration should have been observed. It is not entirely clear how ouabain inhibits net transport in the Maude model if it only affects the exchange pump as Whittembury and others believe. Furthermore changes in cation composition were measured only in nonperfused tubules which were not engaged in fluid translocation.

The data of all of the investigators are certainly provocative and require serious consideration, but in the absence of direct estimates of transport pools, potential differences across the pertinent borders and the permeabilities to the individual ions are difficult to interpret. Certainly many of the findings in slices could as readily be explained by changes in permeability as by activation of a hypothetical new transport system at this juncture.

Whatever the mechanism of Na transport may be or whether there are two pumps or one, Baldamus et al (72) concluded that the active transport system in the proximal nephron is saturated at normal plasma concentrations of Na in the rat. They estimated net isotonic fluid absorption (from which they calculated net Na flux) by the Gertz shrinking-drop technique in the rat proximal tubule at different ambient Na concentrations (range approximately 100–230 meq/liter). The sodium concentration was altered either by direct perfusion of the peritubular capillaries or by peritoneal dialysis. Under similar circumstances the equilibrium concentration difference between Na in lumen and interstitium which develops when raffinose is added to lumen fluid to prevent net water and Na movement was also measured. No change in either the net isotonic absorption or the equilibrium Na concentration difference was observed over the range of interstitial Na concentrations examined. They concluded that active transport of Na is constant and the "pump" saturated. The calculations and conclusions depend, as the authors note, on the absence of a transepithelial PD, which as pointed out may be a hazardous assumption as is reliance on the shrinking-drop technique.

Burg & Orloff (30) found that the rate of isosmotic net fluid absorption in the proximal convolution of isolated perfused tubules of the rabbit was considerably greater than in the straight segment of the proximal tubule. In contrast, PAH transport was more rapid in the straight segment (161) than in the convoluted portion whereas the reverse was true for glucose reabsorption (162).

The infusion of mannitol had been supposed to induce an osmotic diuresis, largely by virtue of restricted absorption in the proximal nephron of water with resultant dilution of intraluminal Na and accelerated net passive influx of salt. In micropuncture studies in the dog Seely & Dirks (163) found that proximal inhibition of net Na transport under these circumstances was insufficient to account for the magnitude of induced diuresis and that greater inhibition of absorption in the distal nephron, particularly in the loop of Henle, was largely responsible for mannitol diuresis. Persson & Ulfendahl (164) compared the osmotic and diffusional permeabilities to water of the proximal tubule in micropuncture studies in the rat. Osmotic permeability as in other epithelial tissues was considerably less than diffusional permeability, from which they concluded, according to dogma, that water flow, in part at least, occurs via aqueous channels or pores. In the distal nephron (165) a similar discrepancy was noted in rats with diabetes insipidus. In antidiuresis in normal rats when ADH was presumably acting, though the diffusional and osmotic permeabilities both rose the latter rose considerably more than the former, which indicated to the author an increase in pore size. The validity of calculating either pore size or changes in pore area on the basis of the discrepancy between osmotic and diffusional permeability has been seriously questioned in recent years, and though the authors noted this, they are insufficiently cautious in our view.

AMMONIA EXCRETION

The role of ammonia in acid-base balance, its distribution in renal cells, urine, and plasma, the theory of nonionic diffusion, and the amino acid precursors from which it is formed in tubule cells are reasonably well understood. Most of the pertinent information was reviewed several years ago by

Pitts (166). The most intriguing and baffling problem still unsolved is the genesis of adaptation. In man, dog, and rat, chronic metabolic acidosis is associated with a marked increase in both production and excretion of ammonia—far out of proportion to the changes in urine pH. Chronic alkalosis reverses the adaptive increase in production and excretion. In recent years renewed interest in the mechanism of adaptation has been generated by Goodman, Fuisz & Cahill (167). Before attempting an evaluation of the numerous papers relevant to the subject we must recognize certain problems. Most pertinent studies have been performed in the dog and rat. Extrapolation of results from one species to the other has been frequent and in our view may not be warranted under all circumstances. Thus, although the urinary changes induced by acid-base alterations are similar in the two species in most respects, differences do exist (168). Furthermore equivalent experimental manipulations in the two species have led to different results which cannot be ignored, particularly if one attempts to ascribe adaptation to a single and identical mechanism in the two. Glutamine is the primary source of ammonia in both rat and dog and yet the enzymatic "machinery" in the cell is not the same. The kidney of the rat can synthesize glutamine, that of the dog cannot (v.i.). For these and other reasons an attempt has been made to discuss many of the observations obtained in the two animal groups separately.

Glutamine is degraded to ammonia similarly in dog and rat. Two major pathways exist: 1. Glutamine may be deamidated to glutamic acid and ammonia (the glutaminase-I reaction) and the glutamic acid converted to α-ketoglutarate and ammonia (the glutamic dehydrogenase step). The carbon skeleton of glutamine, α-ketoglutarate, may, in addition to other paths, traverse the Krebs cycle or be converted to glucose (v.i.). 2. Glutamine may be transaminated with keto acids; the α-ketoglutaramate so formed then converted to α-ketoglutarate and ammonia (glutaminase II reaction). The relative contributions of the two major pathways to ammonia production are difficult to ascertain though most subscribe to the view (169, 170) that the glutaminase I mechanism is the most important metabolic path.

Since it was apparent that glutamine hydrolysis in vivo is accelerated in acidosis, initial interest was focused on the possibility that a rate-limiting enzyme was activated to account for the enhanced ammonia excretion. Davies & Yudkin (171) reported activation of glutaminase I in renal cortical slices of acidotic rats and a decrease in activity in metabolic alkalosis. This was subsequently confirmed (172). Leonard & Orloff (173) however noted that ammonia excretion rose considerably sooner in acidotic rats than did glutaminase activity. Similar findings were recently reported by Alleyne (174). It is also known that cortical glutaminase activity is not elevated in slices from chronically acidotic dogs despite a marked increase in ammonia excretion (168). The latter observation is recalled not to discount the glutaminase thesis in the rat, since it does not of itself, but to re-emphasize the danger of extrapolation of data.

The glutaminase thesis in the rat was ultimately and perhaps finally rejected by Goldstein (175) who was able to prevent induction of glutaminase activation in acidotic rats with actinomycin D without affecting the increase in ammonia excretion. In this regard the report of Bignall, Elebute & Lotspeich (176) should not be misconstrued. Although they state that actinomycin D blocked both enzyme and urinary ammonia "adaptation" in chronic acidotic rats in their studies, this is somewhat misleading. There is no question that glutaminase activation was prevented by actinomycin D treatment and that ammonia excretion was somewhat less in rats so treated than in those given only NH_4Cl. Mean ammonia excretion, however, was 10 meq per hr in control, 100 in NH_4Cl plus actinomycin D-treated animals, and 130 in NH_4Cl-treated animals. Glutaminase activity on the other hand was approximately 80 "units" in both normal and actinomycin D plus NH_4Cl-treated rats and 109 in NH_4Cl-treated rats. Clearly an adaptive increase in ammonia excretion, albeit less than in the acidotic animals not given the inhibitor, occurred without a change in enzyme activity.

It has been argued by Steiner, Goodman & Treble (177) that the failure of Rector & Orloff (168) to observe increased glutaminase I activity in acidotic dogs was a consequence of the dilution of endogenous glutamic acid in the homogenates. Goldstein (178) had previously found that glutaminase I activity is inhibited by glutamate and postulated that the decrease in glutamate concentration in renal tissue in acidosis accounts for enhanced ammonia production. Consequently Steiner, Goodman & Treble (177) argued that the artificial reduction of glutamate concentration in homogenates from alkalotic and acidotic dog cortical tissue would be expected to mask differences between the two. Their objection essentially discounts the principle of the detection of changes in total enzyme activity (concentration) in homogenates, which depends on elimination by dilution of all factors other than the enzyme and appropriate substrate. It also omits recognition that precisely the same technique in rat cortex in which dilution also occurs reveals an increase in glutaminase I activity.

In 1966 Goodman, Fuisz & Cahill (167) proposed that enhanced gluconeogenesis in the kidney induced by acidosis is the primary driving force for the adaptive increase in ammonia production. The carbon endproduct of glutamine, α-ketoglutarate is converted to oxaloacetate and then via a step catalyzed by phosphenolpyruvate carboxykinase (PEPCK) to phosphenolpyruvate and ultimately to glucose. They suggested that acidosis activates PEPCK. Thus a fall in the concentration of α-ketoglutarate consequent to accelerated gluconeogenesis (diversion from the Krebs cycle) will pull the glutamic dehydrogenase step to the right, decrease tissue glutamate, and accelerate glutamine deamidation as well. The latter, essentially activation of glutaminase I secondary to the reduction in glutamate concentration, is based on the observations of Goldstein (178) alluded to earlier. Tissue glutamate concentration is decreased in acidosis in both rat and dog.

Somewhat similar arguments regarding induction of enhanced glutamine degradation via the glutaminase II step secondary to the decrease in the concentration of α-ketoglutarate were also posited (167). In the rat the activity of both is elevated in chronic metabolic acidosis and decreased in alkalosis. Neither is elevated in the dog (168). In support of their thesis, Goodman, Fuisz & Cahill (167) observed that gluconeogenesis from glutamine, glutamic acid, α-ketoglutarate, and oxaloacetate is greater in slices from acidotic than from alkalotic rats whereas glucose production from fructose or glycerol is unaltered in acidosis. They argued against a direct effect of acidosis on the uptake of substrate since even in the absence of exogenous substrate, gluconeogenesis was greatest in slices from acidotic animals. This attractive and original idea was rapidly accepted and a number of studies whose results have been interpreted within the framework of the hypothesis have appeared. Thus Alleyne & Scullard (179) and Alleyne (180), on the basis of analyses of the concentrations of metabolic intermediates in cortical slices and direct estimates of PEPCK activity, noted activation of PEPCK in the kidney of acidotic rats. PEPCK activity in the liver was not altered by acidosis. The increase in enzyme activity correlated with ammonia excretion in the intact animal. Of interest was the observation that both PEPCK activity and ammonia excretion rose within 6 hr of induction of NH_4Cl acidosis without a change in glutaminase I activity. Adrenal steroids also activated renal PTPCK but less than when steroid plus NH_4Cl was employed. The role of steroids in the activation of the pertinent rate-limiting enzyme in metabolic acidosis, however, was excluded by Goodman, Fuisz & Cahill (167) and Goorno, Rector & Seldin (181). Alkaloses induced by oral Na dihydrogen phosphate (179), by hypokalemia (167), and by steroids are all associated with enhanced ammonia excretion and increased activity of PEPCK. In view of this, extracellular pH cannot be a primary factor in the genesis of adaptation. If pH is a factor it is more likely that of the intracellular environment which is unkown.

More recently Alleyne (174) examined in detail the time course of the changes in enzyme activation, gluconeogenesis, and ammoniagenesis in rat cortical slices. Within 2 hr of induction of acidosis in the rat, ammonia excretion rose as did in vitro gluconeogenesis and ammoniagenesis from glutamine and succinate. A good correlation between the two latter processes was not evident until 48 hr after induction of acidosis and was absent at 6 hr. In contrast, neither Goodman, Fuisz & Cahill (167) nor Preuss (182) observed an increase in glucose production (167, 182) or ammonia production (182) in slices early in metabolic acidosis. Alleyne (174) concluded that gluconeogenesis was the primary mechanism responsible for the adaptive increase in ammonia production in acidosis and that both paths for glutamine hydrolysis were accelerated: one (glutaminase I) in response to the decrease in tissue glutamate, the other (glutaminase II) in response to the decrease in tissue α-ketoglutarate.

The lack of correlation between glucose and ammonia production in slices early in acidosis is somewhat disturbing and may indicate that the two processes are not directly linked in the genesis of adaptation. Increased glu-coneogenesis may be a consequence rather than the cause of increased glu-tamine hydrolysis and thus serve as a means for dissipation of the carbon skeleton of glutamine (α-ketoglutarate) in excess of that consumed in the Krebs cycle. Kamm & Cahill (183) noted that hepatic gluconeogenesis in the rat is unaltered by acidosis as did Alleyne (174).

Kamm & Asher (169) found a good correlation between ammonia and glucose production in kidney slices 48 hr after induction of metabolic acido-sis in rats. They point out that conversion of glutamine to ammonia via the glutaminase-I-dehydrogenase pathway should in theory yield 4 ammonias for each glucose formed whereas degradation through the glutaminase II path will yield only 2 ammonias per glucose. Glutamate on the other hand can only yield 2 ammonias per glucose. The ratio obtained in slices from acidotic rats was 6/1 with glutamine as substrate and 2/1 with gluta-mate. They concluded that 75% of the glutamine and 93% of the glutamate converted to ammonia gave rise to glucose. Furthermore they interpreted the observed ratio as evidence that glutamine to a large extent traverses the glutaminase-I-glutamic dehydrogenase pathway. This at the very least is a hazardous conclusion for the following reasons: 1. The ratios are based on net changes, but interpreted as if *only* formation of ammonia and glucose had occurred. It is conceivable that the deficit in glucose reflected by the 6/1 ratio e.g. indicates oxidation of some of the glucose produced. 2. Even were this not the case, the predicted ratio for glutamine on which the calculation and conclusion are based rather than being 4/1 may be 3/1—that expected in the admittedly unlikely event that glutamine is hydrolyzed at equal rates through both pathways.

With the exception of the effect of cyclic 3′,5′-AMP (184) which will be discussed separately, the data in the papers just summarized constitute most of the recent evidence in the rat consistent with the gluconeogenesis theory. None of the data exclude the possibility that gluconeogenesis is secondary to stimulation of ammoniagenesis and merely affords an additional path for the disposal of the products of glutamine hydrolysis. Preuss (182) in a fol-low-up of an earlier report (185) has suggested that acidosis increases the ratio of oxidized to reduced pyridine nucleotides in the kidney which accel-erates the conversion of glutamate to α-ketoglutarate and ammonia along the glutamic dehydrogenase path. It is apparent that this, coupled with ac-celeration of the glutaminase I step attendant upon the predicted decrease in tissue glutamate, could provide an explanation for adaptation. The exper-iments, however, are difficult to interpret since the major conclusions de-pend on the assumption that acute alterations in ammonia and glucose pro-duction in slices of normal rat kidney induced by changes in medium pH are similar to those which occur in vivo and in vitro in the kidneys of chroni-cally acidotic (adapted) and alkalotic animals.

Certain of the results are worthy of note. Slices from rats made acidotic 4 hr before sacrifice did not generate more ammonia or glucose from glutamate than did slices from normal animals, yet tissue glutamate was diminished in the former group. Slices from similarly treated animals when immersed in medium of pH 7.1 for 2 hr produced more ammonia and glucose from glutamate than did slices in medium of pH 7.7. Malonate, a Krebs cycle inhibitor, completely blocked gluconeogenesis at both pHs without significantly decreasing ammonia production. Arsenite, which prevents α-ketoglutarate breakdown, also eliminated gluconeogenesis and though ammonia production fell approximately 70%, the effect of pH was still evident. This dissociation between the two processes, though elicited in a somewhat artificial manner,[1] may well constitute strong evidence against the gluconeogenesis thesis, but only if confirmed in slices from chronically adapted animals. There is no reason to presuppose that adaptation which requires considerable time in vivo, a reflection of a gradual alteration in the rate-controlling step or steps, can be induced acutely in vitro.

In support of the proposed role of the pyridine nucleotides in adaptation, Preuss (182) reported significant increases in NAD/NADH and NADP/NADPH ratios in the renal cortex of rats made acutely acidotic with 20 mM HCl/kg. He neglects to emphasize that were this the only factor responsible for initiating adaptation, one would expect enhanced ammoniagenesis from glutamate by these slices in vitro, which was not the case.

Kamm & Asher (169), in a rebuttal made in defense of the gluconeogenesis theory, reject the inhibitor data of Preuss: 1. They argue that both malonate and arsenite may inhibit enzymes besides succinic dehydrogenase and α-ketoacid oxidase respectively and thereby interfere with glucose production from a variety of substrates. They suggest that under these circumstances products other than glucose may accumulate, particularly if PEPCK activity is increased as they believe. 2. They propose that glucose utilization may have been stimulated in Preuss' studies which would mask an increase in flux of α-ketoglutarate through the gluconeogenic path. 3. Finally, they reiterate that the experiments were not performed in slices from chronically acidotic animals which in their view may be the only valid model to study. Although all three objections may have virtue, only the last goes to the point. The first two are and were amenable to experimental verification by the authors. Whether similar objections will be leveled at Churchill & Malvin (186) is unknown. These authors inhibited gluconeogenesis from glutamine in rat kidney slices with either malonate or phenylpyruvate without affecting ammoniagenesis (malonate) or stimulating it (phenylpyruvate). Though not explicitly stated, it appears that the slices were obtained from chronically acidotic animals. If not, the dissociation is of less interest.

Steiner, Goodman & Treble (177) and Goorno, Rector & Seldin (181)

---

[1] This is not to say that results of studies with slices from chronically acidotic animals, as done by others, are necessarily a closer approximation to the in vivo situation, particularly since all investigators use substrate concentrations [$\pm$10 mM] 10–20 or more times greater than exist in normal plasma.

have presented evidence in the *dog* that ammoniagenesis is secondary to increased PEPCK activity. The former authors compared ammonia excretion and renal glucose production in vivo in control and acidotic dogs. Glucose production by the kidney rose from a mean of approximately .78 μmole/min in the control group to 4.6 in the acidotic group in association with the rise in mean ammonia excretion from 7 to 22 μmoles per min. If accepted at face value the results are consistent with their hypothesis. However, the arteriovenous glucose differences on which the estimate of glucose production is based were significantly different only at the .05 level in the two groups. This is hardly a convincing increase. Renal cortical glutamate concentration was significantly depressed in acidosis, however.

Goorno, Rector & Seldin (181) took the simpler approach and correlated the production of glucose from glutamine and succinate in cortical slices of dog kidney with in vivo ammonia excretion in both acidosis and alkalosis. The results were similar to those of analogous rat studies—enhanced in vitro gluconeogenesis and in vivo ammonia excretion in metabolic acidosis. It is probable that in vivo estimates of renal glucose production were avoided by these workers owing to their appreciation of the inherent difficulties of the technique. But it would have been reasonable to attempt to demonstrate ammoniagenesis from substrate in dog slices, particularly since the increment in glucose production observed was of sufficient magnitude (conceivably) to permit detection of an increase in ammonia production, assuming that the 6/1 ratio or even 4/1 ratio observed in rats (see above) would be approximated. This opportunity did not exist in Churchill & Malvin's study (187) (see below).

At this juncture it should be re-emphasized that no one has demonstrated enhanced in vitro hydrolysis of glutamine to ammonia by kidney slices of chronically acidotic dogs (168, 187). Simpson & Sherrard (188) did observe an increased rate of conversion of labeled glutamine to labeled CO_2 in kidney slices from acidotic dogs, though conceding that this is not necessarily evidence of enhanced hydrolysis to ammonia. They ascribe the failure of Rector & Orloff (168) to the latter's use of an excessively high concentration of substrate which may have inhibited hydrolysis. They fail to note that a significant increment in the rate of hydrolysis of glutamine to ammonia in slices from acidotic rats under precisely the same conditions was observed by those authors (168). Churchill & Malvin (187) also found no effect of acidosis on the capacity of dog slices to produce ammonia from glutamine despite enhanced gluconeogenesis. Though interpreted as evidence against the gluconeogenesis thesis, this is erroneous. Baseline ammonia production was so high (437 ± 42 (SE) μmoles/g/hr) and the increment in glucose production so low (3.2 μmoles/g/hr) as to preclude any possibility of detecting a change in the rate of ammoniagenesis. Of greater significance was their inability to detect an increase in renal glucose production in vivo in acidotic animals despite heroic attempts to do so. The reviewers are impressed by the small effect of acidosis on in vivo glucose production in the Steiner, Goodman & Treble (177) study and the absence of an effect in that of Churchill & Malvin (187). It is probable that the true change is somewhere in between, i.e. negligible, and in our view this constitutes a serious objection to the gluconeogenesis thesis. This conclusion is strengthened by a recent study of Roxe, Disalvo & Balagura-Baruch (189) who found no evidence of net glucose production in dogs in the normal state, in chronic acidosis, in chronic alkalosis, or in respiratory derangements of acid-base balance. They do find evidence of renal gluconeogenesis as indicated by renal release of ^{14}C glucose following injection of labeled precursors.

The role of cyclic 3',5'-AMP in the process under review has been studied in the rat by Pagliara & Goodman (184). The nucleotide increased gluconeogenesis and ammoniagenesis from substrates in the manner to be expected were PEPCK activated, i.e. similar to the pattern in slices from acidotic rats. Tissue glutamate also fell. Parathormone which increases adenyl cyclase activity of kidney slices (190) also stimulates gluconeogenesis from glutamine (184). Ammoniagenesis for unknown reasons was not estimated. Bowman (191) reported enhanced gluconeogenesis with cyclic 3',5'-monophosphate in the perfused isolated rat kidney, but no effect of either parathormone or vasopressin. The relative ineffectiveness of dibutyryl cyclic AMP in cortical slices (184) and its lack of effect in the perfused kidney (191), which because of its greater penetrability and diminished rate of degradation to a physiologically inactive form is generally more effective than cyclic AMP in other tissues, is curious. It may indicate absence of a deacylation system necessary for the conversion of the dibutyryl compound to its active form in this tissue (191). In any event since gluconeogenesis is stimulated in the liver by cyclic AMP, it is not particularly surprising that it is similarly effective in the kidney and the result neither supports nor detracts from the thesis under review. The effects of other hormones or gluconeogenesis in the kidney have also been studied (192).

More recently Pagliara & Goodman (193) have reported effects analogous to those of cyclic AMP in kidney slices with cyclic 3',5'-inosine monophosphate. Since the degradation product 5'-IMP was also effective, the results are not readily interpretable. The authors emphasize that cyclic 3',5'-guanosine monophosphate (cyclic GMP), another naturally occurring nucleotide, inhibits gluconeogenesis and ammoniagenesis in slices incubated with either glutamine or glutamate with an attendant rise in tissue glutamate. The pattern of inhibition of gluconeogenesis from other substrates indicated a block not at the PEPCK step, but rather in the conversion of glutamate to α-ketoglutarate. The authors' conclusion that this may be the physiologic effect of the nucleotide in vivo is weakened since in the absence of substrate the guanosine compound has the opposite effect. It significantly increases both glucose and ammonia production despite an equivalent rise in tissue glutamate. Although it is likely that cyclic GMP may have a function of some sort in the kidney since the requisite specific cyclase system has been detected in this tissue (194), judgment as to its role in ammonia formation is suspended.

Although the present reviewers consider the gluconeogenesis thesis provocative they do not consider it proven, nor in fact a likely explanation for adaptation. It seems very strange indeed that a major homeostatic mechanism, the regulation of acid-base balance by ammonia, should be controlled by a relatively minor gluconeogenic system in a tissue which is never a major source of glucose as Steiner, Goodman & Treble (177) recognize.

Simpson & Sherrard (188) measured the rate of conversion of labeled glutamine to 14 CO_2 in kidney slices and mitochondria from normal dogs at different pH and from chronically acidotic and alkalotic animals. They conclude that the acute effect of acidosis on glutamine uptake and ammonia excretion in vivo is a pH-dependent stimulation of mitochondrial utilization of the amino acid. They argue that this cannot be a consequence of increased gluconeogenesis since the PEPCK system is cytoplasmic. In contrast, increased "utilization" of glutamine evident in slices of chronically acidotic dogs is not evident in the mitochondria. They concede, albeit unwillingly, that gluconeogenesis might be a factor under these circumstances but prefer to assign it a nonregulatory secondary role. They suggest that primary regulation of glutamine hydrolysis and ammonia production in the chronically adapted animal is effected either 1. by a pH-conditioned increase in active glutamine uptake, or 2. by a pH-induced cytoplasmic alteration which increases mitochondrial utilization of the amino acid. Their conclusions are based on the assumption, which they recognize may be unwarranted, that conversion of glutamine to CO_2 is an indirect estimate of glutamine hydrolysis to NH_3. At this point, it should be apparent that the mechanism of adaptation in chronic acidosis is not yet understood, by us at the very least.

It is known that the glutamine synthetase system is present in rat kidney and not in that of the dog in vitro (168, 195). Janicki & Goldstein (196), in an extension of an earlier study (170), assayed the activities of renal glutamine synthetase and renal glutaminase I in tissues derived from a variety of mammals. They report significant synthetase activity in the kidney of rabbit, guinea pig, and rat, but not in those of cat, dog, and pig. Glutaminase activity, present in all, was greatest in those excreting the more acid urine (cat, dog, pig), least in those excreting an alkaline urine (rabbit, guinea pig), and intermediate in the rat. In contrast to Addae & Lotspeich's (197) findings in the dog, metabolic acidosis did not activate liver synthetase in the rat. Neither chronic acidosis nor alkalosis altered renal synthetase activity. Since enzyme assays generally are assumed to reflect total amount of enzyme rather than intrinsic activity, they conclude that the in vivo results which are at variance with theirs in both kidney (198) and liver (197) with respect to synthetase activity must be ascribed to a change in the intrinsic activity in vivo.

Damain & Pitts (198) have estimated the activity of the two enzyme systems in the functioning rat kidney in vivo in both chronic acidosis and alkalosis. Pulse labeling of the kidney with radioactive glutamine and recovery of label in the renal glutamate pool was used to estimate glutaminase activity; the converse, recovery of label from glutamate in the glutamine pool, to estimate synthetase activity. In normal animals the rates of the two reactions were virtually identical so that the minimal quantities of ammonia produced and excreted under these circumstances must derive from the glutaminase II path and from the glutamate dehydrogenase path as well as from other amino acid precursors by transamination coupled to the dehydrogenase step. Of greatest significance was the direct demonstration that metabolic acidosis depressed renal synthetase activity in association with enhanced glutaminase activity.

Clearly in this species increased synthesis of substrate within the organ is not an obligatory step in the renal production of ammonia as it cannot be in the dog which has no synthetase activity whatsoever. In fact the opposite is undoubtedly the case. In alkalosis, synthesis of glutamine is elevated and production of ammonia via glutaminase decreased. As the authors emphasize, both Kamin & Handler (199) and Orloff & Berliner (200) pointed out that fine control of ammonia production in the tubule cell would relate best to removal of ammonia in urine and blood were ammonia produced by a reversible process. Though the synthetase reaction is thermodynamically reversible, glutaminase I is not. The observations of Damian & Pitts (198) provide evidence that both reactions in concert can serve as a single functionally reversible system in the rat. This cannot be the case in the dog in which only the degradative process can be subject to control.

The effects of acute changes in acid-base balance and of urine pH have not been examined in this fashion and may differ, particularly since production is generally assumed to remain constant. On the other hand, glutaminase I activity was depressed in normal rats by infusion of α-ketoglutarate without affecting the synthetase reaction.

A similar effect undoubtedly accounts for the decrease in ammonia production elicited by Balagura-Baruch, Shurland & Welbourne (201) by the injection of α-ketoglutarate in the acidotic dog. In their studies the resultant increase in tissue glutamate and perhaps the rise in α-ketoglutarate inhibited glutaminase I and was responsible for the fall in ammonia production. The fixation of ammonia to α-ketoglutarate (reversal of the dehydrogenase reaction) which Churchill & Malvin (186) consider the probable basis for the decrease in ammonia excretion under these circumstances could only have accounted for a maximum of 25% of the decrease in ammonia release in the dog (201). The infusion of glutamate elicits the appropriate fall in ammonia excretion in the rat (186) but not in the dog (202–204). The latter has been cited as an objection to the gluconeogenesis thesis, which depends on activation of glutaminase I by the fall in tissue glutamate (186), which it may be. It is more likely a consequence of the relatively poor extraction of injected glutamate by the dog kidney (205) and its lack of penetration to the appropriate mitochondrial site.

In vivo studies with labeled precursors have demonstrated that both the amide and amino N_2 of glutamine contribute to urinary ammonia. It is conceivable that recycling of free ammonia derived from the amino position in the dehydrogenase reaction, e.g., ultimately returns it to the amide position in tissue glutamine and that deamidation of glutamine is the only mechanism for the release of ammonia into the urine (204). This obligatory coupling of deamidation (and glutamine synthesis) to ammonia excretion cannot be the case in the dog which lacks the synthetase system. Nor is it in the rat. Lyon & Pitts (205) readily incorporated label from α-ketoglutarate in the renal glutamate pool of all species studied (dog, cat, rat, and guinea pig) indicative of either reversal of the dehydrogenase step or more likely transamination with alanine or aspartate. Incorporation of label in the glutamine pool only occurred in the rat and guinea pig. Even in these species obligatory synthesis of glutamine from ammonia and glutamate cannot be a prerequisite for excretion of ammonia, since if it were, synthetase activity would be greatest in acidosis which it is not (198). In Lyon & Pitts' (205) study labeling was significantly greater in tissue from rats in metabolic alkalosis than in tissue from those in metabolic acidosis.

Glutamine as repeatedly emphasized is the main amino acid precursor of ammonia in the kidney. In acidosis the amount extracted from plasma accounts for virtually all of the ammonia produced by the kidney (206). Oelert & Nagel (207) had reported that production of ammonia by the kidney correlates with filtration rate rather than renal blood flow and concluded that only glutamine filtered and reabsorbed is transformed into ammonia for excretion. This is not the case in metabolic acidosis in the dog. Pilkington, Young & Pitts (208) reconfirmed an earlier observation (209) that renal extraction of glutamine in the acidotic dog greatly exceeds that filtered and reabsorbed. They found that the amount of ammonia produced by the dog kidney is equal to that derived from reabsorbed glutamine plus that transported across the peritubular surface of the cells and thus correlated equally as well with renal blood flow as with GFR. Luminal reabsorption, an active process (209), was virtually complete over a tenfold range of plasma glutamine concentration and was not affected by changes in acid-base balance. Transport across the peritubular surface, on the other hand, was greatly accelerated in acidosis though the nature of the process (active or passive) could not be established. Although specific stimulation of antiluminal transport, were it an active process or enhancement of membrane permeability by acidosis, conceivably is a factor in the adaptive increase in ammonia excretion noted under these circumstances, the authors discount the possibility.

Despite increased renal extractcon of glutamine in acidosis in the dog, the concentration of the amino acid in plasma is maintained relatively constant or may rise slightly (166, 210). The extrarenal source of glutamine responsible for the homeostasis is the liver (197). Addae & Lotspeich (197), in addition to noting increased hepatic production and renal extraction of glutamine in the intact acidotic dog, also obtained evidence that gastrointestinal extraction of glutamine is accelerated. They proposed that the increase in portal venous ammonia, attendant upon intestinal hydrolysis of glutamine, may provide the stimulus for the increase in hepatic synthesis. This is unlikely since no net glutamine synthesis would occur if only the extra ammonia from the portal vein were returned to the liver synthetase system.

In a subsequent study (211) the authors concluded that acidosis per se as well as a slight fall in plasma glutamine may also contribute to the stimulation of hepatic glutamine synthesis. The correlation between net production of glutamine and acidosis was best however. It is notable that enhanced renal extraction of glutamine occurred within 1–2 hr of administering an acid load and was associated with a rise in ammonia excretion (197). It would have been of interest had the authors estimated ammonia production rather than excretion alone since it is generally assumed that acute changes in ammonia excretion are not attended by changes in production. This seems unlikely if an acute increase in glutamine extraction occurs as Addae & Lotspeich (197) have shown. Most recently Weiss & Preuss (212) report that methionine sulfoximine, a selective inhibitor of glutamine synthetase, reduced the activity of this enzyme in liver of acidotic rats without altering ammonia excretion. Thus "adaptation", in their model, occurred despite a decrease in the plasma glutamine concentration of the "inhibited" animal. This does not constitute evidence against Addae & Lotspeich's (197) view that in the *dog* the liver is the extrarenal source of glutamine. Their conclusion that "augmented rates of glutamine production are not the rate limiting factors that are overcome in the increased renal excretion of ammonia in chronic acidosis in the *rat*" had not been seriously questioned by others in the past.

LITERATURE CITED

1. Giebisch, G. 1969. Functional organization of proximal and distal tubular electrolyte transport. *Nephron* 6:260–81
2. Forster, R. P. 1967. Renal transport mechanisms. *Fed. Proc.* 26:1008–19
3. Whittembury, G. 1968. Sodium and water transport in kidney proximal tubular cells. *J. Gen. Physiol.* 51:303–14
4. Morel, F., de Rouffignac, C., Lechene, Cl. 1968. Rôle physiologique du segment grêle des néphrons dans le méchanisme de concentration de l'urine. *Actualités Néphrologiques de L'Hôpital Necker* 233–48
5. 1969. *The Kidney: morphology, biochemistry and physiology.* ed. C. Rouiller, A. Muller. New York: Academic
6. Bank, N. 1968. Physiological basis of diuretic action. *Ann. Rev. Med.* 19:103–18
7. Epstein, F. H. 1968. Calcium and the kidney. *Am. J. Med.* 45:700–14
8. Kriz, W. 1969. Renal countercurrent mechanisms: structure and function. *Am. Heart J.* 78:101–18

9. Hatch, F. E., Johnson, J. G. Intra-renal blood flow. *Ann. Rev. Med.* 20:395–408

10. Cafruny, E. J. 1968. Renal Pharmacology. *Ann. Rev. Pharmacol.* 8:131–50

11. 1970. Schmidt-Nielsen, B., Ed. *Urea and the Kidney.* Amsterdam: Excerpta Med. Found. 495 pp.

12. Windhager, E. E. 1968. *Micropuncture techniques and nephron function.* New York: Appleton. 249 pp.

13. 1969. Thurau, K., Jahrmarker, H., Eds. *Renal Transport and Diuretics.* Berlin-Heidelberg-New York: Springer

14. 1968. Neural control of body salt and water. Physiology Society Symposium. *Fed. Proc.* 27:1127–59

15. Dicker, S. E., Ed. 1970. *Mechanisms of Urine Concentration and Dilution in Mammals.* Arnold (Publ.) Ltd.

16. Walker, A. M., Oliver, J. 1941. Methods for the collection of fluid from single glomeruli and tubules of the mammalian kidney. *Am. J. Physiol.* 134:562–79

17. Walker, A. M., Bott, P. A., Oliver, J., MacDowell, M. C. 1941. The collection and analysis of fluid from single nephrons of the mammalian kidney. *Am. J. Physiol.* 134:580–95

18. Gottschalk, C. W., Leyssac, P. P. 1968. Proximal tubular function in rats with low inulin clearance. *Acta Physiol. Scand.* 74:453–64

19. Schnermann, J., Horster, M., Levine, D. Z. 1969. The influence of sampling technique on the micropuncture determination of GFR and reabsorptive characteristics of single rat proximal tubules. *Pfluegers Arch.* 309:48–58

20. Gertz, K. H., Mangos, J. A., Braun, G., Pagel, H. D. 1965. On the glomerular tubular balance in the rat kidney. *Pfluegers Arch.* 285:360–72

21. Wiederholt, M., Langer, K. H., Thoenes, W., Hierholzer, K. 1968. Funktionelle und morphologische Untersuchungen am proximalen und distalen Konvolut der Rattenniere zur Methode der gespaltenen Olsaule (Split-Oil Droplet Method). *Pfluegers Arch.* 302:166–91

22. Wright, F. S. et al 1969. Failure to demonstrate a hormonal inhibitor of proximal sodium reabsorption. *J. Clin. Invest.* 48:1107–13

23. Hayslett, J. P., Weinstein, E., Kashgarian, M., Epstein, F. H. 1969. Attempts to demonstrate a hormonal natriuretic factor by micropuncture techniques. *Yale J. Biol. Med.* 41:415–21

24. Bojesen, E., Leyssac, P. P. 1969. Proximal tubular reabsorption in the rat kidney as studied by the occlusion time and lissamine green transit time technique. *Acta Physiol. Scand.* 76:213–35

25. Brunner, F. P., Rector, F. C., Jr., Seldin, D. W. 1966. Mechanism of glomerulotubular balance. II. Regulation of proximal tubular reabsorption by tubular volume, as studied by stopped-flow microperfusion. *J. Clin. Invest.* 45:603–11

26. Steinhausen, M., 1963. Eine Methode zur Differenzierung proximaler und distaler Tubuli der Nierenrinde von Ratten in vivo und ihre Anwendung zur Bestimmung tubularer Stromungsgeschwindigkeiten. *Pfluegers Arch.* 277:23–26

27. Arrizurieta-Muchnik, E. E., Lassiter, W. E., Lipham, E. M., Gottschalk, C. W. 1969. Micropuncture study of glomerulotubular balance in the rat kidney. *Nephron* 6:418–36

28. Schnermann, J., Wahl, M., Liebau, G., Fischbach, H. 1968. Balance between tubular flow rate and net fluid reabsorption in the proximal convolution of the rat kidney. I. Dependency of reabsorptive net fluid flux upon proximal tubular surface area at spontaneous variations of filtration rate. *Pfluegers Arch.* 304:90–103

29. Wright, F. S., Howards, S. S., Knox, F. G., Berliner, R. W. 1969. Measurement of sodium reabsorption by proximal tubule of the dog. *Am. J. Physiol.* 217:199–206

30. Burg, M. B., Orloff, J. 1968. Control of fluid absorption in the renal proximal tubule. *J. Clin. Invest.* 47:2016–24

31. Baines, A. D., Gottschalk, C. W., Leyssac, P. P. 1968. Proximal luminal volume and fluid reabsorption in the rat kidney. *Acta Physiol. Scand.* 74:440–52

32. Rodicio, J., Herrera-Acosta, J., Sellman, J. C., Rector, F. C., Jr.,

Seldin, D. W. 1969. Studies on glomerulotubular balance during aortic constriction, ureteral obstruction and venous occlusion in hydropenic and saline-loaded rats. *Nephron* 6:437–56

33. Leyssac, P. P. 1963. Dependence of glomerulotubular balance during imal tubular reabsorption of salt. *Acta Physiol. Scand.* 58:236–42

34. Baines, A. D., Baines, C. J., de Rouffignac, C. 1969. Functional heterogeneity of nephrons. I. Intraluminal flow velocities. *Pfluegers Arch.* 308:244–59

35. Baines, A. D., de Rouffignac, C. 1969. Functional heterogeneity of nephrons. II. Filtration rates, intraluminal flow velocities and fractional water reabsorption. *Pfluegers Arch.* 308:260–76

36. Hanssen, O. E. 1958. A histochemical method for evaluation of excreted sodium ferrocyanide in isolated tubules of the mouse kidney. *Acta Pathol. Microbiol. Scand.* 44:363–71

37. Hanssen, O. E. 1961. The relationship between glomerular filtration and length of the proximal convoluted tubules in mice. *Acta Pathol. Microbiol. Scand.* 53:265–79

38. Hanssen, O. E. 1963. Method for comparison of glomerular filtration in individual rat nephrons. *2nd Int. Congr. Nephrol. Prague,* 527

39. De Rouffignac, C., Deiss, S., Bonvalet, J. P. 1970. Determination du taux individuel de filtration glomerulaire des nephrons accessibles et inaccessibles a la microponction. *Pfluegers Arch.* 315:273–90

40. Wiederholt, M., Hierholzer, K., Windhager, E. E., Giebisch, G. 1967. Microperfusion study of fluid reabsorption in proximal tubules of rat kidneys. *Am. J. Physiol.* 213:809–18

41. Morgan, T., Berliner, R. W. 1969. In vivo perfusion of proximal tubules of the rat: glomerulotubular balance. *Am. J. Physiol.* 217:992–97

42. Gertz, K. H., Braun-Schubert, G., Brandis, M. 1969. Zur Methode der Messung der Filtrationsrate einzelner nahe der Nierenoberflache gelegener Glomeruli. *Pfluegers Arch.* 310:109–15

43. Horster, M., Thurau, K. 1968. Micropuncture studies on the filtration rate of single superficial and juxtamedullary glomeruli in the rat kidney. *Pfluegers Arch.* 301:162–81

44. Jamison, R. L. 1970. Micropuncture study of superficial and juxtamedullary nephrons in the rat. *Am. J. Physiol.* 218:46–55

45. Stumpe, K. O., Lowitz, H. D., Ochwadt, B. 1969. Function of juxtamedullary nephrons in normotensive and chronically hypertensive rats. *Pfluegers Arch.* 313:43–52

46. De Rouffignac, C., Bonvalet, J. P. 1970. Étude chez le rat des variations du debit individuel de filtration glomerulaire des nephrons superficiels et profonds en fonction de l'apport sode. *Pfluegers Arch.* 317:141–56

47. Smith, H. W. 1951. *The Kidney: Structure and function in health and disease.* New York: Oxford. 331 pp.

48. Liebau, G., Levine, D. Z., Thurau, K. 1968. Micropuncture studies on the dog kidney. I. The response of the proximal tubule to changes in systemic blood pressure within and below the autoregulatory range. *Pfluegers Arch.* 304:57–68

49. Levine, D. Z., Liebau, G., Fischbach, H., Thurau, K. 1968. Micropuncture studies on the dog kidney. II. Reabsorptive characteristics of the proximal tubule during spontaneous and experimental variations in GFR and during drug induced natriuresis. *Pfluegers Arch.* 304:365–75

50. Dirks, J. H., Cirksena, W. J., Berliner, R. W. 1965. The effect of saline infusion on sodium reabsorption by the proximal tubule of the dog. *J. Clin. Invest.* 44:1160–70

51. Brenner, B. M., Bennett, C. M., Berliner, R. W. 1968. The relationship between glomerular filtration rate and sodium reabsorption by the proximal tubule of the rat nephron. *J. Clin. Invest.* 47:1358–74

52. Landwher, D. M., Schnermann, J., Klose, R. M., Giebisch, G. 1968. Effect of reduction in filtration rate on renal tubular sodium and water reabsorption. *Am. J. Physiol.* 215:687–95

53. Knox, F. G., Wright, F. S., Howards, S. S., Berliner, R. W. 1969.

Effect of furosemide on sodium reabsorption by proximal tubule of the dog. *Am. J. Physiol.* 217: 192–98

54. Windhager, E. E. 1968. Glomerulotubular balance of salt and water. *Physiologist* 11:103–14

55. Bojesen, E. 1954. The renal mechanism of 'dilution diuresis' and salt excretion in dogs. *Acta Physiol. Scand.* 32:129–47

56. Leyssac, P. P. 1963. Dependence of glomerular filtration rate on proximal tubular reabsorption of salt. *Acta Physiol. Scand.* 58:236–42

57. Rector, F. C., Jr., Brunner, F. P., Seldin, D. W. 1966. Mechanism of glomerulotubular balance. I. Effect of aortic constriction and elevated ureteropelvic pressure on glomerular filtration rate, fractional reabsorption, transit time and tubular size in the proximal tubule of the rat. *J. Clin. Invest.* 45:590–602

58. Wahl, M., Liebau, G., Fischbach, H., Schnermann, J. 1968. Balance between tubular flow rate and net fluid reabsorption in the proximal convolution of the rat kidney. *Pfluegers Arch.* 304:297–314

59. Schnermann, J., Levine, D. Z., Horster, M. 1969. A direct evaluation of the Gertz hypothesis on single rat proximal tubules in vivo: Failure of the tubular volume to be the sole determinant of the reabsorptive rate. *Pfluegers Arch.* 308:149–65

60. Leyssac, P. P. 1969. Renal salt and water excretion in different states of an intrarenal control system. *Proc. Roy. Soc. Med.* 62:1–6

61. Lowitz, H. D., Stumpe, K. O., Ochwadt, B. 1969. Micropuncture study of the action of angiotensin-II on tubular sodium and water reabsorption in the rat. *Nephron* 6:173–87

62. Thurau, K., Schnermann, J. 1965. Die Natriumkonzentration an den Macula densa-Zellen also regulierender Faktor für das Glomerulumfiltrat (Mikropunktionsversuche). *Klin. Wochenschr.* 43:410–13

63. De Wardener, H. E. 1969. Control of sodium reabsorption. *Brit. Med. J.* 3:611–16

64. Earley, L. E., Friedler, R. M. 1966. The effects of combined renal vasodilatation and pressor agents on renal hemodynamics and the tubular reabsorption of sodium. *J. Clin. Invest.* 45:542–51

65. Windhager, E. E., Lewy, J. E., Spitzer, A. 1969. Intrarenal control of proximal tubular reabsorption of sodium and water. *Nephron* 6: 247–59

66. Vereerstraeten, P., Toussaint, C. 1969. Effects of plasmapheresis on renal hemodynamics and sodium excretion in dogs. *Pfluegers Arch.* 306:92–102

67. Daugharty, T. M., Belleau, L. J., Martino, J. A., Earley, L. E. 1968. Interrelationship of physical factors affecting sodium reabsorption in the dog. *Am. J. Physiol.* 215:1442–47

68. Earley, L. E., Martino, J. A., Friedler, R. M. 1966. Factors affecting sodium reabsorption by the proximal tubule as determined during blockade of distal sodium reabsorption. *J. Clin. Invest.* 45:1668–84

69. Koch, K. M., Aynedjian, H. S., Bank, N. 1968. Effect of acute hypertension on sodium reabsorption by the proximal tubule. *J. Clin. Invest.* 47:1696–1709

70. Brenner, B. M., Falchuk, K. H., Keimowitz, R. I., Berliner, R. W. 1969. The relationship between peritubular capillary protein concentration and fluid reabsorption by the renal proximal tubule. *J. Clin. Invest.* 48:1519–31

71. Spitzer, A., Windhager, E. E. 1970. Effect of peritubular oncotic pressure changes on proximal tubular fluid reabsorption. *Am. J. Physiol.* 218:1188–93

72. Baldamus, C. A. et al 1969. Sodium transport in the proximal tubules and collecting ducts during variation of the sodium concentration in the surrounding interstitium. *Pfluegers Arch.* 310:354–68

73. Steinhausen, M., Eisenbach, G. M., Galaske, R. 1970. Countercurrent system in the renal cortex of rats. *Science* 167:1631–33

74. Tobian, L., Coffee, K., McCrea, P. 1967. Evidence for a humoral factor of non-renal and non-adrenal origin which influences renal sodium excretion. *Trans. Assoc. Am. Physicians* 80:200–6

75. Morgan, T., Berliner, R. W. 1969. A study by continuous microperfusion of water and electrolyte

movements in the loop of Henle and distal tubule of the rat. *Nephron* 6:388–405

76. Garella, S., Chazan, J. A., Cohen, J. J. 1969. Factors responsible for proximal sodium conservation as assessed by distal tubular blockade. *Clin. Sci.* 37:775–87

77. Cirksena, W. J., Dirks, J. H., Berliner, R. W. 1966. Effect of thoracic cava obstruction on response of proximal tubule sodium reabsorption to saline infusion. *J. Clin. Invest.* 45:179–86

78. Brenner, B. M., Berliner, R. W. 1969. Relationship between extracellular volume and fluid reabsorption by the rat nephron. *Am. J. Physiol.* 217:6–12

79. Schrier, R. W., McDonald, K. M., Marshall, R. A., Lauler, D. P. 1968. Absence of natriuretic response to acute hypotonic intravascular volume expansion in dogs. *Clin. Sci.* 34:57–72

80. Schrier, R. W., Fein, R. L., McNeil, J. S., Cirksena, W. J. 1969. Influence of interstitial fluid volume expansion and plasma sodium concentration on the natriuretic response to volume expansion in dogs. *Clin. Sci.* 36:371–85

81. Andersson, B., Dallman, M. F., Olsson, K. 1969. Evidence for a hypothalamic control of renal sodium excretion. *Acta Physiol. Scand.* 75:496–510

82. Dorn, J. B., Levine, N., Kaley, G., Rothballer, A. B. 1969. Natriuresis induced by injection of hypertonic saline into the third cerebral ventricle of dogs. *Proc. Soc. Exp. Biol. Med.* 131:240–42

83. Keck, W., Brechtelsbauer, H., Kramer, K. 1969. Wasser- und Natrium-Ausscheidung nach isotonen Kochsalz-Infusionen bei wachen Hunden mit verschiedenem Natriumbestand. *Pfluegers Arch.* 311:119–30

84. Berliner, R. W. 1968. Intrarenal mechanisms in the control of sodium excretion. *Fed. Proc.* 27:1127–34

85. Berne, R. M. 1952. Hemodynamics and sodium excretion of denervated kidney in anesthetized and unanesthetized dog. *Am. J. Physiol.* 171:148–58

86. Blake, W., Jurf, A. N. 1968. Renal sodium reabsorption after acute renal denervation in the rabbit. *J. Physiol.* 196:65–73

87. Bonjour, J., Churchill, P. C., Malvin, R. L. 1969. Change of tubular reabsorption of sodium and water after renal denervation in the dog. *J. Physiol.* 204:571–82

88. Pomeranz, B. H., Birtch, A. G., Barger, A. C. 1968. Neural control of intrarenal blood flow. *Am. J. Physiol.* 215:1067–81

89. Gill, J. R., Jr. 1969. The role of the sympathetic nervous system in the regulation of sodium excretion by the kidney. *Frontiers in Neuroendocrinology* Chap. 8, 289–305

90. Heidenreich, O., Fülgraff, G., Laaff, H., Balshüsemann, E. 1969. Die Wirkung von β-Sympathomimetica und Sympatholytica auf die Nierenfunktion von Hunden. *Arch. Pharmakol. Exp. Pathol.* 263:439–49

91. Gilmore, J. P., Michaelis, L. L. 1968. Diuresis and natriuresis during volume expansion following cardiac reinnervation. *Proc. Soc. Exp. Biol. Med.* 128:645–47

92. Michaelis, L. L., Gilmore, J. P. 1970. Cardiac sympathetics and control of sodium excretion. *Am. J. Physiol.* 218:999–1002

93. Knox, F. G., Davis, B. B., Berliner, R. W. 1967. Effect of chronic cardiac denervation on renal response to saline infusion. *Am. J. Physiol.* 213:174–78

94. McDonald, K. M., Rosenthal, A., Schrier, R. W., Galicich, J., Lauler, D. P. 1970. Effect of interruption of neural pathways on renal response to volume expansion. *Am. J. Physiol.* 218:510–17

95. Waugh, W. H., Kubo, T. 1968. Antinatriuretic effect of exogenous metabolic substrates on the sodium diuresis of saline infusion. *Life Sci.* 7:325–35

96. Waugh, W. H., Kubo, T. 1969. Renal substrates and effect of lipokinetic arylamines on third-factor sodium excretion. *Am. J. Physiol.* 217:267–76

97. Dies, F., Ramos, G., Avelar, E., Matos, M. 1970. Relationship between renal substrate uptake and tubular sodium reabsorption in the dog. *Am. J. Physiol.* 218:411–16

98. Bahlmann, J., McDonald, S. J., Dunningham, J. G., de Wardener,

H. E. 1967. The effect on urinary sodium excretion of altering the packed cell volume with albumin solutions without changing the blood volume in the dog. *Clin. Sci.* 32:395–402

99. Bahlmann, J. McDonald, S. J., Ventom, M. G., de Wardener, H. E. 1967. The effect on urinary sodium excretion of blood volume expansion without changing the composition of blood in the dog. *Clin. Sci.* 32:403–13

100. Knox, F. G., Howards, S. S., Wright, F. S., Davis, B. B., Berliner, R. W. 1968. Effect of dilution and expansion of blood volume on proximal sodium reabsorption. *Am. J. Physiol.* 215:1041–48

101. Wright, F. S., Davis, J. O., Johnston, C. I., Howards, S. S. 1968. Renal sodium excretion after volume expansion with saline and blood. *Proc. Soc. Exp. Biol. Med.* 128:1044–51

102. Coelho, J. B., Bradley, S. E. 1969. Persistence of the natriuretic response to isotonic saline load during hemorrhagic hypotension in the dog. *Proc. Soc. Exp. Med.* 131:265–71

103. Slatopolsky, E. S., Hoffsten, P., Purkerson, M., Bricker, N. S. 1970. On the influence of extracellular fluid volume expansion and of uremia on bicarbonate reabsorption in man. *J. Clin. Invest.* 49:988–98

104. Purkerson, M. L., Lubowitz, H., White, R. W., Bricker, N. S. 1969. On the influence of extracellular volume expansion on bicarbonate reabsorption in the rat. *J. Clin. Invest.* 48:1754–60

105. Kurtzman, N. A. 1970. Regulation of renal bicarbonate reabsorption by extracellular volume. *J. Clin. Invest.* 49:586–95

106. Suki, W. N., Martinez-Maldonado, M., Rouse, D., Terry, A. 1969. Effect of expansion of extracellular fluid volume on renal phosphate handling. *J. Clin. Invest.* 48:1888–94

107. Blythe, W. B., Gitelman, H. J., Welt, L. G. 1968. Effect of expansion of the extracellular space on the rate of urinary excretion of calcium. *Am. J. Physiol.* 214:52–7

108. Robson, A. M., Srivastava, P. L., Bricker, N. S. 1968. The influence of saline loading on renal glucose reabsorption in the rat. *J. Clin. Invest.* 47:329–35

109. Martino, J. A., Earley, L. E. 1968. Relationship between intrarenal hydrostatic pressure and hemodynamically induced changes in sodium excretion. *Circ. Res.* 23:371–86

110. Curran, P. F., MacIntosh, J. R. 1962. Model system for biological water transport. *Nature* 193:347–48

111. Diamond, J. M. 1964. Mechanism of isotonic water transport. *J. Gen. Physiol.* 48:15–42

112. Caulfield, J. B., Trump, B. F. 1962. Correlation of ultrastructure with function in the rat kidney. *Am. J. Pathol.* 40:199–218

113. Bank, N., Koch, K. M., Aynedjian, H. S., Aras, M. 1969. Effect of changes in renal perfusion pressure on the suppression of proximal tubular sodium reabsorption due to saline loading. *J. Clin. Invest.* 48:271–83

114. Bentzel, C. J., Anagnostopoulos, T., Pandit, H. 1970. Necturus kidney: its response to effects of isotonic volume expansion. *Am. J. Physiol.* 218:205–13

115. Sealey, J. E., Kirshman, J. D., Laragh, J. H. 1969. Natriuretic activity in plasma and urine of salt-loaded man and sheep. *J. Clin. Invest.* 48:2210–24

116. Vereerstraeten, P., Toussaint, C. 1970. Mécanismes de l'excrétion du sodium par le rein du chien. *Nephron* 7:15–36

117. Nizet, A., Godon, J. P., Mahieu, P. 1968. Quantitative excretion of water and sodium load by isolated dog kidney: autonomous renal response to blood dilution factors. *Pfluegers Arch.* 304:30–45

118. Nizet, A. 1968. Influence of serum-albumin and dextran on sodium and water excretion by the isolated dog kidney. *Pfluegers Arch.* 301:7–15

119. May, D. G., Carter, M. K. 1970. Effect of vasoactive agents on urine and electrolyte excretion in the chicken. *Am. J. Physiol.* 218:417–22

120. Parmelee, M. L., Carter, M. K. 1968. The diuretic effect of acetylcholine in the chicken. *Arch. Int. Pharmacodyn. Ther.* 174:108–17

121. Hayslett, J. P., Domoto, D. T.,

Kashgarian, M., Epstein, F. H. 1970. Role of physical factors in the natriuresis induced by acetylcholine. *Am. J. Physiol.* 218:880–85

122. Willis, L. R., Ludens, J. H., Hook, J. B., Williamson, H. E., 1969. Mechanism of natriuretic action of bradykinin. *Am. J. Physiol.* 217:1–5

123. Mills, I. H., de Wardener, H. E., Hayter, C. J., Clapham, W. F. 1961. Studies on the afferent mechanism of the sodium chloride diuresis which follows intravenous saline in the dog. *Clin. Sci.* 21:261–64

124. Johnston, C. I., Davis, J. O. 1966. Evidence from cross circulation studies for a humoral mechanism in the natriuresis of saline loading. *Proc. Soc. Exp. Biol. Med.* 121:1058–63

125. Pearce, J. W., Sonnenberg, H., Veress, A. T., Ackermann, U. 1968. Evidence for a humoral factor modifying the renal response to blood volume expansion in the rat. *Can. J. Physiol. Pharmacol.* 47:377–86

126. Rector, F. C., Jr., Martinez-Maldonado, M., Kurtzman, N. A., Sellman, J. C., Oerther, F., Seldin, D. W. 1968. Demonstration of a hormonal inhibitor of proximal tubular reabsorption during expansion of extracellular volume with isotonic saline. *J. Clin. Invest.* 47:761–73

127. Buckalew, V. M., Jr., Martinez, F. J., Green, W. E. 1970. The effect of dialysates and ultrafiltrates of plasma of saline-loaded dogs on toad bladder sodium transport. *J. Clin. Invest.* 49:926–35

128. Bricker, N. S. et al 1968. In vitro assay for a humoral substance present during volume expansion and ureamia. *Nature* 219:1058–59

129. Cort, J. H. et al 1968. Saluretic activity of blood during carotid occlusion in the cat. *Am. J. Physiol.* 215:921–27

130. Howards, S. S., Davis, B. B., Knox, F. G., Wright, F. S., Berliner, R. W. 1968. Depression of fractional sodium reabsorption by the proximal tubule of the dog without sodium diuresis. *J. Clin. Invest.* 47:1561–72

131. Leeber, D. A., Murdaugh, H. V.,

Davis, B. B. 1968. Inhibition of sodium transport by Henle's loop after intravenous saline infusion. *J. Lab. Clin. Med.* 72:220–27

132. Windhager, E. E., Giebisch, G. 1965. Electrophysiology of the nephron. *Physiol. Rev.* 45:214–44

133. Frömter, E., Hegel, U. 1966. Transtubular potential differences in the proximal and distal tubules of the rat kidney. *Pfluegers Arch.* 291:107–20

134. Burg, M. B., Isaacson, L., Grantham, J., Orloff, J. 1968. Electrical properties of isolated perfused rabbit renal tubules. *Am. J. Physiol.* 215:788–94

135. Maude, D. L. 1970. Mechanism of salt transport and some permeability properties of rat proximal tubule. *Am. J. Physiol.* 218:1590–95

136. Maude, D. L. 1968. Stop-flow microperfusion of single proximal tubules in rat kidney cortex slices. *Am. J. Physiol.* 214:1315–21

137. Burg, M. B., Orloff, J. 1970. Electrical potential across proximal convoluted tubules. *Am. J. Physiol.* In press

138. Malnic, G., Aires, M. M. 1970. Microperfusion study of anion transfer in proximal tubules of rat kidney. *Am. J. Physiol.* 218:27–32

139. Ullrich, K. J. 1966. Renal transport of sodium. *Proc. 3rd Int. Congr. Nephrol.* 1:48–61

140. Danielson, B. G., Persson, E., Ulfendahl, H. R. 1970. Transmembrane transport of chloride and iodide in proximal rat tubules. *Acta Physiol. Scand.* 78:339–46

141. Trautner, M., Wieth, J. O. 1968. Renal excretion of chloride, bromide and thiocyanate during water diuresis. *Acta Physiol. Scand.* 74:606–15

142. Malnic, G., Aires, M. M., Vieira, F. L. 1970. Chloride excretion in nephrons of rat kidney during alterations of acid-base equilibrium. *Am. J. Physiol.* 218:20–6

143. Diamond, J. M. 1962. The mechanism of solute transport by the gall bladder. *J. Physiol.* 161:474–502

144. Wheeler, H. O. 1963. Transport of electrolytes and water across wall of rabbit gall bladder. *Am. J. Physiol.* 205:427–38

145. Dietschy, J. M. 1964. Water and

solute movement across the wall of the everted gall bladder. *Gastroenterology* 47:395–408

146. Martin, D. W., Diamond, J. M. 1966. Energetics of coupled active transport of sodium and chloride. *J. Gen. Physiol.* 50:295–315

147. Hogben, C. A. M. 1960. The movement of material across cell membranes. *Physiologist* 3:56–62

148. Kashgarian, M., Stöckle, H., Gottschalk, C. W., Ullrich, K. J. 1963. Transtubular electrochemical potentials of sodium and chloride in proximal and distal renal tubules of rats during antidiuresis and water diuresis (Diabetes insipidus). *Pfluegers Arch.* 277:89–106

149. Rector, F. C., Jr., Clapp, J. R. 1962. Evidence for active chloride reabsorption in the distal renal tubule of the rat. *J. Clin. Invest.* 41:101–7

150. Kleinzeller, A., Knotkova, A. 1964. The effect of ouabain on the electrolyte and water transport in kidney cortex and liver slices. *J. Physiol.* 175:172–92

151. Maude, D. L. 1969. Effects of K and ouabain on fluid transport and cell Na in proximal tubule in vitro. *Am. J. Physiol.* 216:1199–206

152. Whittembury, G., Fishman, J. 1969. Relation between cell Na extrusion and transtubular absorption in the perfused toad kidney: The effect of K, ouabain and ethacrynic acid. *Pfluegers Arch.* 307:138–53

153. Whittembury, G., Proverbio, F. 1970. Two modes of Na extrusion in cells from guinea pig kidney cortex slices. *Pfluegers Arch.* 316:1–25

154. MacKnight, A. D. C. 1968. Water and electrolyte contents of rat renal cortical slices incubated in potassium-free media and media containing ouabain. *Biochim. Biophys. Acta* 150:263–70

155. MacKnight, A. D. C. 1968. Water and electrolyte contents of rat renal cortical slices incubated in medium containing ρ-chloromercuribenzoic acid or ouabain. *Biochim. Biophys. Acta* 163:500–5

156. MacKnight, A. D. C. 1968. Regulation of cellular volume during anaerobic incubation of rat renal cortical slices. *Biochim. Biophys. Acta* 163:557–59

157. MacKnight, A. D. C. 1969. The effects of ethacrynic acid on the electrolyte and water contents of rat renal cortical slices. *Biochim. Biophys. Acta* 173:223–33

158. Willis, J. S. 1968. The interaction of K⁺ ouabain and Na⁺ on the cation transport and respiration of renal cortical cells of hamsters and ground squirrels. *Biochim. Biophys. Acta* 163:516–30

159. Burg, M., Orloff, J. 1964. Active cation transport by kidney tubules at 0 C. *Am. J. Physiol.* 207:983–88

160. Hoffman, J. F., Kregenow, F. M. 1966. The characterization of new energy dependent cation transport processes in red blood cells. *Ann. N.Y. Acad. Sci.* 137:566–76

161. Tune, B. M., Burg, M. B., Patlak, C. S. 1969. Characteristics of ρ-aminohippurate transport in proximal renal tubules. *Am. J. Physiol.* 217:1057–63

162. Tune, B., Burg, M. Unpublished observations

163. Seely, J. F., Dirks, J. H. 1969. Micropuncture study of hypertonic mannitol diuresis in the proximal and distal tubule of the dog kidney. *J. Clin. Invest.* 48:2330–40

164. Persson, E., Ulfendahl, H. R. 1970. Water permeability in rat proximal tubules. *Acta Physiol. Scand.* 78:353–63

165. Persson, E. 1970. Water permeability in rat distal tubules. *Acta Physiol. Scand.* 78:364–75

166. Pitts, R. F. 1964. Renal production and excretion of ammonia. *Am. J. Med.* 36:720–42

167. Goodman, A. D., Fuisz, R. E., Cahill, G. F., Jr. 1966. Renal gluconeogenesis in acidosis, alkalosis, and potassium deficiency: Its possible role in regulation of renal ammonia production. *J. Clin. Invest.* 45:612–19

168. Rector, F. C., Jr., Orloff, J. 1959. The effect of the administration of sodium bicarbonate and ammonium chloride on the excretion and production of ammonia. The absence of alterations in the activity of renal ammonia-producing enzymes in the dog. *J. Clin. Invest.* 38:366–72

169. Kamm, D. E., Asher, R. R. 1970. Relation between glucose and ammonia production in renal cortical slices. *Am. J. Physiol.* 218:1161–65

170. Goldstein, L. 1967. Pathways of glutamine deamination and their control in the rat kidney. *Am. J. Physiol.* 213:983–89

171. Davies, B. M. A., Yudkin, J. 1952. Studies in biochemical adaptation. The origin of urinary ammonia as indicated by the effect of chronic acidosis and alkalosis on some renal enzymes in the rat. *Biochem. J.* 52:407–12

172. Rector, F. C., Jr., Seldin, D. W., Copenhaver, J. H. 1955. The mechanism of ammonia excretion during ammonium chloride acidosis. *J. Clin. Invest.* 34:20–6

173. Leonard, E., Orloff, J. 1955. Regulation of ammonia excretion in the rat. *Am. J. Physiol.* 182:131–38

174. Alleyne, G. A. O. 1970. Renal metabolic response to acid-base changes. II. The early effects of metabolic acidosis on renal metabolism in the rat. *J. Clin. Invest.* 49:943–51

175. Goldstein, L. 1965. Actinomycin D. inhibition of the adaptation of renal glutamine-deaminating enzymes in the rat. *Nature* 205:1330–31

176. Bignall, M. C., Elebute, O., Lotspeich, W. D. 1968. Renal protein and ammonia biochemistry in NH₄Cl acidosis and after uninephrectomy. *Am. J. Physiol.* 215:289–95

177. Steiner, A. L., Goodman, A. D., Treble, D. H. 1968. Effect of metabolic acidosis on renal gluconeogenesis in vivo. *Am. J. Physiol.* 215:211–17

178. Goldstein, L. 1966. Relation of glutamate to ammonia production in the rat kidney. *Am. J. Physiol.* 210:661–66

179. Alleyne, G. A. O., Scullard, G. H. 1969. Renal metabolic response to acid base changes. I. Enzymatic control of ammoniagenesis in the rat. *J. Clin. Invest.* 48:364–70

180. Alleyne, G. A. O. 1968. Concentration of metabolic intermediates in kidneys of rats with metabolic acidosis. *Nature* 217:847–48

181. Goorno, W. R., Rector, F. C., Jr., Seldin, D. W. 1967. Relation of renal gluconeogenesis to ammonia production in the dog and rat. *Am. J. Physiol.* 213:969–74

182. Preuss, H. G. 1969. Renal glutamate metabolism in acute metabolic acidosis. *Nephron* 6:235–46

183. Kamm, D. E., Cahill, G. F., Jr. 1969. Effect of acid-base status on renal and hepatic gluconeogenesis in diabetes and fasting. *Am. J. Physiol.* 216:1207–12

184. Pagliara, A. S., Goodman, A. D. 1969. Effect of adenosine 3′,5′-monophosphate on production of glucose and ammonia by renal cortex. *J. Clin. Invest.* 48:1408–12

185. Preuss, H. G. 1968. Pyridine nucleotides in renal ammonia metabolism. *J. Lab. Clin. Med.* 72:370–82

186. Churchill, P. C., Malvin, R. L. 1970. Relation of renal gluconeogenesis to ammonia production in the rat. *Am. J. Physiol.* 218:353–57

187. Churchill, P.C., Malvin, R. L. 1970. Relation of renal gluconeogenesis to ammonia production in the dog. *Am. J. Physiol.* 218:241–45

188. Simpson, D. P., Sherrard, D. J. 1969. Regulation of glutamine metabolism in vitro by bicarbonate ion and pH. *J. Clin. Invest.* 48:1088–96

189. Roxe, D. M., Disalvo, J., Balagura-Baruch, S. 1970. Renal glucose production in the intact dog. *Am. J. Physiol.* 218:1676–81

190. Chase, L. R., Aurbach, G. D. 1968. Renal adenyl cyclase: anatomically separate sites for parathyroid hormone and vasopressin. *Science* 159:545–47

191. Bowman, R. H. 1970. Gluconeogenesis in the isolated perfused rat kidney. *J. Biol. Chem.* 245:1604–12

192. Joseph, P. K., Subrahmanyam, K. 1968. Effect of growth hormone, insulin, thyroxine and cortisone on renal gluconeogenesis. *Arch. Biochem. Biophys.* 127:288–91

193. Pagliara, A. S., Goodman, A. D. 1970. Effect of 3′,5′-GMP and 3′,5′-IMP on production of glucose and ammonia by renal cortex. *Am. J. Physiol.* 218:1301–6

194. White, A. A., Aurbach, G. D., Carlson, S. J. 1969. Identification of guanyl cyclase in mammalian tissues. *Fed. Proc.* 28:473

195. Krebs, H. A. 1935. Metabolism of amino acids. IV. The synthesis of glutamine from glutamic acid and ammonia and the enzymatic hydrolysis of glutamine in animal tissues. *Biochem. J.* 29:1951–69

196. Janicki, R. H., Goldstein, L. 1969. Glutamine synthetase and renal

ammonia metabolism. *Am. J. Physiol.* 216 :1107–10

197. Addae, S. K., Lotspeich, W. D. 1968. Relation between glutamine utilization and production in metabolic acidosis. *Am. J. Physiol.* 215 :269–77

198. Damian, A. C., Pitts, R. F. 1970. Rates of glutaminase I and glutamine synthetase reactions in rat kidney in vivo. *Am. J. Physiol.* 218 :1249–55

199. Kamin, H., Handler, P. 1951. The metabolism of parentally administered amino acids. III. Ammonia formation. *J. Biol. Chem.* 193 :873–80

200. Orloff, J., Berliner, R. W. 1956. The mechanism of the excretion of ammonia in the dog. *J. Clin. Invest.* 35 :223–35

201. Balagura-Baruch, S., Shurland, L. M., Welbourne, T. C. 1970. Effects of α-ketoglutarate on renal ammonia release in the intact dog. *Am. J. Physiol.* 218 :1070–75

202. Canessa-Fischer, M., Shalhoub, R., Glabman, S., DeHaas, J., Pitts, R. F. 1963. Effects of infusions of ammonia, amides, and amino acids on excretion of ammonia. *Am. J. Physiol.* 204 :192–96

203. Lotspeich, W. D., Pitts, R. F. 1947. The role of amino acids in the renal tubular secretion of ammonia. *J. Biol. Chem.* 169 :611–22

204. Lotspeich, W. D. 1959. *Metabolic aspects of renal function,* 92. Springfield, Ill. : Thomas, 214 pp.

205. Lyon, M. L., Pitts, R. F. 1969. Species differences in renal glutamine synthesis in vivo. *Am. J. Physiol.* 216 :117–22

206. Stone, W. J., Balagura, S., Pitts, R. F. 1967. Diffusion equilibrium for ammonia in the kidney of the acidotic dog. *J. Clin. Invest.* 46 : 1603–8

207. Oelert, H., Nagel, W. 1966. Die Abhangigkeit der Ammonia-Produktion von der GFR bei Ureterablemmung und bei Durchblutungsdrosselung in der Hundeniere. *Arch. Gesamte Physiol.* 292 :129–39

208. Pilkington, L. A., Young, T.-K., Pitts, R. F. 1970. Properties of renal luminal and antiluminal transport of plasma glutamine. *Nephron* 7 :51–60

209. Shalhoub, R. et al 1963. Extraction of amino acids from and their addition to renal blood plasma. *Am. J. Physiol.* 204 :181–86

210. Bartlett, P. D., Gaebler, O. H., Harmon, A. 1949. Effect of anterior pituitary growth hormone preparations on plasma glutamine, total free amino acids and the excretion of urinary amonia. *J. Biol. Chem.* 180 :1021–26

211. Addae, S. K., Lotspeich, W. D. 1968. Glutamine balance in metabolic acidosis as studied with the artificial kidney. *Am. J. Physiol.* 215 :278–81

212. Weiss, F. R., Preuss, H. G. 1970. Glutamine synthetase and plasma glutamine in augmented ammoniagenesis in acidosis. *Am. J. Physiol.* 218 :1697–700

RESPIRATION: ALVEOLAR GAS EXCHANGE · 1058

JOHANNES PIIPER AND PETER SCHEID

Department of Physiology, Max Planck Institute of Experimental Medicine, Göttingen, Germany

This review is restricted to the discussion of a few aspects of alveolar gas exchange, which to the authors appeared to be of basic importance and of current interest:

1. Alveolar-capillary equilibration of CO_2: negative arterial to alveolar P_{CO_2} differences.
2. Evidence for stratified inhomogeneity in the lungs,
3. Analysis of unequal distribution of ventilation, perfusion, and diffusing capacity in the lungs.

The organization plan of the review is based on the subjects, so that it was considered necessary to discuss, even at length, many papers that had appeared before the period of formal coverage by this review (May 1969 to May 1970). Obviously, with such a guiding principle no claim to complete literature coverage can be made. The papers cited have been selected exclusively according to their pertinence to the particular problems treated. Some have been discussed in unusual detail because of their inherent interest, at least to the authors, at the expense of others of possibly greater merit, but of less relevance to this review.

ALVEOLAR-CAPILLARY EQUILIBRATION OF CO_2: NEGATIVE ARTERIAL TO ALVEOLAR P_{CO_2} DIFFERENCES

The occurrence of positive arterial to alveolar P_{CO_2} differences, ΔP_{CO_2} $(a - A)$, in man and in the dog, i.e. that P_{CO_2} in arterial blood is higher than in alveolar (end-tidal) gas, is well known to respiratory physiologists. It is attributed to ventilation of unperfused or relatively underperfused alveolar regions in the lung (alveolar dead space ventilation). But negative ΔP_{CO_2} $(a - A)$ has also been known for a long time to occur and has been explained by differences between the expired alveolar gas and the "true effective mean" alveolar gas, the P_{CO_2} of the latter being assumed to be identical with, or very close to, that in the average end-capillary blood. Recently, the finding of large blood to alveolar P_{CO_2} differences during rebreathing has revived interest in pulmonary CO_2 equilibration, particularly as under the conditions of rebreathing most of the previous explanations for this ΔP_{CO_2} obviously are inoperative.

Normal Breathing: Changes of Alveolar Gas in Time and Space, Sampling Problems

In older work as well as in recent publications there are reports on the occurrence of negative arterial to end-expiratory alveolar P_{CO_2} differences, ΔP_{CO_2} $(a - E')$, in various conditions. Negative ΔP_{CO_2} $(a - E')$ values up to 5 mm Hg (1–6) and even exceeding 8 mm Hg (7,8) have been measured in man and in the dog during exercise. The magnitude of the negative ΔP_{CO_2} $(a - E')$ was related to the arterial P_{CO_2} (7, 8). Bartels and co-workers (4) observed negative ΔP_{CO_2} $(a - E')$ of 1–2 mm Hg in resting conditions, which increased in physical exercise. When during exercise corresponding to an O_2 uptake of 1.5 liters/min the ventilation was temporarily depressed by an additional external breathing resistance, the negative ΔP_{CO_2} $(a - E')$ rose from 1 to 5 mm Hg (9). Matell (10) found negative values of ΔP_{CO_2} $(a - E')$ similar to those observed during exercise when a hypercapnic gas mixture was breathed.

The customary explanation of these findings is based, in the first place, on the presence of respiratory cyclic variations of alveolar gas composition. Thus not only sampling of the last part of an expirate (e.g. by a Rahn sampler), but also the attempts to average P_{CO_2} over that part of the expiration not contaminated by dead space gas, ordinarily leads to an overestimate of alveolar P_{CO_2}. Since during exercise the cyclic variations of alveolar P_{CO_2} are enlarged, the error of overestimate will be exaggerated and may easily lead to a negative ΔP_{CO_2} $(a - E')$.

Besides, the effect of the time delay due to transit of alveolar gas from the alveoli to the mouth must be considered (10). Under the conditions of resting ventilation, this effect may largely cancel out the effect of cyclic variations, since the long time delay due to slow gas flow through the dead space makes the gas reaching the mouth at end-expiration reflect the alveolar gas composition at a much earlier time in the cycle and, therefore, much closer to the time-averaged expired alveolar gas. In exercise with high ventilatory flow rate this compensating delay effect would be expected to be much reduced and, therefore, the gas measured at end-expiration should be close to the gas leaving the lungs at end-expiration, which has higher than average P_{CO_2}.

Even in the theoretical case that the total gas expired from the alveoli of an ideal lung with constant blood flow (and linear CO_2 dissociation curve of blood) is collected for one or several respiratory cycles and compared to the blood sample evenly withdrawn during that time, a ΔP_{CO_2} would be expected to occur. This is because the arterial P_{CO_2} is time-averaged, but the alveolar P_{CO_2} is volume-averaged. The ΔP_{CO_2} would be magnified by presence of postinspiratory or postexpiratory pauses. With a postinspiratory pause, P_{CO_2} in expired alveolar gas must be clearly higher than the time-averaged alveolar P_{CO_2}, because the gas is exhaled from alveoli when their P_{CO_2} is highest, whereas in the blood the true time-averaged P_{CO_2} would be approached.

Although in principle still applicable, all these explanations appear to become quantitatively inadequate when applied to the experimental findings of Salzano et al (11). During submaximal exercise ($\dot{V}o_2$ about 2 liters/min) in human subjects breathing pure O_2 at 1 or 2 atm abs, these authors found P_{CO_2} to be lower in arterial blood than in mixed expired gas. Unfortunately, they gave no quantitative data. When the conventional analysis of alveolar gas exchange is applied, this finding implies a negative value for the physiological dead space and its ventilation. Most authors, however, have found the physiological dead space to increase with increasing metabolic level and ventilation (e.g. 5, 12).

REBREATHING: PROBLEMS OF PHYSICOCHEMICAL EQUILIBRIA

When during rebreathing in a closed system a constant plateau value of P_{CO_2} in the gas has been reached, indicating absence of net CO_2 exchange between blood and gas, the cyclic changes considered above would be expected to disappear. A rebreathing plateau of sufficiently long duration is generally believed to indicate that a complete mixing in the system of rebreathing bag and lungs has been accomplished and, moreover, that a true equilibrium between pulmonary capillary blood and alveolar gas has been attained. Such rebreathing experiments are mostly performed to determine the value of mixed venous P_{CO_2} for calculation of the cardiac output (e.g. 13, 14).

A gas mixture sufficiently high in O_2 to completely oxygenate the blood during rebreathing is often used. In this case the P_{CO_2} value obtained is presumed to represent the P_{CO_2} of oxygenated mixed venous blood (which is higher than the true mixed venous P_{CO_2} because of the Haldane effect).

In checking the CO_2 rebreathing method for determination of the cardiac output, Jones et al (15) found the arterial P_{CO_2} during rebreathing with high O_2 in exercising subjects to be 7 to 10 mm Hg lower than the rebreathing gas value. They hypothesized that certain chemical reactions in the blood might not have reached equilibrium during the contact time and that subsequent equilibration in arterial blood might have led to a decrease of P_{CO_2}. This hypothesis will be analyzed in the following section.

Oxygenation-dependent rate-limiting processes in the blood.—In a rebreathing experiment with oxygenation, the following chemical reactions and equilibria are supposed to occur in pulmonary capillaries:

$$H \cdot Hb \xrightarrow{O_2} Hb^- + H^+ \qquad\qquad 1.$$

$$Hb \cdot NH \cdot COO^- + H^+ \xrightarrow{O_2} Hb \cdot NH_2 + CO_2 \qquad\qquad 2.$$

$$H \cdot B \rightleftharpoons H^+ + B^- \qquad\qquad 3.$$

$$CO_2 + H_2O \rightleftharpoons H_2CO_3 \rightleftharpoons H^+ + HCO_3^- \text{ (cells)}$$
$$\Updownarrow \qquad\qquad\qquad\qquad 4.$$
$$HCO_3^- \text{ (plasma)}$$

Reaction 1, indicating the increase in acidity of hemoglobin upon oxygenation, is the fundamental reaction underlying the Haldane effect. The decrease in carbamate binding effected by oxygenation, reaction 2, has an opposite influence on the acid-base equilibrium because the liberation of CO_2 from carbamate, produced by oxygenation of hemoglobin, is associated with binding of H^+ ions. Reactions 3 and 4 are buffering reactions, the non-bicarbonate buffer HB/B^- being mainly hemoglobin.

If reactions 1 and 2 are assumed to be sufficiently rapid to reach complete equilibrium during the pulmonary contact time, the quantitative relationship between these reactions determines whether there will be a net production or consumption of H^+ ions. According to Rossi-Bernardi & Roughton (16) reaction 1 prevails, leading to acidification upon oxygenation, although to a lesser extent than in the absence of CO_2 and therefore of the carbamate reactions.

If now reaction 4 is assumed to be slow, either because of slow hydration of CO_2 or because of slow exchange of bicarbonate across the red cell membrane so that equilibrium is reached in blood after the contact with alveolar gas has been terminated, then reaction 4 would proceed from right to left, thus leading to a rise of arterial P_{CO_2} above the value in alveolar gas rather than to a drop required for explanation of negative ΔP_{CO_2}.

However, if the liberation of CO_2 from carbamino hemoglobin were relatively slow, CO_2 would be set free in arterial blood after leaving the lung, but the concomitant binding of H^+ ions would make reaction 4 move to the right, thereby decreasing physically dissolved CO_2. According to Rossi-Bernardi & Roughton (16), not 1 meq, as would appear from reaction equation 2, but about 1.5 meq H^+ ions are bound per 1 mmole CO_2 set free. Thus a decrease of P_{CO_2} appears to be feasible, although the concurrent buffering reaction 3 is expected to attenuate and possibly reverse the overall effect on P_{CO_2}. However, according to experimental evidence, reactions 1 and 2 are too rapid to produce such effects (17).

It is essential for the argument that the above explanations cannot operate unless blood is oxygenated during its passage through the lungs. In experiments on exercising subjects in which by rebreathing of a CO_2—N_2 mixture not only the CO_2 output, but also the O_2 uptake was reduced to zero, Jones et al (18, 19) again found P_{CO_2} to be higher in alveolar gas than in arterial blood, the difference being only slightly smaller than in rebreathing experiments with oxygenation (15). Laszlo and co-workers (20, 21), however, found no arterial to alveolar P_{CO_2} difference in isolated rebreathed dog lungs perfused in a closed circuit after half an hour had been allowed for equilibration. Comparison of these opposing results suggests the possibility that a time-dependent process, effective during the first 15 sec of rebreathing before the onset of recirculation, but exhausted later, is involved. It has been intimated that this process is acid-base re-equilibration between lung tissue and blood, brought about by exchange of bicarbonate or hydrogen ions (18, 21).

Lung-blood exchange of bicarbonate (or hydrogen) ions.—During re-breathing maneuvers, the mean P_{CO_2} in pulmonary tissue, normally expected to range between mixed venous and alveolar values, is rapidly raised to a level close to the mixed venous value. This rise in lung tissue P_{CO_2} represents a derangement of acid-base equilibria inside the lung tissue, and between lung tissue and pulmonary capillary blood. Conceivably, the subsequent re-equilibration is achieved by displacement of bicarbonate ions from blood into lung tissue. Thereby the CO_2/bicarbonate equilibrium in blood would be disturbed and re-equilibration in blood would produce a decrease in P_{CO_2} (reaction 4). However, as physically dissolved CO_2 has a high diffusivity, P_{CO_2} differences should disappear rapidly by diffusion exchange.

In blood, bicarbonate ions are mainly generated in red blood cells. If the hydration and bicarbonate chloride exchange (reaction 4) were relatively slow, CO_2 would be transformed into bicarbonate after the blood had left pulmonary capillaries, whereupon arterial P_{CO_2} would be lowered in comparison to alveolar P_{CO_2}, i.e. a negative ΔP_{CO_2} (a−A) would be generated.

Using CO_2–N_2 mixtures for rebreathing, Denison et al (13) found in man that the alveolar P_{CO_2} exceeded the value of mixed venous P_{CO_2} after rebreathing equilibrium had been established for both CO_2 and O_2. At rest the negative P_{CO_2} difference averaged 4.6 mm Hg, and reached 6.7 mm Hg with exercise of 900 kpm/min. The authors presumed that contact with lung tissue had brought about a displacement of the blood CO_2 dissociation curve. Although a clear hypothesis was not presented, pulmonary tissue-blood exchange of H^+ or bicarbonate ions should have been implicated in some manner.

When it is accepted that the experimental results of Jones et al (18) and those of Denison et al (13), both obtained on man in exercise, are consistent with each other, it must be concluded that during rebreathing both mixed venous and arterial blood have lower P_{CO_2} than alveolar gas. This conclusion was confirmed in rebreathing experiments on anesthetized dogs by Laszlo (20). He found in the first 20 to 40 sec of rebreathing, although not later, that both mixed venous and arterial P_{CO_2} were lower than the rebreathing alveolar P_{CO_2}. This result seems not to be explainable by exchange of H^+ or bicarbonate ions, because in principle such exchange processes always must lead to the following gradations of P_{CO_2}: $\bar{v} \geq A \geq a$ (case described above) or $a \geq A \geq \bar{v}$ (e.g. by a hypothetical movement of bicarbonate out of lung tissue into blood).

In order to explain the transitory negative blood to gas P_{CO_2} observed by him, Laszlo (20) appears to intimate that the red cell-plasma CO_2-bicarbonate system had not reached equilibrium before, during, and after contact with alveolar gas. Such slow equilibration may in fact occur when metabolic acids (e.g. lactic acid) are added to the blood (22). However, experiments performed by Guyatt (23) on rebreathing lung lobes in situ provide evidence against such slow equilibration: prolongation of the transit time of blood from the right ventricle to the lungs by means of a tubing incorporated into the divided pulmonary artery had no effect upon the observed negative ΔP_{CO_2} ($\bar{v} - A$) that averaged 4 mm Hg.

Acidification by electrochemical effects.—Gurtner, Song & Farhi (24, 25) investigated the CO_2 equilibration during rebreathing with CO_2–N_2 mixtures in anesthetized dogs, measuring the mixed venous to alveolar P_{CO_2} difference. Their results were similar to those of Denison et al (13): negative P_{CO_2} ($\bar{v} - A$) up to 10 mm Hg were consistent. For explanation, the authors propounded an ingenious and highly stimulating hypothesis based on electrochemical effects hitherto ignored by students of respiratory physiology. We will present a simplified and qualitative description of the theory.

It is assumed that by means of an electrochemical effect, producing local acidification near the endothelium, a radial gradient of P_{CO_2} is generated in the pulmonary capillaries, in the sense that blood elements close to the endothelium (submembrane blood) have higher P_{CO_2} than the remaining major part of the capillary volume (axial blood). Alveolar gas equilibrates with the submembrane blood and therefore its P_{CO_2} is higher than in the axial blood compartment. As the acidifying influence is strictly bound to pulmonary capillaries, the CO_2 dissociation curves of the blood entering and leaving the lung are identical, and P_{CO_2} in mixed venous and arterial blood is the same, but lower than P_{CO_2} in the alveolar gas.

The local acidification, giving rise to local increase of P_{CO_2} in the submembrane blood, is produced by an electrostatic action of the negatively charged endothelial cell membrane upon the ions of the blood. The blood entering the pulmonary capillaries is suddenly exposed to an electric field that is much more effective than in large vessels because of the higher ratio of capillary wall surface area to volume. The time required to attain the equilibrium state in the electrochemical field depends upon the mobility of the ionic species, which is highest for H^+, lower for bicarbonate, and still much lower for protein ions. Thereby an attraction of H^+ ions towards the endothelial membrane is produced, accompanied by a delayed and lesser repulsion of bicarbonate. Consequently, reaction 4 moves to the left, producing an increase of P_{CO_2} in the submembrane blood layer.

The few free H^+ ions of the blood, however, probably contribute little to the increase of the H^+ concentration near the endothelial membrane. Quantitatively more important is the effect on protein buffers: by attraction of H^+ ions towards the membrane the H^+ concentration in the near environment of proteins in the submembrane blood layer is reduced, and this favors the dissociation of H^+ ions from the acidic groups of the protein molecules (decrease of effective pK value). Such a change of dissociation of weak acids induced by electrical fields is known in physical chemistry as the Wien effect.

The authors (24, 25) assume that, in respect to P_{CO_2}, the submembrane blood equilibrates with the alveolar gas, but not with the axial blood.

Although the diffusion pathlength may be in accordance with this assumption, it is not easy to accept P_{CO_2} gradients in blood because of the high diffusivity of physically dissolved CO_2. A diffusional loss of CO_2 from the submembrane blood into the axial blood compartment would be followed by transformation to bicarbonate (thus circumventing the low mobility of bicarbonate) and the increase in P_{CO_2} originally produced by the Wien effect would become very much diluted, although not completely abolished (because of the net overall acidification by the Wien effect). Note that the reduction of the effect would be less if reaction 4 were relatively slow.

The theory devised by Gurtner, Song & Farhi (24, 25) permits recognition of the factors expected to modify the negative ΔP_{CO_2}. As the negative ΔP_{CO_2} is assumed to be brought about by a lack of equilibration of bicarbonate and CO_2 inside pulmonary capillary blood, it should decrease if enough time is allowed for equilibration. On the other hand, the establishment of ΔP_{CO_2} should require a certain time. Hence there should be an optimum contact time, and cardiac output, leading to maximum negative ΔP_{CO_2}. The authors found that the negative rebreathing ΔP_{CO_2} decreased from 10 mm Hg and higher with normal cardiac output (2 liters/min) to close to zero when the cardiac output was reduced to about 0.5 liters/min by bleeding.

According to the theory, the negative ΔP_{CO_2} should also increase with increasing acidity and increasing bicarbonate concentration, and this was borne out by the experimental results. Jones et al (18) found a similar dependence on blood pH. The increase of negative blood to gas ΔP_{CO_2} during rebreathing with increasing exercise intensity (18) is explainable as a combined action of elevated cardiac output and of increased acidity and bicarbonate concentration in mixed venous blood.

In normal breathing (as opposed to rebreathing) a negative ΔP_{CO_2} is not expected to develop according to Gurtner et al (24, 25) because it would be abolished by the CO_2 exchange across the alveolar membrane (however, the theoretical basis of this assertion is not evident from the papers). A negative ΔP_{CO_2} should arise and increase when the net capillary-alveolar CO_2 transfer is decreased; thus the highly negative ΔP_{CO_2} during rebreathing and during transitory hypoventilation is explained.

Highly convincing evidence for the theory was produced by measurements of the distribution of DMO (5-5-dimethyloxazolidine dione) between blood and alveolar space of liquid-filled canine lung lobes in situ (24, 25). The undissociated form of DMO behaved very much like P_{CO_2}. Measurements on artificial membranes with fixed negative charge revealed the importance of protein ions for the Wien effect, since P_{CO_2} differences were generated when plasma was the perfusion fluid, but not when a bicarbonate solution was substituted for plasma.

PHYSIOLOGICAL SIGNIFICANCE

The significance of the negative values for the blood to gas ΔP_{CO_2} found in rebreathing experiments would be rather limited if their occurrence were restricted to the rebreathing condition. In this case, determination of the cardiac output by the CO_2 rebreathing techniques would be chiefly affected. This was originally the main concern of the groups of Jones et al (15) and of Denison et al (13). As the mixed venous P_{CO_2} tends to be overestimated by the rebreathing methods, the venoarterial CO_2 content difference would be overestimated and the value for the cardiac output would turn out too low, particularly in exercise.

The mixed venous P_{O_2} determined by the CO_2–N_2 rebreathing technique showed much better agreement with directly determined P_{O_2} in mixed venous blood (13) and in arterial blood during rebreathing (18). Thus for determination of the cardiac output the rebreathing P_{O_2} method is theoretically preferable to the P_{CO_2} method not only because of higher accuracy due to the lesser slope of the O_2 dissociation curve, but also because of the apparent absence of specific effects impeding gas-blood partial pressure equalization.

We must seriously consider the possibility that during normal breathing (i.e. not in rebreathing) negative ΔP_{CO_2} between pulmonary capillary blood and surrounding alveolar gas also occurs, particularly in exercise. If so, the very basis of all analysis of alveolar gas exchange, the identity of P_{CO_2} between an alveolus and the end-capillary blood leaving this alveolus, would be called in question. The ideal alveolar P_{O_2} would be lower and, therefore, the ideal alveolar to arterial P_{O_2} difference would come out smaller than the value obtained by conventional calculation, if we assume alveolar P_{CO_2} equal to end-capillary P_{CO_2}.

The conventional analysis of alveolar gas exchange data in a lung showing a negative end-capillary to alveolar ΔP_{CO_2} would result in the following errors:

1. underestimate of alveolar and physiological dead space ventilation,
2. overestimate of venous admixture,
3. underestimate of diffusing capacity for O_2 and of the steady-state diffusing capacity for CO based on physiological (CO_2) dead space.

It is of interest that these effects are opposite to those that would occur if alveolar-capillary P_{CO_2} equilibration were incomplete, e.g. due to slowness of carbonic acid dehydration or chloride-bicarbonate exchange across the red cell membrane, leading to a positive end-capillary to alveolar ΔP_{CO_2}.

The above enumeration suffices to show the necessity to confirm or refute the existence of negative blood to gas ΔP_{CO_2} during normal breathing and eventually to work out the conditions and factors determining its value.

Besides the significance for the physiologist and pathophysiologist interested in analysis of alveolar gas exchange, the significance for the gas exchange economy of the organism must not be neglected. If negative ΔP_{CO_2} $(a - A)$ occurred in normal conditions, the same arterial P_{CO_2} could be maintained at a lower level of alveolar ventilation than would be possible if the effect were absent. Therefore its influence would be beneficial, and in heavy exercise it might become of considerable importance.

EVIDENCE FOR STRATIFIED INHOMOGENEITY IN THE LUNGS
ALVEOLAR SLOPE AND ITS POSSIBLE EXPLANATIONS

When N_2 concentration is continuously monitored in expired gas after a single inspiration of pure O_2, one observes a fast increase, indicating washout of the dead space, and thereafter a slow progressive rise (alveolar slope) and not a constant plateau value. The interpretation of this alveolar slope has engaged the minds of physiologists since Krogh & Lindhard (26). In this section we shall discuss the possible interpretations and then concentrate upon the more recent findings concerning one of the possible mechanisms, the stratification.

Three mechanisms may explain the alveolar slope during expiration: 1. continuing respiratory gas exchange, 2. regional inhomogeneities due to $\dot{V}A/VA$ inequalities, 3. stratified inhomogeneity.

Continuing respiratory gas exchange.—Alveolar gas exchange is continued during the course of an expiration. Since the average gas exchange ratio (R) is generally less than 1.0 and diminishes further during expiration, the alveolar N_2 concentration must rise progressively because of shrinkage of its distribution volume. This effect, which in many previous studies could not be properly taken into account, was excluded by Sikand, Cerretelli & Farhi (27) using the simple artifice of comparing the concentrations of two inert gases during expiration after one of these had been inspired. Since the concentrating effect of shrinking lung volume is the same for all inert gases (of negligible solubility), the ratio of two inert gases must remain unaffected. The authors found, however, that after inspiration of a volume of 20% O_2 in argon (Ar) the Ar/N_2 ratio fell continuously during expiration, which indicated a relative rise in N_2 concentration.

Only two mechanisms were left as explanation: regional ventilation inhomogeneities and stratification.

Regional inhomogeneities due to $\dot{V}A/VA$ inequalities.—To explain an alveolar slope by regional inhomogeneities due to unequal distribution of alveolar ventilation $\dot{V}A$, to alveolar volume VA, two conditions must be met: the inspired volume must be unequally distributed to the alveolar volume; and the time course (time constant) of expiration must be correlated with the $\dot{V}A/VA$ ratio. For explanation of a rising alveolar slope, as usually encountered, the relatively hyperventilated regions must expire before the relatively hypoventilated regions.

Sikand, Cerretelli & Farhi (27) could have explained their alveolar slopes by the regional inhomogeneous distribution of ventilation to volume in lungs as reported for the same experimental conditions by West (28) if they had assumed that the better ventilated (basal) regions exclusively contributed to the first part of the expirate, the less ventilated (apical) regions, to the last part. If this had been the case, the CO_2 and O_2 concentrations in expired gas should have displayed a certain pattern reflecting the regional differences in the gas exchange ratio R as calculated by West from his measurements of the $\dot{V}A/\dot{Q}$ inhomogeneity. However, the P_{CO_2} and P_{O_2} values measured during expiration revealed no such changes in R. Therefrom the authors concluded that all lung regions expired with the same time pattern and thus regional inhomogeneities could not have contributed to the alveolar slope.

However, the gravitational inhomogeneity established by West (28) represents a minimum value for total possible inhomogeneities, as recognized by the author himself. There is at least the theoretical possibility that distribution inequalities exist besides, and independently of, the gravitational distributions of $\dot{V}A/VA$ and $\dot{V}A/\dot{Q}$ measured by West. If this hypothetical gravity-independent inhomogeneity is such that there is no or little $\dot{V}A/\dot{Q}$ inequality or that the $\dot{V}A/\dot{Q}$ inequality is not correlated with the $\dot{V}A/VA$ distribution in the manner found by West (see below), an alveolar slope without changes in R could be obtained, of course again with the additional necessary assumption that regions with low $\dot{V}A/VA$ expire last. Experimental results reported by Suda & Martin (29) may be considered to support this possibility. Using the technique of N_2 washout they found higher dispersion of $\dot{V}A/VA$ ratio in small, sublobar, lung areas than for the whole lung. Therefore it appears that the role of regional inhomogeneities in contributing to the alveolar slope cannot yet be excluded.

Stratified inhomogeneity.—The term stratified inhomogeneity designates longitudinal or serial concentration gradients in the airways in contrast to the regional inhomogeneities implying concentration differences between parallel lung regions.

Since the bulk of the lung volume is concentrated into the last few millimeters of the airways, the conducting airways have a considerable length (and a relatively small total cross-sectional area) and, therefore, offer a high resistance to diffusion. Thus concentration gradients established inside the conducting airways or in the zone between the latter (dead space) and the alveolar region are but slowly reduced by diffusion. For explanation of the alveolar slope, the conditions for development of stratified inhomogeneity inside the alveolar space must be investigated.

MORPHOLOGICAL MODELS

One approach to the study of stratified inhomogeneity is provided by the analysis of diffusional equalization processes in theoretical lung models devised as closest possible approximations to the relevant morphological data.

All recent calculations of intrapulmonary diffusion are based on the well-known morphometric studies of Weibel (30); in most cases his Model A with symmetrical dichotomy is used. According to this model the pulmonary airways are represented by a dichotomously branched system of 23 generations of cylindrical elements, the last 7 of which bear alveoli. Although the length and the diameter of the individual elements decrease from generation to generation, the geometrical progression of the number of the elements results in an enormous increase in the total cross-sectional area and in the volume of the elements per generation. If the airway volume is plotted as a function of the distance from the beginning of the tracheobronchial tree, a figure resembling a trumpet or, even more realistically, a thumbtack (31) is obtained.

Two characteristic features important for diffusion calculations result from the morphometry:

1. More than 99% of the lung volume is contained in the last 7 generations of airway elements which bear alveoli in progressively increasing number. The length of the intraluminal pathway through these 7 generations is close to 6 mm.

2. When a tidal volume of 750 ml is delivered into the system as a bolus with a square front, the front reaches the end of the 20th generation, i.e. the region between the first- and second-order alveolar ducts, and its linear distance from the distal end of the alveolar sacs is no more than about 2 mm.

Model of Rauwerda.—The first calculations on diffusion for a model of terminal airways have been published by Rauwerda in his famous thesis (32). He chose the acinus, the unit supplied by one terminal bronchiole, as the unit to be considered. His model for the acinus is a truncated cone with curved bases, resulting from sectioning the space between two concentric spherical surfaces by a cone with its apex at the center of the spheres. The radii of the inner and outer spheres are 1 and 8 mm, respectively, the height of the cone therefore being 7 mm. The resulting ratio of the smaller (proximal) to the greater (distal) surface is 1 to 64 (the opening angle of the cone is immaterial).

A N_2-O_2 concentration step at a distance of 2 mm from the distal surface is set up at time zero, and the change of the concentration difference between the proximal and the distal surface is calculated (the system is closed at both ends). This concentration difference decreased to 16% of its initial value in 0.38 sec, and would have almost disappeared in 1 sec. Rauwerda concluded that no significant stratified inhomogeneity could exist in the acinus during normal breathing.

Model of Cumming et al.—Cumming et al (33) criticized the model of Rauwerda on the grounds that it was closed at its proximal end. It is true that the units considered by Rauwerda by far contain most of the alveolar volume and, therefore, stratification in this volume would influence the alveolar slope. Nevertheless, as the diffusion resistance of the proximal airways is not infinitely high, during the time intervals considered, diffusional exchange between the dead space and the alveolar space should influence the diffusional equalization in the terminal 7 mm of the airways.

Cumming et al (33) retain the truncated cone shape introduced by

Rauwerda, but increase its length in such a manner that no diffusional exchange of any concern could take place through its proximal boundary and thus the question of open or closed end becomes immaterial. Their cone is obtained by cutting a spherical shell of 26 mm outer radius and 5 mm inner radius, resulting in a diffusion distance of 21 mm. If a diffusion front is set up 2 mm from the distal surface the concentration difference across the distal 7 mm, i.e. across the alveolar space, is still 8% of the initial concentration step after 1 sec. The authors concluded that stratified inhomogeneity played a significant role and contributed to the sloping alveolar plateau.

Model of La Force & Lewis.—La Force & Lewis (31) performed calculations for a model resembling the anatomical lung much more closely than the truncated cone models used by Rauwerda and by Cumming et al. The distal 13 generations of airway branches (approximately corresponding to the total length of the model of Cumming et al) were considered, with values for cross section and length as measured by Weibel (30). With approximation methods the time course of diffusion equalization was calculated for concentration steps established at different distances from the terminal end of the system.

The circumstance that the cross section contracts towards the periphery rather than widens if a single air pathway is considered appears to us (in contrast to the authors) to represent no basic difference from the conical models. The real, important advantage of this model resides in its much better agreement with morphometrical data which, as stated above, are not consistent with the truncated cone model.

The authors point out two basic possibilities for treating gas diffusion in airways bearing alveoli. One is to neglect the presence of alveoli and to consider progression of gas diffusion inside the core of the alveolar ducts. The other is to examine diffusion inside the entire unit including the apposed alveoli, but neglecting the existence of the alveolar septa. The authors favor the second model, which departs more markedly from the truncated cone model. It appears to us, however, that the neglect of the alveolar septa should lead to some overestimate of the rapidity of diffusional equalization.

According to the calculations, if the diffusion front is established 2 mm from the terminal end of the system, no discernible gradient persists after 0.1 sec in the last 3 generations constituting 60% of the lung volume, and after 1 sec not even in the last 5 generations making up more than 90% of the lung volume. La Force & Lewis conclude that stratified inhomogeneity is immaterial in normal breathing.

Comparison and criticism.—La Force & Lewis (31) criticized the work of Cumming et al in (33) because the very conspicuous increase of volume in the course of the terminal few millimeters of the pulmonary airways was not adequately taken into account by their truncated cone model (actually this criticism hits Rauwerda less because his model fits the anatomical data better). Cumming et al have considered this drawback. However, they did not calculate the diffusion for the thumbtack model, since they assumed that the effect of the accelerated increase in volume would be to slow down the diffusion equilibration. In contrast, La Force & Lewis believe that the very rapid increase in volume distal to the initial concentration step favors diffusional equalization by means of a dilution effect.

It seems to us that the diffusion equilibration does get slowed if radial diffusion is taken into account. However, as the thumbtack model describes only the dependency of the airway volume upon the axial distance, and since the radial dimensions of one generation of airway elements always are small, it appears to be justified to consider the radial diffusion as infinitely rapid in the thumbtack model too. Therefore, the influence of the geometry would mainly lead to dilution by distally increasing volume, and the conclusion drawn by Cumming et al that diffusion would be slower in a model resembling a thumbtack is not warranted.

Another criticism pertains to the significance of the gradient persisting inside the terminal 7 mm after 1 sec as obtained by Cumming et al (33). If the effects on the alveolar slope are to be derived, the persisting concentration differences in terminal airways should be referred to volume, not to distance. If such transformation is performed with the aid of the data of Weibel (30) a rather different picture emerges. Of course, the total concentration differences remain the same, but now they are limited to the proximal 3 to 4 generations only, whereas in the last 4 airway generations, from which the major part of the alveolar portion of a tidal volume originates, the concentration gradient has practically disappeared in 1 sec equilibration time.

Models and real lungs.—To facilitate the calculations, all the models discussed above had been much simplified, compared with the situation in real lungs. A sharp boundary between the inspired gas and the lung gas at a definite distance from the distal end of the airways was assumed as the initial condition for all calculations. To obtain such a sharp boundary, the following conditions, obviously not met in real lungs, are required.

1. The inspired gas progresses with a square front; there is no parabolic flow profile.
2. No diffusion takes place during inspiration.
3. No convective mixing occurs during inspiration.

Any deviation from these conditions must lead to a reduction of the extent of stratified inhomogeneity in a real lung when compared to that calculated for models. This means that even when significant persisting stratified inhomogeneity is calculated for the model, it is not necessarily present in a real lung.

For detection and evaluation of stratified inhomogeneity in lungs the alveolar slope is generally used (see below). If the alveolar slope is to reflect the stratification as it exists in the lungs, analogous assumptions for the expiration must be made as listed above for the inspiration. Thus it seems that a stratified inhomogeneity of considerable extent must result from calculations performed on a theoretical model in order to explain a measurable alveolar slope.

If the whole lungs are to be approximated by a model unit, homogeneity in structure and function must be assumed. In a lung inhomogeneous in respect to the $\dot{V}A/VA$ ratio the boundary between the inspired gas and the lung gas would be established at variable distances from the distal airway end. In low $\dot{V}A/VA$ units with long effective diffusion distance a stratification may persist and produce an alveolar slope, particularly if such low $\dot{V}A/VA$ units emptied late in expiration. In such a case the stratified and regional inhomogeneities would be interrelated and produce a combined effect.

These considerations show that a real lung may display less or more stratified inhomogeneity than the models.

Experimental Evidence and Analog Models

Liquid breathing.—When, instead of air, liquid is breathed, a stratified inhomogeneity in terms of O_2 and CO_2 pressure gradients is expected to be very markedly magnified because the Krogh diffusion constants of gases in water are about 10^4 (CO_2) to 10^5 (O_2) times smaller than in gas.

Kylstra, Paganelli & Lanphier (34), ventilating dogs artificially with Ringer solution equilibrated with 5 atm O_2, obtained stratification effects from the sequential changes of expired P_{CO_2} and P_{O_2} during expiration. The measured stratification was compared with predictions for a lung model composed of spherical airway units surrounded by capillary network. For the radius of the spherical units a value of 0.85 mm was obtained. This value is much less than the dimensions used in the calculations based on morphological models, and it seems to leave little space for stratified inhomogeneity when air is breathed.

However, because of the higher density/viscosity ratio, turbulence and convective mixing are expected to be more pronounced with liquid breathing, and to reduce potential stratification effects. Moreover, a number of simplifying assumptions had to be made: infinitely rapid inspiration; alveolar space filled exclusively with inspired liquid at the end of inspiration; for O_2 exchange, constancy of diffusion flux across the surface of the units ($=O_2$ uptake); for CO_2 exchange, constancy of P_{CO_2} at the surface of the units (i.e. in blood); expiration infinitely rapid and progressing evenly from the center of the units toward periphery. It is difficult to assess the overall artifact because of these and other assumptions.

Single-breath Ar/N_2 ratio.—The experiments of Sikand, Cerretelli & Farhi (27, 35) in which after inspiration of an Ar-O_2 mixture the Ar/N_2

ratio decreased progressively during expiration have been mentioned. Experiments using this technique were also performed with breath holding. When the Ar/N_2 ratio as measured in expired gas after expiration of 0.75 liters was plotted against the breath-holding time, a decrease was found up to the 10th sec of breath holding, followed by an increase.

This behavior was interpreted as due to diffusion processes in airways on the basis of a model composed of three compartments in serial arrangement. The proximal compartment (0.3 liter) corresponded to the dead space; in the intermediate compartment (3 liters after inspiration of 1.5 liters) the alveolar part of the tidal volume was assumed to be mixed by convection during inspiration, whereas the terminal compartment (1 liter) was assumed to be reached by inspired gas exclusively by diffusion. Each compartment was considered homogeneous in respect to gas concentrations; the diffusion resistances were located at the boundaries between the compartments.

The experimental results could be explained by this model reasonably well, and the authors considered stratified inhomogeneity as the main factor responsible for the alveolar slope. Further (as yet unpublished) analog models composed of more than three compartments and adjusted to morphometric data have been announced by Farhi (35).

Gases of differing diffusivity.—The alveolar stratification and its persistence or disappearance depend on resistances to diffusion which are specifically influenced by the diffusivity (diffusion coefficient) of the gases and, therefore, on their molecular weight. The experiments in which several test gases of highly differing molecular weights were used simultaneously are particularly relevant for detection of intrapulmonary stratification.

Georg et al (36) used the gases He, Ne, and SF_6 (molecular weight ratio 1/5/36, diffusivity ratio 6/2.7/1). Normal and emphysematous subjects inspired a 0.5 liter test gas mixture and the time course of the composition of the immediately following expiration was measured. The heavy gas (SF_6) was preferentially found in the early expirate fraction, the light gas (He) in the last part of the expirate.

In similar experiments Cumming et al (37) found a qualitatively similar separation of Ne and SF_6 after inspiration of a 1 liter test mixture containing these gases. The concentration of neon decreased earlier in the expiration and its alveolar slope was flatter in comparison with SF_6. When breath was held before expiration, the differences between the gases diminished and disappeared, but the alveolar slope, although reduced to about one third of the value without breath holding, clearly persisted. The authors concluded that the major part of the alveolar slope was due to stratification inhomogeneity, whereas the remainder might be partly attributable to regional inhomogeneity.

Some details of the experimental data are not easily understood. During an expiration following 10 sec breath holding, the concentration ratio had become identical with that in the inspired test gas and the alveolar slope of both gases was the same, but during expiration after 30 sec breath holding the alveolar slope, remaining identical for both gases, had further diminished. This further homogenization cannot be easily attributed to diffusion, at least not to diffusion in airway gas, because this should depend on the diffusivity which was different for both gases. Possibly diffusion through pulmonary tissue or convection, e.g. by mechanical action of the heart, was involved.

Following inspiration of air containing traces of H_2 and SF_6, Power (49) measured the ratio H_2/SF_6 in gas samples collected in early expiration (first 500 ml) and later (expirate from 1000 to 2000 ml). Experiments with varied inspired volumes and breath-holding times were performed. In general, the H_2/SF_6 ratio values in both samples were different from the value in inspired test gas, indicating separation of H_2 and SF_6. With longer breath-holding times these differences decreased, but were still measurable after 30 sec. These results support the existence of stratified inhomogeneity in the alveolar space during normal breathing also.

Physiological Significance

Obviously a stratified inhomogeneity would interfere with the effectiveness of alveolar gas exchange: a higher alveolar ventilation would be required for the maintenance of certain arterial P_{CO_2} and P_{O_2} than in the absence of stratified inhomogeneity. The limitation might become important in muscular exercise as the stratification could be enhanced by the short duration of a respiratory cycle. However, the high tidal volume to end-expired volume ratio, leading to deeper penetration of inspired gas into the lungs, and the increased ventilatory flow and the higher rate of change of flow, promoting turbulent mixing, are expected to reduce the stratified inhomogeneity. Thus the overall effect of exercise cannot be easily predicted.

The stratification inhomogeneity is the effect of resistance to diffusion in alveolar gas and may be regarded as additive to the resistance to gas-blood diffusion as represented by the reciprocal of the pulmonary diffusing capacity, D_L.

For a quantitative consideration of the effects of stratifications upon alveolar gas exchange, it is important to realize that stratified inhomogeneity is expected to cause about equal gradients for CO_2, O_2, and CO in relation to their net fluxes, since according to Graham's law the ratio of diffusion coefficients of CO_2, O_2, and CO in gas is 1.71/1.00/0.88, thus rather close to 1.0. Therefore, in the conventional analysis of alveolar gas exchange using the effective ideal alveolar P_{O_2} (calculated setting alveolar equal to arterial P_{CO_2}), the effects of stratified inhomogeneity would be included in the calculated physiological dead space ventilation, specifically in its alveolar component. Possibly a part of the increase in physiological dead space ventilation commonly observed with increased ventilation, particularly in muscular exercise (e.g. 5, 12), is attributable to stratified inhomogeneity.

The results obtained by Wagner, McRae & Read (38) on rats' lungs, indicating a pulmonary capillary flow gradient in the sense of decreasing flow per tissue volume in more peripheral alveolar ducts, are of particular interest in respect to efficiency of alveolar gas exchange, because such a gradient would be apt to compensate the effects of stratified inhomogeneity on alveolar gas exchange. A similar compensating effect could be achieved by capillary blood flowing preferentially countercurrent to O_2 diffusion in the airways, as pointed out by West et al (39).

ANALYSIS OF UNEQUAL DISTRIBUTION OF ALVEOLAR VENTILATION, PERFUSION, AND DIFFUSING CAPACITY IN LUNGS

In the last few years the methods for analysis of distribution inequalities in the lungs have been elaborated and refined. We will discuss the interesting procedure devised by Thews & Vogel (40) in some detail, partly because hitherto it has been published in German literature only.

ANALYSIS OF $\dot{V}_A/V_A$, $\dot{V}_A/\dot{Q}$, AND $D_L/\dot{Q}$ INEQUALITIES ACCORDING TO THEWS & VOGEL

The method is based on analysis of washin and washout processes from measurements of end-expired gas, following a sudden change of the concentrations of three gases in the inspired mixture (40, 41). In practice, after a steady state with an inspired gas containing no CO_2, 12% O_2, and 30% He has been achieved, the inspiratory side of the respiratory valve is connected to another mixture containing 4.8% CO_2, 16% O_2, and no He. The expired concentrations of these gases are continuously monitored.

(a) From He washout the distribution of $\dot{V}_A$ to V_A is determined by isolation of several (usually four) single exponentials characterized by different time constants. Absolute values of $\dot{V}_A$ and V_A are obtained from total ventilation, measured by pneumotachography, and assumed dead space.

(b) From the pattern of increase of end-expired P_{CO_2} the time constants for the CO_2 exponentials corresponding to the compartments established from He analysis are obtained. In theory, the CO_2 washin is analyzed as limited by alveolar ventilation and by perfusion. Thus from a comparison of the corresponding He and CO_2 time constants the perfusion is calculated and therefrom the $\dot{V}_A/\dot{Q}$ ratio is derived for each compartment. The sum of $\dot{Q}$ of all compartments gives the cardiac output.

(c) O_2 exchange in the hypoxic range is considered as limited by ventilation, perfusion, and diffusion. Therefore, from the differences between CO_2 and O_2 time constants the value of the diffusing capacity $(D_{L_{O_2}})$ can be derived for each compartment, their sum yielding the total $D_{L_{O_2}}$.

It is important to point out that the assignment of time constants of the different gases to a single compartment is not arbitrary, but is determined by mathematical relationships between the time constants and the initial amplitudes of the exponential components.

Clearly the validity of such a complex analysis has to be bound to a number of assumptions. The following requirements seem to us to be critical because not adequately met when the procedure is applied to humans.

1. Mixed venous P_{CO_2} and P_{O_2} are required for the calculations, but obviously have not been measured. Since the mixed venous P_{CO_2} has been assumed, the cardiac output value derived from CO_2 exchange parameters has in practice been assumed rather than determined by the method. In other than normal resting conditions and in patients it may be rather hazardous to assume a mixed venous P_{CO_2} for this purpose. Any errors in assumption of mixed venous P_{O_2} must exert effects on the calculated D_{L_0}.

2. The analysis presupposes constancy of mixed venous P_{CO_2} and P_{O_2} for about 1 min after the change in inspired CO_2 and O_2 concentrations. However, it is well known from rebreathing experiments that recirculation begins in about 15 sec.

3. The dissociation curves for CO_2 and for O_2 are assumed to be linear in the range utilized in the procedure. This is obviously not the case for the O_2 dissociation curve when the inspired O_2 fraction is increased from 12 to 16%.

4. Alveolar ventilation and cardiac output are required to remain unchanged during the procedure. However, it is most probable that ventilation increases when 5% CO_2 is administered in inspired gas. Also the cardiac output may easily change in these conditions.

Unfortunately the authors themselves have neglected to discuss any of these discrepancies between the theoretical requirements and the experimental conditions.

The analysis of $\dot{V}_A/V_A$ inequalities from He washout is in principle a conventional method and should present no particular problems. However, the authors have adopted a special method for isolation of the single exponentials from the He washout curve. The method allows separation of more components than would be possible with the conventional graphical method. Although the cardiac output appears to be essentially assumed, its calculated distribution to compartments and the resulting $\dot{V}_A/\dot{Q}$ inequalities may still be reasonably well approximated. As for the determination of the absolute value and of the distribution of the O_2 diffusing capacity, all errors committed in the analysis of alveolar ventilation and perfusion are expected to be propagated and new ones arising from unknown and changing mixed venous P_{O_2} and from nonlinearity of the O_2 dissociation curve will be added. In spite of all these theoretical shortcomings, the values obtained for overall $D_{L_{O_2}}$ reported are in the reasonable range of 13 to 27 ml/min·mm Hg (41, 42).

The analysis performed for a normal young male individual (41) shows a surprisingly restricted inequality of the $\dot{V}_A/\dot{Q}$ ratio which varies no more than from 0.80 to 0.94. Also in an emphysematous patient the $\dot{V}_A/\dot{Q}$ ratio varied by a factor of 1.5 only and the variance of the $D_L/\dot{Q}$ ratio, from 3.0×10^{-3} to 9.2×10^{-3} mm Hg^{-1}, was rather moderate. No simple relationship between $\dot{V}_A/\dot{Q}$ and $D_L/\dot{Q}$ inequality was evident.

Analysis of $\dot{V}A/VA$ and $\dot{V}A/\dot{Q}$ Inequalities according to Lenfant & Okubo

In contrast to most other studies, in which the inhomogeneous lung is approximated by a relatively small number of discrete compartments, Lenfant & Okubo (43, 44) prefer to regard ventilation and perfusion as continuously distributed to volume. Certainly this approach has the basic advantage of being in principle closer to the real situation in inhomogeneous lungs, but a quantitative treatment of the model requires complex mathematical methods involving approximations whose inherent errors easily may limit the accuracy of the analysis. The fundamentals of the mathematical procedures have been described by Gómez (45) and have been applied to analysis of distribution of inspired volume in the lungs by Gómez, Briscoe & Cumming (46). The procedures used by Lenfant & Okubo are closely related to those elaborated by Nakamura et al (47, 48).

In the experimental procedure, after switching from air to pure O_2 breathing, the N_2 concentration was measured in mixed expired gas samples collected for short time intervals, and arterial blood was frequently sampled for P_{O_2} measurement. The distribution pattern of ventilation to volume was obtained by appropriate analysis of the N_2 washout curve in terms of distribution function of lung volume and of total ventilation in respect to washout time constants. The anatomical dead space was considered as a separate parallel ventilation compartment. The distribution function of blood flow to N_2 washout time constant was basically derived from blood-gas O_2 equilibration in each (infinitesimal) lung subdivision, defined by an N_2 washout time constant, with subsequent mixing of the end-capillary blood species from the whole lung, yielding the measured arterial P_{O_2} (corrected for shunt). The nonlinearity of the blood O_2 dissociation curve was taken into account by a special mathematical procedure.

In normal subjects the time constants, reflecting the ratio of volume to ventilation, varied in the range of about one decade, except for the very small time constants apparently associated with anatomical dead space ventilation. The distribution functions of ventilation and blood flow against the time constant were variable from one individual to another, but, on the overall average, they were rather similar, apparently indicating absence of larger systematic variance of the $\dot{V}A/\dot{Q}$ ratio.

Limitations of the Methods for Determination of Inhomogeneities in the Lungs

It seems to us that a basic feature regarding the adequacy of the washin-washout methods discussed above has not been clearly recognized: with all these methods only a part of the inhomogeneities is measurable.

In the procedure of Lenfant & Okubo (43, 44) the lung is subdivided according to the values of the N_2 washout time constant: all regions having a certain time constant value are considered to constitute a single, infinitesimal compartment to which a certain combination of volume, ventilation, and perfusion is apportioned. In reality, it may well be that lung regions of equal washout time constant, i.e. of equal $\dot{V}_A/V_A$ ratio, have different $\dot{V}_A/\dot{Q}$ ratio values. Such an inhomogeneity, however, cannot be detected by the method.

Similarly, in the method of Thews & Vogel (40, 41), although three primarily independent gases are used, the compartments are established from the time constants of the helium washout curve alone. The washin curve of CO_2, which depends on both $\dot{V}_A/V_A$ and $\dot{V}_A/\dot{Q}$ distribution, is analyzed in such a manner that the best-fitting $\dot{V}_A/\dot{Q}$ value is sought for each $\dot{V}_A/V_A$ compartment established from helium washout. In an analogous manner $D_L/\dot{Q}$ values are obtained for each $\dot{V}_A/V_A$ compartment, using the behavior of O_2 in addition to that of CO_2.

In theory, by the method of Thews & Vogel the $\dot{V}_A/\dot{Q}$ compartmentation could be determined correctly, without restriction or bias, only in the absence of $\dot{V}_A/V_A$ inhomogeneity. Similarly, a complete and correct $D_L/\dot{Q}$ analysis can only be performed if there is no $\dot{V}_A/V_A$ and no $\dot{V}_A/\dot{Q}$ inequality. In this respect the method of Lenfant & Okubo shows the opposite behavior. It would fail completely when applied to a lung homogeneous in respect to the $\dot{V}_A/V_A$ ratio, because in this case no compartments could be singled out and, therefore, no $\dot{V}_A/\dot{Q}$ inhomogeneity could be detected.

It follows from the preceding analysis that $\dot{V}_A/\dot{Q}$ inequalities can be determined completely and correctly by both methods only if compartments with the same $\dot{V}_A/V_A$ ratio are also identical in respect to their $\dot{V}_A/\dot{Q}$ ratio, i.e. there is a perfect correlation between the two kinds of inhomogeneity. In contrast, if there exists no correlation between the two kinds of inhomogeneity, both methods would reveal a lung inhomogeneous with regard to the $\dot{V}_A/V_A$ ratio, but, erroneously, homogeneous in terms of the $\dot{V}_A/\dot{Q}$ ratio. In intermediate, practically important, cases of partial correlation the $\dot{V}_A/\dot{Q}$ inequality would be underestimated.

Correlations between $\dot{V}_A/V_A$ and $\dot{V}_A/\dot{Q}$ variances can be produced by external factors simultaneously acting on $\dot{V}_A$, V_A, and $\dot{Q}$. One such factor is gravity, whose effects have been worked out in detail by West (28) and by others. The compartments (horizontal lung slices) of West are based on their location, and their $\dot{V}_A/V_A$ and $\dot{V}_A/\dot{Q}$ ratios have been directly and independently determined. In Table 1 the range of the $\dot{V}_A/V_A$, $\dot{V}_A/\dot{Q}$ and $\dot{Q}/V_A$ ratios as found by West is compared with the values obtained by the authors who used washin-washout methods permitting no localization. Although the extents of the inequalities are not readily comparable as the number of the separated compartments differs greatly, some interesting features are discernible.

(a) With the methods based on washin-washout procedures, the range of the $\dot{V}_A/V_A$ inequalities is larger and that of the $\dot{V}_A/\dot{Q}$ variance is smaller than found by West.

(b) The correlation between the two distribution parameters is qualitatively different. According to West, regions having a high $\dot{V}A/VA$ ratio (dependent lung parts) have a low $\dot{V}A/\dot{Q}$ ratio, but according to the results obtained by washout-washin methods, compartments with a high $\dot{V}A/VA$ ratio tend to have a high $\dot{V}A/\dot{Q}$ ratio.

If the values obtained both by West and by the authors using washin-washout techniques are considered basically correct and comparable, then it must be concluded from the figures in Table 1 that there exists a gravity-

TABLE 1. Patterns of $\dot{V}A/VA$ and $\dot{V}A/\dot{Q}$ inequalities obtained for normal subjects by various methods[a]

Authors	Method	Number of compartments	$\dot{V}A/VA$	$\dot{V}A/\dot{Q}$	$\dot{Q}/VA$
West (28)	$^{15}CO_2$, local counting	9	1.8	0.19	10
Lenfant & Okubo (44)	N_2 washout, arterial Po_2	∞	~5	~1	~5
Thews & Vogel (40)	He washout, CO_2 washin	4	2.9	1.2	2.5

[a] The figures designate the ratio (value in highest $\dot{V}A/VA$ compartment)/(value in lowest $\dot{V}A/VA$ compartment). The figures derived from the continuous distribution functions determined by Lenfant & Okubo (44) are rough approximations.

independent unequal distribution (i.e. inside the horizontal slices of West) in such a manner that high $\dot{V}A/VA$ ratios are associated with low $\dot{Q}/VA$ ratios and, therefore, with particularly high $\dot{V}A/\dot{Q}$ ratios.

The rather weak correlation of the $\dot{V}A/\dot{Q}$ inhomogeneity with the $\dot{V}A/VA$ inequality obtained by use of the washin-washout methods (Table 1) suggests the feasibility of explaining the alveolar slopes for inert gases associated with practically constant R in the experiments of Sikand, Cerretelli & Farhi (27) on the basis of $\dot{V}A/VA$ variance, as reported above.

LITERATURE CITED

1. Galdston, M., Wollack, A. C. 1947. Oxygen and carbon dioxide tensions of alveolar air and arterial blood in healthy young adults at rest and after exercise. *Am. J. Physiol.* 151:276–81

2. Suskind, M., Bruce, R. A., McDowell, M. E., Yu, P.N.G., Lovejoy, F. W., Jr. 1950. Normal variations in endtidal air and arterial blood carbon dioxide and oxygen tensions during moderate exercise. *J. Appl. Physiol.* 3:282–90

3. Filley, G. F., Gregoir, F., Wright, G. W. 1954. Alveolar and arterial oxygen tensions and the significance of the alveolar-arterial oxygen tension difference in normal men. *J. Clin. Invest.* 33:517

4. Bartels, H., Beer, R., Koepchen, H.-P., Wenner, J., Witt, I. 1955. Messung der alveolär-arteriellen O_2-Druckdifferenz mit verschiedenen Methoden am Menschen bei Ruhe und Arbeit. *Pflügers Arch.* 261:133–51

5. Asmussen, E., Nielsen, M.1956. Physiological dead space and alveolar gas pressures at rest and during muscular exercise. *Acta Physiol. Scand.* 38:1–21

6. Whipp, B. J., Wassermann, K. 1969. Alveolar-arterial gas tension differences during graded exercise. *J. Appl. Physiol.* 27:361–65

7. Stegemann, J. 1966. Die Beziehung zwischen arteriellem und endexspiratorischem Kohlendioxyddruck bei künstlicher Beatmung, bei Ruhe und bei verschiedenen Leistungsstufen. *Pflügers Arch.* 292: 140–50

8. Jones, N. L., McHardy, G. J. R., Naimark, A., Campbell, E. J. M. 1966. Physiological dead space and alveolar-arterial gas pressure differences during exercise. *Clin. Sci.* 31:19–29

9. Hanson, J. S., Tabakin, B. S., Levy, A. M. 1967. Exercise arterial blood gas and end-tidal gas changes during acute airway obstruction. *Resp. Physiol.* 3:64–77

10. Matell, G. 1963. Time-courses of changes in ventilation and arterial gas tensions in man induced by moderate exercise. *Acta Physiol. Scand.* 58: *Suppl. 206*, 1–53

11. Salzano, J. V., Bell, W. H., Weglicki, W. B., Saltzmann, H. A. 1967. In *Underwater Physiology*, ed. C. J. Lambertsen, 351–60. Baltimore, Md: Williams & Wilkins. 497 pp.

12. Huch, A., Kötter, D., Loerbroks, R., Piiper, J. 1969. O_2 transport in anesthetized dogs in hypoxia with with O_2 uptake increased by 2:4-dinitrophenol. *Resp. Physiol.* 6: 187–201

13. Denison, D., Edwards, R. H. T., Jones, G., Pope, H. 1969. Direct and rebreathing estimates of the O_2 and CO_2 pressures in mixed venous blood. *Resp. Physiol.* 7:326–34

14. Cerretelli, P., Cruz, J. C., Farhi, L. E., Rahn, H. 1966. Determination of mixed venous O_2 and CO_2 tensions and cardiac output by a rebreathing method. *Resp. Physiol.* 1:258–64

15. Jones, N. L., Campbell, E. J. M., McHardy, G. J. R., Higgs, B. E., Clode, M. 1967. The estimation of carbon dioxide pressure of mixed venous blood during exercise. *Clin. Sci.* 32:311–27

16. Rossi-Bernardi, L., Roughton, F. J. W. 1967. The specific influence of carbon dioxide and carbamate compounds on the buffer power and Bohr effects in human haemoglobin solutions. *J. Physiol. (London)* 189:1–29

17. Forster, R. E. 1969. In CO_2: *Chemical, Biochemical, and Physiological Aspects*, ed. R. E. Forster, J. T. Edsall, A. B. Otis, F. J. W. Roughton, 55–59. Washington, D.C: NASA. 291 pp.

18. Jones, N. L., Campbell, E. J. M., Edwards, R. H. T., Wilkoff, W. G. 1969. Alveolar-to-blood Pco_2 difference during rebreathing in exercise. *J. Appl. Physiol.* 27:356–60

19. Jones, N. L., Campbell, E. J. M. 1969. See Ref. 17, 229–31

20. Laszlo, G. 1969. See Ref. 17, 243–44

21. Laszlo, G., Caldini, P., Bane, H. N. 1968. *Abstr. No. 761. Proc. Int. Union Physiol. Sci., 24th, 1968*

22. Forster, R. E. 1969. See Ref. 17, 275–84

23. Guyatt, A. 1969. See Ref. 17, 244

24. Gurtner, G. H., Song, S. H., Farhi, L. E. 1969. See Ref. 17, 233–41

25. Gurtner, G. H., Song, S. H., Farhi, L. E. 1969. Alveolar to mixed venous Pco_2 difference under conditions of no gas exchange. Resp. Physiol. 7:173–87

26. Krogh, A., Lindhard, J. 1914. On the average composition of the alveolar air and its variations during the respiratory cycle. J. Physiol. (London) 47:431–45

27. Sikand, R., Cerretelli, P., Farhi, L. E. 1966. Effects of $\dot{V}_A$ and $\dot{V}_A/\dot{Q}$ distribution and of time on the alveolar plateau. J. Appl. Physiol. 21:1331–37

28. West, J. B. 1962. Regional differences in gas exchange in the lung of erect man. J. Appl. Physiol. 17:893–98

29. Suda, Y., Martin, C. J. 1968. The intralobar distribution of inspired gas. Fed. Proc. 27:227

30. Weibel, E. R. 1963. Morphometry of the human lung. Berlin, Göttingen, Heidelberg: Springer. 151 pp.

31. La Force, R. C., Lewis, B. M. 1970. Diffusional transport in the human lung. J. Appl. Physiol. 28:291–98

32. Rauwerda, P. E. 1946. Unequal ventilation of different parts of the lung and the determination of cardiac output. PhD thesis, State Univ. Groningen, Groningen, Netherlands. 152 pp.

33. Cumming, G., Crank, J., Horsfield, K., Parker, I. 1966. Gaseous diffusion in the airways of the human lung. Resp. Physiol. 1:58–74

34. Kylstra, J. A., Paganelli, C. V., Lanphier, E. H. 1966. Pulmonary gas exchange in dogs ventilated with hyperbarically oxygenated liquid. J. Appl. Physiol. 21:177–84

35. Farhi, L. E. 1969. In Circulatory and respiratory mass transport, ed. G. E. W. Wolstenholme, J. Knight, 277–93. London: Churchill. 310 pp.

36. Georg, J., Lassen, N. A., Mellemgaard, K., Vinther, A. 1965. Diffusion in the gas phase of the lungs in normal and emphysematous subjects. Clin. Sci. 29:525–32

37. Cumming, G., Horsfield, K., Jones, J. G., Muir, D. C. F. 1967. The influence of gaseous diffusion on the alveolar plateau at different lung volumes. Resp. Physiol. 2:386–98

38. Wagner, P., McRae, J., Read, J. 1967. Stratified distribution of blood flow in secondary lobule of the rat lung. J. Appl. Physiol. 22:1115–23

39. West, J. B., Glazier, J. B., Hughes, J. M. B., Maloney, J. E. 1969. See Ref. 35, 256–72

40. Thews, G., Vogel, H. R. 1968. Die Verteilungsanalyse von Ventilation, Perfusion and O_2-Diffusionskapazität in der Lunge durch Konzentrationswechsel dreier Inspirationsgase. I. Theorie. Pflügers Arch. 303:195–205

41. Vogel, H. R., Thews, G. 1968. Die Verteilungsanalyse von Ventilation, Perfusion and O_2-Diffusionskapazität in der Lunge durch Konzentrationswechsel dreier Inspirationsgase. II. Durchführung des Verfahrens. Pflügers Arch. 303:206–17

42. Vogel, H. R., Thews, G., Schulz, V., v. Mengden, H. J. 1968. Die Verteilungsanalyse von Ventilation, Perfusion und O_2-Diffusionskapazität in der Lunge durch Konzentrationswechsel dreier Inspirationsgase, III. Untersuchung von Jugendlichen, älteren Personen und Schwangeren. Pflügers Arch. 303:218–29

43. Okubo, T., Lenfant, C. 1968. Distribution function of lung volume and ventilation determined by lung N_2 washout. J. Appl. Physiol. 24:658–67

44. Lenfant, C., Okubo, T. 1968. Distribution function of pulmonary blood flow and ventilation perfusion ratio in man. J. Appl. Physiol. 24:668–77

45. Gómez, D. M. 1963. Mathematical treatment of the distribution of tidal volume throughout the lung. Proc. Nat. Acad. Sci. US 49:312–19

46. Gómez, D. M., Briscoe, W. A., Cumming, G. 1964. Continuous distribution of specific tidal volume throughout the lung. J. Appl. Physiol. 19:683–92

47. Nakamura, T., Takishima, T., Sagi,

Y., Sasaki, T., Okubo, T. 1966. A new method of analyzing the distribution of mechanical time constants in the lungs. *J. Appl. Physiol.* 21 :265–70

48. Nakamura, T., Takishima, T., Okubo, T., Sasaki, T., Takahashi, H. 1966. Distribution function of the clearance time constant in lungs. *J. Appl. Physiol.* 21 :227–32

49. Power, G. G. 1969. Gaseous diffusion between airways and alveoli in the human lung. *J. Appl. Physiol.* 27 : 701–9

TEMPERATURE ACCLIMATION IN BIRDS AND MAMMALS[1]

R. R. J. CHAFFEE AND J. C. ROBERTS

Department of Ergonomics, University of California, Santa Barbara

The potential for temperature acclimation is characteristic of many homeotherms, but the mechanisms by which it is achieved may vary considerably from species to species. This review will be concerned almost entirely with a survey of recent (since 1965) studies on temperature acclimation mechanisms in both birds and mammals. Material on closely related areas of research such as hypothermia, hibernation, neonatal and adult thermoregulation, short-term temperature exposure, drug action in temperature control, and cross acclimation either will not be mentioned or will be referred to only in passing where essential to clarify the material on temperature acclimation and acclimatization.

The overall area of temperature acclimation can be subdivided into smaller areas which have received various degrees of emphasis in the last 5 years. Thus, studies on birds have generally emphasized adaptation to natural habitats and relatively few species have been acclimated to heat or cold under laboratory conditions. Rodents, on the other hand, have been acclimated under rigidly controlled laboratory conditions and much is known about their biochemical and physiological responses to prolonged heat and cold. Other mammalian species have not received the attention given laboratory rodents, but recent studies indicate that not all of the adaptive responses, such as biochemical changes, seen in temperature-acclimated rodents can be extrapolated to other species, such as primates (1–3). Thus the area of temperature acclimation presents a vast array of studies which, unfortunately, do not form a highly organized body of information. We have therefore elected to consider birds and mammals separately and to further subdivide the material along the lines which have received major emphasis within the past 5 years.

Before entering into a discussion of the research to be reviewed, reference should be made to recent reviews in closely related areas which may prove interesting to the reader. As mentioned above, hypothermia and hyperthermia will not be considered here. Aspects of these topics have been

[1] Preparation of this review was supported in part by contract No. DADA-17-68-C-8064 from the United States Army Medical Research and Development Command.

reviewed by Cooper (4) and in a recent symposium on depressed metabolism (5). Also a great deal of work has been done on the combined effects of work and temperature in man which will not be considered in detail in this review, since it has been well covered elsewhere (6–16).

The central nervous system plays a major role in temperature acclimation by stimulating first-line defenses which allow the animal to survive until other, more slowly responding, defensive mechanisms can be activated. The topic of central nervous control of temperature regulation has been thoroughly reviewed in the last 5 years by Hardy (17), Bligh (18), Hammel (19), and Benzinger (20). The reader is referred to these reviews and other recent papers on this subject (4, 21–26) as it will not be considered in any detail in this review.

TEMPERATURE ACCLIMATION IN BIRDS

Cold.—With the exception of some species of hummingbirds (Trochilidae), swifts (Apodidae), and poorwills (Caprimulgidae), which become torpid or hibernate in the cold (27), most birds maintain a relatively constant body temperature even when exposed to temperatures well below thermoneutrality. Their ability to do so depends on a combination of behavioral, insulative, metabolic, and other physiological responses. Although birds have not been studied as extensively as mammals, recent research has added greatly to our knowledge of these responses. Since this review is concerned primarily with temperature acclimation or acclimatization, for information on thermoregulation and responses to short-term thermal stress, which will not be covered here, the reader is referred to other reviews (28–31).

Increases in both food consumption and body weight have been reported in laboratory cold-acclimated birds and in wild birds during the winter. In the white-throated sparrow (*Zonotrichia albicollis*), food intake increases linearly as ambient temperature decreases and, although its body weight shows daily fluctuations, its mean body weight increases as acclimation temperature decreases down to −5°C (32). Similarly, cold-acclimated house sparrows (*Passer domesticus*) have a significantly higher body weight than sparrows kept at 22 or 32°C (33), and house sparrows are significantly fatter in the winter than in the summer (34). Moreover, the fatty acids of house sparrows are more unsaturated in the winter than in the summer, a condition which may permit easier mobilization of lipid stores and proper cellular membrane function in the extremities during extreme cold (34). As in the sparrow, increases in food intake and body weight have been reported in cold-acclimated pigeons (35), chicks (36), and cocks (37). Alaskan redpolls, which commonly winter in areas where the environmental temperature may go as low as −60°C, significantly increase both their rate of food intake (selecting high calorie foods such as birch seeds) and their digestive efficiency (% total caloric intake assimilated) at low ambient temperatures (38). This increased food intake at low ambient temperatures permits the build-up of fat stores during the day which subsequently are utilized for thermoregulation during cold nights. Because of its specific dynamic action, the extra food intake also provides some additional heat for maintenance of body temperature.

Insulation plays an important role in cold acclimation in birds both in the laboratory and in the wild. Veghte & Herried (39) have made radiometric measurements which show how effectively several species of Arctic birds can increase their insulation in the cold and thereby reduce their surface temperature and rate of heat loss to the environment. This increase in insulation with decreasing ambient temperature is more pronounced in birds which have been exposed to cold over a period of days than it is in short-term experiments where birds are exposed to sudden changes in ambient temperature, which suggests acclimative changes in plumage insulation or vasoconstriction (40). Also, Fisher et al (37) found that the feather weight and lipid content increased significantly in cocks exposed to cold for 15 months, which again indicates an increase in feather insulation. On the other hand, Rautenberg (35) found that cold-acclimated and control pigeons had the same lower critical temperature and the same rate of increase in heat production with decreasing ambient temperature, which suggests no significant change in the overall insulation. However, feather weight was not determined.

In addition to the earlier studies on seasonal changes in plumage (41), Veghte (42) has shown that both total insulation and tissue insulation of the Alaskan gray jay are higher in fall and winter than in summer, and there is a seasonal shift in the lower critical temperature from 36°C in summer to 7°C in winter. Brooks (38) reports that, unlike many other small birds, Alaskan redpolls have numerous down feathers in the winter which increase insulation. The weight of the body feathers of the house sparrow increases 70% following the autumnal molt and this insulative increase is accompanied by an increase in cold tolerance of 12°C (34).

Measurements of lower critical temperature and metabolic responses to cold indicate that birds from the Arctic are better insulated than tropical birds (27, 41). This also appears to be true of penguins which range from the tropics deep into the Antarctic. Both the length of the feathers and the thickness of the insulative layer of subdermal fat reach their maximum in the southernmost species, Emperor and Adelie penguins (43). Furthermore, the Antarctic species have small, well-feathered heads, while tropical species not only have larger heads, but some also have bare faces (43). The smallest bird thought to be adapted to the Arctic winter by insulation alone is the willow ptarmigan (*Lagopus lagopus*), which unlike most birds is completely covered with feathers down to its toes. In contrast, most small birds which winter in arctic and subarctic regions do not have such adequate insulation and therefore have critical temperatures well above the temperature of the environment (27).

Like the core temperature, skin temperature under the feathers of well-insulated birds also remains relatively constant and fairly high, seldom falling below 30°C (27, 35, 42). Veghte (42) exposed Alaskan gray jays to temperatures between 20 and −50°C and found a maximum variation in skin temperature of only 5°C. Winter jays had lower skin temperatures than summer jays, which would tend to reduce heat loss to the environment. In contrast, Rautenberg's (35) finding of higher skin temperatures in cold-acclimated pigeons than in controls suggests vascular changes similar to those reported in cold-acclimated chickens in which a slight decrease in peripheral resistance and an increase in blood pressure (44, 45) might well cause an increased peripheral blood flow and skin temperature.

In contrast to core temperature, the temperature of the poorly insulated extremities may vary considerably. Thus the bare or poorly insulated legs, characteristic of most birds, may serve as an effective means of regulating heat loss from the body (27, 30, 31, 46, 47). Temperatures close to 0°C have been found in the feet of the Arctic gull (See 27) and winter-acclimatized pheasants (47) at subfreezing ambient temperatures. Cold-acclimated pigeons have higher foot temperatures (ca 16°C) than controls (ca 8°C) when exposed to temperatures as low as −20°C and generally assume a crouching position in the cold which reduces foot exposure (35). Tolerance of such low temperatures in the extremities indicates the existence of tissue adaptations which permit the legs to remain both sensitive and functional at near zero °C.

Earlier studies on seasonal acclimatization to cold in temperate-zone birds show that there is little or no difference in basal metabolic rate between summer and winter (41). However, in laboratory cold-acclimation studies, the metabolic rate of several species of acclimated birds was higher than that of controls over a wide range of ambient temperatures, including the thermoneutral zone (29, 41). Recent studies support these earlier findings. Veghte (42) found no seasonal change in the resting metabolic rate of the Alaskan gray jay at ambient temperatures above −4°C. Hissa & Palokangas (48) found no seasonal variation in the basal metabolism of the titmouse (*Parus major*). On the other hand, Rautenberg (35) found that pigeons acclimated to 10°C in the laboratory had a higher resting metabolic rate than controls at temperatures within the thermoneutral zone.

Two important changes which occur during acclimation to cold are shifts in lower critical temperature which indicate increased insulation, and the increased ability of cold-acclimated and winter birds to tolerate low ambient temperatures by maintaining high rates of heat production for long periods of time. Thus gray jays in winter maintain a higher metabolic rate at ambient temperatures below −35°C than summer jays and can maintain body temperature constant for a longer time at a lower temperature (42). In summer, the minimum ambient temperature at which the white-tailed ptarmigan can maintain its body temperature is −17°C (49) compared to −34°C for the winter ptarmigan (39). The lower limit of temperature tolerance of the house sparrow is −25°C in January compared to 0°C in August (34).

Studies on the relationship between shivering and cold exposure in birds show that below the critical temperature both shivering and O_2 consumption increase linearly as ambient temperature decreases. In both cold-acclimated and control pigeons an increase in metabolic rate and the onset of shivering occur simultaneously at an ambient temperature of about 21°C (35). The facts that cold-acclimated birds do not begin shivering at a lower ambient temperature than controls, and that there is no difference between the ambient temperature at which O_2 consumption increases and that at which shivering first occurs, indicate that nonshivering thermogenesis is not present. Similarly, West (50) found a linear relationship between shivering and metabolic rate in four species of wild birds, which would not be the case if nonshivering thermogenesis occurred and metabolic rate increased prior to the onset of shivering. In evening grosbeaks, the level of shivering at various ambient temperatures was not significantly affected by previous thermal history, nor did the level of shivering at −10°C change significantly between summer and winter (50). This work supports the thesis that shivering and muscular activity are the primary sources of extra heat production in birds exposed to cold and has led to the conclusion that arctic- and temperate-zone birds weighing less than 350–400 g must shiver when they are inactive at most temperatures normally encountered in their environment (50).

Although cold-acclimated sparrows apparently rely on shivering for their increased heat production, Chaffee et al (51, 52) found no increase in pectoral muscle mass of these birds. However, muscle myoglobin levels increased significantly in the cold, a condition which could facilitate O_2 transport and storage in this active tissue (52).

Assays of succinoxidase activity of liver and pectoral muscle of sparrows revealed no significant increases in this enzyme system in response to cold acclimation. In heat acclimation, there was a decrease in liver succinoxidase activity, but no change in that of muscle (51). More recently, Barnett (34) has found that the in vitro metabolism of liver and skeletal muscle tissue slice from cold-acclimated sparrows was higher than that from controls (using glucose as substrate), whereas the metabolism of brain remained unchanged. On the other hand, metabolism of brain and muscle tissue of winter-acclimatized birds was higher than that of summer-acclimatized birds, while that of liver was lower. As a result of these changes in endogenous tissue metabolism, Barnett (34) suggests that nonshivering thermogenesis may occur in isolated tissues. However, more conclusive evidence is needed and the metabolic pathways involved are undetermined.

Nonshivering thermogenesis has not been demonstrated in adult birds. Although norepinephrine (NE) is the mediator of nonshivering thermogenesis in many species of mammals, neither cold-acclimated chickens nor winter-acclimatized pigeons show a metabolic response to this catecholamine (28, 30, 31). Moreover, neither NE, epinephrine (E), nor dopamine stimulated metabolism in the winter-acclimatized titmouse (48). Even in newly hatched chicks (*Gallus domesticus*), which show a marked (150%) increase in metabolic rate with little or no apparent shivering when exposed to a cool environment (25°C), NE causes only a slight (10%) increase in O_2 consumption and E only a 30% increase (53). The NE response essentially disappears and the E response decreases by 1–3 weeks of age (53). This lack of metabolic response to NE in birds may be due, at least in part, to the absence of brown fat (48, 54), which has been implicated in nonshivering thermogenesis in neonate and cold-acclimated mammals (55).

Lin & Sturkie (56) found that plasma levels of both norepinephrine and epinephrine increased in cold-acclimated chickens, reaching a maximum by the 4th week in the cold. Norepinephrine levels remained elevated during 12 weeks in the cold, while epinephrine levels declined after the 4th week and by the 12th week fell within the control range. In light of the lack of metabolic response to NE in adult birds, the significance of these elevated plasma levels of catecholamine in thermogenesis of cold-acclimated chickens remains unclear.

Freeman (57) has found that in neonate chicks, liver and muscle glycogen and plasma glucose levels are significantly decreased during exposure to cold, which suggests that carbohydrates may be a major source of energy during cold stress. However, cold exposure of neonate and young chicks also leads to a fall in overall respiratory quotient (RQ) and a significant increase in plasma free fatty acids (54) which indicates an increase in lipid metabolism in response to cold.

Norepinephrine is only moderately effective in stimulating lipolysis in the neonate chick and it is ineffective in older chickens (57). Furthermore, the β-blocking agent, propranolol, does not interfere with the cold-induced rise in plasma free fatty acids in the chick (57) although it does impair thermoregulation (58). However, propranolol does block the cold-induced decline in muscle glycogen and plasma glucose seen in normal chicks, which suggests that its effect on thermoregulation is the result of an inhibition of carbohydrate metabolism (57).

Recently other hormones have been investigated as possible mediators of thermoregulatory responses in birds. Freeman (57) found thyroid hormones are effective in reducing the rate of decline of rectal temperature in cold-exposed chicks. Hissa & Palokangas (48) have recently reported that the metabolism of the winter-acclimatized titmouse is significantly stimulated by injection of corticosterone, but the mechanism remains to be elucidated. Since avian adipose tissue is particularly sensitive to glucagon, and this hormone, which occurs in high concentration in the avian pancreas, increases plasma free fatty acid levels in birds, Freeman (57) and Hissa & Palokangas (48) have suggested that this hormone is a possible mediator of nonshivering thermogenesis in birds. However, the effects of glucagon on metabolism in cold-acclimated birds must still be studied.

Heat.—As stated earlier, recent studies on birds have emphasized adaptation to natural habitats. This is particularly true with respect to studies on birds in the heat. Although thermoregulatory responses of birds to short-term heat exposure have received considerable attention in the past few years and comparisons have been made between physiological and behavioral responses of birds from hot and temperate regions, relatively few species have been acclimated to prolonged heat under laboratory conditions. Since many of the adaptive responses seen in birds from hot climates, such as decreased activity, food intake, and metabolic rate, occur in heat-acclimated birds as well, both heat acclimation and adaptation are considered here.

A number of studies have been made on birds native to hot environments in an attempt to determine whether their responses to heat differ from those of nonadapted birds. Birds native to hot environments, like those from cold regions, have basal body temperatures not significantly different from those of temperate-zone birds (59, 60). Thus desert birds, in general, have the same body temperature as nondesert species (59, 61) and the upper lethal body temperature is similar for both groups (61). Many birds, when exposed to heat, can tolerate body temperatures as high as 43–44°C for several hours (30, 59–63). A few, like the ostrich, can maintain a near-normal body temperature of 39.7°C for several hours at an ambient temperature of 51°C (61).

Small desert birds avoid some of the diurnal heat stress of their native environment by seeking cooler shaded microclimates (61, 62, 64) and decreasing their activity (62, 64, 65). However, such behavior is not limited to desert birds (30, 60): the white-tailed ptarmigan, native to cooler regions of western North America, seeks cool locations on hot days (49) and both Alaskan redpolls (38) and domestic chickens (30) decrease their activity and food intake when exposed to high ambient temperatures.

In addition to heat, desert birds are frequently faced with a scarcity of water. Birds do not sweat and when ambient temperature exceeds body temperature, heat loss occurs mainly via evaporation from the surfaces of the respiratory tract (29–31, 59–61). It has been suggested (49) that differences in efficiency of evaporative cooling are adaptive since they seem to correlate with habitat. The white-tailed ptarmigan, which may be basically a cold-adapted bird, pants when ambient temperature exceeds 21°C and has a low evaporative efficiency (49). Several species of birds, not all of them native to the desert, have the capacity to dissipate 100% or more of their metabolically produced heat by evaporative cooling at high ambient temperatures (61, 63, 65, 66). At least two species of desert birds, the budgerygah from central Australia (67) and the ostrich (61), reduce their rate of evaporative water loss at high ambient temperatures when deprived of water. While thus conserving body water, deprived birds develop a greater hyperthermia than drinking birds when exposed to heat. Greenwald et al (67) suggest that in the budgerygah, such responses to the combined stresses of heat and water deprivation may be considered physiological adaptations to their hot arid native environment.

An increasing amount of evidence indicates that birds native to hot environments have reduced basal metabolic rates (60, 63). The Inca dove (62) and two species of orioles (63) which inhabit hot regions of the United States have basal metabolic rates 21% and 14% respectively, below those which would be predicted for birds their size. House sparrows from the hot, humid regions of Texas have a lower metabolic rate and a greater evaporative efficiency than sparrows native to cooler regions of North America (68). Similarly, chickens acclimated to 35°C in the laboratory have a lower rate of heat production than either cold-acclimated or control birds (30, 69). Such a reduction in metabolic rate has the advantage, in a hot, often arid environment, of reducing the amount of metabolic heat which must be dissipated by evaporative cooling.

Heat acclimation increases the ability of birds to tolerate high ambient temperatures (29, 30). In the heat, body temperature of acclimated chickens rises more slowly than that of controls (30). House sparrows (68) and orioles (63) from hot regions tolerate higher temperatures than birds from cooler climates. On the other hand, when heat-acclimated (32°C) quail are exposed to cold (5°C) they show greater decreases in hypothalamic, skin, and rectal temperatures than control quail (70).

Such responses may be accounted for in part by the fact that feather insulation is generally decreased in the heat (37, 38, 67) thus facilitating heat loss to the environment by means other than evaporation when ambient temperature is lower than body temperature.

The poorly insulated desert budgerygah has an extremely high upper critical temperature, above 44°C in birds supplied with water (67). This, however, may be an exception rather than the rule among heat-adapted birds, since other studies indicate that birds native to hot climates have upper critical temperatures similar to those of birds from cooler regions (65, 68).

Recent laboratory studies on temperature acclimation in birds clearly show that changes seen during the initial few hours of exposure to heat or cold do not always indicate the changes which will persist after several days of acclimation to a given temperature (45, 69). Whittow et al (45) point out that changes in cardiac output and total peripheral resistance of heat- and cold-acclimated chickens are the reverse of those seen after short-term temperature stress. Harrison & Biellier (69) have followed changes in blood pressure, pulse rate, respiratory rate, O_2 consumption, and body temperatures of chickens from the time of initial ambient temperature change through a period of 9–10 days acclimation. Initial changes in these parameters are usually rapid and tend to overshoot or undershoot the plateau level which is established after 9–10 days (69). Moreover, short-term responses often do not persist or are reversed as acclimation proceeds and a new steady state is reached.

PHYSIOLOGICAL MECHANISMS IN COLD ACCLIMATION IN MAMMALS

Homeotherms which acclimate to cold generally show increased resistance to severe cold stress. In some animals, cold acclimation may be attributed primarily to an increased capacity for thermogenesis, whereas in others it may represent almost exclusively a change in overall insulation. However, in many animals it is well established that there is a delicate resetting of the balance between heat-producing and heat-conserving mechanisms commensurate with the environmental requirements. It is also becoming evident that the mechanisms by which acclimation is achieved may vary markedly from species to species. Recent studies on the physiological mechanisms involved in mammalian cold acclimation have concentrated on (a) changes in basal metabolic rate (BMR), (b) evidence of acclimation of specific tissues and organs, (c) changes in onset or level of shivering, (d) the thermogenic role of brown adipose tissue, and (e) the development of nonshivering thermogenesis and its relationship to the calorigenic action of catecholamines, especially NE.

Barnett & Mount (71) have recently reviewed the literature on the effects of cold on food consumption, behavior, growth, body composition, and reproduction in mammals. In addition, the temperature-induced changes in relative weights of liver, kidney, heart, and brown fat of several species have been summarized (3). In general, the weights of these tissues, as well as the adrenals, tend to increase in the cold and decrease in the heat (3, 71, 72).

Metabolism.—A number of mammalian species show a significant increase in their BMR during cold acclimation, thus increasing their heat production without the intervention of shivering. The BMR of the cold-acclimated rat is 20–21% higher than that of the control (73, 74). The dog (75), cat (76), ground squirrel (77), rabbit (78, 79), and sheep (80–82) also have higher BMRs after cold acclimation. However, no significant increase in BMR was seen in cold-acclimated deer mice (83) or white mice (84, 85). In men acclimated to intermittent cold, neither Joy (86) nor Newman (87, 88) found significant changes in BMR. On the other hand, Hong and his co-workers (89) found a 17% increase in BMR of Korean women divers during winter when exposed regularly to cold water. Wyndham & Loots (90) found little difference in MR (measured at 27°C) of men before and after a year in Antarctica. However, the metabolic response of thin men to acute cold decreased with acclimatization, apparently as a result of increased insulation (90). Similarly, a decreased metabolic response to cold stress and what appears to be insulative acclimatization to cold have been reported in scuba divers after repeated diving in cold water (91). In the latter two studies (90, 91), acclimatization seems to involve changes in peripheral vasoconstriction with lower skin temperatures and higher rectal temperatures during cold stress.

Thyroid.—It has often been suggested that the increased metabolic rate of cold-acclimated animals is related to increased thyroid activity. Moreover, chronic treatment with thyroxine has been considered as a model of cold adaptation (92). When rats are fed a standard commercial diet, or a low I diet supplemented with 5 or 75 μg I/day (93), thyroid weight (93–95), resting O_2 consumption (93, 95), fecal excretion of thyroxine (94, 96, 97), and thyroxine turnover rate (98) increase during cold acclimation. However, plasma protein-bound I (PBI) levels remain unchanged or slightly lower in the cold (93, 95, 99). The thyroid hormone secretion rate increases rapidly in rats (100) and hamsters (101) during the first 10–20 days after cold (4.5°C) exposure, and remains high in rats for up to 190 days (100), while in hamsters it declines within 150 days in the cold to nearly preexposure levels (101). Cold exposure also causes an increased secretion of thyrotropin (TSH) in rats with a peak in plasma TSH at 2 hr followed by a decline (102). Plasma TSH levels remain higher than normal for several weeks in rats exposed to 8°C, but at 15°C return to normal levels by 6–24 hr (102).

Biliary clearance of thyroid hormones is increased in cold-acclimated rats fed ad libitum (96, 103). The mechanism of this increase is not clear. However, Cottle & Veress (104) have shown that cold-acclimated rats excrete more glucuronide derivatives in the urine than controls. This suggests a greater capacity of the liver of cold-acclimated rats to "detoxicate" many compounds, including thyroxine (104). Also, the reported reduction in binding of thyroid hormones to plasma proteins in cold-acclimated rats may contribute to the increased clearance, since this would tend to facilitate the uptake of hormone by the liver (103).

Urinary excretion of iodide increases significantly in ^{125}I-equilibrated rats during the first day after transfer to 5°C (93). Similarly, urinary excretion of ^{131}I following injection of labeled thyroxine or triiodothyronine (T_3) is increased in acutely cold-exposed thyroidectomized rats whether fed or fasted (105). Since there was no increase in the rate of excretion of a tracer dose of ^{131}I, Hillier (105) concluded that cold exposure accelerates the deiodination of both thyroxine and T_3. He (105) further suggested that this may be mediated by release of NE from the sympathetic nervous system, since both NE and E enhance the in vivo deiodination of thyroid hormones. More recently Galton & Nisula (106) have found that rats cold-acclimated for 3 months and fed a low I diet excrete less iodide in the urine than controls even when they receive higher doses of thyroid hormone. Moreover, their (106) in vitro studies with liver, kidney, and muscle revealed no significant changes in the deiodination of thyroxine. They (106) conclude that there is no increase in the amount of thyroxine reaching the peripheral tissues in cold-acclimated rats and that the increased activity of the thyroid is due primarily, if not solely, to the increased loss of thyroxine in the feces.

When propylthiouracil-fed rats are transferred from 28°C to 6°C, their requirement for thyroxine, for both survival and optimum growth, increases manyfold (107) and doses of thyroxine which are lethal at 28°C support a gain in body weight in the cold (107, 108). Hsieh (108) suggests that the normally fed rat may actually suffer from a thyroxine deficiency when exposed to cold. Normal PBI levels and circulatory and metabolic responses to infused NE suggest that cold-acclimated rats are not hyperthyroid (108) and that the increased activity of the thyroid is a response to an increased requirement for thyroxine due possibly to its increased excretion. Although thyroxine is essential for survival in the cold, rats thyroidectomized after cold adaptation can be maintained on relatively low doses of thyroxine and they still respond to cold exposure with an increase in nonshivering thermogenesis (107). Hsieh (107) therefore concludes that "the thyroid gland does not actively control regulatory non-shivering thermogenesis".

Although a number of parameters of thyroid function are significantly increased in cold-acclimated rats, there is now considerable evidence that many of these changes, such as increased fecal secretion of thyroxine, increased resting metabolic rate, and thyroid hypertrophy, are diet dependent and unnecessary once cold acclimation is complete (96–99, 106, 109). Since some commercial laboratory chows are known to contain thyroxine, the increased food intake seen in cold-acclimated rats may result in an increased intake of both thyroxine and bulk in the diet (97). When the intake of non-nutritive bulk is adjusted so that both cold-acclimated and control animals excrete the same amount of feces, the difference in fecal excretion of thyroxine is markedly reduced or abolished (94, 96, 99). Straw (94) found that both fecal and urinary losses of ^{131}I were the same in control and cold-acclimated rats when dietary bulk was controlled, while fecal loss was about three times greater in cold-acclimated rats when diet was not controlled. However, even when fecal loss of ^{131}I is the same in cold-acclimated and control rats, the rate of uptake and release of ^{131}I by the thyroid is increased in the cold (94), as is the rate of disappearance of thyroxine from the blood (96). When only dietary bulk and not dietary thyroxine was controlled, thyroid hypertrophy was seen in the cold (94). Cadot et al (93) have examined thyroid function in rats acclimated to 5° and 30°C using the isotope equilibrium method and controlled dietary iodide. They found no marked differences in thyroid function between the two groups and therefore concluded that the maintenance of the cold-adapted state does not require increased thyroid activity. When rats are fed a low-bulk thyroxine-free diet during acclimation, thyroid weight and resting metabolic rate remain normal (109) and there is no significant increase in thyroxine turnover rate (98). However, cold resistance (97) and sensitivity to NE increase (109) and these rats show the expected hypertrophy of liver, heart, kidney, and adrenals (109) characteristically seen in cold-acclimated rats fed a commercial diet containing thyroxine.

In light of the profound influence which diet can have on thyroid function, it is evident that future studies of the role of the thyroid in cold acclimation will require careful control of the intake of iodine, thyroxine, and bulk in the diet. Furthermore, much of the older data on thyroid function in the cold, not only in rats, but in other species, might well be reexamined in the light of these recent findings.

Organ functions.—Since many animals show an increase in BMR after prolonged cold exposure, studies of the mechanisms involved have led to an investigation of the relative importance of various organs and tissues in contributing to this extra heat production. Zeisberger (110) has recently reported that O_2 uptake of isolated, perfused liver from cold-acclimated rats is 35% higher than that of liver from warm-acclimated animals. He calculates that the metabolism of the liver accounts for 19.3% of the BMR in warm-acclimated rats, compared with 26.5% in cold-acclimated animals. Jansky (111) has reviewed the literature on organ thermogenesis and has put forward the hypothesis that total cytochrome oxidase activity of individual organs might be used to estimate maximum possible O_2 consumption. He gives evidence that in seven rodent species, there is close agreement between the value of "maximal metabolism" measured in vivo and that estimated in vitro based on maximal cytochrome oxidase activity. Davis (112) has studied the contribution of skeletal muscle to nonshivering thermogenesis in cold-acclimated dogs. By measuring arteriovenous O_2 differences in one denervated hindleg, he found that O_2 consumption is higher in the leg of the cold-acclimated dog than in the control. He concludes that denervated skeletal muscle does not contribute significantly to nonshivering thermogenesis in warm-acclimated dogs, whereas it does in cold-acclimated animals.

In addition to evidence of changes in metabolic rate in various internal organs, there are indications of changes in blood flow to these organs in cold-stressed, warm- and cold-acclimated animals. Jansky & Hart (113) found that cold-acclimated rats have a higher cardiac output than controls when measured at 30°C and that exposure to 9°C for 70 min further increases the cardiac output by 46% in both cold- and warm-acclimated animals. Blood flow increased to muscular organs and the adrenals of warm-acclimated rats, whereas in cold-acclimated animals it increased to brown and white adipose tissues, pancreas, kidney, intestine, liver, and other internal organs. They (113) report that extramuscular thermogenesis can account for a greater proportion of the total nonshivering thermogenesis in the cold-acclimated rat than in the control.

Changes in peripheral circulation after cold acclimatization, such as occurs in the hands of fishermen living in cold climates, have been studied extensively (114–116). The higher tolerance to cold and resistance to frost damage is apparently due primarily, if not entirely, to an improvement of the vasodilatory "hunting" reaction. According to Weiner (117) such local acclimatization probably involves the same responses even in diverse ethnic groups. Since the subject of local acclimatization to cold has been reviewed recently by Hampton (114) it will not be considered further here.

Animals native to cold climates, which develop heavy insulation for winter survival, generally have some sparsely furred areas where skin temperature is regulated by vascular changes and through which heat loss to the environment can be increased to prevent overheating (27, 118, 119). Examples of such areas are bare footpads of dogs and porcupines, the lower leg of the reindeer, and the furless tail of the muskrat. Little & Stoner (120) have measured the rate of heat loss from the tail of cold-acclimated (3°C) and control (20°C) rats and find that, at 20°C, heat loss through the tail is greater in the acclimated animals than in the controls. According to Rand et al (121) this difference is probably due to an increased vascularity of the tail during cold acclimation. Thompson & Stevenson (122) have shown, by means of hypothalamic lesions, that such vascular responses in the tail are centrally regulated. Thus, the question of what "triggers" the change in hypothalamic regulation becomes important to an understanding of vascular changes.

In poorly insulated extremities of animals living in the cold, nerves must be adapted to function at low temperatures, and recently studies have been made on the conduction properties of such nerves (118, 123). Miller (118) reports that caudal nerves that are "accustomed" to cold have a lower action potential extinction temperature (to −6°C) and generally better low-temperature operating characteristics than nerves from warm, well-insulated tails. These nerves also survive freezing, and thus probably remain functional in the cold as a result of such thermal characteristics. Petajan (123) has found that immediately after cold exposure there is a reduction in the in vivo nerve conduction velocity of rat ventral caudal nerve, especially when measured at temperatures above 20°C. With prolonged cold exposure (2–4 weeks), however, there is full recovery of nerve function. In comparing temperature-dependent characteristics of various nerves of the beaver (*Castor canadensis*), Miller (124) found that the caudal nerve, which is often exposed to cold, invariably conducts action potentials until it freezes at −5°C, while the phrenic nerve, which is never exposed to cold, fails at 4.5°C. Such studies on nerve conduction characteristics as a function of prolonged cold exposure are of considerable interest and allow for investigation of the biochemical mechanisms involved in maintenance of neural function at low tissue temperatures.

Certain indications of adaptive biochemical differences seen in mammalian tissues subjected to cold have recently been reported by Somero & Johansen (125). Lactic dehydrogenase and pyruvate kinase of arterial smooth muscle of the harbor seal (*Phoca vitulina*) exhibited thermal kinetic properties similar to those observed for enzymes of poikilotherms. Thus the enzyme-substrate affinity is inversely proportional to temperature over the range of temperatures to which the heterothermic flipper tissues are naturally exposed. Whether such enzymatic changes can occur as a cold-acclimation response or are found only in preadapted animals remains to be investigated.

Shivering.—Shivering may be considered an emergency mechanism which functions when cold stress is severe and the rate of heat loss exceeds the capacity of the animal to maintain body temperature by nonshivering means. Although a description of the neural control of shivering is beyond the scope of this review (19, 20, 126–129) mention should be made of recent findings concerning the effects of cold acclimation on shivering level and threshold.

Budd & Warhaft (130) found no difference in shivering in men exposed to 10°C before and after 24 weeks in the Antarctic. On the other hand, Wyndham & Loots (90) found that shivering appeared to decrease in men during 1 year in the Antarctic. Also, Korean women divers have an elevated shivering threshold in winter when they are exposed to severe cold stress (89). Shivering is equally high in both warm- and cold-acclimated ground squirrels and increases linearly with O_2 consumption as ambient temperature decreases (77). The cold-acclimated hamster shivers less than the warm-acclimated hamster relative to both ambient temperature and O_2 consumption (131). Furthermore, in the warm-acclimated hamster, shivering increases progressively at ambient temperatures below 20°C and the electrical activity of the muscles doubles between 30° and 0°C, while in the cold-acclimated animal electrical activity increases only at temperatures below 0°C (131). In the New Zealand rabbit, shivering decreases with time in the cold from 190 μV when a warm-acclimated rabbit is first exposed to 6°C to 76 μV after 3 weeks cold exposure (79). By independently varying the cervical spinal and subcutaneous temperatures of guinea pigs in order to trigger or suppress shivering, Brück & Wünnenberg (132) have found a reduction of approximately 1°C in the threshold temperature at which shivering occurs in animals raised at 3°C compared with those raised at 30°C. According to them (132), this would result in regulation of the deep body temperature of the cold-acclimated guinea pig at a level about 1°C below the controls, thereby reducing the energy requirements for temperature regulation. Surprisingly, short-term cold-acclimated miniature pigs, which show no nonshivering thermogenesis, shiver more than controls at ambient temperatures below 20°C (133).

It is well known that rodents acclimated to cold indoors show many compensatory physiological adjustments different from those seen in outdoor cold-acclimatized rodents (see 28, 41, 83). Similarly, adult sheep, cold-acclimated indoors, shiver more when exposed to −30°C than sheep cold-acclimatized outdoors (80). Since these sheep were shorn before the test, differences in length of fleece could not account for the differences in shivering, nor were there differences in calculated tissue insulation.

Brown adipose tissue.—Since the thermogenic role of brown adipose tissue has recently been thoroughly reviewed by Smith & Horwitz (55), our discussion of this tissue will be limited primarily to papers which have appeared since this review.

In the rat, brown fat mass, O_2 consumption, and estimated caloric output increase following cold exposure such that the estimated heat production of this tissue in the cold-acclimated rat is some 5–8 times higher than that of controls (134). It has been demonstrated that the specific activities (activity/mg N/unit time) of a number of mitochondrial enzymes of brown fat decrease immediately after exposure to cold, and in some cases remain low for up to 4 days (134, 135). During this period, however, N content of the tissue increases so that the total activity of most of these enzymes starts to increase within a few hours after cold exposure (134, 135). Roberts & Smith (134) have followed the changes in tissue mass, N content, and rate of α-ketoglutarate oxidation as a function of time in the cold and have found that the most rapid increases in these parameters occur between 4–8 days in the cold. Thus the development of the increased thermogenic potential of brown fat closely parallels the development of nonshivering thermogenesis in this species.

In a detailed study of changes in the ultrastructure of brown fat in cold-exposed rats, Suter (136) has found that after 3 hr in the cold the brown fat mitochondria enlarge and the arrangement of the cristae becomes irregular. Somewhat later numerous small mitochondria with a simple internal structure appear. By 24 hr the mitochondrial cristae have become more numerous and tend to be transverse and this trend continues throughout cold exposure. A comparison of the changes in mean number of mitochondrial cristae per micron mitochondrial diameter with the estimated values of mitochondrial heat production as a function of time in the cold indicates that the more closely packed the cristae, the greater the brown fat mitochondrial capacity to produce heat (136).

In another study of changes in brown fat ultrastructure following exposure of rats to cold, Thomson et al (135) reported that the outer membrane of most mitochondria appears to be incomplete or lacking between 24–96 hr in the cold with restoration beginning after 96 hr and continuing through 3 weeks in the cold. Such changes in membrane integrity were not seen by Suter (136) and are difficult to interpret.

Although the effects of laboratory cold acclimation on brown fat have been studied extensively in several species (3, 55, 137), few studies have been made on seasonal changes in this tissue in nonhibernating rodents either maintained outdoors (138) or captured in the wild (139) throughout the year. Didow & Hayward (139) found that changes in the relative mass of brown fat in the meadow vole are inversely related to changes in ambient temperature of the animal's microhabitat. Thus the relative mass of brown adipose tissue is lowest in summer, increases rapidly to a maximum in early winter prior to the accumulation of heavy snow when the animals establish protective subnivean nests, and thereafter begins to decrease (139). Similarly, in rats maintained year-round outdoors, Gilbert & Pagé (138) found that brown fat mass and fat-free dry matter increased during the winter, reaching maxima in April and February respectively. The greatest increase in mass occurred between January and February and corresponds to the time of maximal daily temperature fluctuations and lowest minimum daily temperatures. These authors (138) also found that the maximum metabolic response of rats to tyramine occurred in April, when brown fat mass was maximal, rather than in February when the fat-free dry matter was maximal. It is possible, however, that the decrease in total tissue fat-free dry matter between February and April reflects a change in some component other than the mitochondria and therefore does not represent a decreased metabolic capacity of the tissue. Since the maximum response to tyramine and the maximum temperature stress were out of phase, Gilbert & Pagé (138) question whether there is a true relationship between the tyramine response and cold resistance, at least in the Spring.

Since the brown fat of the rat represents only a small portion of the body weight, even in the cold-acclimated animal (55), there has been considerable controversy as to whether the heat produced by this tissue can contribute significantly to the total heat production of the cold-acclimated animal. Recent estimates suggest brown fat accounts for only about 8% of the total heat production in the cold-stressed rat (55). However, removal of the interscapular brown fat from rats, either before or after cold acclimation, (a) reduces cold resistance, (b) decreases the metabolic response to E, NE, and tyramine, and (c) leads to increased secretion of NE in the cold, which suggests a decrease in nonshivering thermogenesis (140). The loss of responsiveness to NE or E in cold-acclimated rats does not occur immediately after removal of the interscapular brown fat, but occurs progressively during the first 4 days after the operation (141) and appears to be quantitatively related to the percent of the total brown fat removed (140). Since the decreased metabolic response to catecholamine cannot be accounted for directly by the O_2 consumption or heat production of the amount of brown adipose tissue removed, it has been proposed that brown fat exerts its influence on nonshivering thermogenesis indirectly. One possibility, suggested by Brück & Wünnenberg (142, 143), is that the heat produced in the brown fat warms thermosensitive elements in the cervical spinal chord, suppressing shivering when the temperature of these elements is above the "shivering threshold". Another possibility, suggested by Leduc & Rivest (140) and Himms-Hagen (141), is that brown fat secretes a humoral agent, and that this agent in turn either elevates thermogenesis in other tissues (140) or increases their ability to produce heat in response to catecholamines (141).

Smith & Horwitz (55) have reviewed much of the literature relating to coupling of oxidative phosphorylation in brown fat mitochondria. Most of the recent evidence indicates that brown fat mitochondria are capable of coupled oxidative phosphorylation and that this can be demonstrated in vitro under the proper incubation conditions (55, 144–148). The sensitivity of brown fat to norepinephrine and the facility with which brown fat mitochondria can be uncoupled in vitro have led a number of workers (144, 146, 148, 149) to propose a hormonally controlled, fatty acid-induced uncoupling, or "loosening" of coupling, in brown fat mitochondria as a mechanism of regulating heat production from this tissue. Rafael et al (148) have proposed a hormonally controlled fatty acid-uncoupling/GTP(ATP)-recoupling cycle. This cycle involves a cold-induced release of NE which stimulates brown fat lipolysis and free fatty acid release. This leads to an un-coupling of oxidative phosphorylation, a "loosening" of respiratory control, and an increase in substrate oxidation (heat production). With removal of the cold stimulus, free fatty acid levels decrease and coupling is rapidly re-stored under the influence of GTP, or ATP, which is formed via substrate-linked phosphorylation even in uncoupled mitochondria (148). Rafael et al (148) were unable to determine from their studies the mechanism by which GTP induced recoupling in fatty acid-uncoupled mitochondria. Hittelman et al (144) found that coupled respiration can be restored in isolated brown fat mitochondria by incubating these particles with ATP + carnitine. They have proposed that endogenous fatty acids, possibly a small, specific frac-tion of those within the mitochondria, act as uncouplers and that in the presence of ATP + carnitine these are transported into mitochondrial com-partments in which they can either be oxidized or isolated so that they can no longer exert their uncoupling effects (144).

In addition to its effect on brown fat lipolysis, it has recently been shown that NE causes a depolarization of brown fat cell membranes both in vitro (150) and in vivo (55, 151). Also, Girardier et al (150) report lower mem-brane potentials in brown fat from cold-acclimated rats than from controls. This has led to the suggestion that changes in the ionic permeability of the cell membrane and in the rate of active transport of Na^+ and K^+, with con-comitant changes in the rate of formation of ADP, might, at least in part, regulate brown fat respiration during exposure to cold (150, 151). In effect, this suggests an increase in Na^+/K^+-ATPase as a source of ADP for mainte-nance of high tissue respiration during cold stress. Herd et al (152) have found that NE stimulates the in vitro activity of an ouabain-sensitive Na^+/K^+-ATPase in brown fat from cold-acclimated rats. Although the direct re-lationship between this and the NE-induced membrane depolarization seen in vivo is not clearly established, it does indicate that NE induces an in-creased ATP turnover (152). Moreover, the resulting increase in ADP for-mation, coupled with the fact that NE-induced lipolysis also increases sub-strate (fatty acid) availability, suggests that the high respiratory rate of brown adipose tissue, induced by cold stress or NE stimulation, may be sus-tained, at least in part, by an energy-utilizing system rather than an un-coupling of oxidative phosphorylation (151, 152).

Norepinephrine and nonshivering thermogenesis.—In the laboratory rat, cold acclimation results in an increased ability to produce heat by nonshiv-ering thermogenesis, an increased sensitivity to NE, and an increased resis-tance to severe cold stress (73, 153). The increased calorigenic response to NE appears to be closely associated with the level of nonshivering thermo-genesis (73, 154–156) and is commonly used as an index of the capacity of an animal to produce heat by nonshivering means. However, the rat is ap-parently not representative of the extent to which such thermogenesis de-velops in cold-acclimated homeotherms in general. Not only does the response to NE vary markedly with age (133, 157–160), but it also varies from species to species (133, 153, 161).

The relationship between cold- or NE-induced thermogenesis and brown fat is well established in the newborn of several species (see Brück 157, 162, 163 and Smith & Horwitz 55 for more details). The capacity for developing nonshivering thermogenesis declines rapidly with age in several species including the rat (160), guinea pig (158, 162), kitten (157), and lamb (159) and is replaced by shivering. This decline in nonshivering thermogenesis is accompanied by a reduction in brown fat (158, 159, 162, 164). In the guinea pig this process can be retarded, but not completely abolished, by raising the animals in a cold environment (158). Alexander & Williams (159) estimate that nonshivering thermogenesis accounts for 31% and shivering 46% of the summit metabolism in the newborn lamb. By 3 weeks of age nonshivering thermogenesis has declined to 4% and shivering has increased to 78% of the summit metabolisms, the balance being interpreted as the true basal metabolism (159). Adult sheep show no response to NE, even when partly shorn and cold acclimated (165).

In several species of adult mammals, nonshivering thermogenesis and the calorigenic response to NE appear to be related to the presence of brown adipose tissue (55, 138, 140, 141, 158, 162). Figure 1 is an attempt to demonstrate this relationship in cold-acclimated animals using data available in the literature. With the exception of the miniature pigs, which were 4–6 weeks old (133), all animals represented are adults. Some of the assumptions made in estimating total brown fat for this figure and the rationale behind these estimates are as follows: (a) multilocular cells typical of brown adipose tissue have been reported in adult humans (166) but no estimate was made of the total amount. In light of the relatively small amount of brown fat reported in other primates (55, 137) it has been estimated that this would not exceed 0.1% of the body weight; (b) the maximum value given by Smith & Horwitz (55) for brown fat in the hedgehog has been taken as representative of the amount one might expect to find in the cold-acclimated hedgehog prior to hibernation; (c) the interscapular brown fat of the mouse is reported to be 0.463% of the body weight (167). It is assumed that in the mouse, as in the rat (168), this represents approximately one-third the total brown fat.

Although data on brown fat mass and NE response frequently came from different sources (see legend, Figure 1) and the number of species represented is relatively small, there is a significant correlation between these two parameters.

Hayward (personal communication) has recently found that relative brown fat protein or fat-free dry matter shows a better correlation with NE response than does brown fat wet weight in a series of small rodents. This relationship is shown in Figure 2, again using data from the literature. In this case it appears that the NE response in hibernators (hedgehog, ground squirrel, hamster, and chipmunk) is lower than would be expected on the

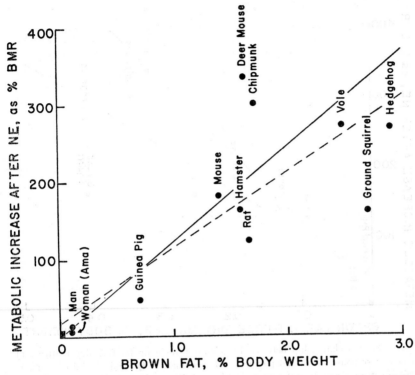

FIGURE 1. Relationship between brown fat (as % body weight) and metabolic response to norepinephrine in cold-acclimated mammals. Vertical bar at $X = 0$ represents the miniature pig (133), sheep (165), and rabbit (78) for which the (X,Y) coordinates are (0,0), (0,0) and (0,10) respectively. Both NE and brown fat data on vole, deer mouse, and chipmunk are from Hayward (personal communication). Assumptions regarding brown fat data on hedgehog, human, and mouse are explained in the text. Brown fat data on guinea pig (158), rat (55), hamster (55), and ground squirrel (169) and NE response data on man (86), woman (89), guinea pig (133, 153), mouse (84, 153), hamster (170), rat (153), ground squirrel (77), and hedgehog (153) are taken from the literature. Solid line = least squares regression line for nonhibernators only ($r = 0.885$). Broken line = regression line for all species ($r = 0.833$). The slopes of these lines are not significantly different.

basis of the amount of brown fat they are assumed to possess. Therefore two regression lines have been calculated, one using only data on cold-acclimated nonhibernators (Figure 2, solid line, $r = 0.983$) and the other using data for all the cold-acclimated species (Figure 2, broken line, $r = 0.825$). Although the slopes of these two lines are not statistically different ($0.05 < p < 0.1$), before any definite conclusions can be drawn with respect to the relationship between NE and brown fat in hibernating species, more work

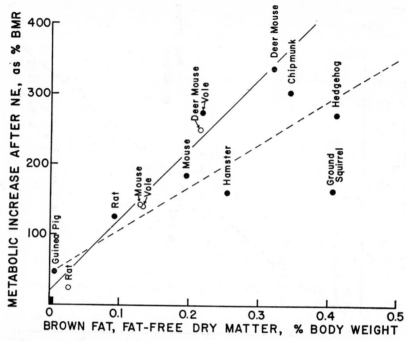

FIGURE 2. Relationship between brown fat protein or fat-free dry matter and metabolic response to norepinephrine in cold-acclimated (●) and control (○) mammals. Vertical bar at $X = 0$ same as in Figure 1. Brown fat and NE response data as in Figure 1 except for data on brown fat protein or fat-free dry matter (per gram tissue or % wet weight) for rat (168), hamster (171), guinea pig (unpublished data), and ground squirrel (172). Solid line = least squares regression line for cold-acclimated nonhibernators only ($r = 0.983$). Broken line = regression line for all cold-acclimated species ($r = 0.825$).

must be done in which these two parameters are measured simultaneously. With the exception of the chipmunk, which comes fairly close to the regression line for nonhibernators, data on NE response and brown fat mass have been taken from different sources in the literature. Since in most hibernators the brown fat mass varies seasonally (55), it is possible that the animals on which NE response was measured were not comparable, with respect to this seasonal cycle, to those in which brown fat was measured. Also, the extent to which hibernators cold acclimate before entering hibernation may vary considerably, thus influencing the extent of the NE response.

In the cold-acclimated nonhibernators, there appears to be a significant correlation between brown fat and NE response. It is interesting that a number of control nonhibernators also show this relationship between brown fat and NE response (Figure 2), when brown fat protein or fat-free dry matter (rather than wet weight) is used as a reference. This no doubt reduces the error in weight otherwise introduced by the infiltration of brown fat with white fat in control animals. Thus species differences in the relative amount of this fat-free dry matter may explain why a significant response to NE is seen in the control mouse, but not the control rat (see Figure 2). The possible mechanisms by which brown fat influences nonshivering thermogenesis in cold-acclimated mammals are discussed in the preceding section and have been reviewed in detail by Smith & Horwitz (55).

An interspecies survey of metabolic acclimation to cold, as determined by the calorigenic response to NE, reveals that a number of species of adult mammals, includuding man, develop some degree of nonshivering thermogenesis in response to prolonged cold stress. This is illustrated in Figures 1 and 2.

Other species which exhibit a calorigenic response to NE, but which were not shown in Figures 1 and 2 because brown fat data were not available, include the bat *Myotis lucifugus* (161), the dog (75), and the cat (76). The bat, when active at room temperature, shows a 10.6-fold increase in metabolic rate in response to NE (161). The dog (75) and cat (76) show a 55% and 36% increase in BMR respectively. The adult rabbit apparently acclimates to cold primarily by increasing its insulation with nonshivering thermogenesis developing as a secondary mechanism when the cold stress is severe (78, 79). Thus, in unshaved adult rabbits, NE increases the metabolic rate only 8–12% (78) above the resting or basal level, whereas in shaved rabbits it is increased by 40–63% (78, 79).

Although in the rat the response to NE varies with the severity of the cold stress or degree of cold acclimation (73), other species show a marked response to NE even when not cold acclimated. Thus, while the unacclimated rat (73) and ground squirrel (77) show significantly less response to NE than their cold-acclimated counterparts, and nonacclimated man (86, 89, 173) and rabbit (78) show none at all, several species of unacclimated mammals, i.e., dog (75), white mouse (84, 153), deer mouse and vole (Hayward, personal communication), hamster (170, 174), Norwegian lemming (175), and hedgehog (153) show a marked response to NE. Moreover, Jeddi (176) has recently pointed out that the response of the control rat (but not the cold-acclimated rat) to NE is significantly higher in unanesthetized animals than in animals anesthetized with pentobarbital, and that anesthesia suppresses 55% of the maximum response to NE in control rats.

Finally, there are those species which show no thermogenic response to NE even after cold acclimation, as for example, birds (28, 30, 31, 48), sheep (165), and miniature pigs (133).

Because several species of newborn mammals show a high capacity for nonshivering thermogenesis and in many cases the cold-acclimated adults of these same species also show varying amounts of such thermogenesis, Brück (157) has proposed that development of nonshivering or chemical thermogenesis during cold acclimation may not be the result of an entirely new mechanism, but may represent the reactivation of a mechanism present in the neonate.

Jansky et al (153) have concluded that homeotherms can be divided into at least three groups with respect to cold acclimation.

1. Those animals in which cold acclimation results in an increase in non-shivering thermogenesis mediated by NE, such as the rat and guinea pig. In this group they also include the rabbit which relies primarily on insulation but develops nonshivering thermogenesis when improvements in insulation are reduced by shaving.

2. Species such as the dog, white mouse, and hedgehog in which both cold- and warm-acclimated animals respond to NE. In these species the role of catecholamines is not clear. Nagasaka & Carlson (75) have suggested that the increased nonshivering thermogenesis seen in the cold-acclimated dog may be due to an increased level of NE in the blood rather than an increased sensitivity of the animal to its calorigenic effects.

3. Species such as birds, miniature pigs, and newborn pigs which show no nonshivering thermogenesis after cold acclimation although in some cases cold resistance is increased. For these species Jansky et al (153) state: "an entirely new mechanism of cold adaptation must be anticipated".

It has been postulated that the hypersensitivity of the cold-acclimated rat to NE may result from tissue saturation (177). Recent studies which test this hypothesis involve depletion of tissue catecholamine levels by reserpine (177, 178) and attempts to mimic cold acclimation by repeated injections of NE with or without an additional cold stimulus (179, 180). Sengupta et al (179) found that NE injected into rats during cold acclimation did not improve their degree of cold acclimation. LeBlanc & Villemaire (180), on the other hand, found that daily injections of NE, thyroxine, or NE + thyroxine into control rats all improved cold resistance and the metabolic response to NE. The most marked effect was found with the combined injection of NE + thyroxine which increased cold resistance to nearly the same level as cold acclimation at 6°C for 35 days.

Injection of reserpine into cold-acclimated rats reduces the cold-induced elevations in BMR, arterial pressure, and heart rate to values not significantly different from those of controls (178). Furthermore, reserpine reduced the sensitivity of cold-acclimated rats to NE and led to a reduction in cold tolerance (177). Thus many of the physiological changes elicited by cold acclimation appear to depend on catecholamines and are at least temporarily lost after depletion of these amines by reserpine.

HEAT ACCLIMATION IN MAMMALS

Animals which acclimate to heat, like those adapted to hot climates, generally show a decreased rate of heat production and/or an increased rate of heat loss. When ambient temperature exceeds body temperature, changes in conductance or insulation may also decrease the rate of heat gain from the environment.

The antelope jack rabbit (*Lepus alleni*) is an excellent example of this latter point. When ambient temperature exceeds body temperature, its conductance decreases, thus impeding the inward flow of heat, while at temperatures between body temperature and thermoneutrality, a high conductance facilitates heat loss (181). Since such conductance changes reduce the requirements for evaporative cooling, the antelope jack rabbit uses less water for evaporation than would be predicted if only its body size were considered (181). Whether heat-acclimated species also use this adaptive mechanism to prevent heat gain when ambient temperature exceeds body temperature is an interesting question.

A growing body of data indicates that many species of small mammals native to hot climates have a depressed metabolic rate relative to that predicted on the basis of body weight (63, 182, 183). Similarly, heat-acclimated (36°C) mice have a significantly lower MR than unacclimated (21°C) mice at ambient temperatures of 32°C and above (184). The metabolic rate of the vole (*Microtus arvalis*) is lower in animals maintained at 30°C and 35°C than in animals kept at 20°C (185). This decrease is not statistically significant, however; the acclimation period at 35°C was short (about 3 days) and a longer acclimation time at this temperature may result in a greater decrease in MR. Seasonal changes in MR of *Microtus* and other species of microtine rodents have been reported to parallel changes in thyroid activity, both MR and thyroid activity being maximal in summer and minimal in winter (186).

Cassuto & Chaffee (187) have hypothesized that, just as cold acclimation results in increased nonshivering thermogenesis, heat acclimation results in a metabolic "chemical thermosuppression". They (187) found that heat-acclimated hamsters have an increased heat tolerance and a decreased cold tolerance compared with controls. The metabolic rate of heat-acclimated hamsters is significantly lower than that of controls over a wide range of ambient temperatures (174, 188, 189). Associated with this reduction in MR is a significant reduction in the relative mass of heat-producing organs (liver, kidney, heart, testes, testes fat pad, brown fat) (187, 189) and in the oxidative enzyme activity of isolated liver mitochondria (187–189), as well as liver glucose 6-phosphatase activity (189). The decrease in oxidative enzyme activity begins the 1st day after heat exposure, reaches its maximum between the 2nd and 5th day, and remains depressed during the whole period of heat exposure (188).

Collins & Weiner (190) and Fregly (191) have recently reviewed the evidence that thyroid activity and release of thyroid hormones are depressed during heat exposure. Cassuto et al (189) have hypothesized that the metabolic and enzymatic changes seen in heat-acclimated hamsters could be nullified by injections of thyroid hormones. The BMR of hamsters (measured at 32°C) can be increased by injections of thyroxine or NE, the effect of either hormone being greater in the heat-acclimated animals than in the controls (174). When both hormones are administered simultaneously the MR of heat-acclimated hamsters increases 110% compared to 60% for controls and the difference between the two groups is abolished (174). Similar hormone injections did not abolish the difference in MR at −15°C, which suggests that factors other than reduced hormonal levels (i.e., reduced levels of oxidative enzymes and decreased mass of heat-producing organs) contribute to the lower heat-production capacity of heat-acclimated hamsters (174). Daily injections of T_3 for 10 days in heat-acclimated hamsters caused an elevation in MR to the same level as that of controls also given T_3, and led to a loss of body weight and severe hyperthermia in heat-acclimated animals (189). The changes in MR following T_3 treatment are reflected in similar changes in liver mitochondrial enzymes. Thus T_3 administration increased the respiration of liver mitochondria 57% in controls and 132% in heat-acclimated animals, so that the enzyme activities of the two groups became similar (189).

Intraperitoneal injection of 2,4-dinitrophenol (DNP) increases the BMR of control hamsters by fourfold and that of heat-acclimated hamsters by sixfold, thus eliminating the difference between the two groups (188). This response resembles that seen after simultaneous injection of thyroxine and norepinephrine. The effect of DNP on respiration of isolated liver mitochondria was also about 50% higher on particles from heat-acclimated animals than on those from controls (188). Cassuto (188) has suggested that the reduced MR of heat-acclimated hamsters is regulated at two levels at least; one a regulatory site on the electron transport chain, which is released by uncouplers and the other a decrease in the concentration of respiratory enzymes.

Rats exposed to heat (34°C) show a significant increase in MR lasting from less than 48–72 hr (depending on age), followed by a decline in MR to levels equal to or less than those of controls (192). Rats acclimated to 30°C for 6–8 weeks have a lower MR (at 30°C) than control or cold-acclimated rats and cannot maintain as high an MR at 5°C as cold-acclimated animals (193). Yousef & Johnson (192) suggest that the initial rise in MR upon exposure to heat may be the result of increased adrenal cortical activity, an initially high thyroid activity, or increased muscular exertion of respiration. They (192) attribute the subsequent decline in MR during acclimation to decreased thyroid and adrenal cortical activity.

Kotby and his co-workers (194, 195) have found that sudden exposure of rats to 34°C causes an increase in plasma corticosterone level to a maximum at 24 hr. Levels remained elevated until day 13 when the plasma corticosterone decreased to slightly below the control value, with a return to control level by day 15 (194). Normal levels were subsequently maintained during 9 weeks continuous exposure to heat (195). Bertin (196), on the other hand, found that both adrenal and plasma levels of corticosterone decreased in rats exposed to 30°C for 48 hr and remained below normal for at least 1 month. After 4 months in the heat, plasma levels of corticosterone returned to normal while adrenal levels remained depressed (196). Collins & Weiner (190), in reviewing the effects of heat on endocrines, report that acute heat stress and hyperthermia lead to an increase in plasma corticoids in many animals, while after prolonged heat exposure, lower plasma glucocorticoid levels and decreased urinary excretion of metabolites suggest that glucocorticoid secretion may be reduced.

As stated earlier, there is considerable evidence that thyroid activity is depressed in the heat (190). Recent studies in the rat support this conclusion. Yousef & Johnson (197) found that thyroid activity was decreased in rats exposed to 34°C compared to controls (28°C). However, when the food intake of the controls was restricted to the level of rats fed *ad libitum* in the heat, the disappearance of much of this difference suggested that the voluntary feed restriction seen in heat-acclimated animals may be a factor in determining decreased thyroid activity (197). Thus, in heat acclimation, as in cold acclimation (96–99, 106, 109), changes in thyroid activity appear to depend, at least in part, on food intake. Yousef & Johnson (198) have also found shifts in the relative amounts of iodine compounds in the plasma of heat-acclimated rats. The relative amount of thyroxine decreases, while that of free I^- and monoiodotyrosine increases during heat acclimation (198). Hutchins (199) found that the reduced excretion of thyroid hormones in heat-acclimated rats is due to a reduced biliary clearance of circulating hormones and not to the observed reduction in bile flow.

Like the hamster, heat-acclimated rats show a significant decrease in the weight of a number of internal organs (72). Succinoxidase and cytochrome oxidase activities of liver decrease during heat acclimation (200). Kidney, heart, and muscle show slight, but not significant, changes in these enzymes (200). In general, the enzyme changes seen during heat acclimation can be mimicked by treatment of unacclimated animals with aldosterone, whose secretion is increased, at least initially, in the heat (190, 200, 201). Henane & Laurent (201) have shown that administration of the aldosterone inhibitor spirolactone to rats at the beginning of heat exposure impairs the process of heat acclimation, but does not affect animals already acclimated to heat. They (201) suggest that, since spirolactone inhibits aldosterone secretion only when the latter exceeds a certain threshold, the secretion of aldosterone is either normal or decreased in completely heat-acclimated animals.

Man, like other animals, also shows true acclimation to heat which manifests itself in the ability to tolerate heat (202–208). With increase in heat stress, the mean rectal temperature is higher and the skewness greater in both acclimatized and unacclimatized men, but at a given level of heat stress the mean rectal temperature is higher and the skewness greater in unacclimatized men.

In accord with the above-mentioned finding that aldosterone plays a role in the heat-acclimation process in rats, Wyndham et al (209) postulate that, in man, the secretion of this hormone, as well as antidiuretic hormone (ADH), increases as a result of the marked central circulatory instability observed in the first few days of acclimation. They (209) hypothesize that this instability stimulates volume receptors which cause an increase in the secretion of both aldosterone and ADH. The result is a retention of salt and water and a consequent expansion in plasma volume and extracellular space. The latter changes stabilize the central circulation with a resultant decrease in the stimulus to the volume receptors and a decrease in aldosterone secretion (209). Braun et al (210) report that administration of aldosterone to men in the heat made it possible for them to march longer, with a lower pulse rate and lower rectal temperature during the first few days of heat exposure. Aldosterone, however, did not shorten the time required for achieving total acclimation. In long-term residents of a hot environment, the excretion of glucocorticoids and aldosterone is not increased (211). These studies (210, 211) further support the thesis (209) that as central circulation is stabilized during heat acclimation, the stimulus for aldosterone secretion declines.

Several studies on the problem of optimum conditions for producing heat acclimation in man (212, 213) and the role of physical conditioning in producing this acclimation (8, 214, 215) indicate that training and physical fitness cannot substitute for heat acclimatization and that to achieve a good state of acclimation for work in heat, men must work at a moderate rate in relatively severe heat. On the other hand, Gisolfi & Robinson (216) have found that interval training significantly improves heat tolerance of men, and might be considered as positive cross acclimation. However, they (216) agree with the concept that exercise alone cannot fully acclimatize men for work in the heat. For a more complete coverage of indices and measurements used in assessing heat acclimatization in man the reader is referred to Fox (217).

Comparative studies have been made on the heat responses of different ethnic groups to a standard metabolic rate (5 kcal/min) and environmental heat stress (32°C wet bulb and low air velocity). Included in these tests were Caucasoids, Bantu, and Kalahari Bushmen in Southern Africa; Arabs and Frenchmen living in the desert; and aborigines and "white" Australians in the Australian tropics (218–225). The results indicate that local environmental heat stresses and physical activity habits are more important determinants of the state of heat acclimatization than are ethnic origin or stature and body size.

Recent studies on the effects of age on heat tolerance and heat acclimatization in man yield somewhat conflicting results (226, 227). Robinson et al (226) found that responses of older men to work in the heat were similar to those observed in the same subjects 21 years earlier. However, Lind et al (227) found indications of a decreased ability to maintain rectal temperature in older men when both young and old men were exposed to hot climatic conditions. Differences in the physical fitness of the older subjects in the two studies (226, 227) may explain the differences in results.

Women appear to be more adversely affected than men by short-term exposure to severe heat stress or to work in the heat (228), perhaps at least in part because women sweat less than men when exposed to severe heat (228–230) or because endocrine differences are an important factor in the early stages of heat acclimatization. After acclimatization, however, body temperature and circulatory reactions of both sexes are similar. Fox et al (230) hypothesize that the observed differences between the sexes might indicate that women are "less heat-acclimatized" than men even when both sexes are living in identical climatic conditions. They (230) explain their hypothesis on the basis of sex differences in such parameters as behavior, clothing, activity, insulation, and sweat mechanism training. On the other hand, Dill et al (231) found that, in children and adults walking at 80 or 100 m per min in the desert, the rate of sweating was related to body surface, metabolic rate, and ambient temperature and not to sex or age. Differences in humidity may account, at least in part, for the differences in results between these two studies (230, 231). Collins et al (232) have discussed in some detail the effect of training of sweat glands on the overall response to heat and the possibility that changes in the central nervous excitability threshold in acclimatization to heat, control sweat output in proportion to heat load. Acclimatization also appears to be an important factor in reducing Na loss in the sweat of men in hot climates (233). For a discussion of differences in sweat rates of lean and obese men and women exposed to heat the reader is referred to the work of Buskirk and his associates (234). Höfler (235) points out a shift in regional distribution of sweating toward the limbs during acclimatization to heat which indicates a better utilization of large surface areas. This in turn seems to indicate a local (body regional) type of heat acclimation somewhat comparable to local acclimation of the circulatory system in cold acclimatization.

A number of studies have been conducted in the past few years on both heat acclimation and heat adaptation in large mammals. Many of the adapted animals studied are desert species, and are faced not only with severe environmental heat, but also a paucity of water, which limits its use for evaporative cooling. There is evidence, however, that some of the "adaptive" mechanisms found in desert species may also be present in "unadapted" mammals and can be activated by exposure to heat and dehydration.

Like the camel (236), the eland (237) and the burro (238) tolerate an increase in body temperature during the day and lose the stored heat to the cooler environment at night by conduction and convection, thus markedly reducing the amount of water required for evaporative cooling. A number of species of large mammals show a decrease in metabolic rate when dehydrated. This also decreases the heat load which much be dissipated by evaporation at high ambient temperatures (236, 239, 240). Dehydration also leads to a reduction of evaporation and a delay in the onset of sweating in response to heat exposure in the steer (239, 241). Taylor, Robertshaw, and their co-workers (237, 240, 242–244) have made an extensive study of the water requirements, water balance, and evaporative cooling in large bovids which inhabit the arid and semiarid regions of East Africa. These animals vary in their water requirements from the oryx, which can survive indefinitely without drinking, to the waterbuck, which is restricted to areas where water is available (240).

In heat-acclimated sheep, the initial steady rate of evaporation becomes shorter and the onset of sweating occurs sooner after exposure to heat than in controls (245). This suggests a sensitization of the sweating mechanism similar to that seen in man (232).

Heat-acclimated cows show significant decreases in heat production, as indicated by decreased MR, pulse rate, food intake, and milk production, and significant increases in heat loss via increased evaporation (both respiratory and surface) and increased tissue conductance (246). Within 60 hr after exposure to 38°C the metabolic rate of cows is significantly reduced and this reduction is accompanied by a significant decline in thyroid activity (247).

Heat acclimation in the pig involves a reduction in MR (248, 249) and in thyroid activity (249). Restricting the food intake of animals in a cooler environment to the level eaten voluntarily by heat-acclimated animals reduces the difference in MR between the groups, but a reduction in MR is still evident in the heat-acclimated animals if the difference in ambient temperature is large (25°C vs 35°C) (248). Pigs raised at 35°C have less hair, are taller and less stocky, and have longer tails and larger ears than their littermates raised at 20°C or 5°C (250). Furthermore, pigs raised in the heat (35°C) have more blood vessels in their skin than those raised in the cold (5°C), although there is no significant difference between pigs raised at 20°C and 35°C (251). Although pigs possess sweat glands they apparently do not sweat even at high environmental temperatures, thus their habit of wallowing in mud is an effective means of increasing evaporative cooling in the heat in the absence of increased sweating (252).

BIOCHEMICAL MECHANISMS

Although much research has been conducted to elucidate the tissue biochemical bases of the observed changes in metabolic rate which occur in proglonged cold or heat exposure, progress has been slow. However, a healthy awareness of the complexity of the problem has developed.

One tacit assumption made in the past was that a basic understanding of biochemical changes and mechanisms in acclimation of the rat would be generally applicable to other mammals and man. This assumption is now recognized by many to be an untenable oversimplification. Thus the approach to the problem is complicated because some biochemical acclimation mechanisms may be species specific, whereas others may apply to the order or class or even possibly to all homeotherms. It would seem, therefore, that before a clear picture of the complex mechanisms of tissue thermogenesis can be obtained, more attention must be given to problems in comparative biochemistry of temperature acclimation.

Enzymes and cofactors.—In rodents the levels of oxidative enzyme activity in liver, kidney, skeletal muscle, and brown fat are generally elevated in cold- and lowered in heat acclimation. However, no such changes are observed in acclimated adult *Macaca mulatta* (3), and very few enzymatic changes are found in acclimated squirrel monkeys *Saimiri sciurea* (1, 2). Thus significant changes in oxidative enzyme levels apparently are not involved in the acclimation process in these monkeys. A number of oxidative enzymatic changes occur in the protoprimate *Tupaia chinensis,* but these are lower in magnitude and fewer than the changes seen in rodents (3). Since this protoprimate weighs about half the usual laboratory rat, i.e. 165 g, body size cannot be considered the determining factor in the extent to which tissue enzymatic changes occur in heat and cold acclimation (3). On the basis of the number and magnitude of oxidative enzyme changes during acclimation to heat or cold, it has been postulated that the species studied may be ranked as follows: rodent > *Suncus* (shrew) > *Tupaia* > *Saimiri* > *Macaca* (3).

As yet, there is no proof that the classical changes in levels of oxidative enzymes seen in vitro in liver, kidney, and skeletal muscle of some cold-acclimated laboratory rodents are directly related to the nonshivering thermogenic increase in MR, or that they are necessary for survival.

The possibility that an enzyme might be changed, not quantitatively, but qualitatively during cold acclimation has been considered (253, 254). Lactic dehydrogenase (LDH) isozyme distribution is altered in brown fat of the hamster (253) and in heart and liver of the rat (254). Whether these isozymic changes are common or the exception, is an important question. In man, during cold acclimation, plasma LDH isozymic changes occur (255). However, plasma changes may not reflect a change in genetic transcription, but may result from differential leakage of LDH from muscle and heart. Such leakage would be in accord with observed changes in cell permeability to creatine phosphokinase in the cold-exposed rat (256).

Changes in cofactor levels also might be responsible for the observed in vitro changes in enzyme activity. Aithal et al (257) have found that in cold-acclimated rats ubiquinone is catabolized more slowly and synthesized more rapidly than in controls. Liver ubiquinone levels increase until day 40, and then level off, possibly in coincidence with completion of acclimation (257). Whether similar changes in ubiquinone occur in other tissues of the rat or in tissues of other species remains to be determined.

An increased utilization of lipid and an increased capacity to oxidize fatty acids have been reported in cold-acclimated rats (258, 259). This has led to an investigation of the effects of cold acclimation on the cofactor carnitine, which is important in lipid metabolism (259, 260). Therriault &

Mehlman (259) found increases in the body pool of carnitine and in the concentration of carnitine in skeletal muscle in cold-acclimated rats. This apparently is not due to retention of carnitine since its half-life and turnover time are reduced to about half the control values and its daily excretion is increased (259). Delisle & Radomski (260) found that total acid-soluble carnitine increased in liver, muscle, and heart of cold-acclimated rats, but free carnitine and acylcarnitine levels increased only in liver. Their results with skeletal muscle do not confirm the marked increase reported by Therriault & Mehlman (259) in cold-acclimated rats. It has been proposed (259) that increased levels of carnitine in the tissues of cold-acclimated rats would lead to increased formation of acylcarnitine, which could then cross the mitochondrial membrane leading to increased oxidation of fatty acids. The latter could contribute to the higher MR seen in cold acclimation, but whether it does is still undetermined. The changes in feedback control which allow for such changes in cofactor levels also present interesting problems.

A number of early studies on mitochondrial preparations containing cytoplasmic contaminants showed "uncoupling" of oxidative phosphorylation (261) in liver mitochondria from cold-acclimated rats. Recent studies on rat liver homogenates (262, 263) confirm these findings and suggest that extramitochondrial contaminants may uncouple rat liver mitochondria in vitro. However, neither isolated mitochondria nor whole homogenates (containing intact mitochondria) of rat brain show any changes in P/O ratio after cold acclimation (264). Moreover, in the chipmunk, which remains active in the cold (2.5°C) for months and thus must be considered acclimated, there is no change in P/O ratio of liver homogenates (265). This lack of "uncoupling" in response to cold acclimation has also been found in other species (3). Thus the evidence fails to confirm that "uncoupling" of mitochondrial oxidative phosphorylation in such tissues as the liver is a general cold-acclimation thermogenic response.

Lipid metabolism.—In cold acclimation, changes may occur in the degree of saturation of certain fatty acids both in stored fat (266, 267) and in structural lipids of mitochondria and endoplasmic reticulum (268, 269). Such chemical changes might be associated with distinct structural changes in these subcellular elements and may, in part, account for the greater fragility of liver mitochondria from cold-acclimated rats than from controls (270); they also introduce the possibility that other subcellular structures such as the lysosomal membrane or the plasma membrane are altered. One indication of the latter is an increased cellular enzyme leakage during cold acclimation (256). If there is a generalized increase in cell membrane permeability in cold acclimation, then leakage of a number of small molecules may also be increased. The increased active transport required to counter such an increase in leakage could serve as an ATPase and thus stimulate cellular metabolism by providing increased levels of ADP. This increased cellular metabolism would, in turn, be reflected in the in vivo metabolic rate.

Harland & Barnett (271) have found that, although there are changes in the composition of body fats in adult mice exposed to prolonged cold, mice raised in the cold did not differ consistently in fat composition from controls. This introduces the possibility that compensatory changes, not involving changes in fat metabolism, can occur in mice raised in the cold, but that such thermogenic biochemical prerogatives may no longer be open to cold-exposed adults. This difference in response as a function of age has also been pointed out with respect to the metabolic response to NE (155). Such age-dependent variations in acclimation responses may make it difficult to compare different animal groups because full physiological maturity has an ill-defined end point in many species.

In humans, exposure to prolonged cold causes regional changes in the composition of subcutaneous fat (272). Specifically a lower percentage of saturated fatty acids and a higher percentage of palmitoleic acid were found in the fat of the extremities, which are often exposed to cold, than in the trunk, which is always protected by clothing. Itoh et al (272) conclude that such changes in fat composition would result in softer adipose tissue in the cold-exposed extremities than in the trunk.

Earlier studies on the effects of cold acclimation on the metabolism of lipids have been reviewed (Masoro 258, white adipose tissue; and Smith & Horwitz 55, brown fat). Cold acclimation alters a number of parameters of lipid metabolism. Recently Shields & Platner (273) have found that cold acclimation has different effects on the oxidation of specific fatty acids, increasing the total in vivo oxidation of palmitate, but not oleate. This points out the danger of using any single fatty acid as an index of altered lipid metabolism resulting from temperature acclimation. Hubbard et al (274) have measured the rate of incorporation of $2\text{-}^{14}\text{C}$-glycerol into glyceride-glycerol of isolated fat cells from cold-acclimated and control rats. When their data are expressed on a μg DNA basis, the rate of incorporation of glycerol into glyceride-glycerol is about 25% lower in cells from cold-acclimated rats than from controls. If the same data are expressed per μg triglyceride the reverse is found. These authors (274) point out the importance of expressing such data in units related to cell number (i.e., DNA) rather than tissue mass (i.e., triglyceride), particularly where the stressor studied can affect the triglyceride content of the cell.

Therriault et al (275) have found that cold acclimation renders adipose tissue more sensitive to the mobilizing action of NE. They (275) have shown that fat cell homogenates and fat cell ghosts from cold-acclimated rats are both more sensitive to the action of NE than are preparations from rats maintained at 25°C in that they accumulate more adenosine 3',5'-monophosphate (CAMP) upon addition of NE + theophylline. There is considerable evidence that CAMP acts as an intracellular second messenger in the lipolytic action of catecholamines and stimulates lipolysis in both brown and white adipose tissue (55, 275, 276). Therriault et al (275) conclude that their data support the thesis that increased NE-induced lipolysis in fat cells isolated from cold-acclimated rats is probably a secondary effect related to an increased sensitivity of the fat cells to the NE-induced accumulation of CAMP. An increased sensitivity of adipose tissue, but not diaphragm muscle, to the lipogenic action of insulin has also been reported in cold-acclimated rats (277).

Cold-acclimated rats respond differently from controls when fed a high fat, cholesterol-containing diet (278). In controls such a diet causes a significant decrease in liver glycogen and an increase in the hepatic concentration of esterified fatty acids (278). This was not found in rats kept at 2°C, where hepatic levels of glycogen and esterified fatty acids were the same as in rats fed a standard diet. In cold-acclimated rats there was an increase in free fatty acids (FFA) in serum and in epididymal fat, indicating an increased mobilization of fatty acids from fat depots (278). Bobek & Ginter (278) conclude that the lipotropic action of cold on liver of rats fed a high fat-cholesterol diet consists of a lowered hepatic synthesis of fatty acids and an increased hepatic fatty acid oxidation.

Recently Platner & Shields (279) have attempted to determine whether or not a "pseudolipotropic" effect of cold exposure is related to Mg metabolism. Their results indicate that dietary Mg is involved in fatty acid metabolism and the pseudolipotropic effect of Mg in cold acclimation is influenced by its dietary level.

McBurney & Radomski (280) have examined the effect of cold acclimation on the turnover of serum free fatty acids and lipoproteins and on the relative extent to which circulating FFA is incorporated into serum triglycerides in the rat. The recovery of the fatty acid label from injected albumin-bound palmitate-1-^{14}C, in the triglyceride fraction of liver, was the same in cold-acclimated and control rats. But there was less label in serum triglycerides in cold-acclimated rats than in controls. When ^{14}C-labeled FFA and lipoproteins (labeled mainly in the triglyceride fraction) were injected into both cold-acclimated and control rats, fractional turnover rates of these compounds were higher in cold-acclimated rats than in the controls. Since only the very low-density lipoprotein-triglyceride pool size was markedly affected (reduced to 30% of control) by cold acclimation, the calculated turnover (fractional turnover $\times$ pool size) of very low-density lipoprotein was only about 48% of that found for the control group. It has been proposed that one of the main functions of this lipoprotein is to store mobilized FFA not immediately required by the tissues (280). McBurney & Radomski (280) suggest that the demands of cold acclimation may reduce the FFA stored in this manner (as their data indicate) and increase the proportion of lipids and lipoproteins being oxidized by the tissues. They (280) further hypothesize that the triglyceride-rich endogenous fraction of very low-density lipoprotein may represent a significant energy source in the cold-acclimated rat.

Itoh et al (272) have recently examined several aspects of lipid metabolism in man in response to cold. They (272) have found that plasma FFA levels are apparently related to the degree of cold exposure, with the lowest levels of FFA occurring in people who are well adapted to cold and the highest levels in people who were not cold exposed. This relationship was not a function of diet or age. On the other hand, plasma lipoprotein lipase activity is significantly higher in the cold-adapted Ainu from northern Japan than in nonadapted Japanese. The possibility that this difference is related to diet could not be ruled out. In several groups of Japanese a positive correlation was found between BMR and plasma FFA levels; however, no such relationship was seen in Ainu in either summer or winter, which suggests that fat metabolism in the cold-adapted Ainu may be different from that of the Japanese (272).

Hluszko et al (281) have found that the RQ of rats exposed to cold (5° C) is lower than that of heat-exposed (30°C) rats, which indicates a greater oxidation of lipids in the cold. This is true even if the diet contains very little lipid. Adjustment to a high lipid diet requires about a week in the cold but a month in the heat. Intestinal absorption of lipids is good, even in heat-acclimated rats fed a high lipid diet. However, chronic heat exposure is often associated with a negative nitrogen balance which according to Collins & Weiner (190) means "it is unlikely that fat will be mobilized as an energy source in high temperature conditions." Hepatic enzymes associated with oxidation of the fatty acid β-hydroxybutyric acid are significantly decreased in the heat-acclimated hamster (187). Thus it appears that in the heat, fat metabolism is decreased. Since the RQ of heat-acclimated rats is slightly higher than that of cold-acclimated animals (281) there appears to be no preferential use of fats in prolonged heat exposure. Thus, loss of weight in some heat-exposed animals is probably associated with the lowered total food intake. On the other hand, the reduced growth rate in the cold may be a result of more rapid mobilization of all food substrates available, and their use in thermogenesis.

Carbohydrate metabolism.—It has long been recognized that total body utilization of carbohydrates increases in animals exposed to cold. Much of the early work in this area has been reviewed by Smith & Hoijer (261), and some of the possible biochemical mechanisms involved have been considered by Hannon (282). Morrison et al (283) have studied the activities of fourteen hepatic enzymes involved in intermediary metabolism of carbohydrates in cold-acclimated rats. They (283) concluded that, in the liver, an increased capacity for gluconeogenesis is the major change in carbohydrate metabolism associated with cold acclimation. They (283) found no alterations in activities of enzymes believed to be rate limiting for glycogenolysis, glycogenesis, or glycolysis after 28 days in the cold (4°C). Similarly, Klain & Hannon (284) found an enhancement of the activities of enzymes associated with gluconeogenesis in liver and kidney of both fasting and fed rats by the end of 48 hr in the cold. In some cases enzymatic differences were maximum at 48 hr, while activity of other enzymes continued to increase up to the 8th day in the cold. Burlington (285) has found that the rate of gluconeogenesis in kidney slices of rats and hamsters is increased after 2 weeks exposure to cold, and concludes that this could supply a substantial amount of glucose for heat production during cold acclimation. Penner & Himms-Hagen (286) have reported that levels of gluconeogenic enzymes in the liver do not reflect the actual changes in the rate of gluconeogenesis. They base their conclusion on in vitro studies of the activities of four "key" gluconeogenic enzymes (phosphoenolpyruvate carboxykinase, pyruvate carboxylase, fructose 1,6-diphosphatase, and glucose 6-phosphatase) compared with the in vivo rate of gluconeogenesis. Although changes in the enzyme levels were generally in the right direction, they were not of sufficient magnitude to account for the increases in gluconeogenesis in vivo. Thus one is faced with the question of whether in vitro assays of enzymatic activity really reflect the optimal "magnitude" of activity in the in vivo enzymatic situation. Since they too found that gluconeogenesis was higher during the first 7 days in the cold than in chronic cold exposure, Penner & Himms-Hagen (286) conclude "that gluconeogenesis is not related to nonshivering thermogenesis." On the other hand, they suggest that increased gluconeogenesis might be important in supplying glucose to support shivering until nonshivering thermogenesis develops.

In accord with these data is Boulouard's (287) finding that adrenal cortical secretion of glucocorticoids tends to reach a peak within a few days after exposure to cold, and returns to nearly control levels by the 18th day. In contrast to the adrenal cortex, which appears to exert its effects mainly during the initial period of cold exposure, Jarratt & Nowell (288) have found that the adrenal medulla not only plays an important role in the development of hyperglycemia in short-term cold exposure, but is also responsible for the high blood sugar level sustained in more prolonged cold exposure until nonshivering thermogenesis is well established.

Vaughan et al (289) have found that hepatic glucose 6-phosphatase and hexosemonophosphate (HMP) dehydrogenase activities increase in cold-acclimating rats during the first 4 weeks of exposure. The increase in HMP dehydrogenase seems to depend on an increased intake of sugar rather than on cold, while the increase in glucose 6-phosphatase is unaffected by diet. Liver glycogen levels decreased in cold-exposed rats fed a mixed diet. These data suggest that hepatic glucose catabolism, as well as gluconeogenesis, may play an important role during cold acclimation in the rat.

Cassuto (290) has looked at glycogen metabolism in liver slices of heat-acclimated hamsters; glycogen breakdown and glucose production were significantly decreased in heat-acclimated animals. Also, both glycogen and glucose 6-phosphate levels were higher in heat-acclimated than in control animals. The latter is probably a result of the decreased activity of hepatic glucose 6-phosphatase seen in heat-acclimated hamsters (189).

Protein metabolism.—In the cold there is an increased oxidation of not only carbohydrates and fats, but also proteins (261, 291). There is also an increase in food intake which usually is inversely related to environmental temperature (292). Moreover, it is now generally accepted that if the cold is severe enough, growth is inhibited in spite of increased food intake (292). Cold stress is effective in overcoming a dietary amino acid imbalance (291, 293). The elevated food intake in the cold results in an increased intake of the limiting amino acid and in the consumption of a greater total quantity of amino acids that can be catabolized for heat production or utilized for tissue protein synthesis (291, 293). This, together with the increased ability to degrade amino acids (291, 293, 294), would seem to indicate that the rates of both protein anabolism and catabolism are increased in the cold.

A number of workers have studied the changes in levels of various proteins in animals acclimating to cold. Trapani (295) found a decreased immune response and an increased antibody decay rate in cold-exposed rats. Similarly, Gubachev (296) found a decreased immunological response in cold-acclimatized humans. Temperature-induced changes in the level and distribution of serum proteins have been demonstrated in several species of mammals. In rats (297) and man (298) there is a net decrease in serum albumin in response to cold. Shields et al (297) have attributed this to a relative increase in the rate of albumin catabolism. On the other hand, Bop & Platner (299) found an increased serum albumin in the cold-acclimatized prairie meadow mouse (*Microtus ochrogaster*). They (299) suggest that this species can satisfy its energy needs in the cold from nonprotein sources without resorting to catabolism of serum albumin. Lózsa et al (300) have found that some of the temperature-induced changes in serum proteins and glycoproteins of the rabbit are not specific. For example, albumin levels decrease and α- and β-globulin levels increase in response to both heat and cold. They (300) regard such changes as manifestations of the general adaptation syndrome. On the other hand, changes in lipoprotein and γ-globulin levels are highly specific with respect to heat or cold exposure (300). Depocas (301) has found that the average cytochrome *c* concentration of all skeletal muscles is higher in cold-acclimated rats than in controls, although the total amount of skeletal muscle cytochrome *c* per rat is about the same. He (301) also found no change in turnover rate of cytochrome *c* and concludes that the rates of synthesis and breakdown of this protein appear to be independent of the environmental temperature, at least in fully acclimated animals. Cytochrome oxidase (302) and myoglobin (52) also show marked increases in response to cold acclimation in a number of species of animals. Thus, it appears that the levels of a number of specific proteins are altered as animals acclimate to cold.

The question of whether there is a more rapid turnover rate with respect to the sum total of all proteins, both structural and nonstructural, in the cold remains unanswered. Lusena & Depocas (270) found that cold acclimation had no significant effect on the rate of turnover or renewal of rat liver mitochondria, or on the amount of mitochondrial protein that could be isolated per gram of liver. Chaffee et al (303) have hypothesized that there is a higher overall amino acid → protein → amino acid turnover rate in cold-acclimated animals. This hypothesis is based on the following findings: (a) the in vivo incorporation of ^{75}Se-selenomethionine into liver and kidney protein increases markedly in cold-acclimated rats and decreases in heat-acclimated animals, and (b) parallel changes were found in whole body turnover rates of ^{75}Se-selenomethionine in rats exposed to 4°, 24°, and 34°C (303, 304). However, these original studies may be questioned because no consideration was given to increased consumption of dietary methionine by the cold rats, which might account for a faster "washing out" of the administered ^{75}Se-selenomethionine. However, the increased rate of incorporation of ^{75}Se-selenomethionine into liver and kidney protein of cold-acclimated rats (304) does not support this criticism for, if there were an increased dilution of the labeled methionine due to increased dietary methionine, the rate of ^{75}Se-selenomethionine uptake by the liver and kidney should have been slower in cold-acclimated animals than in controls. Studies by Yousef & Luick (305) also support the concept of an increased amino acid → protein → amino acid turnover rate in the cold. They (305) found that when food intake was equal in both groups, cold-acclimated mice still showed a faster protein turnover rate than controls. In this study (305), neither extra dietary thyroxine, which might accompany extra food intake (97), nor extra protein intake was responsible for the observed "turnover" changes. Furthermore, Chaffee et al (306) have conducted in vivo ^{75}Se-selenomethionine turnover studies in cold- and heat-acclimated primates using controlled dietary protein and got similar results with respect to cold-acclimated vs control animals.

In vitro studies designed to determine whether biochemical changes occur which support the in vivo findings show that liver ribosomes of heat-acclimated rats have a lower specific activity than do ribosomes from controls (307). This supports the concept of a depressed protein synthesis in the heat. However, no difference in ribosomal activity was found between cold-acclimated and control rats (307). An increase in total hepatic lysosomal cathepsin activity in cold-acclimated animals (307) further supports the concept of an increased rate of protein catabolism in the cold. Unfortunately, no cathepsin studies were made on heat-acclimated rats. One postulated consequence of a faster protein turnover rate in the cold was that it would increase the MR (303, 304). Thus faster amino acid → protein → amino acid recycling might contribute, by a somewhat wasteful use of ATP in protein synthesis and its subsequent hydrolysis, to higher intracellular levels of ADP in the cold, while, conversely, slower recycling would result in lower levels of ADP in the heat (303). This process would thus be somewhat analogous to shivering with respect to replenishment of intracellular ADP. But it would be of a much lower order of magnitude, since no cold-induced differences in protein synthesis (and thus turnover rate) were found in rat skeletal muscle, with its great mass relative to body weight or in brown fat, a highly calorigenic tissue (304).

Unfortunately, evaluations of protein turnover rates are fraught with many technical pitfalls because of the difficulties in defining the effects of dietary protein on the total physiological response to environmental temperature. A number of enzymes can be induced by varying dietary protein levels independent of ambient temperature changes (289, 291, 308). For example, Frascella et al (308) found that, for any given level of dietary protein, kidney phosphoenolpyruvate carboxykinase (PEPck) activity was similar in both cold-acclimated and control rats, but enzyme activity could be increased by increasing dietary protein. On the other hand, cold exposure caused an increase in liver PEPck activity in rats regardless of dietary protein levels and only small changes in the activity of this enzyme could be induced by alterations of protein intake (308). Oratz et al (309) have shown that high environmental temperatures can affect albumin and fibrinogen metabolism in rabbits and postulate that decreased food intake and lowered thyroid activity may be largely responsible for the observed biochemical changes. Dietary protein intake also affects serum and depot lipids (310) and pyridine nucleotide levels (311) in cold-exposed rats. Thus it appears that increased food intake in the cold, already shown to influence metabolism and thyroid function (96–99, 106, 109), may also be a complicating factor in interpreting some of the biochemical changes reported in cold-acclimated animals. Moreover, proof or negation of the hypothesis that an increased rate of cellular amino acid → protein → amino acid recycling accompanies cold acclimation (303) will require further experimentation and this hypothesis may well meet the same fate as have similar proposals of fatty acid recycling (see 55, 258).

Monoamines and associated enzymes in brain tissue.—Since the studies of Feldberg & Myers (312, 313) on the cat indicating that NE and 5-hydroxytryptamine (5-HT) are active in the responses of thermoregulatory centers of the brain, much interest has developed in the possible mechanisms involved. Lomax (314) and Cremer & Bligh (315) have extensively reviewed the literature on the effects of these amines on thermoregulation. Lomax et al (316) discuss the physiological significance of the original hypothesis of Feldberg & Myers (312) in light of the variety of species-specific responses to injected amines. They point out that agents leading to a fall in temperature in one species may cause a rise in another, and that either hypo- or hyperthermic responses may be observed in a single species depending on the dose of the drug injected into the cerebral ventricles (316).

Relatively few studies have been conducted on the effects of intraventricular injection of amines on body temperature in birds (317, 318), so that good comparisons between mammalian and avian responses based on such injections cannot as yet be made. Allen & Marley (319) interpret their results on intravenous injection of various amines (including catecholamines and tryptamines) into chickens as indicating that thermoregulatory responses to such amines are similar in chickens and cats. Whether this is coincidence or represents a common basis of thermoregulatory action of these amines in birds and mammals is a fundamental question. In light of the variation in responses seen in mammals (316), it is clear that any meaningful answer must await further research.

Another basic question is whether these amines perform a transmitter role or augment the action of acetylcholine. Microinjection of cholomimetic agents into the rostral hypothalamus produces hypothermia (See 316). Cholinergic blocking agents, on the other hand, lead to a rise in temperature following central injection, suggesting the blockage of endogenous acetylcholine (316). Lomax et al (316) have investigated the possibility that catecholamines act to influence cholinergic transmission in the thermoregulatory centers of the rat at they do in the cervical ganglion of the cat (320) and conclude that catecholamines change the polarization of cholinergic neurons and thus adjust the sensitivity of thermoregulatory centers. Thus, catecholamines may be a factor in the physiological regulation of the set point of the central thermostat. This type of research obviously is essential to an understanding of thermoregulation in both unacclimated and temperature-acclimated animals since it correlates biochemical action and changes within the brain with the observed physiological action of the central thermostat and changes in the set point.

There has been considerable research recently to determine the effects of temperature acclimation in mammals on levels and turnover rates of brain amines and the enzymes which are associated with their metabolism (321–329). Ingenito & Bonnycastle (330) measured NE and 5-HT levels in whole brain and hypothalamus of heat- and cold-exposed rats. Acute heat failed to cause changes in levels of either of these amines, but acute cold caused a slight decrease in 5-HT in brain, but not in hypothalamus, and no changes in NE levels. Long-term cold exposure produced increases in NE in whole brain, but 5-HT levels returned to normal (330). Similarly, Bhagat (324) found elevated levels of catecholamines and increased turnover rates of ^{3}H-NE in rat brain after chronic environmental cold stress (2°C for 6 hr /day for 20 days). Kuroshima et al (323) found that somewhat milder, shorter-term cold exposure (5°C for 2 weeks) failed to cause differences in rat brain serotonin or norepinephrine, or in the monoamine oxidase activity in whole brain or hypothalamus. Studies by Harri & Tirri (321) indicate that in mice there is an increase in brain 5-HT after 5 hr at 32°C, followed by a return to normal by the 7th day, and that there is a decided drop in 5-HT after 5 hr at 7°C, followed by a return to normal by 24 hr. These studies were done only on whole brain and changes in the hypothalamus alone were not measured. Ingenito (322) studied NE levels in hypothalamus, midbrain, and medulla oblongata of rats following exposure to cold for 1, 15, and 30 days. Compared with controls living at 25°C, hypothalamic levels of NE were increased following 15 and 30 days at 1°C, while levels in the midbrain and medulla increased only slightly and only after 30 days of exposure. Such changes were not related to colonic temperature. Ingenito (322) suggests that the bases for the increased NE level in brain and the increased catecholamine levels seen in peripheral tissues following prolonged cold exposure may be similar. Conversely, studies on levels of catecholamines in various areas of the brain and in other tissues of unacclimated heat-exposed (hyperthermic) rats showed that a decrease in NE occurred only in brain tissues, whereas in other tissues, such as adrenals and heart, catecholamine levels increased as body temperature rose (331). Legrand (331) concludes that the fall in cerebral NE during hyperthermia is associated directly with the central thermoregulatory mechanisms.

Since levels of amines, such as catecholamines and serotonin, are critical for both autonomic and central nervous system thermoregulatory action, it is interesting indeed to consider what effects cold may have on their synthesis. In normal as well as stressed animals, Green & Curzon (332) have found an inverse relationship between brain 5-HT and liver tryptophan pyrrolase. Thus changes in hepatic tryptophan metabolism possibly have a direct influence on thermoregulation by the central nervous system.

To better evaluate the role of amines in temperature acclimation, further coordinated studies are needed which combine precise anatomical dissection of specific brain areas with biochemical analyses of levels and turnover rates of critical amines, precursors, and associated enzyme systems. Such studies, if accompanied by further studies like those of Bhagat (324) and of Nikki (325) involving precise injection of amines into different loci within the hypothalamus of acclimated animals, and those of Roth et al (333) measuring release of catecholamines from discrete regions of the brain, may lead to the elucidation of biochemical bases of changes in the set point in temperature acclimation.

Summary

We have tried to summarize and interrelate results of at least a portion of the research on temperature acclimation and acclimatization in homeotherms which has appeared in the literature during the last 5 years. In addition, some mention has been made of thermoregulatory adaptations and responses to short-term temperature exposure where these may give insight into the possible mechanisms involved in acclimation or acclimatization.

Although adaptation and seasonal acclimatization to heat and cold have been studied in birds, relatively few species have been acclimated to prolonged heat or cold in the laboratory. Moreover, very few biochemical studies have been performed on temperature-acclimated birds. Thus a great deal is still unknown about the mechanisms of temperature acclimation in this class of homeotherms. Shivering appears to be the major metabolic means by which adult birds increase their heat production when exposed to cold, and to date nonshivering thermogenesis has not been demonstrated. Although NE is the mediator of nonshivering thermogenesis in many species of mammals, it does not stimulate MR in cold- or winter-acclimated adult birds. The hormone glucagon has recently been suggested as a possible mediator of thermoregulatory responses in birds; however, its effect on MR of cold-acclimated birds remains to be demonstrated.

There is considerable evidence that both birds and mammals which are adapted to hot climates or acclimated to heat in the laboratory have a reduced metabolic rate. In mammals this is accompanied by a reduction in the size of internal heat-producing organs and a decrease in the activity of oxidative enzymes. A decrease in liver succinoxidase activity has also been reported in heat-acclimated sparrows.

The thermogenic role of brown fat in mammals has received a great deal of attention in the past few years, particularly with respect to its relationship to nonshivering thermogenesis and the metabolic response to NE. Since brown fat represents only a small percent of the body weight, it has been suggested that its influence on such thermogenesis may be exerted indirectly either by warming thermosensitive elements in the cervical spinal cord and thus regulating shivering, or by secretion of a hormonelike product which elevates thermogenesis in the other tissues.

Recent studies on thyroid function in both heat- and cold-acclimated mammals indicate that temperature-induced changes in dietary intake of bulk and thyroxine may be responsible for some of the observed changes in metabolism and thyroid activity. It also appears that diet and changes in food intake may complicate the interpretation of some of the tissue biochemical changes observed in acclimated animals. This is particularly true with respect to certain substrate-inducible enzymes and has led to considerable difficulty in determining whether changes in protein metabolism and protein turnover are a consequence of cold per se or are the result of changes in protein consumption.

Comparative studies on changes in levels of oxidative enzymes in several species of temperature-acclimated mammals reveal that not all of the "classical" changes reported in rodents occur in other species and thus such changes are apparently not necessary for survival.

A number of other biochemical changes have recently been reported in temperature-acclimated mammals. Changes in level and distribution of isozymes have been reported in cold-acclimated rats and man. A major change in carbohydrate metabolism seems to be an increase in gluconeogenesis during the early stages of cold acclimation which could provide an increased supply of glucose to support shivering. Changes in the fatty acid composition of structural lipids of mitochondria and endoplasmic reticulum have been reported in cold-acclimated rats. Such changes could account for the greater mitochondrial fragility and increased cellular leakage of enzymes seen in the cold. If a generalized increase in cell membrane permeability occurs in cold acclimation, the increased active transport required to counter such a leak could serve as an ATPase and thus stimulate cellular metabolism by providing increased levels of ADP.

One promising area for further research is the elucidation of the neurochemical mechanisms which regulate the thermostatlike control of the hypothalamus. Techniques have now been worked out so that the approach to this type of study should not be too difficult. There is already evidence that changes in levels of brain and hypothalamic transmitter amines are affected by temperature acclimation.

ACKNOWLEDGMENT

The authors wish to express their sincere thanks to their colleagues who have so generously provided copies of manuscripts in press and unpublished data for use in this review.

LITERATURE CITED

1. Chaffee, R. R. J. et al 1966. *J. Appl. Physiol.* 21:151–57
2. Chaffee, R. R. J., Horvath, S. M., Smith, R. E., Welsh, R. S. 1966. *Fed. Proc.* 25:1177–81
3. Chaffee, R. R. J. et al 1969. *Fed. Proc.* 28:1029–34
4. Cooper, K. E. 1968. In *Recent Advances in Medicine,* 333–50. London: Churchill. 15th ed. 423 pp.
5. Musacchia, X. J., Saunders, J. F., Eds. 1969. *Depressed Metabolism.* New York: American Elsevier. 630 pp.
6. Blockley, W. V. 1965. *Human sweat response to activity and environment in the compensable zone of thermal stress: a systematic study.* Final Rep. on Contr. NAS 9-3556, prepared for Crew Systems Div. Manned Spacecraft Cent. NASA, Houston, Texas. 112 pp.
7. Dill, D. B. 1969. *Scientia* 104:1–13
8. Edholm, O. G. 1969. *Proc. Roy. Soc. Med.* 62:1175–79
9. Belding, H. S. 1967. *Arch. Environ. Health* 15:660–69
10. Henane, R. 1966. *Rev. Corps Santé Armees* 7:293–318
11. Henane, R. 1967. *Rev. Corps Santé Armees* 8:809–24
12. Hirooka, K. 1968. *Kobe J. Med. Sci.* 14:195–218
13. Minard, D. 1967. *Milit. Med.* 132:306–15
14. Nielsen, B. 1969. *Acta Physiol. Scand. Suppl. 323.* 64 pp.
15. Rautenberg, W. 1969. *Z. Vergl. Physiol.* 62:235–66
16. Wyndham, C. H. 1969. *Environ. Res.* 2:442–69
17. Hardy, J. D. 1965. In *Physiological Controls and Regulations,* 98–116. Philadelphia: Saunders. 362 pp.
18. Bligh, J. 1966. *Biol. Rev.* 41:317–67
19. Hammel, H. T. 1968. *Ann. Rev. Physiol.* 30:641–710
20. Benzinger, T. H. 1969. *Physiol. Rev.* 49:671–759
21. Bullard, R. W., Banerjee, M. R., MacIntyre, B. A. 1967. *Int. J. Biometeorol.* 11:93–104
22. Cranston, W. I. 1966. *Brit. Med. J.* 2:69–75
23. Hensel, H. 1966. *Touch, Heat and Pain. Ciba Found. Symp.,* 275–88

24. Klussmann, F. W., Stelter, W. J., Spaan, G. 1969. *Fed. Proc.* 28:992–95
25. Ogata, K., Sasaki, T., Murakami, N. 1966. *Bull. Inst. Const. Med. Kumamoto Univ.* 16:1–67
26. Smith, R. E. 1969. *Fed. Proc.* 28:1011–15
27. Irving, L. 1964. In *Handbook of Physiology.* Sec. IV. *Adaptation to the Environment,* 361–77. Washington, D.C: Am. Physiol. Soc. 1056 pp.
28. Hart, J. S. 1964. *Symp. Soc. Exp. Biol.* 18:31–48
29. Siegel, H. S. 1969. *Poultry Sci.* 48:22–30
30. Whittow, G. C. 1965. In *Avian Physiology,* 186–271. New York: Cornell Univ. Press. 766 pp.
31. Wittke, G. 1967. *Fortschr. Zool.* 18:301–36
32. Kontogiannis, J. E. 1968. *Physiol. Zool.* 41:54–64
33. Blackmore, F. H. 1969. *Comp. Biochem. Physiol.* 30:433–44
34. Barnett, L. B. 1970. *Comp. Biochem. Physiol.* 33:559–78
35. Rautenberg, W. 1969. *Z. Vergl. Physiol.* 62:221–34
36. Prince, R. P., Whitaker, J. H., Matterson, L. D., Luginbuhl, R. E. 1965. *Poultry Sci.* 44:73–77
37. Fisher, H., Griminger, P., Weiss, H. S. 1965. *J. Appl. Physiol.* 20:591–96
38. Brooks, W. S. 1968. *Wilson Bull.* 80:253–80
39. Veghte, J. H., Herreid, C. F. 1965. *Physiol. Zool.* 38:267–75
40. West, G. C., Hart, J. S. 1966. *Physiol. Zool.* 39:171–84
41. Hart, J. S. 1964. In *Handbook of Physiology.* Sec. IV. *Adaptation to the Environment,* 295–321. Washington, D.C: Am. Physiol. Soc. 1056 pp.
42. Veghte, J. H. 1964. *Physiol. Zool.* 37:316–28
43. Stonehouse, B. 1967. *Advan. Ecol. Res.* 4:131–96
44. Sturkie, P. D. 1967. *J. Appl. Physiol.* 22:13–15
45. Whittow, G. C., Sturkie, P. D., Stein, G., Jr. 1966. *Res. Vet. Sci.* 7:296–301

46. Steen, I., Steen, J. B. 1965. *Acta Physiol. Scand.* 63:285–91
47. Ederstrom, H. E., Brumleve, S. J. 1964. *Am. J. Physiol.* 207:457–59
48. Hissa, R., Palokangas, R. 1970. *Comp. Biochem. Physiol.* 33:941–53
49. Johnson, R. E. 1968. *Comp. Biochem. Physiol.* 24:1003–14
50. West, G. C. 1965. *Physiol. Zool.* 38:111–20
51. Chaffee, R. R. J., Mayhew, W. W. 1964. *Can. J. Physiol. Pharmacol.* 42:863–66
52. Chaffee, R. R. J., Cassuto, Y., Horvath, S. M. 1965. *Can. J. Physiol. Pharmacol.* 43:1021–25
53. Freeman, B. M. 1966. *Comp. Biochem. Physiol.* 18:369–82
54. Freeman, B. M. 1967. *Comp. Biochem. Physiol.* 20:179–93
55. Smith, R. E., Horwitz, B. A. 1969. *Physiol. Rev.* 49:330–425
56. Lin, Y.-C., Sturkie, P. D. 1968. *Am. J. Physiol.* 214:237–40
57. Freeman, B. M. 1970. *Comp. Biochem. Physiol.* 33:219–30
58. Wekstein, D. R., Zolman, J. F. 1968. *Am. J. Physiol.* 214:908–12
59. Dawson, W. R., Schmidt-Nielsen, K. 1964. In *Handbook of Physiology.* Sec. IV. *Adaptation to the Environment,* 481–92. Washington, D.C: Am. Physiol. Soc. 1056 pp.
60. King, J. R., Farner, D. S. 1964. In *Handbook of Physiology.* Sec. IV. *Adaptation to the Environment,* 603–24. Washington, D.C: Am. Physiol. Soc. 1056 pp.
61. Crawford, E. C., Jr., Schmidt-Nielsen, K. 1967. *Am. J. Physiol.* 212:347–53
62. MacMillen, R. E., Trost, C. H. 1967. *Comp. Biochem. Physiol.* 20:263–73
63. Rising, J. D. 1969. *Comp. Biochem. Physiol.* 31:915–25
64. Ricklefs, R. E., Hainsworth, F. R. 1968. *Ecology* 49:227–33
65. Calder, W. A., Schmidt-Nielsen, K. 1967. *Am. J. Physiol.* 213:883–89
66. Lasiewski, R. C., Acosta, A. L., Bernstein, M. H. 1966. *Comp. Biochem. Physiol.* 19:445–57
67. Greenwald, L., Stone, W. B., Cade, T. J. 1967. *Comp. Biochem. Physiol.* 22:91–100
68. Hudson, J. W., Kimzey, S. L. 1966. *Comp. Biochem. Physiol.* 17:203–18
69. Harrison, P. C., Biellier, H. V. 1969. *Poultry Sci.* 48:1034–45
70. Yousef, M. K., McFarland, L. Z., Wilson, W. O. 1966. *Life Sci.* 5:1887–96
71. Barnett, S. A., Mount, L. E. 1967. In *Thermobiology,* 411–77. London and New York: Academic. 653 pp.
72. Ray, D. E., Roubicek, C. B., Hamidi, M. 1968. *Growth* 32:1–12
73. Jansky, L., Bartunkova, R., Zeisberger, E. 1967. *Physiol. Bohemoslov.* 16:366–72
74. LeBlanc, J., Côté, J. 1967. *Can. J. Physiol. Pharmacol.* 45:745–48
75. Nagasaka, T., Carlson, L. D. 1965. *Am. J. Physiol.* 209:227–30
76. Hemingway, A., Price, W. M., Stuart, D. 1964. *Int. J. Neuropharmacol.* 3:495–503
77. Pohl, H., Hart, J. S. 1965. *J. Appl. Physiol.* 20:398–404
78. Kockova, J., Jansky, L. 1968. *Physiol. Bohemoslov.* 17:309–16
79. Heroux, O. 1967. *Can. J. Physiol. Pharmacol.* 45:451–61
80. Webster, A. J. F., Hicks, A. M., Hays, F. L. 1969. *Can. J. Physiol. Pharmacol.* 47:553–62
81. Sykes, A. R., Slee, J. 1968. *Anim. Prod.* 10:17–35
82. Sykes, A. R., Slee, J. 1969. *Anim. Prod.* 11:77–89
83. Roberts, J. C., Hock, R. J., Smith, R. E. 1966. *Fed. Proc.* 25:1275–83
84. Hosek, B., Novak, L. 1968. *Experientia* 24:1214–15
85. LeBlanc, J., Robinson, D., Sharman, D. F., Tousignant, P. 1967. *Am. J. Physiol.* 213:1419–22
86. Joy, R. J. T. 1963. *J. Appl. Physiol.* 18:1209–12
87. Newman, R. W. 1968. *J. Appl. Physiol.* 25:277–82
88. Newman, R. W. 1969. *J. Appl. Physiol.* 27:316–19
89. Kang, B. S. et al 1970. *J. Appl. Physiol.* 29:6–9
90. Wyndham, C. H., Loots, H. 1969. *J. Appl. Physiol.* 27:696–700
91. Skreslet, S., Aarefjord, F. 1968. *J. Appl. Physiol.* 24:177–81
92. Locker, A., Weish, P. 1966. *Helgoländer Wiss. Meeresunters.* 14:503–13
93. Cadot, M., Julien, M.-F., Chevillard, L. 1969. *Fed. Proc.* 28:1228–33
94. Straw, J. A. 1969. *J. Appl. Physiol.* 27:630–33

95. Straw, J. A., Fregly, M. J. 1967. *J. Appl. Physiol.* 23 :825–30
96. Hillier, A. P. 1968. *J. Physiol. London* 197 :123–34
97. Magwood, S. G. A., Heroux, O. 1968. *Can. J. Physiol. Pharmacol.* 46 : 601–7
98. Heroux, O., Petrovic, V. M. 1969. *Can. J. Physiol. Pharmacol.* 47 : 963–68
99. Heroux, O., Brauer, R. 1965. *J. Appl. Physiol.* 20 :597–606
100. Bauman, T. R., Turner, C. W. 1967. *J. Endocrinol.* 37 :355–59
101. Bauman, T. R., Anderson, R. R., Turner, C. W. 1968. *Gen. Comp. Endocrinol.* 10 :92–98
102. Itoh, S., Hiroshige, T., Koseki, T., Nakatsugawa, T. 1966. *Fed. Proc.* 25 :1187–92
103. Cottle, W. H., Veress, A. T. 1966. *Can. J. Physiol. Pharmacol.* 44 : 571–74
104. Cottle, W. H., Veress, A. T. 1966. *Can. J. Physiol. Pharmacol.* 44 : 325–26
105. Hillier, A. P. 1968. *J. Physiol. London* 197 :135–48
106. Galton, V. A., Nisula, B. C. 1969. *Endocrinology* 85 :79–86
107. Hsieh, A. C. L. 1966. *Gunma Symp. Endocrinol.* 3 :239–48
108. Hsieh, A. C. L., Pun, C. W., Li, K. M., Ti, K. W. 1966. *Fed. Proc.* 25 :1205–9
109. Heroux, O. 1968. *Can. J. Physiol. Pharmacol.* 46 :843–46
110. Zeisberger, E. 1966. *Helgoländer Wiss. Meeresunters.* 14 :528–40
111. Jansky, L. 1966. *Fed. Proc.* 25 :1297–1302
112. Davis, T. R. A. 1967. *Am. J. Physiol.* 213 :1423–26
113. Jansky, L., Hart, J. S. 1968. *Can. J. Physiol. Pharmacol.* 46 :653–59
114. Hampton, I. F. G. 1969. *Brit. Antarctic Surv. Bull.* 19 :9–56
115. Itoh, S., Shirato, H., Hiroshige, T., Kuroshima, A., Doi, K. 1969. *Jap. J. Physiol.* 19 :198–211
116. Krog, J., Ålvik, M., Lund-Larsen, K. 1969. *Fed. Proc.* 28 :1135–37
117. Weiner, J. S. 1965. *Int. Soc. Sci. J.* 17 :150–52
118. Miller, L. K. 1967. *Comp. Biochem. Physiol.* 21 :679–86
119. Webster, A. J. F., Blaxter, K. L. 1966. *Res. Vet. Sci.* 7 :466–79
120. Little, R. A., Stoner, H. B. 1968. *Quart. J. Exp. Physiol.* 53 :76–83
121. Rand, R. P., Burton, A. C., Ing, T.
122. Thompson, G. E., Stevenson, J. A. F. 1965. *Can. J. Physiol. Pharmacol.* 43 :279–87
123. Petajan, J. H. 1968. *Am. J. Physiol.* 214 :130–32
124. Miller, L. K. 1970. *Can. J. Zool.* 48 : 75–81
125. Somero, G. N., Johansen, K. 1970. *Comp. Biochem. Physiol.* 34 :131–36
126. Hemingway, A. 1963. *Physiol. Rev.* 43 :397–422
127. Brück, K., Wünnenberg, W. 1968. *Biokybernetik* 1 :154–59
128. Kosaka, M., Simon, E. 1968. *Arch. Ges. Physiol.* 302 :357–73
129. Tanche, M., Chatonnet, J., Satta, S. O. 1965. *Rev. Can. Biol.* 24 :225–28
130. Budd, G. M., Warhaft, N. 1966. *J. Physiol. London* 186 :216–32
131. Pohl, H. 1965. *J. Appl. Physiol.* 20 : 405–10
132. Brück, K., Wünnenberg, W. 1967. *Arch. Ges. Physiol.* 293 :226–35
133. Brück, K., Wünnenberg, W., Zeisberger, E. 1969. *Fed. Proc.* 28 : 1035–41
134. Roberts, J. C., Smith, R. E. 1967. *Am. J. Physiol.* 212 :519–25
135. Thomson, J. F., Habeck, D. A., Nance, S. L., Beetham, K. L. 1969. *J. Cell Biol.* 41 :312–34
136. Suter, E. R. 1969. *J. Ultrastruct. Res.* 26 :216–41
137. Chaffee, R. R. J., Roberts, J. C., Conaway, C. H., Sorenson, M. W., Kaufman, W. C. 1970. *Lipids* 5 : 23–29
138. Gilbert, R., Pagé, E. 1968. *Rev. Can. Biol.* 27 :241–54
139. Didow, L. A., Hayward, J. S. 1969. *Can. J. Zool.* 47 :547–55
140. Leduc, J., Rivest, P. 1969. *Rev. Can. Biol.* 28 :49–66
141. Himms-Hagen, J. 1969. *J. Physiol. London* 205 :393–404
142. Brück, K., Wünnenberg, W. 1966. *Arch. Ges. Physiol.* 290 :167–83
143. Wünnenberg, W., Brück, K. 1968. *Arch. Ges. Physiol.* 299 :1–10
144. Hittelman, K. J., Lindberg, O., Cannon, B. 1969. *Eur. J. Biochem.* 11 :183–92
145. Prusiner, S. B., Cannon, B., Lindberg, O. 1968. *Eur. J. Biochem.* 6 :15–22
146. Prusiner, S. B., Cannon, B., Ching, T. M., Lindberg, O. 1968. *Eur. J. Biochem.* 7 :51–57

1965. *Can. J. Physiol. Pharmacol.* 43 :257–67

147. Rafael, J., Klaas, D., Hohorst, H.-J. 1968. Z. Physiol. Chem. 349 :1711–24

148. Rafael, J., Ludolph, H.-J., Hohorst, H.-J., 1969. Z. Physiol. Chem. 350 : 1121–31

149. Christiansen, E. N., Pedersen, J. I., Grav, H. J. 1969. Nature 222 :857–60

150. Girardier, L., Seydoux, J., Clausen, T. 1968. J. Gen. Physiol. 52 :925–40

151. Horwitz, B. A., Horowitz, J. M., Jr., Smith, R. E. 1969. Proc. Nat. Acad. Sci. 64 :113–20

152. Herd, P. A., Horwitz, B. A., Smith, R. E. 1970. Experientia 26 :825–26

153. Jansky, L., Bartunkova, R., Kockova, J., Mejsnar, J., Zeisberger, E. 1969. Fed. Proc. 28 :1053–58

154. Zeisberger, E., Brück, K. 1967. Arch. Ges. Physiol. 296 :263–75

155. Himms-Hagen, J. 1967. Pharmacol. Rev. 19 :367–461

156. Carlson, L. D. 1966. Pharmacol. Rev. 18 :291–301

157. Brück, K. 1966. Biometeorology 2 : 241–50

158. Brück, K., Wünnenberg, B. 1966. Fed. Proc. 25 :1332–37

159. Alexander, G., Williams, D. 1968. J. Physiol. London 198 :251–76

160. Moore, R. E., Simmonds, M. A. 1966. Fed. Proc. 25 :1329–31

161. Hayward, J. S. 1968. Can. J. Physiol. Pharmacol. 46 :713–18

162. Brück, K. In Brown Adipose Tissue. New York : American Elsevier. In press

163. Brück, K. 1967. Naturwissenschaften 54 :156–62

164. Thompson, G. E., Jenkinson, D. M. 1969. Can. J. Physiol. Pharmacol. 47 :249–53

165. Webster, A. J. F., Heitman, J. H., Hays, F. L., Olynyk, G. P. 1969. Can. J. Physiol. Pharmacol. 47 : 719–24

166. Aherne, W., Hull, D. 1966. J. Pathol. Bacteriol. 91 :223–34

167. Ikemoto, H., Hiroshige, T., Itoh, S. 1967. Jap. J. Physiol. 17 :516–22

168. Smith, R. E., Roberts, J. C. 1964. Am. J. Physiol. 206 :143–48

169. Joel, C. D. 1965. In Handbook of Physiology. Sec. V. Adipose Tissue, 59–85. Washington, D.C : Am. Physiol. Soc. 824 pp.

170. Williams, D. D. 1968. Comp. Biochem. Physiol. 27 :567–73

171. Chaffee, R. R. J., Allen, J. R., Cassuto, Y., Smith, R. E. 1964. Am. J. Physiol. 207 :1211–14

172. Burlington, R. F., Therriault, D. G., Hubbard, R. W. 1969. Comp. Biochem. Physiol. 29 :431–37

173. Budd, G. M., Warhaft, N. 1966. J. Physiol. London 186 :233–42

174. Cassuto, Y., Amit, Y. 1968. Endocrinology 82 :17–20

175. Hissa, R. 1970. Experientia 26 :266–67

176. Jeddi, E., Chatonnet, J. 1969. C. R. Soc. Biol. 163 :168–71

177. LeBlanc, J. 1966. J. Appl. Physiol. 21 :661–64

178. Chevillard, L., Portet, R., Cadot, M., Cabady, M. 1965. Arch. Int. Pharmacodyn. 153 :30–48

179. Sengupta, A. K., Prakash, M. O., Ghose, A. 1968. Jap. J. Physiol. 18 :563–69

180. LeBlanc, J., Villemaire, A. 1970. Am. J. Physiol. 218 :1742–45

181. Dawson, T., Schmidt-Nielsen, K. 1966. J. Cell. Physiol. 67 :463–71

182. Hudson, J. W., Rummel, J. A. 1966. Ecology 47 :345–54

183. Hudson, J. W., Wang, L. C.-H. 1969. In Physiological Systems in Semiarid Environments, 17–33. Albuquerque : Univ. New Mexico Press. 293 pp.

184. Pennycuik, P. R. 1967. Aust. J. Exp. Biol. Med. Sci. 45 :331–46

185. Rigaudière, N. 1967. C. R. Soc. Biol. 161 :1554–58

186. Rigaudière, N. 1969. Arch. Sci. Physiol. 23 :215–42

187. Cassuto, Y., Chaffee, R. R. J. 1966. Am. J. Physiol. 210 :423–26

188. Cassuto, Y. 1968. Am. J. Physiol. 214 :1147–51

189. Cassuto, Y., Chayoth, R., Rabi, T. 1970. Am. J. Physiol. 218 :1287–90

190. Collins, K. J., Weiner, J. S. 1968. Physiol. Rev. 48 :785–839

191. Fregly, M. J. 1968. In 3rd Midwest Conf. Thyroid, 1–20. Columbia : Univ. Missouri. 123 pp.

192. Yousef, M. K., Johnson, H. D. 1967. Life Sci. 6 :1221–28

193. Portet, R., Bertin, R., Chevillard, L. 1967. J. Physiol. Paris 59 :476

194. Kotby, S., Johnson, H. D. 1967. Life Sci. 6 :1121–32

195. Kotby, S., Johnson, H. D., Kibler, H. H. 1967. Life Sci. 6 :709–19

196. Bertin, R. 1969. C. R. Soc. Biol. 163 : 2108–11

197. Yousef, M. K., Johnson, H. D. 1968. *Endocrinology* 82:353–58
198. Yousef, M. K., Johnson, H. D. 1968. *Nature* 217:182–83
199. Hutchins, M. O. 1969. *Proc. Soc. Exp. Biol. Med.* 131:1292–95
200. Bedrak, E., Samoiloff, V. 1967. *Can. J. Physiol. Pharmacol.* 45:717–22
201. Henane, R., Laurent, F. 1966. *C. R. Soc. Biol.* 160:733–36
202. Munro, A. H., Sichel, H. S., Wyndham, C. H. 1967. *Life Sci.* 6:749–54
203. Wyndham, C. H. 1968. *Proc. Symp. Physiol. and Behavioral Temp. Regulat., New Haven, Aug. 1968*
204. Wyndham, C. H. 1965. *J. S. Afr. Inst. Mining Met.* 66:125–55
205. Strydom, N. B., Wyndham, C. H., van Graan, C. H., Holdsworth, L. D., Morrison, J. F. 1966. *S. Afr. Med. J.* 40:539–44
206. Wyndham, C. H., Williams, C. G., Morrison, J. F., Heyns, A. 1967. *J. S. Afr. Inst. Mining Met.* 68:92–100
207. Wyndham, C. H., Strydom, N. B. 1969. *S. Afr. Med. J.* 43:893–96
208. Wyndham, C. H., Strydom, N. B., Williams, C. G., Heyns, A. 1967. *J. S. Afr. Inst. Mining Met.* 68:79–91
209. Wyndham, C. H. et al 1968. *J. Appl. Physiol.* 25:586–93
210. Braun, W. E., Maher, J. T., Byrom, R. F. 1967. *J. Appl. Physiol.* 23:341–46
211. Lemaire, R., Olsen, O., Benceny, C. 1965. *Arch. Sci. Physiol.* 19:141–60
212. Williams, C. G., Wyndham, C. H., Heyns, A. J. A. 1968. *Int. Z. Angew. Physiol.* 26:298–308
213. Williams, C. G., Heyns, A. J. A. 1969. *Int. Z. Angew. Physiol.* 27:198–211
214. Strydom, N. B. et al 1966. *J. Appl. Physiol.* 21:636–42
215. Strydom, N. B., Williams, C. G. 1969. *J. Appl. Physiol.* 27:262–65
216. Gisolfi, C., Robinson, S. 1969. *J. Appl. Physiol.* 26:530–34
217. Fox, R. H. 1965. In *The Physiology of Human Survival*, 53–79. London: Academic. 581 pp.
218. Wyndham, C. H. et al 1964. *J. Appl. Physiol.* 19:598–606
219. Wyndham, C. H. et al 1964. *J. Appl. Physiol.* 19:607–12
220. Wyndham, C. H. et al 1964. *J. Appl. Physiol.* 19:881–84
221. Wyndham, C. H. et al 1964. *J. Appl. Physiol.* 19:885–88
222. Wyndham, C. H., Metz, B., Munro, A. 1964. *J. Appl. Physiol.* 19:1051–54
223. Wyndham, C. H., MacPherson, R. K., Munro, A. 1964. *J. Appl. Physiol.* 19:1055–58
224. Wyndham, C. H., Strydom, N. B., Williams, C. G., Morrison, J. F., Bredell, G. A. G. 1966. *Int. Z. Angew. Physiol.* 23:79–92
225. Wyndham, C. H., Strydom, N. B., van Graan, C. H., Heyns, A., Hodgson, T. 1967. *Int. Z. Angew. Physiol.* 24:315–19
226. Robinson, S., Belding, H. S., Consolazio, F. C., Horvath, S. M., Turell, E. S. 1965. *J. Appl. Physiol.* 20:583–86
227. Lind, A. R., Humphreys, P. W., Collins, K. J., Foster, K., Sweetland, K. F. 1970. *J. Appl. Physiol.* 28:50–56
228. Wyndham, C. H., Morrison, J. F., Williams, C. G. 1965. *J. Appl. Physiol.* 20:357–64
229. Morimoto, T., Slabochova, Z., Naman, R. K., Sargent, F. II. 1967. *J. Appl. Physiol.* 22:526–32
230. Fox, R. H., Löfstedt, B. E., Woodward, P. M., Eriksson, E., Werkstrom, B. 1969. *J. Appl. Physiol.* 26:444–53
231. Dill, D. B., Horvath, S. M., Van Beaumont, W., Gehlsen, G., Burrus, K. 1967. *J. Appl. Physiol.* 23:746–51
232. Collins, K. J., Crockford, G. W., Weiner, J. S. 1965. *Arch. Environ. Health* 11:407–22
233. Ashworth, A., Harrower, A. D. B. 1967. *Brit. J. Nutr.* 21:833–43
234. Bar-Or, O., Lundegren, H. M., Magnusson, L. I., Buskirk, E. R. 1968. *Hum. Biol.* 40:235–48
235. Höfler, W. 1968. *J. Appl. Physiol.* 25:503–6
236. Schmidt-Nielsen, K., Crawford, E. C., Jr., Newsom, A. E., Rawson, K. S., Hammel, H. T. 1967. *Am. J. Physiol.* 212:341–46
237. Taylor, C. R. 1969. *Am. J. Physiol.* 217:317–20
238. Yousef, M. K., Dill, D. B. 1969. *J. Appl. Physiol.* 27:229–32
239. Bianca, W. 1966. *J. Agr. Sci.* 66:57–60
240. Taylor, C. R., Spinage, C. A., Lyman, C. P. 1969. *Am. J. Physiol.* 217:630–34

241. Bianca, W. 1965. *Res. Vet. Sci.* 6: 33–37
242. Taylor, C. R. 1968. *Symp. Zool. Soc. London* 21:195–206
243. Taylor, C. R., Robertshaw, D., Hofmann, R. 1969. *Am. J. Physiol.* 217:907–10
244. Robertshaw, D., Taylor, C. R. 1969. *J. Physiol. London* 203:135–43
245. Hofmeyr, H. S., Guidry, A. J., Waltz, F. A. 1969. *J. Appl. Physiol.* 26: 517–23
246. Kibler, H. H., Johnson, H. D., Shanklin, M. D., Hahn, L. 1965. *Missouri Agr. Exp. Sta. Res. Bull.* 893:1–28
247. Yousef, M. K., Kibler, H. H., Johnson, H. D. 1967. *J. Anim. Sci.* 26: 142–48
248. Ingram, D. L., Mount, L. E. 1965. *Res. Vet. Sci.* 6:300–6
249. Ingram, D. L., Slebodzinski, A. 1965. *Res. Vet. Sci.* 6:522–30
250. Weaver, M. E., Ingram, D. L. 1969. *Ecology* 50:710–13
251. Ingram, D. L., Weaver, M. E. 1969. *Anat. Rec.* 163:517–24
252. Ingram, D. L. 1965. *Nature* 207: 415–16
253. Allen, J. R., Chaffee, R. R. J. 1964. *Physiologist* 7:80
254. Blatt, W. F., Walker, J., Mager, M. 1965. *Am. J. Physiol.* 209:785–89
255. Mager, M., Blatt, W. F., Newman, R. W. 1968. *J. Appl. Physiol.* 24: 616–18
256. Petajan, J. H., Vogwill, M. T., Murray, M. B. 1969. *J. Appl. Physiol.* 27:528–34
257. Aithal, H. N., Joshi, V. C., Ramasarma, T. 1968. *Biochim. Biophys. Acta* 162:66–72
258. Masoro, E. J. 1966. *Physiol. Rev.* 46:67–101
259. Therriault, D. G., Mehlman, M. A. 1965. *Can. J. Biochem.* 43:1437–43
260. Delisle, G., Radomski, M. W. 1968. *Can. J. Physiol. Pharmacol.* 46: 71–75
261. Smith, R. E., Hoijer, D. J. 1962. *Physiol. Rev.* 42:60–142
262. Frehn, J. L., Anthony, A. 1965. *Trans. Ill. State Acad. Sci.* 58: 263–67
263. Frehn, J. L., Munro, D. W., Anthony, A. 1968. *Trans. Ill. State Acad. Sci.* 61:296–307
264. Vincendon, G., Bidet, R., Jund, R., Mandel, P., Kayser, C. 1965. *Bull. Soc. Chim. Biol.* 48:929–44
265. Munro, D. W., Anthony, A. 1965. *Proc. Pa. Acad. Sci.* 39:114–20
266. Kodama, A., Pace, N. 1963. *Fed. Proc.* 22:761–65
267. Williams, D. D., Platner, W. S. 1967. *Am. J. Physiol.* 212:167–72
268. Chaffee, R. R. J., Platner, W. S., Patton, J., Jenny, C. 1968. *Proc. Soc. Exp. Biol. Med.* 127:102–6
269. Patton, J. F., Platner, W. S. 1970. *Am. J. Physiol.* 218:1417–22
270. Lusena, C. V., Depocas, F. 1967. *Can. J. Physiol. Pharmacol.* 45: 683–87
271. Harland, W. A., Barnett, S. A. 1969. *Quart. J. Exp. Physiol.* 54:202–6
272. Itoh, S., Kuroshima, A., Doi, K., Moriya, K., Shirato, H., Yoshimura, K. 1969. *Fed. Proc.* 28:960–64
273. Shields, J. L., Platner, W. S. 1966. *Fed. Proc.* 25:515
274. Hubbard, R. W., Voorheis, H. P., Therriault, D. G. 1970. *Lipids* 5: 114–20
275. Therriault, D. G., Morningstar, J. F., Jr., Winters, V. G. 1969. *Life Sci.* 8:1353–58
276. Reed, N., Fain, J. N. 1968. *J. Biol. Chem.* 243:2843–48
277. Vrana, A., Kazdova, L. 1969. *Life Sci.* 8:1103–8
278. Bobek, P., Ginter, E. 1966. *Nature* 210:204
279. Platner, W. S., Shields, J. L. 1969. *Fed. Proc.* 28:978–82
280. McBurney, L. J., Radomski, M. W. 1969. *Am. J. Physiol.* 217:19–23
281. Hluszko, H. T., Portet, R., Chevillard, L. 1969. *C. R. Soc. Biol.* 163:344–48
282. Hannon, J. P. 1963. *Fed. Proc.* 22: 856–61
283. Morrison, G. R., Brock, F. E., Sobral, D. T., Shank, R. E. 1966. *Arch. Biochem. Biophys.* 114:494–501
284. Klain, G. J., Hannon, J. P. 1969. *Fed. Proc.* 28:965–68
285. Burlington, R. F. 1966. *Comp. Biochem. Physiol.* 17:1049–52
286. Penner, P. E., Himms-Hagen, J. 1968. *Can. J. Biochem.* 46:1205–13
287. Boulouard, R. 1966. *Fed. Proc.* 25: 1195–99
288. Jarratt, A. M., Nowell, N. W. 1969. *Can. J. Physiol. Pharmacol.* 47: 1–6
289. Vaughan, D. A., Vaughan, L. N., Stull, H. D. 1966. *Metabolism* 15: 781–86

290. Cassuto, Y. 1967. *Israel J. Chem.* 5 :137 pp.
291. Klain, G. J., Vaughan, D. A. 1963. *Fed. Proc.* 22 :862–66
292. Sugahara, M., Baker, D. H., Harmon, B. G., Jensen, A. H. 1969. *J. Nutr.* 98 :344–50
293. Anderson, H. L., Benevenga, N. J., Harper, A. E. 1969. *J. Nutr.* 99 : 184–90
294. Beaton, J. R. 1963. *Can. J. Biochem. Physiol.* 41 :1169–79
295. Trapani, I. L. 1966. *Fed. Proc.* 25 : 1254–59
296. Gubachev, I. U. M. 1966. *Vrach. Delo* 6 :105–7
297. Shields, J. L., Platner, W. S., Neubeiser, R. E. 1960. *Am. J. Physiol.* 199 :942–44
298. Blatt, W. F., Kerkay, J. 1967. *Can. J. Physiol. Pharmacol.* 45 :571–75
299. Bop, J. R., Platner, W. S. 1966. *Nature* 211 :634
300. Lózsa, A., Kereszti, Z., Berencsi, G. 1969. *Acta Physiol. Acad. Sci. Hung.* 35 :63–74
301. Depocas, F. 1966. *Can. J. Physiol. Pharmacol.* 44 :875–80
302. Jansky, L. 1965. *Acta Univ. Carolinea-Biol.* 1965 :1–91
303. Chaffee, R. R. J., Yousef, M. K., Johnson, H. D. 1968. *Fed. Proc.* 27 :633
304. Yousef, M. K., Chaffee, R. R. J. 1970. *Proc. Soc. Exp. Biol. Med.* 133 :801–5
305. Yousef, M. K., Luick, J. R. 1969. *Can. J. Physiol. Pharmacol.* 47 : 273–76
306. Chaffee, R. R. J. et al 1969. *Physiologist* 12 :195
307. Chaffee, R. R. J. 1968. *ARL-TR-68-13* 39 pp.
308. Frascella, D. W., Somberg, E. W., Sporn, E. M., Dalton, C., Mehlman, M. A. 1969. *Bull. N.J. Acad. Sci. Spec. Symp. Issue.* March 1969, 77–79
309. Oratz, M., Walker, C., Schreiber, S. S., Gross, S., Rothschild, M. C. 1967. *Am. J. Physiol.* 213 :1341–49
310. Frascella, D. W., Somberg, E. W., Therriault, D. G., Dalton, C., Mehlman, M. A. 1969. *Bull. N.J. Acad. Sci. Spec. Symp. Issue.* March 1969, 46–51

311. Frascella, D. W., Somberg, E. W., Sporn, E. M., Dalton, C., Mehlman, M. A. 1969. *Bull. N.J. Acad. Sci. Spec. Symp. Issue.* March 1969, 80–83
312. Feldberg, W., Myers, R. D. 1963. *Nature* 200 :1325
313. Feldberg, W., Myers, R. D. 1964. *J. Physiol. London* 173 :226–37
314. Lomax, P. 1970. *Int. Rev. Neurobiol.* 12 :1–43
315. Cremer, J. E., Bligh, J. 1969. *Brit. Med. Bull.* 25 :299–306
316. Lomax, P., Foster, R. S., Kirkpatrick, W. E. 1969. *Brain Res.* 15 :431–38
317. Marley, E., Stephenson, J. D. 1968. *J. Physiol. London* 196 :97P–99P
318. Marley, E., Stephenson, J. D. 1968. *J. Physiol. London* 196 :116P
319. Allen, D. J., Marley, E. 1967. *Brit. J. Pharmacol. Chemother.* 31 :290–312
320. DeGroat, W. C., Volle, R. L. 1966. *J. Pharmacol. Exp. Ther.* 154 : 200–15
321. Harri, M., Tirri, R. 1969. *Acta Physiol. Scand.* 75 :631–35
322. Ingenito, A. J. 1968. *Proc. Soc. Exp. Biol. Med.* 127 :74–77
323. Kuroshima, A., Doi, K., Yoshimura, K., Itoh, S. 1969. *Jap. J. Physiol.* 19 :691–700
324. Bhagat, B. 1969. *Psychopharmacologia* 16 :1–4
325. Nikki, P. 1969. *Ann. Med. Exp. Biol. Fenn.* 47 :129–40
326. Gibson, S., McGeer, E. G., McGeer, P. L. 1969. *J. Neurochem.* 16 : 1491–93
327. Simmonds, M. A. 1969. *J. Physiol. London* 203 :199–210
328. Simmonds, M. A., Iversen, L. L. 1969. *Science* 163 :473–74
329. Lichtensteiger, W. 1969. *J. Physiol. London* 203 :675–87
330. Ingenito, A. J., Bonnycastle, D. D. 1967. *Can. J. Physiol. Pharmacol.* 45 :733–43
331. Legrand, M. 1969. *J. Physiol. Paris* 61 :99–118
332. Green, A. R., Curzon, G. 1968. *Nature* 220 :1095–97
333. Roth, R. H., Allikmets, L., Delgado, J. M. R. 1969. *Arch. Int. Pharmacodyn.* 181 :273–82

CENTRAL NERVOUS SYSTEM: AFFERENT MECHANISMS[1]

R. W. RODIECK

Department of Physiology, University of Sydney, Sydney NSW, Australia

On the basis of a survey of *Biological Abstracts* and *Index Medicus,* the number of papers coming under this heading that have been published in the last 2 years is about 2200. A list of these papers would fill the space available for this review twice over. The editors well recognize this problem and have asked for a review that is restricted to a few topics that have recently received particular interest. Because the areas that I have chosen are in their infancy rather than maturity, this review is more a commentary on the new findings and the questions they raise than a summary of the answers these findings provide.

PHYSIOLOGY OF PHOTORECEPTOR OUTER SEGMENTS

In the last 2 years a great deal of interest has been focused upon one of the most fundamental questions in vision; the transducer action of photoreceptors. Although this is basically a physiological question, the picture that emerges draws on a variety of approaches, including chemical, photochemical, immunochemical, electronmicroscopic, electrophysiological, and psychophysical. This area seems destined for further rapid advance.

RETINAL

The primary action of light in vision is thought to be a *cis-trans* isomerization of the C_{11} bond of the retinyl group of the visual pigment; and the mechanism whereby this is effected has been suggested by recent molecular orbital calculations on retinal (109, 145, 198). The calculations indicate that, whereas there is a large energy barrier for torsional rotation about the C_{11} bond from the 11-*cis* to the all-*trans* form, no barrier exists while the molecule is in the lowest triplet state. This excited state has an energy minimum when the molecule is in the all-*trans* configuration, so that both the (presumed) long latency of this triplet state, and its potential energy profile for torsional rotation about C_{11}, favor the photoconversion of 11-*cis* retinal to the all-*trans* form.

[1] Some aspects of this topic are also treated in this volume in the chapter by Arnaldo Lasansky.

Pauling's calculations (154) form the basis for the long-held view that, because of a certain postulated steric hindrance, the 11-*cis* stereoisomer has a higher free energy (by 9.5 kcal mole^{-1}) than the all-*trans* form. This led to the belief that light permits the visual pigment to fall down an energy gradient, and thus triggers the bleaching reaction. However, Hubbard (101) showed experimentally that the free energy difference between these two retinal isomers is only 1.1 to 1.4 kcal mole^{-1}, and this indicates that the postulated steric hindrance does not exist. An explanation for this unexpected finding has been provided by Nash (145), who calculated that the postulated steric hindrance is relieved by rotation about the single bonds adjacent to the isomerized double bond. The calculated minimum potential energy difference achieved is in good agreement with the enthalpy of isomerization of 11-*cis* retinal.

Light certainly does not *trigger* the bleaching reaction. Considering the small difference in free energy between 11-*cis* and all-*trans* retinal, and the fact that opsin sequesters 11-*cis* retinal to form visual pigment, some of the free energy of the light must be used to boost the visual-pigment molecule up a free-energy gradient to form all-*trans* retinal and opsin.

VISUAL-PIGMENT CHEMISTRY

Cattle visual-pigment extracts have been extensively studied and have long been held to be composed of a protein (or lipoprotein) having a molecular weight of about 40,000 and a molar extinction coefficient at 500 nm (e_{max}) of about 42,000 liters mole^{-1} cm^{-1} (126a). However, Heller (94), using the powerful cationic detergent cetyltrimethylammonium bromide (CTAB) and gel-filtration chromatography, finds that cattle visual pigment is a glycoprotein composed of 235 amino acid residues, having a molecular weight of about 27,500 (94, 96, 98) and an e_{max} of 23,100 $\pm$ 800 liters mole^{-1} cm^{-1}. The fraction of nonpolar residues is high (50%) as might be expected for a membrane protein. The molecule resembles in a number of ways other membrane proteins which have been extracted from beef heart mitochondria (82) and human erythrocyte membranes (167, 170). The latter protein has also been shown to be a glycoprotein (167).

Heller & Lawrence (98) have shown that the carbohydrate in the visual-pigment molecule is in the form of a single oligosaccharide chain attached to an aspartyl residue. They have determined the composition of this chain as well as the amino acid sequence of the glycopeptide isolated from a peptic digest of the visual pigment. They suggest that the function of the hydrophilic oligosaccharide moiety on the surface of the visual-pigment molecule is to serve as a vectorial orientation marker during the assembly of the molecule into the membrane mosaic.

Heller (96) has further shown that visual pigments extracted from rat and frog retinas have exactly the same general properties as cattle visual pigment, differing only in the details of their amino acid composition. Thus visual pigments from different species that have the same λ_{max} value are not identical but homologous. For example, although both rabbits and frogs have a rod visual pigment with a λ_{max} at 502 nm, rabbits can develop specific antifrog rhodopsin antibodies (see following).

To what degree are these new findings in conflict with earlier studies? Regarding the molecular weight, recent work by Shields et al (173) and Shichi et al (172) agrees with the lower value but differs somewhat regarding the amino acid composition.

Previous studies on the absorbance spectra of visual pigments have shown a small peak at about 350 nm which has been termed the *β-peak* or *cis-peak*. The recent study of Shichi et al (172) also shows this peak. However, it was absent in Heller's spectrum although he could obtain such a peak by partially bleaching his purified extracts. He concludes that the β-peak is not part of the spectrum of unbleached visual pigment but is due to impurities (bleaching photoproducts) in the extract. Since only Heller's technique separates bleached visual pigment from the unbleached form and since his purified extracts have a lower A_{280}/A_{500} ratio (1.55–1.68) than any others reported, this explanation seems plausible. However, it might be argued that Heller's extraction and purification procedure somehow disrupted the visual-pigment molecule and this change accounts for the differences in the spectrum he obtained. The validity of any such procedures must inevitably be judged by comparison with the behavior of visual pigment in outer segments. In agreement with Heller's interpretation, the best spectrum obtained in this region by microspectrophotometry (MSP) of single outer segments shows no β-peak (63a).

Shichi et al (172) recently determined the peak extinction of cattle visual pigment, and unlike Heller, obtained the older value of 42,000 liters mole^{-1} cm^{-1}. In light of this, Heller (97) redetermined the e_{max} value by essentially the same method that he had used before and again obtained the lower value. He attempted a determination using the method described by Shichi et al, but reported that it gave only very erratic and nonreproducible results. See (171a) for a different view.

The e_{max} value of a visual pigment is an important and fundamental quantity in vision and enters into many calculations. Since it might be argued that Heller's procedures somehow disrupt the visual pigment and this change accounts for the lower value, an independent test is desirable. Again, the best appeal that can be made is to the behavior of visual pigment in outer segments. Recent findings, discussed later in this review, provide sufficient data to independently calculate the value of e_{max} in outer segments. The relevant equation is $D_{max} = 1.5 \cdot e_{max} c$ where D_{max} is the maximum optical density per unit length for axial rays, 1.5 is the chromophore orientation factor for axial rays, and c is the visual-pigment concentration. For frog (red) rods, Liebman & Entine (124) found a maximum optical density at 500 nm of 1.5×10^{-2} μm^{-1}. Standard values in the literature on the concentration of visual pigment in outer segments are themselves based on an assumed value for e_{max} and an independent value is needed here. Fortunately the recent work permits this value to be estimated from the geometry of the situation alone. As discussed later, X-ray diffraction studies of frog rods show the disk-to-disk spacing to be 29.5 nm (29) and that (fixed) disks contain visual-pigment molecules ordered in a square array having sides of 7.0 nm (27). This gives an elemental volume of 1445 nm³ containing four protein layers (i.e. the disk is composed of two membranes, each composed of two protein layers). As discussed later, it appears that virtually all of this protein is visual pigment so that each elemental volume contains four visual-pigment molecules. The concentration of visual pigment in the outer segment is then $2.77 \cdot 10^6$ molecules μm^{-3} or 4.6 mM. Substituting into the above equation provides an e_{max} value of 21,700 liters mole^{-1} cm^{-1} which is close to Heller's value. While these calculations are for frog rods rather than cattle rods, recent work by Dartnall (49) shows that a variety of different retinal-based visual pigments all have about the same photosensitivity so that it is likely that they have about the same e_{max} values as well. Naturally calculations of this type do not prove that the lower value of e_{max} is correct, but they do indicate that many of the recent findings obtained by a number of different workers, taken together, are remarkably self-consistent. The most critical factor is the assumption that almost all of the protein in the outer segment is visual pigment. If only two of the four protein layers of the disk were visual pigment then the calculated value of e_{max} would be 43,400 liters mole^{-1} cm^{-1} or close to the older value.

RETINYL-OPSIN LINKAGE

The traditional view of visual pigment is that of a chromophore (retinal) bound to opsin via a Schiff base linkage. When bleached to metarhodopsin II there seems little doubt that the linkage is of this type and, at this stage, reduction with NaBH$_4$ demonstrates that the retinyl group is attached to the ε-amino group of lysine (2, 31, 95, 96). But NaBH$_4$ fails to reduce unbleached visual pigment, and if a Schiff base is present this must mean that the retinyl group is masked within a hydrophobic region inside the visual-pigment complex. Two alternative types of linkages have recently been proposed. Heller (95), finding that only a single titratable sulfhydryl group is released on bleaching, has proposed that, in the unbleached state, the retinyl group is linked by a substituted aldimine bond to the ε-amino group of lysine as well as a sulfhydryl group of cysteine. Bleaching breaks the latter bond, releasing the titratable sulfhydryl group and converting the bond to a Schiff base. Heller's suggestion seems to be a good one, but it has been ignored in the literature. Instead, there has been much interest in the idea that the retinyl group in the unbleached pigment is bound by a Schiff base linkage to phosphatidyl ethanolamine (PE) rather than to the protein (3, 48, 72, 161, 162). In this scheme, light exposure is thought to cause the retinyl group to migrate to the ε-amino group of lysine. Interest in PE stems partly from the fact that retinal binds to it via a Schiff base, and the resulting N-retinylidene PE (N-RPE) has an absorbance peak in the visible range (445 nm), giving it an orange color. Apparently overlooked is

Heller's (94) finding that CTAB extracts of visual pigment have a normal absorbance in the visible range but *contain no PE,* a finding now fully confirmed by Hall & Bacharach (91). In addition, Andersen et al (6a) have injected ^{3}H-retinal into frogs and later extracted and purified the frog visual pigment. They find that no N-RPE could be extracted from the purified visual pigment under conditions identical to those used by others (3, 162). However, labeled N-RPE could be extracted from the crude extracts. This is not only strong evidence against a role for PE in the retinal linkage but probably explains the basis for the earlier claims for PE.

Quantum Efficiency

Defined in this context as the ratio of the number of pigment molecules bleached to the number of photons absorbed, the quantum efficiency is also equal to the ratio of the photosensitivity of the visual pigment to its extinction. Values for photosensitivity range from 26,300 to 28,500 liters mole^{-1} cm^{-1} (49, 120a). Combined with an e_{max} of 23,100 ± 800 (see above), one obtains a quantum efficiency ranging from 1.10 to 1.28. A quantum efficiency greater than unity implies that a single photon is able to bleach more than one molecule. In principle this could be accomplished by radiationless energy transfer, but the distance between visual-pigment molecules in solution is too great for this to be significant. Visual-pigment fluorescence has been observed (86, 87) but its efficiency is again too low to be significant here. It therefore appears that the best value to assume for the quantum efficiency is unity. In the past few years smaller values in the range from 0.5 to 0.67 have been quoted. However, these values were based either on an ε_{max} value that was probably too large (49, 65) or on studies with bright flashes of light or low temperatures—two situations in which photoregeneration could occur. The critical experiment here has not yet been done, namely the determination of the photosensitivity of visual pigment extracted by CTAB and purified by gel-filtration chromatography.

Bleaching Dynamics in Outer Segments

As noted above the primary action of light is to photoisomerize the visual-pigment chromophore. The molecule is thereby rendered unstable and passes through a series of intermediate thermal reactions, finally hydrolyzing to free retinal and opsin. Until recently these intermediates have been well studied only in solution. There, at physiological temperatures, the occurrence of the intermediates may be divided into three main periods: (*a*) a rapid period, lasting only a few microseconds, where the visual pigment passes, via pre-lumirhodopsin and lumirhodopsin, to metarhodopsin I; (*b*) a period lasting fractions of a millisecond to several milliseconds, where metarhodopsin I is converted to metarhodopsin II; and (*c*) a slow period lasting many minutes, where metarhodopsin II is converted to pararhodopsin (191) and then to free retinal and opsin. Recent work has shown that this sequence applies, not only to visual-pigment solutions, but to the retina, whether in isolation, in the excised eye, or in the living eye. This has been demonstrated using both spectrophotometry of the isolated retina and the early receptor potential (ERP) of the retina under all conditions including the living eye.

Some years ago, Hagins, in an unpublished thesis not available to me, is reported to have used fundal reflectometry of the rabbit eye to demonstrate the occurrence of three long-lived transient intermediates that he labeled A, B, and C. In the eye, the ERP resulting from an intense flash is composed of two components; R_1, which is positive, and R_2, which is negative (43, 151). It was originally believed that R_1 is generated as a result of the conversion of pre-lumirhodopsin, through lumirhodopsin, to metarhodopsin I (152) while R_2 results from the conversion of metarhodopsin I to meta II (44). However, it now appears that both R_1 and R_2 occur during the conversion of visual pigment to meta I (46). R_1 and R_2 are the only fast photovoltages observed from the visual pigment itself, but if an intense flash is presented when bleaching intermediates are present, then an ERP is also observed (9, 44, 150) which is due to photoregeneration. Cone (44) identified the different ERPs observed with the intermediates described by Hagins and thus labeled these ERPs R_A, R_B, and R_C. He also pointed out that intermediate A was most probably meta I, B was meta II, and C corresponded to para. This correspondence between the intermediates observed in the retina and those observed in solution has been fully confirmed by spectrophotometry of the isolated rat retina (46, 71) and frog retina (70). The correspondence between the ERP potentials and the intermediates has also been fully confirmed (46, 62) and these potentials have thus been renamed $R_{meta\ I}$, $R_{meta\ II}$, and R_{para} (46). In summary, bleaching in the eye is like that in solution, but in the eye the ERP provides an additional measure of visual-pigment and intermediate photoproduct concentrations. No ERP is observed for free retinal or retinol since they are not oriented. Where regeneration of visual pigment in the living eye fits into all of this has not yet been determined.

In the isolated rat retina, Frank & Dowling (71) found that the threshold for the b-wave is raised by some 3 log units immediately following a strong bleaching flash, and remains stable at that level thereafter. Since, during this period, the long-lived intermediates are undergoing the changes described above, it seems probable that these intermediates do not in themselves directly affect visual sensitivity.

Donner & Reuter (55–57), studying dark adaptation in the frog retina, reported that: (*a*) meta I is a long-lived intermediate; and (*b*) visual sensitivity is directly related to the concentration of meta II. Similar findings have been reported by Baumann (16, 17). The findings described above naturally bring these claims into question and Frank (70) has discussed possible reasons for these striking differences.

VISUAL-PIGMENT REGENERATION IN THE ISOLATED NEURAL RETINA

It has been universally held that visual pigment does not regenerate in the isolated neural retina [i.e. away from the retinal (pigment) epithelium], although, in the last century, Kühne had reported that partial regeneration could be observed in the isolated neural retina of the frog. This regeneration was rediscovered by Goldstein (76) who found that in the isolated neural retina of the frog, the ERP recovered in the dark to 80 to 90% of its amplitude prior to bleaching. The ERP is a measure of pigment concentration (43) and the frog ERP is dominated by cones (see below) so that Goldstein concluded that regeneration had occurred. Using minispectrophotometry on the isolated neural retina of the rod-dominated rat eye, Cone & Brown (45) showed that as much as 80% of the bleached rhodopsin spontaneously regenerated, provided the isolated retina was sealed in a small chamber. They reported similar results for the frog and monkey. Frank (70) confirmed their finding in the frog, adding that it was not necessary to confine the retina to a small chamber, for some regeneration (14%) could be observed when the retina was perfused. Frank suggested that free retinal (or retinol) is the substance whose local concentration is most critical. Weinstein et al (194) failed to observe regeneration in the rat, and Frank (70) suggests that this may be due to their adding human serum to their perfusion solution. Retinol and retinal are relatively insoluble in aqueous solution but if they could bind to (serum) protein this might facilitate their transportation away from the isolated neural retina.

The mechanism of this form of regeneration is not clear. Frank (70) found that when ultraviolet wavelengths were removed from his light source, regeneration did not occur, which suggested that photoisomerization of the chromophore was necessary. If this is the case, then this form of regeneration could not be significant in the intact eye, since the ocular media filter out ultraviolet. However, Cone & Brown (45) observed regeneration when filters were used to remove from the light flash all wavelengths shorter than 510 nm.

MEMBRANE COMPOSITION

For some time there has been good, but circumstantial evidence that visual pigment is a membrane protein of the outer-segment lamellae and recent evidence reviewed in the following sections makes this certain. With rather indirect methods, the fraction of outer-segment membrane protein that is visual pigment has been held to range from about 25 to 50%. Recent work indicates a higher fraction is visual pigment.

Hall et al (93) injected frogs with ^{3}H-labeled amino acids and later isolated the protein that had become incorporated in the outer segments. They found that between 80 and 85 percent of the radioactivity of washed outer segments was due to visual pigment. This is a lower bound since contamination would tend to reduce this percentage. Hence most, and perhaps virtually all, of the protein of the (rod) outer-segment disks is visual pigment.

Liebman (123), using MSP to study the spectra of outer segments, finds that the A_{280}/A_{500} ratio corrected for dichroism is near that previously reported for visual-pigment extracts. As he points out, the two ratios should be equal if all the outer-segment protein were visual pigment. However, his data show a larger ratio than Heller's recent low value of about 1.6 so that the relevance of the MSP measurements to this question is not yet clear.

Using quite a different technique, Bownds & Gaide-Huguenin (32) also report that virtually all of the protein is visual pigment. They hydrolyzed frog outer segments, performed an amino acid analysis, and compared the number of amino acid residues present in the outer segments with the number of visual-pigment molecules present as estimated by measuring the difference spectrum at 500 nm. They report that, on the average, there are 250 amino acid residues in the outer segment per visual-pigment molecule (or, in their words, per prosthetic group). Since frog visual-pigment molecules contain about 236 residues (see above) there would thus seem to be few residues remaining for proteins other than visual pigment. However, Bownds & Gaide-Huguenin assumed an e_{max} value of 42,000 liters mole^{-1} cm^{-1} and surprisingly failed to consider the lower value reported by Heller. If an e_{max} of 23,100 liters mole^{-1} cm^{-1} is assumed, then their data could equally be used to claim that only about 52% of the amino acid residues belong to the visual pigment.

Thus, while all three reports claim that most of the outer-segment protein is visual pigment, the data in two of them could also be used to claim a smaller fraction. Nevertheless I believe that the technique of Hall et al was freer from experimental difficulties than those used in the other reports. If their finding is accepted, then a fundamental requirement for visual-pigment molecules is that they possess all the properties required of proteins to combine with lipid to form membranes. This would explain the difficulty with which they are solubilized.

Like other plasma membranes, the membrane lipid fraction is high in phospholipids, but, for rods at least, it is exceptionally low in cholesterol (63). Unexpectedly, Falk & Fatt (66) found that the entire lamellar structure of rods disappeared in retinas treated with osmium tetroxide followed by tris (hydroxymethyl) amino methane (TRIS), but the cone outer segments remained unaffected. The external membrane of the rod outer segment and the disk edges were not affected, which indicates that they differed in composition from the disk membrane. There is thus a fundamental, but as yet unkown difference between the composition of rod and cone lamellae. One explanation which might be offered is that rod disks, lacking a structural role, have dispensed with cholesterol, but cone infoldings, which separate exterior from interior, have not, making the cone lamellae less liable to chemical disruption than the rod lamellae. This greater stability of cone infoldings may be the basis for the well-known difficulty in extracting cone visual pigments.

Blasie and co-workers (27, 28), extending an earlier study (26), have used low-angle X-ray diffraction and electronmicroscopy to show that there is a planar liquidlike arrangement of 4 to 5 nm particles in untreated frog disk membrane. Treatment of the disk with antirhodopsin serum identified the particles with the photopigment molecules. Electronmicrographs of phosphotungstate negatively stained disk membrane demonstrated electrolucent spaces about 4 nm in diameter within the disk membrane. In fixed material these spaces lacked the liquidlike arrangement and became ordered in a square array having unit sides of 7.0 nm. The spaces were interpreted as the nonpolar cores of the photopigment molecules. A difficulty with this interpretation is that, if the nonpolar sites were restricted to the core of the molecule, it would be difficult to understand why visual pigments are insoluble in aqueous buffers. Visual pigment has a high fraction of nonpolar residues (see above) and it seems likely that at least some of these lie on the outside of the molecule to promote membrane formation. Hence it is at least possible that the electrolucent holes observed are intermolecular (at nonpolar binding sites) rather than intramolecular.

MEMBRANE STRUCTURE

The classic Davson-Danielli model for biological membranes (protein on the outside, lipid on the inside) has recently come under fire from a number of workers who, while differing in specific details, propose that lipid and protein are interspersed throughout the membrane (see review by Korn 120). The trilaminar unit membrane seen in the electronmicroscope is explained as an artifact of preparation. However, recent work on outer segments strongly supports the older model. Using the freeze-etch technique, Clark & Branton (37) found that the outer segments fractured in such a way as to suggest that the shear passed, not on either side of the disk membrane, but through it. The disk membranes are thus layered. Recent low-angle X-ray diffraction studies on living outer segments by Blaurock & Wilkins (29) and Gras & Worthington (81) have provided sufficient resolution to infer the nature of this layering. The two studies approach the problem of the synthesis of the disk electron density profile from the primary data somewhat differently, but both arrive at a disk about 15 nm thick, composed of two membranes separated by a small intradisk space. The model of Blaurock & Wilkins has the two protein layers of equal thickness, while that of Gras & Worthington (81) has a thicker protein layer bounding the interior of the disk than bounding its exterior. The symmetry of the first model seems in better agreement with the recent evidence that most of the protein of the rod disk membrane is visual pigment. If this is true, then visual pigment forms, not only the exterior layer of the rod disk, but also the interior layer. Since bleaching at either site would presumably result in visual activation, one would be led to suggest that the rod disks are of no significance in visual excitation, other than providing a means of orienting the conjugated chain of the visual-pigment chromophore in a direction perpendicular to the light path. It would be most useful to obtain corresponding data for cones, for there, half the lamellar surface remains extracellular.

PHOTODICHROISM

Some years ago Hagins & Jennings (89) found that photodichroism could not be observed in outer segments when the bleaching light rays were parallel to their long axes. This unexpected finding could be explained as due either to radiationless energy transfer or to rotational freedom of the chromophore in the plane of the disk. The first possibility seems unlikely since the distance between visual-pigment molecules (about 5.6 nm, Ref. 27) is too large for radiationless energy transfer to be efficient, and yet this possibility would require an efficiency close to unity. Pak & Helmrich (153), using the ERP as a measure of pigment bleaching, were unable to demonstrate photodichroism after a retina had been fixed in 2.5% glutaraldehyde or frozen at −10°C. They assumed that under these conditions the chromophore would be fixed and thus argued that the absence of photodichroism cannot be due to rotation of the chromophore. However, this conclusion may be doubted since the assumption that freezing or glutaraldehyde somehow fixes the chromophore is not easy to justify.

Kirschfeld (119) has recently discussed evidence that the central rhabdomere of the eye of the fly may contain orientated and fixed chromophores, indicating that rotation of the chromophore is at least not necessary for vision.

MEMBRANE TOPOLOGY

The classic picture is that the outer segment is linked to the inner segment only via the eccentrically lying connecting cilium. However, in mammalian receptors, Richardson (164) has demonstrated a second cytoplasmic bridge directly between the two segments. It is hard to understand both why this second bridge remained undetected for so long and how the photoreceptors develop to form the topological equivalent of a torus.

The lamellar structure of cone outer segments is formed from an infolding of the plasma membrane and this infolding is also found at the base of the rod outer segments. However, Richardson's (164) micrographs of mamalian rods show no such infoldings and, if anything, suggest that the basal disks are found only near the connecting cilium. It may be that infoldings are seen only in longitudinal sections that are perpendicular to those shown by Richardson.

Elsewhere the rod outer segment appears to contain membranous sacs (disks), pinched off from the basal infoldings and thus held to be topologically free from the external membrane. Convincing evidence has been lacking, however, as to whether a small bridge, overlooked by electronmicroscopists, might connect the disk interior to the extracellular space. If such a bridge did exist it would be of considerable physiological importance. Two recent studies indicate that it does not. Cohen (40) found that lanthanum, while able to fill the extracellular space in the retina, including the infolds of the cone outer segments, was never observed within the rod disks except the most basal or ones with narrow zones of probable damage.

Goldstein (76–79) has shown that the ERP produced by cones is very much larger than that produced by rods, a finding that suggests that only the basal infoldings of the rod outer segments contribute to the rod ERP. For rod disks, the lack of asymmetry, such as provided by a pathway to the exterior, means that contributions from different visual-pigment molecules at different points in the disk cancel.

RENEWAL OF OUTER-SEGMENT MEMBRANE

The excellent work of Young and others (11, 92, 93, 201–207) has established that the outer segments of rods and cones are in a continual state of renewal. Radioactive amino acids were injected into animals and the (radioactive) proteins synthesized from them were located using autoradiography. In frog photoreceptors new protein is formed in the ergastoplasm of the inner-segment myoid and most of it passes around the mitochondria of the ellipsoid to reach the outer segment. As noted above, Hall et al (92, 93) have shown that at least 80% of the new protein of the outer segments is visual pigment (see also 11). The manner by which new protein is incorporated into the lamellar structure of outer segments differs for rods and cones.

In rods, new protein, including the visual-pigment opsin, is taken up only by the basal infoldings or disks. With time these labeled disks are displaced sclerally until they pass off the end (201), to be taken up by the pigment epithelium (10, 205, 206). The renewal rate of visual pigment has been studied by radiobiochemical techniques (92, 93). The results indicate that the visual pigment is stable (not renewed) while it is in the disk membrane, and is not broken down until the disk is shed from the end of the rod outer segment. The disks of the frog red rods are formed at the rate of 36/day and traverse the outer segment in about 6 to 7 weeks. In frogs the renewal rate increases with ambient temperature and in both frogs and rats increases very slightly with intense constant illumination (201).

In cones a localized concentration of radioactive protein in the outer segments indicative of new membrane synthesis is not observed; instead the protein becomes diffusely distributed throughout the outer segment (203). Therefore, it appears that mature rods, but not cones, continue to synthesize outer segment membranes.

What is the significance of the rapid turnover of rod outer-segment disks? The MSP studies show that the density of visual pigment in the apical end of the rod outer segments is not significantly smaller than at the basal end, so there is no need to renew the outer segments to keep the concentration of visual pigment high. It may be that a small amount of denatured visual pigment in the outer segments significantly reduces their sensitivity and that this fraction is minimized by the continual renewal of visual pigment. But this is speculation.

Dewey et al (52) have used antifrog rhodopsin serum obtained from rabbits and the indirect Coon's antibody technique to fluorescein-label all visual pigment in the frog retina. This is a powerful new technique that should find many applications in retinal studies. In agreement with Young's work, they find the visual pigment, not only in the outer-segment disk membrane, but in the myoid and ellipsoid of the inner segment and in the pigment epithelium. Surprisingly, they also report it in the external membrane of the rod outer segment.

ELECTROPHYSIOLOGY

Since Bortoff (30) and Tomita (185–187) first recorded intracellularly from vertebrate photoreceptors, it has been known that these cells hyperpolarize in response to light. In a beautiful study, Penn & Hagins (156) have determined the spatial distribution of extracellular current about rat rods that is associated with this potential change. Arrays of microelectrodes were inserted into the receptor layer of retinal slices under direct vision by infrared microscopy. These arrays permitted them to determine not only the voltage profile as a function of depth, but also the first and second derivatives of this profile. These profiles, together with resistivity measurements, were used to compute the radial and lateral current flows about the receptors. They found that, in the dark, the rod outer segments act as a sink for current drawn from the rest of the cell, including the inner segment. Light acts to reduce this dark current. At least 60,000 charges contribute to this photocurrent for each absorbed photon and this photocurrent gives rise to the receptor potential of the ERG (a-wave, PIII, or late RP).

The light-induced current and hyperpolarization could be due to three factors: (a) an electrogenic pump; (b) an increase in membrane permeability for an ion (or ions) whose equilibrium potential lies below the resting (dark) potential; and (c) a decrease in membrane permeability for an ion whose equilibrium potential lies above the resting potential. Regarding the first possibility, Arden & Ernst (7) showed that the pigeon cone receptor potential recorded with external electrodes could still be generated by light after the addition of ouabain, provided that an ionic concentration gradient for sodium or some other ion was maintained. If external sodium was replaced by TRIS the receptor potential inverted and this is evidence against a light-activated electrogenic pump and thus for an ionic concentration gradient as the causal agent of the pigeon cone receptor potential. In more recent work, Arden & Ernst (8) report that reducing chloride ions in the external medium (by replacement with sulfate ions) reduced the light-evoked receptor potential in quantitatively the same way as reducing external sodium ions. The behavior of the response to changes in the concentration of external chloride was reported to indicate that, like sodium, this ion had its highest concentration in the external medium and produced an inward current. Since these ions have opposite polarities, Arden & Ernst proposed that, during the dark, sodium permeability is high, chloride permeability low. Illumination decreases sodium permeability and reduces chloride permeability so that the ionic currents add rather than cancel. If this were the case, then, unlike the rat rods described by Penn & Hagins, intense illumination could cause the photocurrent to be even larger than the dark current.

In contrast to pigeon cones, Arden & Ernst (7) found that the receptor potential of rat rods is abolished by ouabain and cannot be restored or inverted by altering the external medium, thus raising the possibility for a rod electrogenic pump. However, Sillman et al (176) have shown that, as in pigeon cones, the frog rod receptor potential is not blocked by ouabain, provided that an ionic gradient for sodium is maintained. It is hard to believe that frog and rat rods would differ so fundamentally. These studies (7, 8, 176) make use of presumed properties of ouabain in blocking ionic pumps, but this drug does not block all potassium and sodium pumps, nor is it known to block chloride pumps.

Following the idea that receptor potentials result from permeability changes and concentration gradients, Toyoda et al (188) recorded from single photoreceptors in *Necturus maculosus* and *Gekko gekko* and showed that the response to light is accompanied by an increase in membrane resistance. This increase was not caused by the hyperpolarization itself, since passive hyperpolarization by current injection did not change the membrane resistance, but made the hyperpolarizing response to light larger. Sillman et al (175, 176) studied the rod receptor potential in the excised frog retina and found that, except at very low concentrations, its amplitude varied in direct proportion to the logarithm of the external sodium concentration, and in inverse proportion to the logarithm of the external potassium concentration. This evidence, taken together, strongly supports the idea that the light-activated hyperpolarization results from a decrease in the permeability of the outer-segment membrane to sodium and perhaps other ions. The sodium channels remain open in the dark, producing the dark current. In contrast, the invertebrate photoreceptors that have been studied respond to light by a depolarization and increase in membrane permeability.

The ability of photoreceptors to signal the absorption of a single photon has long fascinated visual physiologists. As noted above, the work of Penn & Hagins indicates that the *gain* of the outer segments is at least 60,000 charges per absorbed photon. Hagins (88), applying communication theory to information flow in photoreceptors, has calculated that the minimum number of charges that must reach the synaptic site for reliable transmission is about 3000. Only a fraction of the charges leaving the outer segment reach the synaptic site, but, judging from the spatial distribution of extracellular current measured by Penn & Hagins (156), it seems possible that the required 5% could do so.

The work of Rodieck & Ford (166) and Ford (69) on the cat and of the above authors on other species indicates that, below saturation, the rod receptor potential has a much slower time course than had been anticipated. To a brief flash it rises fairly rapidly to decay over a second or so. This would make the peak current for one absorbed photon about 60,000 charges per second or about $4 \cdot 10^{-15}$ A. This photocurrent could result from a relatively small permeability change in a large number of sodium channels, or a larger change in a smaller number of channels. Estimates of the *maximum* sodium current through a single activated channel in other nerve membrane range from 6.7 to $40 \cdot 10^{-12}$ A for the frog node of Ranvier (14, 100) to $200 \cdot 10^{-12}$ A for lobster axons (100). These values are thus much larger than the photocurrent for a single absorbed photon. In other words it would be necessary to change the permeability of only a single sodium channel in order to generate the observed photocurrent. A similar conclusion is reached for the *Limulus* retinula cell (15).

This puts a new light on photoreceptor activation, for it is commonly believed that, in order to account for the ability of a single absorbed photon to be signaled, some form of chemical amplification similar to an enzymatic or catalytic process is required between the photochemical event and the electrical signal. Now the *minimum* requirement is that a single photochemical event block a single outer-segment membrane sodium channel.

The density of sodium channels on nerve membrane is estimated to range from $1.3 \cdot 10^9$ cm^{-2} for lobster axon (134) to $8.9 \cdot 10^9$ cm^{-2} for the nodes of Ranvier of frog sciatic nerve (14). If the density of sodium channels on rat rod outer segments were similar, then the number of channels per outer segment would be in the range from 2 to $15 \cdot 10^3$. It may be significant that this is of the same order of magnitude as the number of absorbed photons necessary to fully saturate rods (see below). It is perhaps also worth noting that the rodlike response from *Gekko* single photoreceptors saturates at an intensity about 2 log units lower than that of the conelike response from *Necturus* (188), and that this difference in saturation may reflect the fact that the lamellar infolding of the cone outer segments gives them a much larger surface area (and hence potentially more channels) than the rod outer segments. This would fit in with the psychophysical observations that whereas cones have about the same optical density as rods, they saturate at a higher level while still able (individually) to signal the absorption of a single photon.

In response to a bright light flash the receptor response becomes, not larger, but longer (33, 156). Ganglion cells and at least one of the cell types generating the ERG produce a delayed off-response to bright flashes of light (47, 158–160, 174) that is probably a reflection of this delayed decay of the receptor potential. In the frog retina, very bright flashes can produce a ganglion cell silent period longer than 10 sec that is followed by a discharge (158). One means of interpreting these findings is that the bright flash produces an excess of material sufficient to block all the sodium channels. Only when this excess is inactivated can the photoreceptor begin to return to its depolarized state.

Falk & Fatt (64, 65) investigated the passive electrical properties of a packed suspension of dark-adapted frog rod outer segments and found a behavior similar to that of other biological material. Illumination caused very small admittance changes that were identified partly with changes in the visual-pigment molecules and partly with changes involving the organized structure of the rod. It is not as yet clear how these changes are related to receptor activation.

LINEARITY OF VERTEBRATE PHOTORECEPTOR RESPONSES

Convincing evidence, obtained from different species and using different techniques, indicates that vertebrate photoreceptors produce, to a light flash, a response (V) that depends on light intensity (I) in the following way:

$$\frac{V}{V_{max}} = \frac{I}{I + I_0}$$

V_{max} is the amplitude of the saturated response to a very bright flash and I_0 is a constant having the same dimensions as the stimulus. When $I << I_0$, V becomes proportional to I; when $I = I_0$, $V = \frac{1}{2}V_{max}$; as I becomes larger than I_0 there is a narrow range where an approximately logarithmic relation is obtained [since this relation is part of the series expansion for log $(I + I_0)$]; when $I >> I_0$, $V = V_{max}$. Credit for the discovery of this relation goes to Rushton and his co-workers (4–6, 141–144). It is the relation to be expected from the above discussion on receptor activation if one assumes a number of ionic channels in the membrane that are controlled by some product of visual-pigment activaton. The evidence for this relaton is as follows.

Using intracellular recording from turtle cones, Baylor & Fuortes (20) have shown that the change in transmembrane potential to a light flash obeys this relation with $I_0 = 2700$ photons absorbed per receptor. For light flashes somewhat smaller than this value the response was thus proportional to light intensity.

Using intracellular recording from carp cones, Tomita (186) found that the amplitude of the response was proportional to light intensity over about one third (1 mV) of the maximum response (3 mV). He estimated that the response to a single photon was a few microvolts; hence the linear range extended up to a few hundred photons absorbed per cone per flash. For higher light intensities there was a range for which the stimulus-response relationship became approximately logarithmic as predicted.

Using extracellular recording from rat rods, Penn & Hagins (156) found that the amplitude of the response was proportional to light intensities up to about 250 photons absorbed per rod. As in the turtle cones studied by Baylor & Fuortes, they found that, beyond saturation, the responses became longer rather than larger.

Using intracellular recording from fish S-potentials, Naka & Rushton (140–144) showed that each receptor input obeys the above relation. This implies that the cells that produce S-potentials (almost surely horizontal cells) have a response that is strictly proportional to the receptor input. It also confirms the validity of using changes in the transmembrane potential (or extracellular field) as a measure of the receptor "signal".

Alpern et al (4–6) have devised a powerful psychophysical technique based upon the metacontrast effect to show that human rod signals obey the above relation. This important series of papers describes additional properties of rod signals that are not dealt with in this review. For the rod mechanism, $I_0 = 800$ absorbed photons per rod, a value that also marks the beginning of saturation of the rod mechanism. Thus saturation of the rod mechanism results from a saturation of the rods themselves, rather than the neurons that collect their signals. Correlative evidence comes from the work of Rodieck & Ford (166) who showed that the receptor potential of cat rods saturates at the same level as the (psychophysically measured) human rod mechanism. Baumann (17) has shown the same for the frog ERG.

In all the studies cited above, saturation occurred when only a very small fraction of the visual pigment had been leached. In the cat (Rodieck & Ford 166) the response of the pigment epithelium saturates at the same level as the rod receptor potential. It is known that the pigment epithelium response depends upon receptor activity, but this finding shows that this response is related to the electrical activity of the receptors rather than to the amount of visual pigment bleached. In an extensive investigation of the cat late receptor potential, Ford (69) studied, not the flash response, but the increment response so that the cats were adapted to the stimulus level. Ford effectively measured the slope of the stimulus-response function observed under these conditions. The resulting integrated curve deviates from the above analytic relation and is strongly skewed on a log plot, but it has roughly the same range and peak value and the magnitude of the deviation is less than one might expect from the profound psychophysical changes that light adaptation is known to produce.

Rodieck & Ford (166) found that the components of the electroretinogram (ERG) and local ERG are linearly related to fractional changes in light intensity smaller than about 40%. They also reinterpreted the nature of both the ERG and the local ERG although this work is not reviewed here.

There emerge from this wide variety of studies the following considerations.

(a) Saturation of receptor mechanisms, measured psychophysically, corresponds to a saturation of the receptors themselves, rather than the neural circuitry. In other words it is the linear part of the stimulus-response curve that is important for vision. When a receptor response begins to deviate from linearity it also begins to lose its ability to signal light intensity. The widely held view that a logarithmic relation is involved in the transducer mechanism prior to saturation has no experimental basis.

(b) Vertebrate photoreceptors possess a stimulus-response relation quite different from that in invertebrate photoreceptors such as the *Limulus* ventral photoreceptor (131) or its ommatidial eccentric cell (54). These invertebrate photoreceptors have a generator potential that is approximately logarithmically related to light intensity over a dynamic range of 4 log units. Thus each of these invertebrate receptor cells is able to signal light intensities over a very wide range. The vertebrate rod system also has a dynamic range of about 4 to 6 log units but achieves this by summing the activity of many rods when the light intensity drops below one absorbed photon per rod (i.e. the psychophysical absolute threshold for a spot $\frac{1}{2}°$ in diameter is about ten absorbed photons that are distributed among about 5000 rods).

(c) The Weber region of the psychophysical increment threshold curve may be integrated, as was done by Fechner, to obtain a logarithmic relationship; yet over this range the photoreceptor response is linear. Whatever meaning may be claimed for "Fechner's law" in psychology, its significance in visual physiology is obscure. The only logarithmic relation in vertebrate vision that I know of is the experimentally observed proportionality between the logarithm of b-wave, ganglion cell response, or psychophysical threshold and the concentration of bleached visual pigment (for recent work see 16, 18, 19, 55–57, 71, 168).

NEURAL BASIS OF RECEPTIVE-FIELD ORGANIZATION

Although all vertebrate retinas appear quite similar, their ganglion cells differ radically in the nature of the visual information they transmit. Center-surround organization, first described by Kuffler in the cat, appears the more common, at least in mammals and teleosts. However, some mammalian ganglion cells (particularly in the rabbit and squirrel), as well as those in amphibians, reptiles, and birds, have more complex coding properties. Prominent among these specialized cells are the direction-sensitive units, responding to a specific direction of movement of an object, but not the nature of its contrast.

Until recently, ideas as to the nature of the neural circuitry involved were necessarily speculative. Barlow & Levick (13) suggested that the neural basis of direction sensitivity of rabbit ganglion cells lies at the level of the outer plexiform layer (OPL), horizontal cells playing a primary role. Dowling & Boycott (59) and Rodieck (165) proposed that center-surround receptive fields are organized at the level of the inner plexiform layer (IPL), bipolar cells forming the center, amacrine cells the antagonistic surround. Recent work indicates that the above suggestions are probably incorrect, the level of organization being just the opposite of that proposed.

Dowling (58) found that the density of synaptic contacts in the IPL was much higher in frogs than in primates. He suggested that the neural organization of specialized ganglion cells occurs in the IPL rather than the OPL. In a well-controlled and thorough study, Dubin (61) determined the density of synaptic contacts in the IPL of the frog, rabbit, cat, rat, squirrel, pigeon, and monkey. He found a strong correlation between the complexity of ganglion cell receptive-field organization known for these animals and the density of synaptic contacts in the IPL.

Direct evidence on retinal organization comes from the excellent work of Werblin & Dowling (60, 195, 196) on the *Necturus* retina. They recorded intracellularly from every type of retinal neuron, identifying these cells by injecting them with the dye Niagara blue. They found, in agreement with others (115, 116, 147), that the cells about the OPL (photoreceptors, horizontal and bipolar cells) respond in a sustained and graded manner to visual stimuli, whether flashing, stationary, or moving. The important parameter is the amount of light over the receptive field, not the movement pattern of the stimulus. Bipolar cells are organized in an antagonistic center-surround manner, the center from the receptors, the surround from the horizontal cells. Two types were observed: (*a*) those that depolarized upon illumination of the center; (*b*) those that hyperpolarized upon illumination of the center. With dark adaptation the surround influence was abolished as it is in cat ganglion cells. The suggestion that the ganglion cell surround was due to an amacrine cell contribution could not explain this disappearance.

About the inner plexiform layer the response was transient and depended upon the sequence in which specific areas of the receptive field were illuminated. The activity of these cells could not be predicted from their responses to flashing lights. Amacrine cell receptive fields are also organized in a center-surround manner, but respond only when a moving spot crosses the boundary of the center region. On-center amacrine cells respond only when the spot enters the center, off-center cells only when it leaves. Ganglion cell responses generally resembled either of their inputs (bipolar or amacrine cells) although some ganglion cells (and only ganglion cells) displayed direction sensitivity.

The mudpuppy *Necturus* has an unusual OPL but there is no reason to doubt the generality of these important findings. Intracellular recording from cells throughout the retina has also been made by Kaneko & Hashimoto (115, 116) in the carp and by Norton et al (147) in frog and *Necturus*. While these workers did not determine the cell types from which they recorded, this can, in most cases, be inferred from Werblin's work. Granting this inference, there exist two discrepancies between the work of Kaneko et al on carp and that of Werblin on *Necturus*: (*a*) in carp the surround influence in bipolar cells appears to exist even in the dark; (*b*) no concentric receptive fields seem to exist in carp amacrines.

To summarize, it appears that specialized dynamic organization of ganglion cell receptive fields occurs in the IPL; the simple static form of center-surround organization originates in the OPL, although it may be further modified in the IPL.

COLOR VISION

The most fundamental consideration in color vision is the number of spectrally distinct photoreceptor types contained in a given small retinal area. This photoreceptor variance (i.e. number of different types) must be equal to or larger than the psychophysical variance (i.e. monovariant, divariant, trivariant, etc). For example, in the human parafoveal region there are four receptor types (one type of rod, three types of cones) but psychophysically this region is only trivariant. There is thus a neural reduction in variance.

In an excellent review, Liebman (123) described the technique of microspectrophotometry (MSP) applied to single outer segments, discusses previous work, and presents data on a number of additional species. These findings, together with earlier work with this technique, will be discussed below with regard to certain broad questions of color vision.

Rod Variance

A naive statement of the Duplicity Theory is that cones are for color vision, rods for night vision. It has even been argued that, in specializing to signal dim lights, rods have somehow lost their ability to signal color (192). But rod signals are known to contribute to human color matches at mesopic levels (38, 39, 200). Thus, if this aspect of the Duplicity Theory is to be preserved, it must be restated to say that the rod contribution does not increase the variance of psychophysical color matches. Yet recent work brings even this statement into question.

Liebman & Entine (124) have determined the receptor complement in the frog retina as shown below.

Red rods	502 nm
Green rods	432 nm
Principal cones	575 nm
Accessory cones	502 nm
Single cones	575 nm

Unlike the human, in the frog each morphologically distinct photoreceptor type contains only one type of visual pigment, but the five photoreceptor types share only three types of visual pigment. The principal cone contains a yellow oil droplet, but this is unlikely to make its spectral sensitivity much different from that of single cones, at least over most of the visible range. Hence frog color vision can be trivariant only if the signals from the green rods add to the variance. Behavioral work by Muntz (136–139) has demonstrated that the positive phototaxis observed in frogs depends upon a stimulus containing a *relatively* high contribution of blue light. This phototaxis involves the blue-sensitive green rods and, since it is the *relative* amount of blue light present that is critical, some form of color vision is necessarily involved. Thus, for at least one species, rods contribute to the behavioral variance of color vision.

The frog optic nerve fibers that subserve this phototaxis terminate in the diencephalon, whereas most frog optic fibers terminate in the tectum. This raises the interesting cautionary point that the type of color vision observed may well depend upon the behavioral response criteria. It is at least possible that tests based on positive phototaxis would reveal one form of color discrimination while contrast-discrimination tests based on some form of avoidance reaction would reveal another.

AVIAN COLOR VISION

The inner segments of avian photoreceptors contain brightly colored oil droplets (red, orange, and yellow), whose transmission spectra have now been well described (117, 128). These oil droplets modify the spectral composition of the light that reaches the outer segment. They thus modify the spectral sensitivity of the photoreceptors and thereby have the potential for increasing the photoreceptor variance and could, in themselves, provide a basis for color vision. Walls (192, 193) argued against this possibility and, although his reasoning is not convincing, his view has been widely quoted. However, King-Smith (117) has shown that if all pigeon cones are assumed to contain only one type of visual pigment, then the transmission spectra of their oil droplets perfectly accounts for the psychophysical measured hue discrimination of these birds. Using microspectrophotometry, Liebman (123) now finds that the cones of the pigeon, chicken, and gull contain only a single visual pigment with a λ_{max} at 562 nm ("chicken iodopsin"). Hence it is *only* the oil droplets that provide the variance required for (cone) color vision in these birds.

The pigeon retina contains two regions, known as the red field and the yellow field, each with its own fovea. The red field corresponds to the pecking region of the visual field (73) and differs from the yellow field both in the relative proportions of colored oil droplets and in the transmission properties of the droplets. Within certain limits the relative proportion of different oil droplets cannot directly affect color matches; however, the transmission factors will. Therefore psychophysical data on pigeon color vision should depend upon which of these regions is used by the pigeon in the testing situation.

PENTAVARIANT VISION IN THE TURTLE?

Liebman & Granda (123) have shown that each cone of the freshwater turtle *Pseudemys* contains one of three visual pigments (λ_{max} = 450, 518, and 620 nm). There are four types of cone oil droplets in this retina (red, orange, yellow, and colorless) so that there could be as many as twelve types of cones, each with a different spectral sensitivity. However, the red oil droplet is found only with the 620 nm pigment, the orange droplet with the 560 nm and 620 nm pigments, and the colorless oil droplet only with the 450 nm pigment. The visual pigment(s) associated with the yellow oil droplet was not determined. As Liebman (123) points out, the red and orange oil droplets are associated with the visual pigments whose spectral sensitivities they are best able to effectively modify. Presuming that the yellow oil droplet is associated with only one visual pigment, there are then five types of cones in this (pure cone) retina, making its complement of photoreceptors pentavariant.

COLOR VISION IN CATS

The literature on color discrimination in cats has had its ups and downs. Following a number of conflicting claims, it was shown in 1964 by behavioral experiments that cats possess a weak color discrimination (127, 129, 171). Before that time there were at least nine electrophysiological studies claiming evidence for color vision in cats. Much of this electrophysiological work is conflicting and none of it convincing, although at least one study is still widely quoted at the textbook level.

Daw & Pearlman (51) studied the receptive-field organization of cat retinal ganglion cells at scotopic and photopic levels in the hope of elucidating the neural basis for this color discrimination. They found that the center-surround organization observed at scotopic levels, and due to rod signals, was repeated at photopic levels where the ganglion cells received signals from green-sensitive cones (556 nm). Since only one type of cone was found, they proposed that the weak color discrimination possessed by cats results from a rod contribution to the behavioral variance. In support of this idea, Steinberg (179, 180) found both a rod and cone contribution to cat S-potentials. If both rods and cones were required then cats should possess color discrimination only at mesopic levels. However, Pearlman & Daw (155) tested this point, and found that cats retained the ability to distinguish colors at light intensities sufficient to saturate rods. In a further electrophysiological study at the level of the dLGN (dorsal lateral geniculate nucleus), they found, among the 118 geniculate cells studied, 3 that received an input arising from blue-sensitive cones. Two of these cells were organized in an opponent-color manner (center: blue-on, green-off; surround: blue-off, green-on). It therefore appears that cone variance is both necessary and sufficient to explain cat color vision, a rod contribution to the magnitude of the variance not being required.

COLOR-CODING GANGLION CELLS

The only retinal ganglion cells that have been studied in relation to color vision are the center-surround type. Since the early studies of Wagner et al (189, 190) it has been known that the central region may be influenced by a complement of cones different from that influencing the surround. All the center-surround receptive fields thus far described may be characterized by stating the region of the receptive field over which each receptor mechanism contributes and whether the contribution is excitatory or inhibitory. In the center region each receptor mechanism may excite, inhibit, or not contribute to the response. With three receptor types there are 26 possible center regions (i.e. 3^3-1). Together with 27 possible surrounds (i.e. 3^3 since there may be no surround), there are thus 702 possible receptive-field organizations of this general form. Of these, a total of 20 have thus far been described, distributed among cats (51, 155), goldfish (50), monkeys (80, 197), and squirrels (130). While red-green and green-blue combinations have been described, none has yet been found with a red-blue center-surround organization. The opponent-color type organization that might be anticipated from psychophysical experiments on simultaneous contrast has been observed only in a few cells in the goldfish retina (50) and the cat dLGN (155).

In the monkey dLGN, Wiesel & Hubel (197) found many cells with a center or surround that was activated by either red- or green-sensitive cones, but only a few (1%) that had regions activated only by blue-sensitive cones. Blue-sensitive cones also enjoy a unique position in human psychophysical experiments. These cones are absent from the central fovea, and their mechanism has a higher Weber fraction, a lower visual acuity, a lower flicker fusion frequency (84), and a lower contrast sensitivity for sine-wave gratings (83) than green- or red-sensitive cone mechanisms.

DISCREPANCIES

In the monkey the receptive fields described in the retina by Gouras (80) differ considerably from those described by Wiesel & Hubel (197) in the dLGN. It seems unlikely that this difference is due to a change of organization at the dLGN since Hubel & Wiesel report that they observed the same receptive-field organization when recording from optic tract fibers as they did from the dLGN.

In a microspectrophotometric study of goldfish cones, Marks (126) estimated that the ratio of red:green:blue cones is approximately 11:15:2. Nevertheless no one has yet found a ganglion cell in the goldfish retina that is activated by blue-sensitive cones.

The deep-red-sensitive cones described by Naka & Rushton (142) from studies of fish S-potentials have not been observed by workers using microspectrophotometry although they have specifically looked for them (123). Neither have they been described in studies on ganglion cells or intracellular studies on photoreceptors. Witkovsky (199) reported that, in terms of the stimulus parameters he used, the response properties of carp ganglion cells seemed virtually independent and unrelated to the properties of carp S-potentials.

BINOCULAR SINGLE VISION AND STEREOPSIS

Because of parallax, the retinal images in the two eyes ordinarily differ and the visual system appears to deal with this situation in two principal ways: (a) by combining the neural signals from the two eyes a binocular singleness of vision is somehow achieved; (b) by comparing these signals in some way the important form of depth perception known as stereopsis is achieved. These two facts have long fascinated workers in vision and an extensive psychophysical literature has developed. In the last 3 years related neurophysiological studies have been carried out in Canberra, Berkeley, and Harvard which will be reviewed here. Since these studies make extensive use of the concepts and theories developed from the psychophysical studies, a brief summary of the present psychophysical situation is in order.

PSYCHOPHYSICS

An experimental horopter is a surface established by a subject about a given fixation point. There are a number of different experimental horopters, depending on the instructions given to the subject and on the testing apparatus. The most often quoted horopter is the one in which the subject is asked to establish a "frontoparallel plane" about the fixation point. However, the relevant experimental horopter for this discussion is probably the one where the subject is asked to equate the primary subjective visual directions (Nonius method).

The points on each retina that project optically to a single point on a given horopter surface are said to be *corresponding* while those that do not do so are said to be *disparate* (other definitions are sometimes derived from theoretical notions). The shape of the experimental horopters changes from concave to convex with increasing fixation distance and many years ago Hillebrand suggested that this change was such as to keep the same set of corresponding points. There has been much evidence for and against this possibility (see Ogle 148, 149) but strong evidence in its favor has recently been presented by Flom & Eskridge (68). The invariance of corresponding points with fixation distance indicates that this topological mapping of one retina onto the other is a more fundamental concept than the horopter and that disparities about corresponding points can be spoken of without regard to fixation distance. Points in the visual world that are before or behind the horopter necessarily form disparate retinal points, but, provided that the disparity is not too great, binocular single vision is still achieved (Panum's area). Maximum disparity for single vision increases away from the fixation region and has about the same value in either the horizontal or vertical direction.

Horizontal disparity gives rise to stereopsis, vertical disparity does not. There has been a long-standing controversy regarding the location in the visual system of the mechanism of stereopsis. Helmholtz believed that form vision precedes stereopsis; Hering believed the opposite. Julesz (111–113) has shown, with the use of stereo-pair random-dot patterns, that an appreciation of form vision is not required for stereopsis. Monocular inspection of these patterns gives no cue as to the three-dimensional form that emerges when they are viewed by both eyes in a stereo situation.

The invariance of corresponding points and the stereopsis that can be achieved in the absence of form vision have suggested to some that the visual mechanisms for stereopsis and binocular single vision occur rather early in the visual system, before, for example, the mechanism directly concerned with form vision. This may be true, but some difficult points arise if one presupposes or insists upon a single linear principle of hierarchial organization. For example, Stromeyer & Psotka (183) have found a subject with such a high capacity for eidetic imagery that she can achieve depth perception by viewing one of the dot patterns with one eye and viewing the other, at a later time, with the other eye. When the two patterns were observed successively by the same eye there was no appearance of depth. If the principle used above were applied to this situation, then one would be forced to say that memory occurs in the visual pathway even before binocular single vision, stereopsis, or form vision.

NEUROPHYSIOLOGY

The essential neurophysiological requirement for binocular interaction is that a neuron receives signals from both eyes. Virtually all of the neurophysiological studies have been done on the cat and, unless otherwise noted, the findings described below refer to this animal.

Dorsal lateral geniculate nucleus (dLGN).—Each nucleus receives the fibers from both eyes that project to the contralateral visual field. These fibers form two retinotopic projections: the well-known one to the bulk of the triple-layered dLGN and a second projection to a smaller medial portion (medial interlaminar nucleus). The latter projection has been recently established by both histological (74, 121, 182) and electrophysiological (118) techniques. It has previously been held that the cells in each layer of the dLGN receive signals from only one eye, although a number of workers have reported that a small fraction are binocularly activated. In addition it has been known for some time that the large cells lying between the nuclear layers (central interlaminar nucleus) are directly innervated by both eyes. Against these findings, Grüsser & Sauer (85) have claimed that there is no binocular interaction in the dLGN. Recently it has become clear that the majority of and perhaps all dLGN cells receive signals from both eyes. Marchiafava (125) has demonstrated a retinotopically organized interaction which he interpreted as due to reciprocal presynaptic interaction. However, Suzuki & Kato (184) found that postsynaptic intracellular potentials recorded from the dLGN can be altered by stimulation of either optic nerve. Sanderson, Darian-Smith & Bishop (169) have now demonstrated that most dLGN cells receive, in addition to an excitatory input from one (dominant) eye, a purely inhibitory input from a related point in the other eye. The inhibitory receptive field from the other (nondominant) eye has about the same size as the surround of the direct dominant influence. Singer (177) has confirmed this and has used intracellular recording to demonstrate that this inhibitiion is postsynaptic. The inhibitory effect has not yet been shown to be strong nor to display the complexity or specificity that might be expected for the neural mechanisms subserving binocular single vision or stereopsis. Nevertheless these findings are new, and the role of the dLGN in binocular vision has not yet been thoroughly investigated. Studies on the locations of the receptive fields from the dominant and nondominant eyes might well provide a neurological basis for the notion of corresponding points.

Striate cortex.—The percentage of cells in the striate cortex that have been shown to be influenced by both eyes has risen with time from 0% (102) to 20% (103) to 30% (114) to 80 to 84% (104) and most recently to 100% (99). Most of these cells are influenced about equally by the two eyes but if there is a dominance it is likely to be from the contralateral eye (25, 104). About 16 to 20% of the cells can be activated only by one eye, giving the impression that they are monocular, but Henry et al (99) have shown that these units receive an inhibitory and subliminal excitatory contribution from the nondominant eye. It is not clear at the moment whether the inhibitory influence originates in the LGN or the striate cortex, but in any case all cells of the striate cortex receiving a project from the binocular visual field appear to be binocularly driven.

About 10 years ago Hubel & Wiesel (103, 104) discovered that the adequate visual stimulus for cells in the striate cortex was a line, bar, or edge having a specific orientation. Quantitative aspects of this orientation specificity have recently been presented by Campbell et al (35) and Pettigrew et al (157). Hubel & Wiesel (104) studied the manner in which the signals from each eye interacted upon the single cell in the striate cortex and summarized their findings as follows.

For each of our cells comparison of receptive fields mapped in the two eyes showed that, except for a difference in strength of responses related to eye dominance, the fields were in every way similar. They were similarly organized, had the same axis orientation, and occupied corresponding regions in the two retinas. The responses to stimuli applied to corresponding parts of the two receptive fields showed summation. This should be important in binocular vision, for it means that when the two images produced by an object fall on corresponding parts of the two retinas, their separate effects on a cortical cell should sum. Failure of the images to fall on corresponding regions, which might happen if an object were closer than the point of fixation or further away, would tend to reduce the summation; it could even lead to mutual antagonism if excitatory parts of one field were stimulated at the same time as inhibitory parts of the other. It should be emphasized that for all simple fields and for many complex ones the two eyes may work either synergistically or in opposition, depending on how the receptive fields are stimulated; when identical stimuli are shown on corresponding parts of the two retinas their effects should always sum.

Subsequent work has confirmed much of the above, although some points are now thought to be incorrect. The similarity of the receptive fields from the two eyes has been fully confirmed (12, 34, 157). If it were true that the receptive fields always occupy corresponding points in the two retinas, then this fact would provide a neural basis for the concept of corresponding points. Burns & Pritchard's (34) position regarding the cortical conditions required for fused binocular vision would require that this be exactly true. The signal for disparity would then be the characteristic discharge patterns of the cortical cells when the receptive fields did not exactly overlap. However Barlow et al (12) and Nikara et al (146) have shown that receptive fields do not occupy exactly corresponding regions of the two retinas. If a number of receptive-field positions are plotted in a given region of the visual field, and the centers of those from one eye translated to a single point, the receptive-field centers from the other eye do not translate to a corresponding single point as Hubel & Wiesel anticipated, but form a scatter diagram.

Workers in this area refer to this scatter as *receptive-field disparity*. Since the word *disparity* has a different meaning in the psychological literature, I believe that it would be worthwhile to consider a different terminology. The word *incongruity* could, for example, be substituted.

Near the area centralis this scatter diagram is radially symmetric, having a standard deviation of 0.5° (110, 146). Blakemore (23) found that there was an increase in scatter which was greater along the horizontal axis. Further, away from the area centralis, Joshua & Bishop (110) found that, for horizontal eccentricity, the standard deviation of horizontal scatter increased from 0.5° to 0.9° while that of the vertical scatter decreased from 0.5° to 0.35°. In contrast, both horizontal and vertical scatters remained unchanged for vertical eccentricities up to 20°. Both Nikara et al (146) and Joshua & Bishop (110) stress the necessity for rigid control of eye movements.

For any given position of the two eyes, only a fraction of the cortical cells will have receptive fields from the two eyes that exactly overlap. Hence the receptive-field centers from the two eyes do not in themselves provide a unique set of corresponding points. Barlow et al (12) noted that, with fixed convergence, different units will be optimally excited by objects lying at different distances, and they suggested that this may be the basic mechanism underlying depth discrimination in the cat. Some doubt is thrown on this suggestion when it is recalled that, in humans, stereopsis only occurs for horizontal disparity, vertical disparity being ineffective. For this to be true a cortical neuron must be specific for horizontal disparity while generalizing for vertical disparity. The cells thus far described in the cat do not display this property.

This is not to say that the cat could not achieve some degree of depth discrimination by means of a mechanism that did not distinguish vertical disparity from horizontal disparity. However, despite claims to the contrary, there does not appear to be any experimental evidence, behavioral or electrophysiological, to support the view that the cat possesses stereopsis.

It may be that this scatter is related, not to stereopsis, but to binocular single vision (146). In humans, when vergence movements are blocked to prevent fusion, the size of Panum's area is about 15 min and is the same in the vertical as in the horizontal direction (132). During binocular or monocular fixation each eye drifts and flicks about a region 15 to 20 min in diameter (53, 178). However, Fender & Julesz (67), using stabilized retinal images, showed that eye movements alone could not account for Panum's fusional area. Hence the suggestion of Nikara et al (146) that this scatter forms the basis of Panum's fusional area seems a good one although they were not explicit as to just how binocular single vision is achieved.

Recent work in Canberra (P. O. Bishop, personal communication) suggests that single vision arises under conditions where the striate cells only fire when the specific stimulus and the two receptive fields coincide in space. When they exactly coincide the question of double vision naturally doesn't arise. As the two receptive fields become slightly misaligned the possibility arises of the cell being stimulated by two separate stimulus features or by the same features at slightly different times; however, double vision is prevented by the marked mutual inhibition that occurs between the two receptive fields. Double vision is thought to arise when the misalignment is sufficiently great that the mutual inhibitory effect for slight misalignments can no longer suppress the firing of the cell.

Joshua & Bishop (110) have found that the absolute distance between the receptive-field centers of the two eyes tends to decrease with increasing retinal eccentricity. Whatever the exact neurophysiological basis for corresponding points might be, this finding strongly suggests that, as a function of fixation distance, the cat horopter deviates from the Vieth-Müller circle in qualitatively the same way as does the human horopter.

A specific theory put forward by Joshua & Bishop (110) has been extensively described by Bishop (22). In essence the theory rests on two assumptions. The first is that corresponding points or maximum binocular interaction occurs when the greatest number of cells in some region of the striate cortex have superimposed receptive fields from each eye. The second is that Panum's fusional area is proportional to the standard deviation of the relative scatter of receptive-field centers from the other eye. With these assumptions, they have used their data to construct cat horopters and fusional areas. The theory can be tested since it is possible in principle to behaviorally determine cat horopters and fusional areas.

The Joshua-Bishop theory is probably the simplest consistent with the data, but it has not yet been determined whether the criteria they have chosen are the ones used by the cat. A possible objection to their assumptions is that all cortical cells are treated equally, whereas one might anticipate that those most sensitive to misalignments would carry a greater weight.

To return to Hubel & Wiesel's summary, they found that when the two receptive fields were superimposed the effects from each eye summed. However, Pettigrew et al (157) found that, under these conditions, most units showed either summation or facilitation of the monocular responses, with a minority showing occlusion. When the receptive fields did not superimpose, binocular occlusion could be demonstrated for all units. Small changes in the relative positions of the receptive fields could result in large changes in the response that could not be predicted from studies of the monocular responses alone.

Nasotemporal overlap.—The projection of the nasal retina to the contralateral visual cortex and the temporal retina to the ispsilateral cortex presents a special problem: if this division were sharp there would be no binocular vision for points just before or just behind the fixation point. But it is just this region that is known to have the highest stereoscopic acuity. Using the technique of retrograde degeneration, Stone (181) has shown that, in the cat, there exists a band of overlap about 0.9° wide in which fibers might pass to either optic tract.

But this is not the only pathway across the midline of the cat visual field, for Berlucchi & Rizzolatti (21) have found that, after sagittal section of the optic chiasm, there were still a few binocularly driven units in the striate cortex. After cutting the cat optic tract on one side, Choudhury et al (36) were still able to record early evoked potentials near the lateral edge of area 17 on the same side, provided that the light stimuli were near the central vertical meridian. There have now been three electrophysiological studies of the degree of midline overlap, based on the idea of simultaneously recording the most medial receptive fields in both hemispheres (23, 106, 122), which all agree that there is a central strip 1.5° to 2.0° wide that is bilaterally represented. These findings can be explained either by the bilateral projection of the central retinal strip to the two optic tracts, or to connections through the corpus callosum. In favor of this latter possibility, Blakemore (24) has shown that a human with a split chiasma is nevertheless able to recognize the depth of objects produced by images falling just within the temporal retina of both eyes. Furthermore Mitchell & Blakemore (133) report that depth perception is lost near the fixation region in a "split-brain" human whose corpus callosum had been surgically divided.

One might expect the fibers that pass through the corpus callosum to be monocular. In cats, Gazzaniga et al (75) report that this is so for most, if not all of these fibers.

Monkey.—Hubel & Wiesel (107) studied binocular vision in the monkey and found that most simple cells in the striate cortex (area 17) cannot be activated by both eyes, and those that do apparently do not display the binocular scatter of receptive-field positions reported for the cat. In area 18 they described certain cells termed *binocular depth cells* which required binocular activation to produce a significant response. These cells had two important properties not described for the cat. First, the displacement of the field in one eye, relative to the field in the other, was usually at right angles to the receptive-field orientation. Second, vertically oriented fields were the more common and hence relative horizontal displacement of the receptive-field centers must also be the more common. Thus, for the majority of these cells horizontal displacement had a more pronounced effect than vertical displacement. An essential requirement for a neural basis of stereopsis is thus approached by these cells.

Human—Regan & Spekreijse (163) recorded the evoked potentials (EP) from the scalp when a subject viewed random-dot stereo-pair patterns. The pattern presented to the right eye remained unaltered throughout. The pattern to the left eye was alternated so that, when both patterns were viewed, a central square appeared to change in depth forward and back again. The EP for this stimulus differed from that observed when the patterns to the two eyes were rotated by 90°; in other words, the response to horizontal disparity differed from that to vertical disparity. Controlled experiments showed that this difference could not be explained by eye movements.

COLUMNAR ORGANIZATION IN THE MAMMALIAN CEREBRAL CORTEX

Since the sensory cortex is held to map the array of sensory receptors onto the cortical surface on a point-to-point basis, one might be led to conclude that, at any one point in the sensory world, the recognition of different stimulus parameters would be confined to a vertical organization among the different cortical layers. However, some years ago, Mountcastle (135), in a study of single units in the cat somatic sensory cortex, demonstrated that this was not the case. The neurons studied could be placed in three distinct classes in terms of the modality of the adequate stimulus: (*a*) movement of hairs; (*b*) pressure on the skin and; (*c*) mechanical deformation of deep tissue. Each type was found in all the cortical cellular layers. However, if the penetration of the microelectrode was perpendicular to the cortical surface, then only one of these types was generally found. Thus, the somatic sensory cortex contains modality-specific vertical columns of cells that are intermingled in any given topological region. The shape and size of the columns was not determined, but studies with slanting penetrations suggested that they were not wider than 0.5 mm. Hence, at this detailed level, the concept of a point-to-point projection breaks down, at least in the cat somatic sensory cortex.

Hubel & Wiesel have now shown that columnar organization applies to the striate cortex of the cat (105) and monkey (107, 108) as well. In the cat the orientation specificity of cortical cells has a columnar arrangement (105). In the monkey, not only line orientation, but ocular dominance and perhaps directionality of movements and color sensitivity are mapped in sets of superimposed but independent mosaics. The finding that the columns for each of these parameters are independent is important, for it indicates that the cortical surface is mapped much like a logical (Venn) diagram of overlapping closed contours. Thus the properties of cells at any point on the cortical surface depend in part upon which of each of the different sets of contours include that point. In this light, the retinotopic projection is itself but one of these columnar arrays.

The columns, defined electrophysiologically, have about the same size as the horizontal distribution of cortical dendrites and it seems clear that cortical microcircuitry has become a field ripe for rapid advance.

Perhaps because the sets of columns overlap, they have not been detected using standard histological techniques, although Colonnier (41, 42) has offered some findings in this regard. However, Hubel & Wiesel (108) have devised a clear-cut means of demonstrating columns of ocular dominance in the monkey striate cortex. They placed a lesion in single layers of the dLGN and observed the distribution of degenerated terminals in the striate cortex. The columnar mosaic consists, not of a checkerboard or set of islands, but of a series of roughly parallel stripes having a periodicity of about 1 mm. The number of eye-preference stripes in the entire striate cortex is about 75 for each eye, or a total of about 150. The neurophysiological findings have thus led to a powerful neurohistological approach that has only just begun to be exploited.

The existence of columnar organization in the somatic and striate regions of the cortex suggests that this form of organization would apply to the auditory cortex as well. But Abeles & Goldstein (1), who studied the primary auditory cortex of cats with this possibility in mind, were not able to demonstrate discrete functional columns. They believe that if there are such columns in the auditory cortex they have a diameter less than about 100 μm, which is the limit of resolution of the technique they employed.

LITERATURE CITED

1. Abeles, M., Goldstein, M. H., Jr. 1970. Functional architecture in cat primary auditory cortex: columnar organization and organization according to depth. *J. Neurophysiol.* 33:172–87

2. Akhtar, M., Blosse, P. T., Dewhurst, P. B. 1968. The nature of the retinal-opsin linkage. *Biochem. J.* 110:693–702

3. Akhtar, M., Hirtenstein, M. D. 1969. Chemistry of the active site of rhodopsin. *Biochem. J.* 115:607–8

4. Alpern, M., Rushton, W. A. H., Torii, S. 1969. Encoding of nerve signals from retinal rods. *Nature* 223:1171–72

5. Alpern, M., Rushton, W. A. H., Torii, S. 1970a. The size of rod signals. *J. Physiol.* 206:193–208

6. Alpern, M., Rushton, W. A. H., Torii, S. 1970b. The attenuation of rod signals by backgrounds. *J. Physiol.* 206:209–27

6a. Anderson, R. E., Hoffman, R. T., Hall, M. O. 1970. Studies on the linkage of retinal to opsin. *Nature.* In press

7. Arden, G. B., Ernst, W. 1969. Mechanism of current production found in pigeon cones but not in pigeon or rat rods. *Nature* 223:528–31

8. Arden, G. B., Ernst, W. 1970. Anion and cation currents in pigeon cones. *J. Physiol.* 209:44P–45P.

9. Arden, G. B., Ikeda, H., Siegel, I. M. 1966. Effects of light-adaptation on the early receptor potential. *Vision Res.* 6:357–71

10. Bairati, A., Jr., Orzalesi, N. 1963. The ultrastructure of the pigment epithelium and of the photore-

ceptor-pigment epithelium junction in the human retina. *J. Ultrastruct. Res.* 9 :484–96

11. Bargoot, F. G., Williams, T. P., Beidler, L. M. 1969. The localization of radioactive amino acid taken up into the outer segments of frog (*Rana pipiens*) rods. *Vision Res.* 9 :385–91

12. Barlow, H. B., Blakemore, C., Pettigrew, J. D. 1967. The neural mechanism of binocular discrimination. *J. Physiol.* 193 :327–42

13. Barlow, H. B., Levick, W. R. 1965. The mechanism of directionally selective units in rabbit's retina. *J. Physiol.* 178 :477–504

14. Bass, L., Moore, W. J. 1968. A model of nervous excitation based on the Wien dissociation effect. In *Structural chemistry and molecular biology*, ed. A. Rich, N. Davidson, 356–69. San Francisco : Freeman

15. Bass, L., Moore, W. J. 1970. An electrochemical model for depolarization of a retinula cell of *Limulus* by a single photon. *Biophys. J.* 10 :1–19

16. Baumann, Ch. 1967a. Sehpurpurbleichung und Stäbchenfunktion in der isolierten Froschnetzhaut. I. Die Sehpurpurbleichung. *Pflügers Arch.* 298 :44–60

17. Baumann, Ch. 1967b. Sehpurpurbleichung und Stäbchenfunktion in der isolierten Froschnetzhaut. II. Die Begrenzung der Stäbchenfunktion durch Helladaptation. *Pflügers Arch.* 298 :61–69

18. Baumann, Ch. 1967c. Sehpurpurbleichung und Stäbchenfunktion in der isolierten Froschnetzhaut. III. Die Dunkeladaptation des skotopischen Systems nach partieller Sehpurpurbleichung. *Pflügers Arch.* 298 : 70–81

19. Baumann, Ch., Scheibner, H. 1968. The dark adaptation of single units in the isolated frog retina following partial bleaching of rhodopsin. *Vision Res.* 8 :1127–38

20. Baylor, D. A., Fuortes, M. G. F. 1970. Electrical responses of single cones in the retina of the turtle. *J. Physiol.* 207 :77–92

21. Berlucchi, G., Rizzolatti, G. 1968. Binocularly driven neurons in visual cortex of split-chiasm cats. *Science* 159 :308–10

22. Bishop, P. O. 1970. Neurophysiology of binocular single vision and

stereopsis. In *Handbook of sensory physiology*, ed. H. J. A. Dartnall. Berlin : Springer-Verlag

23. Blakemore, C. 1969. Binocular depth discrimination and the nasotemporal division. *J. Physiol.* 205 : 471–97

24. Blakemore, C. 1970. Binocular depth perception and the optic chiasm. *Vision Res.* 10 :43–47

25. Blakemore, C., Pettigrew, J. D. 1970. Eye dominance in the visual cortex. *Nature* 225 :426–29

26. Blasie, J. K., Dewey, M. M., Blaurock, A. E., Worthington, C. R. 1965. Electron microscope and low-angle X-ray diffraction studies on outer segment membranes from the retina of the frog. *J. Mol. Biol.* 14 :143–52

27. Blasie, J. K., Worthington, C. R., Dewey, M. M. 1969a. Molecular localization of frog retinal receptor photopigment by electron microscopy and low-angle X-ray diffraction. *J. Mol. Biol.* 39 :407–16

28. Blasie, J. K., Worthington, C. R. 1969b. Planar liquid–like arrangement of photopigment molecules in frog retinal receptor disk membranes. *J. Mol. Biol.* 39 :417–39

29. Blaurock, A. E., Wilkins, M. H. F. 1969. Structure of frog photoreceptor membranes. *Nature* 223 : 906–9

30. Bortoff, A. 1964. Localization of slow potential responses in the *Necturus* retina. *Vision Res.* 4 : 627–35

31. Bownds, D. 1967. Site of attachment of retinal in rhodopsin. *Nature* 216 :1178–81

32. Bownds, D., Gaide-Huguenin, A. C. 1970. Rhodopsin content of frog photoreceptor outer segments. *Nature* 225 :870–72

33. Brown, K. T., Murakami, M. 1967. Delayed decay of the late receptor potential of monkey cones as a function of stimulus intensity. *Vision Res.* 7 :179–89

34. Burns, B. D., Pritchard, R. 1968. Cortical conditions for fused binocular vision. *J. Physiol.* 197 :149–71

35. Campbell, F. W., Robson, J. G. 1968. Application of Fourier analysis to the visibility of gratings. *J. Physiol.* 197 :551–66

36. Choudhury, B. P., Whitteridge, D., Wilson, M. E. 1965. The function

of the callosal connections of the visual cortex. *Quart. J. Exp. Physiol.* 50:214–19

37. Clark, A. W., Branton, D. 1968. Fracture faces in frozen outer segments from the guinea pig retina. *Z. Zellforsch. Mikroskop. Anat.* 91:586–603

38. Clarke, F. J. J. 1960. Extra-foveal colour metrics. *Opt. Acta* 7:355–84

39. Clarke, F. J. J. 1963. Further studies of extra-foveal colour metrics. *Opt. Acta* 10:257–84

40. Cohen, A. I. 1968. New evidence supporting the linkage to extracellular space of outer segment saccules of frog cones but not rods. *J. Cell Biol.* 37:424–44

41. Colonnier, M. L. 1966. The structural design of the neocortex. In *Brain and conscious experience,* ed. J. C. Eccles, 1–23. New York: Springer-Verlag

42. Colonnier, M. L. 1967. The fine structural arrangement of the cortex. *Arch. Neurol.* 16:651–57

43. Cone, R. A. 1965. The early receptor potential of the vertebrate eye. *Cold Spring Harbor Symp. Quant. Biol.* 30:483–91

44. Cone, R. A. 1967. Early receptor potential: photoreversible charge displacement in rhodopsin. *Science* 155:1128–31

45. Cone, R. A., Brown, P. K. 1969. Spontaneous regeneration of rhodopsin in the isolated rat retina. *Nature* 221:818–19

46. Cone, R. A., Cobbs, W. H. III 1969. Rhodopsin cycle in the living eye of the rat. *Nature* 221:820–22

47. Crescitelli, F. 1968. Delayed off-responses recorded from the isolated frog retina. *Vision Res.* 8:801–16

48. Daemen, F. J. M., Bonting, S. L. 1969. Internal protonation in retinylidene phosphatidylethanolamine and the redshift in rhodopsin. *Nature* 222:879–81

49. Dartnall, H. J. A. 1968. The photosensitivities of visual pigments in the presence of hydroxylamine. *Vision Res.* 8:339–58

50. Daw, N. W. 1968. Colour-coded ganglion cells in the goldfish retina: extension of their receptive fields by means of new stimuli. *J. Physiol.* 197:567–92

51. Daw, N. W., Pearlman, A. L. 1969. Cat colour vision: one cone process or several? *J. Physiol.* 201:745–64

52. Dewey, M. M., Davis, P. K., Blasie, J. K., Barr, L. 1969. Localization of rhodopsin antibody in the retina of the frog. *J. Mol. Biol.* 39:395–405

53. Ditchburn, R. W., Ginsborg, B. L. 1953. Involuntary eye movements during fixation. *J. Physiol.* 119:1–17

54. Dodge, F. A., Jr., Knight, B. W., Toyoda, J. 1968. Voltage noise in *Limulus* visual cells. *Science* 160:88–90

55. Donner, K. O., Reuter, T. 1967. Dark-adaptation processes in the rhodopsin rods of the frog's retina. *Vision Res.* 7:17–41

56. Donner, K. O., Reuter, T. 1968. Visual adaptation of the rhodopsin rods in the frog's retina. *J. Physiol.* 199:59–87

57. Donner, K. O., Reuter, T. 1969. The photoproducts of rhodopsin in the isolated retina of the frog. *Vision Res.* 9:815–47

58. Dowling, J. E. 1968. Synaptic organization of the frog retina: an electron microscopic analysis comparing the retinas of frogs and primates. *Proc. Roy. Soc. B* 170:205–28

59. Dowling, J. E., Boycott, B. B. 1966. Organization of the primate retina: electron microscopy. *Proc. Roy. Soc. B* 166:80–111

60. Dowling, J. E., Werblin, F. S. 1969. Organization of retina of the mudpuppy, *Necturus maculosus.* I. Synaptic structure. *J. Neurophysiol.* 32:315–38

61. Dubin, M. W. 1970. The inner plexiform layer of the vertebrate retina: a quantitative and comparative electron microscopic analysis. *J. Comp. Neurol.* In press

62. Ebrey, T. G. 1968. The thermal decay of the intermediates of rhodopsin *in situ. Vision Res.* 8:965–82

63. Eichberg, J., Hess, H. H. 1967. The lipid composition of frog retinal rod outer segments. *Experientia* 23:994

63a. Entine, G., Liebman, P. A., Storey, B. T. 1968. Ubiquinone in the retina. *Vision Res.* 8:215–19

64. Falk, G., Fatt, P. 1968a. Passive electrical properties of rod outer segments. *J. Physiol.* 198:627–46

65. Falk, G., Fatt, P. 1968b. Conductance changes produced by light in rod outer segments. *J. Physiol.* 198: 647–99

66. Falk, G., Fatt, P. 1969. Distinctive properties of the lamellar and disk-edge structures of the rod outer segment. *J. Ultrastruct. Res.* 28:41–60

67. Fender, D., Julesz, B. 1967. Extension of Panum's fusional area in binocularly stabilized vision. *J. Opt. Soc. Am.* 57:819–30

68. Flom, M. C., Eskridge, J. B. 1968. Change in retinal correspondence with viewing distance. *J. Am. Optom. Assoc.* 39:1094–97

69. Ford, R. W. 1969. *The cat electroretinogram to incremental stimuli.* PhD thesis. Univ. Sydney, Sydney, Australia

70. Frank, R. N. 1969. Photoproducts of rhodopsin bleaching in the isolated, perfused frog retina. *Vision Res.* 9:1415–33

71. Frank, R. N., Dowling, J. E. 1968. Rhodopsin photoproducts: effects on electroretinogram sensitivity in isolated perfused rat retina. *Science* 161:487–89

72. Fukami, I., Fukami, Y. 1969. Reaction between retinal and phospholipid components of outer segments of rods from cattle retina. *Nature* 223:63

73. Galifret, Y. 1968. Les diverses aires fonctionnelles de la rétine du pigeon. *Z. Zellforsch. Mikroskop. Anat.* 86:535–45

74. Garey, L. J., Powell, T. P. S. 1968. The projection of the retina in the cat. *J. Anat.* 102:189–222

75. Gazzaniga, M. S., Berlucchi, G., Rizzolatti, G. 1967. Physiological mechanisms underlying transfer of visual learning in corpus callosum of cat. *Fed. Proc.* 26:590

76. Goldstein, E. B. 1967. Early receptor potential of the isolated frog (*Rana pipiens*) retina. *Vision Res.* 7: 837–45

77. Goldstein, E. B. 1968. Visual pigments and the early receptor potential of the isolated frog retina. *Vision Res.* 8:953–63

78. Goldstein, E. B. 1969. Contribution of cones to the early receptor potential in the Rhesus monkey. *Nature* 222:1273–74

79. Goldstein, E. B., Berson, E. L. 1969. Cone dominance of the human early receptor potential. *Nature* 222:1272–73

80. Gouras, P. 1968. Identification of cone mechanisms in monkey ganglion cells. *J. Physiol.* 199:533–47

81. Gras, W. J., Worthington, C. R. 1969. X-ray analysis of retinal photoreceptors. *Proc. Nat. Acad. Sci.* 63:233–38

82. Green, D. E., Haard, N. F., Lenaz, G., Silman, H. I. 1968. On the noncatalytic proteins of membrane systems. *Biochemistry* 60:277–84

83. Green, D. G. 1968. The contrast sensitivity of the color mechanisms of the human eye. *J. Physiol.* 196: 415–29

84. Green, D. G. 1969. Sinusoidal flicker characteristics of the color-sensitive mechanisms of the eye. *Vision Res.* 9:591–601

85. Grüsser, O. J., Sauer, G. 1960. Monoculare und binoculare Lichtreizung einzelner Neurone im Geniculatum laterale der Katze. *Pflügers Arch.* 271:595–612

86. Guzzo, A. V., Pool, G. L. 1968. Visual pigment fluorescence. *Science* 159:312–14

87. Guzzo, A. V., Pool, G. L. 1969. Fluorescence spectra of the intermediates of rhodopsin bleaching. *Photochem. Photobiol.* 9:565–70

88. Hagins, W. A. 1965. Electrical signs of information flow in photoreceptors. *Cold Spring Harbor Symp. Quant. Biol.* 30:403–18

89. Hagins, W. A., Jennings, W. H. 1959. Radiationless migration of electronic excitation in retinal rods. *Discuss. Faraday Soc.* 27:180–90

91. Hall, M. O., Bacharach, A. D. E. 1970. Linkage of retinal to opsin and absence of phospholipids in purified frog visual pigment$_{500}$. *Nature* 225:637–38

92. Hall, M. O., Bok, D., Bacharach, A. D. E. 1968. Visual pigment renewal in the mature frog retina. *Science* 161:787–89

93. Hall, M. O., Bok, D., Bacharach, A. D. E. 1969. Biosynthesis and assembly of the rod outer segment membrane system. Formation and fate of visual pigment in the frog retina. *J. Mol. Biol.* 45:397–406

94. Heller, J. 1968a. Structure of visual pigments. I. Purification, molecular weight, and composition of bovine visual pigment$_{500}$. *Biochemistry* 7: 2906–13

95. Heller, J. 1968b. Structure of visual pigments. II. Binding of retinal and conformational changes on light exposure in bovine visual pigment$_{500}$. *Biochemistry* 7:2914–20

96. Heller, J. 1969. Comparative study of a membrane protein. Characterization of bovine, rat, and frog visual pigments$_{500}$. *Biochemistry* 8:675–79

97. Heller, J. 1970. Absorptivity and quantum yield of bleaching in bovine visual pigment$_{500}$. *Nature* 225:636–37

98. Heller, J., Lawrence, M. A. 1970. Structure of the glycopeptide from bovine visual pigment 500. *Biochemistry* 9:864–69

99. Henry, G. H., Bishop, P. O., Coombs, J. S. 1969. Inhibitory and subliminal excitatory receptive fields of simple units in cat striate cortex. *Vision Res.* 9:1289–96

100. Hille, B. 1968. Charges and potentials at the nerve surface. *Divalent ions and pH. J. Gen. Physiol.* 51:221–36

101. Hubbard, R. 1966. The stereoisomerization of 11-*cis*-retinal. *J. Biol. Chem.* 241:1814–18

102. Hubel, D. H. 1958. Unit cortical responses to monocular light stimulation in unanesthetized cats. *Fed. Proc.* 17: Part 1

103. Hubel, D. H., Wiesel, T. N. 1959. Receptive fields of single neurones in the cat's striate cortex. *J. Physiol.* 148:574–91

104. Hubel, D. H., Wiesel, T. N. 1962. Receptive fields, binocular interaction and functional architecture in the cat's visual cortex. *J. Physiol.* 160:106–54

105. Hubel, D. H., Wiesel, T. N. 1963. Shape and arrangement of columns in cat's striate cortex. *J. Physiol.* 165:559–68

106. Hubel, D. H., Wiesel, T. N. 1967. Cortical and callosal connections concerned with the vertical meridian of visual fields in the cat. *J. Neurophysiol.* 30:1561–73

107. Hubel, D. H., Wiesel, T. N. 1968. Receptive fields and functional architecture of monkey striate cortex. *J. Physiol.* 195:215–43

108. Hubel, D. H., Wiesel, T. N. 1969. Anatomical demonstration of columns in the monkey striate cortex. *Nature* 221:747–50

109. Inuzuka, K., Becker, R. S. 1968. Mechanism of photoisomerization in the retinals and implications in rhodopsin. *Nature* 219:383–85

110. Joshua, D. E., Bishop, P. O. 1970. Binocular single vision and depth discrimination. Receptive field disparities for central and peripheral vision and binocular interaction on peripheral single units in cat striate cortex. *Exp. Brain Res.* 10:389–416

111. Julesz, B. 1964. Binocular depth perception without familiarity cues. *Science* 145:356–62

112. Julesz, B. 1965a. Some neurophysiological problems of stereopsis. In *Information processing in sight sensory systems*, ed. P. W. Nye, 135–42. Pasadena, Calif: Calif. Tech. Press

113. Julesz, B. 1965b. Texture and visual perception. *Sci. Am.* 212:38–48

114. Jung, R. 1960. Microphysiologie corticaler Neurone: ein Beitrag zur Koordination der Hirnrinde und des visuellen Systems. In *Structure and function of the cerebral cortex*, ed. D. B. Tower, J. P. Schadé. Amsterdam: Elsevier

115. Kaneko, A., Hashimoto, H. 1968. Localization of spike-producing cells in the frog retina. *Vision Res.* 8:259–62

116. Kaneko, A., Hashimoto, H. 1969. Electrophysiological study of single neurons in the inner nuclear layer of the carp retina. *Vision Res.* 9:37–55

117. King-Smith, P. E. 1969. Absorption spectra and function of the coloured oil drops in the pigeon retina. *Vision Res.* 9:1391–99

118. Kinston, W. J., Vadas, M. A., Bishop, P. O. 1969. Multiple projection of the visual field to the medial portion of the dorsal lateral geniculate nucleus and the adjacent nuclei of the thalamus of the cat. *J. Comp. Neurol.* 136:295–315

119. Kirschfeld, K. 1970. In 1968 *Varena Symposium on Vision*, ed. W. Reichardt

120. Korn, E. D. 1968. Structure and function of the plasma membrane. *A biochemical perspective. J. Gen. Physiol.* 52:257s–278s

120a. Kropf, A. 1967. Intramolecular energy transfer in rhodopsin. *Vision Res.* 7:811–18

121. Laties, A. M., Sprague, J. M. 1966.

The projection of optic fibers to the visual centers in the cat. *J. Comp. Neurol.* 127 :35–70

122. Leicester, J. 1968. Projection of the visual vertical meridian to cerebral cortex of the cat. *J. Neurophysiol.* 31 :371–82

123. Liebman, P. A. 1970. Microspectrophotometry (MSP) of photoreceptors. In *Handbook of sensory physiology*, ed. H. J. A. Dartnall. Berlin : Springer-Verlag

124. Liebman, P. A., Entine, G. 1968. Visual pigments of frog and tadpole (*Rana pipiens*). *Vision Res.* 8 :761–75

125. Marchiafava, P. L. 1966. Binocular reciprocal interaction upon optic fibre endings in the lateral geniculate nucleus of the cat. *Brain Res.* 2 :188–92

126. Marks, W. B. 1965. Visual pigments of single goldfish cones. *J. Physiol.* 178 :14–32

126a. Matthews, R. G., Hubbard, R., Brown, P. K., Wald, G. 1963. Tautomeric forms of metarhodopsin. *J. Gen. Physiol.* 47 :215–40

127. Mello, N. K., Peterson, N. J. 1964. Behavioral evidence for color discrimination in cat. *J. Neurophysiol.* 27 :323–33

128. Meyer, D. B., Cooper, T. G., Gernez, C. 1965. Retinal oil droplets. In *The structure of the eye. II. Symp.* held August 8–13, during the 8th Int. Congr. of Anatomists, Wiesbaden, Germany, ed. J. W. Rohen, 521–33. Stuttgart : Schattauer-Verlag

129. Meyer, D. R., Anderson, R. A. 1965. Colour discrimination in cats. In *Colour vision physiology and experimental psychology*, Ciba Found. Symp., ed. A. V. S. de Reuck, J. Knight, 325–44. London : Churchill

130. Michael, C. R. 1968. Receptive fields of single optic nerve fibers in a mammal with an all-cone retina. 3. Opponent color units. *J. Neurophysiol.* 31 :268–82

131. Millecchia, R., Mauro, A. 1969. The ventral photoreceptor cells of *Limulus*. II. The basic photoresponse. *J. Gen. Physiol.* 54 :310–30

132. Mitchell, D. E. 1966. Retinal disparity and diplopia. *Vision Res.* 6 :441–51

133. Mitchell, D. E., Blakemore, C. 1970. Binocular depth perception and the corpus callosum. *Vision Res.* 10 : 49–54

134. Moore, J. W., Narahashi, T., Shaw, T. I. 1967. An upper limit to the number of sodium channels in nerve membrane? *J. Physiol.* 188 : 99–105

135. Mountcastle, V. B. 1957. Modality and topographic properties of single neurons of cat's somatic sensory cortex. *J. Neurophysiol.* 20 :408–34

136. Muntz, W. R. A. 1962a. Microelectrode recordings from the diencephalon of the frog (*Rana pipiens*) and a blue-sensitive system. *J. Neurophysiol.* 25 :699–711

137. Muntz, W. R. A. 1962b. Effectiveness of different colors of light in releasing positive phototactic behavior of frogs, and a possible function of the retinal projection to the diencephalon. *J. Neurophysiol.* 25 :712–20

138. Muntz, W. R. A. 1963a. The development of phototaxis in the frog (*Rana temporaria*). *J. Exp. Biol.* 40 :371–79

139. Muntz, W. R. A. 1963b. Phototaxis and green rods in Urodeles. *Nature* 199 :620

140. Naka, K. I. 1969. Computer assisted analysis of S-potentials. *Biophys. J.* 9 :845–59

141. Naka, K. I., Rushton, W. A. H. 1966a. S-potentials from colour units in the retina of fish (*Cyprinidae*). *J. Physiol.* 185 :536–55

142. Naka, K. I., Rushton, W. A. H. 1966b. An attempt to analyse colour reception by electrophysiology. *J. Physiol.* 185 :556–86

143. Naka, K. I., Rushton, W. A. H. 1966c. S-potentials from luminosity units in the retina of fish (*Cyprinidae*). *J. Physiol.* 185 :587–99

144. Naka, K. I., Rushton, W. A. H. 1967. The generation and spread of S-potentials in fish (*Cyprinidae*). *J. Physiol.* 192 :437–61

145. Nash, H. A. 1969. The stereoisomers of retinal—a theoretical study of energy differences. *J. Theor. Biol.* 22 :314–24

146. Nikara, T., Bishop, P. O., Pettigrew, J. D. 1968. Analysis of retinal correspondence by studying receptive fields of binocular single units

in cat striate cortex. *Exp. Brain Res.* 6:353–72

147. Norton, A. L., Spekreijse, H., Wagner, H. G., Wolbarsht, M. L. 1970. Responses to directional stimuli in retinal preganglionic units. *J. Physiol.* 206:93–107

148. Ogle, K. N. 1962. The optical space sense. In *The eye* 4: Part II, ed. H. Davson, 211–417. New York: Academic

149. Ogle, K. N. 1964. *Researches in binocular vision.* New York: Hafner

150. Pak, W. L., Boes, R. J. 1967. Rhodopsin: responses from transient intermediates formed during its bleaching. *Science* 155:1131–33

151. Pak, W. L., Cone, R. A. 1964. Isolation and identification of the initial peak of the early receptor potential. *Nature* 204:836–38

152. Pak, W. L., Ebrey, T. G. 1965. Visual receptor potential observed at sub-zero temperatures. *Nature* 205:484–86

153. Pak, W. L., Helmrich, H. G. 1968. Absence of photodichroism in the retinal receptors. *Vision Res.* 8:585–89

154. Pauling, L. 1949. Zur *cis-trans*-Isomerisierung von Carotinoiden. *Helv. Chim. Acta* 32:2241–46

155. Pearlman, A. L., Daw, N. W. 1970. Opponent color cells in the cat lateral geniculate nucleus. *Science* 167:84–86

156. Penn, R. D., Hagins, W. A. 1969. Signal transmission along retinal rods and the origin of the electroretinographic α-wave. *Nature* 223:201–5

157. Pettigrew, J. D., Nikara, T., Bishop, P. O. 1968. Binocular interaction on single units in cat striate cortex: simultaneous stimulation by single moving slit with receptive fields in correspondence. *Exp. Brain Res.* 6:391–410

158. Pickering, S. G. 1968. The extremely long latency response from on-off retinal ganglion cells: relationship to dark adaptation. *Vision Res.* 8:383–87

159. Pickering, S. G., Varju, D. 1967. Ganglion cells in the frog retina: inhibitory receptive field and long-latency response. *Nature* 215:545–46

160. Pickering, S. G., Varju, D. 1969. Delayed responses of ganglion cells in the frog retina: the influence of stimulus parameters upon the length of the delay time. *Vision Res.* 9:865–79

161. Poincelot, R. P., Millar, P. G., Kimbel, R. L., Jr., Abrahamson, E. W. 1970. Determination of the chromophoric binding site in native bovine rhodopsin. *Biochemistry* 9:1809

162. Poincelot, R. P., Millar, P. G., Kimbel, R. L., Jr., Abrahamson, E. W. 1969. Lipid to protein chromophore transfer in the photolysis of visual pigments. *Nature* 221:256–57

163. Regan, D., Spekreijse, H. 1970. Electrophysiological correlate of binocular depth perception in man. *Nature* 225:92–94

164. Richardson, T. M. 1969. Cytoplasmic and ciliary connections between the inner and outer segments of mammalian visual receptors. *Vision Res.* 9:727–31

165. Rodieck, R. W. 1967. Maintained activity of cat retinal ganglion cells. *J. Neurophysiol.* 30:1043–71

166. Rodieck, R. W., Ford, R. W. 1969. The cat local electroretinogram to incremental stimuli. *Vision Res.* 9:1–24

167. Rosenberg, S. A., Guidotti, G. 1968. The protein of human erythrocyte membranes. I. Preparation, solubilization, and partial characterization. *J. Biol. Chem.* 243:1985–92

168. Rushton, W. A. H., Fulton, A. B., Baker, H. D. 1969. Dark adaptation and the rate of pigment regeneration. *Vision Res.* 9:1473–79

169. Sanderson, K. J., Darian-Smith, I., Bishop, P. O. 1969. Binocular corresponding receptive fields of single units in the cat dorsal lateral geniculate nucleus. *Vision Res.* 9:1297–1303

170. Schneiderman, L. J., Junga, I. G. 1968. Isolation and partial characterization of structural protein derived from human red cell membranes. *Biochemistry* 7:2281–86

171. Sechzer, J. A., Brown, J. L. 1964. Colour discrimination in the cat. *Science* 144:427–29

171a. Shichi, H. 1970. Spectrum and purity of bovine rhodopsin. *Biochemistry* 9:1973–77

172. Shichi, H., Lewis, M. S., Irrverre, F., Stone, A. L. 1969. Biochemistry of visual pigments. I. Purification

and properties of bovine rhodopsin. *J. Biol. Chem.* 244:529–36

173. Shields, J. E., Dinovo, E. C., Henriksen, R. A., Kimbel, R. L., Jr., Millar, P. G. 1967. The purification and amino acid composition of bovine rhodopsin. *Biochim. Biophys. Acta* 147:238–51

174. Sickel, W., Crescitelli, F. 1967. Delayed electrical responses from the isolated frog retina. *Pflügers Arch.* 297:266–69

175. Sillman, A. J., Ito, H., Tomita, T. 1969a. Studies on the mass receptor potential of the isolated frog retina. I. General properties of the response. *Vision Res.* 9:1435–42

176. Sillman, A. J., Ito, H., Tomita, T. 1969b. Studies on the mass receptor potential of the isolated frog retina. II. On the basis of the ionic mechanism. *Vision Res.* 9:1443–51

177. Singer, W. 1970. Inhibitory binocular interaction in the lateral geniculate body of the cat. *Brain Res.* 18:165–70

178. St. Cyr, G. J., Fender, D. H. 1969. The interplay of drifts and flicks in binocular fixation. *Vision Res.* 9:245–65

179. Steinberg, R. H. 1969a. Rod and cone contributions to S-potentials from the cat retina. *Vision Res.* 9:1319–29

180. Steinberg, R. H. 1969b. Rod-cone interaction in S-potentials from the cat retina. *Vision Res.* 9:1331–44

181. Stone, J. 1966. The naso-temporal division of the cat's retina. *J. Comp. Neurol.* 126:585–600

182. Stone, J., Hansen, S. M. 1966. The projection of the cat's retina on the lateral geniculate nucleus. *J. Comp. Neurol.* 126:601–24

183. Stromeyer, C. F. III, Psotka, J. 1970. The detailed texture of eidetic images. *Nature* 225:346–49

184. Suzuki, H., Kato, E. 1966. Binocular interaction at cat's lateral geniculate body. *J. Neurophysiol.* 29:909–20

185. Tomita, T. 1965. Electrophysiological study of the mechanisms subserving color coding in the fish retina. *Cold Spring Harbor Symp. Quant. Biol.* 30:559–66

186. Tomita, T. 1968. Electrical response of single photoreceptors. *Proc. IEEE* 56:1015–23

187. Tomita, T., Kaneko, A., Murakami, M., Pautler, E. L. 1967. Spectral response curves of single cones in the carp. *Vision Res.* 7:519–31

188. Toyoda, J. I., Nosaki, H., Tomita, T. 1969. Light-induced resistance changes in single photoreceptors of *Necturus* and *Gekko*. *Vision Res.* 9:453–63

189. Wagner, H. G., MacNichol, E. F., Jr., Wolbarsht, M. L. 1960. The response properties of single ganglion cells in the goldfish retina. *J. Gen. Physiol.* 43:45–62

190. Wagner, H. G., MacNichol, E. F., Jr., Wolbarsht, M. L. 1963. Functional basis for "on"-center and "off"-center receptive fields in the retina. *J. Opt. Soc. Am.* 53:66–70

191. Wald, G. 1968. The molecular basis of visual excitation. *Nature* 219:800–7

192. Walls, G. L. 1942. *The vertebrate eye and its adaptive radiation.* Michigan: Cranbrook Press

193. Walls, G. L., Judd, H. D. 1933. The intra-ocular colour-filters of vertebrates. *Brit. J. Ophthalmol.* 17:641–75, 705–25

194. Weinstein, G. W., Hobson, R. R., Dowling, J. E. 1967. Light and dark adaptation in the isolated rat retina. *Nature* 215:134–38

195. Werblin, F. S. 1970. Response of retinal cells to moving spots: intracellular recording in *Necturus maculosus*. *J. Neurophysiol.* 33:342–50

196. Werblin, F. S., Dowling, J. E. 1969. Organization of the retina of the mudpuppy, *Necturus maculosus*. II. Intracellular recording. *J. Neurophysiol.* 32:339–55

197. Wiesel, T. N., Hubel, D. H. 1966. Spatial and chromatic interactions in the lateral geniculate body of the Rhesus monkey. *J. Neurophysiol.* 29:1115–56

198. Wiesenfeld, J. R., Abrahamson, E. W. 1968. Visual pigments: their spectra and isomerizations. *Photochem. Photobiol.* 8:487–93

199. Witkovsky, P. 1967. A comparison of ganglion cell and S-potential response properties in carp retina. *J. Neurophysiol.* 30:546–61

200. Wyszecki, G., Stiles, W. S. 1967. *Color science concepts and methods, quantitative data and formulas.* New York: Wiley

201. Young, R. W. 1967. The renewal of

photoreceptor cell outer segments. *J. Cell Biol.* 33 :61–72

202. Young, R. W. 1968. Passage of newly formed protein through the connecting cilium of retinal rods in the frog. *J. Ultrastruct. Res.* 23 :462–73

203. Young, R. W. 1969a. A difference between rods and cones in the renewal of outer segment protein. *Invest. Ophthalmol.* 8 :222–31

204. Young, R. W. 1969b. The organization of vertebrate photoreceptor cells. In *The retina,* ed. B. R. Straatsma, M. O. Hall, R. A. Allen, F. Crescitelli, 177–210. Los Angeles : Univ. California Press

205. Young, R. W., Bok, D. 1969. Participation of the retinal pigment epithelium in the rod outer segment renewal process. *J. Cell Biol.* 42 : 392–403

206. Young, R. W., Bok, D. 1970. Autoradiographic studies on the metabolism of the retinal pigment epithelium. *Invest. Ophthalmol.* 9 : 524–36

207. Young, R. W., Droz, B. 1968. The renewal of protein in retinal rods and cones. *J. Cell Biol.* 39 :169–84

NERVOUS FUNCTION AT THE CELLULAR LEVEL: GLIA[1]

ARNALDO LASANSKY

Laboratory of Neurophysiology
National Institute of Neurological Diseases and Stroke
National Institutes of Health
Bethesda, Maryland

INTRODUCTION

The function of neuroglial cells was authoritatively discussed by Kuffler & Nicholls in 1966 (1). The following review is limited to papers which touched on this subject since then, and the period covered extends through May 1970. Myelin sheath formation—the best-known glial function—has been recently, and comprehensively, reviewed by Bunge (2).

PHYSIOLOGICAL PROPERTIES OF GLIAL CELLS

Previous studies on the physiological properties of glial cells in the central nervous system of the leech and amphibia were extended to mammals (3). Negative potential shifts, not associated with impulse activity, were recorded with microelectrodes from the rat optic nerve, and identified as the membrane potential of glial cells by means of iontophoretic injections of Procion yellow followed by histological examination; no distinction was made between astroglia and oligodendroglia. The membrane potential of these glial cells (77–85 mV) was higher than the values reported for mammalian neurons, and it appeared to depend mainly on the transmembrane gradient of potassium ions. Glial cells in the rat optic nerve, however, did not behave as ideal potassium electrodes—although some other glial cells nearly do (1)—but Dennis & Gerschenfeld suggested that this finding may have been the result of cell injury during impalement. A similar deviation from ideal potassium electrode behavior has been reported for Schwann cells surrounding squid giant nerve fibers (4). In this instance, the deviation was interpreted as due to a nonelectroneutral inward transport of K^+ because the membrane potential (40 mV) was relatively insensitive to changes in the external concentrations of Na^+ and Cl^-, and addition of a cardiac glycoside to the bathing fluid caused an immediate hyperpolarization of the Schwann cells, without significant changes in their ionic concentrations.

[1] Some aspects of this topic are also treated in this volume in the chapter by R. W. Rodieck.

241

On the other hand, the membrane potential of glial cells in the optic nerve of *Necturus* provides an accurate indicator of the extracellular K+ concentration. By making use of this property, Cohen, Gerschenfeld & Kuffler (5) established that the ionic environment of cells in the brain of *Necturus* is determined by the ionic concentrations in the cerebrospinal fluid, and not by those in the blood plasma.

Intracellular recordings from 'idle' or 'unresponsive' cells from the cerebral cortex of cats have been the subject of several reports (6–11). Such units are defined by the recording of a stable negative potential shift, which is not accompanied by spontaneous or evoked spikes, or synaptic potentials. It may then be asked whether the recordings can be reliably regarded as membrane potentials and, if so, whether they are indeed obtained from glial cells. Karahashi & Goldring (6) thought it unlikely that microelectrode tip potentials contributed significantly to the observed dc shift, and pointed out that the idle cells were found only under the same experimental conditions necessary for intracellular recordings from discharging cortical neurons. Another indication that the negative dc shifts represent membrane potentials appears to be provided by the observation that rectangular current pulses delivered through the microelectrode by means of a bridge circuit result, at the point of recording, in an exponential charging curve (11). The membrane time constant thus determined was reported to be about 385 μsec; despite the extreme shortness of this time constant, the authors claimed that the charging curve could be distinguished from electrode artifacts, which lasted less than 150–175 μsec. From the value of the time constant—and extrapolating data on the specific capacitance of human astrocytes in tissue culture—Trachtenberg & Pollen (11) concluded that the specific membrane resistance of the idle cells is 200–500 ohm cm². It was implied, therefore, that the idle cells are glial cells—more specifically, astrocytes—but no dye-marking experiments were performed.

Identification of the unresponsive or idle cells of the cat cerebral cortex by means of dye injections was attempted by Kelly, Krnjević & Yim (8), Grossman & Hampton (9), and Grossman, Whiteside & Hampton (10). Fast green- or methyl blue-filled electrodes were used for this purpose, and the dyes were ejected by passing rather large currents (0.25–0.5 μA) during several minutes. Perhaps for this reason, some of the marked cells were reported to show a 'severely disrupted cytoplasm' (9), while in most instances only stained nuclei were found (8). From the appearance of the stained nuclei (8), or of the 'lightly stained cytoplasm' (9, 10) when present, it was concluded that the marked units were glial cells. It may be expected that newly developed dye-marking techniques (12) will provide more convincing images, and perhaps also the means to identify the specific types of glial cells from which the recordings are obtained.

The unresponsive cells in the cat cerebral cortex have been reported to have a membrane potential of 50–80 mV (6), 62 (S.E. 2.2) mV (7), 50–95 mV (9), and 50–92 mV (11). After direct cortical stimulation or repetitive stimulation of thalamic nuclei, they show a depolarizing response (6) which appears to be similar to the potassium-mediated effect described in amphibian (13) and leech (14) glial cells; this similarity is perhaps the best available evidence for one of the possibilities suggested by Karahashi & Goldring (6) : that the unresponsive cells, from which the depolarizing responses are recorded, are glial cells.

Depolarization of the unresponsive cells of the cat cerebral cortex was also observed after iontophoretic application of acetylcholine and γ-aminobutyric acid (7). This effect was interpreted as a change in an electrogenic active transport associated with the uptake of chemical transmitters into glial cells. It seems also possible and simpler, however, that the transmitters have an effect on the surrounding neurons, which may leak K^+ and thus depolarize the glial cells.

Slow glial cell depolarizations, accompanied by a reduction in the membrane impedance, had been observed following strong electrical stimulation in cultures of mammalian cerebellum (15). These responses, however, are not specific to glial cells, and are seen only when the membrane potential is displaced by more than 250 mV (16). According to Wardell (16), they are the consequence of mechanical and dielectric breakdown of the cell membrane.

Depolarizing responses can also be recorded intracellularly from Müller cells in the retina of *Necturus* (17). Their latency, time course, and intensity-response curve resemble those of the electroretinographic b-wave; they also show an off-effect as does the electroretinogram. Because of their long latency, slow time course, and glial origin, Müller cell responses were thought to be secondary to a light-induced release of K^+ from neurons at the distal portion of the inner nuclear layer. It would be interesting to see, therefore, whether the amplitude of these responses is affected by changes in the external K^+ concentration in a way consistent with such an interpretation (13). Furthermore, having the site of K^+ accumulation at distal layers of the retina is a necessity imposed by the assumption that the Müller cell response provides the source of current for the b-wave, which is positive when recorded from the vitreous humor. If the Müller cell response is indeed K^+ mediated, however, one would expect it to include some manifestation of ganglion cell activity, such as could be represented, for instance, by the observed off-effect.

Glial cells in cultures of rat midbrain and cerebellum have been reported to be electrically coupled to neurons (18). These neurons did not show any spontaneous or evoked impulse activity, and were identified on the basis of their morphological features in unstained preparations, and after the intracellular injection of methyl blue.

Responses of retinal horizontal cells.—Much of the mystery surrounding the hyperpolarizing responses of horizontal cells has been taken away by the finding that vertebrate photoreceptor cells are also hyperpolarized by light (19, 20). This type of response is still very intriguing, but for reasons different from those previously assumed. Thus, it is no longer justifiable to suggest that horizontal cells may be glial cells because their responses are unlike those usually found in other neurons, since horizontal cells are probably driven by photoreceptor cells, which also behave unlike other neurons. Furthermore, analogous responses can be recorded from bipolar cells (21, 22).

Electronmicroscopic studies have revealed the site and nature of the contacts between horizontal cell processes and photoreceptor cell endings (23). Because of the surface specializations associated with them, such contacts are likely to represent synapses. According to Dowling (24, 25), horizontal cell processes are presynaptic to bipolar cell dendrites at the outer plexiform layer. From this interpretation, it was concluded that horizontal cells are interneurons which mediate the effect of the periphery of the receptive field of bipolar cells.

CHEMISTRY AND METABOLISM OF GLIAL CELLS

Biochemical studies still suffer from the lack of a reliable technique to separate pure neuronal and glial cell fractions, so that it has not yet been possible to determine the relative contributions of each cell type to the chemistry and metabolism of a specific area of nervous tissue. The best known attempt to obtain this type of information is represented by microchemical studies on neurons and glial cells isolated by dissection from several areas of the mammalian brain (26). A number of serious objections to the validity of this methodology were raised by Kuffler & Nicholls (1). One of their criticisms, concerning the purity of the samples provided by the dissection technique, has been further substantiated and elaborated in a recent electronmicroscopic study of the lateral vestibular nucleus of the rat (27)—which is one of the areas that had been studied by the microchemical methods. Sotelo & Palay (27) point out that the satellite cells of the giant cells of Deiters are astrocytes, not oligodendrocytes as previously assumed. Furthermore, and more relevant to the interpretation of the chemical data, the astrocytic processes envelop not only the neuronal bodies, but also a variety of elements in the surrounding neuropil. Therefore, the glial samples must be heterogeneous, and comparing their properties with those of the neuronal sample would also involve a comparison between the properties of the neuronal bodies and those of synaptic endings and cell processes from various origins.

Methods for the separation of nerve and glial cells in bulk from the cerebral cortex have been reported (28, 29). The method of Rose (28) has been more frequently used (30–34); it consists of mechanical disruption of the tissue, followed by centrifugation on a discontinuous Ficoll gradient. The resulting 'neuronal' and 'glial' fractions appear to be highly heterogeneous. According to Cremer et al (35), the 'neuronal' fraction contains fragmented capillaries and endothelial cells among other contaminants, while the 'glial' fraction contains numerous synaptic endings; consequently, the 'glial' fraction is now referred to as the 'neuropil' fraction (36). It would seem, therefore, that the bulk isolation procedures depending only on mechanical disruption of the tissue have some of the shortcomings of the microdissection techniques, and the results reported following their use are open to the same kind of objections. Nevertheless, a perhaps more promising alternative consists of softening the brain tissue with trypsin prior to disruption (37); this procedure yields a neuronal fraction more than 90% pure, while the purity of the glial cell fraction has been estimated to be at least 73%. The neurons retain only stumps of axons and dendrites, but the published images of isolated neuroglial cells show a surprisingly good preservation of their processes.

Glial cell fractions, believed to consist of 95% oligodendrocytes, have been obtained from the centrum ovale of rat and bovine brains (38). The isolated cells are devoid of processes and plasma membrane; their lipid composition has been the subject of two subsequent reports (39, 40). Nuclear fractions can be isolated from rat brain containing either neuronal, astrocytic, or glial (oligodendroglial and microglial) nuclei (41); these or similar nuclear fractions have been used for studies on protein (42, 43) and RNA (44) synthesis. Two membrane fractions isolated from homogenates of the first stellar nerve of the squid have been tentatively identified as axonal and Schwann cell plasma membranes (45); the axolemmal fraction was identified mainly on the basis of its higher ATPase activity (46).

Tyrosine incorporation in the rabbit retina was radioautographically studied (47). Müller cells showed the highest concentrations of exposed grains, and it was concluded that they are actively engaged in protein synthesis. Subcutaneous astroglial nodules were induced in newborn hamsters by injecting trypsinized cultures of astrocytes (48). The nodules almost lacked cerebrosides, and had a low concentration of gangliosides and RNA. The brain specific protein S-100 (49) was localized mainly to glial cells, and also to neuronal nuclei, by means of fluorescent antibody and immunodiffusion techniques (50). Glial tumors in tissue culture also contain the protein S-100 (51); the S-100 content increases almost tenfold as the cells grow from low density to confluency, and then remains constant. More recently, Cicero et al (52) have observed that in thalamic nuclei undergoing retrograde neuronal degeneration, the level of S-100 increases during the first weeks following cortical ablation, and then declines to about its normal level. The initial increase in S-100 is correlated with early gliosis in the affected nuclei, while the normal levels found later coexist with extensive neuronal loss. Cicero et al (52) concluded that the protein S-100 is largely, or exclusively, confined to glial cells, probably astrocytes. Nevertheless, glial cells were reported to lack any antigenic specificity, according to the results of a study with immunodiffusion and immunofluorescence techniques (53). Only nerve cells would contain immunologically specific antigens, while those present in glial cells were also found in the spleen.

GLIAL CELLS AND THE BLOOD-BRAIN AND BLOOD-RETINAL BARRIERS

As pointed out by Kuffler & Nicholls (1), glial cells in the central nervous system of higher vertebrates do not form continuous perivascular barriers, since open extracellular pathways may be found leading from the basement membrane of capillaries to the neuronal elements in the brain and retina. Additional images of spaces at least 30–70 Å wide between perivascular astrocytic processes were then obtained in the brain of the mouse (54). Thus, the junctions previously described between perivascular astrocytic end-feet do not represent continuous belts; furthermore, those junctions are not tight, since the adjoining glial membranes are separated at the junctional areas by an extracellular gap about 20 Å wide (55). Definitive evidence for the existence of an extracellular pathway between brain neurons and the contraluminal surface of the capillary endothelium has been reported by Brightman (56). He injected horseradish peroxidase into the cerebral ventricles of the mouse, and followed its diffusion within the brain parenchyma. In the vicinity of the capillaries, peroxidase penetrated between astrocytic processes, and infiltrated the capillary basement membrane. The presence of peroxidase was followed throughout the length of the intercellular spaces, so as to exclude the possibility that all the tracer moved across the astroglial layer by means of pinocytosis.

Similar results were obtained in the toad retina (57), which derives part of its blood supply from a capillary network embedded in the vitreous humor and adjacent to the inner limiting membrane. These hyaloid vessels lack a glial investment, so that solutes traversing the endothelium will penetrate into the vitreous humor without having to move across any additional barrier. From the vitreous humor, extracellular pathways lead to the retinal neurons, as shown by following the penetration into the retina of extracellular tracers such as ferrocyanide (58) and peroxidase (57).

It is clear, therefore, that the capillary endothelium is the only continuous cellular barrier intervening between blood and central nervous system neurons in mammals and amphibia. Experiments with electron opaque tracers have also revealed important structural differences between the endothelium of central nervous system capillaries and that of muscle capillaries. These differences can account for the well-known impermeability of brain and retinal capillaries to colloidal substances. From observations on the movement of horseradish peroxidase across the wall of muscle capillarries, Karnovsky (59) concluded that the tight junctions between endothelial cells are not continuous belts but are interrupted by segments where the intercellular spaces are open for diffusion. These junctional discontinuities would be, according to Karnovsky (59), the morphological representation of the small pore system required by the pore theory of capillary permeability. Another pathway across the endothelium of muscle capillaries was demonstrated by Bruns & Palade (60), by using ferritin as an electron opaque tracer. Ferritin, a larger molecule than peroxidase, was not seen to pass between endothelial cells. Instead, it was found within endothelial vesicles in all the locations to be expected if ferritin moved across the endothelium by way of vesicular transport. Bruns & Palade concluded that the endothelial vesicles are the structural equivalent of the large pore system of capillaries. Thus, two extracellular pathways appear to exist across the endothelium of muscle capillaries, but the relative importance of the vesicular and intercellular pathways is still unclear.

In central nervous system capillaries neither extracellular route is available. Thus, Reese & Karnovsky (54) observed that intravenously injected horseradish peroxidase remained confined to the lumen of cerebral capillaries in mice. Although some of the tracer was taken up by endothelial vesicles, there was no evidence that such vesicles were engaged in transport across the endothelial cells. In addition, the tracer failed to penetrate the junctions between endothelial cells; these junctions can be considered, therefore, as zonulae occludentes. Similar findings were reported at the hyaloid (retinal) vessels of the toad: intravenously injected horseradish peroxidase did not penetrate the endothelial junctions, or move across the endothelium via vesicular transport (57). In the amphibian brain the capillary endothelium was also shown to be impermeable to peroxidase (61), although in *Necturus maculosus* the cerebral capillaries are surrounded by large connective tissue spaces (just as the hyaloid vessels in the toad are surrounded by vitreous humor). Lack of extracellular space around central nervous system capillaries, therefore, cannot be proposed as the basis for a barrier to colloidal particles. Instead, this barrier appears to be the result of a lack of extracellular channels across the endothelium.

Since glial cells can be bypassed by solutes penetrating into the central nervous system of some mammals and amphibia, one may have concluded that they make little or no contribution to the blood-brain and blood-retinal barriers. Recent observations in elasmobranchs, however, indicate that such a conclusion is at least not generally valid. In the capillaries of the shark brain, the junctions between endothelial cells are open, so that intravenously injected peroxidase can move across them to infiltrate the capillary basement membrane (62, 63). Beyond this point, diffusion of peroxidase into the brain parenchyma appears to be prevented by tight junctions between perivascular glial cells, but it is still uncertain whether these junctions represent uninterrupted belts. If so, the glial cells would provide in elasmobranchs the first, or only, continuous cellular barrier encountered by solutes leaving the brain capillaries. It may be, therefore, that the study of homeostatic mechanisms in the brain of sharks will give some information on the function of the perivascular glial processes. In at least one important respect, such as the regulation of cerebrospinal fluid K^+ concentration, such homeostatic mechanisms appear to be the same in elasmobranchs as in higher vertebrates (64).

GLIAL CELLS AND THE REGULATION OF THE IONIC ENVIRONMENT

When glial cell depolarization following neuronal activity was first described, it was suggested that the accompanying current flow across the glial cell membranes could redistribute the K^+ accumulated in the extracellular space, without significantly altering the internal K^+ concentration of glial cells (13). As pointed out by Kuffler (65), this role of glial cells as spatial buffers for potassium is probably not their primary function, since it can only become effective when the neuronal activity is focal, instead of distributed over a large area. Trachtenberg & Pollen (11), however, have recently emphasized the significance of this possible neuroglial function, in view of the claim that the specific membrane resistance of glial cells in the cat cerebral cortex seems to be optimal for an adequate value of K+ current, and the length constant of glial cells would be sufficient to carry 'large amounts of K+ at significant distances from the extracellular spaces closest to areas of synaptic contact'. Some of the assumptions involved in the calculation of these electrical constants have been mentioned above, as well as the lack of identification of the impaled units, either by dye marks or by recording a slow depolarizing response to neuronal stimulation.

In any case, it seems logical to think that removal of K+ is not the main function of the neuroglia (65), since a similar purpose could be accomplished by having larger extracellular spaces, such as would result, for instance, by doing away with the glial cells altogether. An experiment of this kind has in fact been carried out in the leech central nervous system by Baylor & Nicholls (14), who found that the accumulation of extracellular K+ following impulse activity was reduced when the glial investment of the neurons was removed. They concluded, therefore, that glial cell processes may act as spatial barriers, which would favor K+ accumulation around groups of neurons, or neuronal processes, enclosed within a common glial wrapping. In this way, neighboring neurons may interact by means of the K+ released during the activity of any one of them, since even small increases in extracellular K+ concentration would be expected to have significant effects on synaptic transmission. Baylor & Nicholls (66) showed also that the sensitivity of a neuron to the outside K+ concentration depends on its previous history of activity, so that integration would be affected in a very complex way by this nonsynaptic K+-mediated mechanism resulting from glial compartmentalization of the neural elements.

Glial cells have also been proposed as extraneuronal sodium stores in the lamellibranch *Anodonta cygnea* (67). Axons in the central nervous system of this mollusc can generate action potentials in Na+-free nonelectrolyte solutions for prolonged periods, although 'appreciable restriction of ion movements to the axon surfaces' was not observed. Nevertheless, the action potentials in sodium-free medium were believed to be sodium-mediated; to support this claim, the authors refer to unpublished experiments said to indicate that the action potentials are not due to anion efflux, nor to influx of other extracellular cations. On this basis, it was postulated that the axonal activity is maintained by a small sodium fraction sequestered within the glial cells. It is not obvious, however, how this sodium would reach the axonal surface, since it was believed not to exchange with ^{22}Na+ in the bathing fluid. Furthermore, the glial cell processes are very sparse and do not form sheaths around the neuronal elements, although 'large axonal profiles are invariably associated with glial processes'. A high concentration of sodium, perhaps partly in a bound form, has been found within the sheath cells of squid nerve fibers (68). Again in this instance, the finding was interpreted to suggest a role of the Schwann cells in maintaining a normal sodium concentration within the periaxonal space, 'under some conditions'. Presumably, the conditions meant are of a physiological nature, but no specific details were given.

GLIAL CELL PROLIFERATION ACCOMPANYING INCREASED NEURAL ACTIVITY

The rate of proliferation of glial cells in the supraoptic nucleus of the rat was estimated radioautographically from the uptake of ^{3}H-thymidine (69). Increased labeling of the glial cells was reported during dehydration —induced by giving the rats a 1% saline solution instead of water for 2 weeks—although no changes were observed under these conditions in glial cells of the optic tract and trigeminal ganglion and nerve. It was noted that the increased rate of proliferation did not necessarily indicate hyperplasia, since the results could also be interpreted as reflecting an increase in the turnover of glial cells. No mention was made, however, of a previous report by Watson (70), who, using the same experimental procedure, failed to detect changes in the DNA synthesis of glial cells in the supraoptic nucleus, among other areas of the central nervous system. Electrical stimulation of preganglionic fibers was reported to increase the ^{3}H-thymidine labeling of satellite cells in sympathetic ganglia (71). The number of glial cells relative to that of neurons has been said to be larger in the visual cortex of rats subjected to a greater environmental complexity and training, as compared to those subjected to an impoverished environment (72). The increased (16%) glia-neuron ratio was seen in 12 out of 17 pairs of rats, but the difference was believed to be significant ($p < 0.02$).

Besides the uncertainty created by inconclusive or conflicting results, the reported glial cell proliferation is difficult to interpret. At least, it cannot be taken as evidence of a direct functional relationship between glial cells and neurons (71, 72), since it may be caused indirectly by changes in the surroundings associated with neuronal activity, such as would result, for instance, from an increase in the local blood flow (1).

SPECIALIZED CONTACTS BETWEEN GLIAL CELLS AND NEURONS

At the intermediate retina (lamina ganglionaris) of dipterans, the photoreceptor cell terminals make specialized contacts with the so-called capitate projections of glial cells (73). The capitate projections are about 0.1–0.5 μ long and 0.1 μ in diameter; they occupy a recess on the surface of the visual cells, and the intervening space—which has a constant width (250 Å) —is occupied by a layer of amorphous material. At least 800 capitate projections invaginate each visual cell terminal; other segments of the visual cells, as well as other nerve elements at the optical cartridges, are free of them. Trujillo-Cenóz (73) suggested that because of their unique appearance, the capitate projections may have more than a merely supporting role, but it is difficult to speculate on what their function may be.

In the ventral nerve cord of the prawn *P. vulgaris*, 'nodal' (glial) cells make pentalaminar junctions with the axons (74). The nodal cells also engage in pentalaminar junctions with other glial cells, which ramify through-out the nerve cord and surround other axons. According to Heuser & Dog-genwheiler (74), the pentalaminar junctions may electrically couple the glial cells to one another and to the axons, so that the resulting chain of glial cells may mediate axon-to-axon electrical interaction.

Pentalaminar junctions have been also observed between glial and reti-nular or eccentric cells in the lateral eye of *Limulus* (75). The junctions involved either the rhabdomeric or nonrhabdomeric surface of the visual cells, and were frequently found in close association to subsurface cisternae within the adjacent visual cell cytoplasm. Similar junctions were present between glial cell processes, but in *Limulus* there was no reason to assume the existence of glial cell chains mediating electrical interaction between visual cells, since the latter are extensively linked to one another by pentala-minar junctions at the level of the rhabdom. In a subsequent study of the lateral eye, Fahrenbach (76) failed to find pentalaminar junctions between glial and visual cells. He attributed this result to the use of what he thought to be a better fixative mixture (lower sucrose concentration). On the other hand, Clark, Millecchia & Mauro (77) used a fixative similar to Fahren-bach's in a study of the ventral eye of *Limulus*, and reported the finding of pentalaminar junctions between glial and visual cells, in this case involving almost exclusively the rhabdomeric surface of the visual cells.

More recently, I have made some observations on the effect of hyper-tonic solutions on the pentalaminar junctions of the lateral eye of *Limulus* (unpublished). When the eye is soaked in a solution having twice the mo-larity of seawater (560 mM/liter NaCl added to artificial seawater), and then fixed in the same solution plus 3% glutaraldehyde, the pentalaminar junctions between glial and visual cells are not found, but those between microvilli at the rhabdom remain unaltered. It may be, then, that the penta-laminar junctions between glial and visual cells are not quite the same as the junctions between microvilli, which probably mediate the electrical cou-pling found between visual cells in the lateral eye (78). On the other hand, the glial to visual cell junctions are found in tissue which is well fixed by any other criterion, and also when moderately hypertonic fixatives are used (75). It would seem unjustified, therefore, to disregard them as artifacti-tious, at least until their possible existence in vivo can be tested by other means.

Neurons devoid of glial sheaths.—In X-irradiated tissue cultures of rat dorsal root ganglia, the perineuronal satellite cells may degenerate during the first days following exposure to radiation, and the neuronal bodies are left covered only by a basement membrane (79). Nevertheless, during a 14-day observation period, the denuded neurons appear to survive just as well as those invested by glial cells. Masurovsky, Bunge & Bunge (79) con-cluded, therefore, that whatever neuronal dependence on glial cells may ex-ist, it must be related to longer-term processes. The soma of leech photore-ceptor neurons also lacks a glial sheath, so that the neuronal membrane is separated from the surrounding connective tissue only by a basement membrane (80).

Transfer of materials from glial cells to neurons.—Following intraperitoneal injections of ³H-histidine to newts, the label was found in Schwann cell bodies, myelin sheath, and axoplasm of brachial plexus nerves (81). On the basis of this observation, and from the time course of the labeling, Singer & Salpeter (81) suggested that protein formed in the Schwann cells 'is carried thence inward into the myelin and finally to the axon'. Similar interpretations were then advanced with respect to the uptake and final destination of an RNA precursor (82). According to Droz & Koenig (83), however, 'labeled proteins in Schwann cells decay at the same rate all along the length of the peripheral nerves', while incorporation into the axon is 'first detected in the proximal segments, and only later in the more distal regions'. Droz & Koenig (83) concluded, therefore, that it is unlikely that Schwann cells contribute more than a small part, if any, of the axonal proteins.

RETINAL PIGMENT EPITHELIUM

Results from several lines of work suggest that the reginal pigment epithelium cells are endowed with some of the functions that have been hypothesized for other glial cells. Nevertheless, not much consideration appears to have been given to the possibility that the pigment epithelium represents a useful model system for the study of neuroglial function. Perhaps this is because the pigment epithelium cells—due to their anatomical relationship to one another, and to the capillaries in the choroid—may seem to be a better analog of epithelial cells in the cerebral choroid plexuses, than of glial cells in the strict sense of the term, that is, cells which occupy interstices between neural elements. While this is partly true, anyone who has examined a well-fixed retina under the electronmicroscope is aware of the close spatial relationship existing between photoreceptor cells and pigment epithelium cell processes; the latter, in fact, intervene between the photoreceptors, and cover them, in a pattern similar to that displayed by glial processes surrounding neurons at other regions of the nervous system.

The pigment epithelium is the main or only diffusion barrier interposed between the choroidal blood and the neural retina (84–86); in this role it resembles the pericapillary glia of lower vertebrates (62, 63). It is puzzling, however, that at the retinal capillaries the main diffusion barrier is represented by endothelial, rather than glial, cells (57, 84). Fluorescent dyes intravenously injected penetrate the pigment epithelium cells, but do not extend beyond their inner surface (84). Substances moving beyond this boundary can penetrate into the neural retina by following extracellular pathways, since extracellular electron opaque tracers—such as ferrocyanide and peroxidase—can be seen to diffuse across the junctional layer at the outer surface of the neural retina (57, 87).

As might have been expected, the pigment epithelium is not just a passive diffusion barrier, since at least chloride ions are preferentially transferred from the inner (retinal) to the outer (choroidal) surface of the toad pigment epithelium in the absence of an electrochemical potential gradient (88). The interest of this observation from the viewpoint of glial cell function is somewhat diminished, however, by the finding that the frog cornea is also engaged in active chloride transport from its aqueous to tear surfaces (89). Of more interest, perhaps, is the observation that the retinal pigment epithelium appears to take up bicarbonate at its inner surface (88), since in this way it may influence the pH in the immediate environment of the photoreceptors. Nevertheless, bicarbonate ions are not transported across the epithelium, and the exact nature of the uptake process remains undetermined.

Intracellular recordings from pigment epithelium cells in the turtle retina show that a single flash of light results in a small hyperpolarization which, upon repetitive stimulation, may build up gradually to an amplitude of about 15 mV (D. A. Baylor, unpublished results). Some of the properties of this response—such as its summation and long time course of decay—resemble those of K^+-mediated depolarizations of glial cells in amphibian optic nerve (13) and leech ganglia (14). The hyperpolarizing nature of the pigment epithelium cells response might be consistent with a K^+-mediated effect, since the receptor cells hyperpolarize and decrease their surface membrane conductance (90, 91)—and probably leak less K^+—during illumination. Nevertheless, it is not known as yet whether the pigment epithelium cell hyperpolarization is due to a change in external K^+ concentration, although it does not appear to arise as a consequence of direct light activation of the pigment epithelium cells, since it is not observed when the neural retina is stripped away (D. A. Baylor, unpublished results). In addition, there is now independent evidence that the pigment epithelium cells are sensitive to changes in visual cell activity. Liebman, Carroll & Laties (92) have studied the action spectrum of the migration of melanin granules in the retinal pigment epithelium of the frog, and concluded that the migration is secondary to light absorption in the red rods. They also suggested that this effect may be mediated by a release of ions or vitamin A from the photoreceptors.

The existence of a pigment epithelium cell response to stimulation of the visual cells is of great interest in view of the well-known exchanges of vitamin A occurring between the pigment epithelium and the neural retina during the course of light and dark adaptation (93). This may very well be an example of a neuron signaling a glial cell so as to elicit a trophic response from it (1). Another type of metabolic interaction between pigment epithelium cells and photoreceptors has been recently demonstrated in the retina of the frog (94). Disc membranes are continuously formed and displaced along the outer segments of rod cells, as determined by following radioautographically the uptake of tritiated aminoacids (95). When the labeled membranes reach the distal end of the outer segments, they are detached from them and reappear within the pigment epithelium cells as inclusion bodies or phagosomes (94). The labeled phagosomes ultimately disappear from the pigment epithelium cells, so that it may be inferred that their membranous material is destroyed and eliminated. Again, this sequence of events is strongly reminiscent of the excretory role already proposed for other neuroglial cells (1, 65).

LITERATURE CITED

1. Kuffler, S. W., Nicholls, J. G. 1966. The physiology of neuroglial cells. *Ergeb. Physiol.* 57 :1–90
2. Bunge, R. P. 1968. Glial cells and the central myelin sheath. *Physiol. Rev.* 48 :197–251
3. Dennis, M. H., Gerschenfeld, H. M. 1969. Some physiological properties of identified mammalian neuroglial cells. *J. Physiol. (London)* 203 : 211–22
4. Villegas, J., Villegas, R., Giménez, M. 1968. Nature of the Schwann cell electrical potential. Effects of the external ionic concentrations and a cardiac glycoside. *J. Gen. Physiol.* 51 :47–64
5. Cohen, M. W., Gerschenfeld, H. M., Kuffler, S. W. 1968. Ionic environment of neurones and glial cells in the brain of an amphibian. *J. Physiol. (London)* 197 :363–80
6. Karahashi, Y., Goldring, S. 1966. Intracellular potentials from "idle" cells in cerebral cortex of cat. *Electroenceph. Clin. Neurophysiol.* 20 :600–7
7. Krnjević, K., Schwartz, S. 1967. Some properties of unresponsive cells in the cerebral cortex. *Brain Res.* 3 :306–19
8. Kelly, J. S., Krnjević, K., Yim, G. K. W. 1967. Unresponsive cells in cerebral cortex. *Brain Res.* 6 : 767–69
9. Grossman, R. G., Hampton, T. 1968. Depolarization of cortical cells during electrocortical activity. *Brain Res.* 11 :316–24
10. Grossman, R. G., Whiteside, L., Hampton, T. L. 1969. The time course of evoked depolarization of cortical glial cells. *Brain Res.* 14 : 401–15
11. Trachtenberg, M. C., Pollen, D. A. 1970. Neuroglia : biophysical properties and physiologic function. *Science* 167 :1248–52
12. Stretton, A. O. W., Kravitz, E. A.

1968. Neuronal geometry : determination with a technique of intracellular dye injection. *Science* 162 :132–34
13. Orkand, R. K., Nicholls, J. G., Kuffler, S. W. 1966. Effect of nerve impulses on the membrane potential of glial cells in the central nervous system of amphibia. *J. Neurophysiol.* 29 :788–806
14. Baylor, D. A., Nicholls, J. G. 1969. Changes in extracellular potassium concentration produced by neuronal activity in the central nervous system of the leech. *J. Physiol. (London)* 203 :555–69
15. Hild, W., Tasaki, I. 1962. Morphological and physiological properties of neurons and glial cells in tissue culture. *J. Neurophysiol.* 25 :277–304
16. Wardell, W. M. 1966. Electrical and pharmacological properties of mammalian neuroglial cells in tissue-culture. *Proc. Roy. Soc. (London) B* 165 :326–61
17. Miller, R. F., Dowling, J. E. 1970. Intracellular responses of the Müller (glial) cells of the mudpuppy retina : their relation to b-wave of the electroretinogram. *J. Neurophysiol.* 23 :323–41
18. Walker, F. D., Hild, W. J. 1969. Neuroglia electrically coupled to neurons. *Science* 165 :602–3
19. Bortoff, A. 1964. Localization of slow potential responses in the Necturus retina. *Vision Res.* 4 :627–35
20. Tomita, T. 1965. Electrophysiological study of the mechanisms subserving color coding in the fish retina. *Cold Spring Harbor Symp.* 30 :559–66
21. Kaneko, A., Hashimoto, H. Electrophysiological study of single neurons in the inner nuclear layer of the carp retina. *Vision Res.* 9 : 37–55
22. Werblin, F. S., Dowling, J. E. 1969.

Organization of the retina of the mudpuppy, *Necturus maculosus.* II. Intracellular recording. *J. Neurophysiol.* 32:339–55

23. Stell, W. K. 1967. The structure and relationships of horizontal cells and photoreceptor-bipolar synaptic complexes in goldfish retina. *Am. J. Anat.* 120:401–24

24. Dowling, J. E., Brown, J. E., Major, D. 1966. Synapses of horizontal cells in rabbit and cat retinas. *Science* 153:1639–41

25. Dowling, J. E., Werblin, F. S. 1969. Organization of the retina of the mudpuppy, *Necturus maculosus.* I. Synaptic structure. *J. Neurophysiol.* 32:315–38

26. Hydén, H. 1967. RNA in brain cells. In *The Neurosciences,* ed. G. C. Quarton, T. Melnechuk, F. O. Schmitt, 248–66. New York: Rockefeller Univ. Press

27. Sotelo, C., Palay, S. L. 1968. The fine structure of the lateral vestibular nucleus in the rat. I. Neurons and neuroglial cells. *J. Cell Biol.* 36:151–79

28. Rose, S. P. R. 1967. Preparation of enriched fractions from cerebral cortex containing isolated, metabolically active neuronal and glial cells. *Biochem. J.* 102:33–43

29. Freysz, L. et al 1968. Quantitative distribution of phospholipids in neurons and glial cells isolated from rat cerebral cortex. *J. Neurochem.* 15:307–13

30. Bradford, H. F., Rose, S. P. R. 1967. Ionic accumulation and membrane properties of neurons and glia from mammalian cerebral cortex. *J. Neurochem.* 14:373–75

31. Rose, S. P. R. 1968. Glucose and amino acid metabolism in isolated neuronal and glial cell fractions *in vitro. J. Neurochem.* 15:1415–29

32. Volpe, P., Giuditta, A. 1967. Biosynthesis of RNA in neuron- and glia-enriched fractions. *Brain Res.* 6:228–40

33. Blomstrand, C., Hamberger, A. 1969. Protein turnover in cell-enriched fractions from rabbit brain. *J. Neurochem.* 16:1401–7

34. Hamberger, A., Blomstrand, C., Lehninger, A., 1970. Comparative studies on mitochondria isolated from neuron-enriched and glia-enriched fractions of rabbit and beef brain. *J. Cell Biol.* 45:221–34

35. Cremer, J. E., Johnston, P. V., Roots, B. I., Trevor, A. J. 1968. Heterogeneity of brain fractions containing neuronal and glial cells. *J. Neurochem.* 15:1361–70

36. Rose, S. P. R., Sinha, A. K. 1969. Some properties of isolated neuronal cell fractions. *J. Neurochem.* 16:1319–28

37. Norton, W. T., Poduslo, S. E. 1970. Neuronal soma and whole neuroglia of rat brain: a new isolation technique. *Science* 167:1144–46

38. Fewster, M. E., Scheibel, A. B., Mead, J. F. 1967. The preparation of isolated glial cells from rat and bovine white matter. *Brain Res.* 6:401–8

39. Fewster, M. E., Mead, J. F. 1968. Lipid composition of glial cells isolated from bovine white matter. *J. Neurochem.* 15:1041–52

40. Fewster, M. E., Mead, J. F. 1968. Fatty acid and fatty aldehyde composition of glial cell lipids isolated from bovine white matter. *J. Neurochem.* 15:1303–12

41. Løvtrup-Rein, H., McEwen, B. S. 1966. Isolation and fractionation of rat brain nuclei. *J. Cell Biol.* 30:405–15

42. Burdman, J. A., Journey, L. J. 1969. Protein synthesis in isolated nuclei from adult rat brain. *J. Neurochem.* 16:493–500

43. Løvtrup-Rein, H. 1970. Protein synthesis in isolated nuclei of nerve and glial cells from rat brain. *Brain Res.* 19:433–44

44. Kato, T., Kurokawa, M. 1970. Studies on ribonucleic acid and homopolyribonucleotide formation in neuronal, glial and liver nuclei. *Biochem. J.* 116: 599–609

45. Camejo, G., Villegas, G., Barnola, F. V., Villegas, R. 1969. Characterization of two different membrane fractions from the first stellar nerves of the squid, *Dosidicus gigas. Biochim. Biophys. Acta* 193:247–59

46. Sabatini, M. T., Dipolo, R., Villegas, R. 1968. Adenosine triphosphatase activity in the membranes of the squid giant fiber. *J. Cell Biol.* 38: 176–83

47. Hodson, S., Marshall, J. 1967. Tyrosine incorporation into the rabbit retina. *J. Cell Biol.* 35:722–26

48. Shein, H. M., Britva, A., Hess, H. H.,

Selkoe, D. J. 1970. Isolation of hamster brain astroglia by *in vitro* cultivation and subcutaneous growth, and content of cerebroside, ganglioside, RNA and DNA. *Brain Res.* 19:497–501

49. Moore, B. W. 1965. A soluble protein characteristic of the nervous system. *Biochem. Biophys. Res. Commun.* 19:739–44

50. Hydén, H., McEwen, B. 1966. A glial protein specific for the nervous system. *Proc. Nat. Acad. Sci.* 55: 354–58

51. Benda, P., Lightbody, J., Sato, G., Levine, L., Sweet, W. 1968. Differentiated rat glial cell strain in tissue culture. *Science* 161:370–71

52. Cicero, T. J., Cowan, W. M., Moore, B. W., Suntzeff, V. 1970. The cellular localization of the two brain specific proteins, S-100 and 14-3-2. *Brain Res.* 18:25–34

53. Mihailovic, L. J., Hydén, H. 1969. On antigenic differences between nerve cells and glia. *Brain Res.* 16:243–56

54. Reese, T. S., Karnovsky, M. J. 1967. Fine structural localization of a blood-brain barrier to exogenous peroxidase. *J. Cell Biol.* 34:207–17

55. Brightman, M. W., Reese, T. S. 1969. Junctions between intimately apposed cell membranes in the vertebrate brain. *J. Cell Biol.* 40:648–677

56. Brightman, M. W. 1967. The intracerebral movement of proteins injected into blood and cerebrospinal fluid of mice. *Progr. Brain Res.* 29:19–37

57. Lasansky, A. 1967. The pathway between hyaloid blood and retinal neurons in the toad. Structural observations and permeability to tracer substances. *J. Cell Biol.* 34: 617–26

58. Lasansky, A., Wald, F. 1962. The extracellular space in the toad retina as defined by the distribution of ferrocyanide. Light and electron microscope observations. *J. Cell Biol.* 15:463–79

59. Karnovsky, M. J. 1967. The ultrastructural basis of capillary permeability studied with peroxidase as a tracer. *J. Cell Biol.* 35:213–36

60. Bruns, R. R., Palade, G. E. 1968. Studies on blood capillaries. II.

Transport of ferritin molecules across the wall of muscle capillaries. *J. Cell Biol.* 37:277–99

61. Bodenheimer, T. S., Brightman, M. W. 1968. A blood-brain barrier to peroxidase in capillaries surrounded by perivascular spaces. *Am. J. Anat.* 122:249–67

62. Brightman, M. W., Reese, T. S., Feder, N. 1970. Assessment with the electron microscope of the permeability to peroxidase of cerebral endothelium and epithelium in mice and sharks. In *Alfred Benson Symposium on Capillary Permeability*, ed. C. Crone, N. Lassen. Copenhagen: Munksgaard. In press

63. Brightman, M. W., Reese, T. S., Olsson, Y., Klatzo, I. 1970. Morphological aspects of the blood-brain barrier to peroxidase in elasmobranchs. *Progr. Neuropathol.* In press

64. Cserr, H., Rall, D. P. 1967. Regulation of cerebrospinal fluid [K+] in the spiny dogfish, *Squalus acanthias. Comp. Biochem. Physiol.* 21:431–34

65. Kuffler, S. W. 1967. Neuroglial cells: physiological properties and a potassium mediated effect of neuronal activity on the glial membrane potential. *Proc. Roy. Soc. (London) B* 168:1–21

66. Baylor, D. A., Nicholls, J. G. 1969. After-effects of nerve impulses on signalling in the central nervous system of the leech. *J. Physiol. (London)* 203:571–89

67. Treherne, J. E., Carlson, A. D., Gupta, B. L. 1969. Extraneuronal sodium store in central nervous system of *Anodonta cygnea. Nature* 223: 377–80

68. Villegas, J., Villegas, L., Villegas, R. 1965. Sodium, potassium, and chloride concentrations in the Schwann cell and axon of the squid giant fiber. *J. Gen. Physiol.* 49:1–7

69. Murray, M. 1968. Effects of dehydration on the rate of proliferation of hypothalamic neuroglia cells. *Exp. Neurol.* 20:460–68

70. Watson, W. E. 1965. An autoradiographic study of the incorporation of nucleic-acid precursors by neurons and glia during nerve stimulation. *J. Physiol. (London)* 180:754–65

71. Schwyn, R. C. 1967. An autoradiographic study of satellite cells in autonomic ganglia. *Am. J. Anat.* 121:727–40

72. Diamond, M. C. et al 1966. Increases in cortical depth and glia numbers in rats subjected to enriched environment. *J. Comp. Neurol.* 128: 117–26

73. Trujillo-Cenóz, O. 1965. Some aspects of the structural organization of the intermediate retina of dipterans. *J. Ultrastruct. Res.* 13:1–33

74. Heuser, J. E., Doggenweiler, C. F. 1966. The fine structural organization of nerve fibers, sheaths, and glial cells in the prawn, *Palaemonetes vulgaris. J. Cell Biol.* 30: 381–403

75. Lasansky, A. 1967. Cell junctions in ommatidia of *Limulus. J. Cell Biol.* 33:365–83

76. Fahrenbach, W. H. 1969. The morphology of the eyes of *Limulus.* II. Ommatidia of the compound eye. *Z. Zellforsch. Mikrosk. Anat.* 93:451–83

77. Clark, A. W., Millecchia, R., Mauro, A. 1969. The ventral photoreceptor cells of *Limulus.* I. The microanatomy. *J. Gen. Physiol.* 54:289–309

78. Smith, T. G., Baumann, F., Fuortes, M. G. F. 1965. Electrical connections between visual cells in the ommatidium of *Limulus. Science* 147:1446–48

79. Masurovsky, E. B., Bunge, M. B., Bunge, R. P. 1967. Cytological studies of organotypic cultures of rat dorsal root ganglia following X-irradiation in vitro. I. Changes in neurons and satellite cells. *J. Cell Biol.* 32:467–96

80. Lasansky, A., Fuortes, M. G. F. 1969. The site of origin of electrical responses in visual cells of the leech, *Hirudo medicinalis. J. Cell Biol.* 42:241–52

81. Singer, M., Salpeter, M. M. 1966. The transport of ³H-1-histidine through the Schwann and myelin sheath into the axon, including a reevaluation of myelin function. *J. Morphol.* 120:281–316

82. Singer, M., Green, M. R. 1968. Autoradiographic studies of uridine incorporation in peripheral nerve of the newt, *Triturus. J. Morphol.* 124:321–43

83. Droz, B., Koenig, H. L. 1969. The turnover of proteins in axons and nerve endings. *Symp. Int. Soc. Cell Biol.* 8:35–50

84. Rodríquez-Peralta, L. A. 1968. Hematic and fluid barriers of the retina and vitreous body. *J. Comp. Neurol.* 132:109–23

85. Brindley, G. S., Hamasaki, D. I. 1963. The properties and nature of the R membrane of the frog's eye. *J. Physiol. (London)* 167:599–606

86. Cohen, A. I. 1965. A possible cytological basis for the "R" membrane in the vertebrate eye. *Nature* 205: 1222–23

87. Lasansky, A. 1965. Functional implications of structural findings in retinal glial cells. *Progr. Brain Res.* 15:48–72

88. Lasansky, A., de Fisch, F. W. 1966. Potential, current, and ionic fluxes across the isolated retinal pigment epithelium and choroid. *J. Gen. Physiol.* 49:913–24

89. Zadunaisky, J. A. 1966. Active transport of chloride in frog cornea. *Am. J. Physiol.* 211:506–12

90. Toyoda, J., Nosaki, H., Tomita, T. 1969. Light-induced resistance changes in single photoreceptors of *Necturus* and *Gekko. Vision Res.* 9:453–63

91. Baylor, D. A., Fuortes, M. G. F. 1970. Electrical responses of single cones in the retina of the turtle. *J. Physiol. (London)* 207:77–92

92. Liebman, P. A., Carroll, S., Laties, A. 1969. Spectral sensitivity of retinal screening pigment migration in the frog. *Vision Res.* 9:377–84

93. Dowling, J. E. 1960. Chemistry of visual adaptation in the rat. *Nature* 188:114–18

94. Young, R. W., Bok, D. 1969. Participation of the retinal pigment epithelium in the rod outer segment renewal process. *J. Cell Biol.* 42: 392–403

95. Young, R. W. 1967. The renewal of photoreceptor cell outer segments. *J. Cell Biol.* 33:61–72

PERIPHERAL MECHANISMS OF VISION 1062

PAUL WITKOVSKY

Departments of Ophthalmology and Physiology
Columbia University, New York, N. Y.

INTRODUCTION

This review is concerned with recent studies[1] of the vertebrate retina, particularly those reporting microelectrode investigations of unit responses and anatomical studies of retinal cytoarchitecture and synapses. From these studies has emerged a more precise appreciation than previously possible of the role played by a given neuronal response in the functional organization of the retina. Given the limitations of space, emphasis of one body of investigations has precluded a thorough review of others. The readers' attention is drawn to recent reviews and symposia concerned with the visual system (1–16), some of which summarize areas of research neglected in this essay. Of particular interest is the projected *Handbook of Sensory Physiology* series by Springer, now in preparation. Volume VII, nos. 1–4 will deal with the visual system. The titles are *The photochemistry of vision, Physiology of photoreceptor organs, Central processing of visual information,* and *Visual psychophysics.*

PHOTORECEPTORS: FUNCTION

Intracellular records have been obtained from cones of carp (17–19), *Necturus* (20, 21), and turtle retinas (22) and from rods of gecko (21) and frog (19) retinas. Localization of the electrode tip has been verified in some cases by dye-deposit techniques (20, 23). Common features are a resting potential of 10–30 mV inside negative and a light-evoked response which is a sustained hyperpolarization. Response amplitude is graded with light intensity over a range of 1.5 to 4.0 log units above threshold, in different studies. The absolute light levels of this dynamic range, however, may vary. Thus, saturation for gecko rods is reported to be 2 log units lower than that for *Necturus* cones (18).

The mechanism of receptor response generation has been analyzed in various retinas. In rat rods in the dark, a potential difference was found between the outer segment and the cell base, the outer segment being rela-

[1] Journal articles appearing January 1967–June 1970 make up the bulk of the citations. This study was supported by NIH grant EY 00280.

tively negative; a light flash transiently reduced the dark potential. Both the dark current and the photocurrent appeared to be dependent upon metabolic processes for both were abolished by 10 mM KCN (24).

A spatial analysis of current distribution (24) showed that during the dark, current flowed out of the inner segment into the outer segment. Photocurrent can be represented by current flow in the opposite direction; that is, the photocurrent might represent a reduction in the dark current or the onset of a light-induced current of opposite sign. Subsequent work favors the first alternative. In gecko and *Necturus* photoreceptors, light induced an immediate increase in the membrane resistance of the cell, proportional to the photovoltage (21). The increase was not a passive result of hyperpolarization, since polarizing the membrane by extrinsic current caused no resistance increase. The data are consistent with the hypothesis that the permeability to some ion or ions is reduced during the light. By applying extrinsic current it was shown that the size and polarity of the photovoltage was dependent on the membrane potential level of the cell. The reversal potential for the response was estimated to be slightly positive to zero, strongly suggesting a principal role for Na^+ in response generation. Further studies on rat (25, 26), frog (27, 28), and pigeon (26) receptors indicate that Na^+ is in fact the principal current carrier. Reduction in $(Na^+)_o$ resulted in a fall in photovoltage according to the relation $V = k \ (Na^+)_o$. The slight deviation from this function at low external sodium concentrations suggests the possible participation of other ions in generation of the response. When the transport mechanism was poisoned by ouabain, a photovoltage was transiently restored by artificially increasing the sodium gradient across the photoreceptor (28).

Tomita (18) has calculated that a fish cone generates 1–10 μV/quantum absorbed, a value in agreement with that calculated for rat rods (24). Thus, the difference in threshold levels for different photoreceptors will depend on the efficiency of quantum capture. Other factors, such as the noise level of the cell, may also play a role. It is interesting that in rat retina which contains only the rod pigment, the receptors begin to saturate at about 2.5 log units above threshold (24), whereas the behaviorally determined increment threshold for the rat operates over a 6 log unit range of adapting luminance (29).

In carp cones and the octopus photoreceptor, the action spectrum of the individual photoreceptor response looks reasonably like a Dartnall nomogram curve for a pigment with the same maximum (18). So far, however, it has been impossible to hold the response long enough to obtain amplitude vs intensity functions at many wavelengths, from which a true spectral sensitivity function to be compared with the nomogram could be derived (17). There is good agreement, however, between the absorption (31) or difference spectrum maxima (32) of goldfish cones and those of the electrophysiologically derived action spectra of single carp cones. For both kinds of data, approximate sensitivity peaks are: blue, 455 nm, green, 535 nm, and red, 620 nm.

The photoreceptor response is reported to be indifferent to the degree to which other photoreceptors are illuminated (22, 30). Baylor & Fuortes (22) estimated that the increase seen in receptor response upon increasing stimulus diameter was due to scattered light falling upon the test receptor.

PHOTORECEPTORS: SYNAPTIC CONTACTS

Photoreceptors make synaptic contacts with bipolar and horizontal cells; the details of these contacts have been partially worked out for several vertebrates (33-40). In general, rods have a single invagination into which enter a variable number of centrally located bipolar dendrites, flanked by two horizontal cell processes. Cones have multiple invaginations, each populated by one central bipolar dendrite and two lateral horizontal cells—a complex called a triad (33-37). In some primates it is known that the two horizontal processes in the triad derive from different cells (37, 38) and that the central bipolar dendrite originates in one kind of midget bipolar (37, 39). In the retinas so far studied, where a given horizontal cell contacts both rods and cones, the cell dendrites enter the cones while the terminal processes of the axon enter rods, e.g. primate (37), cat, and guinea pig.[2] The distinction between rods and cones on which the preceding statement is based derives from an examination of photoreceptor synaptic terminals: cones have multiple invaginations, each populated by a triad, rods have a single invagination into which penetrate a variable number of processes. In the goldfish retina, dendrites from a given horizontal cell connect exclusively with either rods or cones (33). Although teleost horizontal cells have axons, it is not certain whether the axons possess a terminal expansion (41).

In contrast to the horizontal cells, primate bipolar cells receive synaptic input either from rods alone or from cones (37-40). Teleost bipolars are of two groups, one exclusive to cones, another that connects to both rods and cones (33). This kind of information is not yet available for bipolars of other vertebrate retinas. Noninvaginating contacts, called superficial contacts, are made by certain bipolar cells onto cone bases in primate retina (37, 40). At these contacts one sees membrane densities but no synaptic ribbon. Superficial contacts, sometimes associated with a synaptic ribbon and/or membrane specializations, are described between cones and postsyn-

---

[2] Kolb, H. reported at the Association for Research in Ophthalmology meeting, April 1970. In this study, which employed the combined Golgi electronmicroscope technique (see 33, 37-40), horizontal cell axons were not actually traced to the cell body. The inferred identification is reasonable, however, since horizontal cells in many vertebrate retinas have such axons, whereas photoreceptors and bipolar cells do not.

aptic processes in turtle (42), frog (36), and *Necturus* retinas (35), though the identity of the postsynaptic elements is not yet certain.

S-Potentials

It is generally accepted that horizontal cells generate the S-potential (43–45), though in retinas where more than one class of S-potential is generated, some controversy remains.

Transretinal current pulses, scleral side positive, evoke depolarization in the S-potential but have little or no effect when pulse polarity is reversed. Current pulses applied when the light is on elicit a larger response than when applied in the dark, within certain limits and after a delay. These findings have led the investigators to conclude that extrinsic current of appropriate polarity acts presynaptically on the receptor causing the release of a transmitter, which depolarizes the horizontal cell. During the light, transmitter release is reduced, causing the horizontal cell to hyperpolarize and its membrane resistance to increase (46, 47). This explanation applies only to the L-type S-potential. It is important to note that the L-potential itself precedes the membrane resistance increase elicited by a light stimulus, so that the L-potential cannot be the result of the resistance change (48).

S-potentials follow Ricco's law (area $\times$ intensity $= k$) over a large area (up to 10.0 mm in carp) (49) and have a homogeneous receptive field without antagonistic areas (50–52). Naka & Rushton (50) determined that what was transmitted to the cell from a distant light stimulus was current, not scattered light. It is unclear, however, how in fish retinas, such information is transmitted a distance equal to many horizontal cell diameters. Synaptic morphology of the sort seen at chemically transmitting synapses is found between teleost horizontal cells (53). In addition, neighboring horizontal cells in teleosts and elasmobranchs have closely apposed (90–100 Å separation) membranes (53, 54) though further work is needed to characterize these regions as electronically couped "gap" junctions according to recently established criteria (55). Kaneko found that nearby horizontal cells in dogfish were tightly coupled (56). The coupling ratio between two horizontal cells separated by a distance not exceeding one cell diameter ranged from 0.60 to 0.05. In a small number of cases, it was proven that the tested cells were adjacent by passing two different fluorescent dyes, procyon yellow and red, through the recording pipettes, then localizing the cells histologically. There is no suggestion, either morphological or physiological, that retinal horizontal cells in vertebrate classes other than fishes are tightly coupled.

In goldfish retina the latest report (43) states that both C- and L-type potentials are recorded from cells in both the external horizontal cell and internal horizontal cell layers (Cajal's classification) while no response has yet been localized to the intermediate horizontal cell layer which connects exclusively to rods (33). In tench retina, a study of dark-adaptation behavior of the L-response revealed that, following a bright flash, recovery was described by a shift of the V-log I curve by 3 log units along the abscissa (57). Judging from the small change of sensitivity and the apparent retention of maximum sensitivity in the red region of the spectrum in dark- and light-adapted states, it is probable that the dark adaptation of the cone system alone was observed. This is consistent with the anatomical data showing that, in goldfish, the external horizontal cell is connected only to cones (33). Photopic L-potentials in turtle and carp retina had a marked Stiles-Crawford directional effect, indicating cone input (58, 59), whereas dark-adapted L-potentials in carp, whose spectral curves indicated rod input (λ_{max} at 530 nm), lacked directional sensitivity, except in the blue region (59). It was concluded that the dark-adapted cell is receiving input from rods with a small contribution from blue cones. It was not determined whether horizontal cells from the same layer generated both the photopic and scotopic responses. Where more than one cone class contributes to the S-potential, as in certain fish, the interaction between cone inputs is very complex (60–62). The catfish is a simpler experimental subject as its L-potential is driven by a single cone (λ_{max} at 625 nm) (63).

In the cat, L-potentials undergo a clear Purkinje shift upon adaptation and operate over an approximate 6 log unit range, shifting from rod- to conelike responses at about 3.5 log units above absolute dark threshold (64–66). By using stimuli which selectively evoked rod or cone responses, it was shown that the contributions from the two receptor populations added in a linear fashion.

The role of S-potentials in retinal information processing is just beginning to be elucidated. In some vertebrate retinas (e.g. *Necturus*), synapses made by horizontal cells onto bipolar cells are found, in addition to the proximity of processes of these two cells in receptor bases (35). In *Necturus* retina the center of the receptive field of the bipolar cell is about 100 μ, while the horizontal cell receptive field is about 500 μ in diameter. Bipolar cells respond to a central flash with a graded, sustained slow potential, either always depolarizing or always hyperpolarizing, i.e. the polarity does not change with wavelength. An annular flash of inner diameter 250 μ, outer diameter 500 μ has little effect on the bipolar cell, yet when the cell is polarized by a steady central flash, that polarity is reduced or abolished (but not reversed) by the same annulus and the time course of surround inhibition corresponds to the onset of the S-potential. Additional central light, however, repolarizes the cell. Thus, the *Necturus* bipolar cell codes contrast —its reponse reflects the difference in center and surround intensities (20). In other vertebrates the bipolar cell receptive field may have different properties from that found in *Necturus*. In the goldfish retina, for example, the annular flash alone evokes a bipolar response of opposite polarity to that evoked by a central one (43).

In a study of S-potentials and ganglion cells in the carp retina, little correspondence was found between the two responses in terms of adaptation, thresholds, and spectral sensitivity (67). However, in the pike retina Maksimova reports (68) that intracellular polarization by 5–75 mV of the horizontal cells can induce firing in, or sharply modify in specific ways, the light-induced responses of ganglion cells. Since there is no direct connection between horizontal and ganglion cells, these effects must be mediated by direct horizontal to bipolar contacts or via feedback to the receptors. The horizontal cells were reported to have resistances of 20–30 kΩ; resistance values reported for teleost horizontal cells by other investigators have been 1–7 MΩ, so that some of the large currents used (10^{-7} A) may have affected the ganglion cell directly through an extracellular pathway. Nevertheless, the report is a provocative one—Naka,[3] working with catfish retina, has been able to modify ganglion cell activity by small amounts of current (nA) injected in the S-potential compartment.

SYNAPTIC ORGANIZATION OF THE INNER PLEXIFORM LAYER

Neural messages resulting from interactions between photoreceptors, horizontal cells, and bipolar cells are conveyed to the inner plexiform layer by bipolar processes (though one should reserve the possibility that amacrine cells may have ascending processes reaching the outer plexiform layer —see section on retinal pharmacology). The bipolar cell synaptic terminal in the inner plexiform layer is characterized by a synaptic ribbon, increased membrane densification and two postsynaptic processes (34–36, 53, 69–71). In a given case, either both the postsynaptic elements derive from amacrine cells or one from an amacrine, the other from a ganglion cell (34–36, 53). This unit is called a dyad. Dowling has surveyed a number of vertebrate retinas and determined that increased complexity of ganglion cell receptive-field organization, as measured physiologically, is associated with an increased dependence of the ganglion cell on synaptic input from amacrines (36). A striking feature of the bipolar synaptic terminal complex is that close to where an amacrine cell process receives input from a bipolar process, it often makes a reciprocal synapse back onto the bipolar. The inference has been drawn that this represents a feedback loop and an argument that gains control is accomplished at these points made (72).

Although at the ultrastructural level it appears that synapses made by one type of retinal neuron are basically the same in whatever retina studied, the overall shapes of any given class of retinal neuron, as determined by silver and methylene blue staining, are highly varied. In the outer plexiform layer, the extent and level of termination of bipolar and horizontal cell processes seen in the silver-stained cell is highly significant with respect to the kind and number of photoreceptors with which that cell connects (33, 37–40). But in the inner plexiform layer the meaning of the great diversity of cellular arborizations is not yet clear. One feature which has been studied is the extent of the ganglion cell dendritic arbor. In the rat (73) and the cat (74)

[3] Naka, K. reported at the Association for Research in Ophthalmology meeting, April 1970.

the measurements indicate that the dendritic tree is large enough only to subserve the central area of physiologically measured ganglion cell center-surround receptive fields. The importance of laterally oriented elements in the organization of the receptive-field surround is thereby emphasized. Amacrine cells are probably more closely involved with surround organization than are horizontal cells because they make synapses directly onto the ganglion cell. Secondly, synaptic contacts between amacrine processes have been found wherever sought (34–36, 53), whereas horizontal-horizontal cell synapses are prominent only in fish retinas (53, 54). The extent of the horizontal cell receptive field in the cat (64), for example, is clearly insufficient to mediate the far-periphery effect reported in that retina (75). Finally, ganglion cells are known only to receive synaptic input; they have never been identified as the presynaptic unit in a retinal synapse.

RESPONSES OF BIPOLAR AND AMACRINE CELLS

Whether bipolar cells generate spikes as well as slow potentials is not yet certain. In *Necturus* (20) and goldfish (43) they are reported to generate slow potentials only, and in these animals the recording electrodes were localized in bipolar cells by dye-deposit techniques. Clearly, without knowing the variety of amacrine cell responses, it is impossible to sort out which recorded voltages belong to bipolar cells, which to amacrines. A response definitely localized to the amacrine cell, elicited by a diffuse light flash, is: depolarizing transients at "on" and "off" upon which spikes may be superimposed (20). When the receptive field was mapped with small spots, a center-surround organization was revealed, center stimulation evoking an "on" transient, surround stimulation an "off" transient, or the reverse. Another group of amacrines fired at "on-off" irrespective of stimulus location in the field. Moving stimuli elicit a more complex response in that one sees an initial hyperpolarization when the spot enters the field of an "on" center cell and when it leaves the field of an "off" center unit (30). However, responses not clearly of the sustained (bipolar) or transient (amacrine) category discussed above are recorded from inner nuclear layer units in frog and carp retina (44, 76, 77). In one study where marking was attempted, the cells were not definitely localized but ganglion cells may reasonably be excluded as the source (78). The fact that the units did not respond to optic nerve stimulation supports this conclusion. It is noteworthy that in the frog, after spike blockage with tetrodotoxin, ganglion cells are reported to be still driven by light. The authors conclude that although bipolar cells may produce spikes, the graded potentials on which they ride are sufficient to stimulate the ganglion cell (76).

The functional role of amacrine cells is not yet clarified. Probably all ganglion cells receive partial synaptic input from amacrine cells; some may receive all synaptic input from them. Werblin (20, 30) has shown a close resemblance between the response form and receptive-field organization of certain amacrine and ganglion cells and suggests that amacrines play a principal role in organizing dynamic aspects of the visual stimulus. The fact that amacrines feed back onto bipolars at the point where the ganglion cell receives input from the bipolar suggests a role for amacrine cells in control of ganglion cell excitability in the center of the receptive field. It has been reported that all cat ganglion cells have a characteristic transient high-frequency burst which drops to a steady level when only the field center of "on"-center cells is stimulated (79, 80). One may speculate that the initial burst is in response to bipolar cell input. Shortly thereafter, amacrine feedback reduces the steady bipolar input to a lower level. During dark adaptation, the inhibitory surround is known to disappear. If this represents cessation of amacrine cell activity, then a weak central stimulus might evoke a sustained response, without an initial transient, i.e., bipolar excitation without amacrine inhibition. Such a response is in fact reported (80).

PHOTOCHEMISTRY AND RETINAL EXCITABILITY

Several recent studies have considered the relation between photopigment kinetics and retinal sensitivity (81–93). When some photopigment is bleached, neural thresholds rise; both photochemical and neural mechanisms are invoked to account for the loss in sensitivity. In the former category it is necessary to consider (*a*) production and decay of photoproducts and (*b*) loss and subsequent regeneration of photopigment. Neural mechanisms may involve change in sensitivity of individual neural elements or synapses or reorganization of neural complexes, e.g., the summation pool or the receptive field. The link between photochemical and neural changes is not always maintained. In patients with Oguchi's disease, after a bleach, rhodopsin regeneration proceeds at a normal rate while neural recovery is greatly delayed, compared to the normal observer (81).

The log of the final neural threshold following a change in photopigment level is proportional to the level of bleached pigment, in the rat (82, 84), frog (85), and skate (86), with either ERG b-wave or, except in the case of the frog (87), ganglion cell spike activity as the measure. Human psychophysical thresholds also follow this relation (88). It is unlikely that photoproducts play a role in threshold determination over most of the dark-adaptation function, since they have either completely decayed, or in the case of the vitamin A-deficient rat (94), not formed. In the very early stages of dark adaptation, however, very rapid threshold changes occur which cannot be explained by changes in the level of photopigment and whose nature is unknown. In an isolated retina, where no or little regeneration occurs, after bleaching, neural excitability changes over several log units before stabilizing (87). In the intermediate period of dark adaptation, when threshold was changing rapidly (between about 25 and 90 min in the frog), Donner & Reuter found that the simple relation log threshold = k conc. visual pigment did not hold (89). This led them to study photoproduct formation in rhodopsin rods (90, 91). On the basis of these studies they proposed that in the rapid phase of dark adaptation the presence of metarhodopsin II depressed sensitivity and in the later, slower phase it was the rate of rhodopsin regeneration that governed threshold. The latter factor has been shown to be inapplicable in the rat (82–84), skate (86), and human studies (92); and in the frog, their interpretation of photoproduct kinetics is disputed (93). Furthermore, their analysis does not consider a possible contribution from the accessory cone pigment whose maximum sensitivity, 502 nm, is exactly that of rhodopsin (95). However, although there are difficulties with their proposed mechanisms, their data taken together with (83) indicate that the quantitative aspects of adaptational mechanisms need not be identical in every vertebrate retina.

It is well known that large changes in neural excitability occur without appreciable bleaching of photopigment; in the increment threshold function, for example, threshold for seeing rises more than 4 log units above its absolute dark value before a loss of pigment is detectable. A critical thing to determine here is whether the receptor itself adapts, i.e., whether the ratio of the quanta absorbed to the neural signal changes when some pigment is bleached. This is not yet known. Rushton (88) has argued that receptors do not adapt on the basis of experiments with gratings, but his experiments have been repeated and contrary results obtained (96). Barlow (97, 98) proposed that the photoreceptor produces a dark current, equivalent to noise from which a superimposed signal must be extracted. This noise increases in the presence of bleached pigment, but it cannot be concluded that the increase is localized within the receptor. In the octopus receptor, with intracellular recordings, the response to a fixed light is shown to vary, depending on whether a preceding stimulus was bright or dim (18). Although very preliminary, this result indicates some receptor adaptation and similar studies of vertebrate receptors would be very welcome.

Response Properties of Ganglion Cells: Maintained Discharge

Several studies of maintained activity in cat retina in the dark sought to determine whether the activity was endogenous or synaptically activated, and what factors governed the rate of firing. Rodieck (99) concluded that the discharges are driven by photoreceptor transmitter release in the dark, because in absolute darkness the spike activity in three of five pairs of simultaneously recorded cells was weakly correlated. Also, the application of a drug toxic to the pigment epithelium, and hence secondarily so to rods, abolished maintained dark activity but did not completely eliminate light-driven spike firing. The supposition that photoreceptors leak transmitter in the dark is supported by the finding, in the horizontal cell, that conductance is relatively higher in the dark (46, 47).

When a steady background is turned on, after some initial fluctuation, the discharge of on-center units increases, that of off-center units decreases for dim lights (98–100). Stronger lights evoke complex firing patterns, in part due to activation of the receptive-field surround. A rare class of cells that code ambient luminance level via changes in steady firing rate, over a 4 log unit range, is reported in the cat (98), a property of ganglion cells (group V) reported previously in frog retina (101). Detection of a signal near threshold depends on distinguishing it from the noise of the maintained discharge. An elegant exposition of the elements which enter into this detection and the analytic procedures to isolate them is to be found in (102).

GANGLION CELL RECEPTIVE-FIELD ORGANIZATION

Many cat ganglion cell receptive fields are characterized by a concentric center-surround organization. If stimulus conditions are carefully selected to stimulate the central region alone, a characteristic transient burst of spikes which decays to a steady frequency is found for all on-center cells, as already mentioned. Summation within the central area of these cells obeys Ricco's law (area × intensity = k), whether tested with increasing concentric disks or disparate spots. The sensitivity profile of the center is characterized by a central plateau, 0.1°–2.5° in diameter, with exponentially falling sides. Field adaptation studied by the product of area × intensity required to depress the response to a small central flash by a constant amount defines an area equal to the central area of summation, but is not more effective when it encroaches upon the inhibitory surround (79). Why this is so is not entirely clear, since an annular field alone does depress the response to a central flash (103). It was further shown (104) that the gain and latency of the central response depend on the total flux of background plus stimulus falling within the central area of summation. If stimuli are chosen which stimulate surround or center alone, then when they are simultaneously flashed, the net output of the ganglion cell is the algebraic sum of the individual center and surround responses (105). As a first approximation, interaction between center and surround is also linear for phase-locked modulating lights, in cat ganglion cells (106–109). As in Limulus eye (110), nonphase-locked center and surround stimuli can interact to produce dampened or accentuated response modulation, depending on the phase angle.

The linear summation manifested in cat ganglion cell field centers is not found for the goldfish, although Ricco's law holds for concentric stimuli of different diameters. The excitation produced by two small, equally bright spots simultaneously flashed in the receptive-field center was more than that produced by one spot at twice the intensity. The data fit the function—excitation $E = kI^n$, where n is 0.55 (111). In the same retina, the effectiveness of a steady background in suppressing a central response was greatest when the background and test spots were superimposed. Larger backgrounds concentric with the spot were more effective within limits that defined the area of the adaptation pool (112). As in the cat, these limits were not equivalent to the receptive-field size. The ganglion cell membrane thus seems to be the locus of addition of excitatory and inhibitory influences, which may arrive via separate pathways. However, the complexities of retinal circuitry already discussed indicate that the degree of excitation reaching the ganglion cell center is extensively modulated by preganglionic interactions.

MIXING OF PHOTORECEPTOR INPUTS AT THE GANGLION CELL

The same ganglion cell often receives input from both rod and cone pathways (113). It can be shown that both receptor types contribute to a threshold response function, such as spectral sensitivity, in the mesopic state (114). In the primate, when the stimulus is suprathreshold for both rods and cones, the cones preempt the channel because the cone-triggered response has a shorter latency (115). In the goldfish retina, however, the shift from a scotopic to a photopic retina involves a delay of many minutes during which no response can be elicited from the ganglion cell. When the retina is well dark-adapted, bright stimuli evoke rod-triggered responses even though stimulus strength is above cone threshold (116). Long periods of neural inactivity following the presentation of bright adapting fields are also reported in an elasmobranch (86).

Mixing of cone inputs at the ganglion cell is a more complex situation. In general these inputs add: nonopponent cells, or subtract: opponent cells. In opponent cells the spatial distribution of the cone mechanisms may be different (117). In the ground squirrel *Citellus* all opponent cells are blue (λ_{max} at 460 nm) and green (λ_{max} at 525 nm) cone driven, but three subclasses are found (118). Class I cells have no center-surround organization; green fires the cell at "on," blue at "off" or the reverse and these mechanisms are antagonistic and have identical spatial distributions. A similar receptive-field organization is reported in a marine fish (119). In class II cells the green cone mechanism is confined to a small center, the blue to a larger concentric area. The response to blue is always either "on" or "off" wherever evoked. In class III cells, green is confined to the center and blue to the surround and these mechanisms evoke opposite and antagonistic responses.

On the other hand, in the goldfish retina are found opponent cells in which a given cone mechanism elicits opposite responses with center or surrround stimulation (117). Although opponent cells with an organization like class II cells above have been reported with small spot stimulation, the use of annular stimuli revealed that the majority of cells have red "on", green "off" firing in the center, red "off", green "on" firing in the periphery, or the reverse. With appropriate stimuli, center and surround are antagonistic to themselves and each other. The most effective stimulus is a central spot of one color and an annulus of another; this cell is therefore appropriate to mediate simultaneous color contrast (117, 120). A variant of this receptive-field organization is seen in which one cone mechanism in both center and surround is suppressed by the other, but can be uncovered by appropriate chromatic adaptation.

In the primate retina, a class of cells is described which fire tonically to maintained stimuli and which appear to be driven by one of three cone classes (121). The spectral sensitivities of these cells agree well with the difference spectrum maxima of primate yellow-, green-, and violet-sensitive pigments (122). The mechanisms were isolated by chromatic adaptation which suppressed an antagonistic surround driven by a different cone class from that giving the central response. As no cells were studied with a dark background or a chromatically neutral white light background, it is possible that two cone classes contribute to the central response, one of whose sensitivity was reduced by the adapting field. Phasic cells are described which sum information from red and green cones; these presumably signal brightness. Phasic cells conduct their message to the CNS faster than tonic ones (123). It is tempting to assume that the information relayed to the center of tonic cells is carried by the midget or flat midget bipolar cells decsribed in the primate (37, 39, 40). Information about the dark-adaptation properties of these units would thus be useful in deciding whether these ganglion cells are fed by a single class of bipolars, since the midget bipolars connect only to cones (39). Gouras (personal communication) could follow two such cells lying close to the fovea, and found that they did not manifest rod input upon dark adaptation.

Cats have a weak color sense which has been measured behaviorally. An initial investigation found only one cone class (λ_{max} at 556 nm), suggesting that color discrimination depended on rods and cones interacting (124). More work revealed that (a) the cat discriminates colors when rods are saturated and (b) a rare class of opponent cells (λ_{max} at 450, 556 nm) is present in the lateral geniculate nucleus (125).

SPECIALIZED GANGLION CELL RECEPTIVE FIELDS

Careful study of the response properties of ganglion cells has uncovered specialized coding properties of these retinal elements, in addition to the commonly encountered concentric center-surround field. Rabbit retina is particularly rich in this respect. Besides the ambient luminance detectors and directionally sensitive elements already mentioned, three additional types are described (126). *Orientation detectors,* when studied with flashing spots, have excitatory and inhibitory fields separated by a line, similar to the simple fields of cat and monkey cortex. These fields have either vertical or horizontal orientation. *Local-edge detectors* respond to a contrast stimulus in the center of the field, e.g., a grating. The central response is reduced by the presentation of a contrast stimulus in the surround, although stimulation of the surround alone is ineffective. Ground squirrel contrast detectors share some of the properties of rabbit local-edge detectors (127). *Uniformity detectors* manifest a steady discharge which is tonically inhibited, never increased, by a stimulus anywhere in the field. The receptive field of these cells has no antagonistic surround. In contrast to most rabbit ganglion cells, an effective stimulus for this class of cells need not have a precise form or orientation. A similar cell type is reported in the cat retina (128). Spinelli (129) has studied discharge characteristics of cat ganglion cells by sequential presentation of lights arranged in a grid. Receptive fields other than the typical concentric type have been isolated, for example, *bar detectors,* like the rabbit orientation detector, and fields with incomplete surrounds.

Ganglion cells responding selectively to certain directions of movement are found in many vertebrate retinas. In rabbit, the preferred axes of movement are in the horizontal and vertical planes, corresponding to the eye movements produced by contraction of the rectus muscles (130, 131). The property of motion selectivity cannot be directly inferred from the receptive field mapped with flashing lights. Two kinds of fields are found: one that fires at "on" and "off" to a spot flashed anywhere in the field, with no inhibitory surround, and another that fires at "on" to a central flash, "off" to a peripheral one. In rabbit, the former are responsive to faster stimulus speeds than the latter (131).

As shown earlier for the rabbit, ground squirrel directional units fire to two spots flashed sequentially anywhere in the receptive field when separated by a small distance (5' to 15') and flashed in the sequence corresponding to movement in the preferred axis (132). The presence of sequence discrimination in small subunits evenly distributed throughout the field suggested that excitation is carried by bipolar cells which are inhibited by stimulus motion in the null direction. Horizontal cells have been invoked for the inhibitory function (132, 133), though, given that amacrine cells also synapse onto bipolars, amacrines might be the mediator of inhibition. Evidence bearing on this point comes from studies of motion sensitivity in preganglionic units (30, 77). Receptors, horizontal cells, and bipolar cells show no preference to direction of stimulus motion in frog and *Necturus* retinas. Some units, unidentified as to cell type, responded with transients when the stimulus entered or left the field and these transients had different waveforms depending on the stimulus direction. However, clear preferred or null directions were not evident. It was concluded that there is no evidence to support establishment of motion selectivity in the outer plexiform layer and that this function was most likely accomplished at the level of the inner plexiform layer.

Motion-sensitive cells are described in frog retina which do not discriminate direction of movement. The factors which influence the firing of these cells have been studied in great detail. Stimulus size, contrast, and velocity were varied systematically and a number of descriptive equations generated which relate neuronal response to the given parameters (134–139).

THE EFFECT OF DRUGS ON RETINAL GANGLION CELLS

This section concerns studies bearing on putative transmitters in the retina. There is abundant evidence for the presence of adrenergic substances in the retina. In the rabbit retina, L-glutamic decarboxylase, which forms GABA from glutamate, and GABA itself, are found (140). Assays of crudely separated retinal fractions show highest activity in the ganglion cell and inner plexiform layer fraction. The fluorescence staining technique shown to be specific for dopamine or norepinephrine (NE) has been applied to many vertebrate retinas (141–145). Dopamine is the identified substance in most cases, NE in a few cells. The fluorescing cells are most often types of amacrine cells. However, some of these cells have ascending processes which terminate near the receptor bases, a feature seldom or never revealed in silver-stained material, depending on the species. Processes in the outer plexiform layer also fluoresce in certain animals. Consistent with the localization of catecholamines by fluorescence is the presence of dense-cored vesicles in horizontal and amacrine cells (34–36, 53, 146). In other tissues, these vesicles have been depleted by reserpine and restored by the administration of catecholamine precursors. The addition of catecholamines (GABA, NE, L-dopa) topically onto the retinal surface or into the circulation in general causes inhibition of light-induced and spontaneous activity and the prolongation of "on" and "off" inhibition in the cat (147, 148); in the rabbit, NE and dopa decreased "on" activity, but increased "off" firing (149).

Evidence for cholinergic transmission in the retina is the presence of specific acetylcholine esterase in the plexiform layers (150, 151) and the effects of acetylcholine (ACh) on ganglion cell activity. In general, at the lowest effective dose, ACh increases spontaneous activity and the light evoked response of "on" cells (148, 149, 152). Physostigmine potentiates this action and atropine antagonizes it. Many "on" cells, however, are unaffected by ACh (148). By analogy with other systems, it is reasonable to think that ACh is contained in the agranular vesicles seen accumulated on the presumed presynaptic side of retinal synapses, though these vesicles may, of course, contain another transmitter in any given case. Some horizontal and amacrine cells would thus appear on indirect evidence to contain at least two transmitters, since they sometimes possess both agranular and dense-cored vesicles. Finally, certain amino acids have an excitatory, e.g. glutamate, or inhibitory, e.g. alanine, effect on ganglion cell light-evoked responses, and excitatory and inhibitory amino acids negate each other when added in combination (153, 154). Kishida & Naka (154) raise the intriguing possibility that retinal synaptic transmission may be altered metabolically by a change in amino acid levels.

ORIGIN OF ELECTRORETINOGRAM COMPONENTS

The ERG recorded with gross electrodes is a polyphasic waveform whose basic components are named, in order of appearance, a, b, c, and d waves. The a, b and c waves derive from components of different polarity and time course called PIII, PII and PI, respectively, which sum to give the gross ERG. At present it appears that the d-wave results from PIII and PII interaction (155) and will not be further considered.

Intraretinally recorded, focal ERGs manifest components not reflected in the gross ERG. Some of the difficulties in interpreting intraretinal ERGs are discussed (156, 157). This section reviews the recent work on ERG fractionation and the localization of ERG components in responses of particular retinal cells.

In mammals, following clamping of the retinal circulation, a microelectrode situated close to the fovea or area centralis registers a graded sustained wave, similar in form and polarity to the PIII isolated previously by drug or anoxia treatment. This wave is called the late receptor potential (158). Its properties can be related to those of rod and cone systems under appropriate conditions of adaptation and stimulation (155, 158). Depth fractionation of PIII was accomplished by a combination of coaxial recording and drug treatment. One pair of coaxial electrodes recorded the potential between the distal tips of the receptors and a point 100–120 μ proximal to them; a second pair registered the potential developed between the inner pipette of the first pair and a vitreal reference (159–161). In the untreated eye, PIII is recorded between the first pair; a complex wave, mainly reflecting PII, is registered between the second electrode pair. Ammonia vapor treatment removes PII, revealing an underlying wave with a PIII-like response. The two PIII components are termed distal and proximal PIII (159). Distal PIII is almost certainly generated by the photoreceptors because (a) its form and polarity are consistent with intracellular recordings of photoreceptor responses and with the analyses of photoreceptor currents already discussed, (b) the extracellular recording site, particularly in (24), is localized to the receptor region, and (c) PIII latency in rat retina is as brief as 300 μsec, supporting a receptor origin (162). The proximal PIII may arise in horizontal cells, given the resemblance between its waveform and that of intracellular records from those cells, but this identity is not yet established.

PII has long been localized to the inner nuclear layer. The radial orientation of the bipolar cells has made them a prime candidate for PII generation, since PII undergoes a polarity reversal within the inner nuclear layer, yet intracellular records from bipolar cells are sustained waves of either polarity (in *Necturus*), whereas PII is not sustained. In *Necturus,* hyperpolarizing and depolarizing bipolars are found with about equal frequency, a fact suggesting that in the gross extracellular record they would tend to cancel, yet *Necturus* has a prominent typical b-wave. In a recent microelectrode study (163) intracellular responses closely resembling the b-wave in latency, waveform, and threshold were localized to the Muller fiber by dye deposition. The Muller fiber is a glial cell on morphological grounds, so that it is pertinent to compare the b-wave to glial cell responses recorded in *Necturus* optic nerve (164). There it was shown that the glial cell membrane depolarized in proportion to a decrease in the ratio K_i^+/K_o^+ across it, induced by potassium efflux from neurons following stimulation. The time course of this depolarization resembles the b-wave in an approximate way. The Muller fiber response does not follow flickering light above 2–3/sec; the extracellular b-wave follows to 18/sec. The authors argue (163) that it is PIII which follows rapid flicker and this is superimposed on a slow b-wave. Intracellular records resembling a b-wave obtained from frog retina were attributed to "slow bipolars", but the cells in question were not localized histologically (165).

If it may be generally concluded that the vertebrate retinal b-wave is a glial cell response (and more work will be required to establish this), then it becomes of great interest to know why the b-wave is such a good indicator of not only retinal sensitivity, but psychophysically determined thresholds as well. To begin with, the amplitude vs log intensity function of the b-wave operates over a greater range of intensities than that of single retinal neurons (17, 20). This might be reconciled by supposing that the retina contains a mixed population of receptors with the same V vs log I function, but shifted along the intensity axis. Different rod and cone dynamic ranges can provide this, for example. The b-wave would reflect the summed output of all responding neurons at any given intensity. A further and more critical problem is that the b-wave, ganglion cell, and psychophysical increment-threshold functions are all linear on a log-log plot, for more than 6 log units, whereas receptor and horizontal cell functions saturate within 2–3 or fewer log units of threshold. A partial resolution of this dilemma is seen in Werblin's analysis of the bipolar response in *Necturus* (20). At any strength background, a stronger central light will produce a bipolar cell response. The upper limit of the increment-threshold function for the retina will then depend on the saturation of the least sensitive receptor subset to which some bipolars connect. The increment-threshold function for a given ganglion cell will be determined partially by the classes of bipolar cells providing excitation in the center of the field and by the degree to which an antagonistic surround is activated. If these arguments apply, the correspondence between b-wave and ganglion cell functions may be fortuitous, the b-wave depending on, say, potassium leakage from a nonspecific group of retinal neurons and the ganglion cell output being a function of a precise balance between excitation and inhibition in a particular group of neurons innervating it.[4]

The dc component is a graded response recorded by a microelectrode situated in the inner nuclear layer (166). It can be distinguished from the b-wave because it is sustained. Furthermore, the amplitude-intensity function of the cat dc component is much steeper than that of the b-wave (167), rising from 10 to 100% of maximum in about 1.5 log units—similar to the same function for bipolar cells in *Necturus* (20). On the basis of the available evidence it seems to be an extracellular marker of bipolar cell responses.

Amacrine cells do not contribute to the gross ERG. However, an extra-

---

[4] The problem of reconciling the amplitude vs intensity functions of retinal neurons with that of the b-wave has received experimental attention. Werblin, F. presented at the Association for Research in Ophthalmology meeting, April 1970 and Adaptation in the vertebrate retina: Intracellular recording in *Necturus*, in manuscript, 1970.

cellular reflection of their response, called the proximal negative response, has been recorded with a microelectrode located in the vicinity of the inner nuclear—inner plexiform layer border, as judged by depth measurements. On and off transients are seen which are similar to the intracellularly recorded amacrine response in response to a light flash (168). The proximal negative response is easily differentiated from the b-wave as it is highly focal, has a different amplitude vs intensity function, and has a distinctly different waveform.

The PI component had previously been localized to the pigment epithelium. A corroborating report assigns intracellular records to the pigment epithelium layer using physiological markers (169). Slow potentials which greatly outlast the stimulus are seen, with rise and fall time constants of 750–800 msec. The agreement in time course between intracellular response and extracellular b-wave is very good. The response depends on light absorption by rhodopsin as its spectral sensitivity function corresponds well with a rhodopsin absorption curve and it does not undergo a Purkinje shift upon light adaptation. Although the pigment epithelium contains some rhodopsin, the c-wave is probably triggered by rod quantum capture since the isolated pigment epithelium does not give a c-wave and the calculated screening effect which would result if quanta had to pass through the rod outer segments to the pigment epithelium is not observed (170).

EFFERENT INNERVATION OF THE RETINA

The functional role of efferent or centrifugal fibers in retinal physiology is still unknown. The only efferent system thoroughly described in anatomical terms is that innervating pigeon retina (171). In the pigeon, electrical stimulation of the optic nerve gives rise to antidromic impulses in efferent fibers that collide with spikes elicited by stimulation of the isthmooptic nucleus (172). Myelinated efferent fibers which make synapses onto amacrine and bipolar cells have been described in fish retinas.[5] Space limitations prohibit a discussion of possible efferent function, based on indirect evidence, but an excellent review is available (173).

[5] Witkovsky, P. reported at the Association for Research in Ophthalmology meeting, April 1970.

LITERATURE CITED

1. Subcortical visual systems. 1970. *J. Brain, Behavior and Evolution,* ed. D. Ingle. G. E. Schneider. In press

2. Brindley, G. S. 1970. Central pathways of vision. *Ann. Rev. Physiol.* 32: 259–68

3. Bridges, C. D. B. 1967. Biochemistry of visual processes. *Compr. Biochem.* 27:31–78

4. Abrahamson, E. W., Ostroy, S. E. 1967. The photochemical and macromolecular aspects of vision. *Progr. Biophys. Mol. Biol.* 17: 179–215

5. Bonting, S. L. 1969. The mechanism of the visual process. *Curr. Topics Bioenerg.* 3:351–415

6. Spector, A. 1970. Annual Review: Physiological chemistry of the eye. *Arch. Ophthal.* 83:506–22

7. Bouman, M. A. 1969. My image of the retina. *Quart. Rev. Biophys.* 2:25–64

8. Alpern, M. 1968. Distal mechanisms of vertebrate color vision. *Ann. Rev. Physiol.* 30:279–318

9. Baker, H. D., Baker, B. N. 1970. Visual sensitivity. *Ann. Rev. Psychol.* 21:307–38

10. Ripps, H., Weale, R. A. 1969. Color vision. *Ann. Rev. Psychol.* 20:193–216

11. Ripps, H., Weale, R. A. 1970. The photophysiology of vertebrate color vision. *Photophysiology* 5:127–64

12. Jacobs, G. H. 1969. Receptive fields in visual systems. *Brain Res.* 14: 553–73

13. Creutzfeldt, O., Sakmann, B. 1969. Neurophysiology of vision. *Ann. Rev. Physiol.* 31:499–544

14. Perkins, E. S., Ed. 1970. *Recent Research on the retina. Brit. Med. Bull.* 26:No. 2

15. Lolley, R. N. 1969. Metabolic and anatomical specialization within the retina. In *Handbook of Neurochemistry,* Vol. 2, *Structural Neurochemistry,* ed. A. Lajtha, 473–504. New York: Plenum

16. Straatsma, B. R., Hall, M. O., Allen, R. A., Crescitelli, F., Eds. 1970. *The Retina: Morphology, Function and Clinical Characteristics.* Berkeley: Univ. California Press, 630 pp.

17. Tomita, T., Kaneko, A., Murakami, M., Pautler, E. L. 1967. Spectral response curves of single cones in the carp. *Vision Res.* 7:519–31

18. Tomita, T. 1968. Electrical response of single photoreceptors. *Proc. IEEE* 56:1015–23

19. Tomita, T. 1970. Electrical activity of vertebrate photoreceptors. *Quart. Rev. Biophys.* 3:179–222

20. Werblin, F. S., Dowling, J. E. 1969. Organization of the retina of the mudpuppy, *Necturus maculosus.* II. Intracellular recording. *J. Neurophysiol.* 32:339–55

21. Toyoda, J., Nosaki, H., Tomita, T. 1969. Light-induced resistance changes in single photoreceptors of Necturus and Gekko. *Vision Res.* 9:453–63

22. Baylor, D. A., Fuortes, M. G. F. 1970. Electrical responses of single cones in the retina of the turtle. *J. Physiol. (London)* 207:77–92

23. Kaneko, A., Hashimoto, H. 1967. Recording site of the single cone response determined by an electrode marking technique. *Vision Res.* 7: 847–52

24. Penn, R. D., Hagins, W. A. 1969. Signal transmission along retinal rods and the origin of the electroretinographic a-wave. *Nature* 223: 201–5

25. Yoshikami, S., Hagins, W. A. 1970. Ionic basis of dark current and photocurrent of retinal rods. *Biophys. Soc. Abstr.* WPM-13

26. Arden, G. B., Ernst, W. 1969. Mechanism of current production found in pigeon cones but not in pigeon or rat rods. *Nature* 223: 528–31

27. Sillman, A. J., Ito, H., Tomita, T. 1969. Studies on the mass receptor potential of the isolated frog retina. I. General properties of the response. *Vision Res.* 9:1435–42

28. Sillman, A. J., Ito, H., Tomita, T. 1969. Studies on the mass receptor potential of the isolated frog retina. II. On the basis of the ionic mechanism. *Vision Res.* 9:1443–52

29. Muntz, W. R. A., Northmore, D. P. M., Pragnell, V. 1969. Increment thresholds in photopic conditions in the hooded rat. *Nature* 223:1280–81

30. Werblin, F. S. 1970. Response of retinal cells to moving spots: intracellular recording in *Necturus maculosus*. *J. Neurophysiol.* 33:342–50

31. Liebman, P. A., Entine, G. 1964. Sensitive low-light-level microspectrophotometer: detection of photosensitive pigments of retinal cones. *J. Opt. Soc. Am.* 54:1451–59

32. Marks, W. B. 1965. Visual pigments of single goldfish cones. *J. Physiol. (London)* 178:14–32

33. Stell, W. K. 1967. The structure and relationships of horizontal cells and photoreceptor-bipolar synaptic complexes in goldfish retina. *Am. J. Anat.* 121:401–23

34. Dowling, J. E., Boycott, B. B. 1966. Organization of the primate retina: electron microscopy. *Proc. Roy. Soc. B* 166:80–111

35. Dowling, J. E., Werblin, F. 1969. Organization of retina of the mudpuppy, *Necturus maculosus*. I. Synaptic structure. *J. Neurophysiol.* 32:315–38

36. Dowling, J. E. 1968. Synaptic organization of the frog retina: an electron microscopic analysis comparing the retinas of frogs and primates. *Proc. Roy. Soc. B* 170: 205–28

37. Kolb, H. 1970. Organization of the outer plexiform layer of the primate retina: Electron microscopy of Golgi-impregnated cells. *Phil. Trans. Roy. Soc. B* 258:22 pp.

38. Missotten, L. 1970. The synaptic relations of visual cells and neurons in the human retina, studied with electron microscopy after silver impregnation. In manuscript

39. Boycott, B. B., Dowling, J. E. 1969. The primate retina: light microscopy. *Phil. Trans. Roy. Soc. B* 255:109–76.

40. Kolb, H., Boycott, B. B., Dowling, J. E. 1969. A second type of midget bipolar cell in the primate retina. *Phil. Trans. Roy. Soc. B* 255:177–81

41. Parthe, V. 1967. Horizontal and amacrine cells of the retina. *Acta Cient. Venez.* 18:240–49

42. Lasansky, A. 1969. Basal junctions at the synaptic endings of turtle visual cells. *J. Cell Biol.* 40:577–86

43. Kaneko, A. 1970. Physiological and morphological identification of horizontal, bipolar and amacrine cells in goldfish retina. *J. Physiol. (London)* 207:623–33

44. Kaneko, A., Hashimoto, H. 1969. Electrophysiological study of single neurons in the inner nuclear layer of the carp retina. *Vision Res.* 9:37–56

45. Steinberg, R. H., Schmidt, R. 1970. Identification of horizontal cells as S-potential generators in the cat retina by intracellular dye injection. *Vision Res.* In press

46. Byzov, A. L., Trifonov, Yu. A. 1968. The response to electric stimulation of horizontal cells in the carp retina. *Vision Res.* 8:817–22

47. Trifonov, Yu. A. 1968. Study of synaptic transmission between photoreceptor and horizontal cell by electrical stimulation of the retina. *Biofizika* 13:809–17

48. Tomita, T. 1965. Mechanisms subserving color coding. *Cold Spring Harbor Symp. Quant. Biol.* 30: 559–66

49. Norton, A. L., Spekreijse, H., Wolbarsht, M. L., Wagner, H. G. 1968. Receptive field organization of the S-potential. *Science* 160: 1021–22

50. Negishi, K. 1968. Excitation spread along horizontal and amacrine cell layers in the teleost retina. *Nature* 218:39–40

51. Negishi, K., Sutija, V. 1969. Lateral spread of light-induced potentials along different cell layers in the teleost retina. *Vision Res.* 9:881–94

52. Naka, K. I., Rushton, W. A. H. 1967. The generation and spread of S-potential in fish (Cyprinidae). *J. Physiol. (London)* 192:437–62

53. Witkovsky, P., Dowling, J. E. 1969. Synaptic relationships in the plexiform layers of carp retina. *Z. Zellforsch.* 100:60–82

54. Yamada, E., Ishikawa, T. 1965. Fine structure of the horizontal cells in some vertebrate retinae. *Cold Spring Harbor Symp. Quant. Biol.* 30:383–92

55. Brightman, M. W., Reese, T. S. 1969. Junctions between intimately apposed cell membranes in the vertebrate brain. *J. Cell Biol.* 40:648–77

56. Kaneko, A. 1970. Electrical connections between horizontal cells in the dogfish retina. In manuscript

57. Naka, K. I., Rushton, W. A. H. 1968. S-potential and dark-adaptation in

fish. *J. Physiol. (London)* 194: 259–69

58. Pautler, E. L. 1967. Directional sensitivity of isolated turtle retinas. *J. Opt. Soc. Am.* 52:1267–69

59. Pautler, E. L. 1970. Analysis of the L-type S-potential by means of the Stiles-Crawford effect in the carp retina. *Experientia* 26:274

60. Naka, K. I., Rushton, W. A. H. 1966. An attempt to analyze colour reception by electrophysiology. *J. Physiol. (London)* 185:536–55

61. Maksimova, E. M., Maksimov, V. V. 1969. Saturation of S-potentials of fish retina. The L-type reaction. *Biofizika* 14:731–39

62. Maksimova, E. M., Maksimov, V. V. 1969. Saturation of S-potentials of fish retina. Biocomponent reactions. *Biofizika* 14:905–13

63. Naka, K. I. 1969. Computer assisted analysis of S-potentials. *Biophys. J.* 9:845–59

64. Steinberg, R. H. 1969. Rod and cone contributions to S-potentials from the cat retina. *Vision Res.* 9:1319–30

65. Steinberg, R. H. 1969. Rod-cone interaction in S-potentials from the cat retina. *Vision Res.* 9:1331–44

66. Steinberg, R. H. 1969. The rod aftereffect in S-potentials from the cat retina. *Vision Res.* 9:1345–56

67. Witkovsky, P. 1967. A comparison of ganglion cell and S-potential response properties in carp retina. *J. Neurophysiol.* 30:546–61

68. Maksimova, E. M. 1969. The effect of intracellular polarization of horizontal cells on the activity of ganglion cells of fish retina. *Biofizika* 14:537–44. *Neuroscience Translations* 11:114–20

69. Radnót, M., Lovas, B. 1967. Die Ultrastruktur der Synapsen der inneren plexiformen Schicht der Netzhaut. *Acta Ophthal.* 167:566–68

70. Raviola, G., Raviola, E. 1967. Light and electron microscopic observations on the inner plexiform layer of the rabbit retina. *Am. J. Anat.* 120:403–26

71. Allen, R. A. 1970. The retinal bipolar cells and their synapses in the inner plexiform layer. In *The Retina; Morphology, Function and Clinical Characteristics*, ed. B. R. Straatsma, M. O. Hall, R. A. Allen, F. Crescitelli, 101–43.

Berkeley: Univ. California Press. 630 pp.

72. Dowling, J. E. 1967. The site of visual adaptation. *Science* 155:273–79

73. Brown, J. E., Major, D. 1966. Retinal ganglion cell dendritic fields. *Exp. Neurol.* 15:70–78

74. Leicester, J., Stone, J. 1967. Ganglion, amacrine and horizontal cells of the cat's retina. *Vision Res.* 7:695–706

75. McIlwain, J. T. 1966. Some evidence concerning the physiological basis of the periphery effect in the cat's retina. *Exp. Brain Res.* 1:265–71

76. Murakami, M., Shigematsu, Y. 1970. Duality of conduction mechanism in bipolar cells of the frog retina. *Vision Res.* 10:1–10

77. Norton, A. L., Spekreijse, H., Wagner, H. G., Wolbarsht, M. L. 1970. Responses to directional stimuli in retinal preganglionic unit. *J. Physiol. (London)* 206:93–108

78. Kaneko, A., Hashimoto, H. 1968. Localization of spike producing cells in the frog retina. *Vision Res.* 8:259–62

79. Cleland, B. G., Enroth-Cugell, C. 1970. Quantitative aspects of gain and latency in the cat retina. *J. Physiol. (London)* 206:73–92

80. Stone, J., Fabian, M. 1968. Summing properties of the cat's retinal ganglion cell. *Vision Res.* 8:1023–40

81. Carr, R. E., Ripps, H. 1967. Rhodopsin kinetics and rod adaptation in Oguchi's disease. *Invest. Ophthal.* 6:426–36

82. Frank, R. N., Dowling, J. E. 1968. Rhodopsin photoproducts: effects on ERG sensitivity in isolated perfused rat retina. *Science* 161:487–89

83. Weinstein, G. W. 1969. Electroretinographic and ganglion cell sensitivity in the isolated rat retina. *Ophthalmology* 158:691–99

84. Weinstein, G. W., Hobson, R. R., Dowling, J. E. 1967. Light and dark adaptation in the isolated rat retina. *Nature* 215:134–38

85. Baumann, Ch. 1967. Sehpurpurbleichung und Stäbchenfunktion in der Isolierten Frosch netzhaut. III. Die Dunkeladaptation des Skotopische systems nach partieller Sehpurpurbleichung. *Pflügers Arch.* 298:70–81

86. Dowling, J. E., Ripps, H. 1970.

Visual adaptation in the retina of the skate. *J. Gen. Physiol.* In press

87. Baumann, Ch., Scheibner, H. 1968. The dark adaptation of single units in the isolated frog retina following partial bleaching of rhodopsin. *Vision Res.* 8:1127–38

88. Rushton, W. A. H. 1965. Visual adaptation. *Proc. Roy. Soc. B* 162:20–46

89. Donner, K. O., Reuter, T. 1965. The dark adaptation of single units in the frog's retina and its relation to the regeneration of rhodopsin. *Vision Res.* 5:615–32

90. Donner, K. O., Reuter, T. 1967. Dark-adaptation processes in the rhodopsin rods of the frog's retina. *Vision Res.* 7:17–41

91. Donner, K. O., Reuter, T. 1968. Visual adaptation of the rhodopsin rods in the frog's retina. *J. Physiol. (London)* 199:59–87

92. Rushton, W. A. H., Fulton, A. B., Baker, H. D. 1969. Dark adaptation and the rate of pigment regeneration. *Vision Res.* 9:1473–80

93. Frank, R. N. 1969. Photoproducts of rhodopsin bleaching in the isolated, perfused frog retina. *Vision Res.* 9:1415–34

94. Dowling, J. E. 1964. Nutritional and inherited blindness in the rat. *Exp. Eye Res.* 3:348–56

95. Liebman, P. A., Entine, G. 1968. Visual pigments of frog and tadpole (Rana pipiens). *Vision Res.* 8:761–76

96. Barlow, H. B., Andrews, D. P. 1967. Sensitivity of receptors and receptor "pools". *J. Opt. Soc. Am.* 57:837–38

97. Barlow, H. B. 1964. The physical limits of visual discrimination. *Photophysiology,* ed. A. C. Giese, II:163–202. New York and London: Academic

98. Barlow, H. B., Levick, W. R. 1969. Changes in the maintained discharge with adaptation level in the retina. *J. Physiol. (London)* 202:699–718

99. Rodieck, R. W. 1967. Maintained activity of cat retinal ganglion cells. *J. Neurophysiol.* 30:1043–71

100. Sakmann, B., Creutzfeldt, O. D. 1969. Scotopic and mesopic light adaptation in the cat's retina. *Pflügers Arch.* 313:168–85

101. Lettvin, J. Y., Maturana, H. R., Pitts, W. H., McCulloch, W. S. 1961.

Two remarks on the visual system of the frog. In *Sensory Communications,* ed. W. A. Rosenblith, 754–76. MIT Press and Wiley, New York

102. Barlow, H. B., Levick, W. R. 1969. Three factors limiting the reliable detection of light by retinal ganglion cells of the cat. *J. Physiol. (London)* 200:1–24

103. Sakmann, B., Creutzfeldt, O., Scheich, H. 1969. An experimental comparison between the ganglion cell receptive field and the receptive field of the adaptation pool in the cat retina. *Pflügers Arch.* 307:133–37

104. Cleland, B. G., Enroth-Cugell, C. 1968. Quantitative aspects of sensitivity and summation in the cat retina. *J. Physiol. (London)* 198:17–38

105. Enroth-Cugell, C., Pinto, L. 1970. Algebraic summation of centre and surround inputs to retinal ganglion cells of the cat. *Nature* 226:458–59

106. Maffei, L. 1968. Inhibitory and facilitatory spatial interactions in retinal receptive fields. *Vision Res.* 8:1187–94.

107. Maffei, L., Cervetto, L., Fiorentini, A. 1970. Transfer characteristics of excitation and inhibition in cat retinal ganglion cells. *J. Neurophysiol.* 33:276–84

108. Maffei, L., Cervetto, L. 1968. Dynamic interactions in retinal receptive fields. *Vision Res.* 8:1299–1304

109. Maffei, L. 1968. Spatial and temporal average in retinal channels. *J. Neurophysiol.* 31:283–87

110. Ratliff, F., Knight, B. W., Graham, N. 1969. On tuning and amplification by lateral inhibition. *Proc. Nat. Acad. Sci.* 62:733–40

111. Easter, S. S. 1968. Excitation in the goldfish retina: evidence for a non-linear intensity code. *J. Physiol. (London)* 195:253–71

112. Easter, S. S. 1968. Adaptation in the goldfish retina. *J. Physiol. (London)* 195:273–81

113. Steinberg, R. H. 1969. High intensity effects on slow potentials and ganglion cell activity in the area centralis of cat retina. *Vision Res.* 9:317–31

114. Donner, K. O., Rushton, W. A. H. 1959. Rod-cone interaction in the

frog's retina analyzed by the Stiles-Crawford effect and by dark adaptation. *J. Physiol. (London)* 149 :303–17

115. Gouras, P. 1967. The effects of light-adaptation on rod and cone receptive field organization of monkey ganglion cells. *J. Physiol. (London)* 192 :747–60

116. Raynauld, J. P. 1969. *Rod and cone responses of ganglion cells in goldfish retina: a microelectrode study.* PhD thesis, Johns Hopkins Univ.

117. Daw, N. W. 1968. Colour-coded ganglion cells in the goldfish retina: extension of their receptive fields by means of new stimuli. *J. Physiol. (London)* 197 :567–92

118. Michael, C. R. 1968. Receptive fields of single optic nerve fibers in a mammal with an all cone retina. III. Opponent color units. *J. Neurophysiol.* 31 :268–82

119. Hammond, P. 1968. Spectral properties of dark-adapted retinal ganglion cells in the plaice (Pleuronectes platessa, L.). *J. Physiol. (London)* 195 :535–56

120. Daw, N. W. 1967. Goldfish retina: organization for simultaneous color contrast. *Science* 158 :942–44

121. Gouras, P. 1968. Identification of cone mechanisms in monkey ganglion cells. *J. Physiol. (London)* 199 :533–48

122. Marks, W. B., Dobelle, W. H., MacNichol, E. F., Jr. 1964. Visual pigments of single primate cones. *Science* 143 :1181–82

123. Gouras, P. 1969. Antidromic responses of orthodromically identified ganglion cells in monkey retina. *J. Physiol (London)* 204 : 407–20

124. Daw, N. W., Pearlman, A. L. 1969. Cat colour vision: one cone process or several? *J. Physiol. (London)* 201 :745–64

125. Pearlman, A. L., Daw, N. W. 1970. Opponent color cells in the cat lateral geniculate nucleus. *Science* 167 :84–86

126. Levick, W. R. 1967. Receptive fields and trigger features of ganglion cells in the visual streak of the rabbit's retina. *J. Physiol. (London)* 188 :285–307

127. Michael, C. R. 1968. Receptive fields of single optic nerve fibers in a mammal with an all cone retina. I. Contrast-sensitive units. *J. Neurophysiol.* 31 :249–56

128. Rodieck, R. W. 1967. Receptive fields in the cat retina: a new type. *Science* 157 :90–92

129. Spinelli, D. N. 1967. Receptive field organization of ganglion cells in the cat's retina. *Exp. Neurol.* 19 : 291–315

130. Oyster, C. W., Barlow, H. B. 1967. Direction-selective units in rabbit retina: distribution of preferred directions. *Science* 155 :841–42

131. Oyster, C. W. The analysis of image motion by the rabbit retina. *J. Physiol. (London)* 199 :613–36

132. Michael, C. R. 1968. Receptive fields of single optic nerve fibers in a mammal with an all cone retina. II. Directional selective units. *J. Neurophysiol.* 31 :257–67

133. Barlow, H. B., Levick, W. R. 1965. The mechanism of directionally sensitive units in rabbit's retina. *J. Physiol. (London)* 178 :477–504

134. Grüsser, O.-J., Grüsser-Cornehls, U., Finkelstein, D., Henn, V., Patuschnik, M., Butenandt, E. 1967. A quantitative analysis of movement detecting neurons in the frog's retina. *Pflügers Arch.* 293 :100–6

135. Butenandt, E., Grüsser, O.-J. 1968. The effect of stimulus area on the response of movement detecting neurons in the frog's retina. *Pflügers Arch.* 298 :283–93

136. Grüsser, O.-J., Finkelstein, D., Grüsser-Cornehls, U. 1968. The effect of stimulus velocity on the response of movement sensitive neurons of the frog's retina. *Pflügers Arch.* 300 :49–66

137. Grüsser-Cornehls, U. 1968. Response of movement-detecting neurons of the frog's retina to moving patterns under stroboscopic illumination. *Pflügers Arch.* 303 :1–13

138. Grüsser, O.-J., Grüsser-Cornehls, U., Licker, M. D. 1968. Further studies on the velocity function of movement detecting class-2 neurons in the frog retina. *Vision Res.* 8 :1173–86

139. Henn, V., Grüsser, O.-J. 1969. The summation of excitation in the receptive fields of movement-sensitive neurons of the frog's retina. *Vision Res.* 9 :57–70

140. Kuriyama, K., Sisken, B., Haber, B., Roberts, E. 1968. The γ-aminobutyric acid system in rabbit retina. *Brain Res.* 9 :165–68

141. Ehinger, B., Falck, B., Laties, A. M. 1969. Adrenergic neurons in teleost retina. *Z. Zellforsch.* 97:285–97

142. Ehinger, B., Falck, B. 1969. Adrenergic retinal neurons of some new world monkeys. *Z. Zellforsch.* 100: 364–75

143. Ehinger, B., Falck, B. 1969. Morphological and pharmacohistochemical characteristics of adrenergic retinal neurons of some mammals. *Arch. Klin. Exp. Ophthal.* 178:295–305

144. Nichols, C. W., Jacobowitz, D., Hottenstein, M. 1967. The influence of light and dark on the catecholamine content of the retina and choroid. *Invest. Ophthal.* 6:642–46

145. Laties, A. M., Jacobowitz, D. 1966. Histochemical studies of monoamine-containing cells in the monkey retina. *J. Histochem. Cytochem.* 14:823–24

146. Pellegrino de Iraldi, A., Etcheverry, G. J. 1967. Granulated vesicles in retinal synapses and neurons. *Z. Zellforsch.* 81:283–96

147. Straschill, M., Perwein, J. 1969. The inhibition of retinal ganglion cells by catecholamines and gamma-aminobutyric acid. *Pflügers Arch.* 312:45–54

148. Straschill, M. 1968. Action of drugs on single neurons in the cat's retina. *Vision Res.* 8:35–48

149. Ames, A. III, Pollen, D. A. 1969. Neurotransmission in central nervous tissue: a study of isolated rabbit retina. *J. Neurophysiol.* 32: 424–42

150. Nichols, C. W., Koelle, G. B. 1967. Acetylcholinesterase: method for demonstration in amacrine cells of rabbit retina. *Science* 155:477–78

151. Nichols, C. W., Koelle, G. B. 1968. Comparison of the localization of acetylcholinesterase and non-specific cholinesterase activities in mammalian and avian retinas. *J. Comp. Neurol.* 133:1–16

152. Trifonow, J., Ostrowski, M. A., Dettmar, P. 1969. Impulsantworten des Nervus opticus auf Reizung der Netzhaut mit Acetylcholin. *Experientia* 25:370–71

153. Kishida, K., Naka, K. I. 1967. Amino acids and the spikes from retinal ganglion cells. *Science* 156:648–50

154. Kishida, K., Naka, K. I. 1968. Interaction of excitatory and depressant amino acids in the frog retina. *J. Neurochem.* 15:833–42

155. Brown, K. T. 1968. The electroretinogram: its components and their origin. *Vision Res.* 8:633–77

156. Murakami, M., Sasaki, Y. 1968. Analysis of spatial distribution of the ERG components in the carp retina. *Jap. J. Physiol.* 18:326–36

157. Murakami, M., Sasaki, Y. 1968. Localization of the ERG components in the carp retina. *Jap. J. Physiol.* 18:337–49

158. Brown, K. T., Murakami, M. 1968. Rapid effects of light and dark adaptation upon the receptive field organization of S-potentials and late receptor potentials. *Vision Res.* 8:1145–72

159. Murakami, M., Kaneko, A. 1966. Differentiation of PIII subcomponents in cold-blooded vertebrate retinas. *Vision Res.* 6:627–36

160. Pautler, E. L., Murakami, M., Nosaki, H. 1968. Differentiation of PIII subcomponents in isolated mammalian retinas. *Vision Res.* 8: 489–91

161. Tomita, T. 1969. Single and coaxial electrodes in the study of the retina. In *Glass Microelectrodes,* ed. M. Lavellee, O. F. Schanne, N. Hebert, 124–53. New York: Wiley

162. Arden, G. B., Ikeda, H. 1968. The minimum latency of the a-wave. *J. Physiol. (London)* 197:529–49

163. Miller, R. F., Dowling, J. E. 1970. Intracellular responses of the Muller (glial) cells of mudpuppy retina: Their relation to b-wave of the electroretinogram. *J. Neurophysiol.* 33:323–41

164. Orkand, R. K., Nicholls, J. G., Kuffler, S. W. 1966. Effect of nerve impulses on the membrane potential of glial cells in the central nervous system of amphibia. *J. Neurophysiol.* 29:788–806

165. Byzov, A. L. 1968. The component analysis of electroretinogram in the retina of cold-blooded vertebrates and the regulative function of horizontal cells. *Advan. Electrophysiol. Pathol. Visual System 6, ISCERG Symp.,* 217–30. Leipzig: VEB Georg Thieme

166. Steinberg, R. H. 1969. Comparison of the intraretinal b-wave and d.c. component in the area centralis of cat retina. *Vision Res.* 9:317–32

167. Steinberg, R. H. 1969. High-intensity effects on slow potentials and

ganglion cell activity in the area centralis of the retina. *Vision Res.* 9 :333–50

168. Burkhardt, D. A. 1970. Proximal negative response of frog retina. *J. Neurophysiol.* 33 :405–20

169. Steinberg, R. H., Schmidt, R., Brown, K. T. 1970. Intracellular responses to light from the cat's pigment epithelium : origin of the c-wave of the electroretinogram. *Nature.* In press

170. Liebman, P. A., Carroll, S., Laties, A. 1969. Spectral sensitivity of

retinal screening pigment migration in the frog. *Vision Res.* 9 :377–84

171. Cowan, M. 1970. Centrifugal fibres to the avian retina. In *Recent Research on the Retina. Brit. Med. Bull.* 26 : No. 2, 112–18

172. Holden, A. L. 1968. Antidromic invasion of the isthmo-optic nucleus. *J. Physiol. (London)* 197 :183–98

173. Ogden, T. E. 1968. On the function of efferent retinal fibers. In *Structure and Function of Inhibitory Neuronal Mechanisms,* 89–109. Oxford: Pergamon

PHYSIOLOGY OF HEARING[1]　　　1063

DONALD H. ELDREDGE AND JAMES D. MILLER

Central Institute for the Deaf, St. Louis, Missouri

In this review we do not cover all of the current literature relevant to the physiology of hearing. Rather we emphasize that for which useful summary statements can be made: 1. Békésy traveling wave, 2. nonlinear mechanisms, 3. dc potentials and ionic gradients, 4. eighth nerve action potentials, and 5. binaural analysis. Other equally important aspects of the physiology of hearing are omitted or only mentioned.

OUTER AND MIDDLE EARS

Von Bismarck (1) measured in the chinchilla the ratios of the sound pressures at the tympanic membrane to those in the free field as functions of frequency and azimuth. As with man and cat, these ratios are as high as +20 dB for some frequencies between 2 and 4 kHz. These resonances of the ear canal varied with changes in the static pressure within the middle ear.

Tonndorf & Khanna (2) used a laser interferometer to measure tympanic membrane motion and the transfer function for the middle ear of the cat. For constant sound pressure, tympanic membrane displacements were approximately constant out to 800–1000 Hz. At higher frequencies an antiresonance at 4 kHz is superimposed on a function that falls gradually with an average slope of −20 dB per decade. The differences between these measurements and earlier ones, e.g., Guinan & Peake (3), are small and probably were caused by small differences in the arrangement of the outer ear and bulla. However, Tonndorf & Khanna found more complex phase relations as a function of frequency than had been observed earlier. Tonndorf & Khanna (4) also evaluated the quality of the impedance matching by the middle ear of the cat by measuring the round window CM as a function of frequency in air, in Xe, and in He. The changes in resonance suggested that

---

[1] The following abbreviations will be used: CM for cochlear microphonic potential with subscripts to indicate the cochlear turn from which CM was recorded; AP for nerve action potential; EP for the endocochlear dc potential; SP for summating potential; EE cells for excitatory-excitatory cells, which increase their rate of discharge in response to acoustic stimulation of either ear; EI cells for excitatory-inhibitory cells which increase their rate of discharge when one ear is stimulated and decrease their rate when the other ear is stimulated.

in air the impedance was slightly undermatched in a way consistent with a good compromise between optimal power transfer and sufficient bandwidth.

BÉKÉSY TRAVELING WAVE

The traveling wave on the cochlear partition that Békésy (5, p. 504) saw showed a broadly tuned pattern of displacement that moved basally with increasing frequency. Johnstone & Boyle (6) and Johnstone, Taylor & Boyle (7), using a Mössbauer technique, measured tuning curves for the basilar membrane of the guinea pig at about 1.5–2.0 mm from the round window end. Even though the methods are difficult and the measurements are limited in place and in dynamic range, the results are largely consistent with Békésy's (5, p. 504) optical observations which were made more apically in the cochlea and at lower frequencies. The sharper tuning reported as a higher "Q" of 2.5 for the base of the cochlea is consistent with the necessity to maintain the instantaneous, net volume displacement of the basilar membrane equal to that of the stapes. At low frequencies the volume displacement in the traveling wave is distributed over an area of the basilar membrane about equal to the area of the foot plate. For very high frequencies, the traveling wave is limited to a short segment of the basilar membrane, and the ratio of basilar membrane to stapes amplitudes must exceed unity for their volume displacements to remain equal.

CM measurements.—Properties of the traveling wave may be inferred from measures of CM. Such inferences are based on Békésy's (5, p. 680) observation that CM is proportional to basilar membrane displacement. Dallos (8) reviewed the theory of the method of differential electrode techniques first described by Tasaki, Davis & Legouix (9) and repeated some of the measurements. To show that the low-frequency CM recorded from the first turn is generated locally and is independent of that generated in the third turn, he polarized the first turn of the basilar membrane. With polarization CM_1 was altered while CM_3 remained unchanged. Dallos (8), Laszlo, Gannon & Milsum (10), and Engebretson (11) measured differential CM as functions of frequency in each of two or three turns of the guinea pig cochlea. For a given position in the cochlea both the CM for a constant sound pressure and the sound-pressure level (SPL) required for constant CM are broadly tuned. Both Dallos and Engebretson show the sensitivity for CM_3 declining at a rate of 10–12 dB per octave for the first octave above 0.5–0.7 kHz, the most sensitive range, and then declining at rates of 30–40 dB per octave for the next one to two octaves. Engebretson shows similar tuning above a best frequency of 2 kHz for CM_2. The longitudinal tuning of the basilar membrane can be estimated from Engebretson's data. For example, with the auditory bulla opened and with a 500 Hz tone at 40 dB SPL, CM_3 is about 100 μV peak-to-peak, CM_2 is 30 μV, and CM_1 is 7–10 μV. As sound-pressure level is increased, CM_3 grows to a maximum of 1500 μV at 80 dB SPL, CM_2 to a maximum of 2200 μV at 95 dB SPL, and CM_1 to a maximum of 3200 μV at 110 dB SPL. Thus, although the third turn is most sensitive at 500 Hz, both the second and first turns will show higher voltages at higher sound pressures. Similar relations were found by Honrubia & Ward (12). Using pipette electrodes in scala media, they observed the maximum of the longitudinal distribution of CM to shift 4 mm toward the base as tonal intensity was increased from about 60 dB SPL to 110 dB SPL. They interpret this basal shift of the CM maximum as a true shift of the maximum of the traveling wave. The validity of this inference depends on the interpretation of the source(s) of nonlinearity in CM and the extent to which nonlinear CM accurately reflects displacement of the basilar membrane.

Laszlo, Gannon & Milsum (10) reported the phase relations for CM_1, CM_2, and CM_3 referred to the phase of the instantaneous sound pressure at the tympanic membrane. Engebretson reported the phases of CM_2 and CM_3 referred to CM_1. Engebretson found no phase differences among the three turns for frequencies below 150 Hz and nearly 180° less phase difference at higher frequencies for the lags of CM_2 and CM_3 relative to CM_1 than the comparable differences inferred from graphs of Laszlo, Gannon & Milsum. Engebretson found the most sensitive frequencies for the second and third turns to be those that show just more than 180° phase lag with respect to the basal turn in a manner consistent with Békésy's (5, p. 462) observations. The wavelengths inferred from Engebretson's data are long enough to exclude the phase cancellations within the field of the differential electrodes postulated by Whitfield & Ross (13) for frequencies up to about one octave above the most sensitive frequency. With the shorter wavelengths at higher frequencies, phase cancellation probably occurs and may account for much of the reduction in amplitude of CM. The linear CM responses correspond well with Békésy's descriptions and probably reflect the mechanical events accurately. Nonlinear CM responses must be examined more critically.

NONLINEAR MECHANISMS

Sweetman & Dallos (14) and Engebretson & Eldredge (15) reviewed sources of nonlinearity in the ear. Harmonics, combination tones, and two-tone interference are all consequences of nonlinearities and may be produced in the middle ear, in the hydromechanical events of the traveling wave, in the mechanoelectric generation of CM, or in any combination of these three. Similarly, summating potential (SP) may be the consequence of asymmetry in any or all of these mechanisms. There is consensus that all three sources of nonlinearity are present in experimental animals. The questions concern the specific combinations of level, frequency, and place at which the nonlinearities occur and, in each case, the process which is the principal source of the observed distortion. These nonlinearities have been studied in cochlear models (16), in CM responses (11, 14, 15, 17–22), and in the discharge patterns of individual neurons (23, 24).

Because there are so many permutations and combinations of the three potentially nonlinear processes with the dimensions of frequency, level, and place along the basilar membrane, a few organizing principles may clarify the relations among the reported observations. 1. Distortion products introduced by the middle ear should show the same cochlear distributions and amplitudes as if the components were present in the original acoustic signal. 2. In cochlear models Tonndorf (16) finds some hydromechanical nonlinearities that are primarily localized to the region where they are generated and others that are propagated as if they were independent waves. The localized nonlinear responses tend to appear at low levels and to be independent of input amplitude. The propagated distortions tend to be associated with Békésy's eddies (5, p. 420) and to grow with input amplitude. 3. Engebretson's (11) data show an important dichotomy. At a given place along the cochlear partition, the relation between CM and sound pressure is linear up to about 70 dB SPL for frequencies lower than the best frequency for that place, while this relation is nonlinear for sound pressures at least as low as about 30 dB SPL for frequencies higher than the best frequency. Above 85 dB SPL the relation of CM to sound pressure is nonlinear for nearly all frequencies. This same dichotomy can be expressed spatially. For a given frequency, the relation is linear up to about 70 dB SPL for regions basal to the best for that frequency, and is nonlinear for sound pressures at least as low as 30 dB SPL for regions apical to the best for the frequency. More briefly, if the phase lag indicated by CM is less than about 180°, CM grows linearly with sound pressure over a wide range of intensity, and if the phase lag is greater than about 180°, CM grows nonlinearly with sound pressure over almost all the measurable range.

Nonlinear distortion products attributable to the middle ear can be measured in the guinea pig at levels below 80–90 dB SPL (25) but, in general, the middle ear is remarkably linear up to about 100 dB SPL (14).

Sweetman & Dallos (14) used interactions between a bone-conducted tone and the difference-tone components simultaneously present in CM_1 and CM_3 to demonstrate that the distortion products in CM_1 were generated independently from those in CM_3 and that those in each turn were localized. Similarly, Dallos & Sweetman (22) demonstrated that harmonic components in CM_1 and CM_3 were independent and not propagated normally. To show that these localized nonlinearities were in the mechanoelectric process and not in the hydromechanical wave, Dallos et al (17) changed the properties for mechanoelectric transduction by adding polarizing currents across the cochlear partition. When polarization reduced the primary components in the CM, the distortion products were increased absolutely and vice versa. The primary frequencies were below the best frequency. They concluded that the principal nonlinearity was in the mechanoelectric process. This conclusion seems valid for frequencies below the most sensitive frequency at a place. At higher frequencies the evidence is not so decisive but, because here CM is nonlinear at such low levels and voltages, a larger role for the low-level, hydromechanical nonlinearity described by Tonndorf (16) is possible.

Distortion products and tonal interference.—Engebretson (11), Engebretson & Eldredge (15), and Dallos (18) described CM distortion products that are qualitatively and quantitatively similar to those previously described by Wever, Bray & Lawrence (26). Engebretson & Eldredge and Nieder & Nieder (19, 20) have postulated mechanisms and described waveforms associated with the phenomenon of tonal interference originally described by Black & Covell (27). All of the above measurements can be explained in terms of a nonlinear transfer function that can be approximated by a polynomial power series expansion. This class of polynomial nonlinearity yields combination tones of the frequencies $mf_1 \pm nf_2$ which grow as the m power of f_1 and as the n power of f_2. For the special combination tone $2f_1$-f_2 when $1 < f_2/f_1 < 2$, Goldstein & Kiang (23) reported discharges of single fibers in the auditory nerve of the cat to be synchronized with the frequency of the combination tone at low levels of f_1 and f_2 and the degree of synchrony seemed to be almost independent of level in a manner reminiscent of the amplitude-independent hydromechanical nonlinearity described by Tonndorf (16). They also found the degree of synchrony with $2f_1$-f_2 to increase and the total response rate to decrease with increasing frequency separation between f_1 and f_2. Dallos (18) measured CM_1 and CM_3 responses to similar pairs of tones and found quite different relations. The $2f_1$-f_2 component was absent at low levels and was independent of frequency separation, and the growth of all distortions products conformed to the polynomial model. The differences between CM and neural data have not been explained.

Summating potentials.—Logically the cochlea appears to require some mechanism for integrating a neural excitatory process over several acoustic cycles at high frequencies. The SP was first described by Davis, Fernández & McAuliffe (28) as such a negative, dc summation at frequencies above about 2 kHz. The association of SP with the linearization of tonal interference led Davis & Eldredge (29) to believe it was the electrical sign of one-way, longitudinal displacements in the cochlear partition caused by the traveling wave. Whitfield & Ross (13) and Johnstone & Johnstone (30) have shown that SP need only be the consequence of an asymmetrical nonlinearity in the transfer function for basilar membrane amplitude to CM. The analysis by Engebretson & Eldredge (15) shows that both SP and tonal interference can be properties of nonlinear systems in general and that SP can be produced by nonlinearities in the middle ear, in the traveling wave, or in the mechanoelectric process for CM. For this reason it is now desirable in reporting SP to specify which process is believed to be nonlinear and asymmetrical.

There is evidence for intracochlear nonlinearities that produce SP just apical to the place of maximum sensitivity for CM. Honrubia & Ward (31) show that SP in response to 0.9 kHz at 75 dB SPL is greatest near the third turn electrode and the SP in response to 3.0 kHz at 65 dB SPL is greatest near the second turn electrode. For nearly identical positions and frequencies, Engebretson (11) shows that the sensitivity of CM is nearly maximum but that CM growth is nonlinear above 30 dB SPL and the phase shift of the traveling wave is greater than 180°. Since CM basal to these places is linear for the same frequencies and levels, the nonlinearities must occur in the cochlea and not in the middle ear. Honrubia & Ward (32) polarized scala media of the basal turn with direct current either adding to or opposing the endocochlear potential and measured CM_1, SP, and the altered EP. For a tone at 2.5 kHz, CM varied linearly with the artificial change in EP both above and below normal values, while SP varied approximately as a power function of EP. This result supports the idea that the asymmetry is in the mechano-electric transducer for frequencies below the best frequency. The same relations at higher frequencies have not been adequately studied.

The dc electrical responses of the ear here described as SP should grow both with the degree of asymmetrical nonlinearity and with the size of the ac signal in which the asymmetry can be detected. This SP will not change in magnitude with signal duration. Békésy (5, p. 640) and Honrubia & Ward (31) also report dc shifts, at the round window and in scala media respectively, that continue to grow during the presentation of loud tones. The recovery from these shifts shows both a rapid component simultaneous with the end of the sound and a slower component. This slow, SP-like change in EP during and following acoustic stimulation represents a different phenomenon which should be distinguished from the SP produced by asymmetrical nonlinearities.

At one time Davis (33) postulated that SP was the dc response of inner hair cells to one-way, longitudinal displacements of the tectorial membrane relative to the reticular lamina produced by the traveling wave. Even though such displacements can occur, this postulate for SP is no longer necessary, and is contrary to expectations from orientation of the cilia. The SP resulting from asymmetrical nonlinearities may or may not have any function. Later we will suggest that it can serve as a neural inhibitory process.

DC POTENTIALS AND IONIC GRADIENTS

The endolymphatic system (34) is completely lined by an epithelium which may be simple squamous as in Reissner's membrane and in the undifferentiated areas of the semicircular canals, ampullae, utricle, and saccule or which may be highly specialized as over the organ of Corti or over the vascular stria (35). The endolymph enclosed throughout this system (36) has a ratio of K^+ to Na^+ which approaches intracellular proportions. The high concentration of extracellular K^+ is unique to the endolymph and only the epithelial surface is normally exposed to it. The EP, which is about 70–90 mV positive with respect to perilymph and to extracellular fluids, is found only in scala media and not in the nonauditory labyrinth. Tasaki & Spyropoulos (37) demonstrated that the vascular stria was the source of EP, but major questions remain. These are concerned with the permeability of the membranes for the various ions, with the type and location of an ion pump, and with the sources of energy for this pump and for the cochlear potentials.

Ionic relations.—One way to approach the above questions is to measure cochlear potentials after changes in ionic compositions of perilymph and endolymph and to compare the results to models that have been established for membranes of giant axons. Important experiments of this kind began with Tasaki & Fernández (38) and in the period covered by this review include reports by Pražma (39) and Konishi & Kelsey (40, 41). Increases in K^+ in perilymph were used to show that EP did not depend directly on a particular ratio of K^+ to Na^+ across Reissner's membrane. Replacement of NaCl by choline chloride in the perilymph showed that neither CM nor EP required Na^+ in the perilymph on either side of the cochlear partition. Calcium-deficient perilymph did not alter EP. Konishi, Kelsey & Singleton (42) earlier concluded that K^+ was essential in scala media to both CM and EP after observing the changes following the perfusion of scala media with Ringer-Locke's solution.

Bosher & Warren (43) and Mendelsohn & Konishi (44) used anoxia for another demonstration that EP and ionic gradients between endolymph and perilymph can vary independently. Both showed that EP changed from normal positive values to negative values within a few minutes after the onset of anoxia. Although there were measurable decreases in K^+ and increases in Na^+ after 30 min of anoxia, these were not quantitatively consistent with the large changes in EP.

Metabolic sources of energy.—The sources of metabolic energy to maintain EP, CM, and the ionic gradients have received increased attention. The histochemical techniques used include quantitative methods applied to small pieces of tissue and histochemical staining methods. Knowledge of these mechanisms was summarized during a symposium on *Biochemical Mechanisms in Hearing and Deafness* held in 1968 (45) and the published report provides many statements that are still pertinent. The organ of Corti, the stria vascularis, and Reissner's membrane are the three structures usually considered in the search for the places for ion transport and the sources of energy for the cochlear potentials. Three research strategies have been to look for stores of energy in the form of glycogen and glucose, for enzymes that participate in one or more of the energy-releasing metabolic cycles, or for the locations of ATPase as a sign of a place where energy is used.

Using quantitative methods, Matschinsky & Thalmann (46) found both glycogen and glucose in the organ of Corti of the guinea pig. Ishii, Takahashi & Balogh (47), using periodic acid methods, found glycogen in the outer hair cells of guinea pig, in Deiters' cells and some outer hair cells in mice, but not in the organ of Corti of the cat. Thalmann, Matschinsky & Thalmann (48) found enzymes for glycolysis, for the citric acid cycle, and for the pentose-P pathway in organ of Corti and stria vascularis, always in much higher concentrations than in Reissner's membrane. Nakai & Hilding (49), using formazan techniques with electronmicroscopy, found much succinic dehydrogenase and dihydronicotinamide adenine dinucleotide diaphorase in the stria vascularis, with some activity in supporting cells of the organ of Corti and even less in the hair cells. Kluyskens & Verstraete (50) find that isoenzymes of lactic dehydrogenase in cochlear fluids favor aerobic glycolosis. The overall trend suggests minimal levels of activity in Reissner's membrane, significant levels of respiration in the organ of Corti, and levels two to three times higher in the stria vascularis.

Matschinsky & Thalmann (46) found significant levels of ATP and creatine phosphate in both organ of Corti and the stria vascularis. With ischemia, they found ATP to fall rapidly in the stria while remaining at nearly normal levels in the organ of Corti. This is an indication that glycolysis can maintain ATP in the organ of Corti. Nakai & Hilding (51) found histochemical signs of ATPase in the stria and on the endolymphatic surface of most cells in the organ of Corti. No ATPase was found along the sides of hair cells or between nerve endings, but supporting cells had the enzyme on their surfaces. Kuijpers, Van der Vleuten & Bonting (52) found high levels of both Na- and K-activated and Mg-activated ATPase in the stria vascularis in the ratio 2:1, Na-K ATPase to Mg-ATPase. Subsequently, Kuijpers (53) reported levels of Na-K ATPase in stria vascularis that were more than 15 times those in the organ of Corti or Reissner's membrane. Ionic transport appears to be concentrated in the vascular stria.

Metabolic inhibitors.—Various methods of blocking enzyme systems have also been used in an attempt to identify specific enzyme systems as they relate to CM, EP, and AP. Ouabain, which will block Na^+ and K^+ transport in neural membranes, has been used in both perilymph and endolymph (52, 54–56). ATP formation may be inhibited by 2,4–dinitrophenol, and steps in oxidative phosphorylation may be blocked by sodium azide or cyanide. These agents have also been injected into both perilymph and endolymph (54, 56–58). Tetrodotoxin suppresses action potentials in excitable tissues by eliminating the inward Na^+ action current and procaine acts by decreasing resting potential across the membrane and the permeability for K^+ with a related increase of membrane resistance. Konishi & Kelsey (59) introduced tetrodotoxin into both scala tympani and scala media with minimal changes except for depression of AP. Procaine in scala typmpani did not change EP. In this class of experiments, suppression of CM and EP by the metabolic inhibitors was common and, of these agents, cyanide appeared to produce more severe changes. Also injection of inhibitors into scala media tended to produce smaller changes than injection in scala tympani. In general, ouabain, tetrodotoxin, and procaine blocked AP but revealed no clear indications of the place of mechanisms for ion transport. The trend of the reports leads to the rather obvious conclusion that metabolic energy is essential for cochlear potentials and also that the mechanisms underlying CM and EP appear to differ in some ways from those found for nerve action potentials.

Integrity of scala media.—Von Ilberg & Vosteen (60) used microinjections of a suspension of electron-dense, 4×10^{-3} μm particles of thorium dioxide into the endolymph and into the perilymph of the guinea pig and examined the specimens by electronmicroscopy. The thorium dioxide would not pass the zonula occludens junctions between any of the epithelial cells even when the particles did penetrate all other intercellular spaces. The particles were carried across Reissner's membrane in either direction in micropinocytic vesicles. The particles penetrated the organ of Corti from scala tympani readily. They concluded that transcellular transport was required between perilymph and endolymph and that the so-called cortilymph spaces contained perilymph. They further postulated that the most likely path for O_2 supply for the organ of Corti also comes from the blood vessels in scala tympani rather than from the stria vascularis through the endolymph.

Rauch et al (61) find such rapid movement of labeled K^+ across Reissner's membrane from scala vestibuli to scala media that they postulate an active transporting process in the membrane. The membrane is sufficiently impermeable to support large potential differences and ionic gradients. Sohmer & Feinmesser (62) found the scala vestibuli surface could tolerate Ringers's solution made six times normal tonicity with sucrose. However, there is a good possibility that the artificial endolymph such as used by Pražma (39) or the labeled K^+ at 133 meq/liter used by Rauch et al (61) would depolarize and otherwise injure the cells of Reissner's membrane leaving a leaky, freely permeable structure and that such chemical injuries account for the major part of their findings.

Summary.—There is not quite enough information to support firmly any complete model of cochlear metabolic physiology, but the following propositions seem to be consistent with the available observations. The metabolic energy for EP and for the K^+ gradient is supplied in the stria vascularis. Na^+ is actively transported out of scala media into the blood stream at the stria vascularis. K^+ and Na^+ can enter the cochlear duct passively and slowly through the other walls, especially Reissner's membrane. Under these circumstances EP might be a Na diffusion potential as postulated by Johnstone, Schmidt & Johnstone (63). CM is produced when the hair cells modulate, as by a variable resistance, a dc current at the reticular lamina. Both EP and the intracellular resting potentials of the hair cells are possible sources for this current, but truly convincing evidence concerning the relative contributions of each source is lacking. During anoxia as much as 95%

of CM decays in a manner that closely parallels the decay of EP (5, p. 700). During asphyxic anoxia (32) and metabolic anoxia produced by cyanide (57), the hair cell-modulating mechanism appears to function with artificial polarizing currents and continued support of hair cell action by glycolytic energy (46) is possible. Thus roughly 95% of the CM voltage may depend on EP and the role played by the hair cells may be primarily one of modulation. The above observations concerning anoxia are not decisive because the organ of Corti normally also uses oxidation in the citric acid cycle as a source of energy. Note that the principal metabolic requirements for the organ of Corti may be supplied by blood vessels in the scala tympani as suggested by Lawrence (64) and by von Ilberg & Vosteen (60) even though the energy for EP, and thus CM, must be provided through the stria vascularis.

EIGHTH NERVE ACTION POTENTIALS

Tuning to characteristic frequencies.—Galambos & Davis (65), Katsuki et al (66), and Kiang et al (67) agree that, when care is taken to eliminate onset transients and distortion products, each primary auditory neuron is highly tuned to a narrow range of frequencies around a characteristic frequency. As intensity is increased each neuron will respond to wider and wider bands of frequencies. The graphic representation of the combinations of frequency and level to which the unit will respond to a particular criterion forms a "tuning curve" that bounds a neural "response area". Kiang, Sachs & Peake (68) have now shown that, when middle ear resonances are eliminated by relating tuning curves to amplitude of the stapes rather than to sound pressure in the ear canal, there is one, and only one, narrow, most-sensitive frequency range for each neuron. Sensitivity decreases rapidly at lower frequencies and even more rapidly at higher frequencies. Published examples (65–69) suggest that sensitivity may decrease at a rate of 25 dB to 100 dB per octave below the characteristic frequency and at rates in excess of 100 dB per octave above. The transient responses of units with characteristic frequencies below about 4 kHz also are consistent with this high degree of tuning. Poststimulus histograms of probability of response to a transient as a function of time are periodic and half-wave "rectified" in form and often increase for two or three "cycles" before decaying in as many as six or seven "cycles" (67, 69).

Now de Boer (70, 71) and de Boer & Jongkees (72) have examined the temporal properties of the responses of single neurons of the auditory nerve of the cat to white noise. Magnetic tape recordings of both the noise and the train of neural spikes were played back with the reproduction of the noise delayed in a manner that allowed each neural response to trigger the computation of the average of the acoustic waveforms that had just preceded the responses. The resulting temporal coherence is a correlation function in time between the two series and has the form of a tone-pulse with the period of the characteristic frequency of the neuron. The tuning implied by these properties is consistent with decreases of sensitivity of at least 30 dB per octave below and at least 100 dB per octave above the characteristic frequency. This degree of tuning is significantly greater than that shown by the motion of the basilar membrane or than shown by CM.

Timing and periodicity.—Rose et al (73) found similar relations in primary auditory neurons in the squirrel monkey and measured the probability of neural responses to continuous tones as a function of time. Data are presented both as probabilities of intervals since the last spike and as folded histograms in which the measurement of time is reset once each cycle of the tone. For frequencies below 4.5–5.0 kHz and at levels within the respective response areas, all units showed phase-locking to the cycle of the tones and grouping of the intervals between discharges around integral multiples of the period of the stimulating tones. Hind et al (74) measured the phase-locking to pairs of independent tones at suprathreshold levels. As the relative level between tones was changed, the folded histograms showed responses locked to the phase of the more effective tone or to both tones. Brugge et al (75) have extended these observations to complex sounds consisting of two tones locked in harmonic frequency ratios of small integers. The phase and amplitude relations between the component tones were varied systematically and probability of discharge was measured as a histogram of interspike intervals and as a folded histogram with a period equal to that for the fundamental of the complex sound. The temporal patterns for the responses were half-wave rectified and could be approximated by simple addition of component sinusoids in appropriate phases. The relations supported the postulate that neural excitation occurs during deflection of the basilar membrane in one direction only. In addition to the periodic intervals that correspond to the primary tones and to the fundamental of the complex tone, Rose et al (76) found "minor secondary periods". They speculate that these may be one basis for the perception of combination tones.

Pfeiffer & Molnar (24) used folded histograms to measure response probabilities of single units in the cat. Instantaneous sound pressure at the tympanic membrane was used as a phase reference for the histograms. The phasic pattern of the response probabilities changed with tonal frequency in a manner similar to the phase lags reported for the basilar membrane (5, p. 462) and for CM (9, 11).

OTHER PROPERTIES OF NEURAL RESPONSES

In the scheme for sensory receptor action outlined by Davis (77) CM is certainly a receptor potential, but there is no direct evidence that it is a generator potential capable of directly eliciting neural responses. Descriptions of the afferent synapses on the hair cells (78) do not clearly favor either chemical or electrotonic initiation of neural activity. We do not have direct evidence concerning neural excitation and inhibition or enhancement and suppression. However, enough information is available concerning miscellaneous properties of the responses of individual neurons to allow us to infer many features of the sensory receptor mechanism.

Response probabilities for continuous tones.—Spontaneous discharge (69, 73) is a general property of nearly all, if not all, primary auditory neurons. Probability of response can be increased by acoustic stimulation or, under particular circumstances, decreased with respect to the probability of spontaneous activity. The studies of phase-locked responses to low-frequency tones by Rose et al (73) yielded several important findings in this regard. *(a)* At times between the phase-locked responses, the probability of response decreased well below the spontaneous rate. *(b)* There were always some responses at intervals of two, three, or more times the period of the tone even when the period was clearly much longer than the absolute refractory period and the sound level was well above threshold. *(c)* For continuous tones, aside from an indication of a relative refractory period at the time of the next period after a discharge, there was a nearly constant probability of a second firing regardless of the number of cycles that had elapsed since the last discharge. If there were a monotonic recovery of neural excitability and a simple summation of an excitatory process over several periods of a tone, one would expect the probability of neural discharge to increase with the number of cycles since the last discharge and the probability of aperiodic discharges to increase similarly.

Suppression of neural activity.—Although the probability of discharge periodically falls below spontaneous probability in the presence of tones, the evidence for active suppression of responses is clearer in experiments employing two tones or two clicks. Hind et al (74) found the total number of spikes in response to two-tone combinations was usually larger than for the less effective component tone and smaller than for the more effective component. Sachs & Kiang (79) explored these relations more systematically and have interpreted the findings as a suppression or inhibition of the responses to the more effective tone by the less effective tone. In the presence of stimulation by continuous tones at the characteristic frequency, inhibition was produced by second tones that had combinations of frequency and levels just outside of or else just within the response area. This two-tone inhibition was asymmetrical wih respect to the characteristic frequency. At lower frequencies sound pressures at least 10 dB greater than those at the characteristic frequency were required. At higher frequencies inhibition was produced by tones at levels at least as low as those for the continuous tone at the characteristic frequency. Sachs' model (80) for this phenomenon at high frequencies includes an inhibitory multiplier.

Discrepant response areas.—In the guinea pig the sensitivity of CM declines no more than 15 dB per octave in the first octave above the most sensitive frequency (8–11). This is in sharp contrast to declines of about

100 dB per octave for the sensitivity of single neurons under similar conditions. If it is true that a neuron with a certain characteristic frequency is attached to a place along the cochlear duct at which CM is most sensitive to the same frequency and if CM, or some other phenomenon related to amplitude of the basilar membrane, were to play a role in neural excitation, then some process must inhibit or block neural responses to tones above the characteristic frequency. The high-frequency portion of two-tone inhibition is consistent with the existence of this unspecified inhibitory or sharpening process.

Electrical modulation of neural activity.—Earlier Tasaki & Fernández (38) had shown in the guinea pig that the whole-nerve AP could be enhanced by artificial direct current flowing from scala vestibuli to scala tympani and diminished by opposing currents. Konishi, Teas & Wernick (81) have measured the responses of single auditory neurons in the guinea pig in the presence of similar currents and found similar relations. The same authors (82) also used direct currents cycled 5 sec on and 5 sec off and 5 Hz alternating currents. The rates of response to tones were again modulated according to the direction of the current.

Click excitation functions.—Goblick & Pfeiffer (83) studied the discharge probabilities of primary auditory neurons of the cat in response to clicks. As shown earlier (69) these probabilities peak at integral multiples of the period of the characteristic frequency of the neuron and, with reversal of click polarity, the peaks shift by one half-period. They define a click excitation function as some process that corresponds to the observed response probabilities. When two clicks are presented with an interclick interval of precisely one half-period, a phase of excitation for one click is superimposed on a quiet or no-response phase of the other and response probabilities can peak in all half-periods, not just the alternate ones. For each half-period after the first, the intensity ratios of the clicks can be adjusted so that the no-response phase of one click exactly offsets the excitatory phase of the other and the response becomes zero for this half-period. The nulling procedure is very sensitive to relative click levels and the overall pattern for these responses strongly implies that the excitatory phases in the click excitation function alternate with inhibitory or suppressive phases rather than with neutral phases. The important new finding of this study is that the click excitation function is nonlinear with respect to time as well as to amplitude. These measurements cannot be explained by any simple model for neural excitation in the cochlea.

Constraints for models of sensory receptor action.—The precise timing of the probabilities of neural discharge for frequencies below about 4 kHz (23, 24, 69, 73–76, 83) requires a process with the precision of CM or the periodic motion of the basilar membrane. The modification and modulation of neural discharge probabilities by cochlear currents (81, 82) show that CM could modulate response probability above and below a spontaneous rate and that artificial cochlear currents can modulate neural responses to normal acoustic inputs. But the quantitative discrepancies between the sharpness of tuning for the basilar membrane (5, p. 461–62, p. 504) or for CM (8–12) on the one hand and the tuning indicated by probabilities of neural discharges to pure tones (68, 69, 79), to clicks (69, 83), and to wide-band noise (70–72) on the other show that neither CM nor any simple trans-formation of basilar membrane motion can account for the patterns of neural responses.

Any chemical or electrical neural excitatory process with a half-wave rectification and a constant decay time will start by showing periodicity but, when the tonal period becomes short with respect to the decay time, the excitatory process can accumulate from cycle to cycle. This summation will increase with frequency and might thus help to account for the degree of neural sharpening relative to the CM functions at frequencies below the characteristic frequency of the neuron. However, acting alone this summat-ing process will tend to smear rather than to preserve periodicity for con-tinuous tones. Finally, as noted in an earlier section, the rate of decrease above the characteristic frequency (69) and in the two-tone paradigm (79) is so strong as to suggest active inhibition.

In order to assimilate the pertinent findings into a single scheme that describes acoustically induced changes in spontaneous neural activity, it now seems necessary to postulate at least three classes of processes.

1. Basilar membrane motion in one direction is associated with neural excitation by a process such as the release of chemical transmitter and the time for decay of this transmitter is constant. This process is asymmetrical, is equivalent to half-wave rectification, and allows an excitatory process to last longer than one period of a tone. A process of this kind helps to account for the increasing sensitivity with frequency seen for the responses to con-tinuous tones and also the nonlinear variations in time shown by the click excitation functions.

2. The electrical currents associated with CM act, according to their di-rection, either to enhance or to suppress both spontaneous and transmitter-induced neural discharge. Neural response rates are limited between zero and some maximum rate. These limits impose a variable asymmetry (82) on the action of CM such that enhancement predominates at low rates of neural discharge and suppression predominates at higher rates. This rela-tion may explain two-tone inhibition of responses to a characteristic fre-quency by a lower frequency. In any event the phase of suppression must be strong enough to enforce the observed periodic probabilities for neural dis-charge that exist when the time required for decay of the transmitter is long with respect to a period.

3. For frequencies above the characteristic frequency, some process must actively suppress neural responses, even in the presence of magnitudes

of CM larger than those associated with effective stimulation at lower frequencies. For this process, the combinations of place along the basilar membrane and tonal frequency are essentially the same as those described earlier for the SP that is associated with sensitive CM response and with nonlinearity at low sound-pressure levels. If this SP does have any function, it may be related to the above suppression. The only evidence for this additional inhibition is the two-tone inhibition. Nevertheless, if one accepts the first two processes as suggested, a third is necessary.

PERIPHERAL EFFERENT CONTROL

Knowledge of peripheral efferents of the auditory system increased remarkably in the late 1950s and early 1960s, and this knowledge appears in several summaries (84–88). Recent attempts to clarify the structure and function of these efferents have had only modest success and primarily confirm and extend earlier findings.

The general distribution of efferent fibers and endings in the mammalian cochlea described in earlier papers has been confirmed (89–91). Nevertheless, the details of the efferent innervation of the cochlea remain obscure. Rossi (88) states that in rodents there are three efferent bundles to the cochlea: the direct (uncrossed) olivocochlear bundle, the crossed olivocochlear bundle, and a direct bundle from the reticular formation of the pons and medulla to the cochlear, ampullary, and macular receptors. Others suggest that visceral efferents may have a regulatory role in the sensory function of the cochlea (92, 93). Thus, the theorist is confronted with four sets of efferents to explain, the experimentalist merely needs to control them. Morest (94) presents evidence that the dorsomedial periolivary nucleus is the origin of the crossed olivocochlear bundle and that these fibers may be influenced by neural activity at both the input and output of the nucleus of the trapezoid body.

Rupert et al (95) describe discharge characteristics of olivocochlear neurons. Klinke et al (96) examined inhibition of sound-driven afferent neurons by acoustic stimulation of the opposite ear. The inhibitory effects were greatest when the frequencies of the tones at the two ears were similar but not identical; thus, the inhibitory curves were W-shaped as they are for two-tone inhibition in a single ear (79).

Wiederhold (97) confirmed earlier findings that electrical stimulation of the crossed olivocochlear bundle resulted in suppression of sound-driven discharges of single fibers in the eighth nerve of cats. Suppression is greatest when the afferent unit is driven at moderate rates by a tone at its characteristic frequency. The amount of suppression appeared to be greatest for units with characteristic frequencies of 3–10 kHz. The most striking fact was that of the 250 afferent units that were studied, nearly all were inhibited by electrical stimulation of the crossed olivocochlear efferents. This finding is at odds with current hypotheses about cochlear innervation. To summarize an argument detailed by Fex (84), if crossed olivocochlear fibers form synapses only with outer hair cells and if only 10% of the primary afferents arise from outer hair cells, then only 10% of the afferents should be suppressed by stimulation of the crossed efferents. Yet both Fex and Wiederhold find such effects for nearly all afferents. Spoendlin (98) has confirmed his earlier finding that only about 10% of the cat's afferents have synapses with outer hair cells. We think it is likely, therefore, that in the cat the crossed efferents synapse, *en passant,* with almost all of the afferents while they are medial to the tunnel of Corti. This and alternative explanations are given by Fex (84).

In the cochlear nucleus both Comis & Whitfield (99) and Starr & Wernick (100) describe centrifugal inhibitory and excitatory effects on both spontaneous and driven afferent activity.

Three behavioral experiments have been reported wherein experimental animals performed auditory detection or discrimination tasks after transection of the crossed olivocochlear bundles. Capps & Ades (101) found frequency discrimination by squirrel monkeys to be seriously impaired postoperatively. Interpretation of this experiment is difficult because preoperative frequency discrimination was very poor; no control group was tested; and the authors themselves doubted the adequacy of the behavioral technique. Dewson (102) found that rhesus monkeys can discriminate sustained vowels (/i/ vs /u/) in the quiet as well after transection of the crossed olivocochlear bundle as before. In order to discriminate the vowels in the presence of a continuous background noise, however, the monkeys required a more favorable signal-to-noise ratio postoperatively than they did preoperatively. Interpretation of this experiment is complicated because three of the four monkeys had been given brain lesions prior to the experiment. Trahiotis & Elliott (103) compared the performance of three trained cats in which the crossed olivocochlear bundle had been transected with three that had undergone sham operation. All were made monaural by surgical destruction of one cochlea. Quiet absolute thresholds, masking of tones by noise, and temporary threshold shifts produced by exposure to noise were measured. The cats deprived of the crossed efferents required a more favorable signal-to-noise ratio than did the control cats in order to detect tones in noise; no other differences were apparent.

In the Dewson and in the Trahiotis & Elliott experiments the masking noises were sustained throughout the test sessions and the signal durations were at least 300 msec. In the Capps & Ades experiment the tones to be discriminated alternated throughout a trial. Furthermore, all of the tasks on which performance may have been affected involved resolution of spectra, that is, frequency resolving power. Thus, all three experiments suggest that there is a deterioration of frequency resolving power in the presence of sustained stimulation after transection of the crossed olivocochlear bundle.

The behavioral and physiological evidence suggests to us that the olivocochlear efferent system may play an important role in the maintenance of organized auditory responses to sounds or sequences of sounds that are sustained for more than a few tens of milliseconds. We find no recent support for the competing hypotheses that the olivocochlear efferents are involved in habituation or selective attention.

NONAUDITORY INFLUENCES ON RESPONSES TO SOUNDS IN THE AUDITORY PATHWAY

Several recent studies support the generalization that neural responses to sound are stable in all auditory nuclei peripheral to and including the inferior colliculus (104–108). That is, evoked responses of these nuclei do not habituate to repeated stimulation by clicks nor are the responses to sustained sounds altered in unexpected ways. The authors of these papers emphasized that the results described above are only obtained if there is adequate control of the sounds at the eardrum and if the actions of middle-ear muscles are controlled. In apparent opposition to this general conclusion, Kitzes & Buchwald (109) provide evidence that neural responses of auditory nuclei of the brainstem do habituate if these responses are measured by integrating multiple unit activity.

There is general agreement that responses to sound recorded from the medial geniculate body or auditory cortex habituate with repeated stimulation even if the general level of arousal is controlled (104, 105, 107, 110). Ebersole & Galambos (111) found a new nonauditory factor that can influence evoked cortical responses to sound. They show that the amplitude of the evoked response to a click declines as a function of the velocity of eye movements associated with optokinetic nystagmus.

Thus, the recent literature taken as a whole supports the generally held impression that neural responses to sound become more stable as one moves from the cerebral cortex down to the periphery. It is interesting that while much of this research has been part of a search for the function of the descending auditory pathways, the details of their regulatory action remain obscure.

AVERAGE EVOKED POTENTIALS

While there have been many recent papers on the average evoked potentials that can be recorded from the human scalp in response to sound, only those few that are relevant to the generation of these potentials will be reviewed. The average evoked potentials to be considered can be divided into short-latency, midlatency, and long-latency groups. In this context, short latencies are less than about 50 msec, midlatencies are about 50–250 msec, and long latencies are 300 msec or more. It has been commonly held that the potentials of the short-latency group may be generated in the primary projection area of the cerebral cortex although they usually include myogenic components. In contrast, it has been commonly held that the potentials of the mid- and long-latency groups result from many generators diffusely located in the cortex (112–114).

In an important paper Vaughan & Ritter (112) describe the distributions of the amplitudes of average evoked potentials elicited by tone bursts and recorded from electrodes at various locations on the human head. They then construct isopotential contours from the potentials of both the mid- and long-latency groups. The contours for the midlatency group (50–250 msec) are consistent with the hypothesis that only generators localized in the primary projection area contribute to these responses. The best position for the scalp electrode (referred to the chin) is at the vertex, the worst is over the Sylvian fissure. The isopotential contours for the long-latency group, in contrast, are consistent with the hypothesis that generators diffusely located over a broad area of the cerebral cortex contribute to the response. For the specific experimental conditions of Vaughan & Ritter, these generators can be conceived of as being distributed over large cortical regions centered on the parietotemporal association areas.

The observations of Jerger et al (115) are consistent with the hypothesis that the generators of evoked potentials of the midlatency group are localized. They describe a patient with bilateral lesions of the temporal lobe who exhibited no evoked potentials of the midlatency group in response to clicks although he could hear and report the occurrence of each click. In contrast, this patient exhibited clearly defined average evoked potentials in response to flashes of light.

Additional support for the notion that the neurogenic components of average evoked potentials of the short- and midlatency groups are generated in the appropriate primary projection areas of the cerebral cortex can be found in papers by Liberson (113), Williamson et al (116), and Stohr & Goldring (114). These authors find that patients with unilateral lesions of the cortex that include the primary somatosensory projection area exhibit weak or absent average evoked potentials in response to stimulation of the median nerve contralateral to the side of the lesion. This was true for potentials of the short- and midlatency groups whether the electrodes were placed on the scalp or the surface of the brain. These facts as well as the details of the lesions and of the characteristics of the potentials recorded with various configurations of the recording and stimulating electrodes strongly support the notion that somatosensory average evoked potentials of the short- and midlatency groups are generated in the primary somatosensory area of the cerebral cortex and that the involved neural pathway is the medial lemniscus.

Because of the similarities between average evoked potentials elicited by stimulation of the auditory and somatosensory systems and because of the results of Vaughan & Ritter (112) and of Jerger et al (115), it appears that the notion that the neurogenic components of the auditory average evoked potentials of the short- and midlatency groups are from generators localized in the primary auditory projection areas of the cortex must be given careful consideration. The notion that the average evoked potentials of the long-latency group are from generators diffusely located in the cortex appears to stand.

BINAURAL ANALYSIS

Many of the important adaptive functions of the auditory system depend on the ability to analyze differences between the complex waveforms arriving at the two ears and changes in these differences with movement of the head or the sound source. This ability is called binaural analysis (117). Binaural analysis has an important role for the localization of sound sources, identification of sound sources in the face of frequency distortion and reverberation in the transmission path, and selective attention as well. Psychoacoustic investigations of binaural analysis were recently reviewed (117, 118). Recent physiological investigations of binaural analysis are summarized below.

SUPERIOR OLIVARY COMPLEX

The afferents of the right and left auditory pathways first converge at the superior olivary complex. Here recent studies of discharge patterns of single neurons, field potentials, and anatomical connections are relevant to binaural analysis.

The superior olivary complex is a bilaterally symmetrical set of nuclei within the brainstem. In the cat and dog (119–121), the two olivary nuclei, the lateral superior olive (the S segment) and the medial superior olive (the accessory nucleus), and the nucleus of the trapezoid body are most prominent. Also included in the complex are the periolivary nuclei. Warr (119) states that the lateral and medial olives receive fibers from the anteroventral cochlear nuclei and the periolivary nuclei receive fibers from the posteroventral cochlear nuclei. While the nucleus of the trapezoid body receives fibers from the contralateral cochlear nucleus, the subdivision of origin is unknown. Irving & Harrison (122) emphasize species differences in the relative prominence of the nuclei of the superior olivary complex. For example, the medial superior olive is small or absent in bats and dolphins.

Medial superior olive.—The medial superior olive is of special interest because it has cells that are obviously specialized to compare inputs from the right and left cochlear nuclei. In the cat, for example, the cells of the medial superior olive each have two large dendrites: one extends medially, the other laterally. Fibers from the contralateral cochlear nucleus terminate on the medial receptive surface (dendrite and soma) of the cells of the medial superior olive. Fibers from the homolateral cochlear nucleus terminate primarily on the lateral receptive surfaces although a few probably terminate on the proximal portions of the medial receptive surfaces. Therefore, with few exceptions, fibers from the right cochlear nucleus terminate on the right of the cells, while those from the left cochlear nucleus terminate on the left. The above description combines observations on cats (120) and dogs (121); the arrangement is more complex for dog than cat because the nucleus has a semilunar rather than nearly vertical alignment. Within the medial superior olive, Clark (123) observed two kinds of end boutons. One kinds has spheroidal vesicles, the other flat vesicles. Following Uchizono (124), Clark argues that the former boutons are excitatory, the latter inhibitory. If this be true, the peripheral parts of the dendrites receive only excitatory boutons, while proximal parts of the dendrites and the cell bodies receive about an equal number of excitatory and inhibitory boutons. Clark (123) also observed bouton-to-bouton contacts which, he suggests, could provide a mechanism for presynaptic inhibition.

Goldberg & Brown (121, 125) measured the responses to tone bursts of 105 cells in the medial superior olive. About 65% of the cells were classed as excitatory (EE), about 24% as excitatory-inhibitory (EI), and about 11% as monaural. EE cells increase their discharge rate when either ear is stimulated; EI cells increase their discharge rate when one ear is stimulated and decrease their rate when the opposite ear is stimulated; and monaural cells have discharge rates that are influenced by stimulation of one ear, but not the other. These authors rally evidence that EE cells are relatively insensitive to interaural intensity differences, but are quite sensitive to the average of the levels at the two ears and that EI cells are relatively insensitive to the average of the levels at the two ears, but are quite sensitive to interaural intensity differences.

Low-frequency cells of the medial superior olive are elegantly sensitive to the interaural time differences of pure tones (125). For pure tones presented monaurally at either ear these units tend to respond with a fixed relation to the phase of the tone. These phase relations for the two ears often differ. The cells of the medial superior olive respond maximally to binaural tones adjusted to an interaural time difference that would make the monaural responses coincide in time. This time difference is optimal. At the optimal interaural time difference, these cells not only respond at maximal rate but their responses are extraordinarily well synchronized with the phase of the stimulus. Now, as the interaural time is changed from its optimal value, both the discharge rate and the degree of synchrony vary periodically at the frequency of the stimulus. On the basis of their findings, Goldberg & Brown (125) suggest that when excitatory inputs from the two ears reach the dendrites in phase (simultaneously), then the cell fires at its maximum rate, which is higher than for stimulation from either ear alone. The discharge rate falls as the excitatory inputs are separated in time until that separation is maximum, that is, until the interaural phase difference is 180°. When the interaural phase difference is 180°, the cell's discharge rate is lower than that for stimulation of either ear alone. The authors interpret these facts as in-phase facilitation plus out-of-phase inhibition.

We believe the results of Goldberg & Brown (121, 125) for cells of the medial superior olive to be consistent with the following summary. For high frequencies, discharges of EE cells mainly reflect the average of the levels at the two ears, while discharges of EI cells mainly reflect interaural intensity differences. For low frequencies, cells with various characteristic delays reflect the interaural time difference by their discharge rate and degree of synchrony with the phase of the stimulus. The fact that these cells have differing optimal interaural delays is consistent with Jeffress' theory (126) that interaural time differences are translated to place differences within the nervous system. Because of additional complexities, this summary is probably far too simple. For example, a cell is not necessarily an EE cell for all stimulus conditions; it may change to an EI cell when the frequency of the tone burst is moved away from its characteristic frequency (125). Also, while Goldberg & Brown (125) show the existence of optimal delays and comment that this delay is nearly invariant with interaural intensity differences, they did not test whether the optimal delay was invariant with frequency. All of these tests are essential to the concept of "characteristic delay". In addition, these cells exhibit other complexities in response to transient sounds (127).

Watanabe et al (128) and Clark & Dunlop (129) have also recently described responses of neurons in or near the medial superior olive. These authors agree with Goldberg & Brown (121, 125) that most neurons of this region fire in a sustained, usually decreasing, manner to maintained tone bursts with slow rise times. If clicks or tone bursts with instantaneous rise times are used, the discharge patterns are, as one might expect, more varied. Watanabe et al (128) show for some high-frequency cells that if a tone burst starts in one ear before the other, then the leading ear can "capture" the cell. The cell may be unresponsive to stimulation of the lagging ear for as long as 50 msec. This situation is often asymmetrical. For example, a particular cell may be "captured" by a leading stimulus to the left but not the right. Similar results obtained with click stimuli are well known (127, 130).

Lateral superior olive.—The lateral superior olive (S segment) also has cells that code interaural parameters. This nucleus receives a massive projection from the homolateral cochlear nucleus (119–121). The pathway from the contralateral cochlear nucleus includes a synapse at the nucleus of the trapezoid body (131, 132), and the calyces of Held that form these synapses appear to be ideally suited for transmission with minimum delay and error. The cells of the lateral superior olive are morphologically similar to those of the medial superior olive. While the details of their innervation are not as well known, apparently the homolateral afferent axons terminate on both dendritic poles and the cell bodies as well (120).

Boudreau & Tsuchitani (133, 134) detailed the responses of binaural cells in the lateral superior olive that are tuned to high frequencies. These cells have little or no spontaneous activity. They fire in response to ipsilateral tones and this response is inhibited by stimulation of the contralateral ear. The tuning curves for ipsilateral (excitatory) and contralateral (inhibitory) stimulation are nearly identical. Thus, these cells are similar to the EI cells of the medial superior olive, and they are relatively sensitive to interaural intensity differences and relatively insensitive to overall intensity. Furthermore, these authors find that the locus of maximal response in the lateral superior olive shifts to cells with characteristic frequencies higher than the frequency of the stimulus tone as the intensity of the stimulus tone increases. Details of the effects of interaural time differences on the neurons of the lateral superior olive are not yet available.

Periolivary nuclei.—Binaural analysis in the periolivary nuclei has not been extensively studied. Anatomical and electrophysiological evidence suggests that the lateral periolivary nuclei and the nucleus of the trapezoid body are not sites of binaural analysis (119, 121, 125). However, the regions of the complex identified by Warr (119) as the anteromedial and dorsomedial periolivary nuclei do carry out binaural analyses similar to those described in the olivary nuclei (121, 125). The medial periolivary nuclei probably are involved in the control of the descending auditory pathways and, in particular, the olivocochlear efferents.

Field potentials in the superior olivary complex.—Potentials measured with large electrodes provide additional evidence for binaural analysis in the superior olivary complex. The slow potentials associated with ipsilateral and contralateral auditory stimulation change as an electrode penetrates various regions of the superior olivary complex. These changes can be successfully interpreted in terms of the anatomy and function of the region (121, 135). A particularly interesting response is variously known as wave activity, the following response, or the frequency-following response. This periodic response is similar to the cochlear microphonic except that it is of neural origin, has a latency, is maximum at about 800 Hz, and cannot be detected above 4–5 kHz. Weinberger et al (136) suggest that it be called the auditory neurophonic. Both the slow and periodic potentials were used by Wernick & Starr (137) to investigate binaural analysis in the superior olivary complex. Both potentials can be recorded in the lateral and medial olives during monaural stimulation of either ear. The periodic response is slightly larger for ipsilateral than contralateral stimulation in the lateral superior olive, while the opposite is true for the medial superior olive. These authors focus on conditions in which continuous tones of low frequency are presented to the two ears with a small interaural frequency difference. Under these conditions man experiences binaural beats. The beat rate appears as a modulation of the slow potential or as a modulation of the envelope of the periodic response. If the sum of the waveforms produced by appropriate monaural stimulation does not match the waveforms produced by the binaural stimulation, then binaural interaction is said to have occurred. Binaural interaction, so defined, is found in the lateral and medial superior olives, but not in nearby regions. The slow and periodic potentials do not always exhibit binaural interaction at the same electrode positions and, thus, they may be related to different processes. These results support the proposition that the superior olivary complex is a major site for binaural analysis.

Ascending projections.—The axons of the lateral superior olive enter the lateral lemniscus of the homolateral and contralateral sides in about equal numbers. The axons of the medial superior olive enter the lateral lemniscus of the homolateral side as do most of the axons of the periolivary complex (120). Thus, the binaural analysis done in superior olivary complex is projected upward. The responses of higher auditory nuclei should reflect this fact, but, in addition, it is likely that additional binaural analysis is done in these higher centers.

INFERIOR COLLICULUS

Geisler, Rhode & Hazelton (138) compare responses of neurons in the inferior colliculus to noise and to tones. They conclude that most of the properties of the binaural responses to noise bands can be linked to those for tones by a simple model. This model includes a narrowband filter interposed between the neuron and the eardrum and the notion that neurons sensitive to interaural time differences have a characteristic delay. EI cells sensitive to interaural intensity differences are described. In most cases, contralateral stimulation is excitatory, ipsilateral stimulation inhibitory. Also, it is demonstrated that onset discharges and sustained discharges may bear different relations to interaural parameters for a single cell. Another complexity is that not all of the phase-sensitive low-frequency cells exhibit characteristic delays that are invariant with frequency and interaural intensity differences. These authors emphasize that in the inferior colliculus there are complexities that either do not exist or have not yet been found in the superior olivary complex. Some of the differences between these two levels in the auditory system are: 1. phase-locking of discharges to the stimuli is not as common in the inferior colliculus as it is in the superior olivary complex; and 2. the discharge patterns are more complex in the inferior colliculus than in the superior olivary complex.

Benevento & Coleman (139) classify neurons in the inferior colliculus on the basis of their responses to clicks with various interaural differences. There are units sensitive to 1. interaural intensity differences, 2. interaural time differences, 3. neither interaural time nor intensity differences, and 4. both interaural time and intensity differences. Unfortunately for this classificatory scheme, many cells change class when the intensities of the clicks are changed. It is worth noting that both in the superior olivary complex and in the inferior colliculus time-intensity trading is commonly found when transient stimuli are used or in the onset responses to high-frequency tone bursts. Time-intensity trading appears to be rare in the sustained responses to low-frequency tones; here it seems the concept of a characteristic delay often applies.

Altman (140) describes neurons in the inferior colliculus that are particularly sensitive to the direction of movement of a sound source. He demonstrates such neurons both for actual sound sources and for changes in interaural time difference that simulate the movement of a source. The extraction of the direction of movement may represent an analysis first performed in the inferior colliculus. Such an analysis is important not only for determining the direction of movement of a sound source, but also for the use of head and pinna movements in sound localization.

MEDIAL GENICULATE BODY

Altman et al (141) describe the responses of cells in the medial geniculate body of cats anesthetized with chloralose and urethane. Monaural and binaural click stimuli were applied either singly or in trains and interaural parameters were varied. They find three types of response to single clicks: an initial discharge with a latency of 6–30 msec; an initial and a late discharge; or only a late discharge. The late discharge occurs between 500 and 4000 msec after the click. The relation of onset discharges to interaural parameters is similar to those previously described in the inferior colliculus and to those described by Aitkin & Dunlop (142) in the medial geniculate body. The properties of the late discharge are more remarkable. In some cases if an interaural parameter was changed during a slowly presented train of dichotic clicks, the response of the late discharge would not change in the expected manner until after three or four dichotic clicks had been presented. Because of the long latency and duration of these late discharges and because of the lag of changes in response to changed interaural parameters, Altman et al (141) argue that these late discharges play a role in the short-term memory for interaural parameters. They also find cells sensitive to the direction of movement as described for the inferior colliculus, and some of these directionally sensitive units appear to be responsive to only limited portions of the auditory field. Aitkin & Dunlop (142) focused on the initial discharges of cells in the medial geniculate body. They find that units with onset responses to clicks are all binaural in that they can be excited by stimulation of both ears or excited by stimulation of one and inhibited by stimulation of the other. They subdivide onset discharges into two classes, short and long, and detail the properties of each class. Among their more interesting findings is the occurrence of poststimulatory inhibition of long duration. Some units could not respond to a second click for as long as 70 msec after a preceding click, and full recovery was sometimes not complete in 400 msec. This effect was observed for monaural click pairs and for dichotic click pairs, although the inhibitory periods were shorter for the latter than for the former case.

AUDITORY CORTEX

Hall & Goldstein (143) surveyed the responses of units in area AI of the cortex of immobilized cats. Clicks, noise bursts, or tone bursts were presented either monaurally or binaurally. These units discharged near the onset or offset of the stimulus with a period of suppression after the discharges. Most cells responded to stimulation of the contralateral ear. Very few responded only to stimulation of the ipsilateral ear, and only a slightly greater number responded *only* to binaural stimulation. Over all types of stimuli, almost all of the units were influenced, either suppressed or excited, by both ears. Nonetheless, the contralateral ear is clearly more heavily represented than the ipsilateral ear. Brugge et al (144) systematically varied interaural parameters while recording from units in areas AI and AII of the cortex of cats anesthetized with sodium pentobarbital or α-chloralose. Most of the units responded at the beginning or the end of a tone burst as described by Hall & Goldstein (143), although a few did maintain discharges throughout a 500-msec tone. They decribe EI units that are sensitive to interaural intensity differences. But, more generally, they conclude that stimulation of each ear evoked an excitatory-inhibitory sequence of events and that the effects of interaural time and intensity changes could be understood as the net response determined by the manner in which the excitatory and inhibitory events interlaced in time. For low-frequency tone bursts (0.2 to 2.4 kHz), units were found that exhibited characteristic delays at which the probability of discharge was highest and latency the shortest. The probability of discharge and latency then varied periodically with frequency of the stimulus as the interaural delay was changed. Hirsch (145) found similar results for evoked responses measured with electrodes placed at various points on the cortex. Surprisingly, she found the amplitude of the evoked response at a given cortical location to be more closely related to interaural phase than to interaural time differences.

BEHAVIORAL EXPERIMENTS

Masterton, Jane & Diamond (146) have continued their investigations of the effects of lesions in the auditory system on discriminations essential for fine localization of sound sources. They find that bilateral ablation of the inferior colliculus that is deep enough to separate the auditory structures of the forebrain from the hindbrain renders the cat incapable of responding to interaural time or interaural intensity cues. Bilateral ablation of the apical region of the inferior colliculus, which spares a large portion of the underlying lemniscal pathways, does not impair discrimination of lateralized sounds. Lesions which appear to sever the rostral projection of the tectum but spare the inferior colliculus itself abolish lateralization based on interaural time differences. In these cases lateralization based on intensity differences (L vs R) may be related to the depth to which the lesion invades the lateral tegmentum. From their experiments and those of others, these authors theorize that temporal cues for sound localization are extracted in the medial superior olive. This information is relayed to the cortex via the lemniscal pathways. Intensive and spectral cues for sound localization, on the other hand, these authors believe can be mediated via extralemniscal pathways. While there is some evidence for binaural effects in extralemniscal structures (147), it appears that the so-called extralemniscal pathways that can carry the intensive and spectral information for sound localization are intimately related to the traditional lemniscal pathways.

Masterton, Jane & Diamond (146) suggest that cortex is necessary for the integration of the several cues for localization and provides the basis for the perception of auditory space. In their view the role of inferior colliculus in sound localization is limited to reflexive and attentive reactions to sounds such as head, pinna, and eye movements. Perhaps, the relative and absolute decrease in the volume of auditory nuclei of the brainstem as one moves from lower to higher mammals (148) can be taken as support for their hypothesis.

Strominger & Oesterreich (149) showed that complete bilateral section of the brachium of the inferior colliculus abolished sound localization by cats in a situation that allowed head movements and both intensive and temporal cues for sound localization. (This is an apparent conflict with the conclusion of Masterton, Jane & Diamond that use of intensive cues does not require the superficial brachia. However, they studied the extreme case of discrimination of sounds presented monaurally to the right or left ears, whereas in the Strominger & Oesterreich experiment only natural interaural intensity differences could occur.) Bilaterally incomplete section of the brachia was without effect on sound localization in one cat. Unilateral complete section of the brachium produced a severe transient and, in some cases, small permanent impairment of localization. In this case, the permanent deficit may be in the field contralateral to the site of the lesion. Wide bilateral extirpation of auditory cortical areas seems to profoundly impair auditory localization by cats. Strominger (150, 151) demonstrates that bilateral ablation of single auditory areas is without effect except for mild impairments in the case of AI. Various combinations of ablations consistently point to the relative importance of AI. Suga (152, 153) investigated the effects of various surgical lesions of inferior colliculus and auditory cortex on obstacle avoidance by bats. While some of those lesions clearly interfered with obstacle avoidance, others did not. Interpretation is difficult because of the unknown nature of the higher auditory pathways. Of course, there is the same difficulty with cats, but the problem is even greater with bats. Nonetheless, Suga rallied arguments to support his view that the auditory cortex is less important for sound localization in bat than it is in cat, and that it is the ventral portion of the bat's inferior colliculus that is crucial for obstacle avoidance.

COMMENT

The detection of small time differences in relation to spatial perception appears to be a function of highly specialized structures unique to the auditory system. This notion may have to be reconsidered in view of findings of von Békésy that comparable time differences can be detected by the olfactory, gustatory, vibrotactile, and visual systems (154).

ACKNOWLEDGMENT

The preparation of this review was supported by PHS research grant NS 03856 from the National Institute of Neurological Diseases and Stroke to Central Institute for the Deaf.

LITERATURE CITED

1. von Bismark, G. 1967. *The sound pressure transformation function from free-field to the eardrum of chinchilla.* MS thesis. MIT, Cambridge, Mass.
2. Tonndorf, J., Khanna, S. M. 1968. *J. Acoust. Soc. Am.* 44:1546–54
3. Guinan, J. J., Jr., Peake, W. T. 1967. *J. Acoust. Soc. Am.* 41:1237–61
4. Tonndorf, J., Khanna, S. M. 1968. *Ann. Otol. Rhinol. Laryngol.* 77:154–63
5. von Békésy, G. 1960. *Experiments in Hearing*, ed. and transl. E. G. Wever. New York: McGraw-Hill. 745 pp.
6. Johnstone, B. M., Boyle, A. J. F. 1967. *Science* 158:389–90
7. Johnstone, B. M., Taylor, K. J., Boyle, A. J. 1970. *J. Acoust. Soc. Am.* 47:504–9
8. Dallos, P. 1969. *J. Acoust. Soc. Am.* 45:999–1007
9. Tasaki, I., Davis, H., Legouix, J.-P. 1952. *J. Acoust. Soc. Am.* 24:502–19
10. Laszlo, C. A., Gannon, R. P., Milsum, J. H. 1970. *J. Acoust. Soc. Am.* 47:1063–70
11. Engebretson, A. M. 1970. *A study of the linear and nonlinear characteristics of the microphonic voltage in the cochlea.* ScD thesis, Sever Inst. Technol., Washington Univ., St. Louis
12. Honrubia, V., Ward, P. H. 1968. *J. Acoust. Soc. Am.* 44:951–58
13. Whitfield, I. C., Ross, H. F. 1965. *J. Acoust. Soc. Am.* 38:126–31
14. Sweetman, R. H., Dallos, P. 1969. *J. Acoust. Soc. Am.* 45:58–71
15. Engebretson, A. M., Eldredge, D. H. 1968. *J. Acoust. Soc. Am.* 44:548–54
16. Tonndorf, J. 1970. *J. Acoust. Soc. Am.* 47:579–91
17. Dallos, P., Schoeny, Z. G., Worthington, D. W., Cheatham, M. A. 1969. *Science* 164:449–51
18. Dallos, P. 1969. *J. Acoust. Soc. Am.* 46:1437–44
19. Nieder, P., Nieder, I. 1968. *J. Acoust. Soc. Am.* 43:1092–1106
20. Nieder, P., Nieder, I. 1968. *J. Acoust. Soc. Am.* 44:1409–22
21. Dallos, P., Schoeny, Z. G., Worthington, D. W., Cheatham, M. A. 1969. *J. Acoust. Soc. Am.* 46:356–61
22. Dallos, P., Sweetman, R. H. 1969. *J. Acoust. Soc. Am.* 45:37–46
23. Goldstein, J. L., Kiang, N. Y. S. 1968. *Proc. IEEE* 56:981–92
24. Pfeiffer, R. R., Molnar, C. E. 1970. *Science* 167:1614–16
25. Stevens, S. S., Newman, E. B., 1936. *Proc. Nat. Acad. Sci.* 22:668–72
26. Wever, E. G., Bray, C. W., Lawrence, M. 1940. *J. Exp. Psychol.* 27:469–96
27. Black, L. J., Covell, W. P. 1936. *Proc. Soc. Exp. Biol. Med.* 33:509–11
28. Davis, H., Fernández, C., McAuliffe, D. R. 1950. *Proc. Nat. Acad. Sci.* 36:580–87
29. Davis, H., Eldredge, D. H. 1959. *Ann. Otol. Rhinol. Laryngol.* 68:665–74
30. Johnstone, J. R., Johnstone, B. M.

1966. *J. Acoust. Soc. Am.* 40 : 1405–13

31. Honrubia, V., Ward, P. H. 1969. *J. Acoust. Soc. Am.* 45 :1443–50

32. Honrubia, V., Ward, P. H. 1969. *J. Acoust. Soc. Am.* 46 :388–92

33. Davis, H. 1958. *Ann. Otol. Rhinol. Laryngol.* 67 :789–801

34. Iurato, S. 1967. *Submicroscopic Structure of the Inner Ear*, ed. S. Iurato, 59–106, 174. London : Pergamon. 367 pp.

35. Spoendlin, H. 1967. *Vascular stria.* See Ref. 34, 131–49

36. Smith, C. A., Davis, H., Deatherage, B. H., Gessert, C. F. 1958. *Am. J. Physiol.* 193 :203–6

37. Tasaki, I., Spyropoulos, C. S. 1959. *J. Neurophysiol.* 22 :149–55

38. Tasaki, I., Fernández, C. 1952. *J. Neurophysiol.* 15 :497–512

39. Pražma, J. 1969. *Acta Oto-Laryngol.* 68 :53–61

40. Konishi, T., Kelsey, E. 1968. *J. Acoust. Soc. Am.* 43 :462–70

41. Konishi, T., Kelsey, E. 1970. *J. Acoust. Soc. Am.* 47 :1055–62

42. Konishi, T., Kelsey, E., Singleton, G. T. 1966. *Acta Oto-Laryngol.* 62 :393–404

43. Bosher, S. K., Warren, R. L. 1968. *Proc. Roy. Soc. Biol.* 171 :227–47

44. Mendelsohn, M., Konishi, T. 1969. *Ann. Otol. Rhinol. Laryngol.* 78 : 65–75

45. Paparella, M. M., Ed. 1970. *Biochemical Mechanisms in Hearing and Deafness.* Springfield, Ill : Thomas. 380 pp.

46. Matschinsky, F. M., Thalmann, R. 1967. *Ann. Otol. Rhinol. Laryngol.* 76 :638–46

47. Ishii, D., Takahashi, T., Balogh, K. 1969. *Acta Oto-Laryngol.* 67 :573–82

48. Thalmann, I., Matschinsky, F. M., Thalmann, R. 1970. *Ann. Otol. Rhinol. Laryngol.* 79 :12–29

49. Nakai, Y., Hilding, D. 1968. *Acta Oto-Laryngol.* 65 :459–67

50. Kluyskens, P., Verstraete, W. 1969. *Acta Oto-Laryngol.* 67 :206–10

51. Nakai, Y., Hilding, D. 1967. *Acta Oto-Laryngol.* 64 :477–91

52. Kuijpers, W., Van der Vleuten, A. C., Bonting, S. L. 1967. *Science* 157 : 949–50

53. Kuijpers, W. 1969. *Acta Oto-Laryngol.* 67 :200–5

54. Pražma, J. 1969. *Acta Oto-Laryngol.* 67 :631–38

55. Konishi, T., Mendelsohn, M. 1970. *Acta Oto-Laryngol.* 69 :192–99

56. Tanaka, Y., Brown, P. G. 1970. *Ann. Otol. Rhinol. Laryngol.* 79 :338–51

57. Konishi, T., Kelsey, E. 1968. *Acta Oto-Laryngol.* 65 :381–90

58. Tsunoo, M., Perlman, H. B. 1969. *Acta Oto-Laryngol.* 67 :17–23

59. Konishi, T., Kelsey, E. 1968. *J. Acoust. Soc. Am.* 43 :471–80

60. von Ilberg, C., Vosteen, K.-H. 1969. *Acta Oto-Laryngol.* 67 :165–70

61. Rauch, S., Köstlin, A., Schnieder, E. A., Schindler, K. 1963. *Laryngoscope* 73 :135–47

62. Sohmer, H., Feinmesser, M. 1967. *Acta Oto-Laryngol.* 64 :55–64

63. Johnstone, C. G., Schmidt, R. S., Johnstone, B. M. 1963. *Comp. Biochem. Physiol.* 9 :335–41

64. Lawrence, M. 1966. *Laryngoscope* 76 : 1318–37

65. Galambos, R., Davis, H. 1943. *J. Neurophysiol.* 6 :39–57

66. Katsuki, Y., Sumi, T., Uchiyama, H., Watanabe, T. 1958. *J. Neurophysiol.* 21 :569–88

67. Kiang, N. Y. S., Watanabe, T., Thomas, E. C., Clark, L. F. 1962. *Ann. Otol. Rhinol. Laryngol.* 71 : 1009–26

68. Kiang, N. Y. S., Sachs, M. B., Peake, W. T. 1967. *J. Acoust. Soc. Am.* 42 :1341–42

69. Kiang, N. Y. S. 1965. *Discharge Patterns of Single Fibers in the Cat's Auditory Nerve.* Res. Monogr. No. 35. Cambridge, Mass : MIT Press. 154 pp.

70. de Boer, E. 1967. *J. Aud. Res.* 7 : 209–17

71. de Boer, E. 1969. *Proc. Kon. Ned. Akad. Wetensch.* Series C 72 :129–51

72. de Boer, E., Jongkees, L. B. W. 1968. *Acta Oto-Laryngol.* 65 :97–104

73. Rose, J. E., Brugge, J. F., Anderson, D. J., Hind, J. E. 1967. *J. Neurophysiol.* 30 :769–93

74. Hind, J. E., Anderson, D. J., Brugge, J. F., Rose, J. E. 1967. *J. Neurophysiol.* 30 :794–816

75. Brugge, J. F., Anderson, D. J., Hind, J. E., Rose, J. E. 1969. *J. Neurophysiol.* 32 :386–401

76. Rose, J. E., Brugge, J. F., Anderson, D. J., Hind, J. E. 1969. *J. Neurophysiol.* 32 :402–23

77. Davis, H. 1961. *Physiol. Rev.* 41 : 391–416

78. Smith, C. A. 1967. Innervation of

the organ of Corti. See Ref. 34, 107–31
79. Sachs, M. B., Kiang, N. Y. S. 1968. *J. Acoust. Soc. Am.* 43 :1120–28
80. Sachs, M. B. 1969. *J. Acoust. Soc. Am.* 45 :1025–36
81. Konishi, T., Teas, D. C., Wernick, J. S. 1970. *J. Acoust. Soc. Am.* 47 :1519–26
82. Teas, D. C., Konishi, T., Wernick, J. S. 1970. *J. Acoust. Soc. Am.* 47 :1527–37
83. Goblick, T. J., Jr., Pfeiffer, R. R. 1969. *J. Acoust. Soc. Am.* 46 :924–38
84. Fex, J. 1968. In *Hearing Mechanisms in Vertebrates,* ed. A. V. S. De Reuck, J. Knight, 169–81. Boston : Little-Brown. 320 pp.
85. Wersäll, J. 1968. In *Structure and Function of Inhibitory Neuronal Mechanisms,* ed. C. von Euler, S. Skoglund, U. Söderberg, 123–39. *Int. Meet. Neurobiologists, 4th, Wenner-Gren Cent., Stockholm, 1966.* Oxford : Pergamon, Int. Symp. Ser., Vol. 10. 563 pp.
86. Smith, C. 1968. See Ref. 85, 141–46
87. Fex, J. 1968. The mechanisms of centrifugal inhibition in the organ of Corti in mammals. See Ref. 85, 147–55
88. Rossi, G. 1968. Anatomical organization of the efferent cochlear and vestibular system. See Ref. 85, 157–68
89. Ishii, D., Balogh, K., Jr. 1968. *Acta Oto-Laryngol.* 66 :282–88
90. Ishii, T., Murakami, Y., Gacek, R. R. 1967. *Acta Oto-Laryngol.* 64 :267–79
91. Hiraide, F. 1970. *Acta Oto-Laryngol.* 69 :286–93
92. Ross, M. D. 1969. *J. Comp. Neurol.* 135 :453–78
93. Spoendlin, H. 1966. *The Organization of the Cochlear Receptor.* Basel : Karger. 227 pp.
94. Morest, D. K. 1968. *Brain Res.* 9 : 288–311
95. Rupert, A. L., Moushegian, G., Whitcomb, M. A. 1968. *Exp. Neurol.* 20 :575–84
96. Klinke, R., Boerger, G., Gruber, J. 1969. *Pfluegers Arch.* 306 :165–75
97. Wiederhold, M. L. 1967. *A Study of Efferent Inhibition of Auditory Nerve Activity.* PhD thesis. MIT, Cambridge, Mass.
98. Spoendlin, H. 1969. *Acta Oto-Laryngol.* 67 :239–54
99. Comis, S. D., Whitfield, I. C. 1968. *J. Neurophysiol.* 31 :62–68
100. Starr, A., Wernick, J. S. 1968. *J. Neurophysiol.* 31 :549–64
101. Capps, M. J., Ades, H. W. 1968. *Exp. Neurol.* 21 :147–58
102. Dewson, J. H. III 1968. *J. Neurophysiol.* 31 :122–30
103. Trahiotis, C., Elliott, D. N. 1970. *J. Acoust. Soc. Am.* 47 :592–96
104. Wickelgren, W. O. 1968. *J. Neurophysiol.* 31 :757–68
105. Wickelgren, W. O. 1968. *J. Neurophysiol.* 31 :777–84
106. Marsh, J. T., Worden, F. G. 1969. *Brain Res.* 12 :99–111
107. Hall, R. D. 1968. *Electroenceph. Clin. Neurophysiol.* 24 :155–65
108. Saunders, J. C., Chabora, J. T. 1969. *J. Comp. Physiol. Psychol.* 69 : 355–61
109. Kitzes, M., Buchwald, J. 1969. *Exp. Neurol.* 25 :85–105
110. Ellinwood, E. H., Cook, J. D., Wilson, W. P. 1968. *Brain Res.* 7 : 306–9
111. Ebersole, J. S., Galambos, R. 1969. *Electroenceph. Clin. Neurophysiol.* 26 :273–79
112. Vaughan, H. G., Ritter, W. 1970. *Electroenceph. Clin. Neurophysiol.* 28 :360–67
113. Liberson, W. T. 1966. *Am. J. Phys. Med.* 45 :135–42
114. Stohr, P. E., Goldring, S. 1969. *J. Neurosurg.* 31 :117–27
115. Jerger, J., Weikers, N. J., Sharbrough, F. W. III, Jerger, S. 1969. *Acta Oto-Laryngol. Suppl. 258.* 51 pp.
116. Williamson, P. D., Goff, W. R., Matsumiya, Y., Allison, T. 1970. *Electroenceph. Clin. Neurophysiol.* 28 :91
117. Green, D. M., Henning, G. B. 1969. *Ann. Rev. Psychol.* 20 :105–28
118. König, E. 1964. *Int. Audiol.* 3 :54–88
119. Warr, W. B. 1969. *Exp. Neurol.* 23 :140–55
120. Stotler, W. A. 1953. *J. Comp. Neurol.* 98 :401–31
121. Goldberg, J. M., Brown, P. B. 1968. *J. Neurophysiol.* 31 :639–56
122. Irving, R., Harrison, J. M. 1967. *J. Comp. Neurol.* 130 :77–86
123. Clark, G. M. 1969. *Brain Res.* 14 : 293–305
124. Uchizono, K. 1968. Inhibitory and excitatory synapses in vertebrate and invertebrate animals. See Ref. 85, 33–59

125. Goldberg, J. M., Brown, P. B. 1969. *J. Neurophysiol.* 32:613–36
126. Jeffress, L. A. 1948. *J. Comp. Physiol. Psychol.* 41:35–39
127. Moushegian, G., Rupert, A. L., Langford, T. L. 1967. *J. Neurophysiol.* 30:1239–61
128. Watanabe, T., Liao, T., Katsuki, Y. 1968. *Jap. J. Physiol.* 18:267–87
129. Clark, G. M., Dunlop, C. W. 1969. *Exp. Neurol.* 23:266–90
130. Galambos, R., Schwartzkopff, J., Rupert, A. 1959. *Am. J. Physiol.* 197:527–36
131. Rasmussen, G. L. 1967. In *Sensorineural Hearing Processes and Disorders*, ed. A. B. Graham, 61–75. Boston: Little-Brown. 543 pp.
132. van Noort, J. 1969. *The Structure and Connections of the Inferior Colliculus.* PhD thesis. Univ. Leiden
133. Boudreau, J. C., Tsuchitani, C. 1968. *J. Neurophysiol.* 31:442–54
134. Tsuchitani, C., Boudreau, J. C. 1969. *J. Acoust. Soc. Am.* 46:979–88
135. Clark, G. M., Dunlop, C. W. 1968. *Exp. Neurol.* 20:31–42
136. Weinberger, N. M., Kitzes, L. M., Goodman, D. A. 1970. *Experientia* 26:46–48
137. Wernick, J. S., Starr, A. 1968. *J. Neurophysiol.* 31:428–41
138. Geisler, C. D., Rhode, W. S., Hazelton, D. W. 1969. *J. Neurophysiol.* 32:960–74
139. Benevento, L. A., Coleman, P. D. 1970. *Brain Res.* 17:387–405
140. Altman, J. A. 1968. *Exp. Neurol.* 22:13–25
141. Altman, J. A., Syka, J., Shmigidina, G. N. 1970. *Exp. Brain Res.* 10:81–93
142. Aitkin, L. M., Dunlop, C. W. 1968. *J. Neurophysiol.* 31:44–61
143. Hall, J. L. II, Goldstein, M. H., Jr. 1968. *J. Acoust. Soc. Am.* 43:456–61
144. Brugge, J. F., Dubrovsky, N. A., Aitkin, L. M., Anderson, D. J. 1969. *J. Neurophysiol.* 32:1005–24
145. Hirsch, J. E. 1968. *J. Neurophysiol.* 31:916–27
146. Masterton, R. B., Jane, J. A., Diamond, I. T. 1968. *J. Neurophysiol.* 31:96–108
147. Jaffe, S. L., Hagamen, W. D. 1969. *Electroenceph. Clin. Neurophysiol.* 26:419–23
148. Zvorykin, V. P. 1970. *Neurosci. Transl.* No. 12:63–72
149. Strominger, N. L., Oesterreich, R. E. 1970. *J. Comp. Neurol.* 138:1–18
150. Strominger, N. L. 1969. *Exp. Neurol.* 24:348–62
151. Strominger, N. L. 1969. *Exp. Neurol.* 25:521–33
152. Suga, N. 1969. *J. Physiol.* 203:707–28
153. Suga, N. 1969. *J. Physiol.* 203:729–39
154. von Békésy, G. 1969. *Proc. Nat. Acad. Sci.* 64:142–47

CYCLIC NUCLEOTIDES[1]

J. G. Hardman, G. A. Robison,[2] and E. W. Sutherland[3]

Departments of Physiology and Pharmacology
Vanderbilt University School of Medicine, Nashville, Tennessee

Cyclic nucleotides have been the subject of a number of reviews during the past few years. Major emphasis in most of these has been on cyclic AMP, the first of the 3',5'-nucleotides found to occur naturally. Topics covered by these reviews have included lipolysis (1–3), steroidogenesis (1, 2), hepatic carbohydrate metabolism (4), carbohydrate metabolism in general (5), calcium metabolism (6), effects on enzymes (2, 5), myocardial contractility (1, 7), neurobiological aspects (8, 9), bacterial protein synthesis (10), and the relation of adenyl cyclase to hormone receptors (11, 12). In addition, two previous *Annual Reviews* (13, 14) attempted to cover a variety of topics, and an often-promised monograph on the subject has been completed (15). The role of cyclic AMP in adrenergic physiology is discussed elsewhere in this volume (16).

In view of the above, the need for another review can be questioned. In such a rapidly expanding field, however, frequent reviewing does seem to serve a useful purpose. It helps to keep the reviewers up to date, at least, and we can hope that others will be similarly served. We propose to discuss several aspects of the subject not previously covered, and will place special emphasis on cyclic GMP. As of this writing, this is the only other 3',5'-nucleotide known to occur naturally. Although it was discovered several years ago in urine (17), it is only within recent years that detailed studies of this nucleotide have been published.

Intracellular Levels

Cyclic AMP.—The alteration of intracellular levels of cyclic AMP by a number of hormones has been discussed previously (1, 2, 15). Hormones that have been shown to raise intracellular cyclic AMP levels in their target tissues include the catecholamines, glucagon, ACTH, MSH, LH, vasopressin, parathyroid hormone, prostaglandins, and, more recently, thyrocalcitonin (18, 19). Where studied carefully, these hormones seem to act by stimu-

---

[1] The authors are grateful to the several individuals who allowed them to read manuscripts in advance of publication.

[2] Investigator, Howard Hughes Medical Institute.

[3] Career Investigator, American Heart Association.

lating adenyl cyclase. Insulin, melatonin, prostaglandins, and catecholamines may under some conditions produce a fall in cyclic AMP levels in some tissues. The mechanism of action of these agents is unknown. To date, neither formation nor destruction of the nucleotide has been clearly established as the process affected.

Cyclic GMP.—Cyclic GMP levels in tissues have been much less extensively studied than cyclic AMP levels. In fact, only recently have sensitive methods been available for detection of cyclic GMP (20–23). The intracellular levels of this nucleotide are, like those of cyclic AMP, extremely low compared to the analogous 5′ mono-, di- and triphosphates. The cyclic nucleotide generally comprises between 0.1 and 0.01% of the total adenine or guanine nucleotide content. Comparative determinations of both nucleotides have been made in only a limited number of studies, but levels of cyclic AMP in mammalian tissues have consistently been found to be at least an order of magnitude higher than those of cyclic GMP (20, 22, 23). This relative distribution is not universal, however, since crickets contain two to three times more cyclic GMP than cyclic AMP (22) and hen eggs and sea urchin sperm contain comparable amounts of the two cyclic nucleotides (24). Minnows and earthworms also contain somewhat higher concentrations of cyclic GMP than found in mammalian tissues (22).

Generally, cyclic GMP has been detected in rat tissues in concentrations between 10^{-8} and 10^{-7} moles per kg (20, 22, 23). Discrepancies of some two to threefold exist in tissue levels of cyclic GMP reported by different groups (20, 22), but since little is known about factors that may influence these levels (e.g. anesthetic, age, sex, fixation technique), such discrepancies are difficult to resolve at present. Extremely high levels of cyclic GMP (6×10^{-6} moles per kg) have been reported to occur in rat diaphragm incubated in vitro without substrate (25). A dissociation between cyclic AMP and cyclic GMP was observed in the mouse brain following decapitation; cyclic AMP levels were elevated at a time when cyclic GMP levels were unaltered or slightly lowered (23, 26).

Unlike cyclic AMP, cyclic GMP has been the subject of only a limited number of studies pertaining to alteration of its tissue levels in response to hormones and other agents. Theophylline, an inhibitor of cyclic nucleotide phosphodiesterase, caused a rapid increase in cyclic GMP levels in rat kidney (20) and small intestine (22). Acetylcholine more than doubled the cyclic GMP content of the perfused rat heart, while not changing or slightly lowering cyclic AMP levels (27); isoproterenol, which in combination with theophylline markedly raised the cyclic AMP level, led to a significant decrease in the concentration of cyclic GMP. Injections of epinephrine or glucagon that elevated cyclic AMP in rat liver in situ had no effect on cyclic GMP levels (20). Hepatic concentrations of cyclic GMP in alloxan-diabetic rats treated or untreated with insulin were likewise indistinguishable from normal (20). Neither ACTH nor epinephrine had any effect on cyclic GMP in fat (23).

Extracellular fluid levels of cyclic GMP vary in altered hormonal states in rat and man, as discussed in a later section. These studies and those summarized above leave no doubt that cyclic AMP and cyclic GMP levels can be changed quite selectively by a number of hormonal and other factors.

Cyclic GMP has been detected in bacteria (28), but has not been shown to exist in the cells of higher plants. Evidence for the formation of cyclic AMP in higher plants has been presented (29).

Other cyclic nucleotides.—To date, other cyclic 3',5'-nucleotides have not been reported in nature. Cyclic deoxy-AMP can be formed from deoxy-ATP by adenyl cyclase (30, 31) but has not been identified in a biological source. Neither cyclic IMP nor cyclic UMP could be detected in rat liver by a radioimmunoassay that would have detected 10^{-8} moles per kg (32). Cyclic UMP was not detectable in urine by methods that would have allowed the measurement of levels as low as 1% of the cyclic AMP and cyclic GMP present (21, 33).

FORMATION

Cyclic AMP.—Although cyclic GMP will be emphasized in this section as in others, some recent observations on the formation of cyclic AMP can be mentioned. As is by now well known, cyclic AMP is formed from ATP under the catalytic influence of adenyl cyclase. Although bacterial adenyl cyclase has been purified more than 100-fold (34), it has so far not been possible to achieve a similar degree of purification of the particulate mammalian system. The bacterial enzyme was used to show that the adenyl cyclase reaction could be reversed under appropriate conditions (35). The implication that the 3'-phosphate bond was of the high-energy type was later confirmed, for cyclic GMP as well as cyclic AMP, by calorimetric experiments (36).

An important series of experiments with adenyl cyclase from adrenal tumors has been reported (37). Phosphatidylethanolamine and sonication were used to obtain a preparation that was "soluble" in the sense that activity did not sediment when subjected to a force of 105,000 × g for 1 hr. Although electronmicroscopy disclosed the presence of small membrane fragments, the activity nevertheless behaved on agarose gels like a globular protein. The important difference between this "soluble" preparation and those previously described (e.g. 38, 39) was that it retained a substantial degree of hormonal sensitivity, in this case to ACTH. Pure monoiodo ACTH-^{125}I bound only to those fractions containing ACTH-sensitive adenyl cyclase activity. ACTH and five derivatives of ACTH inhibited the binding of ACTH-^{125}I in direct proportion to their biological activity; hormones and other proteins lacking biological activity were inert (37). These studies emphasize in a very striking way the close relation between hormone receptors and adenyl cyclase (11) and encourage hope that a highly purified preparation of hormone-sensitive adenyl cyclase will eventually become available.

The nature of the relation between hormone receptors and adenyl cyclase is of course still obscure. Recent studies have disclosed that catalytic activity and hormonal sensitivity do not necessarily develop hand-in-hand. Activity in hemolysates of amphibian erythrocytes did not respond to catecholamines until after metamorphosis (40). Similarly, although adenyl cyclase is present in preparations of newborn rat brains, it does not respond to norepinephrine for the first few days postpartum, following which sensitivity to norephinephrine develops rapidly (41). In the latter studies, the accumulation of cyclic AMP in chopped slices was used as an index of cyclase activity, since sensitivity to norepinephrine is easily lost in broken-cell preparations of brain (9). The significance of brain adenyl cyclase has yet to be established. A substantial part of the activity in brain preparations may be derived from glial cells (42).

Despite the obvious impurity of mammalian adenyl cyclase preparations, the use of an ATP-regenerating system has made kinetic studies feasible, in the sense that the influence of ATPase, at least, can be minimized. Estimates of the apparent K_m for ATP, using adenyl cyclase from several tissues (e.g. 43–46), have ranged from 0.08 to 0.5 mM. Stimulation by fluoride has been seen in preparations of all adult mammalian tissues studied, and there is general agreement that fluoride increases the V_{max} without altering the affinity for ATP. However, the mechanism of the fluoride effect is still obscure. Incubation of a brain preparation with Triton-X100 led to an increase in activity which could not be furtther increased by the addition of fluoride (47). The significance of this is unknown at present. Either Mg^{++} or Mn^{++} is required for adenyl cyclase activity, whereas Ca^{++} has usually been found to be inhibitory (44, 45). On the other hand, ACTH may actually require Ca^{++} in order to stimulate the enzyme (48).

The stimulation of adenyl cyclase activity in renal cortical preparations by parathyroid hormone (49, 50) has been recommended as the basis of a bioassay for this hormone.

Cyclic GMP.—That the metabolism of cyclic GMP was at least partially independent of that of cyclic AMP was suggested early by observations that the urinary excretion of the two nucleotides varied independently in altered hormonal states (21, 51). It is now known that cyclic GMP is formed from GTP by an enzyme system, guanyl cyclase, which is distinctly different from adenyl cyclase in a number of respects.

Guanyl cyclase, in contrast to the entirely particulate adenyl cyclase, is partially soluble in most tissues of the rat so far examined (52–54). Varying amounts of guanyl cyclase are found in particulate fractions of different tissues, however, and all of the enzyme appears to be particulate in the rat small intestine (22). This tissue and lung (52, 53) have the highest activities yet found among mammalian tissues. By far the most active source of guanyl cyclase found so far, however, is the sperm of the sea urchin *Strongylocentrotus purpuratus* (55). The guanyl cyclase activity here is up to 1000 times higher than in rat tissues and, as in the rat small intestine, is found entirely in the particulate fraction. This unusually high activity in sea urchin sperm does not appear to be characteristic of mammalian sperm, where levels of the enzyme are virtually undetectable under comparable assay conditions (24).

Guanyl cyclase activity depends strongly on the presence of Mn^{++} (22, 52–54). The apparent K_m for Mn^{++} is about 0.5 mM (52, 53, 55). Magnesium or calcium ions are extremely poor substitutes for Mn^{++} (52–54), although Ca^{++} does appear to increase activity in the presence of subsaturating concentrations of Mn^{++} (56). Most adenyl cyclase systems studied utilize Mg^{++} almost as well as Mn^{++}, but adenyl cyclase in sea urchin sperm resembles guanyl cyclase in being strongly dependent on Mn^+ for activity (24, 55). Another area of contrast between adenyl and guanyl cyclases involves their responsiveness to fluoride. The stimulatory effect of fluoride on adenyl cyclase, seen in nearly all adult mammalian preparations studied, has not been found with guanyl cyclase, which is unaltered by fluoride (52, 53). On the other hand, several adenyl cyclase systems, including those in sea urchin and human sperm (24) and bacteria (57), are also insensitive to fluoride. Adenyl cyclase in the newborn rat brain is almost if not entirely unresponsive to stimulation by fluoride (41, 47).

Hormones known to affect adenyl cyclase activity in various tissues have been found, under similar conditions, to have no effect on guanyl cyclase activity. Hormones tested and found ineffective include epinephrine, glucagon, and insulin in broken cell preparations of several tissues (52) and ACTH in adrenal cortical preparations (58). Adenosine triphosphate and a number of other nucleotides, as well as oxaloacetate and phosphoenolpyruvate, are inhibitory to guanyl cyclase (22, 52, 53), but only ATP appears to inhibit at physiological concentrations. Heavy metals, including Hg^{++}, Zn^{++}, and Cd^{++}, are strongly inhibitory; this inhibition can be reversed or prevented by dithiothreitol or reduced glutathione (52). Guanyl cyclase in particulate fractions has exhibited increased activity when incubated in the presence of Triton (22, 55). Triton has a similar effect on adenyl cyclase in rat brain preparations (47, 59) although this may not occur in all tissues (22).

It seems clear that in most if not all mammalian tissues studied, adenyl cyclase and guanyl cyclase represent separate and distinct enzyme systems. However, this may not be the case throughout all of nature. It seems possible, for example, that the same enzyme system may have both adenyl and guanyl cyclase activities in sea urchin sperm (24, 55). Both activities in these cells are found entirely in particulate fractions, both are highly dependent on the presence of Mn^{++}, both are stimulated to about the same extent by Triton, and both are insensitive to stimulation by fluoride. In addition, each of these activities is susceptible to inhibition by the nucleoside triphosphate that serves as the substrate of the other, i.e., guanyl cyclase is inhibited by ATP whereas adenyl cyclase is inhibited by GTP. Attempts to separate these two activities in preparations of sea urchin sperm have to date been unsuccessful.

DESTRUCTION

Cyclic AMP.—Cyclic nucleotide phosphodiesterases are the only known enzymes involved in the metabolism of cyclic AMP and cyclic GMP. Other metabolic pathways may exist, however, and the presence of one in the toad bladder has been suggested (60). The plural of phosphodiesterase is used above since evidence is accumulating to indicate that more than one form of the enzyme exists in several tissues (61–64) and even within a single cell type (65). Indeed, earlier demonstrations of the existence of phosphodiesterase activity in both soluble and particulate fractions (66, 67) had raised the possibility of more than one form of the enzyme.

Although a number of drugs inhibit phosphodiesterase activity in vitro (e.g. 66, 68–71), its physiologic regulation is still undefined. Several naturally occurring substances have been reported to be inhibitory (e.g. 72, 73), but the physiological significance of these observations is unclear. There is disagreement about possible effects of insulin to increase phosphodiesterase activity in several tissues (74–77). An earlier report that nicotinic acid stimulated adipose tissue phosphodiesterase activity (78) has not been confirmed (79–81).

The finding that calcium can, under some conditions, stimulate crude preparations of rat brain phosphodiesterase (82) is intriguing. However, proteolytic enzymes also have been shown capable of activating brain phosphodiesterase (83) and an activating effect of calcium on muscle phosphorylase kinase was found to be due to activation of a proteolytic enzyme (84). The possibility of a similar effect on phosphodiesterase should be considered.

The physiological significance of a protein activator of brain phosphodiesterase (85) has not been clarified. Activation induced by this substance seems to be independent of the previously reported activation by proteolytic enzymes (83).

A report of the metabolism of cyclic AMP by the perfused rat liver (86) is difficult to interpret because of the rapid degradation of the nucleotide by the whole rat blood used to perfuse the liver.

Cyclic GMP.—Similar rates of hydrolysis of cyclic AMP and cyclic GMP at substrate levels in the 10^{-3} M range have been seen with phosphodiesterase preparations from rat brain and beef heart (64, 72). Cyclic GMP appears to be hydrolyzed much more slowly than cyclic AMP, by preparations from dog heart (87), rabbit brain (88), and frog erythrocytes (65). The two nucleotides at 10^{-3} M levels were hydrolyzed at nearly the same relative rates by homogenates and subcellular fractions of several rat tissues, the ratio of the rates of hydrolysis being in all cases tested near unity (64). The report of a relatively high rate of cyclic GMP hydrolysis in a particulate fraction from rat liver (76) was not confirmed (64). When the relative rates of the two cyclic nucleotides were compared at 10^{-6} M concentrations, cyclic GMP was hydrolyzed considerably faster than cyclic AMP in most preparations examined, but in particulate fractions from heart and skeletal muscle cyclic AMP was hydrolyzed faster, apparently because of the presence of a phosphodiesterase having a lower apparent K_m for cyclic AMP than for cyclic GMP (64).

Unlike the formation of cyclic GMP, which clearly involves in most tissues a cyclase system distinct and easily separable from adenyl cyclase, the degradation of cyclic GMP cannot be said unequivocally to involve an absolutely specific phosphodiesterase. Indeed, in at least two cell types (64, 65, 89) both cyclic nucleotides apparently serve as substrates for the same enzyme, although with substantially different affinities. For example, with a purified phosphodiesterase from heart, the apparent K_m for cyclic GMP is about 10^{-6} M, at least an order of magnitude lower than that of cyclic AMP (64). Both nucleotides interfere with the hydrolysis of each other by this preparation in a manner predictable from their K_m values. Similar mutual competitive inhibition of cyclic nucleotide hydrolysis has also been seen with phosphodiesterase from frog erythrocytes (65, 89). These observations do not necessarily lead to the conclusion that the cyclic nucleotides inhibit the hydrolysis of each other under physiological circumstances. Indeed in most if not all tissues studied so far, their concentrations appear to be much too low for them to be effective phosphodiesterase inhibitors. These observations should be kept in mind, however, in interpreting cyclic AMP-like effects of high concentrations of exogenous cyclic GMP on various intact cell systems.

Although cyclic AMP and cyclic GMP do seem to be able to serve as substrates for the same enzyme, several observations indicate that their hydrolysis in cells may involve more complicated systems and interactions. The two cyclic nucleotides did not interfere with the hydrolysis of each other by a relatively crude brain phosphodiesterase preparation which appeared to have two K_m's for cyclic AMP and only one for cyclic GMP (62). These observations led to the suggestion that this preparation contained distinct phosphodiesterases for each of the two nucleotides, but whether the substrate specificities were relative or absolute is not clear. Imidazole, known for some time to stimulate the hydrolysis of cyclic AMP by phosphodiesterase from beef heart (66), also stimulated cyclic AMP hydrolysis by a brain phosphodiesterase preparation but inhibited cyclic GMP hydrolysis (70). In these studies, cyclic AMP competitively inhibited the hydrolysis of cyclic GMP but cyclic GMP had no effect on the hydrolysis of cyclic AMP. Low concentrations of cyclic GMP (down to 10^{-7} M) actually stimulated, by two- to threefold, cyclic AMP hydrolysis by a liver phosphodiesterase preparation (64, 90). Cyclic AMP, on the other hand, did not stimulate cyclic GMP hydrolysis. The stimulatory effect of cyclic GMP was most pronounced with cyclic AMP concentrations near the physiological range (near 10^{-6} M). These findings raise the possibility that cyclic GMP influences cyclic AMP levels in some cells by accelerating rather than inhibiting its rate of degradation.

EXTRACELLULAR LEVELS

In addition to the rates of formation and degradation of cyclic nucleotides, the rate at which cells extrude these agents may be a factor in the regulation of their internal concentrations. Very little is known about how cyclic nucleotides exit from cells, but at least one cell type, the avian erythrocyte, appears able to pump cyclic AMP out against a concentration gradient (91) and *E. coli* may have a similar capability (92). Cyclic AMP seems to function extracellularly in promoting aggregation and differentiation of the cellular slime mold (93), but extracellular functions of cyclic nucleotides in other organisms are unknown. Concentrations of cyclic AMP and cyclic GMP in plasma are in the 10^{-8} M range (94), seemingly much too low to elicit responses from intact cells, but extraordinarily high concentrations (10^{-5} M and above) of cyclic AMP occur in human seminal plasma from vasectomized as well as normal subjects (24) and levels of this magnitude do produce effects in some intact cell systems. The growth of interest in extracellular fluid levels of cyclic nucleotides has resulted not so much because of the likelihood of uncovering an extracellular function for the agents but primarily because the levels in plasma and urine dramatically reflect, in several instances at least, hormone- or drug-induced alterations in tissue levels of the nucleotides. Extracellular fluids thus provide a relatively convenient source for studying changes in cyclic nucleotide levels that may be of value, for example, in aiding in the diagnosis or study of various endocrinopathies.

Normal humans excrete from about 2 to 9 μmoles of cyclic AMP per day (66, 94) and about 0.4 to 3 μmoles of cyclic GMP (33, 94). Rats excrete considerably more of the cyclic nucleotides relative to body weight. A rat weighing 100 g excretes daily about 0.06 μmole of cyclic AMP and 0.01 to 0.03 μmole of cyclic GMP (21, 33). Extreme fluctuations in urine volume cause little if any change in the total amount of nucleotides excreted (20, 21).

In humans, all of the cyclic GMP found in urine can be accounted for by glomerular filtration of plasma (94). By contrast, only part of the cyclic AMP in urine is derived from plasma, with a smaller but nevertheless substantial contribution coming from the kidney itself.

The plasma cyclic nucleotides represent a dynamic pool in a steady state. The half-time for the disappearance from plasma of injected radioactive cyclic AMP or cyclic GMP is around 30 min (94), whereas that for cyclic AMP in rats is only about 2 min (95). Less than 20% of injected labeled cyclic nucleotides appear in urine (94, 95), which indicates that extrarenal factors account for the removal of most of the material that disappears from plasma. Metabolism of the nucleotides by elements of blood may account for part of this extrarenal removal, but in vitro studies suggest that this is too slow to be a major factor in human blood (94). The apparent volumes of distribution of both the tritiated nucleotides exceed extracellular space, and that of cyclic GMP is substantially larger than that of cyclic AMP (94).

The sources of the normal plasma levels of the cyclic nucleotides are unknown. Under appropriate hormonal stimulation (discussed below), the liver and kidney appear capable of adding cyclic AMP to plasma.

Cyclic AMP has also been found in cerebrospinal fluid (96), milk (97), bile (86), and gastric juice (98), in addition to plasma, urine, and seminal fluid. Cyclic AMP has been measured in extracellular media from perfused livers (99), incubated epidiymal fat pads (100), human fat cells (101), human platelets (102), and cellular slime molds (103), in addition to the previously mentioned avian erythrocytes and bacteria.

Hormonal effects.—Hypophysectomy and, to a lesser extent, adrenalectomy lowered the excretion of cyclic GMP in rats with little or no effect on cyclic AMP, and thryroparathyroidectomy reduced the excretion of both nucleotides (21, 51). Effects of adrenalectomy and thyroparathyroidectomy were reversed by cortisol and thyroxine, respectively, but a combination of the two hormones only partially reversed the effect of hypophysectomy on cyclic GMP excretion, indicating the involvement of perhaps another pituitary factor. Reduced glomerular filtration is known to be a consequence of adrenal cortical or thyroid hormone deficiency states and may have been in part responsible for the reduced nucleotide excretion. Other defects are probably involved, however, since the cyclic GMP level in plasma of hypophysectomized rats is significantly lower than normal (104).

A striking increase in the amount of cyclic AMP excreted in urine occurs in the rat and man in response to glucagon administration (21, 99). The increment in urinary cyclic AMP can be accounted for by glomerular filtration of an increased plasma level of the nucleotide after glucagon (99). The latter presumably results from an increased amount of cyclic AMP entering the plasma from the liver since the perfused rat liver releases cyclic AMP in response to glucagon. This is a selective effect of glucagon in that cyclic GMP levels in urine and plasma are unaltered by the hormone. Whether or not glucagon is responsible for any of the normal plasma level of cyclic AMP is unknown.

Parathyroid hormone (PTH) also causes an increased urinary excretion of cyclic AMP in rat and man (6, 95, 105, 106) and this apparently results from an effect of the hormone on renal adenyl cyclase (6, 106) as does the modest elevation in plasma cyclic AMP caused by PTH (106). Doses of PTH that produced large changes in cyclic AMP excretion had no effect on cyclic GMP, although higher doses of the hormone affected cyclic GMP to some extent (106).

Calcium infusions reduce the amount of cyclic AMP excreted in urine (95, 106) with little apparent change in the plasma level (106). This could result in large measure, if not entirely, from suppression of endogenous PTH secretion, although a direct inhibition of renal adenyl cyclase by Ca^{++} might contribute to the effect.

In contrast to the reduction in urinary cyclic AMP following calcium infusions, an increase in cyclic GMP excretion was observed in man (106, 107). This appears to have come from elevated plasma levels of the nucleotide. That the elevation in urinary cyclic GMP seen with high doses of parathyroid hormone resulted from altered calcium levels seems possible, although serum calcium levels were not detectably elevated in these experiments (106).

The possibility that the effect of Ca^{++} on urinary cyclic GMP might have been caused by thyrocalcitonin release seems to have been excluded by experiments in which infusions of this hormone had no effect on urinary cyclic GMP levels while elevating both plasma and urinary cyclic AMP (107). In contrast to the changes seen after parathyroid hormone, most or all of the increment in urinary cyclic AMP after thyrocalcitonin could be accounted for by the elevated plasma level.

An earlier report (108) implying that antidiuretic hormone was responsible for virtually all the cyclic AMP in urine has not been substantiated. Supraphysiologic doses of the hormone have produced modest increases in urinary cyclic AMP (95, 109) but doses which produce striking changes in urine osmolality seem to have no effect on excretion of either cyclic AMP or cyclic GMP (105, 107). Moreover, there is little or no change in cyclic nucleotide excretion in individuals in extreme states of hydration or dehydration (110).

Up to threefold elevations in plasma cyclic AMP, and much smaller elevations in cyclic GMP, were seen in response to epinephrine infusions in man (99). The *beta*-adrenergic blocking agent propranolol prevented the rise in plasma cyclic AMP in response to epinephrine whereas the *alpha*-adrenergic blocking agent phentolamine did not (111). By contrast, the change in plasma cyclic GMP after epinephrine was reversed by phentolamine but not by propranolol. The predominantly *beta*-adrenergic agent isoproterenol elevated plasma cyclic AMP without increasing the level of cyclic GMP; norepinephrine with or without the concomitant administration of propranolol was more effective than epinephrine in elevating plasma cyclic GMP (107, 111). How direct or indirect are the effects of catecholamines on plasma cyclic nucleotides, particularly cyclic GMP, is an unresolved question.

Clinical implications.—The diagnostic usefulness of extracellular fluid levels of cyclic nucleotides, especially cyclic AMP, has been suggested by a number of observations. Patients with idiopathic, pseudo- and surgical hypoparathyroidism excrete lower than normal amounts of cyclic AMP in the urine (105, 109). Thyroxine-treated thyroparathyroidecomized rats excrete virtually normal amounts of cyclic AMP, however (21, 99). Hyperparathyroid patients excrete abnormally high amounts of cyclic AMP and this abnormality seems corrected by the removal of parathyroid adenoma (106, 109). Patients with pseudohypoparathyroidism, who have high plasma levels of endogenous parathyroid hormone, do not exhibit an increase in urinary cyclic AMP levels in response to the injected hormone (105). This and other findings led to the interesting conclusion (6, 105) that these patients may have a defective PTH-sensitive adenyl cyclase in bone and kidney. It seems possible that similar defects are involved in certain other endocrine disorders. Patients with affective disorders have been reported to excrete abnormal amounts of cyclic AMP (112–114). Levels were high in manic and low in depressed patients and were apparently changed by the administration of drugs that alter these states. Women in late pregnancy excrete higher than normal amounts of cyclic AMP (109). The relationships of these altered urinary cyclic AMP levels to the associated conditions are not clear and may be quite indirect. Nevertheless, such findings indicate that alterations in extracellular levels of cyclic nucleotides may be encountered in a variety of endocrinopathies or other conditions.

Unfortunately, too little is known about the sources and hormones responsible for the normal levels of cyclic nucleotides in plasma and urine to permit more than speculative conclusions regarding abnormal levels. Studies are badly needed. Furthermore, since apparently all the cyclic GMP and from 50 to 80% of the cyclic AMP in urine is derived from plasma (94), factors that alter glomerular filtration can have pronounced effects on the excretion of the nucleotides and must be taken into consideration in interpreting changes in urine levels.

ACTIONS OF CYCLIC NUCLEOTIDES

Actions of cyclic AMP in many cell-free and intact cell systems have been extensively discussed in previous reviews, and some anomalous effects of cyclic AMP compared with those of its dibutyryl derivative are discussed in the last section of this chapter. Present insight into the biological role of cyclic AMP has developed largely from a line of investigation that has not been followed in parallel in attempts to uncover a role for cyclic GMP. Cyclic AMP was discovered in the process of elucidating the mechanism of the hepatic glycogenolytic actions of epinephrine and glucagon. A knowledge of the first appreciated function of cyclic AMP thus led to the discovery of the nucleotide. On the other hand, cyclic GMP was first identified in nature as a constituent of urine and the knowledge of its existence stimulated a still ongoing search for its function.

Cell-free systems.—Cyclic GMP was shown nearly a decade ago to be a very ineffective substitute for cyclic AMP in activating dog liver phosphorylase (115). It had about 0.2% and cyclic IMP about 2.5% of the potency of cyclic AMP. This relative order of potency of the three nucleotides has usually been observed when their effects have been compared on cyclic AMP-responsive enzyme activities in cell-free systems. Glycogen synthetase kinase from rat and rabbit skeletal muscle can be activated to the same extent by both cyclic AMP and cyclic GMP in high concentrations (116, 117), but the relative potencies of the two are similar to those observed with liver phosphorylase. Michaelis K_a values are about 0.7 and 10 μM for cyclic AMP and cyclic GMP, respectively, with a rabbit muscle kinase preparation (117). Rat liver glycogen synthetase kinase likewise requires some 100 times as much cyclic GMP (and 10 times as much cyclic IMP) as cyclic AMP to produce half-maximum activation (118).

The effects of cyclic AMP on muscle glycogen synthetase kinase (117) and liver phosphorylase activity (119) are unaltered by cyclic GMP. Additive effects result when the nucleotides are combined in concentrations that alone elicit submaximal responses.

The effects of cyclic nucleotides on the enzymes involved in glycogen phosphorolysis and synthesis now appear to involve, as an early step in a cascade of events, activation of a protein kinase (120). Indeed in skeletal muscle the same protein kinase has been identified as phosphorylase kinase kinase and glycogen synthetase kinase (121, 122). This enzyme appears to be similar and may in some cases be identical to the cyclic AMP-sensitive protein kinases studied by others using different proteins as substrates (117, 120, 123–128). Not unexpectedly, cyclic GMP has often been found to be a relatively ineffective substitute for cyclic AMP in activating these kinases from a variety of sources. A protein kinase from adipose tissue required so much cyclic GMP for activation that contamination with cyclic AMP could not be ruled out (124). Similar ineffectiveness of cyclic GMP is seen with cyclic AMP-sensitive protein kinases from heart (129), brain (125), skeletal muscle (125), adrenal cortex (126), frog bladder (127), and liver (130). Cyclic GMP did not share the ability of cyclic AMP to reactivate ATP-inactivated pyruvate dehydrogenase from pig heart, a process seemingly involving activation of a protein kinase (131).

A notable exception to the general ineffectiveness of cyclic GMP in stimulating protein kinase activities has been found in lobster muscle (132). Here two fractions of protein kinase activity have been isolated, one of which has a much higher affinity for cyclic GMP than for cyclic AMP (apparent K_a values are 0.08 and 4 μM, respectively) while the other has the reverse order of affinity. Protein kinase activities with greater affinities for cyclic GMP than cyclic AMP have also been reported in bovine brain and bladder (133). The natural substrates and functions of these kinases have not been identified.

The mechanism by which cyclic nucleotides stimulate protein kinase activity is unknown, but recent studies indicate that they may act by binding to and thereby relieving the inhibition produced by an inhibitory protein (122, 124, 126). It has been suggested (126) that the relief of inhibition results from a dissociation of the binding protein from the kinase. Possibly the binding protein and the kinase are ordinarily bound to one another in the form of a loosely associated complex, analogous perhaps to the regulatory and catalytic subunits of aspartate transcarbamylase (134). In line with this, the addition of a protein inhibitor from muscle increased the apparent binding affinity of the muscle kinase system for cyclic AMP (122). Cyclic AMP-binding proteins have been detected in all vertebrate tissues examined so far (e.g. 126, 135–137). Conceivably these cyclic AMP-binding and kinase-inhibitory proteins will be found to have many properties in common with a cyclic AMP-binding protein that exists in *E. coli* (10, 138, 139). In the metazoan systems studied, cyclic AMP interferes with the ability of the protein to inhibit kinase activity, whereas in the bacterial system the protein and cyclic AMP seem to act together to promote the synthesis of messenger RNA. The binding of labeled cyclic AMP to the kinase-inhibitory protein from adrenal glands was competitively inhibited by cyclic GMP, but in very high concentrations (135). Cyclic GMP was 100 times less potent than non-radioactive cyclic AMP in preventing the binding of labeled cyclic AMP.

The stimulatory effect of cyclic AMP on β-galactosidase synthesis in cell-free extracts of *E. coli* is inhibited by cyclic GMP (138). This seems to be the result of cyclic GMP, again in high concentrations, competitively inhibiting the binding of cyclic AMP to a receptor protein which is involved in the initiation of transcription of β-galactosidase messenger RNA (10, 138, 139). The apparent dissociation constant for cyclic AMP binding is about $1 \times 10^{-6}M$ and the apparent K_i for cyclic GMP is about $1–2 \times 10^{-5}M$ (139). Cyclic GMP does exist in *E. coli* (28), but whether it can reach concentrations of this magnitude remains to be seen. The binding of cyclic AMP to G-factor, a component of the translation apparatus, was neither inhibited nor reproduced by cyclic GMP (140). The significance of the reported binding of cyclic AMP to this factor in the regulation of bacterial protein synthesis is unclear.

Effects of cyclic GMP on the formation of cyclic AMP have not been reported. Cyclic GMP did not share the inhibitory effect of GTP, GDP, and GMP on adenyl cyclase activity of fat cell membranes (141). The ability of cyclic GMP to either inhibit or accelerate the hydrolysis of cyclic AMP by phosphodiesterase preparations in vitro was discussed in an earlier section.

Intact cell systems.—The presence of nucleotides in high concentrations on the outside of cells is, with rare exceptions, an artificial condition. Cyclic

AMP and cyclic GMP do occur in extracellular fluids, but, as discussed in a previous section, the levels of the nucleotides in plasma are in the $10^{-8}M$ range. To elicit responses from intact cell systems, concentrations of exogenous cyclic nucleotides from 10^{-5} to $10^{-2}M$ have been necessary, presumably because of the poor ability of the nucleotides to enter cells. The physiological significance of responses obtained under these conditions may be questioned and indeed should be, especially in the absence of other lines of supporting evidence. A comparison of the effect of exogenous cyclic nucleotides with those of corresponding 5'-nucleotides or nucleosides is a minimum control requirement. However, even a comparatively specific effect of a cyclic nucleotide might be the fortuitous result, for example, of the cyclic nucleotide entering the cell with greater ease than its analog. To say the least, cautious interpretation of effects of exogenous cyclic nucleotides is a necessity.

The relative impotence of cyclic GMP in reproducing effects of cyclic AMP in cell-free systems was not reflected superficially when effects of the two nucleotides on the perfused rat liver were compared. Exogenous cyclic GMP and cyclic AMP appeared to be nearly equipotent with respect to their abilities to stimulate glucose output, glycogenolysis, gluconeogenesis, lactate uptake, urea production, tyrosine transaminase induction, and K^+ release (142–144). The near equipotency of the two nucleotides in the perfused liver seemed paradoxical in view of the relatively weak ability of cyclic GMP to substitute for cyclic AMP in cell-free systems. One possible indirect effect of cyclic GMP was eliminated when cyclic AMP levels in livers perfused with cyclic GMP were found not to be elevated (142, 144), as might have occurred had cyclic GMP inhibited the hydrolysis of cyclic AMP by phosphodiesterase. Alternatively, the apparent equipotency of the two nucleotides could have resulted from the weaker of the two (cyclic GMP) having a greater ability to enter or accumulate within the hepatocytes. The apparent spaces of exogenous cyclic GMP and cyclic AMP in the perfused rat liver were determined and found to be surprisingly different (144). The cyclic GMP space was about 70% while that of cyclic AMP was about 20%, virtually the same as the extracellular space. The apparent concentration of cyclic GMP in intracellular water thus approached the concentration of 10^{-5} to 10^{-4} M in the perfusion medium in these experiments. Such concentrations would be expected to alter the activities of, for example, glycogen phosphorylase and synthetase on the basis of studies in cell-free systems. Thus the apparent equipotency of cyclic GMP and cyclic AMP in at least one intact cell system appears to have resulted from the ability of the intrinsically weak exogenous cyclic GMP to attain a very high level inside the cells. A similar explanation may exist for the apparently high relative potency of cyclic GMP in mimicking steroidogenic effects of cyclic AMP in rat adrenal quarters in vitro (142, 145), but an indirect effect via phosphodiesterase inhibition should also be considered.

Effects of cyclic GMP on intact fat cells appear to depend to some extent on the medium employed. In Krebs-Ringer phosphate medium modified by replacing Ca^{++}, Mg^{++}, and K^+ with Na^+, exogenous cyclic GMP and cyclic AMP are reportedly lipolytic although GMP appears to be much less potent (146–149). In unmodified Krebs-Ringer phosphate medium, both cyclic AMP and cyclic GMP inhibited hormonally stimulated lipolysis (146, 147). However, under both sets of conditions, the cyclic AMP levels in the fat cells were elevated by exposure to cyclic GMP, presumably as a result of phosphodiesterase inhibition (147). While this probably explains the lipolytic effect of cyclic GMP, the explanation for the antilipolytic effect of cyclic GMP in the presence of elevated cyclic AMP levels is not readily apparent.

Cyclic GMP was nearly as effective as cyclic AMP in suppressing the growth of four tumorigenic cells lines in culture and was much more effective than cyclic AMP in inhibiting a nonmalignant cell line (150). These effects were determined after incubations of 2 to 4 days; since they were also produced, at least partially, by $2',3'$-cyclic nucleotides, their physiological significance is unclear.

Cyclic GMP did not possess the reported ability of high concentrations of cyclic AMP to potentiate the action of interferon on monolayers of chick fibroblasts (151).

Effects of cyclic GMP that are unlike those of cyclic AMP may be of more potential interest as leads to its possible role. Such reports are few in number, however. The reported inability of cyclic GMP to mimic the effect of cyclic AMP on water permeability while producing a cyclic AMP-like effect on short circuit current in the toad bladder (152) was especially intriguing. The results of earlier studies of the effects of ionic alterations on the response to vasopressin had suggested another second messenger with just these properties (153).

Contrasting effects of exogenous cyclic AMP and cyclic GMP on the metabolism of kidney slices have been reported (154, 155). Cyclic AMP (and cyclic IMP) elicited responses closely resembling those to acidosis, as for example an increased production of glucose and ammonia from glutamine and glutamate (154). On the other hand, cyclic GMP (but not $5'$-GMP) led to a decreased production of glucose and ammonia from glutamine and glutamate but not from α-ketoglutarate (155). The suggestion that cyclic GMP accomplished this by inhibiting glutamate dehydrogenase should be pursued since other guanine nucleotides are recognized as potent inhibitors of the enzyme (156).

Cyclic GMP reproduced the effects of parathyroid hormone more closely than did cyclic AMP when the nucleotides were infused into thyroparathyroidectomized rats (157). In other studies involving their injection into rats, cyclic GMP did not reproduce the effects of cyclic AMP on the induction of hepatic phosphoenolpyruvate carboxykinase (158) or serine dehydratase (159). When interpreting either positive or negative results of experiments involving the injection of cyclic nucleotides into animals, even more caution is necessary than with simpler intact cell systems. In addition to factors such as differences in ability to accumulate within cells, the relative stabilities of the nucleotides in extracellular fluids and the strong possibility of complicating indirect effects must be taken into account.

A variety of nucleotides and nucleosides are capable of mimicking some of the anabolic effects of estrogen when applied to the rat uterus (160). These agents include 5'-GMP, although cyclic GMP was apparently not tested. The dibutyryl derivative of cyclic AMP was more potent (161) and acted more rapidly (162) than the other nucleotides tested.

There are obviously too few reported effects of cyclic GMP on either intact or broken cell systems to clearly indicate a biological role for this substance. It nevertheless seems clear that its function in nature, if it has one, must differ from that of cyclic AMP.

Additional Considerations

In this concluding section we should like to mention and speculate about a few observations related to cyclic nucleotides that seem especially interesting or puzzling or both, and which may or may not be entirely explicable in terms of present concepts. The feature common to all of these observations is that they represent or suggest areas where more research is needed.

The difficulty of interpreting the effects of exogenous nucleotides on intact cells and tissues was mentioned previously. These effects are poorly understood in general, but some observations are especially puzzling. Usually, in systems in which cyclic AMP itself produces an effect, one of the acyl derivatives has been more effective; the dibutyryl derivative, now commercially available, has been the most widely studied. Two reasons for their greater potency have been suggested: 1. they resist hydrolysis by the phosphodiesterase, and may therefore be allowed to accumulate in higher concentrations at the normal site of action of cyclic AMP; and 2. they may penetrate cell membranes more effectively than cyclic AMP. It is possible that both factors contribute, although not necessarily to the same extent in all cells. In any event, the observation that the dibutyryl derivative is more potent than cyclic AMP itself has been made by so many investigators in such a variety of systems that it has come to be expected.

In a few cases, however, cyclic AMP itself was more effective than the dibutyryl derivative. Intestinal relaxation (163), inhibition of HeLa cell growth (164), and stimulation of renal gluconeogenesis (165) can be cited as examples. The most likely explanation appears to be that one or both of the acyl moieties have to be removed before the effect can be produced, and the responding cells in these experiments may have lacked the capacity to do this. However, this has yet to be proved.

Equally or even more puzzling are those cases where the dibutyryl derivative produces the predicted effect (mimicking the effect of the hormones that stimulate the formation of endogenous cyclic AMP) but where cyclic AMP itself actually produces the *opposite* effect. Effects on glucose uptake in mammalian skeletal muscle (166), on glucose oxidation in fat cells (149), and on melanocyte dispersion in lizard skin (167) can be cited as examples here. The effects of cyclic AMP in these cases resembled the effects of insulin or adrenergic α-receptor stimulation. It can be suggested, as a possible explanation of these observations, that some cells contain a system for catalyzing the conversion of cyclic AMP to an antimetabolite of cyclic AMP and that exogenous cyclic AMP is at times converted to this hypothetical factor so rapidly that the effect of the product predominates. This may provide a useful working hypothesis for future studies. It is of interest in this regard that in the rabbit ileum, where both types of adrenergic receptors mediate relaxation (168, 169), exogenous cyclic AMP produced an effect resembling that produced by α-agonists, whereas the dibutyryl derivative acted more like a β-agonist (169). Conversion of cyclic AMP to an antimetabolite would be consistent with observations made in a variety of systems that α-receptor stimulation is associated with a fall in the level of cyclic AMP (11, 12, 101, 102, 170–174).

These speculations involving alternate routes of cyclic AMP metabolism can be considered in the light of studies on the formation and partial purification of an endogenous inhibitor of cyclic AMP (119). This material noncompetitively inhibits the effect of cyclic AMP to stimulate liver phosphorylase activation in vitro. Although this factor may at times be undetectable, conditions which increase its accumulation seem generally similar to those that enhance the accumulation of cyclic AMP. Added cyclic AMP also increased the accumulation of the inhibitor in broken cell preparations from several tissues, whereas the 6-N-monobutyryl (but not the 2'-O-monobutyryl' or the dibutyryl) derivative prevented its formation. These and other findings, including the failure to separate the inhibitor from cyclic AMP by several chromatographic procedures and sensitivity of the inhibitor to attack by phosphodiesterase, provide strong evidence that many cells do have the capacity to convert cyclic AMP to a derivative which could act as an antimetabolite of cyclic AMP.

Evidence that cyclic AMP is the intracellular second messenger mediating the positive inotropic response to glucagon and the catecholamines has been reviewed previously (7, 13). A recent report of great interest has been that the ability of glucagon to stimulate cardiac adenyl cyclase is lost in tissue obtained from failing hearts, whereas the catecholamines retained their effectiveness (175). Cardiac failure was induced in these experiments by aortic constriction in cats. Interestingly, treatment of isolated fat cells with trypsin had previously been shown to lead to an apparently irreversible loss of the receptors for glucagon, with little or no damage to adrenergic receptors (176, 177). Although glucagon itself probably does not play an important role in regulating myocardial contractility, the loss of the glucagon response in failing hearts may provide a useful clue to at least some aspects of the pathology of cardiac failure. Perhaps the release of proteolytic and other enzymes in response to cell damage also destroys certain important receptors. On the basis of work with isolated fat cells (176, 177), it might be predicted that failing hearts would also be relatively unresponsive to insulin. More extensive damage may even reduce the response to epinephrine, as has been reported in guinea pig hearts (178).

Among other observations for which explanations are not readily apparent are the following: apparent similarities of effects of insulin and glucagon on hepatic enzyme induction (179); the inability of cyclic AMP to mimic oxytocin on toad bladder epithelium in spite of its ability to do so on the intact bladder (180); the ability of both parathyroid hormone and thyrocalcitonin to elevate cyclic AMP levels although they have functionally opposite effects (18, 19); the apparent biphasic character of the lipolytic effect of epinephrine (181); the ability of both α- and β-adrenergic receptors to mediate superficially similar responses in intestine (168, 169) and heart (182); the ability of theophylline to prevent the elevation of cyclic AMP in brain in response to electrical stimulation (183); the inability of fluoride to elevate cyclic AMP levels in intact cells despite its ability to stimulate adenyl cyclase activity in broken cells (184).

We are not in a position to guarantee or in some cases to evaluate intelligently the reliability of all of these observations, and many of them may ultimately be explained in relatively simple terms. Others, however, may require modification or extension of present concepts.

LITERATURE CITED

1. Sutherland, E. W., Robison, G. A., Butcher, R. W. 1968. Some aspects of the biological role of adenosine 3′,5′-monophosphate (cyclic AMP). *Circulation* 37:279–306

2. Butcher, R. W., Robison, G. A., Hardman, J. G., Sutherland, E. W. 1968. The role of cyclic AMP in hormone actions. *Advan. Enzyme Regul.* 6:357–89

3. Jeanrenaud, B. 1968. Adipose tissue dynamics and regulation, revisited. *Ergeb. Physiol.* 60:57–140

4. Exton, J. H., Park, C. R. 1968. The role of cyclic AMP in the control of liver metabolism. *Advan. Enzyme Regul.* 6:391–407

5. Sutherland, E. W., Robison, G. A. 1969. The role of cyclic AMP in the control of carbohydrate metabolism. *Diabetes* 18:797–819

6. Aurbach, G. D., Potts, J. T., Chase, L. R., Melson, G. L. 1969. Polypeptide hormones and calcium metabolism. *Ann. Intern. Med.* 70:1243–65

7. Epstein, S. E., Skelton, C. L., Levey, G. S., Entman, M. 1970. Adenyl cyclase and myocardial contractility. *Ann. Intern. Med.* 72:561–78

8. Weiss, B., Kidman, A. D. 1969. Neurobiological significance of cyclic 3′,5′-adenosine monophosphate. *Advan. Biochem. Psychopharmacol.* 1:131–64

9. Costa, E., Greengard, P., Eds. 1970. *The role of cyclic AMP in neuronal function. Advan. Biochem. Psychopharmacol.* 3. New York: Raven

10. Pastan, I., Perlman, R. 1970. Cyclic adenosine monophosphate in bacteria. *Science* 169:339–44

11. Robison, G. A., Butcher, R. W., Sutherland, E. W. 1969. On the relation of hormone receptors to adenyl cyclase. *Fundamental Concepts in Drug-Receptor Interactions*, ed. J. F. Danielli, J. F. Moran, D. F. Triggle, 59–91. London: Academic. 261 pp.

12. Robison, G. A., Sutherland, E. W. 1970. Sympathin E, symathin I, and intracellular level of cyclic AMP. *Circ. Res. 26 (Suppl. I)*, 1:147–61

13. Robison, G. A., Butcher, R. W., Sutherland, E. W. 1968. Cyclic AMP. *Ann. Rev. Biochem.* 37:149–74

14. Breckenridge, B. McL. 1970. Cyclic AMP and drug action. *Ann. Rev. Pharmacol.* 10:19–34

15. Robison, G. A., Butcher, R. W., Sutherland, E. W. 1970. *Cyclic AMP*. New York: Academic. In press

16. Axelsson, J. 1971. Catecholamine Functions. *Ann. Rev. Physiol.* 33:1–30

17. Ashman, D. F., Lipton, R., Melicow, M. M., Price, T. D. 1963. Isolation of adenosine 3′,5′-monophosphate and guanosine 3′,5′-monophosphate from rat urine. *Biochem. Biophys. Res. Commun.* 11:330–34

18. Murad, F., Brewer, H. B., Vaughan, M. 1970. Effect of thyrocalcitonin on adenosine 3′,5′-cyclic phosphate formation by rat kidney and bone. *Proc. Nat. Acad. Sci.* 65:446–53

19. Chase, L. R., Aurbach, G. D. 1970. The effect of parathyroid hormone on the concentration of adenosine 3′,5′-monophosphate in skeletal tissue in vitro. *J. Biol. Chem.* 245:1520–26

20. Goldberg, N. D., Dietz, S. B., O'Toole, A. G. 1969. Cyclic guanosine 3′,5′-monophosphate in mammalian tissues and urine. *J. Biol. Chem.* 244:4458–66

21. Hardman, J. G., Davis, J. W., Sutherland, E. W. 1969. Effects of some hormonal and other factors on the excretion of guanosine 3′,5′-monophosphate and adenosine 3′,5′-monophosphate in rat urine. *J. Biol. Chem.* 244:6354–61

22. Ishikawa, E., Ishikawa, S., Davis, J. W., Sutherland, E. W. 1969. Determination of cyclic GMP in tissues and of guanyl cyclase in rat intestine. *J. Biol. Chem.* 244:6371–76

23. Steiner, A. L., Parker, C. W., Kipnis, D. M. 1970. The measurement of cyclic nucleotides by radioimmunoassay. See Ref. 9

24. Gray, J. P. 1970. *Adenosine 3′,5′-monophosphate and guanosine 3′, 5′-monophosphate: Formation and occurrence in gametes and embryos.* PhD dissertation. Vanderbilt Univ., Nashville

25. Walaas, O., Walaas, E., Wick, A. 1969. The stimulatory effect by insulin on the incorporation of ^{32}P radioactive inorganic phosphate

into intracellular inorganic phosphate, adenine nucleotides and guanine nucleotides of the intact isolated rat diaphragm. *Diabetologia* 5:79–87

26. Goldberg, N. D., Lusk, W. D., O'Dea, R. F., Wei, S., O'Toole, A. G. 1970. The role of cyclic nucleotides in brain metabolism. See Ref. 9

27. George, W. J., Polson, J. B., O'Toole, A. G., Goldberg, N. D. 1970. Elevation of guanosine 3′,5′-cyclic phosphate in rat heart after perfusion with acetylcholine. *Proc. Nat. Acad. Sci.* 66:398–403

28. Goldberg, N. D. Personal communication

29. Pollard, C. J. 1970. Influence of gibberellic acid on the incorporation of 8-^{14}C adenine into adenosine 3′,5′-cyclic phosphate in barley aleurone layers. *Biochim. Biophys. Acta* 201:511–12

30. Hirata, M., Hayaishi, O. 1966. Enzymatic formation of deoxyadenosine 3′,5′-phosphate. *Biochem. Biophys. Res. Commun.* 24:360–64

31. Rosen, O. M., Rosen, S. M. 1969. Properties of an adenyl cyclase partially purified from frog erythrocytes. *Arch. Biochem. Biophys.* 131:449–56

32. Steiner, A. L., Parker, C. W., Kipnis, D. M. 1970. The assay of cyclic nucleotides by radioimmunoassay. *J. Clin. Invest.* 49:93a

33. Price, T. D., Ashman, D. F., Melicow, M. M. 1967. Organophosphates of urine including adenosine 3′,5′-monophosphate and guanosine 3′,5′-monophosphate. *Biochim. Biophys. Acta* 138:452–65

34. Hirata, M., Hayaishi, O. 1967. Adenyl cyclase of *Brevibacterium liquefaciens*. *Biochim. Biophys. Acta* 149:1–11

35. Greengard, P., Hayaishi, O., Colowick, S. P. 1969. Enzymatic adenylation of pyrophosphate by 3′,5′-cyclic monophosphate; reversal of the adenyl cyclase reaction. *Fed. Proc.* 28:467

36. Greengard, P., Rudolph, S. A. Sturtevant, J. M. 1969. Enthalpy of hydrolysis of the 3′ bond of adenosine 3′,5′-monophosphate and guanosine 3′,5′-monophosphate. *J. Biol. Chem.* 244:4798–4800

37. Lefkowitz, R. J., Roth, J., Pricer, W., Pastan, I. 1970. ACTH receptors in the adrenal: Specific binding of ACTH-^{125}I and its relation to adenyl cyclase. *Proc. Nat. Acad. Sci.* 65:745–52

38. Klainer, L. M., Chi, Y. M., Freidberg, S. L., Rall, T. W., Sutherland, E. W. 1962. Adenyl cyclase. IV. Effects of neurohormones on the formation of adenosine 3′,5′-monosphosphate by preparations from brain and other tissues. *J. Biol. Chem.* 237:1239–43

39. Levey, G. S., 1970. Solubilization of myocardial adenyl cyclase. *Biochem. Biophys. Res. Commun.* 38:86–92

40. Rosen, O. M., Rosen, S. M. 1968. The effect of catecholamines on the adenyl cyclase of frog and tadpole hemolysates. *Biochem. Biophys. Res. Commun.* 31:82–91

41. Schmidt, M. J., Palmer, E. C., Dettbarn, W. D., Robison, G. A., 1970. Cyclic AMP and adenyl cyclase in the developing rat brain. *Develop. Psychobiol.* 3:53–67

42. Perkins, J. P., MacIntyre, E., Riley, W. D. 1970. Adenyl cyclase in cultured human astrocytes. *Mol. Pharmacol.* In press

43. Bär, H. P., Hechter, O. 1969. Adenyl cyclase assay in fat cell ghosts. *Anal. Biochem.* 29:476–89

44. Birnbaumer, L., Pohl, S. L., Rodbell, M. 1969. Adenyl cyclase in fat cells. I. Properties and the effects of adrenocorticotropin and fluoride. *J. Biol. Chem.* 244:3468–76

45. Drummond, G. I., Duncan, L. 1970. Adenyl cyclase in cardiac tissue. *J. Biol. Chem.* 245:976–83

46. Perkins, J. P., Moore, M. M. 1970. Activation of adenyl cyclase *in vitro*. Relation of stimulation by NaF and by Mg^{++}. *Mol. Pharmacol.* Submitted for publication.

47. Perkins, J. P., Moore, M. M. 1970. Adenyl cyclase of rat cerebral cortex. Activation by NaF and detergents. *J. Biol. Chem.* In press

48. Bär, H., Hechter, O. 1969. Adenyl cyclase and hormone action. III. Calcium requirement for ACTH stimulation of adenyl cyclase. *Biochem. Biophys. Res. Commun.* 35:681–86

49. Marcus, R., Aurbach, G. D. 1969. Bioassay of parathyroid hormone in vitro with a stable preparation of adenyl cyclase from rat kidney. *Endocrinology* 85:801–10

50. Melson, G. L., Chase, L. R., Aurbach, G. D. 1970. Parathyroid hormone-sensitive adenyl cyclase in isolated renal tubules. *Endocrinology* 86: 511–18

51. Hardman, J. G., Davis, J. W., Sutherland, E. W. 1966. Measurement of guanosine 3',5'-monophosphate and other cyclic nucleotides. Variations in urinary excretion with hormonal state of the rat. *J. Biol. Chem.* 241:4812–15

52. Hardman, J. G., Sutherland, E. W. 1969. Guanyl cyclase, an enzyme catalyzing the formation of guanosine 3',5'-monophosphate from guanosine triphosphate. *J. Biol. Chem.* 244:6363–70

53. White, A. A., Aurbach, G. D. 1969. Detection of guanyl cyclase in mammalian tissues. *Biochim. Biophys. Acta* 191:686–97

54. Schultz, G. Böhme, E., Munske, K. 1969. Guanyl cyclase. Determination of enzyme activity. *Life Sci* 8:1323–32

55. Gray, J. P., Hardman, J. G., Bibring, T., Sutherland, E .W. 1970. High guanyl cyclase activity in sea urchin spermatozoa. *Fed. Proc.* 29: 608 Abstr.

56. Hardman, J. G., Sutherland, E. W. Unpublished observations

57. Tao, M., Lipmann, F. 1969. Isolation of adenyl cyclase from *Escherichia coli*. *Biochemistry* 63:86–92

58. Schorr, I., McMillan, B., Mahaffee, D., Ney, R. 1970. Regulation and subcellular distribution of adenyl cyclase and guanyl cyclase in the normal and neoplastic adrenal. *Program 52nd Meet. Endocrine Soc., St. Louis, June,* p. 48

59. Schmidt, M. J., Freeman, B. L., Robison, G. A. Unpublished observations

60. Gulyassy, P. F. 1968. Metabolism of adenosine 3',5'-monophosphate by epithelial cells of the toad bladder. *J. Clin. Invest.* 47:2458–68

61. Hardman, J. G., Sutherland, E. W., 1965. A cyclic 3'5'-nucleotide phosphodiesterase from heart with specificity for uridine 3',5'-phosphate. *J. Biol. Chem.* 240:3704–5

62. Brooker, G., Thomas, L. J., Appleman, M. M., 1968. The assay of adenosine 3'5'-cyclic monophosphate in biological materials by enzymatic radioisotopic displacement. *Biochemistry* 7:4177–84

63. Thompson, W. J., Appleman, M. M. 1970. Separation and characterization of multiple forms of 3',5'-cyclic AMP phosphodiesterase. *Fed. Proc.* 29:602 Abstr.

64. Beavo, J. A., Hardman, J. G., Sutherland, E. W., Hydrolysis of guanosine and adenosine 3',5'-monophosphates by rat and beef tissues. *J. Biol. Chem.* 245:5649–55

65. Rosen, O. M. 1970. Preparation and properties of a cyclic 3',5'-nucleotide phosphodiesterase isolated from frog erythrocytes. *Arch. Biochem. Biophys.* 137:435–41

66. Butcher, R. W., Sutherland, E. W. 1962. Adenosine 3',5'-phosphate in biological materials. I. Purification and properties of cyclic 3',5'-nucleotide phosphodiesterase and use of the enzyme to characterize adenosine 3',5'-phosphate in human urine. *J. Biol. Chem.* 237:1244–50

67. DeRobertis, E., Arnaiz, G. R. D. L., Alberici, M., Butcher, R. W., Sutherland, E. W. 1967. Subcellular distribution of adenyl cyclase and cyclic phosphodiesterase in rat brain cortex. *J. Biol Chem.* 242:3487–93

68. Honda, F., Imamura,H. 1968. Inhibition of cyclic 3',5'-nucleotide phosphodiesterase by phenothiazine and reserpine derivatives. *Biochim. Biophys. Acta* 161:267–69

69. Moore, P. F. 1968. The effects of diazoxide and benzothiadiazine diuretics upon phosphodiesterase. *Ann. N.Y. Acad. Sci.* 150:256–60

70. O'Dea, R. F., Haddox, M. K., Goldberg, N. D. 1970. Kinetic analysis of a soluble rat brain cyclic nucleotide phosphodiesterase. *Fed. Proc.* 29:473 Abstr.

71. Beavo, J. A., Rogers, N. L., Crofford, O. B., Hardman, J. G., Sutherland. E. W., Newman, E. V. Effects of xanthine derivatives on lipolysis and on adenosine 3',5'-monophosphate phosphodiesterase activity. *Mol. Pharmacol.* 6:597–603

72. Cheung, W. Y. 1967. Properties of cyclic 3',5'-nucleotide phosphodiesterase from rat brain. *Biochemistry* 6:1079–87

73. Mandel, L. R., Kuehl, F. A. 1967. Lipolytic action of 3, 3'5-triodo-1-thyronine, a cyclic AMP phosphodiesterase inhibitor. *Biochem. Biophys. Res. Commun.* 28:13–18

74. Senft, G., Schultz, G., Munske, K.,

Hoffmann, M. 1968. Influence of insulin on cyclic 3',5'-AMP phosphodiesterase activity in liver, skeletal muscle, adipose tissue, and kidney. *Diabetologia* 4:322–29

75. Müller-Oerlinghausen, B., Schwabe, U., Hasselblatt, A., Schmidt, F. H. 1968. Activity of 3',5'-AMP phosphodiesterase in liver and adipose tissue of normal and diabetic rats. *Life Sci.* 7:593–98

76. Menahan, L. A., Hepp, K. D., Wieland, O. 1969. Liver 3',5'-nucleotide phosphodiesterase and its activity in rat livers perfused with insulin. *Eur. J. Biochem.* 8:435–43

77. Kupiecki, F. P. 1969. Reduced adenosine 3',5'-monophosphate phosphodiesterase activity in the pancreas and adipose tissue of spontaneously diabetic mice. *Life Sci.* 8:645–49

78. Krishna, G., Weiss, B., Davies, J. I., Hynie, S. 1966. Mechanism of nicotinic acid inhibition of hormone induced lipolysis. *Fed. Proc.* 25:719

79. Peterson, M. J., Hillman, C. C., Ashmore, J. 1968. Nicotinic acid: Studies on the mechanism of its antilipolytic action. *Mol. Pharmacol.* 4:1–9

80. Kupiecki, F. P., Marshall, N. B. 1968. Effects of 5-methylpyrazole-3-carboxylic acid (U-19425) and nicotinic acid on lipolysis in vitro and in vivo and on cyclic 3',5'-AMP phosphodiesterase. *J. Pharmacol. Exp. Therap.* 160:166–70

81. Therriault, D. G., Winters, V. G. 1970. Studies on the effect of nicotinic acid on cyclic nucleotide phosphodiesterase activity in rat heart and adipose tissue. *Life Sci.* 9:421–28

82. Kakiuchi, S., Yamazaki, R. 1970. Stimulation of the activity of cyclic 3',5'-nucleotide phosphodiesterase by calcium ion. *Proc. Japan Acad.* 46:387–92

83. Cheung, W. Y. 1969. Cyclic 3',5'-nucleotide phosphodiesterase: preparation of a partially inactive enzyme and its subsequent stimulation by snake venom. *Biochim. Biophys. Acta* 191:303–15

84. Krebs, E. G., Huston, R. B., Hunkeler, F. L. 1968. Properties of phosphorylase kinase and its control in skeletal muscle. *Advan. Eyzyme Regul.* 6:245–55

85. Cheung, W. Y. 1970. Cyclic 3',5'-nucleotide phosphodiesterase. Demonstration of an activator. *Biochem. Biophys. Res. Commun.* 38:533–38

86. Levine, R. A., Lewis, S. E., Shulman, J., Washington, A. 1969. Metabolism of cyclic adenosine 3',5'-monophosphate 8-^{14}C by isolated, perfused rat liver. *J. Biol. Chem.* 244:4017–22

87. Nair, K. G. 1966. Purification and properties of 3',5'-cyclic nucleotide phosphodiesterase from dog heart. *Biochemistry* 5:150–57

88. Drummond, G. I., Perrott-Yee, S. 1961. Enzymatic hydrolysis of adenosine 3',5'-phosphoric acid. *J. Biol. Chem.* 236:1126–29

89. Goren, E., Erlichman, J., Rosen, O. M., Rosen, S. M. 1970. A possible role for cyclic nucleotide phosphodiesterase in the regulation of the intracellular concentration of cyclic 3',5'-AMP. *Fed. Proc.* 29:602 Abstr.

90. Beavo, J., Hardman, J. G., Sutherland, E. W. Stimulation of adenosine 3',5'-monophosphate hydrolysis by guanosine 3',5'-monophosphate. Manuscript in preparation

91. Davoren, P. R., Sutherland, E. W. 1963. The effect of *l*-epinephrine and other agents on the synthesis and release of adenosine 3',5'-phosphate by whole pigeon erythrocytes. *J. Biol. Chem.* 238:3009–15

92. Makman, R. S., Sutherland, E. W. 1965. Adenosine 3',5'-phosphate in *Escherichia coli*. *J. Biol. Chem.* 240:1309–14

93. Bonner, J. T., Barkley, D. S., Hall, E. M., Konijn, T. M., Mason, J. W., O'Keefe, G., Wolfe, P. B. 1969. Acrasin, acrasinase, and the sensitivity to acrasin in *Dictyostelium discoideum*. *Develop. Biol.* 20:72–87

94. Broadus, A. E., Kaminsky, N. I., Hardman, J. G., Sutherland, E. W., Liddle, G. W. Kinetic parameters and renal clearances of plasma adenosine 3',5'-monophosphate and guanosine 3',5'-monophosphate in man. *J. Clin. Invest.* In press

95. Chase, L. R., Aurbach, G. D. 1967. Parathyroid function and the renal excretion of 3',5'-adenylic acid. *Proc. Nat. Acad. Sci.* 58:518–25

96. Robison, G. A., Buxbaum, D. M. Unpublished observations

97. Kobata, A., Kida, J., Ziro, S. 1961. Occurrence of 3',5'-cyclic AMP in milk. *J. Biochem.* 50 :275–76

98. Bieck, P., Oates, J. A., Robison, G. A. Unpublished observations

99. Broadus, A. E., Kaminsky, N. I., Northcutt, R. C., Hardman, J. G., Sutherland, E. W., Liddle, G. W. Effects of glucagon on adenosine 3',5'-monophosphate and guanosine 3',5'-monophosphate in human plasma and urine. *J. Clin. Invest.* In press

100. Butcher, R. W., Sneyd, J. G. T., Park, C. R., Sutherland, E. W. 1966. Effect of insulin on adenosine 3',5'-monophosphate in the rat epididymal fat pad. *J. Biol. Chem.* 241 :1651–53

101. Burns, T. W., Langley, P. E., Robison, G. A. 1970. Lipolytic activity of human adipose tissue : effects of α and β adrenergic blocking agents on 3',5' cyclic adenosine monophosphate and glycerol release. *Clin. Res.* 18 :86

102. Cole, B., Robison, G. A., Hartmann, R. C. 1970. Effects of prostaglandin E_1 and theophylline on aggregation and cyclic AMP levels of human blood platelets. *Fed. Proc.* 29 :316 Abstr.

103. Konijn, T. M., Chang, Y. Y., Bonner, J. T. 1969. Synthesis of cyclic AMP in *Dictyostelium discoideum* and *Polysphondylium pallidum.* *Nature* 224 :1211–12

104. Patterson, W. D., Hardman, J. G., Sutherland, E. W. Unpublished observations

105. Chase, L. R., Melson, G. L., Aurbach, G. D. 1969. Pseudohypoparathyroidism : Defective excretion of 3',5'-AMP in response to parathyroid hormone. *J. Clin. Invest.* 48 : 1832–44

106. Kaminsky, N. I., Broadus, A. E., Hardman, J. G., Jones, D. J., Ball, J. H., Sutherland, E. W., Liddle, G. W. Effects of parathyroid hormone on plasma and urinary adenosine 3',5'-monophosphate in man. *J. Clin. Invest.* In press

107. Kaminsky, N. I., Ball, J. H., Broadus, A. E., Hardman, J. G., Sutherland, E. W., Liddle, G. W. Hormonal effects on extracellular cyclic nucleotides in man. *Trans. Assoc. Am. Physicians.* In press

108. Takahashi, K., Kamimura, M., Shinko, T., Tsuji, S. 1966. Effects

109. Taylor, A. L., Davis, B. B., Pawlson, G., Josimovich, J. B., Mintz, D. H. 1970. Factors influencing the urinary excretion of 3',5'-adenosine monophosphate in humans. *J. Clin. Endocrinol.* 30 :316–24

110. Broadus, A. E., Kaminsky, N. I. Unpublished observations

111. Ball, J. H., Kaminsky, N. I., Broadus, A. E ., Hardman, J. G., Sutherland, E. W., Liddle, G. W. 1970. Effects of catecholamines and adrenergic blocking agents on cyclic nucleotides in human plasma. *Clin. Res.* 18 :336

112. Paul, M. I., Ditzion, B. R., Janowsky, D. S. 1970. Affective illness and cyclic AMP excretion. *Lancet* 1 :88

113. Abdulla, Y. H., Hamadah, K. 1970. 3',5' cyclic adenosine monophosphate in depression and mania. *Lancet* 1 :378–81

114. Paul, M. I., Ditzion, B. R., Pauk, G. L., Janowsky, D. S. 1970. Urinary adenosine 3',5'-monophosphate excretion in affective disorders. *Am. J. Psychiatry* 126 : 1493–98

115. Rall, T. W., Sutherland, E. W. 1962. Adenyl cyclase. II. The enzymatically catalyzed formation of adenosine 3',5'-phosphate and inorganic pyrophosphate from adenosine triphosphate. *J. Biol. Chem.* 237 :1228–32

116. Walaas, O., Walaas, E., Osaki, S. 1968. The effect of nucleoside 2',3'-cyclophosphates and nucleoside 3',5'-cyclic phosphates on UDP glucose : α-1,4-glucan α-4-glucosyltransferase. *Control of Glycogen Metabolism,* ed. W. J. Whelan, 139–52. New York : Academic. 221 pp.

117. Schlender, K. K., Wei, S. H., Villar-Palasi, C. 1969. UDP-glucose : Glycogen α-4 glucosyltransferase I kinase activity of purified muscle protein kinase. Cyclic nucleotide specificity. *Biochim. Biophys. Acta* 191 :272–78

118. Glinsmann, W. H., Hern, E. P. 1969. Inactivation of rat liver glycogen synthetase by 3',5'-cyclic nucleotides. *Biochem. Biophys. Res. Commun.* 36 :931–36

119. Murad, F., Rall, T. W., Vaughan, M. 1969. Conditions for the formation,

partial purification and assay of an inhibitor of adenosine 3',5'-monophosphate. *Biochim. Biophys. Acta* 192:430–45

120. Walsh, D. A., Perkins, J. P., Krebs, E. G. 1968. An adenosine 3',5'-monophosphate-dependent protein kinase from rabbit skeletal muscle. *J. Biol. Chem.* 243:3763–65

121. Soderling, T. R., Hickenbottom, J. P. 1970. Inactivation of glycogen synthetase and activation of phosphorylase b kinase by the same cyclic 3',5' AMP-dependent kinase. *Fed. Proc.* 29:601 Abstr.

122. Reimann, E. M., Walsh, D. A. 1970. Characterization of the adenosine 3',5'-monophosphate-stimulated protein kinase from rabbit skeletal muscle. *Fed. Proc.* 29:601 Abstr.

123. Langan, T. A. 1968. Histone phosphorylation: Stimulation by adenosine 3',5'-monophosphate. *Science* 162:579–80

124. Corbin, J. D., Krebs, E. G. 1969. A cyclic AMP-stimulated protein kinase in adipose tissue. *Biochem. Biophys. Res. Commun.* 36:328–36

125. Kuo, J. F., Greengard, P. 1969. Cyclic nucleotide-dependent protein kinases. IV. Widespread occurrence of adenosine 3',5'-monophosphate-dependent protein kinase in various tissues and phyla of the animal kingdom. *Proc. Nat. Acad. Sci.* 64:1349–55

126. Gill, G. N., Garren, L. D. 1970. A cyclic 3',5'-adenosine monophosphate dependent protein kinase from the adrenal cortex: Comparison with a cyclic AMP binding protein. *Biochem. Biophys. Res. Commun.* 39:335–43

127. Jard, S., Bastide, F. 1970. A cyclic AMP-dependent protein kinase from frog bladder epithelial cells. *Biochem. Biophys. Res. Commun.* 39:559–66

128. Jergil, B., Dixon, G. H. 1970. Protamine kinase from rainbow trout testes. *J. Biol. Chem.* 245:425–34

129. Krebs, E. G. Personal communication

130. Langan, T. A. Personal communication

131. Wieland, O., Siess, E. 1970. Interconversion of phospho and dephospho forms of dog heart pyruvate dehydrogenase. *Proc. Nat. Acad. Sci.* 65:947–61

132. Kuo, J. F., Greengard, P. 1970. Cyclic nucleotide dependent protein kinases. VI. Isolation and partial purification of a protein kinase activated by guanosine 3',5'-monophosphate. *J. Biol. Chem.* 245:2493–98

133. Kuo, J. F., Sanes, J., Greengard, P. 1970. Guanosine 3',5'-monophosphate-dependent protein kinases. *Fed. Proc.* 29:601 Abstr.

134. Wiley, D. C., Lipscomb, W. N. 1968. Crystallographic determination of symmetry of aspartate transcarbamylase. *Nature* 218:1119–21

135. Gill, G. N., Garren, L. D. 1969. On the mechanism of action of adrenocorticotropic hormone: The binding of cyclic-3',5'-adenosine monophosphate to an adrenal cortical protein. *Proc. Nat. Acad. Sci.* 63:512–19

136. Salomon, Y., Schramm, M. 1970. A specific binding site for 3',5'-cyclic AMP in rat parotid microsomes. *Biochem. Biophys. Res. Commun.* 38:106–11

137. Cheung, W. Y. 1970. Adenosine 3',5'-monophosphate: demonstration of a binding site specific for the cyclic nucleotide. *Life Sci.* 9:861–68

138. Zubay, G., Schwartz, D., Beckwith, J. 1970. Mechanism of activation of catabolite-sensitive genes: A positive control system. *Proc. Nat. Acad. Sci.* 66:104–10

139. Emmer, M., de Crombrugghe, B., Pastan, I., Perlman, R. 1970. Cyclic AMP receptor protein of *E. coli:* Its role in the synthesis of inducible enzymes. *Proc. Nat. Acad. Sci.* 66:480–87

140. Kuwano, M., Schlessinger, D. 1970. Binding of adenosine 3',5'-cyclic phosphate to G factor of *Escherichia coli,* and its effects on GTPase, RNase V, and protein synthesis. *Proc. Nat. Acad. Sci.* 66:146–52

141. Cryer, P. E., Jarett, L., Kipnis, D. M. 1969. Nucleotide inhibition of adenyl cyclase activity in fat cell membranes. *Biochim. Biophys. Acta* 177:586–90

142. Glinsmann, W. H., Hern, E. P., Linarelli, L. G., Farese, R. V. 1969. Similarities between effects of adenosine 3',5'-monophosphate and guanosine 3',5'-monophosphate on liver and adrenal metabolism. *Endocrinology* 85:711–19

143. Conn, H. O., Kipnis, D. M. 1969. The effect of various 3',5'-cyclic

nucleotides on gluconeogenesis and glycogenolysis in the perfused rat liver. *Biochem. Biophys. Res. Commun.* 37 :319–26

144. Exton, J. H., Hardman, J .G., Sutherland, E. W., Park, C. R. Manuscript in preparation

145. Mahaffee, D., Watson,, B., Ney, R. L. 1970. The relationship between nucleotide structure and the stimulation of adrenal steroidogenesis. *Clin. Res.* 18 :73

146. Manganiello, V., Murad, F., Vaughan, M. 1969. Cyclic 3′,5′-GMP and glycerol production by fat cells. *Fed. Proc.* 28 :876

147. Murad, F., Manganiello, V., Vaughan, M. 1970. Effects of guanosine 3′,5′-monophosphate on glycerol production and accumulation of adenosine 3′,5′-monophosphate by fat cells. *J. Biol. Chem.* 245 :3352–60

148. Braun, T., Hechter, O., Bär, H. P. 1969. Lipolytic activity of ribonucleotide and deoxyribonucleotide 3′,5′-cyclic monophosphates in isolated fat cells. *Proc. Soc. Exp. Biol. Med.* 132 :233–36

149. Kitabchi, A. E., Solomon, S. S., Brush, J. S. 1970. The insulin-like activity of cyclic nucleotides and their inhibition by caffeine on the isolated fat cells. *Biochem. Biophys. Res. Commun.* 39 :1065–72

150. Heidrick, M. L., Ryan, W. L. 1970. Cyclic nucleotides on cell growth in vitro. *Cancer Res.* 30 :376–78

151. Friedman, R. M., Pastan, I. 1969. Interferon and cyclic-3′,5′-adenosine monophosphate: potentiation of antiviral activity. *Biochem. Biophys. Res. Commun.* 36 :735–40

152. Bourgoignie, J., Guggenheim, S., Kipnis, D. M., Klahr, S. 1969. Cyclic guanosine monophosphate. Effects on short circuit current and water permeability. *Science* 165 :1362–63

153. Orloff, J., Handler, J. 1967. The role of adenosine 3′,5′-phosphate in the action of antidiuretic hormone. *Am. J. Med.* 42 :757–68

154. Pagliara, A. S., Goodman, A. D. 1969. Effect of adenosine 3′,5′-monophosphate on production of glucose and ammonia by renal cortex. *J. Clin. Invest.* 48 :1408–12

155. Pagliara, A. S., Goodman, A. D. 1970. Effect of 3′,5′-GMP and 3′,5′-IMP on production of glucose and ammonia by renal cortex. *Am. J. Physiol.* 218 :1301–6

156. Wolff, J. 1962. The effect of thyroxine on isolated dehydrogenases. III. The site of action of thyroxine on glutamic dehydrogenase, the function of adenine and guanine nucleotides, and the relation to sedimentation changes. *J. Biol. Chem.* 237 :236–42

157. DeLong, A., Rasmussen, H. 1970. Cyclic nucleotides and bone mineral metabolism. *Program 52nd Meet. Endocrine Soc., St. Louis, June,* p. 122

158. Yeung, D., Oliver, I. T. 1968. Induction of phosphopyruvate carboxylase in neonatal rat liver by adenosine 3′,5′-cyclic monophosphate. *Biochemistry* 7 :3231–39

159. Jost, J. P., Hsie, A. W., Hughes, S. D., Ryan, L. 1970. Role of cyclic adenosine 3′,5′-monophosphate in the induction of hepatic enzymes. I. Kinetics of the induction of rat liver serine dehydratase by cyclic adenosine 3′,5′-monophosphate. *J. Biol. Chem.* 245 :351–57

160. Hechter, O., Yoshinaga, K., Halkerston, I. D. K., Birchall, K. 1967. Estrogen-like anabolic effects of cyclic 3′,5′-adenosine monophosphate and other nucleotides in isolated rat uterus. *Arch. Biochem. Biophys.* 122 :449–65

161. Griffin, D. M., Szego, C. M. 1968. Adenosine 3′,5′-monophosphate stimulation of uterine amino acid uptake *in vitro. Life Sci.* 7 :1017–23

162. Sharma, S. K., Talwar, G. P. 1970. Action of cyclic adenosine 3′,5′-monophosphate in vitro on the uptake and incorporation of uridine ribonucleic acid in ovariectomized rat uterus. *J. Biol. Chem.* 245 : 1513–19

163. Kim, T. S., Shulman, J., Levine, R. A. 1968. Relaxant effect of cyclic 3′,5″-AMP on the isolated rabbit ileum. *J. Pharmacol. Exp. Therap.* 163 : 36–42

164. Ryan, W. L., Heidrick, M. L. 1968. Inhibition of cell growth in vitro by adenosine 3′,5′monophosphate. *Science* 162 : 1484–85

165. Bowman, R. H. 1970. Gluconeogenesis in the isolated perfused rat kidney. *J. Biol. Chem.,* 245 :1604–12

166. Chambaut, A., Eboue-Bonis, D., Hanoune, J., Clauser, H. 1969. An-

tagonistic actions between dibutyryl adenosine 3',5'-cyclic monophosphate and insulin on the metabolism of the surviving rat diaphragm. *Biochem. Biophys. Res. Commun.* 34:283–90

167. Hadley, M. E., Goldman, J. M. 1969. Effects of cyclic 3',5'-AMP and other adenine nucleotides on the melanophores of the lizard (*Anolis carolenensis*). *Brit. J. Pharmacol.* 37:650–58

168. Andersson, R., Mohme-Lundholm, E. 1969. Studies on the relaxing actions mediated by stimulation of adrenergic α and β-receptors in taenia coli of the rabbit and guinea pig. *Acta Physiol. Scand.* 77:372–84

169. Bowman, W. C., Hall, M. T. 1970. Inhibition of rabbit intestine mediated by α and β adrenoceptors. *Brit. J. Pharmacol.* 38:399–415

170. Turtle, J. R., Kipnis, D. M. 1967. An adrenergic receptor mechanism for the control of cyclic 3'5'-adenosine monophosphate synthesis in tissues. *Biochem. Biophys. Res. Commun.* 28:797–802

171. Abe, K., Robison, G. A., Liddle, G. W., Butcher, R. W., Nicholson, W. E., Baird, C. E. 1969. Role of cyclic AMP in mediating the effects of MSH, norepinephrine, and melatonin on frog skin color. *Endocrinology* 85:674–82

172. Robison, G. A., Arnold, A., Hartmann, R. C. 1969. Divergent effects of epinephrine and prostaglandin E_1 on the level of cyclic AMP in human blood platelets. *Pharmacol. Res. Commun.* 1:325–32

173. Salzman, E. W., Neri, L. L. 1969. Cyclic 3',5'-adenosine monophosphate in human blood platelets. *Nature* 224:609–10

174. Marquis, N. R., Becker, J. A., Vigdahl, R. L. 1970. Platelet aggregation. III. An epinephrine-induced decrease in cyclic AMP synthesis. *Biochem. Biophys. Res. Commun.,* 39:783–89

175. Gold, H. K., Prindle, K. H., Levey, G. S., Epstein, S. E. 1970. Effects of experimental heart failure on the capacity of glucagon to augment myocardial contractility and activate adenyl cyclase. *J. Clin. Invest.* 49:999–1006

176. Kono, T. 1969. Destruction and restoration of the insulin effector system of isolated fat cells. *J. Biol. Chem.* 244:5777–84

177. Rodbell, M., Birnbaumer, L., Pohl, S. L. 1970. Adenyl cyclase in fat cells. III. Stimulation by secretin and the effects of trypsin on the receptors for lipolytic hormones. *J. Biol. Chem.* 245:718–22

178. Sobel, B. E., Henry, P. D., Robison, A., Bloor, C., Ross, J. 1969. Depressed adenyl cyclase activity in the failing guinea pig heart. *Circ. Res.* 24:507–12

179. Wicks, W. D. 1969. Induction of hepatic enzymes by adenosine 3',5'-monophosphate in organ culture. *J. Biol. Chem.* 244:3941–50

180. Parisi, M., Ripoche, P., Bourguet, J. 1969. The isolated epithelium of the frog urinary bladder; Responses to oxytocin, 3',5'-adenosine monophosphate, and theophylline. *Pflügers Arch.* 309:59–69

181. Allen, D. O., Hillman, C. C., Ashmore, J. 1969. Studies on a biphasic lipolytic response to catecholamines in isolated fat cells. *Biochem. Pharmacol.* 18:2233–40

182. Govier, W. C. 1968. Myocardial *alpha* adrenergic receptors and their role in the production of a positive inotropic effect by sympathomimetic agents. *J. Pharmacol. Exp. Therap.* 159:82–90

183. Kakiuchi, S., Rall, T. W., McIlwain, H. 1969. The effect of electrical stimulation upon the accumulation of adenosine 3',5'-phosphate in isolated cerebral tissue. *J. Neurochem.* 16:485–91

184. Øye, I., Sutherland, E. W. 1966. The effect of epinephrine and other agents on adenyl cyclase in the cell membrane of avian erythrocytes. *Biochim. Biophys. Acta* 127:347–54

MOTOR MECHANISMS: THE ROLE OF THE PYRAMIDAL SYSTEM IN MOTOR CONTROL

1065

VERNON B. BROOKS[1] AND S. DAVID STONEY, JR.[2]

Department of Physiology
New York Medical College
New York, N.Y.

I. INTRODUCTION[3]

During the past century, three major factors have been singled out for study in the control of voluntary movement: the force of the movement towards the target, the speed of the movement, and the displacement towards the target. Neurophysiological systems underlying these factors have recently begun to be identified. Do they amount to "control" systems? Control

[1,2] Supported in part by USPHS Research and Training Grants NS-05508 and NS-05544, and by National Science Foundation grant GB 80108.

[2] Present address: Division of Neurobehavioral Sciences, Medical College of Georgia, Augusta, Georgia 30902.

[3] The following abbreviations will be used: ASG, anterior sigmoid gyrus; CM (nucleus), centromedian nucleus; CM (synapse), corticomotoneuronal synapse; EBR, external basilar region; EDC, extensor digitorum communis muscle; EMG, electromyogram; EPSP, excitatory postsynaptic potential; FDS, flexor digitorum sublimis muscle; FRA, flexor reflex afferents; ICMS, intracortical microstimulation; IP,

337

systems may be defined by the information that is processed, and by the end result that is achieved. Movement control systems only can assume biological reality, however, if inputs can be specified, for instance in terms of natural adequate stimuli, final outputs as muscular adjustments, and places of input-output coupling in terms of nuclei and pathways. Furthermore, it should be possible to demonstrate the ability of the niclei to act as "central detecting apparatus, . . . able to read profiles of appropriate neural activity" (143). What role does the pyramidal tract play in voluntary movements? Does it have unique functions? How strong are its influences, and how are they brought to bear?

The paucity of simple unifying answers has shaped this review, which contains two separate but related sequences: one a detailed documentation of facts and the other a conceptual guide. Details of peripheral inputs are considered in Sections II and III, details of outputs in Sections III and IV, while general consideration is given to input-output relations in Section II, and to control systems in Section V. Pyramidal input-output relations are emphasized, with reference to peripheral inputs, and outputs as force, speed, and displacement of limb movements. Control of posture and of sensory feedback are deemphasized because they have recently been treated by others (cf 64, 129, 227).

Lesions of the pyramidal tract in man have been associated with the so-called pyramidal tract syndrome. This includes paresis of voluntary movement, exaggerated tendon reflexes, the Babinski sign, spasticity, and depression of cutaneous reflexes. Recent work (27, 43, 71, 116, 117, 220) has reassessed the significance of directly, and indirectly, involved structures adjacent to the pyramids, and has plotted long-term recovery. These studies, foreshadowed in many respects by the work of Tower (209), have raised serious questions regarding the validity of the pyramidal syndrome. The main findings were that 2–22 months after pyramidotomy there is little gross impairment of motor function in monkeys or cats, provided there has been minimal involvement of the adjacent midbrain tegmentum or medial lemniscal system. Pyramidotomy deficits appeared mainly as decreased muscular strength, particularly in distal flexors (27, 43); decreased flexor and extensor tone, particularly of distal flexors (27); decreased "agility" or "dexterity" of hand and finger movements (27, 43, 71, 117); increased reaction time to visual cues (27); increased use of synergistic muscles, which tends to transform limb fixation into movement (71), and marked preference for use of the unaffected limb (27). Although lesions can sometimes reveal what a particular part of the brain is doing, the method may fail if there is compensation, or release of action, by another structure. New an-

---

interpositus nucleus; IPSP, inhibitory postsynaptic potential; MSI, motorsensory cortex; PL, palmaris longus muscle; PSG, posterior sigmoid gyrus; PT, PTN, pyramidal tract, pyramidal tract neuron; RN, red nucleus; SI, primary sensory cortex; SII, secondary sensory cortex; T, threshold; VA, ventral anterior nucleus; VL, ventrolateral nucleus; VPL, ventroposterolateral nucleus.

swers to questions of pyramidal functions will come from physiological studies.

The reader is referred here to recent publications on motor control. Neural mechanisms have been the topic for Marchiafava (129), with special attention to the pyramids for Wiesendanger (227) and Phillips (161). Cerebrocerebellar interrelations have been fully reviewed by Evarts & Thach (64) with stress on movement initiation. Pathways of central inhibition have been reviewed by Eccles (59), and the red nucleus by Massion (131). Some specialty symposia have yielded collections of papers, notably those edited by Purpura & Yahr on the thalamus (cf 10), Yahr & Purpura on motor control (cf 225), Freedman on spatially oriented behavior (cf 155), and Leibovic on information processing (cf 58). Other symposia on motor control have been reported briefly by Brooks et al (41) and as comprehensive overview essays by Evarts et al (65). (The latter volume unfortunately did not appear in time to be reviewed.) Tokizane & Shimazu (203) and Granit (75) have written on the functional organization of muscles, and of muscle spindles, respectively. Lundberg (124) has dealt with reflex control of stepping, and Brodal (30) has correlated a vast amount of functional neuroanatomy. The survey of selected literature for this review was completed in June 1970.

II. INPUT ORGANIZATION

Much has been learned about the nature and organization of peripheral inputs to motorsensory cortex since Adrian & Moruzzi (2) demonstrated short-latency activation of the pyramidal tract by peripheral stimulation. Most studies since then have avoided the response depression produced by barbiturate anesthetics, and experiments have been carried out either with chronic animals, with animals surgically prepared under inhalation anesthesia and tested under local anesthesia, or with animals anesthetized with chloralose.

The characteristics of sensory inflow in chloralose-anesthetized animals have received extensive coverage in some recent reviews (3, 45, 129, 227). We will examine this literature first, because the special properties of chloralose have raised some problems. For instance, Marchiafava (129) particularly stressed . . . "convergence of different modalities onto individual cells . . . , with no recognizable patterns of spatial localization based either on modality of input or on the production of excitation versus inhibition. This . . . contrasts sharply with the somatotopic cerebellar terminations of the other branch of the proprioceptive system included within the spinocerebellar pathways. . . ." Wiesendanger (227) also stressed that . . . "one single pyramidal tract cell may react to somatosensory stimuli from wide receptive fields of the body surface, to acoustic stimuli, and to visual input." These authors suggest that convergent cortical input patterns reflect integration occurring at the thalamic level, although there may also be subthalamic (150) as well as cortical convergence (33). However, we must not neglect another important type of input to motor cortex that is somatotopic, radially organized, and place- as well as modality-specific. These results were obtained by prolonged study of responses of each cell to natural adequate stimuli. Although there was much convergence of sensory inputs to motor-sensory cortex (MSI) neurons in chronically implanted or locally anesthetised animals, such convergence did not obscure the basic somatotopic pattern of somesthetic, kinesthetic, and proprioceptive muscle inputs (see 19, 175, 225). In order to bring perspective to these various conclusions, we need to compare major findings obtained under the different experimental conditions.

A. Input from Skin and Joints

Peripheral receptive fields.—All early studies on cats under local (36, 37) or chloralose anesthesia (46, 47, 158) emphasized the convergence of sensory inputs to MSI in general and to pyramidal tract (PT) neurons in particular. Many cells could be excited from very large peripheral receptive fields, e.g. by natural or electrical stimulation of the skin of all four appendages ("somatic polyvalent" in Buser's terminology), and many cells could be activated by several adequate stimuli, e.g. by somatic sensory inputs as well as by visual and auditory inputs ("polysensory") (47). Visual fields of such cells were however relatively nonspecific: the cells gave off-responses to circular or elliptical light sources, often through both eyes, and never to moving light stimuli (99). Work on chloralose-anesthetized animals will be considered first, and thereafter that on locally anesthetized animals with natural stimulation, performed at the same time by Brooks' group, who introduced the terms "local" and "wide" fields (36, 37).

Buser & Imbert (47) and Towe and his collaborators (205–208, 226) confirmed the sensory convergence. Although it was more widespread in their samples than that found by Welt et al (225), they recognized the same predimple rostrocaudal gradient in the distribution of convergence as had Brooks, Rudomin & Slayman (36, 37). Cells in the anterior sigmoid gyrus (ASG) were most likely to exhibit wide receptive fields and to receive polymodal inputs. In contrast, cells in posterior sigmoid gyrus (PSG) tended to be driven from comparatively smaller, local, fields and were less susceptible to polymodal inputs (47). Since general conclusions about input projections hinge on quantitative data from representative cell samples, the arguments in this section are presented in some numerical detail.

Towe and his co-workers (140, 206–208, 226) made an elegant population analysis of over 1500 neurons at four sites in cat's pericruciate cortex. They directed attention to 1. the recording site, ASG or PSG, midsylvian, or coronal; 2. the extent of peripheral receptive fields, as judged by neural responses to electrical stimulation of the foot pad of the four limbs; 3. whether the neurons (PT cells) contributed axons to the pyramidal tract, as judged by antidromic excitation from the medullary pyramid; and 4. the spatiotemporal distribution of excited neurons, identified on the above basis, following peripheral stimulation. It was found (see 204, 205 for summaries) that pre- or postcruciate PT cells could almost always be driven by electrical stimulation of each of the four appendages (firing probabilities greater than 0.5). Cells with such "wide" peripheral fields were classified as *m* neurons. Cells from which a pyramidal projection could not be demonstrated (non-PT cells) fell into two distinct classes, whose proportions depended on the rostrocaudal level at which the sample was taken. In ASG, about 50% of non-PT cells received wide-field input and were also classified as *m* cells. In PSG, however, only 25% of non-PT cells were *m* cells. These non-PT *m* cells, as a class, tended to lie in the lower two thirds of the cortex. The other class of non-PT cells, classified as non-PT *s* cells, could be excited only from the contralateral peripheral focus and were concentrated in the upper half of cortex. The proportion of non-PT *s* cells increased from about 20% in ASG to 50% in PSG. Furthermore, the more superficially located non-PT *s* cells responded with shorter latencies, but had higher thresholds and lower iterative firing abilities to peripheral electrical stimulation than the deeper-lying wide-field *m* cells. Sensitivity to submodalities of natural stimulation was not uniformly distributed. PT *m* cells were most often excited by hair deflection, whereas non-PT *s* cells were more often touch-sensitive (205). Towe et al (208) stated that "the partitioning into *s* and *m* sets accounts for more of the variance in the neuronal response properties than any other partitioning yet tested". They also pointed out that the distributions of excited *m* cells across time and depth within cortex are remarkably similar for stimulation of each of the four paws. For example, ipsilateral forepaw stimulation produced a pattern of activation of postcruciate *m* cells which was "merely delayed 6–8 msec and somewhat desynchronized" compared to that from contralateral forepaw (207). Intracellular recordings (221, 226) on chloralosed cats confirmed this conclusion by showing that PSP patterns were similar in many MSI neurons following electrical stimulation of fore- and hindlimb. A similar conclusion was suggested by Buser & Imber (47) who had found comparable latency ranges for responses from fore- and hindlimb of 700 MSI units. Tests with natural adequate stimuli of 53 PSG neurons by Morse et al (140) showed that, in chloralosed cats, 42% responded to touch, 34% to hairbending, and none to joint movement.

Towe et al (208) reasoned that *s* neuron discharge, which only accompanied cortical responses to stimulation of the contralateral forepaw, might account for the earlier population response evoked by that stimulation. They considered, and rejected, an organization wherein stimulation of contralateral forepaw initially activated superficial *s* cells which then relayed later excitation to deeper cells. A model of this sort has some precedence in visual cortex (84) where neurons in layers V and VI display more complex response properties than superficial neurons. This is thought to be due to convergence of many superficial, "simple" cells within radially aligned columns onto deep, "complex" cells. However, such a scheme cannot account for the experimental evidence in MSI, because deep-lying *m* cells were activated at lower threshold by peripheral electrical stimulation and could follow iterative stimulation to higher rates than s cells. Towe et al proposed, therefore, that s neurons only "modulate" the excitability of m neurons which also receive input from two other pathways. One pathway was thought to be responsible for the early activation of layer V m neutrons by contralateral stimulation with the aid of facilitation from s neurons, while the other pathway was thought to activate PT m neurons in layer III about 6 msec later (208).

In summary, results obtained from chloralosed animals show that peripheral stimulation at any locus leads to a statistically definable spatiotemporal pattern of cell discharge in MSI. The first neurons to be activated, on the average, lie superficially in a particular part of the contralateral hemisphere. Discharge of s neurons is followed first by discharge of large PT m neurons in layer V and then by discharge of PT m neurons in layer III. Since almost all PT neurons belong to the m set that is activated bilaterally, their discharge, in sum, would be common to MSI cortices of both hemispheres. Thus peripheral somatic stimulation could produce "reflex" excitation of a large proportion of the pyramidal system. Excitation first appears at the appropriate contralateral MSI locus and may be focused by s neuron discharge. In view of this widespread distribution of somatic excitation, not to mention bombardment from visual and auditory systems, it is difficult to imagine that local sensory inflow could have a dominant role in providing sufficiently precise information to accurately initiate or guide limb movement. In fact, Towe et al (208) proposed that the cat's pyramidal system is more important in an 'excitability-modulating capacity' than as a 'primary motor system'. This conclusion was based on the input characteristics of the pyramidal system found under chloralose anesthesia, on anatomical evidence suggesting divergence of pyramidal activity at the spinal level (176), and on the paucity of effects of pyramidal transection in chronic cats (208).

However, before discarding the pyramids as a well-ordered system, it is necessary to consider experiments with locally anesthetized or chronically prepared cats, for these may provide some insights into possible effects of anesthesia. Brooks, Rudomin & Slayman (36, 37) began the study of peripheral receptive fields of PT cells in MSI. Cats prepared under inhalation anesthesia were tested after local anesthetization of all injured tissues and pressure points, and after immobilization by a neuromuscular blocking agent. They found, in an initial sample of 208 PT and non-PT cells in the forelimb focus, brisk responses to natural stimulation of the contralateral forelimb; hair deflection, light touch, taps, sustained pressure, and passive joint movement were effective stimuli. Receptive fields of PT and non-PT cells could be quite restricted, especially when located near the tip of the limb. Some cells however, particularly PT cells, exhibited much larger, wide receptive fields that could be discontinuous, ipsi- or bilateral, and for which several stimuli could be adequate. These cells share properties with Towe's m cells and with Buser's somatic polyvalent cells as determined by electrical stimulation. Some also could be polymodal; and some others, particularly large PT cells, exhibited labile fields, i.e., field size or adequate stimuli could change during the course of observation (34, 36, 37, 39, 225). Careful serial study of receptive fields was extended in further work by Brooks' group to another 300-odd cells (38, 225) of which 75% had local input (225). Hairbending or light touch were effective up to twice as often as deep pressure or passive joint movement. While PT cells with wide receptive fields were found equally often in ASG and PSG, non-PT cells exhibiting such properties were more numerous in ASG. Sampling bias could change these proportions drastically, for instance: labile fields were found more frequently after much pyramidal activation; without such, less than 10% of the fields were labile (38, 225). The percentage of cells driven by passive joint movement also varied in different studies, probably because skin fields were tested more exhaustively. Towe's, Buser's, and Brooks' samples agreed however in that about one third of the cells studied were PT cells (see 225). Brooks' results are in agreement with those obtained by Buser's group in that "two major types of body representation exist in the sigmoid cortex, one grading over into the other. The posterior one mostly contains neurons with fixed local receptive fields, while the anterior one contains more fixed wide and labile receptive fields" (33). The actual ratios differed, however, in that local input obtained only for 10% of the sample of Buser, and for 4% of Albe-Fessard (4). In another sample of 100 cells studied with local anesthesia, but still with electrical skin stimuli, Buser found the same distribution as with chloralose (47). It is plain that electrical and natural stimulation yield different distributions, as did natural stimulation in chloralosed and nonchloralosed cats (140). Since PT and non-PT cells in unanesthetized animals had much the same ratios of adequate stimuli and of local to wide fields, whereas in chloralosed animals PT cells were a grossly preferred target for convergence, one might conclude that normal animals have governors that gate convergence to PT cells. A detailed comparison of the data from these various groups of investigators is given in (225), and an overview in (35).

In summary, on the basis of over 500 carefully studied cells in MSI, Brooks and his associates defined the distribution of adequate stimuli as about 60% from superficial receptors (activated by hairbending or light touch), 30% from deep receptors (activated by deep pressure or joint movement), and about 10% as mute. Seventy-five percent of all cells had local receptive fields. The distributions of types of receptive fields and of adequate stimuli were confirmed by Asanuma et al (19), on a sample of 288 neurons from MSI in nonparalyzed cats, tranquilized with low doses of pentobarbital. They confirmed the ratio of 2–3:1 of cells with local to wide peripheral receptive field. The relative effectiveness of different submodalities of somatic stimulation was also confirmed: cells responsive to cutaneous stimulation (hair deflection and light touch) outnumbered, nearly 2:1, the cells responsive to deep inputs (passive joint movement and pressure).

Another dimension was introduced into the study of MSI by Welt et al (225) through combination of systematic serial examination of receptive fields and of cortical histology. Three quarters of 215 neurons within radially aligned columns were discovered to have overlapping local topography. Neurons with local inputs thus provided a radially oriented somatotopic framework, which contained the remaining quarter of neurons with wide receptive fields. Their foci usually included the areas represented by local-field cells in the same radial columns. With histologically confirmed angled penetrations, distances separating cells with less than half-overlapping local fields provided an estimate of 0.1–0.5 mm for the tangential diameter of the radial columns. Columns in MSI received a mixture of inputs from skin, deep receptors and joints having common topography. In contrast, Mount-castle et al (142, 145, 162) had shown that radial columns of 1 mm diameter in cat's primary sensory cortex receive common topographic and modality specific inputs as tested with and without barbiturate anesthesia (also see 38). The radial arrangement in MSI was confirmed by Asanuma, Stoney, Abzug (see 19 and cf Section III).

The studies cited above have all dealt with the cat. Primate precentral motor cortex has not yet been investigated as thoroughly. Bard (23) recorded cortical evoked potentials resulting from tactile stimulation of the periphery in barbiturate-anesthetized monkeys. Light touch to the contralateral forearm and hand evoked easily recordable potentials in postcentral gyrus but not in precentral gyrus. Kruger and his associates (109, 127) showed that electrical stimulation of peripheral muscle and cutaneous nerves evoked independent potentials in pre- and postcentral gyri. Precentral responses had a longer latency than postcentral ones, and their amplitudes were essentially unchanged after acute ablation of postcentral gyrus. Single-unit recording has been little used in primates, but it supports the work with evoked potentials. Albe-Fessard & Liebeskind (6) reported, for 33 chloralosed monkeys, that 87 of 114 carefully studied precentral cells responded to passive movement of the limbs, but that only one responded to tactile stimulation. In contrast, 84 of 118 cells in postcentral gyrus responded to local tactile stimulation. Receptors in muscles as well as in joint tissues were implicated in this study. (See Section on 'muscle receptors' for detailed consideration of these results.) Fetz & Baker (67) reported similar ratios: 189 of 233 precentral cells in 3 chronically implanted monkeys responded to passive joint movement. Only 18 neurons responded to tactile stimulation, often from wide bilateral fields.

In summary, the predominance of muscle and joint inputs to the precentral gyrus of primates contrasts sharply with the input pattern to the cat motor cortex where more than half of the neurons are easily driven by light tactile stimulation. This difference and the looser coupling from periphery to primate motor cortex may in part reflect sampling bias in the studies on cat, but more likely it is also a real difference, related to the greater manual dexterity of primates.

Input pathways.—Contralateral, local, and modality specific receptive fields of cells in MSI have been suggested to reflect input from the medial lemniscus (33). In fact, polysynaptic activation of PT cells from VPL has been demonstrated by Amassian & Weiner (10). Some of this input may be relayed via SI in view of the corticocortical connections between SI and MSI (96, 156, cf 139). Cooling of SI reduced the amplitude of the late relayed pyramidal response to VPL stimulation, bud did not change the early discharge (9). ICMS in SI (of up to 40 μA) activated PT and nonPT cells in MSI. The corticocortical linkages between these areas appear to be primarily between radial columns with overlapping peripheral inputs (Thompson, Stoney & Asanuma 202).

It is apparent that different degrees of sensory convergence have been found in unit-studies with chloralosed and with unanesthetized preparations. Since the organization of sensory inputs to the pyramidal system is fundamental to the control of movement, it is important to see if these results can be reconciled by examining the input pathways. Albe-Fessard (3) and Buser (45) have contended that ipsilateral body representation and auditory and visual inputs, i.e. "extralemniscal" inflow to MSI, arise in an ascending system from the brainstem reticular formation, particularly nucleus gigantocellularis. This region projects to the medial thalamus, particularly CM, which in turn projects to the ventral part of VL and the lateroventral part of VA. The latter regions, which project to largely to ASG, contain neurons with properties compatible with a role in relaying "extralemniscal" activity: polysensory response characteristics, timed to precede cortical responses (see Section IVC). Interference with the thalamic relays for this system by local cooling or KCl injection reversibly blocked the polysensory responses of MSI, leaving the specific response of SI unchanged (45). Furthermore, it has been shown in chronically implanted cats that the responsiveness of MSI and of CM neurons to extralemniscal inputs vary together; for instance it is lowest when the animal is alert, and it increases greatly in slow-wave sleep (3).

A further clue to the parallelism between CM and MSI input is that chloralose greatly augments both responses. These common changes in reactivity to extralemniscal inputs provide additional evidence for the notion that activity in the CM-VA/VL pathway may underlie the extensive convergence of sensory input to MSI in chloralosed preparations. Voronin & Tanengol'ts (221) suggest that auditory, visual, and multiple skin inputs to MSI converge subcortically in chloralosed cats. Their view is based on the similar shapes of PSPs in 35 cells and their similar susceptibilities to inverting currents. The authors allow that chloralose may at least in part be responsible for such a "unifying" action, since the same criteria had previously shown that inputs from VL and CM do converge at the cortical level in encéphale (165) or lightly pentorbarbitalized (126) cats (cf 33, and Section III).

Thus it appears that the characteristics of the CM-VA/VL relays are compatible with a possible role as a unifying center. Towe et al (208) suggested the existence of such a "coadunating" thalamic center to explain fixed patterns of sequential m neuron discharge following stimulation at any peripheral site. In this context, we recall that Thompson and his co-workers had earlier reached the same conclusion based on their study of evoked potentials recorded simultaneously from different cortical association areas in cats (200, 201). At least part of their "pericruciate association area" is coextensive with area 4, as defined cytoarchitectonically (80). Amplitudes of evoked responses recorded from different sites were highly correlated, although they were individually variable. Recovery cycles determined by using two stimuli of different modalities were identical regardless of whether the second stimulus was of the same or a different modality. They concluded that "an auditory, somatic sensory, or visual stimulus activates one and the same central association system which projects in an equivalent fashion to the same four cortical association fields" (200). Furthermore, Thompson found that responses to somatic, visual, and auditory inputs were identical at the thalamic level, and in fact were coextensive throughout the diffuse thalamic system from the rostral mesencephalic reticular formation posteriorly through the centromedian nucleus (CM), the midline nuclei, and the ventral anterior nucleus (VA) (199).

Chloralose appears to release deeper centers from a selective tonic inhibition of cortical origin, according to several lines of evidence. Responses evoked in CM by sensory stimulation become larger after decortication, and subsequent chloralose administration cannot increase them further (3, 132, 133, 137). Furthermore, corticofugal modulation of CM responsiveness is specific for input of the same modality as that of the ablated cortical receiving area (3, 132, 133). It seems doubtful that this effect of chloralose is the sole cause for enhanced extralemniscal reactivity; other mechanisms and systems may be involved. For example, stimulation of cortical sensory receiving areas can facilitate responsiveness of CM and MSI to extralemniscal inflow (45, 48, 49). This influence on CM is specific for inputs of the same modality as those received by the cortical area tested, e.g. visual or auditory. In addition there are corticocortical connections between primary-sensory receiving areas and MSI. This was proved by the continued responsiveness of MSI to stimulation of visual and auditory cortex after extensive thalamic destruction to eliminate subcortical conduction (93). The striatum (107, 108) and caudate nucleus (45) may also influence the input balance, because their stimulation inhibits CM responsiveness to extralemniscal inflow.

The ventroposterolateral nucleus (VPL) may be another thalamic nucleus involved in chloralose facilitation of sensory input. This is suggested by the finding that peripheral receptive fields of some cells in VPL expand and acquire extralemniscal reactivity under chloralose anesthesia (25). Study of chronically decorticate cats (26) suggested that neurons in VPL with extralemniscal input properties are not thalamocortical relay cells, but rather may be interneurons. Even more convincingly, a "population analysis" (cf 204) by Harris (78) showed that 30% of 640 VPL cells in chloralosed cats displayed properties very similar to those of MSI *m* cells. Although their responses to peripheral stimulation tended to precede the discharge of MSI *m* neurons, they did not project preferentially to the pericruciate cortex as assessed by antidromic or synaptic activation through cortical surface stimulation. Such a distribution would have been expected if *m* cells in VPL were serving as a relay to MSI *m* cells. It is therefore apparent that several modes of action, probably in several different pathways as well as in MSI, can account for the enhanced responsiveness of MSI seen under chloralose anesthesia.

Whatever the mechanisms, the fact remains that the degree of convergence of sensory inputs under chloralose to MSI is approached in chronically implanted cats only during slow-wave sleep. Therefore the type of sensory input to MSI obtained in locally anesthetized preparations is more likely to resemble that found in the awake functioning cat. This conclusion is supported by Sakata & Miyamoto's study of MSI neurons in unanesthetized unrestrained cats (175). Receptive-field characteristics of 96 neurons closely resembled those of MSI neurons recorded in paralyzed (225) and nonparalyzed (19) locally anesthetized preparations. The important contribution made by studies with chloralosed animals is the demonstration of the potential influences of many inputs on MSI and PT cells within it. The efficacy of these inputs depends on the functional states of the respective primary cortical receiving areas and on the states of a central core in brainstem and thalamic nuclei.

Finally, it should be noted that sensory inflow to MSI in general and to PT cells specifically has, with few exceptions (67, 175), been tested under static conditions using anesthetized or immobilized animals. Receptive fields can be labile, but in addition fixed fields can change in size or even adequate stimulus as a function of limb position, and excitability within fixed skin fields can depend upon the direction of stroking the skin within it (36, 37). These results, as well as those showing pyramidal effects on somatosensory transmission at the spinal cord, dorsal column nuclei, and thalamus (see 129, 227 for recent reviews), suggest that static tests of afferent inputs may give a distorted picture of information inflow during a movement. Corticofugal influences on somatosensory transmission in nucleus gracilis can be relatively selective: there is presynaptic inhibition of neurons activated by hair deflection and postsynaptic excitation of neurons activated by light touch (72). Furthermore, presynaptic inhibition itself can be specific for one or another functional class of fibers (95). The fact that pyramidal collaterals end in VL (50) and in other subcortical sites (210) indicates that their postsynaptic influence affects not only somatosensory inflow, but afferent input in general (cf Section III). It appears, therefore, that corticofugal outflow during motor activity might exert quite specific shaping influences on somatosensory input (cf 58). These results provide a warning against overemphasizing input characteristics of motor cortical neurons as determined under static conditions.

Receptors.—The preceding studies of organization of sensory input to MSI did not, in any systematic fashion, attempt to identify the peripheral receptors involved. To do so would have required extensive dissection and manipulation of peripheral tissues, which in many instances would have been contrary to the design and conditions of the experiments. Are properties of peripheral receptors mirrored as faithfully by neurons in MSI as they are in SI (145)? One might expect this to be true at least for those cells that receive input through the medial lemniscus (10), which is known to replicate peripheral patterns of activity (143). No such quantitative experiments have been performed with MSI cells. In the following paragraphs the response characteristics of MSI neurons will be related to properties of peripheral receptors.

As previously noted, the natural stimuli most frequently effective for producing excitation of MSI neurons were hair deflection, light touch, brisk taps, sustained pressure, and passive movement of joints. It is likely that each of these stimulates several types of peripheral receptors. Hair deflection presents probably the most coherent case. Three rapidly adapting types of receptors that are "event detectors" and that might be termed "detectors of movement" (143) have been identified in cats, rabbits, and monkeys by Iggo et al (42, 92). The most sensitive major group was associated with down hairs, was innervated by fibers in the Aδ range (Group III), and formed sensory units with small receptive fields. The receptive fields of individual fibers supplying this type often overlapped similarly sized fields of a second major group, which was associated with guard hairs, and was supplied by fibers in the Aβ range (Group II). A third, smaller group associated with tylotrichs was found to be also supplied by myelinated fibers in the Aβ range, and had somewhat larger receptive fields. While it seems likely that some of these receptors could project to MSI units one cannot be certain of their proportions.

For other types of natural stimulation, identification of the receptors becomes more difficult. "Light touch" may activate a discrete set of receptors, for slowly and rapidly adapting primary afferents mostly in Aβ, and partly in the Aα ranges (Groups I and II) have been demonstrated to display "touch" receptive fields (42, 91, 92). Such touch units are likely to provide information about movement as well as steady intensity (143) by virtue of their 'on' transients which reflect rate of stimulus application, and their steady discharges which reflect stimulus intensity. It should be noted, however, that light touch of an intact limb may activate subdermal receptors, e.g. Pacinian corpusles, which may contribute to the ascending volley. "Deep pressure" very likely involves receptors located in deep-lying tissues, since neither of the preceding two categories is effective. Since there exists a class of cutaneous receptors, however, which respond only to high transdermal pressure gradients (44), this conclusion could be questioned for data obtained from intact preparations. Precise identification would require surgical isolation of the skin from the deep-lying receptors. Even in this case, localization of the receptor to deep tissues would still not serve to identify it precisely, since muscles, tendons, or periosteal tissues could contain the receptors. A recent study by Silfvenius (182) showed that deep-lying interosseous Pacinian afferents from the forelimb interosseous nerve project to area 4 in close approximation to the Group Ia projection focus (see below).

Evoked potential studies have shown that joint nerves project to the pericruciate region (13, 102, 113). Gardner (69) has recently reviewed the central pathways from joint afferents. He points out that all studies based on lesions, and on electrophysiological and behavioral methods indicate that joint input may reach cerebral cortex by way of the dorsal column-medial lemniscus system, the spinocervicothalamic system, and, at least in primates, the spinothalamic system. Their degree of independence from the major projection to SI is not clear. Körner & Landgren (102), who studied evoked potentials produced by electrical stimulation of low threshold afferents in the elbow and knee joint nerves of cats, found that "projections from . . . knee joint afferents overlapped with the dorsal and medial areas of the low threshold muscle afferents in the postsigmoid gyrus". The organization of the ascending paths for these joint and muscle afferents was similar, since lesions of the dorsal funiculus abolished elbow joint potentials were abolished by transection of the dorsolateral fascicle. (See below on "muscle afferents," cf 114.) Slowly adapting Ruffini and Golgi endings, in capsular and ligament tissues respectively, may be appropriate joint sense organs.

Joint input is known to be necessary for conscious appreciation of joint position, and for accurate operation of the motor system (136). Joint receptors may "function as absolute detectors of movement" by virtue of the nearly linear relation between their initial discharge rate and the rate of change of position of the joint in their "excitatory angle". Since their tonic discharge rate varies as a function of joint angle, provided it is within the excitatory range, these receptors may also function as "absolute detectors of position" (143). Peripheral joint receptors and central neurons excited by passive joint movement display discrete excitatory angles. Cells in VPL or postcentral gyrus have wide angles, and respond maximally to passive movements of full extension or full flexion. Excitatory angles for these neurons usually subtended more than half of the total range of movement. Their discharge rates declined monotonically as the joint was moved to intermediate positions (143). Central detection of joint movement however presents problems of receptor identification, because activation of CNS by passive joint movement may be caused by signals from joint or muscle receptors, unless tenotomy has been carried out, as discussed in Section IIB.

In summary, more than half of the neurons in cat MSI (of which one third of tested cells were PT cells) receive skin input. Three quarters of the cells tested under local anesthesia, but less than half of those under chloralose, have local receptive fields. Wide fields and polysensory inputs are more pronounced in ASG than PSG. Such extralemniscal reactivity may be due primarily to thalamic convergence, that can be enhanced by chloralose. Population analyses of spatiotemporal discharge patterns show that activation of MSI cells is ordered and statistically predictable.

B. INPUT FROM MUSCLES

Group Ia.—Hagbarth & Vallbo have shown by multi- (76) and single-unit (77) recording from their own tibial, peroneal, and median nerves that Group I muscle afferents can be stimulated by passive joint movement. Units were identified as muscle receptors in general because their responses to voluntary muscle contractions were more pronounced than those that could be induced by local mechanical stimulation intense enough to deform deep structures. Spindle afferents specifically were identified (216) by their slowly adapting responses to local pressure on muscles and to passive joint movement, and by the lack of correlation of their discharge to active force (see Section VB).

A cerebral projection of Group I afferents from muscle spindles has been established in the cat, and it most probably also exists in the monkey. A discussion of their possible function is given in Sections III-V. Here we will examine their projections in detail. Low-strength stimulation of forelimb muscle nerves of cats evoked potentials with short latencies between the postcruciate dimple and the cruciate sulcus (151, 152). This part of PSG, according to Hassler & Muhs-Clement (80), incorporates part of field 3a and part of caudal 4γ, both of which contain giant pyramidal cells. Oscarsson & Rosén concluded that Group Ia afferents were responsible for the cortical Group I potentials, because they exhibited a close proportionality to the amplitude of the Group Ia volley recorded from the dorsal funiculus, they could be duplicated by short pulls on the tendons of forelimb muscles, and they were depressed by steady pull on the tendons of forelimb muscles or by close intraarterial injection of succinylcholine (151, 152).

The functional distribution of these projections is not yet clear. While the rostral part of the Group Ia projection area includes cortical regions that upon electrical stimulation give rise to motor activity in forelimb muscles (18, 19, 122, 175), foci for evoked potentials produced by forelimb muscle and cutaneous nerve stimulation have different cortical distributions. Cutaneous volleys produced maximum activity in three distinct parts of cortex: one region near the suprasylvian sulcus (corresponding to SII); another region near the caudal end of the coronal sulcus (corresponding to SI); and finally, a region at and lateral to the tip of the cruciate sulcus which often overlapped with the Group Ia projection zone (151, 152). Intra- and extracellular analyses of cortical neurons activated from forelimb Group I afferents revealed monosynaptic excitation and disynaptic inhibition by thalamocortical volleys (74, 153). It was suggested that they might be cortical inhibitory interneurons since only non-PT cells were activated (74). However, PT cell activation was demonstrated by Swett & Bourassa in PSG by stimulation of Group I fibers in deep radial nerve. Since averaging techniques were necessary to detect a relayed pyramidal discharge, perhaps only a small proportion of the pyramidal population was driven to frank discharge (193, cf 10). The majority of Group I-activated cells received convergence from different muscle groups (working at the same joint, at different joints, and from antagonistic muscle groups). Half of the 57 cells tested also received cutaneous input (74, 193). Some neurons, however, were "mainly or exclusively activated from one or a few muscle groups" (153).

The course and characteristics of neurons in ascending Group I pathways in the cat have been clarified by selected spinal lesions. Interruption of either the dorsal funiculus or the spinocervical tract demonstrated that forelimb cutaneous afferents ascend through both pathways with some selectivity towards the cortical projection foci. Forelimb Group I muscle afferents projected exclusively through the dorsal funiculus (152) and made monosynaptic connections with three groups of neurons in the caudal brain stem and cervical spinal cord (172). Two groups, one located in the dorsal horn of the rostral cervical cord and the other corresponding to the external cuneate nucleus, appear not to give rise to axons which ascend to VPL. The third group, corresponding to the main cuneate nucleus, contains antidromically identified cuneothalamic relay cells in its ventral caudal portions (170, 172).

Convergence of cutaneous and low threshold muscle afferents was demonstrated in 36 out of 151 cuneothalamic relay cells and convergence from adjacent and synergistic muscles was present in about the same number of cells. Only one half of the cuneothalamic relay neurons responded exclusively to one of six muscle nerves tested. Cuneothalamic relay neurons were predominantly inhibited by cortical stimulation, an effect due, at least in part, to depolarization of presynaptic terminals of first-order fibers (170).

Rosén also identified Group I-activated cells within thalamus (171). In confirmation of Andersson, Landgren & Wolsk (16) and Mallart (128), thalamocortical relay cells tended to be localized to the rostral two thirds of VPL overlying the main projection focus for cutaneous input from the forelimb. Their projections were tested antidromically by stimulation of the cortical surface. Eighty-three of 100 Group I receptive neurons projected to the cortical Group Ia focus only, and 15 projected to both the Group Ia focus and to SII (171). This distribution fits with earlier results of Landgren et al (113) showing a weak Group I projection deep within the anterior suprasylvian sulcus; and also with the observation of Andersson et al (16) that 4 out of 10 thalamic Group I-activated neurons could be antidromically excited from both PSG and cortex around the suprasylvian sulcus. Thirty-three out of 83 thalamocortical relay cells received convergence of cutaneous input from the superficial radial nerve. Convergence of Group I input from adjacent and synergistic muscles was greater in the thalamus than in the cuneate nucleus (171).

The above studies have dealt almost exclusively with the pathways and projection foci from forelimb. Initial attempts to define muscle spindle inputs from hindlimb muscles were generally unsuccessful (128) except for a

hint from Landgren, Silfvenius & Wolsk (113) who detected, in one experiment, a response to Group Ia input from hindlimb in the caudal part of the
upper bank of the suprasylvian fold. Subsequently, Landgren & Silfvenius
(114) recorded hindlimb Group Ia evoked responses on PSG, slightly medial and rostral, and somewhat overlapping, the forelimb Group I focus.
There was, in addition, a second focus on the medial wall of PSG near the
cruciate sulcus. Landgren & Silfvenius suggested that the overlapping foci
for fore- and hindlimb Group I projections might play a role in the coordination of movements involving both limbs (114). Group I inputs from forelimb and hindlimb follow different spinal paths (cf 152): transection of
the dorsal columns at high cervical levels did not influence the cortical
evoked responses from hindlimb, whereas additional transection of the ipsilateral dorsolateral fascicle abolished them.

What role does Group Ia input to the cortex play? To answer this question Swett & Bourassa compared muscle and cutaneous inputs to cortex
with chronically implanted nerve- and cortical electrodes in awake, unrestrained cats. Sensory discrimination thresholds were tested with operant
conditioning of animals trained to press a bar for food reward in response
to electrical stimulation of the deep or superficial radial nerves (29, 192).
Behavioral threshold to superficial radial nerve stimulation coincided with
threshold activation of nerve and cortex. Since the same animals responded
to deep radial nerve volleys only at intensities at or above Group II afferent
fiber threshold, the authors concluded that stretch receptors cannot subserve
conscious kinesthesia and that evoked cortical responses are not necessarily
associated with sensory discrimination. The lack of sensory experience upon
stretching muscles was confirmed directly in humans undergoing hand surgery under local skin anesthesia by Gelfan & Carter (70). Oscarsson & Rosén (151, 152) noted such evidence and suggested that a possible functional
role of the Group I projection to cortex may be to serve as a feedback channel providing the motor cortex with information useful for integrating motor
output (cf 161). Oscarsson et al (153) point out that the pattern of extensive convergence of inputs from different muscles, including antagonists,
and from cutaneous nerves seen at the cortex indicates that only crude
spatial informaiton is forwarded to that level. Rosen's analysis of convergence at other levels in the Group Ia projection pathway led him to suggest
that "information from Group I afferents is integrated in two steps. The
first step is convergence from synergistic muscles occurring at the thalamic level. The second step occurs at the cortical level and implies convergence from afferents in various muscle groups of more unrelated function"
. . . (171).

The study of projection of muscle afferents to primate motorsensory
cortex has lagged behind that in the cat; however, recent evidence confirms
the existence of Group Ia input to area 3a (see 3 and 161a). Lamarre &
Liebeskind (111) reported cortical evoked potentials produced by stimulation
of hindlimb muscle nerves in five monkeys. Responses appeared in both post-

central and precentral gyri after single nerve shocks at strengths just sub-threshold for eliciting Group II activity in the peripheral nerve. Latencies of precentral evoked responses were about 1.0 msec longer than those for post-central cortex. Thresholds for evoking cortical potentials fell to 1.3 times nerve threshold when brief repetitive stimulation was used (111). Unit recording revealed complicated patterns of convergence of afferents from different muscles to precentral neurons (5, 6). Of 114 cells in precentral gyrus of chloralosed monkeys, 87 responded to passive movement of the limbs (5, 6, and see Section IIA). The majority of the cells lying below 1 mm in cortex were driven tonically by displacements of the contralateral limb; phasic re-sponses were rare. "Fewer, but still an important number" were also excited or inhibited by similar or opposite movements of the opposite limb (3). For receptor identification, muscles were disinserted following surgical removal of the skin from chloralosed animals (5, 6). Cortical units were discharged by traction and by local pressure applied to these muscles. Receptors in joint capsules were also implicated in some cases: cells discharged in response to pin pricks and electrical stimulation of the articular aponeurosis. Direct electrical stimulation of muscles separated from their insertions also could produce short-latency discharges.

In summary, Group Ia input from fore- and hindlimb reaches cat PSG just rostral to the dimple after ascent in the lemniscal and spinocervical systems respectively. Curiously, the participation of PT cells appears small, and no Group Ia input to ASG has been reported at all. Muscle spindle af-ferents reach the precentral cortex of monkeys, showing many similarities with data obtained from cats, particularly with respect to complexity of convergence patterns.

Groups Ib, II, and III.—Little is known about central projection of Ib (tendon organ) input, because it is difficult to distinguish a control inflec-tion representing Ib activation in the compound action potentials of fore-limb nerves (151). However, Landgren & Silfvenius (114) found that a sec-ond component was added to evoked potentials recorded from the hindlimb cortical Group I focus when the strength of nerve stimulation exceeded 1.5 T. This second component appeared in concert with the ingoing Group Ib volley recorded from dorsal root filaments, and they both reached maximum amplitude at about 2.0 T. Thus, at least the hindlimb Group Ia projection focus seems to receive input from Group Ib fibers of hindleg muscle nerves.

Inputs from Group II muscle afferents appear to follow the same course as the Group I pathway. Rosén (170) reported that 46 of 151 Group I relay neurons in the cuneate nucleus received excitatory convergence from Group II muscle afferents. Usually this Group II convergence originated from the same nerve that contributed Group I excitation. Convergence was less fre-quently encountered in the thalamus; only 13 of 84 Group I thalamocortical relay neurons tested were also excited by Group II input. According to Os-carsson et al (151, 153) convergence of Group I and Group II inputs was even less frequent at the cortical level, as judged by the virtual absence of change of PSPs in cortical neurons or of surface responses when stimulus strength was increased from 2 to 10 times nerve T (153). Other studies, however, suggest that Group II and Group III inputs from muscle reach MSI. Landgren et al (113) reported that late components with threshold about 1.5–2 T were added to the forelimb Group I potentials recorded from anterior suprasylvian sulcus. Subsequently, Landgren & Silfvenius (114) showed that evoked responses recorded at the rostromedial edge of the hindlimb Group I focus were augmented when the strength of nerve stimulation exceeded 2.5 T. The latency of this component, which they interpreted as added by Group II afferents, was 17–35 msec. Additional late components appeared when muscle nerves were stimulated with strengths above 10T. The finding that 17 extracellularly recorded PT cells (not responsive to Group I volleys) were activated 10–15 msec following volleys in cutaneous and high-threshold muscle afferents from forelimb (74) shows that a Group II projection from forelimb to pericruciate cortex includes both skin and muscle components.

In summary, groups of adjacent PT cells, in cat and primates, receive peripheral inputs from skin, joints, and perhaps also muscle receptors. The first two project somatotopically to cells forming radial columns, providing a framework for a minority of cells receiving much sensory and spatial convergence. Such convergence occurs at all levels in the CNS, including motor cortex, but its appearance is exaggerated under chloralose anesthesia. Muscle input reaches area 3a predominantly. The main inputs to rostral motor cortex are mediated primarily through VL and those to caudal cortex through VPL. Muscle (and joint) inputs predominate in primate cortex but not in cat.

III. INPUT-OUTPUT COLUMNS

In the preceding sections we explored evidence to show that sensory input to MSI in general, and to PT cells in particular, is relatively precise in unanesthetized animals. The present task is to relate this inflow to motor outflow. The relations will be examined once more in Sections VB, C, and D, with special emphasis on force, speed, and displacement in movement.

Intracortical microstimulation (ICMS).—In a recent review Evarts (61) accepted Phillips' position (160) that there is no "fine-grained anatomical mosaic at the head of the corticospinal outflow" when tested by cortical surface stimulation with current adequate to cause muscular contraction. The accent is on "surface" because Phillips had cautioned that surface stimulation "has already been pushed to the limits of its resolving power" but he left the door open with a quote from Hines (81), that "weak stimulation permits restriction of responses to single muscle . . .". Progress in defining how cells with common motor outflow are organized was made by Asanuma & Sakata (18). They systematically explored MSI of cats anesthetized with pentobarbital, applying local repetitive stimulation through an intracortical microelectrode (ICMS). Thresholds for facilitation (or inhibition) of forelimb muscle-nerve monosynaptic reflexes from ICMS were as low as 1/100 of thresholds from surface stimulation. The cortical zones from which low-intensity (6–10 μA) stimulation could produce reflex facilitation of any given motoneuron pool were confined to radially aligned cortical segments of about 1.0 mm diameter. These "efferent zones" for different forelimb motoneuron pools were not arranged in any clear systematic fashion, and spatially independent inhibitory zones were observed. Overlap between the edges of adjacent zones was frequent, as stimulation often produced effects in two or more motoneuron pools, but without obvious functional significance in the combinations of facilitation produced. Acute partial section of the pyramidal tract greatly raised the threshold for facilitation.

Comparison of the "efferent zones" (18) with "afferent radial arrays" found in the same postcruciate volume of cat's cortex by Brooks' group (225, reviewed in Section IIA) suggested that the independent lines of research may have revealed two aspects of "minimal input-output building blocks" of motor cortex. A functional relationship between input-and output-columns was strongly suggested by a subsequent study of Asanuma, Stoney & Abzug (19), who used the same microelectrode for recording of unit responses to natural peripheral stimulation and for ICMS of the same site to evoke a "motor effect". After surgical preparation under inhalation anesthesia, locally anesthetized cats, which had received a tranquilizing dose of pentobarbital, were used. Bipolar EMG electrodes in 6–8 forelimb muscles allowed identification of the muscle(s) activated. When threshold for evoking short-latency (35–45 msec) EMG responses was less than 10 μA, the neuron previously observed at that point was considered to reside in the cortical efferent colony for the muscle activated. Ten μA was chosen on the basis of studies showing that the effective field radii for direct excitation of PT cells by single pulses was less than 100 μ (191).

An important new relationship was found from comparison of the topography of the skin receptive fields of all units assigned to respective colonies in such fashion and confirmed by histology. There was a high degree of organization: neurons of efferent colonies which activated muscles with simple action—like dorsiflexion of the paw, for instance—received input from peripheral receptive fields largely on the dorsal surface of the paw and digits. By the same token, cortical neurons activating muscles for paw ventroflexion had receptive fields predominantly on the ventral surface of the paw and forearm. Neurons in efferent zones associated with muscles with more complex actions—dorsiflexion and lateral deviation of the paw, for instance—were driven from peripheral receptive fields on both the dorsum and lateral side of the paw. Efferent zones projecting to more than one muscle received input arising out of skin areas intermediate to those of the constituent single muscles. Asanuma et al (19) summarized their interpretation as follows: . . . "The fact that skin regions that project most heavily to the efferent colonies lie in the pathway of muscle action (and, therefore, in the course of a manipulatory sequence they are likely to be excited following muscle contraction) suggests that the cutaneous input may also subserve a positive feedback function. If this is so then the input-output configuration which we have described resembles a built-in tracking system which tends to cause a portion of the limb to move toward an impinging tactile stimulus, i.e. to follow the source of stimulation" (19). This functional point will be discussed in Section VD. Proprioceptive input reached radially aligned efferent zones mainly from the distal joint involved in the action of the muscle associated with the particular efferent zone. This relation has not yet been analyzed precisely.

Consideration of the input to efferent zones implies that for each muscle there is one skin area with the densest overlap of peripheral receptive fields projecting to the cortical cells activating that muscle. A stimulus in this zone would produce the most intense synaptic bombardment for that efferent zone; and therefore, the skin area of densest overlap is likely to be the preferred skin trigger zone with the lowest threshold for the efferent column governing that muscle. The trigger zone always lies in the path of limb movement which would be produced by the action of that muscle, although not all parts of the constituent receptive fields do so (cf 35). Since the motor effects from single input-output columns are likely to be weak, they probably would not provide skin input with an obligatory overriding role in movement control. Rather, it would seem more reasonable to expect tight input-output coupling to produce selective bias. Much as the origin of afferent input confers "local sign" to spinal flexion reflexes, so the peripheral origin of sensory input to MSI confers "local sign" to the excitability levels of cortical efferent colonies. Normal function would be assisted by the convergence of various adequate peripheral stimuli and of central influences to cells within these radially organized input-output blocks (cf 35). Their simplest, reflexlike actions are only a minimal function, that may participate in normal movement without dominating it. Precedent for such a view is found in the role of the simple stretch reflex in spinal motor action (see 35).

An independent study of MSI input-output relations in chronically implanted unrestrained cats was performed by Sakata & Miyamoto (175). Movements produced by intracortical stimulation with 30–50 msec pulse trains ranging from 1.5–30 μA "were observed by visually inspecting the parts and their directions of motion as well as by noting the twitch of the muscles". Intracortical stimulation near neurons which received input from a particular forelimb region, e.g. the paw dorsum, produced muscular responses which moved the limb away from the point of contact, e.g. ventroflexion. These results, in contrast to those by Asanuma et al (19), suggest that peripheral input to MSI neurons produces an aversive bias rather than a pursuit or following bias. We have not been able to reconcile these results. However, the fact that Asanuma et al (19) used intramuscular EMG recording to detect short-latency responses with the lowest threshold (usually unobservable to the naked eye) may be significant. Aversion, i.e. withdrawal, would perhaps be the subsequent natural reaction of a cat to the sensory inflow produced by an unexpected (and experimentally unobserved) muscle twitch. Results from primates, while presently inconclusive (see below, 67), suggest that sensory feedback to motor cortex is positive rather than negative. In conceptual agreement with the conclusions of Asanuma et al (19), a colony of cortical neurons which causes activation of a particular muscle receives peripheral input which biases limb movement toward the site of contact of the adequate peripheral stimulus (67). Additional experiments are needed for clarification of input-output relations of primate motor cortex and for reconciliation of the different conclusions reached by studies of cat MSI.

Studies of primate cortex by ICMS have dealt most with proprioception because of the sparse cutaneous input (cf Section IIA). Is there a precise relationship between muscle input and motor output? Woolsey (230) observed that motor responses evoked from postcentral gyrus following chronic ablation of the precentral gyrus were invariably localized to that part of the periphery which projected to the area stimulated. He noted that "it appears clear . . . that a basic relationship exists between the origin of the input signals to the postcentral gyrus and the destination of motor volleys leaving this area" (230). Fetz & Baker (67) in a short report dealing with chronically implanted monkeys confirmed that PT cells respond phasically to passive limb movement rather than tonically to limb position, as did the units described by Albe-Fessard et al (3, 5). Fetz & Baker noted that cells isolated along the same penetration often responded to movement of the same joint, confirming Evarts' previous similar finding with voluntary movements (61), and were able to relate input and output, using ICMS. They reported that "when the cortex was stimulated at a point where cells responded to passive movement of a joint in one direction, the muscles of that joint which had the lowest response threshold were those which opposed that movement" (67). This would tend to return the limb towards its original position. Albe-Fessard et al (7, 8, 121) described in short reports that input and output were closely related for precentral motor cortex in semichronic tranquilized monkeys and chimpanzees. Movements produced by ICMS were much more localized than those evoked by surface stimulation: movements were . . . "observed in the same peripheral regions that send afferents to the cortical area being stimulated" (8). These results may reflect dense or synaptically effective projections (cf 160) to particular motoneuron pools from cortical colonies, which receive afferent input closely related to the target muscle. Such an organization is compatible with the early studies of Ruch, Chang & Ward (173), who suggested that primate corticospinal elements with like spinal destination tend to be concentrated in discrete areas of precentral cortex. Thus primate cortex may contain input-output columns analogous to those in cat. Caution must be retained, however, because Group I input is widely convergent to cortical cells of the monkey (5,

6, cf Section IIB). Furthermore, experiments with surface stimulation of baboon cortex by Phillips and his colleagues (112, 160) show convergence of monosynaptic action on spinal motoneurons from wide regions of precentral cortex.

Collateral interactions.—One of the most studied neural mechanisms which govern the effectiveness of input-output coupling is feedback through axon collaterals of PT cells. Collateral facilitation and inhibition operate both through short recurrent collaterals within the cortex and through longer subcortical loops (cf Section IVC). This facilitation and inhibition, lasting fractions of a second, can be generated experimentally by repetitive antidromic pyramidal stimulation. Intracortical recurrent axon collaterals of large PT cells in cats distribute inhibition to neighboring cells, and those of small PT cells primarily facilitation, as shown by tests of thresholds, latencies, and intracortical depths of cells. These, and other, properties of fast and slow PT cells have recently been succinctly summarized by Oshima (154). The development of thought on collateral interactions has been traced in (98) and (210).

Testing the effects of pyramidal activation on peripherally evoked excitability of cells in motor cortex of intact cats under local anesthesia revealed shrinkage of peripheral receptive fields and of the foci within them during collateral inhibition (39). Brooks & Asanuma (39) thus found that the inhibition sharpened contrast between the most vigorous and the less effective peripheral sensory inputs, but never sufficiently to convert a "wide" receptive field into a "local" one or a "labile" field back to its "fixed" base (34, 39). These results fit with the conclusion that cortical cells with local and wide fields are activated through separate subcortical input routes (33, 208, 225, and cf Section IIA). The sharpening of contrast between foci and less intense areas of peripheral input to individual cells in motor cortex enhances their discriminative power in response. The outer shell of functional radial columns of these cells is thus more sharply delineated by the suppression of afferent and efferent subliminal fringes. This amounts to collateral inhibition of tangential spread of excitation in the cortical sheet, which may assist shifted overlap and thus input-output focusing in motor cortex (185, 225). Several other functions have been proposed for collateral inhibition: Stefanis & Jasper (185), and Granit before them, stressed the stabilization of output frequency (cf 210), and Paillard (155) proposed that collateral facilitation may contribute to calibration of position sense, which is more acute after active than after passive movement. He reiterated the point made by Phillips (160) that the requisite "sense of effort" (136) may derive from such cortical feedback giving rise to "sensation of innervation" (65, cf 194 and Section VA).

Pyramidal collateral facilitation and inhibition in cat's cortex affect PT and non-PT cells, including corticorubral cells that were identified by backfiring from the red nucleus (RN) (210, and cf Section IVC). Are the collateral events intracortical? Inhibition lasting up to 200 msec and briefer facilitation interposed at about 40 msec after the end of conditioning pulses were shown to be produced by antidromic stimulation of the deafferented internal capsule. Data were expressed as inhibitory curves of firing probabilities of extracellularly recorded unit potentials, or of surface potentials of intact locally anesthetized cats (17). Similar degrees and durations of facilitation and inhibition were obtained upon stimulation of the cerebral peduncle of cats with encéphale isolée by Stefanis & Jasper (185), using extra- and intracellularly recorded unit potentials. Stimulation of the medullary pyramid (39), of the capsule (17), or of the peduncle (185) produced very similar patterns of facilitation and inhibition, making it likely that medullary stimulation generated intracortical recurrent interactions. Phillips' (159) caution about bulbar stimulation must be recalled, however, just as he applied it to his own trailblazing results with intracellular recordings reflecting facilitation and inhibition: . . . "The most probable, but not the only possible, cause of these reactions is impulse traffic in the recurrent axon collaterals of the activated Betz cells". Yet, the degree of inhibition varied rather regularly with intensity of pyramidal conditioning (39) and remarkably so with the levels of test cell activity in cat's cortex (39, 98). The latter relationship was measured in sufficient detail by Kameda, Nagel & Brooks for 13 cat's PT cells to reveal its adherence to the operating rules of recurrent inhibition in other systems: a given intensity of pyramidally induced inhibition subtracted roughly the same number of impulses from equivalent portions of cell responses within the physiological range, no matter what the intensity of the test responses (98).

The efficacy of these effects was about the same as that in spinal recurrent inhibition of tonic motoneurons in relation to appropriate physiological ranges of discharge frequency. It would be remarkable if such regular results were produced by several additive and interacting cortical and subcortical inhibitory systems. Potentials evoked in cat's cortex by bulbar or peduncular stimulation were used as indicators in many studies of collateral action, as judged by volume or surface recordings. Results obtained with cooling of the cortical surface (73) and with laminar analysis (88) agree that the short-latency "α" wave reflects prodromal events. There is also agreement that the β wave reflects collaterally induced postsynaptic responses, but vector analysis (88) revealed also a prodromal β component.

Subcortical modulation of afferent input to cat's cortex through the pyramids is now well established at many levels of the neuraxis. These self-adjustments, multiply achieved by pre- and postsynaptic inhibitions and by postsynaptic facilitation of subcortical afferent lines, have been reviewed elsewhere (64, 129, 161, 227), but one subcortical event is particularly relevant here. Facilitatory collateral influences have been suggested as possible causes (1, 33) for the major and long-lasting changes of peripheral input to PT cells, making their receptive fields "labile" (see Section IIA). Such changes consisted of sudden enlargements of receptive fields and acquisition of new adequate stimuli. This raised state of excitability could last minutes or even hours (1, 37, 38). Pyramidal collaterals were implicated on the one hand by the realization that "labile" fields were found five times more often when electrical stimulation of the medullary pyramids was interspersed frequently with tests of natural adequate activation of the cells (225). On the other hand, antidromically produced collateral inhibition, thought to be intracortical, reduced the extent of labile fields but could not shrink them back to their "fixed" basic proportions and inputs (34, 39). Pyramidal feedback into the lemniscal and reticular afferent systems may thus be part of a self-regulating long loop on the afferent as well as on the efferent side.

In summary, evidence suggests that cat's motorsensory cortex is organized in radial columns of 1 mm diameter that constitute functional minimal input-output blocks. Each column innervates primarily only one spinal motor nucleus, and receives topographically specific skin and joint input from the limb innervated by that nucleus. It is suggested that through this pyramidal reflex pathway, skin input can cause the limb to pursue a moving tactile stimulus. Primate cortex, which has a predominance of proprioceptive inputs, also has colonies of cells apparently organized at the minimal level according to relevant muscles. Precision of these minimal input-output relations is sharpened by cortical collateral inhibition.

IV. OUTPUT ORGANIZATION

How do the pyramids influence muscles? We will first examine their relatively direct actions on spinal alpha motoneurons (IVA), then on α-γ coactivation and on spinal interneurons (IVB), and finally their less direct supraspinal actions through subcortical nuclei and the cerebellum (IVC). Monosynaptic activation of primate α motoneurons has been discussed extensively by Phillips (160, 161), and will not be taken up here. Actions on sensory relay nuclei will not be considered, because that topic has been treated adequately in other recent reviews (59, 129, 160, 227).

A. PRIMARY ACTIONS ON ALPHA MOTONEURONS

Two schools of thought have been based on studies with cats. The first, championed by Lundberg et al (cf 123, 124) and Preston et al (164), suggests that pyramidal action on motoneurons is subservient to internuncial activity of segmental reflex arcs. In contrast, Vasilenko & Kostyuk (217) maintain that pyramidal outflow reaches motoneurons through a multisynaptic 'private' channel which is largely independent of segmental reflex activity.

Vasilenko & Kostyuk (217) showed that MSI stimulation evoked spinal potentials in "pyramidal" cats in two distinct foci of negativity. The earliest focus developed in the ventrolateral part of the dorsal horn (the external basilar region or EBR) 1.4 msec after arrival of the descending wave in the pyramidal tract. A second focus of negativity developed along the medial border of the dorsal horn (the "medial basilar nucleus") after 2.3 msec, and in the ventral horn after 3.7 msec. By stimulating cutaneous and muscle nerves they were able to show that relevant spinal receiving areas (primarily the intermediate zone of Cajal) did not appreciably overlap the areas activated by pyramidal volleys (217). Subsequent intracellular recording from spinal neurons showed that EBR neurons could not be activated from the periphery, and that their discharge latency was compatible with monosynaptic connections of motoneurons (218, 232). Average response latencies to cortical stimulation in the pertinent groups of spinal cells were as follows: discharge of PT fibers, 8.06 msec; EPSPs of EBR cells, 9.06 msec; discharge of EBR cells, 10.76 msec; and EPSPs of motoneurons, 12.63 msec. However, interneurons in the intermediate zone, responsive to flexor reflex afferents (FRA) input, discharged 6.2 msec after EPSP appearance in motoneurons (232). On the basis of these results the authors suggested (217, 218, 232) that EBR interneurons provide a pathway, largely independent of segmental reflex arcs, whereby pyramidal outflow may influence motoneurons. The late activation of cells in the intermediate zone would represent pyramidal adjustment of segmental reflex organization in a fashion appropriate for forthcoming or concurrent movement (232).

Fetz (66) also studied field potentials evoked in the lumbar spinal cord by stimulation of the pyramidal tract. He observed some separation in time of activity peaks set up by cutaneous and pyramidal volleys respectively, but he could not confirm clear functional separation. "Source density" was calculated for each evoked potential to reduce inaccurate estimates of the distribution of sources generating them. Fetz noted that PT activation of lumbar interneurons typically appeared with 10–20 msec latencies and that almost all cells were influenced by natural or electrical stimulation of the periphery.

Asanuma, Stoney & Thompson (20) examined the characteristics of cervical interneurons activated by ICMS of forelimb motorsensory cortex of the cat. They found that ICMS, which facilitated monosynaptic reflexes of identified forelimb muscle nerves, activated neurons throughout the intermediate spinal gray. Essentially all of those interneurons received input from the periphery. Since such low-threshold facilitation of monosynaptic reflexes had previously been shown to be abolished following acute PT section (18), it is likely that they too were dealing with pyramidal outflow. The peripheral inputs were usually from several of the main forelimb muscle and cutaneous nerves. No meaningful pattern was detected of afferent input related to the motoneuron pool with which the neurons were identified by ICMS. Contrary to the results of Vasilenko et al (232), Asanuma et al (20) found that the majority of cervical neurons activated by ICMS exhibited initial spikes preceding or coinciding with the first increase in the excitability of the test motoneuron pool, determined by monosynaptic testing. Furthermore, the overall envelope of activity evoked by ICMS closely matched the time course of facilitation of the motoneuron pools produced by ICMS. This fact, plus the finding that most of the interneurons could only be activated from very restricted cortical loci, led them to conclude that the inter-neurons could be internuncials on the pyramidal-motoneuronal pathway.

These data assign a coordinating role to corticofugal systems, superim-posing their special demands on the spinal system. This view is compatible with that of Lundberg (124) and with results obtained by Asanuma & Ward (21). The latter authors showed that ICMS (20 μA max) in layers V and VI of cat's pericruciate cortex produced sustained contractions of a particular forelimb muscle without accompanying relaxation of the antago-nistic muscle. By stimulating two sites, they found all possible combinations of contractions of the antagonistic muscle pair: simultaneous stimulation could cause coactivation, reciprocal activation, or solitary activation de-pending on the precise localization of the stimulating electrodes. Whether or not the corticofugal motor outflow makes use of segmental reflex mecha-nisms such as reciprocal inhibition apparently depends on what particular groups of corticofugal neurons are activated. The same interactions were observed when one of the stimulating electrodes was in the white matter, which suggests the spinal cord rather than the motor cortex as the site of interaction. Since muscle relaxation could occur without concomitant change in the activity level of the agonist, it is unlikely to have been due to activity around the gamma loop produced by α-γ coactivation (see Section IVB). Asanuma et al (20, 21) concluded that functional differentiation in MSI is accomplished by discrete spatial separation of excitatory and inhibi-tory zones for each muscle.

A similar conclusion was reached about human supraspinal control by Kots (103), who employed monosynaptic testing with the H reflex to deter-mine reflex excitability during single voluntary extensions or flexions of the ankle. The mechanogram and the electromyogram picked up from the skin, accompanying foot movement, were recorded simultaneously. Excitability of gastrocnemius motoneurons was determined by stimulating the popliteal nerve and recording the muscle H reflex. Excitability of gastrocnemius mo-toneurons (the agonist in extension) gradually increased during the last 60 msec of the latent period before onset of voluntary extension. With volun-tary flexion, reflex excitability of gastrocnemius motoneurons (the antago-nist in flexion) was unchanged throughout the latent period until the onset of movement, but excitability dropped sharply at the beginning of the flex-ion myogram of gastrocnemius. Thus, with extension, when gastrocnemius is agonist, the amplitude of its H response increased before its contraction, but no change preceded flexion (monitored by EMG of tibialis anterior) when gastrocnemius is antagonist. Kots (103) considered that the timing of inhibition of the antagonist nucleus near the beginning of spike activity of the agonist pool may be due to spinal reciprocal interaction. He concluded that: "The supraspinal command evidently incorporates facilitatory influ-ences addressed to the spinal motoneurons of the agonist but does not con-tain inhibitory influences to the motoneuronal pool of the antagonist" (103).

The details of pyramidal action depend in good measure on the type of muscle under consideration. Preston and his co-workers (164, 213) have surveyed pyramidal influences on motoneurons of muscles acting on the cat's ankle and on the monkey's elbow. Using intracellular recording and monosynaptic reflex testing in "pyramidal preparations", they found that cat motoneuron pools required repetitive pyramidal volleys for facilitation and inhibition. Pyramidal effects were evoked by stimulation of motorsensory cortex after partial transection of the midbrain, sparing only the pyramidal tract and closely adjacent structures.

In contrast, excitation and inhibition of motoneuron pools of baboons and monkeys could be produced with single volleys (188). Comparison of different muscle groups in cats and primates revealed characteristic patterns of pyramidal influence. Motoneuron pools of proximal limb muscles that functioned in an antigravity role received predominantly inhibitory influences from the pyramidal tract. Conversely, proximal flexor motoneuron pools were generally facilitated. These patterns, suggested Preston et al, reflected the need of the motor cortex to arrest the tonic antigravity postural mechanisms to permit volitional movements (164, 213). When distal muscles of the forelimb were considered, the above pattern of pyramidal influence became blurred. Particularly in the primates, but to some degree also in cats, distal muscles acting about the wrist or the carpal joints of the paw tended to receive primarily facilitation from pyramidal tract activation (164). Thus, distal forelimb muscles, regardless of their anatomical or physiologic classification, receive what could be described as a "flexor" pattern of pyramidal influence. Preston et al noted that these findings suggest "an organization and function for cortical control of distal forelimb musculature differing from that of the hindlimb and the more proximal forelimb musculature" (164).

Subsequent analyses of pathways mediating these effects through selected lesions of descending tracts revealed some surprising results (189, 190). In cats, transection of the ipsilateral dorsolateral funiculus at L_3 reduced, but did not abolish, flexor facilitation and converted extensor inhibition into a powerful facilitation of about the same duration. Curiously, essentially the same effects could be produced by a transection which included only ventral and ventrolateral cord. A C_4 transection of dorso- and ventrolateral fasciculi abolished all cortical effects, as did transection of the pyramids in the medulla. The authors suggested that at least two descending pathways, each capable of independently driving motoneurons, mediate cortical facilitation to flexor motoneurons. Inhibition of extensor motoneurons, however, appears to require the integrity of "one or more descending pathways other than the corticospinal tract" (190).

Similar investigations in "pyramidal" baboons (189) showed that lumbar dorsolateral column transections abolished early facilitation evoked by cortical stimulation, but did not greatly impair late facilitation. Cortical inhibition was also abolished by such a lesion. Transection of ventral quadrants of the cord produced little effect on the patterns of cortically induced facilitation and inhibition. Stewart & Preston (189) concluded that the primate, just as the cat, has collaterals from the pyramidal tract which mediate cortically evoked excitability changes to motoneurons, but that activation of segmental motoneurons is "less dependent on supporting influences traversing other descending systems in the primate pyramidal preparation than in similar cat preparations" (189).

The degree of corticospinal control of a motoneuron pool appears to be reflected in the discharge patterns of motor units recorded in the periphery. Tokizane & Shimazu (203) related average firing rates and interspike interval variability of motor units in human muscles during different degrees of voluntary contraction. They observed that motor units fell into one of two distinct groups: one group (their kinetic or K-type) exhibited marked irregularities in interspike intervals during even moderate voluntary contractions, and was incapable of regular, low rates of discharge. The other group (their tonic or T-type) displayed regular discharge rates during moderate contractions and was capable of significantly lower rates of rhythmic discharge. The quantitative character, as well as the proportion, of K and T motor units varied in different muscle groups. There was an overall decrease of regularity of firing of arm motor units as compared to motor units of the leg. K motor units were more frequently found in arm muscles than in leg muscles, and both K and T units of the arm less often exhibited slow rhythmic discharges with low interspike interval variability. Comparison of proximal and distal muscle groups of the arm revealed a similar shift. Although the relative regularity of motor unit discharge of different muscles tended, overall, to decrease with smaller muscles, this was not considered to be the prime variable since striking exceptions occurred. Rather, the authors noted that firing irregularity increased in direct proportion to the extent of precentral cortical representation. Since many of the regularly firing muscles were important in postural adjustments, Tokizane & Shimazu (203) felt that regularity reflected the susceptibility of the governing motoneurons to segmental, particularly γ loop, influences.

In summary, the pyramidal outflow can influence, in a precise fashion, one or a small number of muscles without affecting other muscles of the same or other segmental levels. Furthermore, it can, by activation of interneurons of segmental reflex arcs, produce patterns of muscular activity in large part determined by the pattern of segmental reflex connections, e.g. reciprocal inhibition. The exact mechanisms by which solitary effects are produced—whether by mediation of a "private line" type of interneuron or by selective activation of other neurons which also receive input from the periphery or by both—remains to be clarified. Cortical dominance over motoneurons may be revealed by their degree of discharge irregularity during voluntary contractions.

B. The Gamma (γ) Loop

In the preceding section (IVA) we discussed pyramidal influences on spinal α motoneurons. While they can call forth muscle power unaided, in fact they do so in conjunction with γ motoneurons. This involves the loop through muscle spindles (135) at some stage in the evolving movement (58). The development of thought on γ loop function has most recently been summarized by Granit (75) and Phillips (161). The question arises: what is the role of the spindles in pyramidal control (cf 157), and how do the pyramids engage γ motoneurons? The facts are considered below, and will be reconsidered in the context of special functions in Section V.

Spindle function.—Dynamic spindles respond to increases of load, in addition to reflecting muscle length and its changes. Bursts of impulses from spindles of inspiratory muscles contracting against tracheal occlusion were first demonstrated by von Euler's group (52). They called this a load-compensating reflex, which involves the governance of the spindles by spinal γ motoneurons. Under physiological conditions supraspinal excitation or inhibition of muscles almost always has corresponding effects on their primary spindles, as was emphasized by Granit (75).

Since γ motoneuron bias can change spindle discharge rate whether the muscle is relaxing or contracting, spindle function is enlarged from the provision of negative feedback in a closed-loop "length-servo" for maintenance of constant muscle length (135), to become the detector of differences between extra- and intrafusal muscle lengths in an open-loop "follow-up servo" under dynamic fusimotor control (134). The stretch reflex can then be used to make muscle length follow changes in spindle length as set by supraspinal commands.

Granit (75) predicted that . . . "Load compensation is by no means restricted to respiration. It will follow movement like a shadow and whenever muscles go from a more isotonic to a more isometric form of contraction in carrying weights—lifting limbs alone or limbs with weights added . . ." (75). This prediction has been confirmed for animals (178, 179) and humans (76, 77, 216). Severin, Shik & Orlovskii (178, 179) used a new experimental preparation: the mesencephalic cat that permits single fiber recording during walking induced by midbrain stimulation. The head of the preparation was fixed in a holder and the legs touched a moving treadmill belt. Electrodes were inserted stereotaxically into the brainstem at P2, L4, H0, for intermittent stimulation at 30 pulses/sec. The essential result obtained was that single spindle and Golgi afferent fibers from ankle extensors and flexors, recorded in dorsal root filaments, discharged most strongly when the muscle contracted in the support (or stance) phase of induced stepping, instead of the relaxed swing phase. Twenty-seven spindle afferents were identified on the basis of a firing pause, in their stretch-evoked discharge, after single shock stimulation of flexor or extensor muscles by implanted electrodes. Local mechanical stimulation of muscles through the skin was sometimes capable of showing in which muscle the spindle was located. Fibers from Golgi tendon organs were identified on the basis of their giving a burst response to electrical stimulation of the muscle. Activation of spindle afferents during locomotion did not precede the electrical activity in extrafusal fibers; spindle afferents from extensors were most active "precisely during active contraction".

Hagbarth & Vallbo (76, 77, 216) provided evidence for the load compensating reflex in higher functions, presumably involving the cerebral cortex. They studied proprioceptive responses to voluntary movements of their feet and hands, by recording multiple (76) and unit (77) responses from their tibial and median nerves. Units that very likely were spindle fibers (both Group Ia and II) usually started firing simultaneously with or slightly after initiation of EMG activity in the muscle of origin of the fiber during isometric and isotonic contractions. The work was extended to 15 subjects by Vallbo (216), who found that 30 out of 35 spindle endings increased their discharge during voluntary contractions.

Gamma (γ) motoneurons.—Granit's suggestion of the general existence of the load compensating reflex also contained an opinion about its mode of operation. He thought that . . . "alpha output is likely to be adjusted by the length servo for optimum compensation . . ." (75), i.e. that γ drive inevitably governs α drive in spinal "α-γ linkage". This has not been borne out by studies of induced walking of mesencephalic cats (179), or by experiments with humans (216). Instead, a more flexible interdependence of the α and γ system has emerged. This will be discussed in relation to force and speed control in Sections VB and C, but first we must examine the facts. Records from single ventral root fibers in mesencephalic cats suggested that γ motoneuron discharge could precede or follow onset of α discharge during induced walking, indicating flexibility of α-γ linkage of supraspinal coactivation (179).

The follow-up servo function through the γ route was shown to be less effective than "α-γ coactivation" by Phillips (161). He reasoned that . . . "It should be possible to show 1) that the neural apparatus of the cortical hand area includes a projection . . . to fusimotor neurons, in addition to the powerful monosynaptic (CM) projection to α motoneurons; 2) that the hand muscles contain spindles which are unloaded by movement and made to discharge by fusimotor activation; and 3) that the spindles supply excitatory feedback to the α motoneurons." The three points were substantiated as follows.

Parallel coupling of extra- and intrafusal muscle fibers was shown by Koeze, Phillips & Sheridan (101) by recording the discharges of single spindle afferents of (extensor digitorum longus) EDC, from dorsal root filaments in lightly anesthetized baboons, using responses to electrical stimulation of the surface of the opposite precentral arm area. Independent α and γ responses could sometimes be elicited alone. Furthermore, corticospinal volleys failed to excite spindle afferents at frequencies effective for the monosynaptic CM synapses, but below strengths to activate them even at light anesthetic levels. Another observation was that during cortically induced tonic contractions, bursts of spindle acceleration occurred independently. Koeze et al (101) concluded that the actions on muscle spindles and on motor units were capable of functional independence. "The experiment demonstrates that the cortex has access to a fusimotor system that is powerful enough to offset the unloading effect of 'isometric' contraction, and that its response is roughly coextensive in time with the α response. It could therefore be related accurately to phasic movements. The corticofugal pathway has not been defined and may be corticorubro-spinal, cortico-interneuonal, etc. . . ." Clough et al (51) investigated whether feedback from one muscle is confined to motoneurons of the same muscle by measuring the quantity of monosynaptic excitation intracellularly from α motoneurons of the same and of other hand muscles. When muscle afferents had been electrically stimulated in motor nerves from single muscles or functionally related groups of muscles, they showed that the spindles of EDC or of palmaris longus (PL) sent only little excitation to motoneurons of other muscles, which is consistent with the follow-up length-servo theory. But this was not the case for flexor digitorum sublimis (FDS), whose spindles sent more excitation to motoneurons of the intrinsic muscles of the hand than to the motoneurons of FDS itself. The authors found these results easier to reconcile with the theory of α-γ coactivation than with a follow-up servo (161).

Koeze (100) undertook further similar experiments with the baboon's hindlimb muscle (tibialis anticus) that is activated reflexly in posture and locomotion to a much greater extent than the hand. He could not, however, demonstrate any low-threshold activation of fusimotor neurons, using as criterion one more acceleration of spindle afferent discharge before contraction, from which he concluded that the γ loop is not active in threshold movements of the cat's hindlimb evoked by cortical surface stimulation.

The question of relative potency in driving motoneurons was analyzed, and it was found that for single muscles (EDC, FDS, PL) the CM input produced more depolarization than spindle feedback from the muscles' own spindles. Spindle and CM inputs to motoneurons also differed by a property of CM synapses which is not shared by spindle afferents' synapses—their transmitting potency was increased when a few impulses were delivered at frequencies of 200/sec and over (161). The latter point may however be related to recruitment of cortical cells.

Recent measurements of EPSP shape indices suggest that CM synapses may, on average, be located on more distal parts of the dendritic tree of the motoneuron than Ia synapses (163). Experiments in which CM- and graded spindle excitation produced by stretch were added . . . "suggest that even large totals of monosynaptic spindle input at high frequencies can have, at best, a marginal or auxiliary effect on the α motoneurons of the baboon's EDC. Such a conclusion favours the hypothesis of α-γ coactivation against the hypothesis of the follow-up length-servo in its original form. Clough et al (51) found that the largest spindle inputs are directed mainly to those motoneurons which also receive the largest CM inputs, . . . which . . . should improve the selectivity of cortical control by α-γ coactivation."

In view of the organization of motor cortex in colonies for individual muscles (19, 161), one would expect functional cortical coactivation of spinal α and γ motoneurons to require proximity of their "upper motoneurons". Such proximity has been demonstrated most recently by facilitating static and dynamic spindles in forelimb muscles of the cat through pericruciate stimulation, monitored by recording from dorsal root filaments (219, 231). Pyramidal mediation of the pericruciate facilitatory influence was proved by its continuation after section of the brainstem sparing the cerebral peduncle (231), or of the medulla sparing the pyramid (231), or after lesion of the red nucleus (219). On the efferent side, γ fibers in hindlimb motor nerves have been shown to be activated by stimulation of the medullary pyramid in decerebrate cats whose medulla was cut except for the pyramid, cortical stimulation strengths that evoked muscle contractions being avoided (115, 227). Responses from fascicles of hindlimb nerves to cortical stimulation in similar preparations have confirmed the above conclusions (68). Cortical activation of γ motoneurons of flexors and extensors facilitated 58 out of 79 peroneal (flexor) units and inhibited 97 out of 149 triceps surae (extensor) units. In addition, these studies (68) have revealed parallel pyramidal effects on α and γ motoneurons, which may be of importance in their coactivation.

Shik's experiments with walking of the mesencephalic cat induced by brainstem stimulation indicated a considerable degree of independence in the relative timing of α and γ discharge, measured in ventral root fibers (179). This implies flexibility of α-γ linkage at the midbrain level of coordination (cf 124).

Evidence suggesting involvement of motor cortex in governance of γ discharge also comes from Vallbo's studies of spindle afferents with 15 human subjects. He reported that "the afferent activity was on the whole very precise in its onset and cessation, and it coincided in time with the α motoneuron discharge as revealed by the EMG activity" (216).

Regulation of spinal interneurons.—So far evidence has been marshaled concerning corticofugal effects on motoneurons, both of the α and γ size range. Turning to interneurons now, what functional role can be assigned to their corticofugal innervation, besides polysynaptic support of segmental flexor reflexes (123, 124)? Can the pyramidal system influence the balance between antagonistic muscles which is regulated by spinal reciprocal inhibition? Evidence has been advanced from Lundberg's laboratory that the cat's corticospinal tract shares this capability with other corticofugal systems (124). Lundberg & Voorhoeve (125) showed by reflex testing and intracellular recording that corticospinal activation facilitated segmental reflexes as well as reciprocal inhibition on the Ia pathway, and also Ib and flexor reflex afferent actions. The pyramids were proved to be the pathway responsible because acute section abolished the effects. In complementary fashion, extrapyramidal systems also facilitated reflex transmission through excitatory actions on interneurons. Hongo & Jankowska (82) increased reflex inhibition through Ia and Ib circuits, as well as cutaneous FRA reflex excitation, by cortical stimulation around the postcruciate dimple of pyramidotomized cats. By making acute spinal quadrant lesions, they proved that the effects descended through the dorsal and ventral lateral funiculi, i.e. most probably through the rubrospinal and reticulospinal systems. Since the monosynaptic test reflexes were unaffected, interneurons rather than motoneurons were thought to have been excited by the cortical conditioning stimulation. This was indeed found for 18 out of 34 cells tested, with the remainder at least facilitated. The effects may have been in part due to primary afferent depolarization of Ib and cutaneous fibers, but not of Ia fibers.

Recent evidence suggests that spinal recurrent inhibition may release the reciprocal control exerted by the Ia pathway on antagonistic flexors and extensors (86). Intracellular recording from interneurons revealed that Renshaw cells inhibit Ia interneurons in lamina VII of the cat's lumbar ventral horn (85). The inhibitory effect from motor axon collaterals was limited to the Ia pathway, since no reduction was found in IPSPs evoked in motoneurons by Ia or FRA volleys. Spatial convergence from corticospinal, corticorubrospinal, and vestibulospinal tracts and recurrent axon collaterals of motoneurons has been demonstrated. Stimulation of supraspinal systems and of Ia afferents at suitable intervals gave large motoneuron IPSPs when separate stimulation at those strengths gave none. These convergent test-IPSPs were decreased by Renshaw action evoked by preceding ventral root stimulation (87).

Hongo, Jankowska & Lundberg (83) studied the effects of stimulating the cat's red nucleus on synaptic transmission of various primary afferents to motoneurons. Intracellular recording from spinal interneurons revealed mainly EPSPs accounting for the rubral facilitation (probably monosynaptic) of Ia inhibition and of Ib excitation of antagonists as well as of some Ib inhibitions. Together with these effects there was also facilitation of reflexes to input from low-threshold joint and cutaneous receptors, as well as from high-threshold cutaneous ones. The authors point out that corticofugal effects on interneurons would aid, rather than hinder, α-γ coactivation because they would coordinate reciprocally active muscles. The corticofugal effects also obtain for spinal interneurons activated by Ib input. Hongo et al (83) comment on the importance of Ib function:

Many tendon organs have a very low threshold for contraction. . . . Furthermore, the . . . very large . . . receptive field from which any motor nucleus draws its Ib effect . . . indicates that Ib reflex actions regulate movements in which muscles operating at different joints are engaged. . . . Expectedly there would be a highly different demand on the Ib reflexes in gait of different speed. Much higher tensions would be produced in fast running or jumping than in pacing, hence the need for regulation of the transmittability, particularly of the inhibition between extensors. . . . The problem in complex movements arises from the fact that certain muscles seem to be linked together in Ia inhibition. The available evidence . . . suggests . . . : When higher centres give the command for a more complex movement involving perhaps extension at one joint and flexion at another, or coactivation of extensors and flexors at the same joint, there is a mobilization of the appropriate Ib reflexes subserving this movement . . . (83)

In summary, it seems that α and γ motoneurons can be called into action by the pyramids independently of each other. This "coactivation" can offset the unloading of spindles during muscular contraction, thus maintaining loop gain in the "load compensating reflex". There is no direct evidence for initiation of movement through the γ loop. Pyramidal governance of movement is supported by muscle sense organs better suited for feedback control rather than for initiation of movements. The pyramids appear capable of "priming" interneurons in segmental reflex arcs, of funneling afferent inflow suitable for movements, and of governing the balance between antagonistic muscles.

C. ACTIONS ON SUPRASPINAL CENTERS

The distinctive peripheral input characteristics of units in cat's ASG and PSG, described in Section II, reflect differences in their central connections. Here only some contrasts between ASG and PSG are considered with relevance to input-output relations. For general information, the reader is referred to Brodal (30), and for cerebrocerebellar orientation to Evarts & Thach (64) [see Section I].

VL and VPL.—Rinvik (167) has been one of the most recent to point out that cat's ASG and PSG are predominantly associated with VL and VPL respectively, in terms of both thalamocortical and corticothalamic connections. He found that terminal degeneration from corticothalamic fibers gradually increased in VL as lesions were placed at successively more rostral cortical levels starting with the postcruciate dimple. The amount of terminal degeneration increased abruptly at the level of the cruciate sulcus, and conversely, the amount of terminal degeneration in VPL decreased. Jones & Powell (97), who studied terminal degeneration after cortical lesions which appear to have infringed relatively little on area 4 γ (80), also concluded that the sensory cortex sent fibers to VPL in a topographically organized manner. They confirmed that the pattern of degeneration appeared to conform with a concentric lamellar pattern of representation of the body surface as described by Mountcastle & Henneman (144). Specificity of corticothalamic connections has been verified electrophysiologically. Stimulation of ASG is msot likely to yield antidromic invasion and postsynaptic facilitation (and/or inhibition) of VL neurons (57, 174). Stimulation of PSG, in contrast, is most likely to yield antidromic invasion and postsynaptic facilitation (and/or inhibition) of neurons in VPL (181).

Even more precise information has been provided by Andersen, Junge & Sveen (15): the area of sensorimotor cortex to which a thalamocortical relay neuron sends its axon is likely to be the very area which is most effective in facilitating synaptic transmission of the same thalamic cell. In agreement with the conclusions reached above, VL stimulation evoked the largest responses on ASG, and VPL the largest responses on PSG (139, 177). Blum, Halpern & Ward (28) also suggested that colonies of PT cells were activated either from VL or from sensory cortex, but not from both, on the basis of study of 41 PT cells. The cat's lateral (169) VL projects highly topographically (57) and monosynaptically to large PT cells (10) that then tend to oscillate at 4–5/sec (119). The power of evoking pyramidal tract discharges from the cat's VL decreases during reticular arousal, judged by surface and volume recording (186) and by intracellular studies revealing attenuation of their synchronization mechanisms (166). Corticofugal connections from motorsensory cortex were established by intracellular recording in VL. They were ipsilateral (57) and monosynaptic to a majority of VL relay cells (215).

Red nucleus (RN).—Anatomical studies indicate functional differences between pre- and postcruciate connections to RN. Rinvik & Walberg (168) observed that maximal terminal degeneration of pars magnocellularis of RN followed lesions of the precruciate cortex, and that RN received "only scattered fibers" from postcruciate cortex. These connections have been reviewed elsewhere (64), and moreover, RN has been the subject of a special recent review by Massion (131). Of relevance here may be that cats' RN cells were shown by Tsukahara, Fuller & Brooks (210) to be inhibited disynaptically for approximately 50 msec by fast PT fibers, and facilitated monosynpatically by slow ones, conducting at 50 and 15 m/sec respectively. That these effects were mediated through pyramidal branches going to RN was proved by appropriate brain sections in these acute experiments. Termination of the pyramidal branches in RN was inferred from the distribution of "closed-end" field potentials generated by pyramidal stimulation around the red nucleus. Finally, the field potential indicators of fast and slow fiber activities had thresholds and amplitudes that correlated well with those of IPSPs and EPSPs respectively recorded from RN cells (210). Tests of conductance changes by passing hyperpolarizing current pulses during pyramidally induced IPSPs suggested that the collateral inhibitory synapses are on the somatic region of RN cells, while absence of conductance changes during EPSPs implied that excitatory synapses are on distal dendrites (211).

Others.—Other instances of different projections from ASG and PSG have been documented. Sousa-Pinto & Brodal (183) found that the inferior olive received a somatotopic projection from ASG and rostral coronal cortex, but not from PSG. Likewise, the cortical projection to the lateral reticular nucleus arises mainly from ASG (32). P. Brodal (31) reported that both banks of the cruciate project to the pons in a somatotopic fashion. However, he noted that "anterior sigmoid gyrus and the anterior part of the coronal gyrus project to, at least in part, other regions of the pontine nuclei than do the posterior sigmoid gyrus and the posterior part of the coronal gyrus" (31). Corticospinal fibers from PSG were found to be distributed mainly to the dorsal gray, and fibers from ASG more ventrally in cat (147). A similar spinal distribution descends from pre- and postcentral cortex in monkey (110). Electrophysiological and anatomical studies have generally confirmed each other. Morrison & Pompeiano (138) observed that stimulation of the pyramidal tract, following chronic ablation of ASG, yielded normal dorsal root potentials indicating afferent depolarization, but little or no ventral root discharge. Along the same line, Andersen, Eccles & Sears (14) showed that dorsal root potentials could only be evoked by stimulation of postcruciate white matter after ablation of ASG and PSG. Marchiafava & Pompeiano (130) reversed the procedure and found that after chronic removal of PSG, normal flexion responses could still be produced by PT stimulation. A recent study by Fetz (66) indicated that PT stimulation produced differential effects on spinal interneurons receiving pre- and postcruciate PT projections. Neurons of lamina IV and V were predominantly inhibited, while more ventral cells in lamina V and VI were predominantly excited. The former group of cells is in close contact with afferent cutaneous fibers and may give rise to ascending axons.

It has been suggested that these results indicate that PT fibers from ASG, which project most ventrally in the spinal cord, are predominantly concerned with "motor" signals, while PT fibers from PSG are predominantly concerned with modulating incoming sensory inflow (66, 110). However, motor responses are produced with equal ease by extremely weak focal intracortical stimulation of either pre- or postcruciate cortex (18, 19, 175); the postcruciate dimple marks the cytoarchitectonic boundary between area 4 γ and other areas (80). Perhaps the distinctive characteristics of pre- and postcruciate cortex cited should not be interpreted to indicate discrete separation of function. Thus, rather than assigning one part of area 4 γ a "motor" function and another part an "input biasing" function, it would seem more parsimonious to assign all the area 4 a motor function. The more caudal part receives and acts on relatively precise sensory information from the periphery and sends a major secondary projection to modulate that input at various levels. The more rostral part receives more complex information, including that from cerebellum, and sends a major secondary projection back to the cerebellum and the relays on the cerebellar-cortical pathway.

Cerebrum and cerebellum.—Functional and anatomical cerebral-cerebellar connections have been reviewed by Evarts & Thach (64). In the following we highlight recent relevant evidence of cerebrocerebellar input-output relations.

The pyramidal influences on the red nucleus, referred to in Section III, may be a governor of the balance between cerebral and cerebellar inputs to this extrapyramidal center. RN cells are convergent relay stations of the ipsilateral corticorubral and contralateral cerebellar efferent systems, since they receive powerful monosynaptic excitatory connections from the contralateral nucleus interpositus (IP) of the cerebellum. Since IP is excited tonically by the inferior olive and is inhibited by Purkinje cells in the cerebellar cortex, RN cells are excited by the inferior olive, using IP as a relay; and they are disfacilitated by cerebellar cortex. Somatic, visual, and auditory inputs can thus excite and disfacilitate RN cells through this "cerebellar reflex" pathway, which in turn is inhibited by fast, and facilitated by slow, pyramidal fibers (210). This particular pyramidal action may be a "switching" from cerebellar to cerebral control of spinal targets common to both the corticospinal and the corticorubrospinal systems. Since these two descending paths generally act synergically, discharge of fast PT cells would weaken the cerebellorubral influence on the cord, and that of small PT cells would strengthen it (210). Axon branches of both fast and slow PT cells in the pontine nuclei can activate mossy fibers, but only branches of slow PT cells can fire olivary cells to give climbing fiber responses (154). Cerebral and cerebellar influences also meet in VL: the dentate and interposed nuclei send monosynaptic excitation, as well as polysynaptic inhibition, to separate populations of VL relay cells (215).

Implied in all theories of movement is the importance of information flow about the momentary state of the movement from the periphery to the cerebellum, and thence to the cerebrum as well as from cerebrum to cerebellum. Eccles (58) has characterized the interaction of the periphery and some critical parts of the brain as ". . . a dynamic control of an evolving movement by feedback loops up to the cerebellar cortex." The cerebrum also informs the cerebellum what commands are being sent down, and the cerebellum in turn gives . . . "to the cerebrum an ongoing comment on its PT discharges" (58). Ito (94) envisaged the cerebellar comment as predicting what the (skilled, learned) movement will be, thus offering correction through an internal loop before external feedback can reach the cerebral cortex.

Thach (196) has attempted to obtain data on timing. He showed that Purkinje cells in an intermediate portion of the hemisphere of the culmen generated simple and complex spikes, referable to mossy and climbing fiber input. Simple, but not complex, spikes, discharged consistently in a pattern closely in time with a self-paced, oscillatory rapidly alternating arm movement, performed by monkeys for liquid reward. Thach further found that

the discharge frequency of nuclear cells varied in a consistent temporal relation to successive movement cycles of the ipsilateral limbs. This constitutes evidence for participation, although not of control, by a cerebellar system which is known to project to motor cortex. In subsequent studies (197,
198), monkeys were required to hold a lever against a stop, and at a light
signal to move it quickly to an opposite stop. The discharge rate of most
cells in dentate and IP (197) and of Purkinje cells (198) increased in relation to the movement, rather than to the signal. In this step-tracking
task, 15 out of 52 Purkinje cells showed discharge changes not only for
simple but also for complex spikes (198). More dentate cells (42/50)
changed before movement than IP cells (18/41). The distribution time of
frequency change for 52 Purkinje cells in intermediate cortex coincided
well with that of IP cells (198). Since the direction of frequency change
tended to be the same for Purkinje and for nuclear cells, and since the pathway to Purkinje cells is longer and has more synapses than that to nuclear
cells, Thach suggested (198) that . . . "the role of Purkinje cells is to modify through restraint the already initiated output of the nuclear cell" . . .
Dentate cells changed earlier than IP, and in fact, early enough so that
their discharge could not have been influenced by feedback from the moving
wrist (197). Thach pointed out however that these experiments do not yet
establish whether dentate output preceded or followed pyramidal discharge
(197).

In summary, ASG and PSG have distinct (and reciprocal) connections
with several supraspinal targets. Cerebral and cerebellar influences commin-
gle in VL and in RN, where pyramidal collaterals can influence their respective spinal effectiveness. Our knowledge of the timing of pyramidal and
cerebellar unit discharges during voluntary movements is not yet accurate
enough to permit definition of the control sequence.

V. ARE THERE THREE CONTROL SYSTEMS?

A. Nature of Movement Control

A control system was defined in the Introduction as an entity with identifiable inputs (for instance in terms of natural adequate stimuli), outputs
(for instance in terms of muscular adjustment), and input-output couplings
that can read profiles of neural activity. The last item of course is the most
mysterious. Although we can approach the problem with unit neurophysiology, answers may well depend . . . "not only on the types of units observed,
but also upon whether or not they are observed simultaneously, and the important temporal relations between their discharge patterns taken into account" . . . (90). In the following, we introduce our consideration of control
systems with a brief review on the role of sensory feedback in intermittent
and in continuous control.

Sensory feedback.—The question has been asked many times: how important is sensory feedback for the execution of voluntary movements? The well-known studies by Mott & Sherrington (141) dramatically illustrate the degradation of motor performance when afferent input is abolished. They provided support for the "chain-reflex" hypothesis of movement control—namely that continuous sensory input impinging on different levels of the neuraxis, particularly as feedback information, exclusively determines patterns of motor output.

Many lines of evidence now strongly suggest that this explanation cannot account for all types of movement. Taub & Berman have sought answers to this question by deafferenting monkeys' arms bilaterally from C_2 to T_3. In a recent summary (194) they described that six such animals could learn, and that another six could relearn, to flex a forelimb to a buzzer or click that was response-terminated to avoid an electric shock to the forearm. The same was true for another four monkeys that executed less overt movements: they grasped and squeezed a cylinder instead of moving the arm. These animals could appose thumb and forefinger to a degree and could climb and walk, even when blindfolded. Even more surprising, when the spinal cord was completely deafferented by section of all dorsal roots in subsequent operations on three animals, the conditioned behavior was retained as well as the ability to walk. No certain explanation can be offered how these abilities are retained, but Taub & Berman consider "central efferent monitoring" through, for instance, pyramidal collaterals to the dorsal column nuclei, and thence back to the cerebral cortex (cf Section II, and 65). The idea of endogenous motor patterns, more or less independent of sensory inflow, is not new and resembles the fixed-action patterns described by ethologists to account for many aspects of instinctive behavior. Invertebrate physiologists have provided evidence that motor patterns can be generated by central mechanisms which do not require reinforcement or guidance from sensory input. These topics are reviewed by Evarts et al (65). Be that as it may, normal vertebrate motor behavior appears to use continuous sensory input although responses may be intermittent.

Intermittent vs continuous control.—Our definition of control need not be limited to a single individual movement. It has been known for a long time that some movements are too fast to permit correction during their course, although executions of subsequent repetitions may benefit from the initial experience. Examples of such fast, smooth movements are stepping (cf 124, 224) and rapid finger tapping (cf 187). Other movements, as for instance of tracking behavior, proceed more slowly, and are accompanied by corrective oscillations (cf 184, 187). That movement patterns undergo marked deterioration in the absence of sensory inflow is well established (cf 155, 161). How far it acts continuously to modify or "control" motor outflow is, however, the subject of much controversy. Indeed, it is not yet settled to what degree motor control itself is intermittent or continuous, or if the two are not a continuum. For fast movements control would be intermittent, for slow movements it could be both. Stetson (187), who was particularly concerned with these differences, pointed out that movements with repetition rates approaching 10/sec, such as are seen in skilled typists and pianists, are essentially ballistic, and unmodifiable during their course. Alternations of protagonist and antagonist muscles, which may last about 0.1 sec, are likely beyond control by feedback loops, since minimal feedback times from periphery to higher centers are about 0.1 sec (58).

Errors associated with rapid movements were greater than the errors associated with slow movements (157). Stetson (187) hypothesized that sensory feedback was important for guidance only when movements exceeded 0.4–0.6 sec in duration. More rapid movements, he inferred, were preprogramed in the CNS. Monkeys perform tracking tasks in similar fashion to humans. Kozlovskaya, Uno, Atkin & Brooks (106) have described fast continuous (0.4–0.6 sec) and slow discontinuous movements for cebus monkeys that were trained to move a handle between two target zones through a horizontal arc. Slow movements, composed of successive steps each lasting about 0.2 sec, became more numerous when task conditions became unstable or difficult. Performance of fast movements did not depend on external cues during their individual execution, but that of slow movements did.

The intermittent nature of movement control, implied by the apparently pre-set fast movements, as well as by stepwise corrective slow ones, also becomes evident through the "psychological refractory period". Telford (195) discovered that the reaction time to the second of two signals, following each other within 0.5 sec, was longer than when the intervals separating the signals were 1 sec or more. He concluded that voluntary responses were followed by a psychological refractory phase during which another stimulus could elicit a response only after a delay in excess of the simple reaction time. Craik (53, 54) attempted to equate this psychological refractory period with the delays observed in tracking tasks, where about 0.3 sec elapsed between observation of misalignment and initiation of correction.

This has been analyzed more quantitatively by Naves & Stark (146). Stark (184) proposed that hand movements in tracking tasks are controlled by a system that samples data at rates related to response times. When input was predictable, the movements of the hand could precede those of the target at even high tracking frequencies. Tracking above 3–4 cps (intervals of about 0.3 sec) could not be performed for unpredictable inputs. Stark concluded that "for unpredictable inputs, the human tracking system acts as a position control system. . . . Its intermittency is related to . . . control of the muscle by ballistic voluntary inputs and a stabilizing proprioceptive reflex loop. The actuating signal includes a combination of error and input (pursuit tracking)." The question of intermittent vs continuous control has been treated most recently by Eccles (58). He suggested a dynamic loop hypothesis of movement control in which integrative information flows between muscles, cerebrum, and cerebellum. Loop times of about 30 and 100 msec were suggested for cat and human respectively. Continuous information feedback is implicit in Eccles' view, although correction may occur discontinuously. Whether continuous sensory input from the periphery needs to reach motosensory cortex for the control of movement is still an open question. Assessment of input and action on it may occur at some other site, and may be prerequisite to generation of corrective movements. An example from animal experiments was given by Evarts (61) who has pointed out that the initial discharge of PT cells cannot depend on feedback from muscle since it precedes muscular contraction.

Three systems?—Are accuracy of displacement, speed, and force of movement under independent control? The older experiments on human performance say that this is so. Woodworth (229) found that discrimination (and presumably control) of force and extent (i.e. the change in position) were related but separate functions. He also noted (228) that accuracy of movement was independent of its speed when there was no visual feedback (cf 157). These data could be interpreted in favor of independent control systems, but they also relegate feedback control to a minor position. Bates (24), on the other hand, proposed force as the basic output quantity. He reasoned that velocity should be considered the first integral, and displacement the second integral, of force. From this he deduced that generation of a given velocity and even more that of a given displacement, should be a more complex task than generation of a desired force. In fact, since the PT output under consideration here is contraction of muscles, one may argue that force is the primary output variable under pyramidal control. Speed and displacement then would be no more than secondary consequences of force control (cf 61).

Experiments by Evarts with unit records from trained monkeys (see Section VB) suggest that output variables can be separated, as was proposed by Stetson (187). Ths may be true and we share this view, but with the caution voiced by Humphrey (90) who has shown that even under controlled conditions, simultaneous records from several selected cells may yield significant correlations for dynamic components of force, for movement velocity, and to a lesser degree for displacement. In the experimental situation, responses may be required which independently stress force, or speed, or displacement, and thus reveal correlations with PT cell discharge (60–63). Since PT cells are thought to function as part of minimal input-output columns in primate cortex, as they do in cat cortex (see Section III), we suggest that such columns act as a central detecting apparatus able to read profiles of inputs to give appropriate outputs. This implies that all columns can participate in control of force, speed, and displacement, and that none are exclusively engaged with any single output. Movements with different, force, speed, or displacement would require different spatiotemporal patterns of columnar activity to give such functional separate controls. In this section we will reconsider the evidence presented heretofore, to see what cause can be made for pyramidal control systems governing force, speed, and displacement in movement.

B. THE FORCE CONTROL SYSTEM

The force of limb movement depends primarily on the number of motor units activated, their degree of synchronicity, and the relative forces of antagonistic muscles. Pyramidotomy decreases muscle tone, particularly of the flexors (27, cf Section I). Evarts (62) found that many precentral PTNs tend to discharge as a function of the force exerted about the wrist when trained monkeys displace a handle with wrist movements through an arc between two mechanical stops in a fixed interval of time. Discharge of PTNs related to the reciprocal action of particular flexors and extensors, and modification of their discharge preceded the onset of muscle action (60). The discharge of many PTNs in conditioned monkeys could depend on the direction of movements, particularly when no load had to be overcome, but most often it depended on force or its apparent rate of change when a load had to be overcome to move the handle. Under conditions requiring joint displacement (62), activation of 26 out of 31 precentral PTNs seemed to vary with change of force and its rate of change, rather than its steady intensity, indicating their linkage to dynamic factors in movement. Discharge frequency of about half of the cells varied monotonically with load (62). When the monkeys were required to maintain a fixed posture and when thus there was no need for joint displacement (63), many PTNs discharged in relation to the amount and direction of force that the monkey had to exert to keep the handle steady rather than to the prevailing level of torque. Evarts concluded that output of motor cortex PTNs in this situation is related to the patterns of muscular contraction acting about the joint of the moving part rather than to the resultant joint displacement or position (63).

In commenting on his data (61), the postulation was made that PTNs near one another might be expected to control the same muscle, and that their discharges would be in a fixed relationship while that for PTNs innervating different muscles should be plastic. In fact only a few were found locked in positive correlation, recalling the frequently differential input of joint- or skin-driven pairs of cells recorded in cat's motor cortex (36). A common denominator uniting neighboring monkey's PTNs apparently was the joint to whose movement the cells were related. An even lower, or minimal, common denominator was a particular muscle moving that joint, as found by Fetz & Baker (67) who combined Evarts' technique with ICMS (cf Section III).

Evarts' data, obtained by visual inspection of discharge records from single cells, have found general support from records taken under similar conditions from several neurons simultaneously by Humphrey et al (89, 90). The monkey was trained to move a vertical handle from side to side by alternate flexion-extension of the wrist, against variable loads. He was required to displace his wrist to within ± 5° of a 30° angular displacement (as indicated by a signal light, not by a mechanical stop), and to maintain that position for 0.5–1.0 sec before moving to the alternate position. Quantitative correlation of discharge of PT and non-PT cells could predict the dynamic force output of the movement. Specifically, linear combination of computer-smoothed spike frequencies from 29 sets of 3–8 neurons have yielded predictions of the time course of some measures of the movement. When a set of cells had been selected, each of whose firing indicated that the movement occurred but whose discharge patterns were not identical, prediction accuracy remained steady for as long as 40 min under given load conditions. The most accurately predicted measure of movement was the net force exerted (in one illustrated example with a correlation coefficient of 0.84). The rate of change of force (df/dt) was but poorly correlated for groups of cells ($r = 0.43$) and other measures of dynamic force relation served better. Little was found in the activity of a given set of cortical cells that would allow estimates of the magnitude of the steady force exerted by the animal in supporting a load, or of the absolute amplitude of the force excertions during movement.

These experiments establish that PT cells participate in the control of force of movement. Our definition of a control system also requires physiologically identifiable inputs and outputs. As has been pointed out in Section IA, little is known about the supraspinal involvement of muscle tension receptors: the Golgi tendon organs. Granit (75), Phillips (161), and Evarts (62) have recently pointed to nuclear bag organs of muscle spindles as likely sense organs to influence cortical governance of force, stressing that Ia afferent fibers project to the motorsensory cortex (cf Section IIB). This is a curious arrangement, because the primary dynamic muscle spindles reflect muscle length (and its rate of change), as well as intrafusal tension rather than extrafusal muscle tension, as had been pointed out by Matthews (134) who had already implicated them in supraspinal force adjustment (see Sections IIB and IVB).

Phillips (161) made the theoretical case of how length and speed measurements by primary spindles (and length measurements by secondary endings) could alter PTN activation of α and γ motoneurons, and thus change force of movement. Essentially he argued that slowing down of the movement by an "unexpected" resistance would speed up spindle discharge. He also showed how properly timed responses to changes of load can prevent oscillations, typical of feedback imbalance. Thus transducers of length and speed can presumably function in cerebral regulation of force. Their convergence into columns of cortical cells with input from skin and joints is still unclear, however (cf Section IIB). The mediation of PT output through "α-γ coactivation" and the "load compensating reflex" in voluntary movement has been discussed in Sections IVA and B, as has been PT governance of the balance between antagonistic motoneuron pools. This balance determines the net force exerted by a moving limb when encountering passive resistance.

In summary, it appears that specification of change of force can be an important function of the pyramidal system. The primary spindles, although not force-sensitive, appear to participate in adjustment of pyramidal output, while the role of force sensors is still unknown. The pyramids can govern muscle force by coactivation of α and γ spinal motoneurons, and by adjusting the relative strengths of antagonistic muscles through influencing spinal interneurons. These items satisfy the requirements for defining a force control system that can operate through cortical input-output columns. It might not function as an isolated entity in normal movements, except possibly in isometric contractions.

C. The Speed Control System

Force and speed of movements are determined by the same parameters, i.e., the number of motor units activated, their degree of synchronicity, and the relative forces of the antagonistic muscles concerned. The net force used in a displacement movement is the difference between opposing muscular forces, which is a function of change of speed rather than of speed itself, since force = mass $\times$ acceleration (cf 60, 64, 75). Control over force and speed can scarcely be separated when limb displacements are unopposed by an external load, and they are correlated even when there is a load (cf 90). However, common experience tells us that we can move a limb at a given speed and yet with different degrees of effort, depending on the stiffness of the joint which depends on the relative co-contraction of antagonistic muscles. Stetson (187) called these "loose" and "tight" movements. Ordinarily force and speed controls would interact, except in pure isometric contractions.

Can one define properties of a speed control system, and its connection to pyramidal function? Lesion experiments reveal no slowing of movement, only increases of reaction time (27, 116, and cf Section I). Beck (27) showed that medullary pyramidotomy failed to change the time taken by trained monkeys to move a hand from one place to another. This negative evidence does not however rule out pyramidal participation in speed control. One may ask the question: is speed of movement encoded in the firing patterns of PT cells? Records from individual PT cells of monkeys rapidly executing a lever-turning task between two mechanical stops within prescribed time limits leave an equivocal answer. A positive answer was obtained in similar experiments by Humphrey et al (89, 90), in which monkeys chose their own speed in a tracking task. The correlation between simultaneous firing patterns of several cortical neurons with movement velocity was nearly as good as that with force ($r = 0.76$, see Section VA). Once a suitable equation had been established for a set of simultaneously observed units, predictions of wrist velocity were accurate for several load conditions. These experiments suggest that PT cells participate in the control of speed of movement, but not necessarily independently of force control. The output presumably acts through α-γ coactivation and interneuronal balancing of antagonists, as has been discussed in the section on force (VA).

What are the input sensors? The speed-sensitive initial discharge of joint receptors has been considered in Section IIA. These receptors are known to project to precentral cortex of monkey (6). Measurements of rate can be considered to provide "predictive" information, if the existence of neural readout systems is assumed, that compute the future consequences of rates. Evidence that such computations are made with data from joint receptors comes from Merton's experiment (136). He demonstrated loss of sense "of range of rapidity" of passive movements of the top joint of the thumb after an hour and a half of ischemic block at the wrist, which spares the operant muscles (136). This does not, of course, prove that motor cortex is involved. Active movement provides more accurate information about final position than does passive movement: Paillard (155) showed that blindfolded subjects can locate one hand with the other more accurately if they move the exploring hand than if it is moved for them. Errors in the judgment of the final position increased greatly as the time separating positioning and judging increased to over 10 sec. Paillard drew attention to the similarity of the time course of this deterioration of precision of localization and that of adaptation of the speed-sensitive discharge of joint and muscle receptors. Participation by motor cortex can only be inferred.

In Sections IVB and VB it has been shown that the speed-sensitive primary spindles (Section IIB) function in force control. In displacement movements they are bound to also function in speed control, since the two parameters are linked. The dynamic primary spindles forward information on rate of length change of muscles through the medial-lemniscal and spinocerebellar paths (149). Spindles do not seem to specifically measure acceleration, as tested on cat's ankle extensors during experimentally induced length changes of various forms (120). Matthews (134) has pointed out that . . . "the velocity response of the primary ending enables it to 'predict' the length of the muscle after the delay time of the reflex . . ." How could this predictive measurement be used in speed control? Matthews proposed . . . "that in voluntary movements the relative amounts of α and γ activity were adjusted to be appropriate for the velocity of shortening 'expected'. If shortening then proceeded faster than 'intended' by the higher centres it would be slowed by servo action, and if shortening were hindered by some unexpected load it would be speeded up by servo action" . . . (134). Phillips (161) envisaged that the degree of α and γ coactivation would be adjusted by cerebral cortex, as set forth in Section IVB. Spindles and speed of human voluntary contractions were linked by Vallbo (216), who measured single fiber responses from primary dynamic spindles of tibial and median nerves in 15 subjects. These spindles discharged during voluntary contractions with external shortening, and their discharge varied closely with the speed of contraction (see Section II for identification of receptor).

Evidence for involvement of the dentatothalamic system that impinges on motor cortex in speed control has accrued from studies in animals and humans. For instance, Brooks et al (40, 106, cf Section VA) studied the

performance of monkeys trained to perform a step-tracking task which prescribed displacement control at voluntary speeds. The monkeys turned an
unloaded handle, through a horizontal arc centered at the elbow at their
own speed from one target zone to another. An auditory cue was given
when the handle was within the target zones (that were about 10° wide and
not bounded by mechanical stops), and another when it had been held there
for about 1 sec. When part of the dentate nucleus ipsilateral to the operant
arm was cooled for a few minutes to 25°–10° C with an implanted cooling
probe, there appeared reversible increases of magnitude and variability in
velocity of individual movements (40, 104). Increased peak velocities were
reached and were followed by longer periods of deceleration, implying simultaneous derangements of speed and force. [Shik's group (148) produced
similar increases of terminal limb velocities after cerebellar damage in dogs'
hindlimbs during running induced by midbrain stimulation.] Loss of speed
control could be caused only by dysfunction of the dentate nucleus: cooling
of n. interpositus did not produce these effects (214). These results fit the
functions proposed for these cerebellar nuclei, as elaborated by Eccles (58),
involving dentate predominantly with cortical movement control, and IP
less so. Although Brooks' experiments seem to involve the dentate in speed
control, no direct evidence has been produced linking the effects of dentate
cooling to pyramidal tract function (see Section IVC).

Hassler (79) described a speeding up of to-and-fro movements made by
patients with their arm upon request when the posterior part of the ventral
oral nucleus (V.o.p.) was stimulated repetitively, and less frequently with
stimulation of the anterior part of VL (V.o.a.) and never with the somatosensory thalamic nuclei (VPL). Hassler (79) described the V.o.p. effect:
". . . When asked, the patients gave reasons for the thalamically induced acceleration as follows: 'Everything was faster' . . . 'it goes faster all by itself'.
. . . Stimulation of V.o.p. also produced acceleration of speech, with subjective reasons given such as 'I felt urged' . . . 'I know I counted faster . . .' "
Hassler concluded: "The conscious patients stimulated in V.o.p. identify
themselves with the stimulus-evoked acceleration inasmuch as they experience the acceleration as their genuine intention and not as a strange influence . . ." "Thus the acceleration of active movements of the extremities as
well as of articulation is one of the main functional features of the V.o.p.
stimulation. This nucleus contains synapses between the dentatothalamic
neurons and the thalamocortical ones to area 4γ. The function of this neuronal chain is to accelerate facilitation of the motor cortex and voluntary
movements at the same time" . . . (79). In the light of more recent evidence
we might rephrase this function as "influencing" rather than specifically
"accelerating".

In summary, speed of muscle contraction and of movement vary with
muscular force in displacement movements. Although there is no detailed
evidence for pyramidal control of speed, frequency of discharge of groups
of precentral cells does vary with speed. These cells receive input from
speed-sensitive primary spindles and joint receptors, of which the latter

seem to be essential for correct estimation of passive movement speed. The lateral cerebellum, through the dentate nucleus, appears to influence movement speed, as can its way station to motor cortex, the ventrolateral nucleus. These items come close to fulfilling the requirements for defining a speed control system that can operate through cortical input-output columns. However, this may be no more than a special function of the force control system.

D. Displacement Control System

A control system for displacement is more difficult to define than those for force and speed. Displacement is relatively independent of the number of active motor units. Force and speed of movement can vary with the number, discharge frequency, and synchrony of active motor units in even a single spinal motor nucleus. Variations in force and speed can therefore be viewed simply as additions or subtractions of active motor units. In contrast, variations in displacement must reflect the distribution of activity in several motor nuclei. Therefore it follows that displacement can be controlled with accuracy only by a number of cortical columns, each one of which reaches only a single spinal motor nucleus.

Electrophysiological results support this conclusion. Evarts (61–63) reported that displacement was not well represented in discharge patterns of individual PTNs, although his results . . . "do not show PTN activity to be unrelated to displacement, but rather indicate that PTN activity is related to force . . . it is quite impossible to conclude that PTNs as a group do not represent displacement at all . . ." (61). Evarts' thought found quick experimental verification. Humphrey et al (90) showed that instrumentally conditioned voluntary wrist displacements of monkeys could be predicted with some accuracy ($r = .56$; $p < .001$) when simultaneous discharge patterns of from 3–8 PT cells were analyzed. This correlation, however, indicates that only 31% of the variability between expected and obtained displacements can be accounted for by PT discharge patterns, in contrast to 71% of the variations in force (see Section VB). We might look forward to better correlations from larger sets of appropriate cells, an expectation compatible with Bates' recognition that displacement is the most complex of the three factors in movement control (24, Section VA).

Several modes of action are possible for the pyramidal system as a displacement controller. None of the available evidence fits the model discussed and rejected by Evarts (63), conceiving that PT neurons act "as displacement controllers, whose outgoing signals call for changes in the position of the moving part without specifying the forces required." Rather, the data from behavioral and electrophysiological studies strongly implicate the pyramidal system in force and speed control (see Sections VB and C), as well as displacement control.

There is little direct evidence that the pyramidal system determines displacement towards a final position. Ward (222, 223) studied motor reactions produced in chronically implanted cats and monkeys by surface elec-

trical stimulation. He noted that changes of limb posture prior to cortical
stimulation yielded responses which always brought the responding extrem-
ity to the same "final position". Stimulation of the same cortical surface
point, or even of subcortical white matter, could cause either flexion or extension depending on whether the initial position of the limb was on the
flexor or extensor side of the presumed final position. Ward concluded
(222) that specific limb displacements rather than either muscles or movements are represented in the motor cortex. It may be significant that reversals of response were best observed as the preparatory phase of rhythmic
"batting" or "digging" responses elicited by prolonged stimulation. Simple
movements, however, such as flexion or extension, without rhythm, usually
had final positions at "the maximal extent of movability of the responding
leg in the direction of the movement, i.e., maximal extension or maximal
flexion . . ." (222). Furthermore, response latencies exceeded 0.3 sec, and
often were 3–10 sec. These complexities make it difficult to compare these
results with those more recently obtained and discussed in Section III. In
view of the extremely large effective field radii for excitation of PT cells by
surface stimulation (112) it would seem reasonable to assign responses obtained by Ward to recruitment of spinal motoneurons during changing segmental facilitation.

Behavioral studies based on lesions fail to provide a clear answer on
pyramidal displacement control. As indicated in Section IC, monkeys
trained to move their forelimb, by elbow or shoulder movements, through a
vertical arc into a prescribed target of 10° to obtain a fruit juice reward,
performed normally, without dysmetria, after pyramidotomy (27). This test
and other observations on movements of pyramidotomized monkeys (71,
117) suggest that position control is not much affected by the absence of a
pyramidal tract. Apparently, other descending pathways are available which
provide pyramidotomized animals with near normal displacement control
(cf 118), for all but the most distal musculature.

Behavioral studies based on temporary dysfunction show that the dentatothalamic system affects displacement (until compensation takes place). Reversible cooling of the dentate nucleus in monkeys trained to perform a
tracking task into 10° targets by horizontal elbow flexion and extension (40,
104, cf Section VA, B, C) led to grossly hypermetric fast movements (106).
In slow movements (106), the deceleration phase lengthened with concurrent overshoot beyond the targets. Animals experienced in the cooling procedure, however, started to decelerate earlier in the movement, i.e. farther
from the targets, and with the help of auditory cues stopped accurately
within them. Unexpected withdrawal or presentation of such cues, which
did not change performance of trained animals, caused dysmetria during
dentate cooling. This implies that the external cue was needed, apparently
because internal cues from the operant arm failed (105). It is not known
whether the compensation for the dysmetria is a product of pyramidal function.

While it is difficult to conceive of output signals which directly specify absolute displacement, it is easier to conceive of error signals varying as a function of the differences between intended and actual displacements, as has been implied by Phillips (161) and by Evarts (63). According to this model (63), . . . "other parts of the sensorimotor system would sense the resistance experienced by the moving part and elicit appropriate patterns and magnitudes of muscular contraction." One would have to assume that some central apparatus can predict the intended target position, perhaps like the cerebellum (cf 58, 94), and that the CNS would "pay attention" to a particular input, whose magnitude varied with the distance of the limb from the target position. Such an arrangement could drive motoneurons, whose effect would be braked by appropriately timed increase in antagonist action (cf Section IVA, and 187).

What types of receptors could provide the necessary input? As has been pointed out in Sections IIA and VC, the initial discharge of joint receptors could serve displacement because it is speed-sensitive, and their tonic discharge would also qualify, since it is a monotonic function of joint angle. Muscular receptors would not provide precise error signals about limb position, since their output reflects intrafusal tension due both to α-γ coactivation and to extrafusal tension (see Sections IIB, IVB, and VB, C). Phasic input from skin receptors, excited by hair deflection and touch, would be unsuited for providing *continuous* error signals, as it only signals solitary events (see Section IIB). However, phasic input might be admirably suited to call forth *transient* displacements such as occur in tracking, or pursuit movements (cf Section VA). The input-output relations of radial columns in cats' motor cortex appear capable of handling just that type of information flow (see Section III). Columns in primate motor cortex may perhaps use their relatively sparse skin input (cf Section IIA) in similar fashion. Two cortical reflexes whose properties are compatible with tight coupling through input-output columns (35) are discussed below.

Relevance to cortical reflexes.—Denny-Brown has described a cortically mediated pursuit reflex: the instinctive "tactile" grasping reaction. In this paragraph we have condensed many quotes from his descriptions. Instinctive grasping occurs in many normal human adults when their attention is distracted; and it becomes prominent after mesial frontal lesions (56, 180). It is easily elicited in children, and in infants over 6 months (212). It is abolished by ablation of the precentral gyrus (56). The reaction is an orientation of the hand or foot in space such as to bring a light contact stimulus into the palm or sole, leading them to grasping (56). It is an active enfolding of the stimulating object by the hand, accomplished in a series of steps or preliminary adjustments, by which the hand engages with, and closes around the stimulating object (180). It is a stereotactic contactual response (56), the adequate stimulus for which is stationary light touch. It results in a succession of extension-flexion movements of the fingers, accompanied by projection and turning of the whole arm so as to bring the tactile contact into the palm of the hand (the "closing" and "pursuit" reactions). The elementary response of the closing reaction is an extension of the hand in the direction perpendicular to the skin at the point of uneven contact, such as to bring the contact into the palm of the hand. In the palm the same contact leads to the "trap reaction" (55). The motor reaction is delicate, highly integrated, weakly performed and intermittent (cf Section VA), as if the further contact with the stimulus resulting from one closing movement leads inevitably to a further adjusting movement, and this to repetition of the cycle, thus giving the performance its progressive character. The instinctive grasp reaction therefore necessitates the existence of a mechanism which would appear to involve a highly discriminative sensory component (180).

Phillips and his colleagues (51) noted that this cortical reflex also fits the control of spinal proprioceptive patterns as seen in the baboon. They showed that cortical activation was strongest for those spinal motoneurons that received the greatest input from muscle spindles (cf Sections IIIB and C). They stressed that in evoking contraction of the long flexors in the tactile-conditioned grasp reflex, passive stretch of the intrinsic flexors may be more important than stretch of the long flexors themselves (51). In the instinctive response, touch to the hand would trigger intrinsic muscle action. Such mechanisms are of course considered to be only fractions of the complex human grasping response, which presumably is built upon and involves the function of many simple input-output columns. Tight preferential input-output coupling for cortical cells reveals only minimal building blocks, from which natural cortical function is thought to be synthesized (35).

Asanuma et al (19; also see 225) considered also another cortical reflex: tactile placing (22). They stated that:

> The present findings suggest that afferent inputs originating from restricted peripheral loci may "reflexly" induce contraction of a particular muscle or muscles through a loop including the motorsensory cortex. The "tactile placing reaction" is a reflex-type reaction which is known to be mediated by the pericruciate cortex. It is possible to explain a part of the placing reaction by input-output relationships that we have described. For example, contact with dorsum of the paw leads to paw dorsiflexion, which is one of the initial movements in the placing reaction. However, our findings do not, by themselves, lead to a complete understanding of the cortical mechanisms subserving this reaction. For example, a placing reaction can be elicited by contact with any aspect of the forearm, and each of these reactions surely involves different combinations and sequences of muscle contraction. (19)

The difficulty is that too many kinds of contact can lead to too many kinds of movement, to allow a simple input-output relation to explain them all. Amassian has shown recently (11, 12) that this type of contact placing is initiated by a lifting-withdrawal phase, followed by a directed landing phase. The initial EMG response in contact placing for a dorsal paw stimulus is in ventroflexors of the paw and arm, which implies that contractual positive cortical feedback may operate during landing, but that it is inhibited during initial lifting. Furthermore, the latency of the earliest EMG changes in the placing reaction were usually on the order of 80 msec (11, 12) whereas latencies of less than 50 msec might be expected for "reflex" conduction through cortical efferent colonies [allowing 15–25 msec for afferent conduction to MSI, and 25–35 msec for efferent conduction to muscle (see 18, 19, 208, 221)]. Thus, it would appear that the placing reaction is an adaptive response superimposed on and necessarily overriding the place-specific input bias. A similar argument can be made about the possible role of efferent colonies in the instinctive grasp response.

The two cortical reflexes, placing and grasping, were classed together by Denny-Brown (56), who noted their parallel susceptibility to parietal lesions, and their parallel release by frontal lesions. A recent study by Goldberger (71) has extended and differentiated previous findings. Tactile placing and grasping responses were abolished in four monkeys after contralateral pyramidotomy near the olivary level. A crude form of contact placing (but not grasping) was restored by adding spinal lesions of the ventrolateral and ventral funiculi at the side of pyramidal spinal descent, i.e. contralateral to the pyramidal lesion. Spatiality, however, was largely absent; the placement of the foot was forward regardless of the locus of foot stimulation. The postoperative reflex may represent a lower-level reaction lacking cortical control (71).

In summary, groups of primate PT cells can encode voluntary displacement, but not as precisely as force or speed. This may be a matter of sampling, because displacement must involve a greater number of cortical input-output columns than does variation of force or speed. Pursuit tracking movements have properties for which radial columns of PT cells (as established in the cat) could provide input-output coupling from skin and joints to appropriate muscles. These items approximate the requirements for defining a displacement control system. However, this may be no more than a combination of appropriate force (and speed) control input-output units.

LITERATURE CITED

1. Adkins, R. J., Morse, R. W., Towe, A. L. 1966. *Science* 153:1020–22
2. Adrian, E. D., Moruzzi, G. 1939. *J. Physiol. London* 97:153–99
3. Albe-Fessard, D. 1966. In *Contributions to Sensory Physiology*, ed. W. D. Neff, 2:101–60. New York: Academic. 263 pp.
4. Albe-Fessard, D., Dumont-Tyc, S., Jankowska, E. 1961. *J. Physiol. Paris* 53:243–44
5. Albe-Fessard, D., Liebeskind, J., Lamarre, Y. 1965. *Compt. Rend. Acad. Sci.* 261:3891–94
6. Albe-Fessard, D., Liebeskind, J. 1966. *Exp. Brain Res.* 1:127–46
7. Albe-Fessard, D., Derome, P., Gallouin, F. 1968. *J. Physiol. Paris* 60:*Suppl.* 2, 385–86
8. Albe-Fessard, D., Derome, P., Gallouin, F. 1969. *J. Physiol. London* 201:93P–94P
9. Amassian, V. E. 1967. Discussion in *The Neurophysiological Basis of Normal and Abnormal Motor Activities*, ed. M. D. Yahr, D. P. Purpura, 288–92. New York: Raven. 500 pp.
10. Amassian, V. E., Weiner, H. 1966. In *The Thalamus*, ed. D. P. Pur-

pura, M. D. Yahr, 255–82. New York: Columbia Univ. Press. 438 pp.

11. Amassian, V. E., Rosenblum, M., Weiner, H. 1969. *Fed. Proc.* 28: 455

12. Amassian, V. E., Rosenblum, M., Weiner, H. 1970. *Fed. Proc.* 29: 792Abs

13. Andersen, H. T., Korner, L., Landgren, S., Silfvenius, H. 1967. *Acta Physiol. Scand.* 69:373–82

14. Andersen, P., Eccles, J. C., Sears, T. A. 1964. *J. Neurophysiol.* 27: 63–77

15. Andersen, P., Junge, K., Sveen, O. 1967. *Nature* 214:1011–12

16. Andersson, S. A., Landgren, S., Wolsk, D. 1966. *J. Physiol. London* 183:576–91

17. Asanuma, H., Brooks, V. B. 1965. *Arch. Ital. Biol.* 103:220–46

18. Asanuma, H., Sakata, H. 1967. *J. Neurophysiol.* 30:35–54

19. Asanuma, H., Stoney, S. D., Jr., Abzug, C. 1968. *J. Neurophysiol.* 31:670–81

20. Asanuma, H., Stoney, S. D., Jr., Thompson, W. D. 1970. *Brain Res.* In press

21. Asanuma, H., Ward, J. E. 1970. *Brain Res.* In press

22. Bard, P. 1933. *Arch. Neurol. Psychiat.* 30:40–74

23. Bard, P. 1938. *Bull. N.Y. Acad. Med.* 14:585–607

24. Bates, J. A. V. 1947. *J. Inst. Elec. Eng.* 94:Part IIa, No. 2:298–304

25. Bava, A., Fadiga, E., Manzoni, T. 1966. *Arch. Sci. Biol.* 50:101–33

26. Bava, A., Fadiga, E., Manzoni, T. 1968. *Arch. Ital. Biol.* 106:204–26

27. Beck, C. H., Chambers, W. W. 1970. *J. Comp. Physiol. Psychol.* 70:1–22

28. Blum, B., Halpern, L. M., Ward, A. A., Jr. 1968. *Exp. Neurol.* 20: 156–73

29. Bourassa, C. M., Swett, J. E. 1967. *J. Neurophysiol.* 31:515–29

30. Brodal, A. 1969. *Neurological Anatomy,* 255–303. New York: Oxford Univ. Press, 2nd ed. 807 pp.

31. Brodal, P. 1968. *Exp. Brain Res.* 5: 210–34

32. Brodal, P., Marsala, J., Brodal, A. 1967. *Brain Res.* 6:252–74

33. Brooks, V. B. 1963. *Electroencephalog. Clin. Neurophysiol. Suppl.* 24: 13–32

34. Brooks, V. B. 1965. In *Studies in Physiology,* ed. D. R. Curtis, A. McIntyre, 13–17. Heidelberg: Springer. 276 pp.

35. Brooks, V. B. 1969. In *Information Processing in the Nervous System,* ed. K. N. Leibovic, 231–43. New York: Springer. 373 pp.

36. Brooks, V. B., Rudomin, P., Slayman, C. L. 1961a. *J. Neurophysiol.* 24: 286–301

37. Brooks, V. B., Rudomin, P., Slayman, C. L. 1961b. *J. Neurophysiol.* 24: 302–25

38. Brooks, V. B., Levitt, M. 1964. *Physiologist* 7:95

39. Brooks, V. B., Asanuma, H. 1965. *Arch. Ital. Biol.* 103:247–78

40. Brooks, V. B., Horvath, F., Atkin, A., Kozlovskaya, I., Uno, M. 1969. *Fed. Proc.* 28:396

41. Brooks, V. B., Jasper, H. H., Patton, H. D., Purpura, D. P., Brookhart, J. M. 1970. *Brain Res.* 17:539–52

42. Brown, A. G., Iggo, A. A. 1967. *J. Physiol. London* 193:707–33

43. Bucy, P. C., Ladpli, R., Ehrlich, A. 1966. *J. Neurosurg.* 25:1–20Gg

44. Burgess, P. R., Perl, E. R. 1967. *J. Physiol. London* 190:541–62

45. Buser, P. 1966. *The Thalamus,* 323– 47. See Ref. 10

46. Buser, P., Ascher, P. 1960. *Arch. Ital. Biol.* 98:123–64

47. Buser, P., Imbert, M. 1961. In *Sensory Communication,* ed. W. A. Rosenblith, 607–26. New York: Wiley. 844 pp.

48. Buser, P., Ascher, P., Bruner, J., Jassik-Gerschenfeld, D., Sindberg, R. 1963. *Progr. Brain Res.* 1:294– 322

49. Buser, P., Kitsikis, A., Wiesendanger, M. 1968. *Brain Res.* 10:262–65

50. Clare, M. H., Landau, W. M., Bishop, G. H. 1964. *Exp. Neurol.* 9:262–67

51. Clough, J. F. M., Kernell, D., Phillips, C. G. 1968. *J. Physiol. London* 198:145–66

52. Corda, M., Eklund, G., Euler, C. v. 1965. *Acta Physiol. Scand.* 63: 391–400

53. Craik, K. J. W. 1947. *Brit. J. Med. Psychol.* 38:56–61

54. Craik, K. J. W. 1948. *Brit. J. Med. Psychol.* 38:142–48

55. Denny-Brown, D. 1950. *J. Nerv. Ment. Dis.* 112:1–45

56. Denny-Brown, D. 1960. *Handbook of Physiology, Sec. I, Neurophysiol-*

ogy, ed. J. Field, 2:781–96. Washington, D.C: Am. Physiol. Soc. 1439 pp.

57. Dormont, J. F., Massion, J. 1970. *Exp. Brain Res.* 10:205–18

58. Eccles, J. C. 1969. *Information Processing in the Nervous System,* ed. K. N. Leibovic, 245–69. New York: Springer. 373 pp.

59. Eccles, J. C. 1969. *The Inhibitory Pathways of the Central Nervous System.* Springfield, Ill: Thomas. 135 pp.

59a. Engberg, I., Lundberg, A. 1969. *Acta Physiol. Scand.* 75:614–30

60. Evarts, E. V. 1966. *J. Neurophysiol.* 29:1011–27

61. Evarts, E. V. 1967. In *Neurophysiological Basis of Normal and Abnormal Motor Activities,* 215–51. See Ref. 9

62. Evarts, E. V. 1968. *J. Neurophysiol.* 31:14–27

63. Evarts, E. V. 1969. *J. Neurophysiol.* 32:375–85

64. Evarts, E. V., Thach, W. T. 1969. *Ann. Rev. Physiol.* 31:451–98

65. Evarts, E. V., Bizzi, E., Burke, R. E., DeLong, M., Thach, W. T. 1970. *Neurosci. Res. Program Bull.* 8. In press

66. Fetz, E. E. 1968. *J. Neurophysiol.* 31:69–80

67. Fetz, E. E., Baker, M. A. 1969. *Physiologist* 12:223

68. Fidone, S. J., Preston, J. B. 1969. *J. Neurophysiol.* 32:103–15

69. Gardner, E. 1967. *Ciba Found. Symp. Myotatic, Kinesthetic and Vestibular Mechanisms,* 56–76. 331 pp.

70. Gelfan, S., Carter, S. 1967. *Exp. Neurol.* 18:469–73

71. Goldberger, M. E. 1969. *J. Comp. Neurol.* 135:1–26

72. Gordon, G., Jukes, M. G. M. 1964. *J. Physiol. London* 173:291–319

73. Gorman, A. L. F., Silfvenius, H. 1967. *Electroencephalog. Clin. Neurophysiol.* 23:360–70

74. Grampp, W., Oscarsson, O. 1968. In *Structure and Functions of Inhibitory Neuronal Mechanisms,* ed. C. von Euler, S. Skoglund, U. Söderberg, 351–55. New York: Pergamon. 563 pp.

75. Granit, R. 1968. *Proc. Roy. Soc. Med.* 61:69–78

76. Hagbarth, K. E., Vallbo, A. B. 1968. *Exp. Neurol.* 22:674–94

77. Hagbarth, K. E., Vallbo, A. B. 1969.

Acta Physiol. Scand. 76:321–34

78. Harris, F. A. 1970. *Nature* 225:559–62

79. Hassler, R. 1966. In *The Thalamus,* 419–38. See Ref. 10

80. Hassler, R., Muhs-Clement, K. 1964. *J. Hirnforsch.* 6:377–423

81. Hines, M. 1944. In *The Precentral Motor Cortex,* ed. P. C. Bucy, 4: 459–95. Urbana, Ill: Univ. of Illinois. 605 pp.

82. Hongo, T., Jankowska, E. 1967. *Exp. Brain Res.* 3:117–34

83. Hongo, T., Jankowska, E., Lundberg, A. 1969. *Exp. Brain Res.* 7:365–91

84. Hubel, D. H., Wiesel, T. N. 1962. *J. Physiol. London* 160:106–54

85. Hultborn, H., Jankowska, E., Lindstrom, S. 1968. *Brain Res.* 9:367–69

86. Hultborn, H., Jankowska, E., Lindstrom, S. 1968. *Acta Physiol. Scand.* 73:41A

87. Hultborn, H., Udo, M. 1969. *Acta Physiol. Scand. Suppl.* 330:182

88. Humphrey, D. R. 1968. *Electroencephalog. Clin. Neurophysiol.* 24: 116–29

89. Humphrey, D. R., Schmidt, E., Thompson, W. D. 1970. *Fed. Proc.* 29:791Abstr.

90. Humphrey, D. R., Schmidt, E. M., Thompson, W. D. 1970. *Science* 170:758–62

91. Hunt, C. C., McIntyre, A. K. 1960. *J. Physiol. London* 153:88–98

92. Iggo, A. A. 1968. In *The Skin Senses,* ed. D. R. Kenshalo, 84–105. Springfield, Ill: Thomas. 636 pp.

93. Imbert, M., Bignall, K. E., Buser, P. 1966. *J. Neurophysiol.* 29:382–95

94. Ito, M. 1968. *Proc. 4th Symp. Role of the Vestibular Organs in Space Exploration.* In press

95. Janig, W., Schmidt, R. F., Zimmermann, M. 1968. *Exp. Brain Res.* 6:116–29

96. Jones, E. G., Powell, T. P. S. 1968. *Brain Res.* 9:71–94

97. Jones, E. G., Powell, T. P. S. 1968. *Brain Res.* 10:369–91

98. Kameda, K., Nagel, R., Brooks, V. B. 1969. *J. Neurophysiol.* 32:540–53

99. Kitsikis, A., Wiesendanger, M., Buser, P. 1968. *J. Physiol. Paris* 60:*Suppl. 2,* 477

100. Koeze, T. H. 1968. *J. Physiol. London* 197:87–105

101. Koeze, T. H., Phillips, C. G., Sheridan, J. D. 1968. J. Physiol. London 195:419–49
102. Körner, L., Landgren, S. 1969. Acta Physiol. Scand. 76:5A–7A
103. Kots, Y. M. 1964. Biophysics 15:167–72
104. Kozlovskaya, I., Atkin, A., Horvath, F., Uno, M., Brooks, V. B. 1969. Excerpta Med. Int. Congr. Ser. No. 193:241
105. Kozlovskaya, I., Horvath, F., Atkin, A., Brooks, V. B. 1970. Physiologist 13:244
106. Kozlovskaya, I., Uno, M., Atkin, A., Brooks, V. B. 1970. Commun. Behav. Biol. 5:153–56
107. Krauthamer, G. M., Albe-Fessard, D. 1964. Neuropsychologia 2:73–83
108. Krauthamer, G., Albe-Fessard, D. 1965. J. Neurophysiol. 28:100–24
109. Kruger, L. 1956. Am. J. Physiol. 186:475–82
110. Kuypers, H. G. J. M. 1958. J. Comp. Neurol. 110:221–55
111. Lamarre, Y., Liebeskind, J. C. 1965. J. Physiol. Paris 57:259
112. Landgren, S., Phillips, C. G., Porter, R. 1962. J. Physiol. London 161:112–25
113. Landgren, S., Silfvenius, H., Wolsk, D. 1967. J. Physiol. London 191:543–59
114. Landgren, S., Silfvenius, H. 1969. J. Physiol. London 200:353–72
115. Laursen, A. M., Wiesendanger, M. 1966. Acta Physiol. Scand. 67:165–72
116. Laursen, A. M., Wiesendanger, M. 1967. Brain Res. 5:207–20
117. Lawrence, D. G., Kuypers, H. G. J. M. 1968. Brain 91:1–14
118. Lawrence, D. G., Kuypers, H. G. J. M. 1968. Brain 91:15–36
119. Leblanc, F. E., Cordeau, J. P. 1969. Brain Res. 14:255–70
120. Lennerstrand, G., Thoden, U. 1968. Acta Physiol. Scand. 73:234–50
121. Liebeskind, J., Gardner, E. B., Derome, P., Doetsch, G., Rhodes, J., Novin, D., Albe-Fessard, D. 1969. J. Physiol. Paris 60:Suppl. 2, 371
122. Livingston, A., Phillips, C. G. 1957. Quart. J. Exp. Physiol. 42:190–205
123. Lundberg, A. 1966. In Nobel Symposium I, Muscular Afferents and Motor Control, ed. R. Granit, 275–305. New York: Wiley. 466 pp.
124. Lundberg, A. 1969. The Norwegian Academy of Science and Letters, The Nansen Memorial Lecture, 1969, 5–42. Oslo: Universitetsforlaget
125. Lundberg, A., Voorhoeve, P. 1962. Acta Physiol. Scand. 56:201–19
126. Lux, H. D., Nacimiento, A. C., Creutzfeldt, O. D. 1964. Pflügers Arch. 281:170–80
127. Malis, L. I., Pribram, K. H., Kruger, L. 1953. J. Neurophysiol. 16:161–67
128. Mallart, A. 1968. J. Physiol. London 194:337–53
129. Marchiafava, P. L. 1968. Ann. Rev. Physiol., 30:359–400
130. Marchiafava, P. L., Pompeiano, O. 1964. Arch. Ital. Biol. 102:500–29
131. Massion, J. 1967. Physiol. Rev. 47:383–436
132. Massion, J., Meulders, M. 1960. J. Physiol. Paris 52:172–73
133. Massion, J., Meulders, M. 1961. Arch. Int. Physiol. 69:26–9
134. Matthews, P. B. C. 1964. Physiol. Rev. 44:219–88
135. Merton, P. A. 1953. Ciba Symp. The Spinal Cord, 247–60
136. Merton, P. A. 1964. Symp. Soc. Exp. Biol. 8:387–400
137. Meulders, M., Massion, J., Colle, J., Albe-Fessard, D. 1963. Electroencephalog. Clin. Neurophysiol. 15:29–38
138. Morrison, A. R., Pompeiano, O. 1965. Arch. Ital. Biol. 103:538–68
139. Morse, R. W., Towe, A. L. 1964. J. Physiol. London 171:231–46
140. Morse, R. W., Adkins, R. J., Towe, A. L. 1965. Exp. Neurol. 11:419–40
141. Mott, F. W., Sherrington, C. S. 1895. Proc. Roy. Soc. B 57:481–88
142. Mountcastle, V. B. 1957. J. Neurophysiol. 20:408–34
143. Mountcastle, V. B. 1968. In Medical Physiology, ed. V. B. Mountcastle, 2:1345–71. St. Louis: Mosby. 1858 pp.
144. Mountcastle, V. B., Henneman, E. 1949. J. Neurophysiol. 12:85–100
145. Mountcastle, V. B., Talbot, W. H., Sakata, H., Hyvarinen, J. 1969. J. Neurophysiol. 32:452–84
146. Naves, F., Stark, L. 1968. Biophys. J. 8:257–302
147. Nyberg-Hansen, R., Brodal, A. 1963. J. Comp. Neurol. 120:369–91
148. Orlovskii, G. N., Severin, F. V., Shik, M. L. 1966. Biophysics 11:578–88
149. Oscarsson, O. 1966. In Nobel Sympo-

sium I, Muscular Afferents and Motor Control, 307–16. See Ref. 123

150. Oscarsson, O. 1967. The Neurophysiological Basis of Normal and Abnormal Motor Activities, 292–93. See Ref. 9

151. Oscarsson, O., Rosén, I. 1963. J. Physiol. London 169:924–45

152. Oscarsson, O., Rosén, I. 1966. J. Physiol. London 182:164–84

153. Oscarsson, O., Rosén, I., Sulg, I. 1966. J. Physiol. London 183:189–210

154. Oshima, T. 1969. In Basic Mechanisms of the Epilepsies, ed. H. H. Jasper, A. A. Ward, Jr., A. Pope, 253–61. Boston: Little, Brown. 835 pp.

155. Paillard, J., Brouchon, J. 1968. In The Neuropsychology of Spatially Oriented Behavior, ed. S. J. Freedman, 37–55. Homewood, Ill: Dorsey. 290 pp.

156. Pandya, D. N., Kuypers, H. G. J. M. 1969. Brain Res. 13:13–36

157. Partridge, L. D. 1961. Am. J. Phys. Med. 40:96–103

158. Patton, H. D., Towe, A. L., Kennedy, T. T. 1961. J. Neurophysiol. 23:501–14

159. Phillips, C. G. 1959. Quart. J. Exp. Physiol. 41:1–25

160. Phillips, C. G. 1966. In Brain and Conscious Experience, ed. J. C. Eccles, 389–421. New York: Springer. 591 pp.

161. Phillips, C. G. 1968. Proc. Roy Soc. B 173:141–74

161a. Phillips, C. G., Powell, T. P. S., Wiesendanger, M. 1970. J. Physiol. London 210:59–60P

162. Poggio, G. F., Mountcastle, V. B. 1963. J. Neurophysiol. 26:775–806

163. Porter, R., Hore, J. 1969. J. Neurophysiol. 3:443–51

164. Preston, J. B., Shende, M. C., Uemura, K. 1967. In Neurophysiological Basis of Normal and Abnormal Motor Activities, 61–72. See Ref. 9

165. Purpura, D. P., Shofer, R. J. 1964. J. Neurophysiol. 27:117–32

166. Purpura, D. P., McMurtry, J. G., Maekawa, K. 1966. Brain Res. 1:63–76

167. Rinvik, E. 1968. Brain Res. 10:79–119

168. Rinvik, E., Walberg, F. 1963. J. Comp. Neurol. 120:393–407

169. Rispal-Padel, L., Massion, J. 1970. Exp. Brain Res. 10:331–39

170. Rosén, I. 1969. J. Physiol. London 205:209–36

171. Rosén, I. 1969. J. Physiol. London 205:237–55

172. Rosén, I. 1969. Brain Res. 16:55–71

173. Ruch, T. C., Chang, H. T., Ward, A. A. 1948. Res. Publ. Assoc. Res. Nerv. Ment. Dis. 26:61–83

174. Sakata, H., Ishijima, T., Toyoda, Y. 1966. Jap. J. Physiol. 16:42–60

175. Sakata, H., Miyamoto, J. 1968. Jap. J. Physiol. 18:489–507

176. Scheibel, M. E., Scheibel, A. B. 1966. Brain Res. 2:333–50

177. Schlag, J., Villablanca, J. 1967. Brain Res. 6:119–42

178. Severin, F. V., Orlovskii, G. N., Shik, M. L. 1967. Biophysics 12:575–86

179. Severin, F. V., Shik, M. L., Orlovskii, G. N. 1967. Biophysics 12:762–72

180. Seyffarth, H., Denny-Brown, D. 1948. Brain 71:109–83

181. Shimazu, H., Yahagisawa, N., Garoutte, B. 1965. Jap. J. Physiol. 15:101–24

182. Silfvenius, H. 1970. Acta Physiol. Scand. 79:6–23

183. Sousa-Pinto, A., Brodal, A. 1969. Exp. Brain Res. 8:364–86

184. Stark, L. 1968. Neurological Control Systems — Studies in Bioengineering. New York: Plenum. 428 pp.

185. Stefanis, C., Jasper, H. 1964. J. Neurophysiol. 27:855–77

186. Steriade, M., Iosif, G., Apostol, V. 1969. J. Neurophysiol. 32:251–65

187. Stetson, R. H., Bouman, H. D. 1935. Arch. Neerl. Physiol. 20:179–254

188. Stewart, D. H., Preston, J. B. 1967. J. Neurophysiol. 30:453–65

189. Stewart, D. H., Preston, J. B. 1968. J. Neurophysiol. 31:938–46

190. Stewart, D. H., Preston, J. B., Whitlock, D. G. 1968. J. Neurophysiol. 31:928–37

191. Stoney, S. D., Jr., Thompson, W. D., Asanuma, H. 1968. J. Neurophysiol. 31:659–69

192. Swett, J. E., Bourassa, C. M. 1967. J. Neurophysiol. 30:530–45

193. Swett, J. E., Bourassa, C. M. 1967. J. Physiol. London 189:101–17

194. Taub, E., Berman, A. J. 1968. In The Neuropsychology of Spatially Oriented Behavior, 173–92. See Ref. 155

195. Telford, C. W. 1935. J. Exp. Psychol. 14:1–35

196. Thach, W. T. 1968. J. Neurophysiol. 31:785–97

197. Thach, W. T. 1970. *J. Neurophysiol.* 33:527–36
198. Thach, W. T. 1970. *J. Neurophysiol.* 33:537–47
199. Thompson, R. F. 1962. *Int. Congr. Physiol. Sci., 21st, Leiden, 1962.* Ser. No. 48, 1057
200. Thompson, R. F., Johnson, R. H., Hoopes, J. J. 1963. *J. Neurophysiol.* 26:343–64
201. Thompson, R. F., Smith, H. E., Bliss, D. 1963. *J. Neurophysiol.* 26:365–78
202. Thompson, W. D., Stoney, S. D., Jr., Asanuma, H. 1970. *Brain Res.* 22:15–27
203. Tokizane, T., Shimazu, H. 1964. *Functional Differentiation of Human Muscle.* Springfield, Ill: Thomas. 62 pp.
204. Towe, A. L. 1965. *Proc. Symp. Information Processing in Sight Sensory Systems,* ed. P. N. Nye, 142–56. Pasadena: Calif. Inst. Technol.
205. Towe, A. L. 1968. In *The Skin Senses,* 552–74. See Ref. 92
206. Towe, A. L., Patton, H. D., Kennedy, T. T. 1963. *Exp. Neurol.* 8:220–38
207. Towe, A. L., Patton, H. D., Kennedy, T. T. 1964. *Exp. Neurol.* 10:325–44
208. Towe, A. L., Whitehorn, D., Nyquist, J. K. 1968. *Exp. Neurol.* 20:497–521
209. Tower, S. S. 1940. *Brain* 63:36–90
210. Tsukahara, N., Fuller, D. R. G., Brooks, V. B. 1968. *J. Neurophysiol.* 31:467–84
211. Tsukahara, N., Fuller, D. R. G. 1969. *J. Neurophysiol.* 32:35–42
212. Twitchell, T. E. 1965. *Neuropsychologia* 3:247–59
213. Uemura, K., Preston, J. B. 1965. *J. Neurophysiol.* 28:393–412
214. Uno, M., Kozlovskaya, I., Atkin, A., Brooks, V. B. 1970. *Electroencephalog. Clin. Neurophysiol.* In press
215. Uno, M., Yoshida, M., Hirota, I. 1970. *Exp. Brain Res.* 10:121–39
216. Vallbo, A. B. 1970. *Acta Physiol. Scand.* 78:315–33
217. Vasilenko, D. A., Kostyuk, P. G. 1965. *Fed. Proc. Transl. Suppl.* 25:569–76
218. Vasilenko, D. A., Kostyuk, P. G. 1966. *Neurosci. Transl. No. 1*:66–72
219. Vedel, J. P., Mouillac-Baudevin, J. 1970. *Exp. Brain Res.* 10:39–63
220. Voneida, T. J. 1967. *Exp. Neurol.* 19:483–93
221. Voronin, L. L., Tanengol'ts, L. T. 1969. *Fed. Proc. Transl. Suppl.* 28:89–99
222. Ward, J. W. 1938. *J. Neurophysiol.* 1:463–75
223. Ward, J. W. 1952. *Res. Publ. Assoc. Nerv. Ment. Dis.* 30:223–34
224. Watt, D., Jones, G. M. 1968. *Proc. Ann. Sci. Meet. Aerospace Med. Assoc., 1968, Bal Harbour,* p. 174
225. Welt, C., Aschoff, J. C., Kameda, K., Brooks, V. B. 1967. In *Neurophysiological Basis of Normal and Abnormal Motor Activities,* 255–93. See Ref. 9
226. Whitehorn, D., Towe, A. L. 1968. *Exp. Neurol.* 22:222–42
227. Wiesendanger, M. 1969. *Ergeb. Physiol.* 61:73–136
228. Woodworth, R. S. 1899. *Psychol. Monogr.* 3:1–114
229. Woodworth, R. S. 1901. *Psychol. Rev.* 8:350–59
230. Woolsey, C. N. 1958. In *Biological and Biochemical Bases of Behavior,* ed. H. F. Harlow, C. N. Woolsey, 63–82. Madison, Wisconsin: Univ. Wisconsin Press. 476 pp.
231. Yokota, T., Voorhoeve, P. E. 1969. *Exp. Brain Res.* 9:96–115
232. Zadorozhny, A. G., Vasilenko, D. A., Kostyuk, P. G. 1970. *Neurophysiology* 2:17–25 (In Russian)

BRAIN-ADENOHYPOPHYSIAL COMMUNICATION IN MAMMALS 1066

F. E. YATES

Biomedical Engineering, University of Southern California
Los Angeles, California

S. M. RUSSELL AND J. W. MARAN

Department of Physiology, Stanford University, Stanford, California

INTRODUCTION

Scope of this review.—This review concerns interactions between the brain and the pituitary gland. However, hormones of the pars intermedia (α- and β-MSH)[1] or pars nervosa (antidiuretic hormone-vasopressin, oxytocin) are not considered except insofar as they may affect function of the pars distalis, and the same is true for the pineal gland and its (hormonal?) constituents. In brief, we consider how the secretions of ACTH, TSH, growth hormone, prolactin, FSH, and LH are adjusted by the brain.

Since neuroendocrinology has been rapidly developing, its history is frequently recounted. For background, the reader may consult the articles by McCann & Porter (1) or by McCann, Dhariwal & Porter (2). Other reviews and books that are pertinent to the history of the topics covered in this review may be found in (3–9). We especially recommend the authoritative review of the chemistry of releasing factors by Burgus & Guillemin (5).

In documenting assertions, we have used recent references, in keeping with the purposes of the *Annual Reviews*. We have also favored the more easily accessible papers over those published in journals less readily available in the United States. These choices suit the convenience of students and investigators, but they belie the historical order of development of the field. For that, and for proper credit to first discoveries, we expect the reader to rely upon the bibliographies of the recent papers we have cited.

[1] Some abbreviations in this review are: MSH, melanocyte-stimulating hormone; ACTH, adrenocorticotropin; CRF, corticotropin-releasing factor; LRF, luteinizing hormone-releasing factor; TRH, TRF, thyrotropin-releasing factor; FRF, follicle-stimulating hormone-releasing factor; PIF, prolactin-inhibiting factor; PRF, prolactin-releasing factor; TSH, thyroid-stimulating hormone, thyrotropin; LH (ICSH), luteinizing hormone; LTH, luteotropic hormone (synonymous with prolactin in the rat, but not in most species); cyclic AMP, 3',5' adenosine monophosphate.

Trends in neuroendocrinology.—Current work in neuroendocrinology has the following main themes, many of which appear in the body of this review:

1. Identification of the structure of pituitary and hypothalamic hormones
2. Definition of mechanism of action of hypothalamic hormones on the pituitary
3. Search for internal feedback loop closure at the brain or pituitary (i.e., study of ACTH, LH, FSH, TSH as feedback agents)
4. Search for sites of external feedback loop closure at brain or pituitary (i.e., study of growth hormone, prolactin, estrogens, progesterone, glucocorticoids, thyroid hormones as feedback agents)
5. Definition of coupling relations among various neuroendocrine systems (i.e., which hormones affect the performance of the systems governing other hormones?)
6. Identification of neural pathways and transmitters involved in endocrine functions
7. Identification and explanation of periodic functions of neuroendocrine systems (rhythms)
8. Quantification of the hormonal biases of behavior, especially in primates
9. Discovery of hormones not now recognized or appreciated

FEATURES OF THE VENTRICULAR, HYPOTHALAMIC, PORTAL VESSEL PITUITARY UNIT

Neurons, glia, ependymal cells, and portal vessels in the median eminence.—The ependyma lining the third ventricle in the area of the anterior hypothalamus in monkeys differs from the ependyma elsewhere in the ventricular system. In this region it is double-layered, and the layer against the cerebrospinal fluid has bulbous projections that vary in size with the menstrual cycle of females (10). The deeper layer, against neuronal and glial cells, has basal processes that extend toward the pars tuberalis of the adenohypophysis. In monkeys and rats, these processes make direct contacts with cells and the periendothelial space of vessels of the primary plexus in the postchiasmatic region of the hypophysial-portal system (10, 11). The primary plexus of the toad hypothalamic-adenohypophysial portal system has two types of loops: short—localized in the external region of the median eminence, surrounded by nerve endings and glial cells, and long—localized near the ependymal lining of the median eminence. Both the ascending and descending limbs of the long vessels are surrounded by nerves, ependymal processes, and glial cells (12). The vascular endings of the ependymal processes have dense granules that may be transported substances.

Two types of nerve fibers, containing vesicles 1500–3000 and 500–1000 Å in diameter, respectively, are present in the median eminence, the infundibulum, and the posterior pituitary of the human. It has been proposed that one type of neuron stores monoamines, and the other stores releasing factors (13). Kobayashi et al (14) have suggested that three categories of vesicles are present in neurons of the median eminence: synaptic vesicles, vesicles with catecholamine-containing granules, and vesicles transformed from neurosecretory granules; the latter granules presumably carry neurohypophysial hormones.

The anatomical arrangements described above place the capillary loops and neurons of the median eminence very close to cerebrospinal fluid of the third ventricle (15). Ten years ago Löfgren proposed that the hypothalamus may influence adenohypophysial function through secretory substances transported to the pars distalis from the cerebrospinal fluid (16). Further details of the anatomy of the median eminence, and the possibilities for transport from cerebrospinal fluid to blood in the hypothalamic-hypophysial portal system have been described by Kobayashi & Matsui (17).

The possibility for transport of substances from cerebrospinal fluid to adenohypophysis suggests that not all releasing factors are necessarily stored in the median eminence region of the brain. They could be synthesized and stored elsewhere, and delivered via cerebrospinal fluid to the portal vessels in the median eminence. Nevertheless, all the known releasing and inhibiting factors have been extracted from stalk-median eminence tissue, so we have no reason to doubt that storage does occur there. The physiological operation of a releasing factor transport route from neurons anywhere, through cerebrospinal fluid, ependyma, portal system endothelial cells, portal blood, and adenohypophysis remains to be proved. Meanwhile, one interpretation of experiments involving intraventricular injections of test substances is that the substances reached and acted upon cells of the adenohypophysis through such a transport route.

Cells of the adenohypophysis.—The nomenclature of pituitary cell types classified as acidophils, basophils, or chromophobes is based on their staining characteristics and light microscopy. The division of pituitary cells into somatotrophs, mammotrophs, corticotrophs, thyrotrophs, and gonadotrophs (LH and FSH cells) is based on the secretory product of the cells. Ultrastructural classification of the cells is based very largely on the content, size, and location of secretory granules. Under these circumstances it is difficult to relate to each other published findings based upon classifications at different levels.

The separate classifications of the pituitary cell types by secretory products and by electronmicroscopy can be made to converge by immunohistochemical methods (18). The peroxidase-labeled antibody method has been used to localize the pituitary hormones in cells examined by electronmicroscopy. Growth hormone, ACTH, prolactin, and TSH appear in separate cells. FSH and LH possibly appear within the same cell. No ACTH-containing cells were found in the pars distalis near the pars intermedia, but some were found in the pars intermedia itself. Unfortunately, those may have been merely α-MSH cells detected by a crossreacting antiserum.

New techniques involving digestion of pituitary tissues by trypsin, filtration through steel mesh, treatment of the filtered cells by elastase and collagenase, and zonal centrifugation (19) have allowed isolation of different types of anterior pituitary cells from rats. Transplanted pellets of isolated chromophobes have been placed in the cerebral cortex, under the renal capsule, or into the hypophysiotropic area of the hypothalamus of hypophysectomized rats (20). Under the latter circumstances, differentiation of chromophobes into both acidophils and basophils can be observed.

Dependence of cells of adenohypophysis on ions and cyclic AMP.—Cells of the adenohypophysis have resting membrane potentials, with inside negative, as might be expected. The polarity of the potential can be reversed if the cells are incubated in a high K^+ medium (21). Since high K^+ externally is known to stimulate release of at least some hormones (TSH, LH, ACTH), the coupling between the action of hypothalamic releasing factors and pituitary hormone release may involve membrane depolarization as an electrical stage.

It is also not surprising that the effects of high external K^+ concentration depend upon the presence of Ca^{++} (22). In the absence of Ca^{++} in the external medium, cells of the adenohypophysis are not depolarized by high K^+.

The in vitro synthesis of at least some hormones (prolactin and growth hormone) by incubated rat pituitaries also depends upon the concentration of K^+ and Ca^{++} externally (23). The ion effects are different on different hormones, as well as different on the processes of synthesis and release for a given hormone.

ADRENAL GLUCOCORTICOID NEUROENDOCRINE SYSTEM

Anatomical issues.—Siperstein & Miller (24) have shown that the "adrenalectomy cell" of the pituitary of adrenalectomized animals, and the "ACTH cell" of the pituitary of normal animals appear to be the same cell. This cell is a very large, irregularly shaped chromophobe that is present in only small numbers normally. These cells fit in the interstices between other cells; they have secretory granules 200 mμ in diameter; and they increase in size and number after adrenalectomy. The content of secretory granules increases at first when cortisol is given. This result suggests that the initial effect of cortisol is to decrease release but not the synthesis of ACTH. Cortisol also prevents the development of the adrenalectomy cells following adrenalectomy. A study by Nakayama et al (25) supports the views of Siperstein concerning the identity of the ACTH-secreting cell of the rat adenohypophysis. They note that corticotrophs make up only 0.16% of the population of anterior pituitary cells normally and that few secretory granules are present.

Another attempt to identify the corticotropin cells in the rat hypophysis was made by Baker et al (26) who used peroxidase-labeled antibody. Corticotrophs were least numerous near the junction with the pars intermedia. Some experiments have indicated that ACTH is present in and may be released from posterior pituitary neural tissue (27), but it is not certain that it is synthesized by corticotrophs located there.

Recently Gosbee et al (28) have shown by an autoradiographic technique that the uptake of labeled thymidine, which is presumably related to mitosis rates of cells, changed most strikingly in a cell type restricted to the pars intermedia of the pituitary when animals were subjected to adrenalectomy or cortisol administration. The cells of the anterior pituitary showed no marked histological changes, nor changes in mitosis rate, as the physiological state of the adrenocortical system was varied. They concluded that the pars intermedia may be in some way involved in ACTH release. We found some support for their provocative suggestion by means of microinjections of ovine CRF into the pars intermedia of rats pretreated with dexamethasone and pentobarbital (Wei, E., Dhariwal, A. P. S., and Yates, F. E.—unpublished observations). Much more ACTH was released if the CRF was injected in or near the pars intermedia than if the same dose was injected more laterally in the pars distalis. Our results could indicate that the pars intermedia does have a concentration of corticotrophs, or that the corticotrophs are clustered in the pars distalis near the junction with the pars intermedia [a suggestion made unlikely by the data of Baker et al (26)], or that chemical or mechanical disturbance of the pars intermedia and pars nervosa during CRF assays alters the response of the corticotrophs in the pars distalis to CRF. We conclude that some relationship, not yet precisely defined, may exist between the pars intermedia and ACTH release.

Localization of the site of storage of CRF, and the possibly different site of production, has been more difficult than might be expected. The many reports of successful extractions of CRF-like materials from pituitary stalk-hypothalamic median eminence tissue indicate that CRF is probably stored in that region. Porter et al (29) carefully exposed the blood supply to the pituitary of rats and selectively interrupted various channels. The maximal secretion rate of corticosterone from one adrenal, about 1 μg/min, decreased after hypophysectomy to very low levels within 60 min. Under these conditions posterior lobectomy (neurohypophysectomy) caused only a very slight decrease in corticosterone secretion rate. The authors correctly point out that it is far from ideal to have a system under maximal or supramaximal stimulation while testing for inhibitory influences.

The surprising thing in the above study was that transection of the three to five major portal vessels in the upper stalk, which drain the postchiasmatic eminence, had no effect on maximal corticosterone secretion rate. Since this preparation has an intact peduncular artery and caudal hypophysial artery inflow, as well as intact long portal vessels from the postpeduncular eminence and short portal vessels from the posterior lobe, pituitary blood flow presumably remains high. Evidently, sufficient CRF reaches the anterior pituitary through these vessels to sustain maximal adrenal performance. If CRF ever flows from the postchiasmatic eminence, that flow is not necessary for maximal adrenal performance. Previously, we had reported, on the basis of microinjections of CRF, that the CRF spread more readily into the pituitary from the postpeduncular than from the postchiasmatic region (30). We interpreted our results to mean that if fluid is injected into the posterior, medial basal hypothalamus it is more likely to enter portal vessels than if injected more anteriorly. Endogenous CRF may similarly enter portal vessels more readily from that same region. When the peduncular artery is cut, blood flow to the postpeduncular eminence, the stalk, and part of the posterior lobe is reduced; corticosterone secretion is diminished from 1.0 to about 0.7 μg/min. If the lower stalk is sectioned, the secretion rate drops from 1.0 to about 0.6 μg/min, and blood flow from all parts of the median eminence is stopped. The major conclusion from the work of Porter et al is that the primary capillary plexuses in the postchiasmatic eminence and in the posterior pituitary are not necessary to distribute CRF to the anterior pituitary during maximal ACTH release. The stalk and posterior peduncular eminence remain the only regions of CRF delivery that appear to be obligatory for the maximum performance of the system. These conclusions do not distinguish whether the apparently necessary vascular channels are so because they are the only ones carrying CRF, or because they are the only ones distributed to corticotrophs in the secondary plexus present in the pars distalis. In an earlier study, Porter (31) successfully dissociated effects of hypothalamic lesions on ACTH release from their effects on pituitary blood flow.

CRF activity not attributable to vasopressin has been localized in synaptosomes and granules present in homogenates made from median eminence tissue of rats (32). Synthesis and release of CRF can change independently, so that the content of CRF in hypothalamic tissue can increase following noxious stimuli (33), or cycle with the circadian rhythm in plasma corticosterone levels of the rat (34, 35).

CRF assays.—Several groups have compared various assay methods for CRF (36, 37). Our laboratory has used direct injection of test materials into the anterior pituitary of pharmacologically prepared rats as a means to assay CRF (30). Although this method gains sensitivity and specificity by presentation of the test materials to the region of the responsive cells, it loses sensitivity if dexamethasone is used in the pharmacological preparation of the animals, because dexamethasone inhibits the pituitary response to CRF (38, 39). Our assay is possible because the capacity of the pituitary to detect dexamethasone is more easily saturated than is its capacity to detect CRF. Thus, a large enough dose of CRF applied locally can override a maximal inhibition of the pituitary with dexamethasone. Even under these constraints, the intrapituitary microcannulation technique for CRF assay is still about six times more sensitive than are intravenous assays of CRF in median eminence-lesioned rats. An additional advantage of the pituitary microinjection assay is that CRF is distinguishable from vasopressin, while this distinction is frequently difficult to make in other assays of CRF extracted from hypothalamic tissue (36, 37).

Vasopressin itself, when injected directly into the anterior pituitaries of unanesthetized dogs without pharmacological treatment, causes a brisk ACTH release that justifies viewing it as a corticotropin-releasing factor (39). The pituitary response to vasopressin is as readily inhibited by dexamethasone as is the response to ovine CRF (39). Since vasopressin also potentiates the pituitary response to CRF (40), any physiological release of ACTH by vasopressin may be through enhancement of the response of the corticotroph to CRF, rather than through action as an independent CRF.

Structural and functional relations between CRF and vasopressin.—No recent progress has been reported on the structure of CRF. Ten years have passed since two CRFs were first proposed, one related to α-MSH (α-CRF), the other to vasopressin (β-CRF) but distinct from it (41). A new study has compared analogs of lysine vasopressin for CRF activity (42), using for assay the rat pretreated with chlorpromazine, morphine and pentobarbital. This preparation has the advantage that corticosteroid inhibition of the pituitary response to CRF is avoided. It has the disadvantage that its specificity is not known. In this assay two derivatives of vasopressin (1-deamino-4-decarboxamido-8-lysine vasopressin and 4-decarboxamido-8-lysine vasopressin) both had CRF, antidiuretic, and vasopressor activities. The CRF/pressor activity ratios of these two analogs and of a hypothalamic CRF material were higher than that of lysine vasopressin; the former analog had a strikingly higher ratio than that of the other substances. Therefore, it was clear once again that antidiuretic potency and pressor activity are not directly proportional to CRF potency.

Corticotropin release and vasopressin release are often associated (43). The stresses of ether, histamine, or noise all produce increments in the plasma concentration of ACTH and vasopressin whose release is in long and short pulses, respectively. The shapes of these pulses are difficult to compare, however, because of differences in the sensitivities of the assays for the two substances. It is tempting to assume a causal relationship between the simultaneous releases of vasopressin and ACTH. Again, however, it should be remembered that animals lacking vasopressin can still release ACTH, both in response to stress, and in the maintenance of the basal, circadian rhythm of corticosterone secretion (40, 44).

Mechanism of action of CRF.—The CRF-like action of vasopressin in causing ACTH release from pituitary tissue in vitro can be enhanced if cyclic AMP levels of the gland are first increased by inhibiting phosphodiesterase with theophylline (45). Furthermore, pituitaries of adrenalectomized animals that are presumably secreting ACTH at a high rate have increased levels of cyclic AMP. Dexamethasone inhibits the ACTH-releasing effects of both vasopressin, and exogenous dibutyl cyclic AMP.

Although it appears that corticosteroid inhibition of ACTH release may involve protein synthesis, the process of ACTH release by CRF does not (46). The process of ACTH release appears to be estrogen-dependent to some extent in the female rat: ACTH secretion in response to crude CRF in vitro is diminished by prior ovariectomy, and the defect is at least partially restored by estrogen therapy (47).

CNS lesions and adrenocortical function.—Current work on the adrenal glucocorticoid system after CNS lesions seems depressingly like that of 10 or 15 years ago. The same problems remain unsolved, most of the findings are confirmatory and as ambiguous as ever. This state of affairs reflects the intrinsic difficulty of defining the neural part of neuroendocrinology. Brodish has demonstrated again that extensive lesions involving the anterior, medial basal hypothalamus diminish and delay the onset of the stress response of the adrenocortical system (48). Pituitaries of such lesioned animals release ACTH readily after the animals are injected with blood from hypophysectomized donors. Presumably this blood is CRF-rich. The delayed stress response can be inhibited by dexamethasone, as can the response of normal animals. Increase in stimulus intensity (multiple stresses) shortens the delay. These effects may mean that in the presence of the lesions, fewer viable CRF-releasing neurons remain, that they are recruited with greater difficulty during stresses, and that their population is so small that they cannot sustain CRF release very long.

In rats with forebrains removed, Dunn & Critchlow (49) left varying amounts of hypothalamic tissue ranging from complete hypothalamus to only basal hypothalamic tissue. In some cases they left only the pituitary. After being stressed by immobilization plus hemorrhage, or by ether, the animals with only the pituitary left, as well as the animals with complete hypothalamic islands, failed to respond. The animals with basal hypothalamic tissue remaining gave a feeble response. All responses were measured from very high "pre-stress" levels. Such experiments show that hypothalamic tissue has some ability to support ACTH release in the absence of connections with other parts of the brain.

Rats with medial basal hypothalamic islands, or with the anterior connections of the hypothalamus severed, lose the afternoon rise in plasma corticosterone levels (50).

Still other studies showing that the pituitary adrenal system can be activated in rats with medial basal hypothalamic islands or partial deafferentation of the hypothalamus have appeared (51, 52). It should not be imagined, however, that adrenocortical function is normal in animals whose neural connections to the medial basal hypothalamus are damaged.

Some areas of the pons are claimed to be necessary for traumatic stress-induced ACTH release in rats under pentobarbital anesthesia (53, 54). Since the lesions in the pons interrupted no known sensory pathway to the hypothalamus, it was concluded that the lesions may have interrupted a "facilitatory" area.

In animals with transplanted, heterotopic pituitaries the low level of ACTH secretion produced by the transplants is not necessarily interfered with by median eminence lesions (55). More recently the same laboratory has found that in such preparations, which have their own pituitaries removed, ablation of the cerebral cortex increased plasma corticosterone levels. If the whole forebrain except a hypothalamic island was removed, the levels were the same as seen after removal of the cerebral cortex alone (56). The transplants were very responsive to injections of crude CRF. It was concluded that ACTH release from ectopic pituitaries is primarily dependent on a neural humor of hypothalamic origin that passes into the general circulation, but that the amount of the hypothalamus needed to provide the neurohumor seems to be greater than that destroyed by the median eminence lesions in the earlier work. The now well-known effects of forebrain removal on ACTH release from the remaining, isolated pituitary have been confirmed in monkeys (57), in which such isolation of the pituitary is consistent with at least normal cortisol secretion rate.

That the adrenocortical system has residual function in the presence of extensive damage to the brain, including forebrain removal and isolation of the pituitary, is definitely established, but how that residual function is maintained is unknown. It may be that the isolated pituitary, or even the pituitary connected to a hypothalamic island, is subjected to or responsive to chemical influences that are not normally operative.

CNS stimulation and adrenocortical function.—A new study of the role of the reticular activating system in the regulation of ACTH secretion has been reported by Taylor (58). She showed that stimulation of the reticular formation of the rostral pons or caudal midbrain led to an increase in cortisol secretion rate if the initial secretion rate was low, or a decrease if it was high. The decreases were not prominent, and the dependence of the response upon the initial conditions may have been a statistical accident since the groups were rather small. Nevertheless, the possibility that the action taken by the reticular activating system depends upon the initial condition of the adrenocortical system remains itself very interesting and worthy of further study.

Redgate (59) re-examined the effects on ACTH release in the cat of electrical stimulation of the brainstem and limbic system. Stimulation of the amygdaloid-septal complex led to a prompt rise in ACTH levels in plasma (bioassayed) whereas stimulation of the medullary reticular formation, lemniscal systems, medial midbrain structures, or posterior lateral hypothalamus led only to a delayed (by 5–10 min) rise. The most remarkable finding in this report is that no increase in ACTH release was obtained following stimulation of the hypothalamus at the base of the third ventricle, whether the cats were anesthetized or not. It may be that the electrodes were not near the CRF-releasing neurons, or that these neurons are surrounded by inhibitory neurons which dominate when the stimulation is given, or finally, that the stimulus parameters were not suitable. The author concludes that at least two paths for ACTH release exist: one in the forebrain for prompt release and one in the midbrain for delayed release.

Certainly, there is more than one afferent pathway to the CRF-releasing cells of the medial, basal hypothalamus. Different stresses activate different pathways: lesions effective in interfering with the ACTH release in response to leg break in anesthetized rats had no effect on the release in response to rubber band tourniquets (60). By means of various hypothalamic lesions it was established that the pathway by which a single leg break causes ACTH secretion is contralaterally distributed at the level of the basal hypothalamus. This pathway enters the anterior quadrant within 1 mm of the ventral brain surface. The pathway by which the tourniquet stress activates ACTH release was not defined, but is clearly different.

Internal (ACTH) feedback loop in the adrenal glucocorticoid system.— The question of whether or not increases in plasma levels of ACTH inhibit CRF release remains unresolved. The adrenalectomized animal, with high initial levels of ACTH, still releases ACTH readily after stress (61). More than 10 years ago the administration of ACTH was shown to increase the pituitary content of ACTH in adrenalectomized rats and impair the fall in content which ordinarily follows stress in such animals (62). Exogenous ACTH given for several days interferes with the release of endogeneous ACTH after some, but not all, stresses in otherwise normal rats (63, 64), even though the prestressed plasma corticosteroid levels may be normal. Among the various possible explanations for this result are that the high ACTH transients in plasma inhibit some pathways for activation of the adrenocortical system, or that the transients in plasma corticosterone levels produced by the intermittent ACTH injections have done the same. In vivo experiments with ACTH given systemically are not likely to answer the question about the existence of an internal feedback loop.

Work with hypothalamic implantation of ACTH has recently been summarized (65). The authors believe that an internal feedback loop exists, but whether the discovery concerns a physiological loop is still unsettled.

Corticosteroid inhibition of CRF or ACTH release (external feedback loop).—The history of the search for the site of corticosteroid inhibition of the adrenoglucocorticoid system has been well presented by Kendall (66). Initially, it was widely believed that corticosteroids inhibited ACTH release by action on the adenohypophysis. Subsequently the favored view was that the inhibitory action occurred in the brain, possibly at multiple sites. Recent reinvestigation has indicated without question that the ACTH-releasing process of the pituitary can be inhibited by corticosteroids (39; 66 for references). The current conviction that the pituitary is a site of corticosteroid inhibition of ACTH release challenges all previous demonstrations which depended on corticosteroid implants in the brain and suggested that the brain contains such inhibitory sites. Kendall has demonstrated rapid spread of corticosteroids from intracerebral regions to the pituitary (67).

It is not clear whether there are corticosteroid-sensitive, inhibitory feedback sites in the brain which affect CRF release. It is clear, however, that corticosteroid-sensitive neurons do exist in the hypothalamus (68). Of a population of 337 neurons, 57 had their firing rates depressed by dexamethasone, 4 were activated by dexamethasone, and 276 showed no change. The sensitive cells were diffusely scattered over a large stretch of tissue near the midline of the hypothalamus and midbrain. It was later discovered that the septal region also contains dexamethasone-sensitive neurons (Steiner, F. A. —personal communication). What these corticosteroid-sensitive neurons do is the mystery.

An interesting result most easily interpreted by the assumption that the brain does contain a corticosteroid-sensitive inhibitory feedback site was obtained by Hedge & Smelik (69). They concluded that in dexamethasone-pretreated rats, mechanical stimulation of the hypothalamus will release CRF, but that replenishment of CRF by new synthesis is impaired.

Rate-sensitive feedback—A new finding.—In addition to the possibility that the corticosteroid inhibitory feedback affecting ACTH release is multistage with a feedback point at the pituitary and possibly one or more in the brain, other characteristics of this feedback have been proposed. An observation made in our laboratory (70) indicates that the external, inhibitory feedback loop operates in two different time domains. An initial, very prompt inhibitory response has the properties of a unidirectional rate-sensitive pathway: even when the absolute levels of plasma corticosterone are low, if the rate of increase is high, the stress response of the adrenocortical system to histamine is completely inhibited. At a later time, when plasma corticosterone levels have been increased by an intravenous infusion of corticosterone so that they are high, but steady (the derivatives are then zero, or small), histamine again activates ACTH release and no inhibition is seen. After a delay of 2 hr, the steady elevation of plasma corticosterone levels finally activates a feedback pathway with absolute-level detection characteristics, and the system is again inhibited. The interplay of these two feedback operations separated by a long delay may cause the adrenocortical response to stress to be multiphasic. Our discovery of the separate derivative-sensitive rapid feedback pathway and the level-sensitive slow feedback pathway may help explain why experiments involving single intravenous injections of corticosteroids are so likely to expose the operation of a negative feedback loop. If a test stress is applied shortly after such intravenous injection, when the first derivative of corticosteroid concentration is large, inhibition is usually seen. If the test stress is applied somewhat later in the interval when the first derivative of plasma corticosterone levels is small, and the 2 hr delay in the level-sensitive feedback pathway has not elapsed, no inhibitory feedback action is detected. Most of the literature dealing with the location of the corticosteroid inhibition of ACTH release concerns the slow, delayed feedback pathway. The location of the rate-sensitive feedback path is not known.

Delayed, level-sensitive feedback.—The slow, delayed corticosteroid-inhibitory feedback path that closes at the pituitary involves protein synthesis (46), and that presumably causes the delay. Although this feedback involves a protein synthetic step, it still seems to exert its effect against ACTH release rather than against ACTH synthesis (71). The delayed feedback pathway readily saturates, with respect to its ability to detect corticosteroids, so that it is always possible to choose a stress input of large enough magnitude, or a large enough dose of CRF, to activate the adrenocortical system in spite of a maximal corticosteroid signal in the delayed, level-sensitive feedback pathways (30, 38, 40, 63, 72). This point deserves emphasis. If a supramaximal stress is applied to an animal after a very large dose of dexamethasone has been given several hours in advance, and a stress response occurs, it should not be concluded that the activation of the adrenocortical system by the stress necessarily occurred through corticosteroid-resistant pathways. Since the pituitary response to CRF can be inhibited by corticosteroids, the correct interpretation of such an experiment is that the delayed corticosteroid feedback detector was saturated with corticosteroids, and that the maximal inhibition resulting was not sufficient to bring a supramaximal stress input below maximal strength.

Ceiling-effect fallacy.—We cannot emphasize too strongly that tests for inhibitory relationships between variables in a biological system require that the interacting variables be at intermediate values in their physiological ranges. Inhibition cannot be properly tested in the adrenocortical system when its output is at either zero or maximal levels. Thus, to answer the question whether a certain stress input to the adrenocortical system passes through a corticosteroid inhibitory feedback point, the stress must be graded so that it does not drive the adrenocortical system to its maximal response. Once the stimulus strength has been so graded, it can then be determined whether the response can be affected by corticosteroids under conditions in which their plasma levels are also within the physiological dynamic range. Until such care is taken, it will be very difficult to interpret experiments leading to claims that the basal operation of the adrenocortical system can be inhibited by corticosteroids, but the stress response cannot.

Zimmermann & Critchlow (73) have shown that corticosterone injections in unanesthetized female rats cause a decrease in the plasma levels of corticosterone in the afternoon, at the time of the peak in the circadian rhythm for corticosterone. The "basal" levels in their experiments are very much higher than those found in other laboratories where anesthetized rats are usually studied. The decrease in plasma corticosterone levels seen in spite of the large subcutaneous injection of corticosterone was accounted for by a high transient (up to 150 μg/100 ml) of plasma corticosterone shortly after the injection. The levels then decreased below those seen in saline-injected controls. The increment in plasma corticosterone above basal levels caused by exposure of the animals to ether was not altered by the corticosterone injection. The authors concluded that high but physiological levels of circulating corticosterone can inhibit "non-stress" pituitary adrenal function but not "stress" responses. Although our laboratory once advanced a similar interpretation of data of this kind (63), we now think an alternative explanation is more likely.

For a given submaximal stress input, the extent to which corticosteroids can inhibit the expected ACTH release is a nonlinear function of the dose (plasma concentration?) of the corticosteroid (63). Furthermore, as we have noted above, the corticosteroid detector saturates before the stress input path saturates (63). These two features of the delayed corticosteroid inhibitory feedback pathway combine to confuse interpretation of experiments of the kind performed by Zimmerman & Critchlow (73). Specifically, if the initial condition of the adrenocortical system is about halfway up the normal dynamic range for the system, just before a stress is applied, and if the stress then drives the system to its maximum position, as in their experiments, a given dose of corticosteroids will depress the initial condition more than the stress-response level, because of the nonlinearity of the dose-response relation between corticosteroids and ACTH release. Thus, the "stress increment" may actually widen after corticosteroid treatment, as occasionally seen by Zimmermann & Critchlow (74). Even if the "stress increment" appears to be unaltered by corticosteroids, this does not mean that the stress response was uninhibited, because an increment from low initial conditions represents less ACTH release in this nonlinear system than does the same increment in plasma corticosterone levels from higher initial conditions. In this particular situation, the true state of affairs can be seen only by examining plasma levels of ACTH itself, because the adrenal cortex is the first element in the whole adrenal glucocorticoid neuroendocrine system to reach saturation. This saturation pitfall is to be avoided when questions of inhibition are being asked.

In addition to all the properties described above, the delayed corticosteroid feedback pathway also changes its sensitivity during the circadian rhythm in the adrenocortical system (75). Synthetic corticosteroids in humans inhibit endogenous cortisol secretion most effectively when they are given in the early morning hours, while between 8 a.m. and midnight only massive doses of potent synthetic steroids will inhibit cortisol secretion. Interestingly, the conclusion of the authors of this study was exactly opposite that of Zimmerman & Critchlow (73): they concluded (75) that the basal

circadian performance of the adrenocortical system in humans is resistant
to corticosteroid inhibition, whereas activation superimposed upon it—in
this case occurring during sleep—is corticosteroid-sensitive.

In addition to variations in sensitivity to corticosteroids occurring in the
delayed negative feedback pathway during the circadian period, it is evident
that the inhibitory effectiveness of a given dose of corticosteroids is
strongly dependent on the time interval between administration of the steroid and the application of stimuli known to release ACTH (76), for a
given time of day. This feedback system is sufficiently rich in functional
complexity that generalizations are hard to come by. The few that exist can
be found in computer simulations of the system or its components (72, 77,
78).

Peculiar functional states of the corticosteroid feedback path.—The ability of dexamethasone to suppress ACTH release is apparently impaired in
humans by the antiepileptic drug diphenylhydantoin (79). In rare patients
with Cushing's syndrome, a paradoxical response to dexamethasone is seen
(80), in which the already elevated production of ACTH is often *increased*
by dexamethasone. In the case cited, the patient had a basophilic adenoma
of the pituitary. Possibly such pituitary tissue binds dexamethasone at corticosteroid receptor sites, but does not respond to it. In that case the dexamethasone would act as an anticortisol at the pituitary feedback site, and
would open the loop. Alternatively, dexamethasone might directly stimulate
ACTH production or release, as a positive feedback agent. These two possibilities have not yet been distinguished, although in principle it should be
easy to tell them apart by determining whether cortisol itself increases or
decreases ACTH secretion in these patients.

Another peculiarity of the corticosteroid feedback system may have been
uncovered in recent studies (81) of pituitary-adrenal function in squirrel
monkeys which have extraordinarily high plasma cortisol levels (over 400
μg/100 ml in the resting (?) state). After stress, the levels increase to more
than 1000 μg/100 ml. Cortisol turnover in these monkeys is like that of
other primates. Apparently, they operate their adrenal glucocorticoid system
at a much higher point than do other animals. The fraction of cortisol that
is unbound in plasma is that normal for other monkeys. What adaptations
these animals have made to this peculiarity in the operating point of the
adrenal glucocorticoid system is unknown.

Uptake of corticosteroids by brain.—McEwen and his colleagues have
studied the distribution and uptake throughout the body of radioactively labeled corticosteroids (82–84). They could not overcome the two difficulties
inherent in such work: it is not certain that the radioactivity found in tissue
is in the native hormone injected rather than in a metabolite; nor is it certain that where hormones are bound they have physiologically interesting
actions. In spite of these difficulties, several important results were ob-

tained. Following injection of tritiated corticosterone into adrenalectomized rats there was a general uptake of labeled hormone by CNS tissue, but hippocampus and septum took up the steroid "specifically", which meant that the peak concentration relative to that present in the blood was greater than unity in those two regions of the brain only. In those regions the concentration was 4 to 5 times that in cortex. In normal rats the hippocampus did not take up the tracer specifically, though the septum did. Apparently the endogenous corticosterone levels saturate the sites available in the hippocampus.

It was later shown (83) that much of the corticosteroid taken up in the hippocampus was associated with the nuclear fraction of cells; whether these were neurons or glia was unknown. The nuclear binding was very specific for corticosterone: only corticosterone could displace labeled corticosterone from the binding sites, whereas in the hippocampus overall, dexamethasone and cortisol could compete with corticosterone. The septum was too small to permit isolation of cell nucleii for this kind of analysis.

The above results suggest the possibility that the hippocampus is the site of corticosterone detection in the 2 hr-delayed, level-sensitive feedback. Enzyme synthesis could be responsible for the lagged effect. The nuclear binding of corticosterone seems to involve a macromolecular nucleic acid-protein complex (84), though it may have been produced artificially during preparation.

Intermittent and periodic function in the adrenal glucocorticoid system.
—It is well known that the adrenal glucocorticoid system has periodic performance. The circadian rhythm in plasma glucocorticoid levels is very conspicuous in normal animals of many different species. In man the rhythm is endogenous, but the dark-light transition provides the synchronization of the endogenous rhythm with the circadian geophysical rhythms (85). Neither the transition from light to dark, nor the duration of darkness, provides timing signals. Less well established is a circannual rhythm in this system (86).

Recently, it has become apparent that the adrenal glucocorticoid system may have periodic performance at frequencies higher than once per day. Hellman et al in a study of two normal subjects and one subject with Cushing's syndrome (87, 88), by means of specific and precise methods combined with rapid sampling, found that cortisol is secreted intermittently. For 75% of the 24 hr period the adrenal cortex is not secreting at all.

When intermittency is discovered in a biological system, the next question that arises is whether the bursts are random or periodic. Hellman et al do not take a position on this question, but from their data and the data of Orth & Island (85) it appears that there is about one secretory burst every 3 hr. Berson & Yalow's data (89) can be interpreted as showing approximately eight bursts of cortisol secretory activity in humans every 24 hr. Hellman et al thought the bursts of secretion were associated with periods of REM sleep (which occur every 90 min during sleep, at twice the average frequency of the bursts in adrenal cortical function in the 24 hr period). However, the cortisol secretion bursts were easily uncoupled from REM sleep. Whether the eight secretory bursts of cortisol within 24 hr represent a high frequency rhythm with a 3 hr period, or represent intermittency within a 24 hr rhythm, is still unclear.

THYROID NEUROENDOCRINE SYSTEM

TRH.—The history of the achievement of the first identification of a hypothalamic releasing hormone has been presented in full detail (5). It began in 1962 with proof from Guillemin et al that extracts of hypothalamic tissue contained a substance that stimulated the secretion of TSH from the adenohypophysis, in an assay system with satisfactory specificity (90). By 1966, studies by Schally et al on porcine hypothalamic materials had isolated a TRF that after hydrolysis yielded three amino acids: histidine, glutamic acid, and proline (91).

In 1969, Schally et al published further details concerning the purification of the natural, porcine thyrotropin-releasing substance (92). The purified material was 32 percent (dry weight) histidine, glutamic acid, and proline. Burgus et al have also achieved a highly purified TRF preparation (93).

Eight synthetic peptides based on histidine, proline, and glutamic acid or glutamine were all inactive (94). Guillemin and co-workers tested six tripeptides containing histidine, proline, and glutamic acid, and found them inactive until acetylation, after which the sequence Glu-His-Pro became active as a TRF both in vitro and in vivo (95). The acetylation step which had activated the tripeptide Glu-His-Pro apparently did so by causing formation of pyroglu at the N terminal of the tripeptide (96). (The term pyroglu, also abbreviated PCA, refers to 2-pyrrolidone-5-carboxylyl.) On the basis of further derivatization and infrared and nuclear magnetic resonance spectroscopy, it was concluded that the structure of TRF was (pyro) Glu-His-Pro-R.

It was considered that the radical (R) of the C terminal might be an amide (specifically Pro-NH$_2$). Further comparison of synthetic PCA-His-Pro-NH$_2$ and ovine TRF by mass spectrometry of methyl or trifluoroacetyl derivatives indicated that the synthetic substance was identical with the natural hormone (97). The activity of the same synthetic substance was also compared with that of natural porcine TRH and it was concluded that they were the same substance, and that, therefore, porcine and ovine TRH were also identical (98). Further comparisons of the physical properties of the synthetic L-(pyro)Glu-L-His-L-Pro-NH$_2$ and the natural porcine TRH supported the view that they were identical (99).

A summary of the biological activity of synthetic polypeptide derivatives related to the structure of hypothalamic TRF was presented by Guillemin and co-workers in 1970 (100). In that report on synthetic substances, and in a parallel report on the purification of the natural TRH (93), it was concluded that the synthetic PCA-His-Pro-NH$_2$ corresponded to the minimal active core of ovine TRH, although the possibility was not ruled out that the natural material might be slightly different from the synthetic substance. The available data continue to support the view that the synthetic substance is identical with the natural substance.

In 1970, Schally's laboratory reported an extensive study of the biological properties of L-(pyro)Glu-L-His-L-Pro(NH$_2$), and again showed that it is identical to porcine TRH (101), and that the simpler tripeptide, L-glutaminyl-L-histidyl-L-prolinamide, which has the open glutaminyl form instead of the cyclized (pyro)Glu form, is inactive as TRH (102).

Natural TRH is inactivated by blood and other tissues (cerebral cortex, liver, kidney, and muscle) (103). A proteolytic enzyme of bacterial origin, PCA-peptidase, hydrolyzes such substrates (104).

Mechanism of action of TRH.—Although the available evidence is slender, it now appears that TRH stimulates both synthesis and release of TSH (105). When natural TRH was added to incubated anterior pituitary tissue from male rats, TSH concentration was increased in both media and tissues. Although it has been claimed that TSH release can be stimulated by cyclic AMP or by theophylline (106–108), confirmation is needed. TSH release is stimulated by epinephrine (106); this effect is augmented by phentolamine (an α-adrenergic inhibitor) and partially blocked by propranolol (a β-adrenergic inhibitor). These results suggest that the pituitary thyrotropic cells may have α-inhibitory and β-stimulatory adrenergic receptors. However, the effective doses of cyclic AMP and epinephrine were about 10^{-3} M (106), whereas the effective doses of the natural TRH (at least in other preparations) were about 10^{-9} M. Thus the physiological significance of the TSH-releasing activity of cyclic AMP or epinephrine is still uncertain.

Synthetic TRH in vivo.—Given intravenously to men (109) and orally to mice (110), synthetic TRH was effective in provoking TSH release. The resistance of the TRH molecule to the action of most proteolytic enzymes is probably responsible for its effectiveness when given orally.

Thyroid feedback system (external loop).—Crude hypothalamic extracts with TRH activity (111) provoke TSH release after intrapituitary injection. The response can be inhibited by doses of thyroxine that are within the physiological range (1–12 μg/100 g BW per day) (112). Similarly, the TSH releasing action of synthetic TRH can be inhibited by triiodothyronine (101). These experiments further support the view that the thyroid system has a negative feedback loop closed at the level of the anterior pituitary.

In studies of endocrine negative feedback systems the action of the feedback loop is usually evaluated by administering the inhibitory hormone.

Less common, because it is technically more difficult, is the experiment in which circulating levels of the inhibitory hormone are diminished. Such an experiment in thyroid physiology was accomplished by an exchange transfusion between a normal recipient dog and a thyroidectomized-hypophysectomized donor dog (113), or by plasmapheresis (114). The exchange transfusion caused no immediate increase in thyroid hormone secretion in the recipient dog, but several weeks afterwards the levels of thyroid hormone in the blood of the recipient (which had been decreased by dilution immediately after the transfusion) were restored to normal (113). After plasmapheresis, within 2 hr an increase in thyroid secretion occurs (114). These results have been interpreted to mean that the pituitary-thyroid inhibitory feedback system operates very slowly in the case of an acute reduction of circulating, unbound thyroid hormone. From studies of thyroid hormone metabolism it is already known that the pituitary-thyroid system is dominated by a very long time constant for thyroxine metabolism.

Although the closed-loop system has a slow response to decreases in thyroid hormone levels, dynamic asymmetry is a property of at least some endocrine systems (70, 115), and so a slow response to a decrease in levels of an inhibitory hormone does not mean that the inhibition produced by increased levels of the hormone is also necessarily slow. In fact, it may be rapid: thyroid hormones are well known to inhibit thyroxine release from the thyroid gland rapidly. Furthermore, when synthetic TRH is given intravenously in man, plasma TSH levels are increased 5 min later (109) and the response of the thyroid gland to TSH is also rapid (111).

Hypothalamic activation of the thyroid system.—Whether thyroid hormones act on the brain to inhibit TRH release is still an open question. In a study of hypophysectomized rats with implantation of heterotopic pituitaries under their kidney capsules, Kajihara & Kendall found that both hypothalamic lesions and hypothalamic implants of thyroxine could inhibit TSH secretion (indirectly measured) of the transplanted pituitaries (116). Unfortunately, thyroid function was already markedly depressed in the animals with heterotopic pituitaries and further depression produced by lesions or thyroxine implantations was difficult to measure.

Stimulation and inhibition of TRH release.—It has been clearly demonstrated in unanesthetized monkeys that stimulation of various regions of the hypothalamus may either increase or decrease TSH secretion (measured indirectly) (117). A related finding in rats is that stimulation of the medial basal hypothalamus will increase plasma TSH levels (measured directly) (118). In the monkeys, stimulation of the medial supraoptic region, the medial anterior hypothalamus, or the median eminence all generally activated the thyroid system, whereas stimulation of the preoptic region, parts of the median eminence, or the posterior mammillary region inhibited the thyroid system in some animals.

GROWTH HORMONE NEUROENDOCRINE SYSTEM

Structure and assay of growth hormone.—The amino acid sequence of human growth hormone has been determined (119). Bovine growth hormone, which is inactive in primates, produces fragments after digestion with chymotrypsin which have the activity of human growth hormone (120).

The concentration of growth hormone in plasma is now usually measured by radioimmunoassay. In primates, particularly, this assay method has been very successful. In rats, however, it has been less certain that the immunoreactive substance is the biologically active hormone. Fortunately, Frohman & Bernardis (121) have found that immunoreactive growth hormone in rat plasma increases in rats subjected to electrical stimulation of the ventral medial hypothalamic nucleus (but not in rats stimulated in the cerebral cortex). This result indicates that under conditions somewhat like those in which growth hormone secretion has been proved to be increased in monkeys (stimulation of medial, tuberal hypothalamus) (122), a species for which the radioimmunoassay is considered reliable, an increase of immunoreactive growth hormone is found also in the rat.

In collaboration with Frohman, we have found that levels of growth hormone in rat plasma determined by radioimmunoassay are increased following intrapituitary injections of growth hormone-releasing factor (GRF) (Frohman, L. A., J. A. Maran & A. P. S. Dhariwal, unpublished observations). Thus, in spite of the earlier uncertainty, it now appears that radioimmunoassay of rat growth hormone provides a satisfactory means to explore physiological variations in growth hormone levels in plasma of this species.

Localization of somatotrophs.—The fluorescent antibody technique has successfully distinguished the acidophilic, prolactin-secreting cells from growth hormone-secreting cells (123). A double antibody technique has been used to localize with peroxidase the distribution of growth hormone in the rat hypophysis. This technique has also demonstrated that the prolactin cells and the growth hormone cells are different (124).

It is still not known whether the human adenohypophysis contains different cells for growth hormone and prolactin production. Conway et al mapped regions of growth hormone production indirectly and found that these regions corresponded to those high in acidophils (125).

GRF.—Growth hormone-releasing factor from porcine hypothalami has been highly purified (126). It is an acidic polypeptide with high glutamic acid and alanine content. The structure of GRF is not known for any species.

The action of GRF on the pituitary appears to involve stimulation of both release and synthesis of growth hormone (127, 128). The growth hormone content of both medium and tissue is increased when growth hormone-releasing factors are added to tissue cultures of anterior pituitaries.

Unfortunately, results of experiments in which tissue content and medium content of a pituitary hormone are examined and summed after exposure of the tissue to hypothalamic releasing factors in vitro do not directly localize the site of action of the releasing factor. If a releasing factor stimulates release, and if the biosynthetic pathway producing the hormone has a product inhibition of an earlier catalytic step, then release would disinhibit synthesis and both would appear to be stimulated. Nevertheless, the more immediate effect of releasing factor would be on release itself. Conversely, if release has mass action characteristics, stimulation of synthesis could provoke release itself. The resolving power of such experiments is low.

Action of GRF.—The action of GRF appears to involve cyclic AMP (107, 129). The release of growth hormone is associated with extrusion of granules into the interstitial space between the somatotroph and the sinusoid (130).

Pituitary transplantation experiments—pitfalls.—The ability of the anterior pituitary to make or release growth hormone may depend on the presence of glucocorticoid and thyroid hormones. A clonal strain of rat pituitary tumor cells that secrete growth hormone spontaneously, showed increased growth hormone production in the presence of cortisol (131).

When rat pituitaries were transplanted to sites remote from the hypothalamus, growth hormone production fell and growth was impaired (132). The question arises whether the diminution in growth hormone secretion was caused by the removal of the pituitary from hypothalamic influence, or by the reduction in TSH and ACTH secretion secondary to the relocation of the pituitary. If thyroxine is administered to hypophysectomized rats bearing pituitary transplants under the renal capsules, their rate of growth is enhanced, whereas the same dose of thyroxine has no effect on the growth rates of animals whose pituitaries have been removed and replaced with in situ grafts.

The tentative conclusion from the above studies (132) is that the growth hormone-releasing process of the anterior pituitary requires that somatotrophs be exposed to thyroid hormones and glucocorticoids, and that GRF be present. When the animal with transplanted pituitaries is subjected also to hypothalamic lesions, and a further diminution in growth hormone production seems to occur (133), the obvious conclusion would be that the hypothalamus was producing GRF, which was reaching the transplanted pituitaries through the systemic circulation. However, because of the coupling between adrenal, thyroid, and growth hormone systems at the pituitary, the hypothalamic lesions could have been decreasing either adrenal or thyroid function still further, and the further diminution in growth hormone secretion could be secondary to these effects.

GIF.—A substance capable of inhibiting growth hormone release (GIF) is present in hypothalamic extracts (134). Pituitaries incubated in vitro which spontaneously release growth hormone can be inhibited by hypothalamic GIF (128). So far the appearance of GIF in hypothalamo-hypophysial portal blood has not been demonstrated, nor is it clear what physiological conditions would permit hypothalamic release of GIF. The detection of GIF in portal blood might require that GRF be absent, since administration of the two together interferes with the effects of both (128).

Growth hormone feedback loop.—The growth hormone-releasing effect of arginine, which is well known, is diminished in the first week after parturition in women (135). At the same time, the growth hormone system is still under the influence of placental somatomammotropin. If human chorionic somatomammotropin is accepted by the growth hormone-releasing system as a growth hormone, and if there is a negative feedback loop regulating growth hormone secretion, then these results are interpretable as an example of the operation of that feedback loop. Obviously, these interpretations are highly conjectural, and cannot be taken as proof that a negative feedback loop exists. The authors of the paper were careful not to claim otherwise.

More directly, the existence of a growth hormone negative feedback loop has been tested through implantation of growth hormone in various regions of the brain (136). Pituitary weight and growth hormone content were diminished by growth hormone implantation in the anterior median eminence of the hypothalamus, in the posterior median eminence, and in the posterior dorsal hypothalamus. Unfortunately, a small effect was observed after implantation of the hormone in the cerebral cortex.

Evidence that growth hormone may inhibit its own release has been provided by Sakuma & Knobil (137). They showed in unanesthetized monkeys that the strong releases of endogenous growth hormone provoked by insulin or vasopressin are impaired by a prior infusion of human growth hormone. The infusion brought the levels of growth hormone to high, but still physiological, values before the insulin or vasopressin tests. Changes in blood sugar or free fatty acids were not a likely cause of the impairment of the response, and it was concluded that growth hormone had inhibited growth hormone release.

Activation of GRF release.—The brain will activate the growth hormone system under a wide variety of conditions, and either norepinephrine or dopamine injected into cerebrospinal fluid of the lateral ventricles will release GRF. Serotonin will not, so norepinephrine is a probable transmitter for GRF release (138). Insulin-induced hypoglycemia and arginine infusions are standard and reliable clinical tests for the growth hormone-releasing function of the brain and anterior pituitary. Growth hormone release occurs normally during the periods of sleep characterized by slow waves in the electroencephalogram. These are the non-REM (rapid eye movement) sleep periods. The growth hormone release observed in these circumstances is so pronounced that it has been concluded that sleep may support anabolism in this manner (139). Surprisingly little conclusive evidence is available on the role of fatty acids or triglycerides in growth hormone release. The transient rise and fall in plasma free fatty acids provoked by heparin has been used as a means to determine the relationship between fatty acid levels and growth hormone levels (140). Unfortunately, the studies were very unconvincing: the increases in plasma growth hormone concentration were very small, and though they were attributed to the falling limb of the plasma free fatty acid curve, they could equally well be attributed in the short-term experiments to the rising limb of the curve, if it is supposed that the system has a small lag in it.

A more direct test through the intravenous infusion of hydroxybutyrate, 20% soybean oil emulsion, or sodium octanoate indicated some interaction between changes in plasma ketone or lipid levels and growth hormone secretion (141). Insulin-induced hypoglycemia was used as the stimulus for growth hormone release, and the effects of the ketone or lipid infusions on the response to the stimulus were studied. Soybean oil emulsion or sodium octanoate inhibited the growth hormone response to insulin-induced hypoglycemia, whereas infusions of β-hydroxybutyrate did not. Since insulin decreases free fatty acid levels, these results could be interpreted to mean that the insulin test for growth hormone release is mediated by hypolipemia instead of hypoglycemia. However, if hypoglycemia is prevented by simultaneous administration of glucose with the insulin, growth hormone release does not occur (142). Although the situation is unclear, it will be surprising if growth hormone release is not conditioned in some way by variations in plasma levels of lipid substrates, as it is by glucose and amino acid levels.

The regulation of growth hormone secretion by plasma levels of metabolites (glucose, amino acids) appears to involve an effect of the metabolites on the CNS rather than on the pituitary. The growth hormone release following insulin-induced hypoglycemia is prevented by hypothalamic lesions (143).

Estrogen and growth hormone release.—Estrogens enhance the growth hormone-releasing response of normal men to arginine infusions (144). Furthermore, the response is stronger in women during the midcycle stage of the menstrual cycle than it is during the phase near or at menstruation itself (145, 146). Clomiphene citrate, which may act as an antiestrogen by occupying estrogen receptor sites, is effective in preventing the midcycle increase in the growth hormone-releasing response to arginine infusions (146). It seems that in humans the growth hormone-releasing process is highly modifiable by estrogens. The mechanism and site for this action of the estrogens is not known.

Dexamethasone, in contrast to estrogens, has no effect on growth hormone release in acute experiments, even when it prevents ACTH release (147).

Adrenergic receptors and growth hormone release.—In addition to its dependence on metabolite levels, thyroid hormone levels, glucocorticoid levels, estrogen levels, and the state of the CNS (as evidenced by slow wave sleep), the growth hormone-releasing process also depends on adrenergic receptors. Alpha-adrenergic blockade with phentolamine clearly decreases the growth hormone-releasing response to provocative tests (148) and decreases resting growth hormone levels in plasma (149). Blockade of β-adrenergic receptors by propranolol has the opposite effect.

It seems clear that growth hormone release is stimulated by α receptors and inhibited by β receptors. These receptors have opposite effects on the secretion of insulin and TSH. Apparently the effects may be independent of changes in glucose levels in the blood. Infusions of phentolamine into the hypothalamus of conscious baboons depressed plasma growth hormone levels (150). If the phentolamine did not spread into the pituitary, then it can be concluded that the α receptors which stimulate the growth hormone system are located in or near the hypothalamus.

PROLACTIN

Functions.—Prolactin is an extraordinary substance whose wide-ranging and interesting actions have been well discussed by Bern & Nicoll (151).

The complete amino acid sequence of prolactin (ovine lactogenic hormone) has been determined (152). There are three homologous segments in human pituitary growth hormone and ovine prolactin, comprising in total about 45% of each molecule (153). It should be noted here, however, that contrary to the statement of Bewley & Li (153), humans may not control both growth and lactation with the one molecule. In monkeys, at least, independent secretion of prolactin and growth hormone has been shown (154).

PRF.—As far as is now known, in all birds prolactin release is stimulated by a hypothalamic, prolactin-releasing factor (PRF) (155). In mammals, the isolated pituitary secretes prolactin spontaneously, and the secretion can be inhibited by a hypothalamic prolactin-inhibiting factor (PIF) (156, 157). More recently, evidence suggesting the existence of a prolactin-releasing factor in mammalian hypothalamic tissue has been presented (158, 159). Apparently the secretion of prolactin, like that of growth hormone and MSH, may be regulated by both stimulating and inhibiting substances.

PIF.—Mammalian hypothalamic prolactin-inhibiting factor may be norepinephrine (160, 161). Norepinephrine (and epinephrine) strongly inhibited release of newly synthesized, labeled prolactin from rat pituitaries incubated in vitro with radioactive leucine (160). Growth hormone release was unaffected. In a similar preparation Birge et al (161) showed that the inhibitory action of norepinephrine (or epinephrine) on prolactin release in vitro could be prevented by both α- and β-adrenergic blocking agents. The major effect of norepinephrine appeared to be inhibition of prolactin release, rather than a primary inhibition of synthesis. It is now necessary to demonstrate that norepinephrine flows in hypothalamic hypophysial portal blood in concentrations sufficient to inhibit prolactin release from mammotrophs.

Effects of estrogens and thyroid hormones on prolactin release.—Just as estrogens enhance pituitary release of ACTH and growth hormone, as described above, they also appear to enhance prolactin release (162) or synthesis (163), probably by a direct action on the pituitary, as well as presumably at the hypothalamus by inhibition of PIF secretion (164, 165). Thyroid hormones also promote prolactin release by an action on the pituitary ,(166). In contrast, progesterone has no effect on prolactin secretion from the pituitary in vitro (167) but can stimulate prolactin release in vivo (162). Presumably progesterone acts by inhibiting the release of PIF from the hypothalamus. Unfortunately, at least one report shows that hypothalamic content of PIF is decreased instead of being increased by progesterone (168).

Prolactin in the estrous cycle.—Radioimmunoassays of serum prolactin levels in the rat have shown that during normal estrous cycling, a large pulse of prolactin secretion is present during proestrus, estrus, and metestrus (169). The exact relation of this surge of prolactin release to that of the LH surge that occurs on the day of proestrus in the rat is not yet clear. In any case, both hormones have a strongly pulsed release at or near estrus. The two pulses could be independent, or have common causality, or one could cause the other. Gonadotropin release is not known to affect prolactin release.

Some indirect evidence suggests that prolactin may stimulate gonadotropin release (170, 171). Pituitary FSH release from immature female rats can be stimulated by prolactin implants in the median eminence, and the onset of puberty is advanced by such implants. Also, prolactin levels in serum surge upward on the day of vaginal opening that defines the onset of puberty in the rat (172).

Prolactin inhibitory feedback loop.—Implantations of prolactin in the median eminence of the rat will terminate pregnancy (173) if the implant is made before placental support of the corpus luteum is firmly established, by the seventh day; such implants will interfere with mammary development in estrogen-treated rats (in which estrogen is presumably provoking prolactin secretion through an inhibition of PIF release at the hypothalamus, rather than by its direct pituitary action) (174); they will inhibit lactation in post-partum rats (175); and, finally, they will decrease serum prolactin levels in female rats between the fourth and eighth postpartum day (176). Further-more, median eminence implants of prolactin, but not FSH or LH, will in-hibit luteal function in the rat as evidenced by shortened pseudopregnancy, and impaired deciduomata formation (177). These results indicate that pro-lactin in the hypothalamus stimulates the release of PIF, and thereby inhib-its its own release from the pituitary. As is usual with hypothalamic implant studies, it is not easy to determine to what extent the brain is ordinarily stimulated to produce PIF by some function of plasma prolactin levels in intact animals.

REPRODUCTION

Introduction.—Over 50% of all published work in neuroendocrinology during the past year was on reproduction. Anyone facing the prospect of reviewing neuroendocrine aspects of reproduction as part of a larger topic such as ours, must severely restrict his scope. We have chosen to review the plasma concentrations of reproductive hormones in female mammals during their reproductive cycle, and to use that information to deduce which of the many experimentally demonstrated relationships among these signals are operationally significant in normal females.

Among the important topics in reproductive physiology omitted from this review are: biochemistry of gonadal and other hormones; chemistry and mechanism of action of releasing factors; male reproduction; neuro-transmitters in the pathways activating neurons that secrete hypothalamic hormones; hormonal basis of sexual behavior; effects of neonatal treat-ments with androgens or estrogens; puberty; pregnancy; and lactation. We have also deliberately omitted citing any experiments using only pituitary contents of gonadotropins as primary data.

Bibliographic sources for topics not covered in this review of reproduc-tion.—Several recent reviews deal effectively with various aspects of repro-duction. Everett (178) and Armstrong (8) have discussed many of the cur-rent problems in the field; Harris & Naftolin have offered a brief, pertinent discussion of the predominant views now current (179). An important at-tempt to synthesize the functional relationships among the many variables in the reproductive system has been accomplished by Schwartz (180), whose review includes a valuable mixture of primary data, with hypothesis testing implemented by computer simulation.

Reproduction in the male has been reviewed by Davidson & Bloch (181). The chemistry of hypothalamic releasing factors has been discussed well in a recent volume of the *Annual Review of Biochemistry* (5). Mecha-nism of action of hypothalamic releasing factors has been treated by Ge-schwind (182). Effects on reproductive function of treatment with hormones during prenatal and early postnatal periods have been reviewed by Barraclough (183). Catecholamines as neural transmitters in neural-endocrine pathways have been discussed by Fuxe & Hökfelt (184).

The electrophysiological effects of steroid hormones on brain, including the hormonal basis of sexual behavior and the effects of neonatal treatments with androgens or estrogens, were the subject of an excellent conference sponsored by the University of California, Los Angeles, in May 1970. The proceedings of this conference are being published (185) and include valuable articles on reproductive physiology by J. Davidson, by S. M. McCann, and by K. Brown-Grant. We were fortunate to see prepublication copies of some of the manuscripts, and these have influenced the following discussion.

Hormones involved in the reproductive cycles of female mammals.—The possibly relevant hormones in the female reproductive cycle of mammals are LRF and LH; FRF and FSH; PIF and prolactin; progesterone and 20α-hydroxy-pregn-4-ene-3-one; 17α-OH-progesterone; estradiol and estrone; luteolysin (?); prostaglandin (?); melatonin (?). Adrenal androgens are probably not significant normally, though there is doubt on this point. Of the hormones listed, only six or seven have proven importance in the operation of the reproductive cycle in female humans, monkeys, or rats.

Reproductive cycles.—Since cyclicity is a conspicuous property of the reproductive performance of mammals, the origins of the periodicity should be of profound interest in this branch of neuroendocrinology. In physics, as in applied mathematics, problems of periodicity and stability have led to important theoretical developments that can serve as valuable background in biology. Below we describe a simple categorization of oscillatory systems that may help frame hypotheses about reproductive cycles.

Two views concerning the origins of periodicity.—If a system shows periodic behavior, the periodicity may have either of two very different origins. In one case, a system can be intrinsically oscillatory. In the other case, it may be nonoscillatory and driven by a periodic function at its input.

In a linear system, intrinsic oscillation can arise from an arrangement of an energy input, with feedback loops and appropriate parameter values. The boundary conditions uniquely determine the behavior of the system. If the system is nonlinear and also nonconservative, as are biological systems, it may exhibit limit cycle oscillations. In this nonlinear case the performance does not depend upon specific starting conditions, but the same oscillatory behavior can be reached from many different initial conditions.

The theories concerning stability and oscillations in nonlinear systems cannot be succinctly stated here. Their significance in biology has been discussed by Iberall & Cardon (186). Whether the human female reproductive system is regarded as being linear or nonlinear (and it is certainly nonlinear), the important point is that it might be intrinsically oscillatory because of the nature of its structure and unit processes.

In contrast to the intrinsically oscillatory system (linear or nonlinear) described above, is a nonoscillatory system, which may be made to give periodic performance when it is coupled to or driven by an oscillator or timer. Much of the work on the reproductive system of female rats seems to lend itself to an interpretation based on the assumption that the periodic function arises from a timer in the brain. Unfortunately, the available data do not actually distinguish clearly between the two cases discussed above in primates.

Localization in brain of signals for gonadotropin release in rats.—Reproductive cyclicity in the female rat is believed to depend on neurons in the medial preoptic area. It is also believed that positive feedback effects of ovarian steroids are exerted in the same area. In contrast, adjustments of gonadotropin secretion involved in compensatory ovarian hypertrophy after unilateral ovariectomy, or in the negative feedback inhibitions of gonadotropin-releasing factor secretion caused by ovarian steroid hormones, are determined by neurons lying in the medial, basal hypothalamic areas extending from the optic chiasm posteriorly to the pituitary stalk, and the arcuate and ventromedial hypothalamic nuclei. The evidence for these views is highly varied in nature and quality, and has been recently discussed by McCann et al (187). Some of the arguments are given below.

In the rat, situations exist in which cyclic release of gonadotropins is not seen. For example, they are lacking in: prepuberal animals of both sexes; males; females with lesions of the medial preoptic area; animals with anterior deafferentation of the hypothalamus eliminating connections from the preoptic area to the medial basal hypothalamus; females treated with androgens neonatally; pregnant animals; or those exposed to constant light. Nevertheless, in such animals gonadotropin outputs can be affected, or ovulation can be made to occur in some instances. For example, in the animal made acyclic by exposure to constant light or early androgen treatment, ovulation can be induced by electrical stimulation of the preoptic area, the median eminence, or the arcuate nucleus (188).

The negative feedback arrangements required for compensatory ovarian hypertrophy involve neurons whose connections are lost by anterior cuts in the hypothalamus at the rostral border of the ventromedial and arcuate nuclei (189). Animals with lesions farther forward (in the retrochiasmatic region), disconnecting the medial preoptic area from the medial basal hypothalamus, stop cycling and fail to ovulate (190) but they still are capable of compensatory ovarian hypertrophy (189). Since the animal with a retrochiasmatic lesion is in constant estrus, it presumably can maintain estrogen secretion. This fact supports the view that a continuous release of gonadotropins (pattern not specified) can be sustained by the anteriorly deafferented, medial basal hypothalamus (190). However, estrous cycles cannot be maintained in animals with suprachiasmatic lesions (191).

As would be expected, median eminence lesions severely alter all gonadotropin release; for example, plasma LH and FSH levels drop and prolactin levels rise (187).

Evidence that a negative feedback action of estrogens on gonadotropin secretion occurs in the medial, basal hypothalamus, rather than in the suprachiasmatic-preoptic area, comes from studies in ovariectomized animals with rostral hypothalamic cuts. The postcastration rise in LH was not altered by the lesions. It was concluded that a negative feedback action of estrogen is intact in such animals and that it involves regions caudal to the lesion, in the hypothalamus (190).

A positive feedback effect of progesterone on gonadotropin release in rats has been localized in an area rostral to the medial basal hypothalamus, probably in the preoptic area (190). The site of the more definite positive feedback effect of estrogen on gonadotropin release has not definitely been localized, but estrogen implants in hypothalamic or preoptic areas cause ovulation or precocious puberty (192, 193), so these areas may be the sites of stimulatory action of estrogens on gonadotropin release.

Although much work has been done with implantation of estrogens into brain and pituitary, the well-known possibility that estrogens placed in the brain may spread to the pituitary makes the interpretation of such experiments so difficult that we have not emphasized this kind of evidence.

A line of research now being vigorously pursued concerns uptake of radioactively labeled estrogens by brain and pituitary. Obviously, in such studies it is never clear that uptake or binding is synonymous with the identification of the estrogen by a physiologically important estrogen receptor. Estrogen is bound by cells of the anterior pituitary (194–200) in rats and cows. The uptake may have been specific, because the concentration of radioactivity appeared to be higher in pituitary tissue than in blood, cerebral cortex, or liver. Labeled estrogens were also taken up (specifically?) by neurons (?) (in some cases uptake was shown not to be localized in glial or ependymal cells) in various regions of the brain including: medial preoptic nucleus, suprachiasmatic preoptic nucleus, arcuate nucleus, lateral part of the ventromedial nucleus, lateral septal nucleus, terminations of the stria terminalis, amygdaloid complex, median eminence, "anterior hypothalamus" (195, 196, 198, 199–205). These data were obtained from rats, mice, and cows.

Brain estrogen receptors do not respond to estradiol as do uterine receptors (206).

Another approach to localization of brain cells affecting gonadotropin release involves recording activity of multiple units in various regions during the female reproductive cycle. During the 2 hr period in the afternoon of the day of proestrus in rats, when an LH surge is being established (described below), a burst of multiple unit electrical activity occurs in the basal hypothalamus, the arcuate nucleus, the ventromedial hypothalamic nucleus, the medial preoptic area, septum, amygdala, and the bed nucleus of the stria terminalis (207). This study was extremely valuable in that the normal estrous cycle was examined.

Other studies, in which some experimental derangements of reproductive function were made and electrical activity in the brain recorded, are more difficult to interpret (208–210). The difficulty stems from the fact that the experimental maneuvers might have changed electrical activity in those parts of the brain concerned with either sexual behavior or generalized motor activity, both of which are well known to vary during the estrous cycle. Consequently, until the electrical patterns of those neurons governing gonadotropin release can be distinguished from those of neurons governing motor, sexual, or other behavior, approaches of this kind will remain extremely difficult to interpret by themselves, although in combination with other techniques (for example, hormone uptakes, biogenic amine turnovers, lesions, stimulations) they may contribute usefully to the identification of the various regions of the brain involved in reproduction.

It is still too soon for a clear synthesis of all the various lines of evidence describing those parts of the brain involved in reproduction. The constellation of findings described above is consistent with the notion that the cyclicity of the female reproductive system (at least in rats) depends upon some activity of the medial preoptic area, and that a region of the anterior, medial basal hypothalamus is capable of sustaining gonadotropin release acyclically. This latter region is also a site at which ovarian steroids may inhibit secretion of gonadotropin-releasing factors.

Relationships among reproductive hormones.—In Table 1 we have indicated various effects experimentally proven or proposed for the reproductive hormones listed above. Recent references have been used for most of the documentation, even of long known facts, since they provide updated discussions and bibliographies. The data have been taken mainly from experiments in female rats, though ewes or primates are also included as sources. We have attempted to indicate sites of action for effects on gonadotropin release by specifying the gonadotropin release process itself if the effect is at the pituitary, or the appropriate releasing factor secretion process if the effect is at the brain. In either case, gonadotropin release is changed. When the site of action is not known we specify both processes, conjoined with "and/or".

Table 1 provides a set of data on mechanisms that serve as the basis for our interpretation of the second set of data giving patterns of concentrations of reproductive hormones in the sera or plasmas of female humans, monkeys, or rats. From these two data sets we later draw conclusions about the physiological system arrangements that lead to cyclic ovulation in spontaneous ovulators.

Our opinion about causalities, based upon Table 1.—

1. The gonadotropins FSH and LH, and prolactin all can inhibit their

TABLE 1. Characteristics of reproductive hormones

Hormone	Experimentally demonstrated characteristics and functions pertinent to the female reproductive cycle
1. LRF	Causes LH release (211) Is itself released by dopamine (212, 213)
2. FRF	Causes FSH release (214) Is itself released by dopamine (215) Inhibits its own release (?) (216)
3. PIF	Inhibits prolactin release (156) Is itself norepinephrine (160)
4. PRF	Increases prolactin secretion (159)
5. LH (ICSH)	Causes ovulation of prepared follicle (217, 218) Inhibits its own release (219, 220), probably by decreasing LRF secretion Stimulates progesterone secretion (221, 222) Causes luteinization in concert with other hormones (223) Causes luteolysis in rats (224) Increases estrogen secretion alone (222), but does this much better with FSH (225) In concert with FSH, supports follicular growth (225)
6. FSH (Many preparations have been contaminated with LH)	Triggers and/or sustains follicular growth (217) and amino acid uptake (226) Inhibits its own release (220, 227), probably by decreasing FRF secretion Stimulates its own release by increasing FRF secretion (228) Causes ovulation of prepared follicle, but ovulation not followed by normal corpus luteum (217, 229, 230) Helps maintain corpus luteum in conjunction with other hormones (223) Stimulates estrogen secretion, if LH is also present (217), and possibly even if LH is not present (225, 231)
7. Prolactin	Helps maintain corpus luteum in conjunction with other hormones (223), and is especially important in rats for this function Increases FRF release (170) Inhibits its own release by increasing PIF secretion (175–177)
8. Progesterone (Progestins, 20α-hydroxy-pregn-4-ene-3-one)	Secreted by granulosa cells (263) Increases prolactin secretion by decreasing PIF release (162) Stimulates FRF and/or FSH surge (232, 233) Inhibits FRF and/or FSH release (234, 235) Stimulates LH release (236–240), probably by increasing LRF secretion (190) Inhibits preovulatory surge of LRF and/or LH (241, 242) Inhibits LRF and/or LH release generally (235, 243), but the effect may not be strong (244–247) In 4-day cycling rat, delays ovulation when given on diestrus day, but abolishes that delay if a repeated dose is given (248); in 5-day cycling rat, advances ovulation 1 day if given on day 3 (249, 250)
9. Estradiol (Estrogens, estrone)	Secreted by ovarian theca interna cells along with 17α-OH-progesterone (264) Increases LRF and/or LH release (244, 258, 305, 311) Increases LH release in males (251) and females (252) Decreases LRF secretion (251, 253–255) Decreases LH release (256) Decreases FRF and/or FSH releases when they are initially high (232, 257) Has little or no effect on FRF and/or FSH releases when they are initially low (258) Increases prolactin release (162, 163) Decreases PIF release (164, 165) Increases prolactin release and/or decreases PIF release (257) Helps maintain corpus luteum (223) Causes precocious puberty if placed in preoptic area (192) Provokes ovulation if placed in anterior hypothalamus, basal tuberal region, pituitary or third ventricle (193) Advances ovulation by one day in the 5-day cycling rat (259)
10. Melatonin	Interferes with gonadal growth and function (260)
11. Prostaglandin $F_{2\alpha}$ (Luteolysin?)	Luteolytic in rat (261) Initiates labor in pregnant humans (262)

own releases through inhibitory (negative) feedback effects on the brain. These effects are *not* an essential feature of the normal functional arrangements underlying female reproductive cycles.

2. Estrogens have multistage inhibitory feedback effects on the processes leading to gonadotropin release, at sites in brain (e.g. medial basal hypothalamus, arcuate and ventromedial nuclei) and pituitary. The effects are more marked on FSH levels than on LH levels.

3. Estrogens also have stimulatory (positive) feedback effects on the processes leading to gonadotropin release. These effects occur mainly in a region of the brain different from the locus of inhibitory feedback (e.g. medial preoptic area) but also (at least for LH release) on the pituitary.

4. The brain site for the inhibitory feedback effect of estrogens lies functionally between the site of stimulatory feedback and the site of gonadotropin-releasing factor secretion.

5. The stimulatory and inhibitory effects ascribed to estrogens in items 2–4 above can be ascribed to progesterone as well, on the basis of selected experiments. However, none of these actions of progesterone is as potent (on the basis of molar concentration or physiological level) as the corresponding action of estrogen, and patterns of progesterone levels in blood play no essential role in the mechanisms underlying cyclicity in the female reproductive system. (Progesterone does play an essential role at the endometrium, but those actions necessary for the maintenance of pregnancy are not in the scope of this review.)

6. The female reproductive system is characterized by redundancy. FSH and LH have many common actions during all three stages of the cycle: follicular, ovulatory, and luteal. Because of the redundancy, loss of one signal may not necessarily cause failure of the system. For example, in the absence of LH, FSH is revealed as an ovulatory hormone. In a given species the pattern of signal strengths may differ from that in other species, but in general, the FSH signal predominates as initiator of the follicular stage at the ovary, and LH predominates as initiator of the ovulatory stage at the ovary. The length of the luteal phase is much more constant than that of the follicular phase. LH is the predominant initiator of luteinization, but a constellation of low-level signals including both FSH and LH is needed for maintenance of luteal function.

7. Luteolysis in primates is an intrinsic property of the corpus luteum. In other species extrinsic luteolytic signals may also operate (prostaglandins, LH).

8. Theca interna cells make and secrete estrogens and 17α-OH-progesterone in similar patterns. This process is only weakly coupled to gonadotropins after initiation, which is strongly coupled.

9. Granulosa cells make and secrete progesterone and 20α-OH-pregn-4-ene-3-one in similar patterns. This process is only weakly coupled to gonadotropins after initiation, which is strongly coupled.

10. Stimulatory effects at brain, pituitary, and ovary have strong, posi-

tive, rate-sensitive characteristics. They are more sensitive to positive rate of change of hormonal levels, than to the absolute value of the levels.

11. Inhibitory actions of hormones in the female reproductive system are more sensitive to absolute levels than to either positive or negative rates of change of the levels.

12. The origin of the cyclicity of the female reproductive system in spontaneous ovulators is entirely within the system itself in primates, but requires a mixture of periodic input functions (timers, clocks) and system properties in other species (such as the rat). In reflex ovulators periodicity is lost entirely, and input functions drive ovulation. Thus there is a spectrum of driving signals for ovulation ranging from a completely *input-dependent* reproductive system (rabbits) to a system nearly *input-independent* (humans). The rat system which lies between these extremes shows some properties of each.

Patterns of concentrations of reproductive hormones in sera or plasmas during reproductive cycles.—Five of the major reproductive hormones that circulate in plasma (LH, FSH, progesterone, estradiol, prolactin) or related hormones (20α-hydroxy-pregn-4-ene-3-one, 17α-OH-progesterone, and estrone) have been measured by techniques adequate for detecting physiological levels in normal animals. The methods include radioimmunoassay, competitive protein binding, double isotope dilution derivative analysis, gas chromatography, or thin layer chromatography. As a result, one can now begin to interpret experimental data such as those shown in Table 1 in the light of the normal patterns of the hormones.

Reproductive hormones in normal women at midcycle: In normal women a striking, midcycle increase in plasma LH concentration occurs (232, 265–286). Studies of hospitalized women with presumably normal reproductive systems have proved that the LH "surge" occurred prior to ovulation (268–270). The time interval between the peak of the LH concentration and ovulation could not be established exactly, but has been estimated to be approximately 48 hr or less (268–270). Indirect evidence of the occurrence of ovulation, such as the increase in body temperature associated with progesterone release from the corpus luteum, has also indicated that the midcycle LH surge is preovulatory (265, 268, 277).

The shape of the LH surge determined in any particular investigation obviously will depend on sampling rates. At relatively high sampling rates the LH surge can be seen occasionally to have a complex waveform, with more than one peak (268) or a shoulder on the trailing edge of a main peak (275).

Similar studies have established the existence of a midcycle FSH surge (232, 265–267, 269–272, 276, 277, 282, 284, 285, 287). The FSH peak usually occurred simultaneously with the LH peak (269, 270, 285) but was less marked. We have found no studies describing complexities in the shape of the midcycle FSH surge.

The pattern of prolactin concentration in normal women during a reproductive cycle has not been reported. However, because many investigators have had difficulty proving that prolactin and growth hormone are separate substances, separately released in the human, it is of interest that growth hormone levels in normal women also show a midcycle peak that precedes the LH peak (266). We believe, however, that it is reasonably clear that in nonhuman primates the release of prolactin occurs independently of that of growth hormone (154). Therefore, we do not claim that the described growth hormone peak represents or is necessarily associated with a prolactin peak in humans.

From the evidence in Table 1, and the concentration of gonadotropins in plasma described above, we conclude that the proximate cause of ovulation in normal women is an abrupt release of both FSH and LH, with the LH surge providing the predominant, and probably sufficient, signal. The question then is, what causes the abrupt release of these gonadotropins?

Plasma levels of estradiol and 17α-OH-progesterone also show a midcycle peak (274, 282, 285, 286, 288–290). The exact relationship between the rise in estrogen levels and the rise in gonadotropin levels can be established only by studies with relatively rapid sampling in the immediate preovulatory period. The available data indicate that the estrogen rise starts before the gonadotropin rise. The estrogen peak need not itself necessarily precede the LH/FSH peaks for a causal relation to exist, because the time or magnitude of a peak may not be the physiologically significant aspect. The rate of change of a variable could be the significant signal.

The plasma levels of progestins (progesterone, 20α-hydroxy-pregn-4-ene-3-one) have been studied more thoroughly than have those of estrogen. We have tried to compare the times of onset of rises in progestin levels with onset of rises in gonadotropin levels, rather than the times of peak concentrations, to deduce the relationship between progestin and gonadotropin release in women.

From the data in Table 1 it is clear that progesterone itself can cause gonadotropin release under some experimental conditions (190, 232, 233, 237–240). When it does so in humans, the time interval from administration of progesterone to peak gonadotropin release (FSH and LH) is approximately 24 hr (232). Nevertheless, not a single study involving simultaneous determination of progesterone and LH in women has revealed a significant rise in progesterone levels preceding the onset of the rise in LH levels (266, 269, 270, 271, 275, 277, 281, 283, 285, 286). Therefore, it now seems assured that in the human the preovulatory release of gonadotropins is not caused by progesterone.

Since gonadotropins can cause progestin release from unruptured follicles, a preovulatory rise in plasma progestins may occur (269, 270, 281) after the earlier preovulatory estrogen and gonadotropin surges. The progestins might then enhance the ovulatory effectiveness of the gonadotropins, and cause the secondary peak in the LH surge, if it is observed.

Levels of reproductive hormones during the follicular phase of the reproductive cycle in women: FSH levels during the follicular phase of the menstrual cycle have been reported to follow two slightly different patterns: 1. FSH levels rise to a peak very early, starting up even before the first day of menstruation that marks the end of the preceding cycle, and then decrease until the immediate preovulatory surge of FSH occurs (232, 266, 267, 271, 276, 285, 286) ; or 2. FSH levels rise in the early follicular phase and remain relatively steady until the preovulatory surge occurs (265, 287). The former seems to be the usual pattern. Characteristic of all patterns reported is the feature that FSH levels rise early in the follicular phase and become higher than at any other time in the cycle, except (in most cases) for the preovulatory peak itself. There is no rise in FSH levels immediately before the preovulatory estrogen surge. In fact, FSH levels are usually falling slowly at that time. However, the high FSH levels early in the follicular phase do form a pattern that might be expected to favor follicular maturation, and subsequent, delayed, but accelerating estrogen secretion, as a byproduct of follicular growth.

The pattern of LH concentration in plasma during the follicular phase of the menstrual cycle is slightly different from that of FSH. LH levels start to increase at about the first day of menstruation (265, 267, 272, 275), but after FSH levels have already begun to increase (285). The pattern also differs from that of FSH in that the levels do not decrease prior to the preovulatory surge, but increase slowly (266, 285).

Mean levels of both LH and FSH are higher in the follicular than in the luteal phase (232, 266, 267, 271, 284, 285). As in the case of FSH, there is no pulse of LH in the follicular phase that accounts for the preovulatory rise in estrogen secretion in humans, but rising LH levels may support follicular maturation.

Estrogen levels are lower during the follicular phase of the cycle than they are during the luteal phase (282, 288, 289). Progesterone levels are extremely low during the follicular phase, and higher during the luteal phase (266, 275, 277, 281). Progesterone production remains low until a corpus luteum is formed, and is not an important product of the maturing follicle, except, perhaps, just before ovulation (285) when the LH surge may provoke the follicle to start secreting it.

The maturing follicle produces both estrogen and 17α-OH-progesterone, an estrogen precursor. The plasma levels of the latter substance are seen to rise, along with estrogens, toward the end of the follicular phase (281, 285), probably as a consequence of follicular growth and increasing rates of estrogen production.

Plasma levels of hormones during the luteal phase in women: After ovulation, plasma levels of both LH and FSH fall steadily and slowly, until several days before the onset of menstruation, when FSH levels start to increase (285). LH levels fall throughout the whole luteal phase and do not rise until menstruation has started (285).

Immediately after the preovulatory surge, estrogen levels fall, but soon begin to increase again until a midluteal peak is achieved at the time that gonadotropin levels fall (282, 286, 289, 290). After the peak the levels decrease, and reach their nadir just before onset of menstruation. As the levels fall, FSH levels start to rise. Progesterone levels increase just after the LH peak, and rise to a midluteal phase peak and decline (285), in a way similar to that described for estrogen.

Circadian effects in women: Although a circadian rhythm in LH concentration has been reported (265) for the luteal phase, the hormone patterns described for all phases of the cycle do not depend upon time of day (285).

Hormonal levels in nonhuman species: As might be hoped, the relationships between LH, progesterone, and ovulation in the monkey appear to be the same as they are in the human (309, 310). The LH surge precedes both the rise in plasma progesterone levels and ovulation.

Plasma LH levels in the rat peak late in the afternoon of proestrus (236, 300–302), prior to ovulation which occurs in the early morning of the following day. An increased estrogen secretion rate may precede the LH peak by 8 hr (300). Less certain is the claim that progestin secretion rates (progesterone and 20α-hydroxy-pregn-4-ene-3-one, measured separately) increase on the afternoon of proestrus before plasma LH levels begin to rise (236). Simultaneous frequent measurements of plasma concentrations of gonadotropins, estrogens, and progestins have not been made in the rat. Causal relationships among these hormones, with respect to the process of ovulation, are therefore impossible to specify confidently. Plasma FSH (303) and prolactin (169, 304) also increase on the afternoon of proestrus, possibly starting up before the LH surge, but in the absence of simultaneous, frequent measurements we cannot be certain. Except for the fact that an LH surge seems to be required for ovulation in the rat, little else appears to be established about the hormonal preparations for ovulation and luteal formation. Schwartz has claimed that an increase in LH levels precedes the estrogen surge, which then causes the preovulatory LH surge (299).

Of the four hormones of major importance in the female reproductive cycle, only plasma LH has been measured frequently in the ewe. Plasma LH levels increase at the time of estrus (305–308). It is not yet certain whether an estrogen peak precedes the LH peak.

Luteolysis in women.—The events terminating the luteal period in the human are not known. We believe that senescence with functional failure after 10–14 days is an intrinsic property of the human corpus luteum, in the absence of fertilization of the egg and supplementary gonadotropin production by the trophoblast. In some species a luteolysin does seem to exist, and it may be a prostaglandin (261) or LH itself (224). The uterus may be a source of luteolytic activity in some species, but it is apparently not in humans (291).

Though neither the uterus nor prostaglandins provide luteolytic signals

TABLE 2. Proposed causal relationships in typical menstrual cycle

(Parentheses denote weak coupling and/or effects of doubtful significance)

Day of cycle	Stage	Event	Proximate cause
24–28	Late luteal; early follicular	End of luteal function—and sharp decline in E* and P* secretions Start of rise in FSH Start of maturation of a new crop of follicles	1. Instrinsic senescence process in human corpus luteum and previously ripened but unruptured follicles 2. Fall in levels of E (and P) with relaxation of feedback inhibition of FSH 3. Rise in FSH
1–5	Early follicular; menses	Menstruation; start of rise in LH Follicle beginning E secretion	4. Same as 2. The negative feedback inhibition of LH by E (and P) relaxes more slowly than that of FSH, when signal removed 5. Rising FSH (and LH) levels—strong coupling
6–12	Follicular	E secretion increasing FSH levels plateau, and start slow decline LH levels relatively steady, without slow decline	6. Semiautonomous, nonlinear, continued maturation of follicle. (The growth is now only weakly coupled to FSH and LH.) 7. Inhibitory feedback effect of rising E levels on FSH Stimulatory threshold not reached; half-life of FSH is long 8. Short LH half life requires higher production rate, so that less negative feedback sensitivity to E is observed for LH than FSH
13	Preovulatory	E secretion accelerating LH levels starting to rise again	9. Same as 6—nonlinear maturation 10. E levels reach rate-sensitive stimulatory feedback threshold for effects on LH, after delay
14	Preovulatory	FSH levels start to rise E secretion falling, P secretion starts	11. E levels reach stimulatory rate-sensitive feedback threshold for effects on FSH, after a delay 12. Starting P secretion transiently interferes with E synthesis. FSH stimulates P secretion
15	LH peak	Explosive rise in LH to peak; smaller rise in FSH to peak Rapid fall in LH and FSH from peak	13. Positive feedback stimulation sensitive to an increasing rate of rise of E—after a delay 14. Metabolism of LH and FSH, after positive, stimulatory derivative of E levels is over
16	Ovulatory	Ovulation Corpus luteum formation Increased P secretion, from luteinizing granulosa cells	15. Follicular rupture process initiated by LH (and FSH) surges 16. Ovulation 17. Corpus luteum maturation, strongly coupled to LH (and FSH) surges

* E =estradiol, P =progesterone.

TABLE 2. *(Continued)*

Day of cycle	Stage	Event	Proximate cause
17	Postovulatory Early luteal	E and P levels increasing	18. Corpus luteum and unruptured, ripened follicle crop continued maturation (now only weakly coupled to gonadotropins); previous inhibition of E secretion by start of P secretion ended
18–22	Luteal	E and P rising to midluteal peak	19. Same as 18
22–23	Midluteal	E and P at peak	20. Semiautonomous maturation of corpus luteum complete; spontaneous senescence of corpus luteum and previously ripened but unruptured follicles begins

in the normal menstrual cycle, prostaglandin $F_{2\alpha}$ may initiate labor (262) or abortion in pregnant women and the effect could be on the corpus luteum. The details are not yet clear. Biological effects of prostaglandins have been recently reviewed (292).

Causal chains of events in menstruation.—In Table 2 we have proposed a comprehensive account of causal relationships underlying the human menstrual cycle. Such a proposal involves much conjecture, but with the recent improvement in primary data in the field of reproductive physiology, the guesswork is diminishing. To be as useful as possible, our conclusions, based on the above literature review, are presented in detail, even though the details are not all equally defensible.

We believe it important to distrust unaided and untested intuitions when dealing with a subject as complicated as the nonlinear menstrual cycle. Therefore we have had the network of interrelationships in Table 2 severely tested by a computer simulation. The simulation has demonstrated the scheme to have at least the validity that it will cycle, and will start to do so from a variety of initial conditions. Furthermore, it is capable of generating all the relevant hormonal waveforms described in this review (personal communication from Gregory B. Yates). The successful simulation does not use or require a "clock" or timing pulse in the brain. The periodicity was intrinsic in the system itself.

Other mathematical models and simulations of the female reproductive cycle.—We have reviewed, and list below in chronological order, all other models of the female reproductive system of which we are aware. Unfortunately, it is not possible to describe the models briefly in any fair and useful manner. They vary greatly in purpose, form, function, and adequacy. On the basis of their published performance, none appears to generate the hormonal waveforms described in this review as exactly as our model, based upon the assumptions in Table 2, seems to do, although that of Vande Wiele et al (286) comes close. The models may be found in the following references: Lamport, 1940 (293); Rapoport, 1952 (294); Danziger & Elmergreen, 1957 (295); Horrobin, 1969 (296); Thompson, Horgan & Delfs, 1969 (297); Schwartz, 1969—rat estrous cycle (298); Schwartz, 1969—extension of previous model (180); Vande Wiele et al, 1970 (286); Schwartz, 1970—extension of her previous model (299).

We mention our unpublished model only to assure the reader that the postulations in Table 2 are actually capable of explaining the observed hormonal patterns. How correct these explanations are remains to be seen. In any case, computer simulations keep one from explaining too much with words used much too glibly.

Analysis of the reproductive cycle of women can be advanced by simulations based upon data obtained by more rapid sampling of blood, through several consecutive cycles, with accurate, simultaneous determinations of LH, FSH, estradiol, progesterone and prolactin in those samples. Hopefully, subjects can be found with stamina (and blood) enough.

Concluding Remarks

The scope of neuroendocrinology, which involves brain-adenohypophysial communication, now includes both the responses of the brain to hormones, with respect to feedback, morphogenetic and behavioral processes, and the responses of peripheral endocrine and metabolic systems to humoral agents released by the brain. The subject as a whole is beyond the capacities of a single review, and we regret the inevitable shortcomings of our account of the field. We expect that in the future, wiser reviewers will wish to cast their nets less broadly than we have done, and use a finer mesh. The minnows escaped us, but we hope the larger catch makes good digesting.

Our zeal for computer simulation as a means of testing networks of (often facile) verbal hypotheses serves us well, we think, in the section on Reproduction. Though we remained hard-headed mechanists to the end, as we survey what we have written about neuroendocrinology, we concede the aptness of William Beaumont's remark:

> The reader will perceive some slight seeming discrepancies, which he may find it difficult to reconcile; but he will recollect that the human machine is endowed with a vitality which modifies its movements in different states of the system, and probably produces some diversity of effects from the same causes.

ACKNOWLEDGMENTS

We wish to thank Miss Jeanette Blood for assistance in preparation of the manuscript, and Gregory B. Yates for carrying out the computer simulation. Work done in our laboratory was supported by United States Public Health Service grant AM 04612. Miss Russell and Mrs. Maran were supported by predoctoral fellowships from the National Institute of General Medical Sciences.

LITERATURE CITED

1. McCann, S. M., Porter, J. C. 1969. Hypothalamic pituitary stimulating and inhibiting hormones. *Physiol. Rev.* 49 :240–84
2. McCann, S. M., Dhariwal, A. P. S., Porter, J. C. 1968. Regulation of the adenohypophysis. *Ann. Rev. Physiol.* 30 :589–640
3. Meites, J., Ed. 1970. *Hypophysiotropic Hormones of the Hypothalamus: Assay and Chemistry.* Baltimore: Williams & Wilkins. 338 pp.
4. Haymaker, W., Anderson, E., Nauta, W. J. H., Eds. 1969. *The Hypothalamus.* Springfield, Ill: Thomas. 805 pp.
5. Burgus, R., Guillemin, R. 1970. Hypothalamic releasing factors. *Ann. Rev. Biochem.* 39 :499–526
6. Stear, E. B., Kadish, A. H., Eds. 1969. *Hormonal Control Systems,* Math. Biosci. Suppl. New York: American Elsevier. 304 pp.
7. Gual, C., Ebling, F. J. G., Eds. 1969. *Progr. Endocrinol.* Amsterdam: Exerpta Med. Int. Congr. Ser., Vol. 184. 1276 pp.
8. Armstrong, D. T. 1970. Reproduction. *Ann. Rev. Physiol.* 32 :439–70
9. Ganong, W. F., Martini, L., Eds. 1969. *Frontiers in Neuroendocrinology, 1969.* New York: Oxford Univ. Press. 442 pp.
10. Kumar, A. 1968. Sexual differences in the ependyma lining the third ventricle in the area of the anterior hypothalamus of adult rhesus monkeys. *Z. Zellforsch.* 90 :28–36
11. Voitkevich, A. A., Dedov, I. I. 1969. Neurovascular contacts of the median eminence of the neurohypophysis. *Dokl. Akad. Nauk SSR* 186 :373–76
12. Rodriguez, E. M. 1969. Ependymal specializations. I. Fine structure of the neural (internal) region of the toad median eminence, with particular reference to the connections between the ependymal cells and the subependymal capillary loops. *Z. Zellforsch.* 102 :153–71
13. Bergland, R. M., Torack, R. M. 1969. An electron microscopic study of the human infundibulum. *Z. Zellforsch.* 99 :1–12
14. Kobayashi, T., Yamamoto, K., Kaibara, M., Ajika, K. 1968. Electron microscopic observation on the hypothalamic-hypophyseal system in the rat. III. Effect of reserpine treatment on the axonal inclusions in the median eminence. *Endocrinol. Jap.* 15 :321–35
15. Duvernoy, H., Koritke, J. G. 1968. Les vaisseaux sous-épendymaires du recessus hypophysaire. *J. Hirnforsch.* 10 :227–45
16. Löfgren, F. 1959. New aspects of the hypothalamic control of the adenohypophysis. *Acta Morphol. Neer. Scand.* 2 :220–29
17. Kobayashi, H., Matsui, T. 1969. Fine structure of the median eminence and its functional significance. In *Frontiers in Neuroendocrinology, 1969,* ed. W. F. Ganong, L. Martini, 3–46. New York: Oxford Univ. Press. 442 pp.
18. Nakane, P. K. 1970. Classifications of anterior pituitary cell types with immunoenzyme histochemistry. *J. Histochem. Cytochem.* 18: 9–20
19. Ishikawa, H. 1969. Isolation of different types of anterior pituitary cells in rats. *Endocrinol. Jap.* 16 :517–29
20. Yoshimura, F., Harumiya, K., Ishikawa, H., Ohtsuka, Y. 1969. Differentiation of isolated chromophobes into acidophils or basophils when transplanted into the hypophysiotrophic area of hypothalamus. *Endocrinol. Jap.* 16 :531–40
21. Milligan, J. V., Kraicer, J. 1970. Adenohypophysial transmembrane potentials; polarity reversal by elevated external potassium ion concentration. *Science* 167 :182–84
22. Kraicer, J., Milligan, J. V., Gosbee, J. L., Conrad, R. G., Branson, C. M. 1969. *In vitro* release of ACTH: Effects of potassium, calcium and corticosterone. *Endocrinology* 85 :1144–53
23. MacLeod, R. M., Fontham, E. H. 1970. Influence of ionic environment on the in vitro synthesis and release of pituitary hormones. *Endocrinology* 86 :863–69
24. Siperstein, E. R., Miller, K. J. 1970.

Further cytophysiologic evidence for the identity of the cells that produce adrenocorticotrophic hormone. *Endocrinology* 86:451–86

25. Nakayama, I., Nickerson, P. A., Skelton, F. R. 1969. An ultrastructural study of the adrenocorticotrophic hormone-secreting cell in the rat adenohypophysis during adrenal cortical regeneration. *Lab. Invest.* 21:169–78

26. Baker, B. L., Pek, S., Midgley, A. R., Jr., Gersten, B. E. 1970. Identification of the corticotropin cell in rat hypophyses with peroxidase-labeled antibody. *Anat. Rec.* 166:557–67

27. Mialhe-Voloss, C., Baulieu, É.-É. 1958. Étude qualitative des corticostéroides libérés par la surrénale du rat *in vitro* sous l'influence des hormones corticotropes antehypophysaire et posthypophysaire. *C. R. Acad. Sci.* 246:639–42

28. Gosbee, J. L., Kraicer, J., Kastin, A. J., Schally, A. V. 1970. Functional relationship between the pars intermedia and ACTH secretion in the rat. *Endocrinology* 86:560–67

29. Porter, J. C., Mical, R. S., Tippit, P. R., Drane, J. W. 1970. Effect of selective surgical interruption of the anterior pituitary's blood supply on ACTH release. *Endocrinology* 86:590–99

30. Dhariwal, A. P. S., Russell, S. M., McCann, S. M., Yates, F. E. 1969. Assay of corticotropin-releasing factors by injection into the anterior pituitary of intact rats. *Endocrinology* 84:544–56

31. Porter, J. C. 1969. Site of corticotropin-releasing factor (CRF) releasing elements: Effect of lesions on ACTH release and adenohypophysial blood flow. *Endocrinology* 84:1398–403

32. Mulder, A. H., Geuze, J. J., deWied, D. 1970. Studies on the subcellular localization of corticotrophin releasing factor (CRF) and vasopressin in the median eminence of the rat. *Endocrinology* 87:61–79

33. Hiroshige, T., Sato, T., Ohta, R., Itoh, S. 1969. Increase of corticotropin-releasing activity in the rat hypothalamus following noxious stimuli. *Jap. J. Physiol.* 19:866–75

34. Hiroshige, T., Sakakura, M., Itoh, S. 1969. Diurnal variation of corticotropin-releasing activity in the rat

hypothalamus. *Endocrinol. Jap.* 16:465–69

35. David-Nelson, M. A., Brodish, A. 1969. Evidence for a diurnal rhythm of corticotrophin-releasing factor (CRF) in the hypothalamus. *Endocrinology* 85:861–66

36. Chan, L. T., deWied, D., Saffran, M. 1969. Comparison of assays for corticotrophin-releasing activity. *Endocrinology* 84:967–72

37. DeWied, D., Witter, A., Versteeg, D. H. G., Mulder, A. H. 1969. Release of ACTH by substances of central nervous system origin. *Endocrinology* 85:561–69

38. Russell, S. M., Dhariwal, A. P. S., McCann, S. M., Yates, F. E. 1969. Inhibition by dexamethasone of the *in vivo* pituitary response to corticotropin-releasing factor (CRF). *Endocrinology* 85:512–21

39. Gonzalez-Luque, A., L'Age, M., Dhariwal, A. P. S., Yates, F. E. 1970. Stimulation of corticotropin release by corticotropin-releasing factor (CRF) or by vasopressin following intrapituitary infusions in unanesthetized dogs: Inhibition of the responses by dexamethasone. *Endocrinology* 86:1134–42

40. Yates, F. E. et al 1971. Potentiation by vasopressin of corticotropin release induced by corticotropin-releasing factor. *Endocrinology.* In press

41. Guillemin, R., Schally, A., Andersen, R., Lipscomb, H., Long, J. 1960. Sur l'existence de deux types de substances à activité hypophysiotrope: α-CRF et β-CRF. *C. R. Acad. Sci.* 250:4462–64

42. Arimura, A., Schally, A. V., Bowers, C. Y. 1969. Corticotropin releasing activity of lysine vasopressin analogues. *Endocrinology* 84:579–83

43. Lutz, B., Koch, B., Mialhe, C. 1969. Libération des hormones antidiurétique et corticotrope au cours de différents types d'agression chez le rat. *Hormone Metab. Res.* 1:213–17

44. Czakó, L., László, F., Kovács, K., Faredin, I., Tóth, I. 1969. Diurnal variations of the plasma cortisol level in diabetes insipidus. *Acta Med. Acad. Sci. Hung.* 26:197–202

45. Fleischer, N., Donald, R. A., Butcher, R. W. 1969. Involvement of adenosine 3',5'-monophosphate in

release of ACTH. *Am. J. Physiol.* 217:1287–91

46. Arimura, A., Bowers, C. Y., Schally, A. V., Saito, M., Miller, M. C. III 1969. Effect of corticotropin-releasing factor, dexamethasone and actinomycin D on the release of ACTH from rat pituitaries *in vivo* and *in vitro*. *Endocrinology* 85:300–11

47. Coyne, M. D., Kitay, J. I. 1969. Effect of ovariectomy on pituitary secretion of ACTH. *Endocrinology* 85:1097–102

48. Brodish, A. 1969. Effect of hypothalamic lesions on the time course of corticosterone secretion. *Neuroendocrinology* 5:33–47

49. Dunn, J., Critchlow, V. 1969. Pituitary-adrenal response to stress in rats with hypothalamic islands. *Brain Res.* 16:395–403

50. Palka, Y., Coyer, D., Critchlow, V. 1969. Effects of isolation of medial basal hypothalamus on pituitary-adrenal and pituitary ovarian functions. *Neuroendocrinology* 5:333–49

51. Feldman, S., Conforti, N., Chowers, I., Davidson, J. M. 1970. Pituitary-adrenal activation in rats with medial basal hypothalamic islands. *Acta Endocrinol.* 63:405–14

52. Makara, G. B., Stark, E., Palkovits, M., Révész, T., Mihály, K. 1969. Afferent pathways of stressful stimuli: corticotrophin release after partial deafferentation of the medial basal hypothalamus. *J. Endocrinol.* 44:187–93

53. Gibbs, F. P. 1969. Central nervous system lesions that block release of ACTH caused by traumatic stress. *Am. J. Physiol.* 217:78–83

54. Gibbs, F. P. 1969. Area of pons necessary for traumatic stress-induced ACTH release under pentobarbital anesthesia. *Am. J. Physiol.* 217:84–88

55. Kendall, J. W., Allen, C. 1968. Studies on the glucocorticoid feedback control of ACTH secretion. *Endocrinology* 82:397–405

56. Sirett, N. E., Kendall, J. W. 1969. Hypothalamic control of ACTH release from ectopic pituitary glands. *Endocrinology* 85:784–88

57. Kendall, J. W., Roth, J. G. 1969. Adrenocortical function in monkeys after forebrain removal or pituitary

stalk section. *Endocrinology* 84:686–91

58. Taylor, A. N. 1969. The role of the reticular activating system in the regulation of ACTH secretion. *Brain Res.* 13:234–46

59. Redgate, E. S. 1970. ACTH release evoked by electrical stimulation of brain stem and limbic system sites in the cat: the absence of ACTH release upon infundibular area stimulation. *Endocrinology* 86:806–23

60. Greer, M. A., Allen, C. F., Gibbs, F. P., Gullickson, C. 1970. Pathways at the hypothalamic level through which traumatic stress activates ACTH secretion. *Endocrinology* 86:1404–9

61. Hodges, J. R., Vernikos, J. 1959. Circulating corticotrophin in normal and adrenalectomized rats after stress. *Acta Endocrinol.* 30:188–96

62. Kitay, J. I., Holub, D. A., Jailer, J. W. 1959. Inhibition of pituitary ACTH release: An extra-adrenal action of exogenous ACTH. *Endocrinology* 64:475–82

63. Dallman, M. F., Yates, F. E. 1968. Anatomical and functional mapping of central neural input and feedback pathways of the adrenocortical system. *Mem. Soc. Endocrinol.* 17:39–72

64. Stark, E., Ács, Z., Szalay, K. S. 1969. Further studies on the hypophyseal-adrenocortical response to various stressing procedures in ACTH-treated rats. *Acta Physiol.* 36:55–61

65. Motta, M., Sterescu, N., Piva, F., Martini, L. 1969. The participation of "short" feedback mechanisms in the control of ACTH and TSH secretion. *Acta Neurol. Psychiat. Belg.* 69:501–7

66. Kendall, J. W. 1971. Feedback control of ACTH secretion. In *Frontiers in Neuroendocrinology, 1971.* New York: Oxford Univ. Press. In press

67. Kendall, J. W., Grimm, Y., Shimshak, G. 1969. Relation of cerebrospinal fluid circulation to the ACTH-suppressing effects of corticosteroid implants in the rat brain. *Endocrinology* 85:200–8

68. Steiner, F. A., Ruf, K., Akert, K. 1969. Steroid-sensitive neurones in rat brain: Anatomical localization and responses to neuro-

humours and ACTH. *Brain Res.* 12:74–85

69. Hedge, G. A., Smelik, P. G. 1969. The action of dexamethasone and vasopressin on hypothalamic CRF production and release. *Neuroendocrinology* 4:242–53

70. Dallman, M. F., Yates, F. E. 1969. Dynamic asymmetries in the corticosteroid feedback path and distribution-metabolism-binding elements of the adrenocortical system. *Ann. N.Y. Acad. Sci.* 156:696–721

71. Fleischer, N., Rawls, W. 1970. Adrenocorticotropin (ACTH) synthesis and release in rat pituitary monolayer culture: The effect of dexamethasone. *Endocrinology.* In press

72. Yates, F. E., Brennan, R. D., Urquhart, J. 1969. Adrenal glucocorticoid control system. *Fed. Proc.* 28:71–83

73. Zimmermann, E., Critchlow, V. 1969. Suppression of pituitary-adrenal function with physiological plasma levels of corticosterone. *Neuroendocrinology* 5:183–92

74. Zimmermann, E., Critchlow, V. 1969. Negative feedback and pituitary-adrenal function in female rats. *Am. J. Physiol.* 216:148–55

75. Ceresa, F., Angeli, A., Boccuzzi, G., Molino, G. 1969. Once-a-day neurally stimulated and basal ACTH secretion phases in man and their response to corticoid inhibition. *J. Clin. Endocrinol. Metab.* 29:1074–82

76. Sirett, N. E., Gibbs, F. P. 1969. Dexamethasone suppression of ACTH release: effect of the interval between steroid administration and the application of stimuli known to release ACTH. *Endocrinology* 85:355–59

77. Yates, F. E., Brennan, R. D. 1969. Study of the mammalian adrenal glucocorticoid system by computer simulation. In *Hormonal Control Systems*, Math. Biosci. Suppl., ed. E. B. Stear, A. H. Kadish, 20–87. New York: American Elsevier. 304 pp.

78. Urquhart, J., Li, C. C. 1969. Dynamic testing and modeling of adrenocortical secretory function. *Ann. N.Y. Acad. Sci.* 156:756–78

79. Asfeldt, U. H., Buhl, J. 1969. Inhibitory effect of diphenylhydantoin on the feedback control of cortico-trophin release. *Acta Endocrinol.* 61:551–60

80. French, F. S., Macfie, J. A., Baggett, B., Williams, T. F., Van Wyk, J. J. 1969. Cushing's syndrome with a paradoxical response to dexamethasone. *Am. J. Med.* 47:619–24

81. Brown, G. M., Grota, L. S., Penney, D. P., Reichlin, S. 1970. Pituitary-adrenal function in the squirrel monkey. *Endocrinology* 86:519–29

82. McEwen, B. S., Weiss, J. M., Schwartz, L. S. 1969. Uptake of corticosterone by rat brain and its concentration by certain limbic structures. *Brain Res.* 16:227–41

83. McEwen, B. S., Weiss, J. M., Schwartz, L. S. 1970. Retention of corticosterone by cell nuclei from brain regions of adrenalectomized rats. *Brain Res.* 17:471–82

84. McEwen, B. S., Plopinger, L. 1970. Association of ³H-corticosterone 1,2 with macromolecules extracted from brain cell nuclei. *Nature* 226:263–65

85. Orth, D. N., Island, D. P. 1969. Light synchronization of the circadian rhythm in plasma cortisol (17-OHCS) concentration in man. *J. Clin. Endocrinol.* 29:479–86

86. Haus, E., Halberg, F. 1970. Circannual rhythm in level and timing of serum corticosterone in standardized inbred mature C-mice. *Environ. Res.* 3:81–106

87. Hellman, L. et al 1970. Cortisol is secreted episodically by normal man. *J. Clin. Endocrinol. Metab.* 30:411–22

88. Hellman, L. et al 1970. Cortisol is secreted episodically in Cushing's syndrome. *J. Clin. Endocrinol. Metab.* 30:686–89

89. Berson, S. A., Yalow, R. S. 1968. Radioimmunoassay of ACTH in plasma. *J. Clin. Invest.* 47:2725–51

90. Guillemin, R., Yamazaki, E., Jutisz, M., Sakiz, E. 1962. Présence dans un extrait de tissus hypothalamiques d'une substance stimulant la secretion de l'hormone hypophysaire thyréotrope (TSH). Première purification par filtration sur gel Sephadex. *C. R. Acad. Sci.* 255:1018–20

91. Schally, A. V., Bowers, C. Y., Redding, T. W., Barrett, J. F. 1966.

Isolation of thyrotropin releasing factor (TRF) from porcine hypothalamus. *Biochem. Biophys. Res. Commun.* 25 :165–69

92. Schally, A. V., Redding, T. W., Bowers, C. Y., Barrett, J. F. 1969. Isolation and properties of porcine thyrotropin-releasing hormone. *J. Biol. Chem.* 244 :4077–88

93. Burgus, R. et al 1970. Characterization of ovine hypothalamic hypophysiotropic TSH-releasing factor. *Nature* 226 :321–25

94. Schally, A. V. et al 1968. Hypothalamic neurohormones regulating anterior pituitary function. *Rec. Progr. Hormone Res.* 24 :497–588

95. Burgus, R. et al 1969. Dérivés polypeptidiques de synthèse doués d'activité hypophysiotrope TRF. *C. R. Acad. Sci.* 268 :2116–18

96. Burgus, R., Dunn, T. F., Desiderio, D., Vale, W., Guillemin, R. 1969. Dérivés polypeptidiques de synthèse doués d'activité hypophysiotrope TRF. Nouvelles observations. *C. R. Acad. Sci.* 269 :226–28

97. Burgus, R., Dunn, T. F., Desiderio, D., Guillemin, R. 1969. Structure moléculaire du facteur hypothalamique hypophysiotrope TRF d'origine ovine : mise en évidence par spectrométrie de masse de la séquence PCA-His-Pro-NH₂. *C. R. Acad. Sci.* 269 :1870–73

98. Folkers, K., Enzmann, F., Bøler, J., Bowers, C. Y., Schally, A. V. 1969. Discovery of modification of the synthetic tripeptide-sequence of the thyrotropin releasing hormone having activity. *Biochem. Biophys. Res. Commun.* 37 :123–26

99. Nair, R. M. G., Barrett, J. F., Bowers, C. Y., Schally, A. V. 1970. Structure of porcine thyrotropin releasing hormone. *Biochemistry* 9 :1103–6

100. Burgus, R. et al 1970. Biological activity of synthetic polypeptide derivatives related to the structure of hypothalamic TRF. *Endocrinology* 86 :573–82

101. Bowers, C. Y., Schally, A. V., Enzmann, F., Bøler, J., Folkers, K. 1970. Porcine thyrotropin releasing hormone is (Pyro)Glu-His-Pro-NH₂. *Endocrinology* 86 :1143–53

102. Folkers, K. et al 1970. Synthesis and relationship of L-glutaminyl-L-histidyl-L-prolinamide to the thyrotropin releasing hormone. *Biochem.*

Biophys. Res. Commun. 39 :110–13

103. Redding, T. W., Schally, A. V. 1969. Studies on the inactivation of thyrotropin-releasing hormone (TRH). *Proc. Soc. Exp. Biol. Med.* 131 :415–20

104. Amoss, M., Burgus, R., Ward, D. N., Fellows, R. E., Guillemin, R. 1970. Evidence for a pyroglutamic acid (PCA) N-terminus in ovine hypothalamic luteinizing hormone-releasing factor (LRF). *Program 52nd Meet. Endocrine Soc.*, p. 61 (Abstract)

105. Mittler, J. C., Redding, T. W., Schally, A. V. 1969. Stimulation of thyrotropin (TSH) secretion by TSH-releasing factor (TRF) in organ cultures of anterior pituitary. *Proc. Soc. Exp. Biol. Med.* 130 : 406–12

106. Wilber, J. F., Peake, G. T., Utiger, R. D. 1969. Thyrotropin release in vitro : stimulation by cyclic 3′-5′-adenosine monophosphate. *Endocrinology* 84 :758–60

107. Steiner, A. L., Peake, G. T., Utiger, R. D., Karl, I. E., Kipnis, D. M. 1970. Hypothalamic stimulation of growth hormone and thyrotropin release in vitro and pituitary 3′,5′-adenosine cyclic monophosphate. *Endocrinology* 86 :1354–60

108. Cehovic, G. 1969. Rôle de l'adénosine 3′-5′-monophosphate-cyclique dans la libération de TSH hypophyaire. *C. R. Acad. Sci.* 268 :2929–31

109. Hall, R., Amos, J., Garry, R., Buxton, R. L. 1970. Thyroid-stimulating hormone response to synthetic thyrotrophin-releasing hormone in man. *Brit. Med. J.* 1 :274–77

110. Vale, W., Burgus, R., Dunn, T. F., Guillemin, R. 1970. Release of TSH by oral administration of synthetic peptide derivatives with TRF activity. *J. Clin. Endocrinol.* 30 :148–50

111. Averill, R. L. W. 1969. Responses to thyrotropin-releasing factor (TRF) by intrapituitary infusion of hypothalamic extracts. *Endocrinology* 84 :514–19

112. Averill, R. L. W. 1969. Depression of thyrotropin-releasing factor induction of thyrotropin release by thyroxine in small doses. *Endocrinology* 85 :67–71

113. Suematsu, H., Matsuda, K., Shizume, K., Nakao, K. 1969. Thyroid response to acute reduction of cir-

culating thyroid hormone level. *Endocrinology* 84:1161–65

114. Suematsu, H., Matsuda, K., Shizume, K., Nakao, K. 1970. Effect of plasmapheresis on thyroid hormone secretion. *Endocrinology* 86:1281–86

115. Yates, F. E., Brown-Grant, K. 1969. A new look at classical endocrine feedback loops. *Excerpta Med. Int. Congr. Ser.* 184:515–22

116. Kajihara, A., Kendall, J. W. 1969. Studies on the hypothalamic control of TSH secretion. *Neuroendocrinology* 5:53–63

117. Thomas, S., Anand, B. K. 1970. Effect of electrical stimulation of the hypothalamus on thyroid secretion in monkeys. *J. Neurovisc. Relat.* 31:399–408

118. Martin, J. B., Reichlin, S. 1970. Thyrotropin secretion in rats after hypothalamic electrical stimulation or injection of synthetic TSH-releasing factor. *Science* 168:1366–68

119. Li, C. H., Dixon, J. S., Liu, W.-K. 1969. Human pituitary growth hormone XIX: The primary structure of the hormone. *Arch. Biochem. Biophys.* 133:70–91

120. Sonenberg, M., Dellacha, J. M., Free, C. A., Nadler, A. C. 1969. Growth hormone activity in man of chymotryptic digests of bovine growth hormone. *J. Endocrinol.* 44:255–65

121. Frohman, L. A., Bernardis, L. L. 1970. Growth hormone secretion in the rat: metabolic clearance and secretion rates. *Endocrinology* 86:305–12

122. Smith, G. P., Root, A. W. 1968. Plasma growth hormone and 17-OH-CS responses to hypothalamic and hippocampal stimulation in conscious monkeys. *Fed. Proc.* 27:319 (Abstract)

123. Nayak, R., McGarry, E. E., Beck, J. C. 1970. Studies with fluorescein-conjugated antisera to growth hormone. III. Localization and inhibition studies with antisera to porcine growth hormone. *Can. J. Physiol. Pharmacol.* 48:39–42

124. Baker, B. L., Midgley, A. R., Jr., Gersten, B. E., Yu, Y.-Y. 1969. Differentiation of growth hormone- and prolactin-containing acidophils with peroxidase-labeled antibody. *Anat. Rec.* 164:163–67

125. Conway, L. W., Schalch, D. S., Utiger, R. D., Reichlin, S. 1969. Hormones in human pituitary sinusoid blood: concentration of LH, GH and TSH. *J. Clin. Endocrinol. Metab.* 29:446–56

126. Schally, A. V. et al 1969. Isolation of growth hormone-releasing hormone (GRH) from porcine hypothalami. *Endocrinology* 84:1493–506

127. Mittler, J. C., Sawano, S., Wakabayashi, I., Redding, T. W., Schally, A. V. 1970. Stimulation of release and synthesis of growth hormone (GH) in tissue cultures of anterior pituitaries in response to GH-releasing hormone (GH-RH). *Proc. Soc. Exp. Biol. Med.* 133:890–93

128. Krulich, L., McCann, S. M. 1969. Effect of GH-releasing factor and GH-inhibiting factor on the release and concentration of GH in pituitaries incubated *in vitro*. *Endocrinology* 85:319–24

129. Müller, E. E., Pecile, A., Naimzada, M. K., Ferrario, G. 1969. The involvement of cyclic 3′,5′-adenosine monophosphate in the growth hormone release mechanism(s). *Experientia* 25:750–51

130. Couch, E. F., Arimura, A., Schally, A. V., Saito, M., Sawano, S. 1969. Electron microscope studies of somatotrophs of rat pituitary after injection of purified growth hormone releasing factor (GRF). *Endocrinology* 85:1084–91

131. Bancroft, F. C., Levine, L., Tashjian, A. H., Jr. 1969. Control of growth hormone production by a clonal strain of rat pituitary cells. Stimulation by hydrocortisone. *J. Cell Biol.* 43:432–41

132. Peng, M.-T., Pi, W.-P., Wu, C.-I. 1969. Growth hormone secretion by pituitary grafts under the median eminence or renal capsule. *Endocrinology* 85:360–65

133. Beddow, D. G., McCann, S. M. 1969. Effect of median eminence lesions on the function of multiple pituitary homografts with particular reference to the secretion of gonadotrophins and growth hormone. *Endocrinology* 84:595–605

134. Krulich, L., Dhariwal, A. P. S., McCann, S. M. 1968. Stimulatory and inhibitory effects of purified hypothalamic extracts on growth hormone release from rat pituitary *in vitro*. *Endocrinology* 83:783–90

135. Katz, H. P., Grumbach, M. M., Kap-

lan, S. L. 1969. Diminished growth hormone response to arginine in the puerperium. *J. Clin. Endocrinol. Metab.* 29:1414–19

136. Katz, S. H., Molitch, M., McCann, S. M. 1969. Effect of hypothalamic implants of GH on anterior pituitary weight and GH concentration. *Endocrinology* 85:725–34

137. Sakuma, M., Knobil, E. 1970. Inhibition of endogenous growth hormone secretion by exogenous growth hormone infusion in the Rhesus monkey. *Endocrinology* 86:890–94

138. Müller, E. E., Pecile, A., Felin, M., Cocchi, D. 1970. Norepinephrine and dopamine injection into lateral brain ventricle of the rat and growth hormone-releasing activity in the hypothalamus and plasma. *Endocrinology* 86:1376–82

139. Parker, D. C., Sassin, J. F., Mace, J. W., Gotlin, R. W., Rossman, L. G. 1969. Human growth hormone release during sleep: electroencephalographic correlation. *J. Clin. Endocrinol. Metab.* 29:871–74

140. Tsushima, T., Matsuzaki, F., Irie, M. 1970. Effect of heparin administration on plasma growth hormone concentrations. *Proc. Soc. Exp. Biol. Med.* 133:1084–87

141. Blackard, W. G., Boylen, C. T., Hinson, T. C., Nelson, N. C. 1969. Effect of lipid and ketone infusions on insulin-induced growth hormone elevations in rhesus monkeys. *Endocrinology* 85:1180–85

142. Roth, J., Glick, S. M., Yalow, R. S., Berson, S. A. 1963. Hypoglycemia: a potent stimulus to secretion of growth hormone. *Science* 140:987–88

143. Abrams, R. L., Parker, M. L., Blanco, S., Reichlin, S., Daughaday, W. H. 1966. Hypothalamic regulation of growth hormone secretion. *Endocrinology* 78:605–13

144. Merimee, T. J., Rabinowitz, D., Fineberg, S. E. 1969. Arginine-initiated release of human growth hormone. *N. Engl. J. Med.* 280:1434–38

145. Merimee, T. J., Fineberg, S. E., Tyson, J. E. 1969. Fluctuations of human growth hormone secretion during menstrual cycle: Response to arginine. *Metabolism* 18:606–8

146. Fiedler, A. J., Tyson, J. E., Merimee, T. J. 1969. Arginine-induced growth hormone release after clomiphene treatment. *J. Clin. Endocrinol. Metab.* 29:1110–13

147. Sakuma, M., Knobil, E. 1970. Failure of high rates of glucocorticoid infusion to inhibit growth hormone secretion in the Rhesus monkey. *Endocrinology* 86:895–97

148. Parra, A., Schultz, R. B., Foley, T. P., Jr., Blizzard, R. M. 1970. Influence of epinephrine-propranolol infusions on growth hormone release in normal and hypopituitary subjects. *J. Clin. Endocrinol. Metab.* 30:134–37

149. Werrbach, J. H., Gale, C. C., Goodner, C. J., Conway, M. J. 1970. Effects of autonomic blocking agents on growth hormone, insulin, free fatty acids and glucose in baboons. *Endocrinology* 86:77–82

150. Toviola, P., Gale, C. C., Werrbach, J. H., Goodner, C. J. 1969. Intrahypothalamic infusion of biogenic amines: effect on temperature regulation and neuroendocrine function in baboons. *Physiologist* 12:377 (Abstract)

151. Bern, H. A., Nicoll, C. S. 1968. The comparative endocrinology of prolactin. *Rec. Progr. Hormone Res.* 24:681–713

152. Li, C. H., Dixon, J. S., Lo, T.-B., Pankov, Y. A., Schmidt, K. D. 1969. Amino-acid sequence of ovine lactogenic hormone. *Nature* 224:695–96

153. Bewley, T. A., Li, C. H. 1970. Primary structures of human pituitary growth hormone and sheep pituitary lactogenic hormone compared. *Science* 168:1361–62

154. Nicoll, C. S., Parsons, J. A., Fiorindo, R. P., Nichols, C. W., Jr., Sakuma, M. 1970. Evidence of independent secretion of prolactin and growth hormone in vitro by adenohypophysis of Rhesus monkeys. *J. Clin. Endocrinol. Metab.* 30:512–19

155. Chen, C. L., Bixler, E. J., Weber, A. I., Meites, J. 1968. Hypothalamic stimulation of prolactin release from the pituitary of turkey hens and poults. *Gen. Comp. Endocrinol.* 11:489–94

156. Pasteels, J. L. 1961. Premiers résultats de culture combinée in vitro d'hypophyse et d'hypothalamus dans le but d'en apprécier la sécrétion de prolactine. *C. R. Acad. Sci.* 253:3074–75

157. Talwalker, P. K., Ratner, A., Meites, J. 1963. In vitro inhibition of pituitary prolactin synthesis and release by hypothalamic extract. *Am. J. Physiol.* 205:213–18

158. Mishkinsky, J., Khazen, K., Sulman, F. G. 1968. Prolactin-releasing activity of the hypothalamus in post-partum rats. *Endocrinology* 82:611–13

159. Nicoll, C. S., Fiorindo, R. P., McKennee, C. T., Parsons, J. A. 1970. Assay of hypothalamic factors which regulate prolactin secretion. In *Hypophysiotropic Hormones of the Hypothalamus: Assay and Chemistry*, ed. J. Meites, 115–50. Baltimore: Williams & Wilkins. 338 pp.

160. MacLeod, R. M. 1969. Influence of norepinephrine and catecholamine-depleting agents on the synthesis and release of prolactin and growth hormone. *Endocrinology* 85:916–23

161. Birge, C. A., Jacobs, L. S., Hammer, C. T., Daughaday, W. H. 1970. Catecholamine inhibition of prolactin secretion by isolated rat adenohypophyses. *Endocrinology* 86:120–30

162. Chen, C. L., Meites, J. 1970. Effects of estrogen and progesterone on serum and pituitary prolactin levels in ovariectomized rats. *Endocrinology* 86:503–5

163. Kanematsu, S., Sawyer, C. H. 1963. Effects of intrahypothalamic and intrahypophysial estrogen implants on pituitary prolactin and lactation in the rabbit. *Endocrinology* 72:243–52

164. Ramirez, V. D., McCann, S. M. 1964. Induction of prolactin secretion by implants of estrogen into the hypothalamo-hypophysial region of female rats. *Endocrinology* 75:206–14

165. Nagasawa, H., Chen, C. L., Meites, J. 1969. Effects of estrogen implant in median eminence on serum and pituitary prolactin levels in the rat. *Proc. Soc. Exp. Biol. Med.* 132:859–61

166. Chen, C. L., Meites, J. 1969. Effects of thyroxine and thiouracil on hypothalamic PIF and pituitary prolactin levels. *Proc. Soc. Exp. Biol. Med.* 131:576–78

167. Meites, J., Nicoll, C. S. 1962. In vivo and in vitro effects of steroids on pituitary prolactin secretion. In *Hormonal Steroids. Biochemistry,*

Pharmacology, and Therapeutics, ed. L. Martini, A. Pecile. 2:307–16. New York & London: Academic. 673 pp.

168. Sar, M., Meites, J. 1968. Effects of progesterone, testosterone, and cortisol on hypothalamic prolactin-inhibiting factor and pituitary prolactin content. *Proc. Soc. Exp. Biol. Med.* 127:426–29

169. Amenomori, Y., Chen, C. L., Meites, J. 1970. Serum prolactin levels in rats during different reproductive states. *Endocrinology* 86:506–10

170. Voogt, J. L., Clemens, J. A., Meites, J. 1969. Stimulation of pituitary FSH release in immature female rats by prolactin implant in the median eminence. *Neuroendocrinology* 4:157–63

171. Clemens, J. A., Minaguchi, H., Storey, R., Voogt, J. L., Meites, J. 1969. Induction of precocious puberty in female rats by prolactin. *Neuroendocrinology* 4:150–56

172. Voogt, J. L., Chen, C. L., Meites, J. 1970. Serum and pituitary prolactin levels before, during, and after puberty in female rats. *Am. J. Physiol.* 218:396–99

173. Clemens, J. A., Sar, M., Meites, J. 1969. Termination of pregnancy in rats by a prolactin implant in median eminence. *Proc. Soc. Exp. Biol. Med.* 130:628–30

174. Mishkinsky, J., Nir, I., Sulman, F. G. 1969. Internal feedback of prolactin in the rat. *Neuroendocrinology* 5:48–52

175. Clemens, J. A., Sar, M., Meites, J. 1969. Inhibition of lactation and luteal function in postpartum rats by hypothalamic implantation of prolactin. *Endocrinology* 84:868–72

176. Voogt, J., Meites, M. S., Meites, J. 1970. Serum prolactin, LH and FSH in female rats implanted with prolactin in median eminence (ME). *Program 52nd Meet. Endocrine Soc.,* 124 (Abstract)

177. Chen, C. L., Voogt, J. L., Meites, J. 1968. Effect of median eminence implants of FSH, LH or prolactin on luteal function in the rat. *Endocrinology* 83:1273–77

178. Everett, J. W. 1969. Neuroendocrine aspects of mammalian reproduction. *Ann. Rev. Physiol.* 31:383–416

179. Harris, G. W., Naftolin, F. 1970. The hypothalamus and control of ovulation. *Brit. Med. Bull.* 26:3–9

180. Schwartz, N. B. 1969. A model for the regulation of ovulation in the rat. *Rec. Progr. Hormone Res.* 25: 1–55

181. Davidson, J. M., Bloch, G. J. 1969. Neuroendocrine aspects of male reproduction. *Biol. Reprod. Suppl.* 1:67–92

182. Geschwind, I. I. 1969. Mechanism of action of releasing factors. In *Frontiers in Neuroendocrinology, 1969*, ed. W. F. Ganong, L. Martini. 389–431. New York: Oxford Univ. Press. 442 pp.

183. Barraclough, C. A. 1968. Alterations in reproductive function following prenatal and early postnatal exposure to hormones. *Advan. Reprod. Physiol.* 3:81–112

184. Fuxe, K., Hökfelt, T. 1969. Catecholamines in the hypothalamus and the pituitary gland. In *Frontiers in Neuroendocrinology, 1969*, ed. W. F. Ganong, L. Martini, 47–96. New York: Oxford Univ. Press. 442 pp.

185. Sawyer, C. H., Gorski, R., Eds. 1971. *Steroid Hormones and Brain Function.* Los Angeles: Univ. of California Press. In press

186. Iberall, A. S., Cardon, S. Z. 1964. Control in biological systems — a physical review. *Ann. N.Y. Acad. Sci.* 117:445–515

187. McCann, S. M., Crighton, D. B., Watanabe, S., Dhariwal, A. P. S., Watson, J. T. 1969. Regulation of gonadotrophin and prolactin secretion. In *Hormonal Control Systems*, Math. Biosci. Suppl., ed. E. B. Stear, A. H. Kadish, 193–228. New York: American Elsevier. 304 pp.

188. Terasawa, E., Kawakami, M., Sawyer, C. H. 1969. Induction of ovulation by electrochemical stimulation in androgenized and spontaneously constant-estrous rats. *Proc. Soc. Exp. Biol. Med.* 132:497–501

189. Köves, K., Halász, B. 1969. Data on the location of the neural structures indispensable for the occurrence of ovarian compensatory hypertrophy. *Neuroendocrinology* 4:1–11

190. Taleisnik, S., Velasco, M. E., Astrada, J. J. 1970. Effect of hypothalamic deafferentation on the control of luteinizing hormone secretion. *J. Endocrinol.* 46:1–7

191. McCann, S. M., Ramirez, V. D. 1964. The neuroendocrine regulation of hypophyseal luteinizing hormone secretion. *Rec. Progr. Hormone Res.* 20:131–81

192. Smith, E. R., Davidson, J. M. 1968. Role of estrogen in the cerebral control of puberty in female rats. *Endocrinology* 82:100–8

193. Döcke, F., Dörner, G. 1965. The mechanism of the induction of ovulation by oestrogens. *J. Endocrinol.* 33:491–99

194. Attramadal, A. 1970. Cellular localization of ³H-oestradiol in the hypophysis: An autoradiographic study in male and female rats. *Z. Zellforsch.* 104:597–614

195. Attramadal, A., Aakvaag, A. 1970. The uptake of ³H-oestradiol by the anterior hypophysis and hypothalamus of male and female rats. *Z. Zellforsch.* 104:582–96

196. Anderson, C. H., Greenwald, G. S. 1969. Autoradiographic analysis of estradiol uptake in the brain and pituitary of the female rat. *Endocrinology* 85:1160–65

197. Stumpf, W. E. 1968. Cellular and subcellular ³H-estradiol localization in the pituitary by autoradiography. *Z. Zellforsch.* 92:23–33

198. Eisenfeld, A. J. 1970. ³H-estradiol: *In vitro* binding to macromolecules from the rat hypothalamus, anterior pituitary and uterus. *Endocrinology* 86:1313–18

199. Kahwanago, I., Heinrichs, W. L., Herrmann, W. L. 1970. Estradiol "receptors" in hypothalamus and anterior pituitary glands: Inhibition of estradiol binding by SH-group blocking agents and clomiphene citrate. *Endocrinology* 86:1319–26

200. Kahwanago, I., Heinrichs, W. L., Herrmann, W. L. 1969. Isolation of oestradiol "receptors" from bovine hypothalamus and anterior pituitary gland. *Nature* 223:313–14

201. McGuire, J. L., Lisk, R. D. 1969. Localization of estrogen receptors in the rat hypothalamus. *Neuroendocrinology* 4:289–95

202. Warenbourg, M. 1970. Fixation de l'oestradiol ³H au niveau des noyaux amygdaliens, septaux et du systeme thalamo-hypophysaire chez la souris femelle. *C. R. Acad. Sci.* 270:152–54

203. Stumpf, W. E. 1968. Estradiol-concentrating neurons: topography in the hypothalamus by dry-mount

autoradiography. *Science* 162 : 1001–3

204. Attramadal, A. 1970. Cellular localization of ³H-oestradiol in the hypothalamus : An autoradiographic study in male and female rats. *Z. Zellforsch.* 104 :572–81

205. Kato, J., Inaba, M., Kobayashi, T. 1969. Variable uptake of tritiated oestradiol by the anterior hypothalamus in the postpubertal female rat. *Acta Endocrinol.* 61 :585–91

206. Whalen, R. E., Maurer, R. A. 1969. Estrogen "receptors" in brain : An unsolved problem. *Proc. Nat. Acad. Sci.* 63 :681–85

207. Kawakami, M., Terasawa, E., Ibuki, T. 1970. Changes in multiple unit activity of the brain during the estrous cycle. *Neuroendocrinology* 6 :30–48

208. Terasawa, E. I., Whitmoyer, D. I., Sawyer, C. H. 1969. Effects of luteinizing hormone on multiple-unit activity in the rat hypothalamus. *Am. J. Physiol.* 217 :1119–26

209. Terasawa, E., Sawyer, C. H. 1969. Changes in electrical activity in the rat hypothalamus related to electrochemical stimulation of adenohypophyseal function. *Endocrinology* 85 :143–49

210. Endröczi, E. 1969. Effect of sex hormones on the electrical activity of brain stem and diencephalon in castrated female rats. *Acta Physiol. Acad. Sci. Hung.* 35 :31–39

211. Kastin, A. J. et al 1969. Stimulation of LH release in men and women by LH-releasing hormone purified from porcine hypothalami. *J. Clin. Endocrinol. Metab.* 29 :1046–50

212. Schneider, H. P. G., McCann, S. M. 1969. Possible role of dopamine as transmitter to promote discharge of LH-releasing factor. *Endocrinology* 85 :121–32

213. Kamberi, I. A., Mical, R. S., Porter, J. C. 1970. Effect of anterior pituitary perfusion and intraventricular injection of catecholamines and indoleamines on LH release. *Endocrinology* 87 :1–12

214. Kamberi, I. A., McCann, S. M. 1969. Effect of biogenic amines, FSH-releasing factor (FRF) and other substances on the release of FSH by pituitaries incubated *in vitro*. *Endocrinology* 85 :815–24

215. Kamberi, I. A., Schneider, H. P. G., McCann, S. M. 1970. Action of dopamine to induce release of

FSH-releasing factor (FRF) from hypothalamic tissue *in vitro*. *Endocrinology* 86 :278–84

216. Kniewald, Z., Massa, R., Motta, M., Martini, L. 1970. Feedback mechanisms and the control of the hypothalamo-hypophysial complex. In *Steroid Hormones and Brain Function,* ed. C. H. Sawyer, R. Gorski. Los Angeles : Univ. of California Press. In press

217. Lostroh, A. J., Johnson, R. E. 1966. Amounts of interstitial cell stimulating hormone and follicle stimulating hormone required for follicular development, uterine growth and ovulation in the hypophysectomized rat. *Endocrinology* 79 :991–96

218. Malven, P. V., Sawyer, C. H. 1966. Formation of new corpora lutea in mature hypophysectomized rats. *Endocrinology* 78 :1259–63

219. David, M. A., Fraschini, F., Martini, L. 1966. Control of LH secretion : Role of a "Short" feedback mechanism. *Endocrinology* 78 :55–60

220. Desjardins, C. 1969. Alteration of hypophyseal LH and FSH release by exogenous LH and FSH in orchidectomized mice. *Proc. Soc. Exp. Biol. Med.* 130 :535–38

221. Savard, K., Marsh, J. M., Rice, B. F. 1965. Gonadotropins and ovarian steroidogenesis. *Rec. Progr. Hormone Res.* 21 :285–365

222. McCracken, J. A., Uno, A., Goding, J. R., Ichikawa, Y., Baird, D. T. 1969. The *in vivo* effects of sheep pituitary gonadotrophins on the secretion of steroids by the autotransplanted ovary of the ewe. *J. Endocrinol.* 45 :425–40

223. Greenwald, G. S., Rothchild, I. 1968. Formation and maintenance of corpora lutea in laboratory mammals. *J. Anim. Sci.* 27 :Suppl. I, 139–62

224. Rothchild, I. 1965. The corpus luteum-hypophysis relationship. The luteolytic effect of luteinizing hormone (LH) in the rat. *Acta Endocrinol.* 49 :107–19

225. Hori, T., Ide, M., Miyake, T. 1969. Pituitary regulation of preovulatory estrogen secretion in the rat. *Endocrinol. Jap.* 16 :351–60

226. Ahrén, K., Kostyo, J. L. 1963. Acute effects of pituitary gonadotrophins on the metabolism of isolated rat ovaries. *Endocrinology* 73 :81–91

227. Corbin, A., Daniels, E. L., Milmore,

J. E. 1970. An "internal" feedback mechanism controlling follicle stimulating hormone releasing factor. *Endocrinology* 86:735–43

228. Ojeda, S. R., Ramírez, V. D. 1970. Failure of estrogen to block compensatory ovarian hypertrophy in prepuberal rats bearing medial basal hypothalamic FSH implants. *Endocrinology* 86:50–56

229. Goldman, B. D., Mahesh, V. B. 1969. A possible role of acute FSH-release in ovulation in the hamster, as demonstrated by utilization of antibodies to LH and FSH. *Endocrinology* 84:236–43

230. Goldman, B. D., Mahesh, V. B. 1968. Fluctuation in pituitary FSH during the ovulatory cycle in the rat and a possible role of FSH in the induction of ovulation. *Endocrinology* 83:97–106

231. Hori, T., Ide, M., Miyake, T. 1968. Ovarian estrogen secretion during the estrous cycle and under the influence of exogenous gonadotropins in rats. *Endocrinol. Jap.* 15:215–22

232. Odell, W. D., Swerdloff, R. S. 1968. Progestogen-induced luteinizing and follicle-stimulating hormone surge in postmenopausal women — a simulated ovulatory peak. *Proc. Nat. Acad. Sci.* 61:529–36

233. Kalra, P. S., Krulich, L., Quijada, M., Kalra, S. P., Fawcett, C. P. 1970. Effects of gonadal steroids on plasma gonadotropins and prolactin. *Program 52nd Meet. Endocrine Soc.*, 126 (Abstract)

234. Schally, A. V. et al 1970. Studies on the site of action of oral contraceptive steroids. II. Plasma LH and FSH levels after administration of antifertility steroids and LH-releasing hormone (LH-RH). *Endocrinology* 86:530–41

235. Labhsetwar, A. P. 1969. Influence of progesterone on the pituitary and plasma levels of LH and FSH in the female rat. *Biol. Reprod.* 1:189–96

236. Goldman, B. D., Kamberi, I. A., Siiteri, P. K., Porter, J. C. 1969. Temporal relationship of progestin secretion, LH release and ovulation in rats. *Endocrinology* 85:1137–43

237. Uchida, K., Kadowaki, M., Miyake, T. 1969. Effect of exogenous progesterone on the preovulatory progesterone secretion in the rat. *Endocrinol. Jap.* 16:485–91

238. Taleisnik, S., Caligaris, L., Astrada, J. J. 1969. Sex difference in the release of luteinizing hormone evoked by progesterone. *J. Endocrinol.* 44:313–21

239. Nallar, R., Antunes-Rodrigues, J., McCann, S. M. 1966. Effect of progesterone on the level of plasma luteinizing hormone (LH) in normal female rats. *Endocrinology* 70:907–11

240. Caligaris, L., Astrada, J. J., Taleisnik, S. 1968. Stimulating and inhibiting effects of progesterone on the release of luteinizing hormone. *Acta Endocrinol.* 59:177–85

241. Smith, E. R., Weick, R. F., Davidson, J. M. 1969. Influence of intracerebral progesterone on the reproductive system of female rats. *Endocrinology* 85:1129–36

242. Spies, H. G., Stevens, K. R., Hilliard, J., Sawyer, C. H. 1969. The pituitary as a site of progesterone and chlormadinone blockade of ovulation in the rabbit. *Endocrinology* 84:277–84

243. Schally, A. V., Carter, W. H., Saito, M., Arimura, A., Bowers, C. Y. 1968. Studies on the site of action of oral contraceptive steroids. I. Effect of antifertility steroids on plasma LH levels and on the response to luteinizing hormone-releasing factor in rats. *J. Clin. Endocrinol. Metab.* 28:1747–55

244. Radford, H. M., Wheatley, I. S., Wallace, A. L. C. 1969. The effects of oestradiol benzoate and progesterone on secretion of luteinizing hormone in the ovariectomized ewe. *J. Endocrinol.* 44:135–36

245. McCann, S. M. 1962. Effect of progesterone on plasma luteinizing hormone activity. *Am. J. Physiol.* 202:601–4

246. McDonald, P. G., Clegg, M. T. 1967. The effect of progesterone on serum luteinizing hormone concentrations in the ewe. *J. Reprod. Fert.* 13:75–82

247. Kaufman, A. B., Rothchild, I. 1966. The corpus luteum-hypophysis relationship: the effect of progesterone treatment on the release of gonadotrophins in the rat. *Acta Endocrinol.* 51:231–44

248. Kobayashi, F., Hara, K., Miyake, T. 1969. Effects of steroids on the

release of luteinizing hormone in the rat. *Endocrinol. Jap.* 16:251–60

249. Everett, J. W., Sawyer, C. H. 1949. A neural timing factor in the mechanism by which progesterone advances ovulation in the cyclic rat. *Endocrinology* 45:581–95

250. Haller, E. W., Barraclough, C. A. 1968. Hypothalamic regulation of ovulation — effects of urethane and progesterone. *Proc. Soc. Exp. Biol. Med.* 129:291–95

251. Schneider, H. P. G., McCann, S. M. 1970. Estradiol and the neuroendocrine control of LH-release in vitro. *Endocrinology* 87:330–38

252. Kanematsu, S., Sawyer, C. H. 1964. Effects of hypothalamic and hypophysial estrogen implants on pituitary and plasma LH in ovariectomized rabbits. *Endocrinology* 75:579–85

253. McCann, S. M. 1962. A hypothalamic luteinizing-hormone-releasing factor. *Am. J. Physiol.* 202:395–400

254. Schneider, H. P. G., McCann, S. M. 1970. Release of LH-releasing factor (LRF) into the peripheral circulation of hypophysectomized rats by dopamine and its blockade by estradiol. *Endocrinology* Vol. 87. In press

255. Lawton, I. E., Sawyer, C. H. 1970. Role of amygdala in regulating LH secretion in the adult female rat. *Am. J. Physiol.* 218:622–26

256. Ramirez, V. D., Abrams, R. M., McCann, S. M. 1964. Effect of estradiol implants in the hypothalamo-hypophysial region of the rat on the secretion of luteinizing hormone. *Endocrinology* 75:243–48

257. McCann, S. M. et al 1970. Studies on the feedback actions of gonadal steroids on gonadotropin and prolactin secretion: effects, sites and mechanism of action. In *Steroid Hormones and Brain Function*, ed. C. H. Sawyer, R. Gorski. Los Angeles: Univ. of California Press. In press

258. Swerdloff, R. S., Odell, W. D. 1969. Serum luteinizing and follicle stimulating hormone levels during sequential and nonsequential contraceptive treatment of eugonadal women. *J. Clin. Endocrinol. Metab.* 29:157–63

259. Everett, J. W. 1948. Progesterone and estrogen in the experimental control of ovulation time and other features of the estrous cycle in the rat. *Endocrinology* 43:389–405

260. Wurtman, R. J., Anton-Tay, F. 1969. The mammalian pineal as a neuroendocrine transducer. *Rec. Progr. Hormone Res.* 25:493–522

261. Pharriss, B. B., Wyngarden, L. J. 1969. The effect of prostaglandin $F_2\alpha$ on the progestogen content of ovaries from pseudopregnant rats. *Proc. Soc. Exp. Biol. Med.* 130:92–94

262. Karim, S. M. M. 1968. Appearance of prostaglandin $F_2\alpha$ in human blood during labour. *Brit. Med. J.* 5631:618–20

263. Channing, C. P. 1970. Influences of the in vivo and in vitro hormonal environment upon luteinization of granulosa cells in tissue culture. *Rec. Progr. Hormone Res.* 26:589–622

264. Channing, C. P. 1969. Steroidogenesis and morphology of human ovarian cell types in tissue culture. *J. Endocrinol.* 45:297–308

265. Midgley, A. R., Jr., Jaffe, R. B. 1968. Regulation of human gonadotropins: IV. Correlation of serum concentrations of follicle stimulating and luteinizing hormones during the menstrual cycle. *J. Clin. Endocrinol. Metab.* 28:1699–703

266. Yen, S. S. C., Vela, P., Rankin, J., Littell, A. S. 1970. Hormonal relationships during the menstrual cycle. *J. Am. Med. Assoc.* 211:1513–17

267. Goebelsmann, U., Midgley, A. R., Jr., Jaffe, R. B. 1969. Regulation of human gonadotropins: VII. Daily individual urinary estrogens, pregnanediol and serum luteinizing and follicle stimulating hormones during the menstrual cycle. *J. Clin. Endocrinol. Metab.* 29:1222–30

268. Thomas, K., Walckiers, R., Ferin, J. 1970. Biphasic pattern of LH midcycle discharge. *J. Clin. Endocrinol. Metab.* 30:269–72

269. Yussman, M. A., Taymor, M. L. 1970. Serum levels of follicle stimulating hormone and luteinizing hormone and of plasma progesterone related to ovulation by corpus luteum biopsy. *J. Clin. Endocrinol. Metab.* 30:396–99

270. Yussman, M. A., Taymor, M. L., Miyata, J., Pheteplace, C. 1970.

Serum levels of follicle-stimulating hormone, luteinizing hormone, and plasma progestins correlated with human ovulation. *Fert. Steril.* 21: 119–25

271. Cargille, C. M., Ross, G. T., Yoshimi, T. 1969. Daily variations in plasma follicle stimulating hormone, luteinizing hormone, and progesterone in the normal menstrual cycle. *J. Clin. Endocrinol. Metab.* 29 :12–19

272. Stevens, U. C. 1969. Comparison of FSH and LH patterns in plasma, urine and urinary extracts during the menstrual cycle. *J. Clin. Endocrinol. Metab.* 29 :904–10

273. Burger, H. G., Catt, K. J., Brown, J. B. 1968. Relationship between plasma luteinizing hormone and urinary estrogen excretion during the menstrual cycle. *J. Clin. Endocrinol. Metab.* 28 :1508–12

274. Corker, C. S., Naftolin, F., Exley, D. 1969. Interrelationship between plasma luteinizing hormone and oestradiol in the human menstrual cycle. *Nature* 222 :1063

275. Neill, J. D., Johansson, E. D. B., Datta, J. K., Knobil, E. 1967. Relationship between the plasma levels of luteinizing hormone and progesterone during the normal menstrual cycle. *J. Clin. Endocrinol. Metab.* 27 :1167–73

276. Faiman, C., Ryan, R. J. 1967. Serum follicle-stimulating hormone and luteinizing hormone concentrations during the menstrual cycle as determined by radioimmunoassays. *J. Clin. Endocrinol. Metab.* 27 :1711–16

277. Saxena, B. B., Demura, H., Gandy, H. M., Peterson, R. E. 1968. Radioimmunoassay of human follicle stimulating and luteinizing hormones in plasma. *J. Clin. Endocrinol. Metab.* 28 :519–34

278. Crosignani, P. G., Nakamura, R. M., Hovland, D. N., Mishell, D. R., Jr. 1970. A method of solid phase radioimmunoassay utilizing polypropylene discs. *J. Clin. Endocrinol. Metab.* 30 :153–60

279. Orr, A. H., Elstein, M. 1969. Luteinizing hormone levels in plasma and urine in women during normal menstrual cycles and in women taking combined contraceptives or chlormadinone acetate. *J. Endocrinol.* 43 :617–24

280. Johanson, A. J., Guyda, H., Light, C.,

Migeon, C. J., Blizzard, R. M. 1969. Serum luteinizing hormone by radioimmunoassay in normal children. *J. Pediat.* 74 :416–24

281. Strott, C. A., Yoshimi, T., Ross, G. T., Lipsett, M. B. 1969. Ovarian physiology: Relationship between plasma LH and steroidogenesis by the follicle and corpus luteum; effect of HCG. *J. Clin. Endocrinol. Metab.* 29 :1157–67

282. Mikhail, G., Wu, C. H., Ferin, M., Vande Wiele, R. L. 1970. Radioimmunoassay of plasma estrone and estradiol. *Steroids* 15 :333–52

283. Johansson, E. D. B., Wide, L. 1969. Preovulatory levels of plasma progesterone and luteinizing hormone in women. *Acta Endocrinol.* 62: 82–88

284. Odell, W. D., Swerdloff, R. S. 1968. Radioimmunoassay of luteinizing and follicle-stimulating hormones in human serum. In *Radioisotopes in Medicine: In Vitro Studies.* AEC Symp. Ser. No. 13, 165–83

285. Ross, G. T. et al 1970. Pituitary and gonadal hormones in women during spontaneous and induced ovulatory cycles. *Rec. Progr. Hormone Res.* 26 :1–62

286. Vande Wiele, R. L. et al 1970. Mechanisms regulating the menstrual cycle in women. *Rec. Progr. Hormone Res.* 26 :63–103

287. Odell, W. D., Parlow, A. F., Cargille, C. M., Ross, G. T. 1968. Radioimmunoassay for human follicle-stimulating hormone — physiological studies. *J. Clin. Invest. Metab.* 47 :2551–62

288. Corker, C. S., Exley, D. 1970. The determination of plasma estradiol-17-beta by competitive protein binding radioassay. *Steroids* 15 :469–83

289. Dufau, M. L., Dulmanis, A., Catt, K. J., Hudson, B. 1970. Measurement of plasma estradiol-17-beta by competitive binding assay employing pregnancy plasma. *J. Clin. Endocrinol. Metab.* 30 :351–56

290. Baird, D. T., Guevara, A. 1969. Concentration of unconjugated estrone and estradiol in peripheral plasma in nonpregnant women throughout the menstrual cycle, castrate and postmenopausal women and in men. *J. Clin. Endocrinol. Metab.* 29 :149–56

291. Beling, C. G., Marcus, S. L., Markham, S. M. 1970. Functional ac-

tivity of the corpus luteum following hysterectomy. *J. Clin. Endocrinol. Metab.* 30:30–39

292. Ramwell, P. W., Shaw, J. E. 1970. Biological significance of the prostaglandins. *Rec. Progr. Hormone Res.* 26:139–87

293. Lamport, H. 1940. Periodic changes in blood estrogen. *Endocrinology* 27:673–79

294. Rapoport, A. 1952. Periodicities of open linear systems with positive steady states. *Bull. Math. Biophys.* 14:171–83

295. Danziger, L., Elmergreen, G. L. 1957. Mathematical models of endocrine systems. *Bull. Math. Biophys.* 19:9–18

296. Horrobin, D. F. 1969. The female sex cycle. *J. Theor. Biol.* 22:80–88

297. Thompson, H. E., Horgan, J. D., Delfs, E. 1969. A simplified mathematical model and simulations of the hypophysis-ovarian endocrine control system. *Biophys. J.* 9:278–91

298. Schwartz, N. B. 1969. Modeling and **control** in gonadal function. In *Hormonal Control Systems,* Math. Biosci. Suppl., ed. E. B. Stear, A. H. Kadish, 299–55. New York: American Elsevier. 304 pp.

299. Schwartz, N. B., Waltz, P. 1970. Role of ovulation in the regulation of the estrous cycle. *Fed. Proc.* In press

300. Miyake, T. 1968. Interrelationship between the release of pituitary luteinizing hormone and the secretions of ovarian estrogen and progestin during estrous cycle of the rat. In *Integrative Mechanism of Neuroendocrine System,* ed. S. Itoh, 139–49. Hokkaido, Japan: Hokkaido Univ. Sch. of Med. 203 pp.

301. Kobayashi, F., Hara, K., Miyake, T. 1968. Luteinizing hormone concentrations in pituitary and in blood plasma during the estrous cycle of the rat. *Endocrinol. Jap.* 15:313–19

302. Monroe, S. E., Rebar, R. W., Gay, V. L., Midgley, A. R., Jr. 1969. Radioimmunoassay determination of luteinizing hormone during the estrous cycle of the rat. *Endocrinology* 85:720–24

303. McClintock, J. A., Schwartz, N. B.

1968. Changes in pituitary and plasma follicle stimulating hormone concentrations during the rat estrous cycle. *Endocrinology* 83:433–41

304. Niswender, G. D., Chen, C. L., Midgley, A. R., Jr., Meites, J., Ellis, S. 1969. Radioimmunoassay for rat prolactin. *Proc. Soc. Exp. Biol. Med.* 130:793–97

305. Goding, J. R. et al. 1969. Radioimmunoassay for ovine luteinizing hormone. Secretion of luteinizing hormone during estrous and following estrogen administration in the sheep. *Endocrinology* 85:133–42

306. Niswender, G. D., Roche, J. F., Foster, D. L., Midgley, A. R., Jr. 1968. Radioimmunoassay of serum levels of luteinizing hormone during the cycle and early pregnancy in ewes. *Proc. Soc. Exp. Biol. Med.* 129:901–4

307. Niswender, G. D., Reichert, L. E., Jr., Midgley, A. R., Jr., Nalbandov, A. V. 1969. Radioimmunoassay for bovine and ovine luteinizing hormone. *Endocrinology* 84:1166–73

308. Wheatley, I. S., Radford, H. M. 1969. Luteinizing hormone secretion during the oestrous cycle of the ewe as determined by radioimmunoassay. *J. Reprod. Fert.* 19:211–14

309. Kirton, K. T., Niswender, G. D., Midgley, A. R., Jr., Jaffe, R. B., Forbes, A. D. 1970. Serum luteinizing hormone and progesterone concentration during the menstrual cycle of the rhesus monkey. *J. Clin. Endocrinol. Metab.* 30:105–10

310. Monroe, S. E., Atkinson, L. E., Knobil, E. 1970. Patterns of circulating luteinizing hormone and their relation to plasma progesterone levels during the menstrual cycle of the Rhesus monkey. *Endocrinology* 87:453–55

311. Brown, J. M. et al. 1969. The release of luteinizing hormone in the ewe following oestradiol administration. *J. Physiol.* 201:98–100

312. Ferin, M., Tempone, A., Zimmering, P. E., Vande Wiele, R. L. 1969. Effect of antibodies to 17 β-estradiol and progesterone on the estrous cycle of the **rat**. *Endocrinology* 85:1070–78

THE REGIONAL CIRCULATION

GORDON ROSS

Department of Physiology, University of California
School of Medicine, Los Angeles, California

This review will be concerned with the description and evaluation of recent investigations of the skeletal muscle, cutaneous, splanchnic, renal, and cerebral circulations. No attempt is made to be comprehensive. The microcirculatory aspects of capillary exchange are discussed elsewhere in this volume (1). Vascular adjustments involved in overall circulatory homeostasis and in integrated responses such as exercise will be mentioned only in the context of their local relevance to a particular vascular bed. Papers of primarily methodological, pharmacological, or clinical orientation will not be reported except when they illuminate a physiological mechanism. I propose to emphasize the neurohumoral responses of the peripheral vessels and those local circulatory changes which can be correlated with the functional status of the organs supplied. It is not yet possible to describe these aspects of the regional circulation in terms of the basic physiology of the vascular smooth muscle cell and the manner in which its excitatory and contractile mechanisms are influenced by neurotransmitters, humoral, metabolic, and ionic factors. Since the progress towards this ideal has recently been the subject of several excellent reviews (2–6) it will not be further discussed in this presentation.

Before the individual vascular beds are considered, some general aspects of blood vessel innervation will be reviewed.

INNERVATION OF BLOOD VESSELS

Continuing use of histochemical, specific fluorescence, and electronmicroscopic techniques has added further knowledge of blood vessel innervation. The variation from species to species and in different blood vessels of the same species is very striking.

In general, the adrenergic innervation of the large conduit arteries is confined to the adventitiomedial junction (6, 7) and the "synaptic cleft" is relatively large. Neuromuscular distances less than 0.08 μ are very uncommon (6). The mean shortest diffusion path from nodes to smooth muscle in the rabbit pulmonary artery is 1.9 μ (7). The problem of how muscle cells in the deeper layers of the media are activated is unsettled. These cells may be hundreds of microns from neural elements. Activation could occur by diffusion of transmitter or by electrical coupling with excited cells in the more superficial layers. It has been calculated that the rabbit pulmonary artery contains 9.3×10^7 nodes per g weight of artery wall and that approximately 50 pg norepinephrine is released per g artery by each nerve impulse. Approximately 80% is taken up again into the nerve fiber and the remainder diffuses into the adjacent tissues. The transmitter overflows preferentially through the adventitia and the amount reaching the inner layers of the media is small and may be below the threshold for contraction (8). It should be recognized that these calculations were made under in vitro conditions. The different patterns of neural stimulation, the pressure gradients across the wall, the perfusion of the vasa vasorum, the presence of circulating vasoactive agents, and possibly many other factors make extrapolation to the in vivo situation extremely difficult. The other possibility for activation of non-innervated cells, namely electrical coupling, has an anatomical basis in some vessels where nexuses have been demonstrated (6). On the other hand, nexuses were reported to be rare in the pulmonary artery (7) and in some blood vessels contraction occurs in the absence of demonstrable electrical activity (4, 8).

As one proceeds downstream along the arterial tree, nerve fibers do extend into the media at least in some arteries (9) and the minimal neuromuscular intervals become smaller, e.g., $0.08\ \mu$ in pancreatic arterioles (10), $0.1\ \mu$ in coronary arterioles (11), and $0.02\ \mu$ in the spleen (12). The terminal arterioles and precapillary sphincters of rabbit fascia are reported to be closely accompanied by unmyelinated nerves, some of which make membranous contact with the smooth muscle cells (13). These small neuromuscular intervals and the thin muscle layer would allow rapid responses to neural stimulation. Endothelial protrusions making close contacts with muscle cells have also been observed in arterioles (12, 13) and provide a very short diffusion pathway by which circulating vasoactive substances could influence arteriolar muscle.

Some veins, e. g., cutaneous, renal, portal, mesenteric, and hepatic, receive a moderately dense innervation, but it is usually less intense than in the corresponding arteries (15, 16). Other veins are only sparsely innervated (15, 17). The rat portal vein contains about 4×10^6 varicosities per cm^2 of nerve plexus which is the same density as that in rabbit pulmonary artery (18). Norepinephrine is apparently released only in sufficient amounts to activate muscle cells close to the nodes and myogenic propagation of the stimulus is responsible for the strong and rapid contractile response of the vein to nerve stimulation. It was calculated that at 4 impulses/sec the transmitter concentration in the vicinity of the nerve terminals was $8 \times 10^{-6}\ M$ and at 16 impulses/sec $2 \times 10^{-5}\ M$, i.e., about 1000 times higher than the concentration of circulating norepinephrine in this animal. Cocaine produced a greater increase in sensitivity to exogenous norepinephrine than could readily be explained by the increased concentration likely to occur in the greater part of the extracellular space of the muscle. It was therefore suggested that the muscle cells closest to the nerves played a key role not only in neural responses, but in responses to exogenous norepinephrine, possibly because they had more abundant α receptors or because they acted as pacemakers.

Schenk & El Badawi (9) have reported that arterial and arteriolar cholinergic innervation is as widespread and often as prominent as the adrenergic supply. Cholinergic fibers were demonstrated in the heart, tongue, gut, and skeletal muscle. They have also been shown in splenic (12), uterine (19), renal (20), and anterior cerebral (21) arteries. Bolme & Fuxe (22) found acetylcholinesterase-containing nerves in the adventitiomedial junctional area of arteries of 30–100 μ diam in hindlimb skeletal muscles of dogs and cats, but not in arteries larger than 100 μ or in veins of any size. Adrenergic terminals were more frequent than cholinergic and occurred in all arterial and arteriolar vessels. The density of adrenergic terminals around veins was much less than around arteries. No differences in adrenergic or cholinergic innervation were observed between red and white muscles. In contrast to the limb muscles, acetylcholinesterase-rich terminals were present only in the larger arteries of the masseter and not in the smaller vessels. Cholinergic terminals were not found in skeletal muscle of man, several types of monkey, polecat, rat, badger, and hare (23). Both small and large arterial vessels supplying the gut of the cat and dog are associated with cholinergic nerves (11, 22), but their functional significance remains doubtful.

Two interesting cholinergic mechanisms have been demonstrated in the domestic fowl. The anterior mesenteric artery of this animal possesses a prominent outer longitudinal layer with an excitatory cholinergic innervation. Contraction of this muscle has little effect on mesenteric blood flow, but potentiates the responses of the adrenergically innervated media (24). The fowl also possesses a renal portal system with a sphincter which is opened by a cholinergic mechanism to permit blood flow through the kidney. The guinea pig uterine artery has a dual innervation (19). Adrenergic fibers supply the entire arterial tree, whereas cholinergic nerves supply only the main trunk and short portions of the secondary branches. Arteries from virgin guinea pigs exposed to bretylium were only slightly dilated by periarterial nerve stimulation and these responses were uninfluenced by physostigmine. In contrast, much larger responses, blocked by hyoscine and enhanced by physostigmine, occurred in arteries from pregnant animals. The uterine artery therefore has three types of neural control: adrenergic constrictor, cholinergic dilator, and an additional dilator mechanism with an unknown transmitter. The increased responsiveness of the vessel during pregnancy is accompanied by an increased concentration of acetylcholinesterase on the postsynaptic membrane (25). Bell suggests that increased cholinergic dilator responses may contribute to the uterine hyperemia of pregnancy. However, this seems unlikely since the resistance vessels of the uterus have not been shown to receive a cholinergic innervation.

The human ductus arteriosus contains adrenergic terminals (26) and both cholinergic and adrenergic fibers have been demonstrated in the ductus, aorta, and pulmonary artery of the fetal lamb (27). Both types of fiber were seen in the outer third of the media as well as in the adventitia. Neuromuscular intervals as small as 0.0075 μ were observed in the ductus, which raises the strong possibility that the smooth muscle of this vessel is under direct neural control. The significance of this in relation to closure of the ductus remains to be established.

ADRENOTROPIC RECEPTORS

Moran (28) has authoritatively reviewed the history and development of the dual-receptor hypothesis and its importance for the understanding of adrenergic cardiovascular responses. Adrenergic vasoconstriction is produced by activation of α receptors and the primary effect of sympathetic nerve stimulation will be determined in part by the number and distribution of these receptors. α-Adrenotropic receptor activity is prominent in the precapillary vessels of skin, white adipose tissue, skeletal muscle, kidney, spleen, liver, and gastrointestinal tract and weak in the heart and brain. The α responses of veins, except for those of the skin and splanchnic area, are less marked than those of the corresponding arteries. β Receptors are not usually considered to be innervated, but if the α receptors are blocked, sympathetic nerve stimulation can induce vasodilatation in several tissues (29–31). This indicates that the transmitter has access to β receptors and occupation of these receptors may modify α responses to nerve stimulation in the nonblocked animal. This is supported by the potentiation of sympathetic vasoconstriction by propranolol in some vascular beds (32, 33). There is no doubt that β-receptor activity is an important determinant of vascular responses to circulating catecholamines. This activity is prominent in skeletal muscle and in the gastrointestinal tract where physiological amounts of epinephrine induce vasodilatation (34–36), less prominent in the heart, spleen, and liver (30, 31, 37–39), and weak in the kidney (40). Epinephrine dilatation is reversed and norepinephrine constriction is enhanced by β-receptor blockade (31, 32, 33, 36–39). The β receptors therefore limit the degree of vasoconstriction which can be achieved by a given concentration of catecholamines. This may be important in preserving adequate organ perfusion, particularly in the splanchnic area, during stress situations.

Studies with various agonists and antagonists (41–43) suggest that neither α nor β receptors are homogeneous. There are at least two varieties of β receptors. The β-1 receptors, which include those of the heart and intestinal smooth muscle, are selectively blocked by 4-(2-hydroxy-3-isopropylaminopropoxy) acetanilide (practolol) which has a relatively weak action on the β-2 receptors which include those of vascular and bronchial smooth muscle. On the other hand, 1-(4′-methylphenyl)-2-isopropylamino-propanol (H 35/25) selectively blocks β-2 receptors. These selective blocking agents constitute important pharmacological tools which enable cardiac and peripheral vascular β-adrenergic effects to be separately studied in the intact animal.

The nature of the adrenotropic receptors remains unknown although some interesting speculations have been advanced (45–47). The view that adenyl cyclase is the β receptor (47) receives its support mainly from studies on the heart and as yet there is little evidence linking this enzyme to adrenergic vasodilatation.

CIRCULATION IN SPECIAL REGIONS

SKELETAL MUSCLE

Cholinergic mechanisms.—There have been several recent studies of sympathetic cholinergic vasodilatation. Its participation in the orienting reflex in dogs was shown by an atropine-sensitive increase in hindlimb blood flow elicited by a nonspecific sound stimulus (48). Cholinergic vasodilatation could also be established as a conditioned reflex response using either an electrical shock or treadmill exercise as the unconditioned stimulus.

In another study (49), cholinergic dilatation induced by hypothalamic or lumbar sympathetic chain stimulation or by acetycholine infusion increased the disappearance rate of ^{125}I and ^{133}Xe from intramuscular depots in the limbs. In contrast, hypothalamic stimulation did not increase the disappearance rate of isotope from the masseter—a finding which correlates with the lack of cholinergic innervation of the small vessels of this muscle. When limb flow had returned to control levels the disappearance rate was often reduced to below prestimulation values. It was concluded that the primary cholinergic response was arteriolar dilatation with a secondary autoregulatory constriction of precapillary sphincters. These results differ from those of others who found that acetylcholine infusions increased the capillary filtration coefficient, whereas vasodilator nerve stimulation reduced it (50). Stimulation of lumbar vasodilator fibers or intra-arterial infusions of acetylcholine in the skeletal muscle of the dog's hindlimb produced only a transient increase in O_2 consumption, whereas vasodilatation due to inhibition of vasoconstrictor tone was associated with an increased O_2 uptake which was sustained for the entire period of increased flow (51). These results support the view that cholinergic influences have little effect on precapillary sphincters.

The reasons for the "escape" of muscle resistance vessel from cholinergic dilator nerve stimulation have been sought by comparing the responses of the dog gracilis to stimulation of the lumbar sympathetic chain and to infusions of acetylcholine (52). Nerve stimulation produced an initial large transient dilatation followed by a smaller persistent dilatation. Both phases were abolished by atropine. Acetylcholine gave a monophasic dilatation which persisted throughout the infusion, which indicates that the cholinergic receptors do not become insensitive to transmitter. The decline of the response to nerve stimulation was therefore a property of the nerve ending and it was suggested that the transmitter output of some or all of the cholinergic fibers might decline with time. However, Folkow, Haeger & Uvnäs have found acetylcholine in blood for stimulation periods longer than 2 min (53). An autoregulatory constriction was unlikely to have been the reason for the adaptation because, under the condition of constant flow, perfusion pressure fell during the dilatation.

Djojosugito et al (51) found that capillary filtration coefficient decreased during cholinergic nerve stimulation, but returned towards normal rather than decreasing further during the escape of the resistance vessels. They suggested that the decline in flow or "escape" might be due to an increased tone in resistance vessels upstream from a point just proximal to the capillaries which was the supposed site of impact of the cholinergic fibers. However, acetylcholinesterase-rich terminals have subsequently been found in small intramuscular arteries of 30 to 100 μ (22) and the compensatory constriction would therefore have to occur in vessels larger than 100 μ which seems unlikely. An alternative hypothesis compatible with Mauskopf & Renkin's work (52) is that the initial arteriolar dilatation leads to contraction of precapillary sphincters which wanes as the arteriolar dilatation lessens, perhaps because of reduced transmitter release. A recent finding of great interest is the presence of cells which contained either acetylcholinesterase or catecholamines enmeshed in the plexus of nerve fibers around the arterioles of the gracilis (54). Surprisingly, vasodilatation induced by hypothalamic stimulation was not blocked by hexamethonium. It was conjectured that these ganglion cells formed part of the sympathetic vasodilator pathway and that atropine blockade was due to block of muscarinic receptor sites on these cells. These unusual findings await confirmation.

Histaminergic vasodilatation.—Tripelennamine and 48/80 reduced norepinephrine reflex vasodilatation in rats (55). The limb vasodilatation induced by carotid sinus nerve stimulation in conscious dogs was also reduced by tripelennamine, but only when given intra-arterially (56). Since the dilatation evoked by sinus nerve stimulation was greater than th' t evoked by ganglionic blockade, the authors considered that the reflex vasodilatation was an active process rather than a mere inhibition of sympathetic constrictor tone. However, local autoregulatory processes could have limited the dilatation to ganglionic blockade as could an increase in circulating constrictor agents, e.g., angiotensin, produced in response to the fall in arterial pressure. The hypothesis that reflex vasodilatation is mediated by histaminergic nerves because it is reduced by antihistamines is weakened by the complex pharmacological actions of these agents which dilate limb vessels (56), constrict those of the mesentery, and potentiate vascular responses to topical catecholamines (57). Other weaknesses of the hypothesis have been discussed in recent reviews (58–60).

Adrenergic neural vasodilatation.—Vasoconstriction produced in the canine gracilis muscle by stimulating its sympathetic nerves or by intra-arterial norepinephrine was potentiated by β-adrenergic blocking agents (29). Moreover, adrenergic vasoconstriction induced reflexly or by stimulating the sympathetic chain in atropinized dogs was converted to a maintained vasodilatation after intra-arterial infusion of the α-receptor blocking agent dibozane. Isoproterenol increased the permeability-surface area (PS) product in some animals and reduced it in others. Sympathetic vasodilatation after dibozane (1,4-bis(1,4-benzodioxan-2-yl methyl) piperazine) produced the same effect on PS as did isoproterenol in each animal. These observations indicate that norepinephrine released from sympathetic vasoconstrictor fibers normally reaches β-adrenoceptive sites in skeletal muscle resistance vessels and, to this extent, these receptors must be considered to be innervated.

Adrenergic vasoconstriction.—Acute denervation increased blood flow in the gracilis muscle of the anesthetized rat, but did not alter the number of open capillaries, which suggests that precapillary sphincters are not under neural control at rest (62). It has previously been shown that the precapillary sphincters do not participate in the circulatory changes induced by reflex sympathetic activation or inhibition (63). The precapillary sphincters are clearly innervated (17) and constrict vigorously to direct sympathetic nerve stimulation and to norepinephrine. This implies either that the sphincters are unresponsive to the patterns of impulse discharge at rest and during reflex activity or that the neural influences are effectively opposed by local chemical factors.

The sympathetic control of the large arteries of the limb was demonstrated by the finding that the diameter of the femoral artery increased after denervation and decreased during sympathetic nerve stimulation (64). Following stimulation, a dilatation occurred whose nature is obscure and deserves further study. The veins of skeletal muscle appear to be under minimal sympathetic control. Sympathetic nerve stimulation produced minimal nonsignificant responses of venous segments draining dog gracilis (65). This lack of response may be related to the paucity of adrenergic terminals (66) and to the thin muscle layer in these vessels. This study confirms that muscle venoconstriction, unlike that in the splanchnic area, is not a significant means for translocating functionally important amounts of blood to the central circulation.

The organization of the sympathetic outflow to the vasculature of the dog's hindlimb was studied by stimulating different anatomical sections (61). Constrictor responses were obtained from the anterior spinal nerve roots from T10 to L4 with maximum responses from T12, 13, and L1. The constrictor fibers then entered the lumbar paravertebral chain between L1 or above and L5, and they left the chain between L4 and S1. The maximum response to sympathetic chain stimulation was obtained from the L4-5 level.

Circulation in red and white muscle.—Hilton and his colleagues (67) have continued their comparative studies of blood flow in red (soleus) and white (gastrocnemius) muscle in cats. Slow muscle had a much higher resting flow, gave smaller constrictor responses to sympathetic nerve stimulation, showed weak β-receptor activity, and exhibited a smaller functional hyperemia. Hudlická (68) showed that resting blood flow rates were three times as high in slow as in fast muscle of adult chickens. The differences in blood flow began at 10 days of age and were maximal at 28 days, whereas the difference in the speed of contraction is present at hatching and different enzyme patterns are present at 4 days (68). Reis, Moorhead & Wooten (69) found that the differences in perfusion rates of red and white muscle disappeared during sleep because of a fall in red muscle flow, whereas in the defense reaction flow increased in white muscle, but not in red, so that again the perfusion rates became similar. These observations indicate that different control mechanisms are operative in each type of muscle.

Functional hyperemia.—At a recent conference (70) several papers considered the role of local factors in exercise hyperemia. Rodbard (71) provided evidence, mainly based on a hydraulic model, that local regulation of blood flow in many situations, including exercise, depends more on the transmural pressure of the capillary than on the tone of the arterioles which are considered to be mainly "on, off" valves. The behavior of the model is interesting and instructive, but its applicability to the physiological situation has not been established. The critical issue is whether tissue pressure does alter in magnitude and direction and with a similar time course as the model predicts. In vivo tissue pressure measurements are extremely difficult to make and the required data are not available. In contrast to Rodbard's view of the "on, off" function of arterioles, graded arterial constriction has been reported by several observers (e.g., 72).

Mellander (73) summarized the work of his group indicating the importance of tissue hyperosmolality. The evidence is that 1. exercise increases venous osmolality and the magnitude and time course of this increase parallels the exercise hyperemia; 2. infusion of hyperosmolar solutions produces hyperemia equivalent to that obtained in exercise; 3. both exercise and hyperosmolar infusions produce similar microcirculatory changes, i.e., decreased precapillary resistance, increased capillary filtration, and a reduction in the precapillary/postcapillary resistance ratio; and 4. interstitial deposits of ^{133}Xe were cleared more rapidly when injected in hypertonic than in isotonic solution. Studies on the rat portal vein (74) suggest that hyperosmolality might reduce the volume of the smooth muscle cells and cause changes in the ionic gradients across the cell membrane leading to inhibition of pacemaker activity, intercellular propagation, and excitation-contraction coupling. It is perhaps questionable, however, whether the rat portal vein is a good model for changes occurring in the arteriolar vessels of cat or man. A recent careful study has demonstrated that the magnitude of the dilator effect of intra-arterial hypertonic solutions in the human forearm was linearly related to the increase in plasma osmolality and to the initial resistance (75). The results were considered compatible with the suggestion that hyperosmolality is a major determinant of exercise hyperemia. However, in these studies the maximal blood flow increases were only about 100% and venous plasma osmolality during exercise producing a similar flow increase was not measured.

The importance of hyperosmolality in exercise hyperemia is challenged by studies on the dog gracilis (76). During the first minute of motor nerve stimulation there was an increase in osmolality and in the concentration of K and Mg in the venous effluent. At the fifth minute of stimulation osmolality and Mg concentration had returned to prestimulation levels and only K remained elevated. The percent resistance drop produced by exercise was also much greater than that produced by intra-arterial infusions of hyperosmolar solutions which produced identical changes in venous osmolality. Stainsby & Barclay (77) confirmed that hyperosmolar solutions increased muscle blood flow in the dog, but there was a distinct tendency for the flow increase to lessen during continuing infusion. These studies are difficult to evaluate in the context of exercise hyperemia since venous osmolalities were not measured. Skinner & Costin (78) reported that increasing the osmolality of the blood perfusing the dog gracilis muscle to a level approaching the maximum observed with exercise produced only a modest decrease in vascular resistance, but increased the vasodilatation induced by hypoxia and hypokalemia. This work underlines the necessity for understanding the interrelationships of known vasodilator materials since alteration in the blood concentration of one factor may alter the sensitivity to other metabolites.

These studies, taken together, indicate that tissue hyperosmolality has not yet been proved to be the dominant cause of exercise hyperemia. Interpretation of the effects of intra-arterial hyperosmolar solutions is difficult because this route of administration causes shrinkage of blood cells, altering their rheological properties, as well as shrinkage of endothelial cells which would affect capillary exchange and might influence arteriolar smooth muscle via the myoendothelial junctions described by Rhodin (13). During exercise the hyperosmolality develops in the tissue fluid and its effects are not likely to be strictly comparable to those produced by raising the osmolality of arterial blood even though both procedures might give rise to equivalent degrees of venous hyperosmolality.

An interesting and important investigation by Duling (79) has indicated that large O_2 losses may occur through the walls of small arteries and arterioles and that a significant fraction of the O_2 supply to tissues diffuses through precapillary vessels. Oxygen tensions were measured on the external surface of precapillary vessels in the suffused cheek pouch of anesthetized animals. With a suffusion solution Po_2 of 39 mm Hg, a femoral arterial Po_2 of 67 mm Hg, and a tissue Po_2 of 8 mm Hg, O_2 tension fell from 35 mm on small arteries to 20 mm at terminal arterioles. When the animals breathed 95% O_2, small artery Po_2 was 152 mm and terminal arteriolar Po_2 was 37 mm while femoral artery Po_2 was 427 mm Hg. Similar values were found for the hamster cremaster muscle. Duling suggests that if the precapillary smooth muscle is sensitive to changes in Po_2 at levels compatible with normal in vivo O_2 tension, then O_2 may be a primary determinant of local blood flow. A reduction in blood flow or an increase in tissue metabolism would lower the Po_2 of vascular smooth muscle and would induce dilatation. This hypothesis is attractive, but as the author points out, the responses observed may have been due to alterations in the concentration of tissue metabolites rather than to the direct effects of changing tissue O_2 tensions. The responsiveness of human skeletal muscle vessels to hyperbaric O_2 has been recently demonstrated by Reich et al. (80). Breathing pure O_2 at 1 and 3 atm pressure reduced resting blood flow in the calf and the magnitude and duration of exercise hyperemia were curtailed by O_2 at 3 atm. Different results were obtained by Bond, Blackard & Taxis (81) who found no evidence that exposure to O_2 at 2 atm pressure reduced muscle blood flow in anesthetized dogs. Moreover, equally good autoregulation in response to pressure changes occurred over a wide range of venous Po_2.

Kontos et al (82) have further explored the role of hypoxia and hypercapnia in the local regulation of skeletal muscle flow. The vasodilator response of the human forearm to breathing low O_2 gas mixtures was only 26% of that induced by brachial artery compression resulting in a similar deep forearm venous blood Po_2. On the other hand, the dilator response to hypercapnia was 64% of the response to a degree of ischemia which produced a similar venous Pco_2. Indirect neural effects were excluded by local adrenergic blockade. The results suggest that hypoxia is a relatively minor cause of the dilator response to moderate ischemia and confirm previous observations in animals. On the other hand, the role of tissue Pco_2 was quantitatively more important. Since the vasodilator response to ischemia in the human forearm was markedly reduced by prior infusion of the alkaline buffer tromethamine, the effect of CO_2 may be mediated by a reduction in intracellular pH. Local hypercapnia seemed to be relatively unimportant in exercise hyperemia since the increases in venous Pco_2 were small and intraarterial tromethamine only slightly reduced the dilator response.

Red muscles develop a much smaller functional hyperemia than white muscles and have a less active myosin ATPase. Moreover, contraction of white muscle results in an increase in venous blood phosphate, whereas contraction of red muscle does not. This suggested that release of phosphate might be responsible for the functional hyperemia of white muscle (83). Infusions of isosmotic NaH_2PO_4 solutions increased blood flow in fast and slow muscle, but the amounts required to match the maximum dilatations obtained in contracting muscle produced larger increases in venous phosphate than were observed in functional hyperemia. Nevertheless, these observations suggest that inorganic phosphate should be added to the growing list of substances which might be implicated in exercise hyperemia.

A review of the large numbers of papers dealing with exercise hyperemia provides little hope that a single agent will be found to be the cause of this response. In the early studies the discussion centered around oxygen lack and "metabolites". Later the "metabolites" were fractionated and H^+, K^+, CO_2, adenosine compounds, and Krebs cycle intermediates have all been conisdered as mediators of the response. In the last few years, hyperosomolality came to the fore and now we have phosphate. I incline to the view that exercise hyperemia is caused by the subtle interaction of all the factors mentioned above and probably others as yet unknown. The apparent preponderance of any one agent in a particular experimental situation may well be related to the abnormal conditions under which the study is performed.

Interaction between neural and hormonal factors.—Donald, Rowlands & Ferguson (84) compared the blood flow changes in normal and sympathectomized hindlimbs of conscious dogs during exercise. The magnitude of the exercise flow and the decline of the postexercise hyperemia were similar in both as were the exercise venous O_2 saturations. This indicated that the sympathetic nervous system had little effect on exercising limb blood flow. However, during exercise sufficient to increase flow fivefold, moderate stimulation of the lumbar sympathetic trunk reduced flow by almost 50%. This implies that the sympathetic neural discharge to exercising muscle in dogs is at a low level. In addition, sympathetic constriction was antagonized by local factors since the percent reduction of flow produced by a given stimulus progressively diminished with increasing muscular work. The influence of some of these factors has been studied by Skinner & Costin (78) who found that hypoxia alone reduced sympathetic constriction but larger reductions, and even abolition of the constrictor response, were obtained by a combination of hypoxia and hyperkalemia, or hypoxia and hyperosmolality, or all three factors together.

The ability of sympathetic activity to influence hyperemic responses in man is shown by the reduction in reactive hyperemia, exercise hyperemia, and thermal hyperemia in the forearm when changing from a lying to a standing posture (85). The magnitude of both reactive and functional hyperemia is therefore not solely related to metabolic changes, but may be modified by neural factors.

ADIPOSE TISSUE

Close intra-arterial infusions of several anterior pituitary hormones or of glucagon mobilized free fatty acids (FFA) and increased blood flow in rabbit epigastric adipose tissue (86). These changes persisted for some time after stopping the infusions. Intra-arterial FFA produced no consistent change in blood flow. Extracts of stimulated adipose tissue produced pronounced long-lasting vasodilatation, whereas extracts of nonstimulated fat pads produced smaller transient dilatation. The vasoactive extracts contained a substance resembling prostaglandin E_1 and it was suggested that this agent was the cause of the vasodilatation accompanying lipolysis. In the same series of experiments norepinephrine produced persistent vasoconstriction and no increase in FFA. Canine mesenteric adipose tissue is also metabolically unresponsive to catecholamines and to sympathetic nerve stimulation, both of which produce slight vasoconstriction (87). On the other hand, canine subcutaneous tissue reacts to local nerve stimulation by vasoconstriction and release of FFA. The vasoconstriction is accompanied by a diminished clearance of depot Xe and, surprisingly, by an increased capillary filtration coefficient. This suggests that the number of open capillaries is diminished by contraction of precapillary sphincters and that capillary permeability is increased. After α-adrenergic blockade, nerve stimulation produced vasodilatation, FFA release was potentiated, and the increase in capillary filtration coefficient was greatly reduced. This unique behavior of the microcirculation has been reported by Rosell (88) who himself advises caution in interpreting these unusual results until more direct methods of evaluating capillary function have been applied. Prostaglandin E-like activity was found in the venous effluent following nerve stimulation, but was not considered to be responsible for the adrenergic vasodilatation since prostaglandin E_1 inhibits lipolysis in this tissue.

The importance of the adrenergic control of the circulation of adipose tissue is indicated by the responses to fasting and hemorrhage. Fasting increased blood flow in several white fat depots in rats (89, 90), but not after denervation (89). Severe bleeding reduced blood flow to canine subcutaneous tissue to zero in some animals and irreversible vascular damage was produced. Similar changes occurred after denervation and circulating catecholamines were presumably responsible since a high level of protection was afforded by phenoxybenzamine (91). These findings indicate that the circulation of subcutaneous fat may be more severely compromised in shock than any other organ.

Sympathetic nerve stimulation induced thermogenesis and vasodilatation in brown fat of cold-exposed guinea pigs. β-Adrenergic blockade prevented the thermogenic response but only partially blocked the blood flow increase (92). This suggests that the vasodilatation is in part secondary to metabolic changes which are dependent on β adrenoreceptors. The mediator of the residual dilatation is unknown. The physiology of brown fat has recently been reviewed in detail (93).

SKIN

Adrenergic responses.—Rolewicz, Whitmore & Zimmerman (94) were able to stimulate selectively the sympathetic nerves to the arteries and small vessels and to the veins of the dog's hindpaw. The increase in resistance was greater and developed more rapidly in the arterial than in the venous segment. Arterial nerve stimulation substantially increased the concentration of norepinephrine in the venous effluent, whereas venous nerve stimulation produced a minimal increase. Phenoxybenzamine produced a greater percent increase in effluent norepinephrine during venous than during arterial nerve stimulation. In a subsequent study (95), isolated venous segments concentrated twice as much radioactive norepinephrine from the external medium as did arterial segments. The differences disappeared after exposure to cocaine. These findings suggest that there are fewer adrenergic terminals in the veins and that they have a more efficient reuptake mechanism. Abdel-Sayed et al (96) showed that cutaneous veins in dogs constricted strongly to nerve stimulation in striking contrast to the minimal responses of muscle veins in the same animal. The greater response of the cutaneous veins, which has obvious implications for the thermoregulatory function of the skin, may be partly related to their denser adrenergic innervation and thicker muscle layer.

Continuing studies of the potentiation of adrenergic constriction of cutaneous veins by local cooling have shown that the potentiation is unaltered by amounts of tranylcypromine and pyrogallol adequate to inhibit monoamine oxidase and catechol-O-methyl transferase respectively (97). The effect of cooling is not, therefore, due to diminished enzymatic destruction of catecholamines and previous work has shown that it is not due to interference with reuptake of norepinephrine by the nerve terminal (98). The effect of temperature does not seem to be a direct one on the contractile machinery since veins constricted by potassium or barium chloride were relaxed by cooling. Changes in the excitation coupling mechanism may be responsible (99). In contrast to its effects on veins, cooling diminished the responses of the skin resistance vessels to norepinephrine and sympathetic nerve stimulation, possibly through the production of partial α-adrenergic blockade (96).

The partition of blood flow between skin and muscle in the human forearm has been studied during leg exercise (100). At rest, approximately 50% of forearm flow was distributed to skin and 50% to muscle. Mild leg exercise produced no change in forearm muscle flow, but a reduction in skin flow. Moderate exercise reduced muscle and skin flow, but late in the exercise skin flow increased. Severe exercise reduced muscle and skin flow throughout the period but skin flow increased after the termination of exercise. These results suggest that sympathetic constrictor activity associated with exercise can delay the onset of cutaneous vasodilatation required for heat dissipation. Increased sympathetic activity also reduced the hyperemia induced by local heating (85).

Cholinergic responses.—Most investigators, including, recently, Ballard, Abboud & Mayer (101), have found no evidence of a cholinergic vasodilator mechanism in the skin. On the other hand, Brody & Shaffer (102) have reported that low-frequency lumbar sympathetic nerve stimulation following pretreatment with guanethidine produced dilatation in the dog's paw which was blocked by atropine.

Other neurogenic dilator responses.—Stimulation of the sympathetic nerves to the canine paw can produce substantial dilator responses which persist for some time after the stimulus is withdrawn and which are not blocked by atropine, propranolol, or antihistamines (101–104). This neurogenic vasodilatation is associated with the discharge of a substance into the blood draining the paw which elicits dilatation in skin but not in muscle. The nature of this material, which is presumably the neurotransmitter, remains to be determined. There is some evidence that this system is activated by chemoreceptor stimulation (101).

THE SPLANCHNIC CIRCULATION

Stomach.—Jansson, Lundgren & Martinson have reviewed their work on the neurohumoral control of the cat stomach (105). Stimulation of high threshold vagal efferent fibers produced relaxation, increased secretion, and increased blood flow. The elevated flow was mainly secondary to the increased secretion but, whereas atropine blocked secretion completely, the flow increase was only "reduced to a large extent". This raises the possibility that the noncholinergic, nonadrenergic neurotransmitter responsible for vagal inhibition of the stomach (106) may also affect blood flow. Cowley & Code (107) studied the aminopyrine clearance of the nonsecreting gastric mucosa of conscious dogs. Intravenous infusions of pitressin and norepinephrine and a single rapid intravenous injection of gastrin pentapeptide reduced the clearance whereas epinephrine increased it without inducing secretion. The effect of epinephrine on the secreting stomach is uncertain since it reduced mucosal flow and secretion in a gastrin-stimulated pouch (108) and produced a further increase in flow in a histamine-stimulated preparation (109).

The possible existence of arteriovenous shunts has been reexamined in anesthetized dogs (110). After the injection of 20 μ radioactive microspheres into the left ventricle, the radioactivity of the gastric venous effluent increased with time. No microspheres were found in the centrifuged effluent and radioactivity was present only in the plasma. This study confirms other work indicating that the percentage of gastric flow passing through arteriovenous anastomoses is extremely low (111, 112) and draws attention to elution of isotope as a possible source of error in radioactive microsphere methods.

Pancreas.—Aune & Semb (113) have studied pancreatic blood flow with the H_2 clearance method. This technique enables blood flow to be measured serially in conscious animals and its application to the pancreas represents a significant advance in the study of the circulation of this relatively inaccessible organ. The average pancreatic flow in fasting conscious dogs was 76 ml/min/100 g and was reduced to 49 ml/min/100 g by pentobarbital anesthesia. Blood flow was increased by secretin and cholecystokinin but the increase was often transient, even in the face of persistent augmentation of secretion. No effect on the H_2 clearance of the stomach was observed. Different results were obtained by Goodhead et al (114) who reported that secretin increased pancreatic secretion and blood flow to a comparable degree and at the same time increased blood flow throughout the gastrointestinal tract. Cholecystokinin, urecholine, and pentagastrin also increased pancreatic secretion and blood flow in this study.

Vagal stimulation produced an intense atropine-resistant vasodilatation and increased secretion in the pancreas of the pig (115). The vasodilatation had a short latent period, was well developed before the secretory response began, and subsided more rapidly than the secretory rate. Injections of acetylcholine produced effects similar to those of vagal stimulation, but were abolished by atropine. Secretin and cholecystokinin produced much smaller blood flow increases which began at the same time as the secretory response. There was no clearcut correlation between secretion and blood flow. The vasodilatation induced by vagal stimulation is probably mediated partly by metabolic vasodilator substances liberated in association with increased secretion and partly by specific vasodilator fibers via a transmitter not yet characterized. The neural component seems to be larger in the pig than in other species. Angiographic studies of the human pancreas indicate that secretin injected into the celiac or mesenteric arteries increases the diameter of pancreatic arteries and increases opacification of the capillaries and veins (116). These observations indicate that secretin increases human pancreatic blood flow and dilates the larger arteries as well as the smaller resistance vessels.

Spleen.—Recent studies have confirmed the relative absence of autoregulation in the spleen since flow changed proportionately when arterial pressure was varied over the range 40–140 mm Hg (117, 118). On the other hand, changes in venous pressure increased vascular resistance. A 33 mm Hg venous pressure increment increased resistance by an average of 26% and by 100% in individual cases. Thus the spleen, like the intestine and liver, possesses a pronounced "venovasomotoric" reaction (118). Fillenz (12) has shown that the splenic artery of the cat possesses both a cholinergic and an adrenergic innervation but only adrenergic fibers were present within the spleen. The innervation of the smooth muscle of the trabeculae was sparse. Unfortunately the innervation of the splenic veins, which are important in splenic emptying, was not discussed in detail.

Isoproterenol may substantially reduce splenic vascular resistance (38, 119). The capacitance vessels were initially dilated and then constricted (119). All responses were abolished by propranolol suggesting that β-receptor activation of splenic veins may induce both dilatation and constriction. Norepinephrine infusions constricted both resistance and capacitance vessels and this constriction was converted to a dilatation by phenoxybenzamine. Propranolol did not enhance norepinephrine constriction of the resistance vessels in this study although a considerable potentiation of the constrictor response to both injections and infusions or norepinephrine by β-adrenergic blockade has been reported by others (38). Epinephrine produced variable effects on splenic resistance vessels before blockade but invariably constricted after blockade. The capacitance vessels were con-

stricted before and after blockade. Sympathetic nerve stimulation reduced
splenic flow and weight (31). Flow tended to recover during continued
stimulation, but this "autoregulatory escape" was later in onset, slower in
development, and less complete than the comparable response in the intestinal circulation. Angiotensin and pitressin reduced splenic flow but had little
effect on the capacitance vessels.

Liver.—Takeuchi et al (120) have confirmed the many previous observations that autoregulation occurs in the hepatic arterial bed of dogs and
additionally showed that autoregulation persisted after severe hepatocellu-
lar damage produced by carbon tetrachloride. This is suggestive evidence
that the autoregulation is due to a myogenic response of the hepatic resistance vessels. No reciprocity of hepatic arterial and portal venous flow was
observed and the status of this controversial issue remains open. Ungvary &
Donath (14) have studied the adrenergic innervation of the liver and observed a unique appearance of the hepatic veins of the dog. The usual adventitiomedial nerve plexus was absent but there was a dense innervation of
all the layers of the media. This study demonstrates the anatomical basis for
the early changes in hepatic hemodynamics seen in certain types of shock in
this animal.

Contrary to previous reports, recent work has indicated that β-adrener-
gic receptors are present in the hepatic arterial resistance vessels as shown
by an isoproterenol-induced dilatation which was blocked by propranolol
(30, 39). Epinephrine and norepinephrine produced only vasoconstriction
and this was augmented by β-adrenergic blockage (39). Hepatic nerve
stimulation also produced vasoconstriction of the hepatic arterial bed and
this was reversed by phenoxybenzamine (30) indicating that neuronally released norepinephrine has access to β-adrenoreceptive sites. Rapid intraportal administration of catecholamines produced flow changes in the innervated and denervated hepatic arterial bed within a few seconds of injection
long before the agents could have recirculated (39). Similarly, Wangensteen et al (121) found that intraportal acetylcholine increased hepatic arterial flow. Vasoactive substances entering the circulation of the liver by way
of the portal vein therefore gain rapid access to the hepatic arterial resistance vessels. This is obviously important since the gut is the source of a
number of vasoactive agents. Circulating catecholamines have little direct
effect on portal flow which was initially unchanged following their intraportal administration. Their effects are mainly secondary to vascular changes
in the gastrointestinal and splenic circulations.

The importance of the liver as a blood reservoir in the cat has been confirmed (121). Hepatic blood volume was approximately 14% of the total
blood volume and half of this could be expelled by hepatic sympathetic
nerve stimulation with no change in portal blood flow or capillary filtration
coefficient. The adrenergic responses of the liver differ from those of the
intestine in that no sustained reduction in the area of exchange vessels oc-

curred. The rapidity and degree of "autoregulatory escape" of the hepatic arterial resistance vessels is also smaller (39).

Blood flow through the hepatic artery of the cat was reduced by intra-arterial or intravenous administration of glucagon (123). This effect is unique since other vascular beds either are dilated by glucagon or are unresponsive. Despite the arterial constriction, total hepatic flow increases as a result of increased portal vein flow secondary to mesenteric vasodilatation (124). Secretin also reduced hepatic arterial flow but the latency of response following close intra-arterial administration was longer than for glucagon and its action may therefore be indirect (125). The radiological studies of Uden (116) indicate that human hepatic arterial vessels may also be constricted by secretin.

Intestine.—Goodhead (126), using the ^{86}Rb-fractionation method, determined that mean flow in the canine duodenum varied from 104 ml/min/100 g in the proximal portion to 155 ml/min/100 g in the distal part. These values do not differ greatly from earlier determinations. On the other hand, colonic flow was 124 ml/min/100 g which is considerably higher than previously reported values.

Adrenergic responses: The superior mesenteric artery and its branches receive a dense adrenergic innervation in cats, dogs, and man (16, 127, 128). The norepinephrine content of the mesenteric arteries is considerably higher than that in other vessels and is five times that of the femoral artery (129). The veins receive a less dense innervation (16, 127).

Sympathetic nerve stimulation can reduce blood flow in the gut to zero but as stimulation continues flow returns to approximately control levels. At the termination of stimulation, flow increases rapidly and then falls slowly to the initial value. Throughout stimulation the capacitance vessels remain constricted and the capillary filtration is reduced. Norepinephrine infusions produce similar effects (for references see 58). The recovery of flow during continuing exposure to a constrictor influence has been termed autoregulatory escape and the subsequent increase in flow, reactive hyperemia. These terms are perhaps unfortunate. Autoregulation implies in a general sense the ability of a tissue to regulate its blood flow according to its metabolic needs and in a particular sense the ability to maintain a constant flow in the face of changing pressure gradients. Recent evidence suggests that the mechanisms responsible for mesenteric escape differ from those of autoregulation. Richardson & Johnson (130) found that escape occurred over a wider range of pressures than autoregulation, that autoregulation was dependent upon the initial state of the vascular bed whereas escape was not, that escape occurred in some preparations which did not exhibit autoregulation, and that autoregulation and escape could occur simultaneously without attenuation of either response. Escape during constrictor responses also appears to be a rather specific phenomenon. It occurs with epinephrine, norepinephrine, and angiotensin but not with methoxamine or pitressin (131).

For these reasons it is suggested that the term autoregulatory escape be abandoned and replaced by terms which do not imply the mechanism, e.g., flow recovery, norepinephrine escape, or sympathetic escape. Similarly the magnitude of the subsequent hyperemia seems to vary with the constrictor agent used and the term reactive hyperemia should perhaps be replaced by postinfusional hyperemia or poststimulation hyperemia.

The mechanism of escape has been much discussed (58, 131–133). It has been suggested that initially all vascular elements are constricted but subsequently vessels in the submucosa or deep mucosa relax whereas superficial mucosal resistance vessels remain constricted, i.e., that blood is "shunted" from mucosa to submucosa. Several difficulties are associated with this hypothesis: 1. There has been no clear anatomical demonstration of shunts. The early findings of Spanner (134) have not been confirmed. 2. Microsphere studies have failed to demonstrate a greater percentage of 20 μ microspheres in the liver following their injection into the superior mesenteric artery during epinephrine infusion (135). This indicates that if shunting occurs, it takes place through vessels smaller than 20 μ. 3. There is no increase in mesenteric venous O_2 content during the escape as might be expected if shunt vessels opened (136). If the shunt occurred through exchange vessels in a tissue with similar metabolic activity as the ischemic zone, a change in venous O_2 would not necessarily occur. However, it is difficult to conceive that the submucosa of the cat which is composed of dense connective tissue could have the same metabolic rate as the highly cellular mucosa. 4. The "shunting" hypothesis does not explain why escape is not seen during methoxamine or pitressin infusion or why the magnitude and rapidity of escape is diminished by β-adrenergic blockade (36, 131). 5. Escape occurs in a number of other tissues, e.g., liver (39) and spleen (31), and even in isolated arteries and arterioles (32, 33, 137) so that it does not demand a specialized vascular structural basis such as occurs in the small intestine.

Richardson & Johnson (130) believed that their data could best be explained by a secondary relaxation of the same vascular elements which were initially constricted. This relaxation would have to be more prominent and more prolonged than the constrictor effect in order to explain the subsequent hyperemia. It seems possible that a vasodilator substance might be liberated by sympathetic nerve stimulation, catecholamines, or angiotensin, but not by methoxamine or pitressin. The effect of β-adrenergic blockade might then be explained by the enhancement of catecholamine constriction which would more effectively antagonize the vasodilator agent. This view is of course purely speculative, but it should be possible to test it, possibly by a bioassay method. "Escape" also occurs during the administration of vasodilator agents but here also the phenomenon shows specificity since it occurs during infusions of prostaglandin and bradykinin but not of acetylcholine (138), isoproterenol (131), dilator doses of epinephrine (36), or dopamine (139). An angiographic study in man failed to demonstrate any constrictor effect of intramesenteric arterial infusions of epinephrine on the superior mesenteric artery or its branches. After β-adrenergic blockade, however, epinephrine greatly reduced the diameter of these vessels (140). This suggests that both α and β adrenoreceptors are present in human mesenteric arteries and raises the possibility that "escape" may occur in man.

The mechanism of action of norepinephrine has been studied in an isolated mesenteric artery preparation (141). Theophylline and sodium nitrite produced a Ca-dependent inhibition of the constrictor response. Theophylline also reduced or abolished pitressin constriction indicating that its action was not merely due to α-adrenergic blockade. Isoproterenol, a known stimulator of adenyl cyclase in some tissues, did not inhibit norepinephrine constriction. The action of theophylline was therefore probably not related to accumulation of cyclic AMP. It was speculated that theophylline may have interfered with the availability of Ca^{++} to the contractile proteins. Norepinephrine mesenteric constriction is also antagonized by a number of other agents, including prostaglandin E_1 (142), histamine, and betahistine (143). Malik & Ling (144) have described the effect of acetylcholine on the response of perfused rat mesenteric arteries to sympathetic stimulation. Very low concentrations of acetylcholine (50 pg/ml) increased the constrictor response but high concentrations reduced or abolished it. The block was abolished by amphetamine, atropine, or increased concentrations of Ca in the perfusion fluid. It was speculated that exogenous acetylcholine acted upon the postulated "cholinergic link" mechanism of adrenergic transmission but this cannot be the whole story since acetylcholine partially blocked the response to norepinephrine. It would be instructive to determine whether this interaction between acetylcholine and sympathetic nerve stimulation occurs in other vascular beds. Its physiological significance has not been established but it is of interest that in some tissues cholinergic and adrenergic fibers may lie close together in the same Schwann cell, and in the iris and heart contacts that may represent axo-axonal synapses have been observed (145).

The cardiovascular effects of dopamine were recently reviewed (146). It has a predominantly vasodilator action on the mesenteric resistance vessels but an initial constriction may occur, especially with larger doses. The renal vascular bed behaves similarly. Despite the close structural relationship between dopamine, epinephrine, and norepinephrine, the renal and mesenteric vasodilatation persists after β-adrenergic blockade. It has therefore been proposed that specific dopamine receptors are present in the gut and kidney. Support for this view comes from recent observations that renal and mesenteric dilatation induced by dopamine is selectively inhibited by haloperidol (147). However the effect of the latter is extremely transient and the dose range over which specific dopamine blockade is demonstrable is very narrow. Larger doses also reduce the dilator effects of bradykinin and isoproterenol.

Cholinergic mechanisms: Cholinergic nerve fibers can be demonstrated in close association with intestinal arterial vessels (9, 22) but neurogenic mesenteric cholinergic vasodilatation has never been demonstrated in mammals. Interesting effects have however been shown in the domestic chicken and have been described in an earlier section.

Other neural mechanisms: Pelvic nerve stimulation produced an intense but poorly sustained dilatation of the colonic mucosa, particularly in the distal two thirds (148). Secretion also increased and the secretory fluid was found to have vasodilator activity. It was suggested, by analogy with the salivary glands, that kinins might be involved but direct evidence for this has not been obtained.

Peptides: Said & Mutt (149) have described a peptide isolated from gut which dilated the femoral, hepatic, and mesenteric vascular beds. It was inactivated in the liver and its activity was distinct from, and many times greater than, that of secretin or cholecystokinin. Glucagon (123), secretin (125), and cholecystokinin (150) are potent mesenteric vasodilators and secretin and cholecystokinin appear to be effective in amounts in the physiological range. Fara, Rubinstein & Sonnenschein (150) have shown that 3–6 min after milk was placed in the cat duodenum, superior mesenteric flow increased by 50–100%, duodenal motility increased, and sedation occurred. The effect was due to the lipid component of the milk. The flow and motility responses, but not the sedative effects, were blocked by atropine. Cholecystokinin mimicked most aspects of the response but inhibited duodenal motility. These interesting results suggest that fat in the duodenum increases mesenteric blood flow by releasing vasodilator substances which may include cholecystokinin. Atropine blockade may be due to interference with cholecystokinin release (151). It was subsequently shown (152) that intraduodenal instillation of corn oil or 1-phenylalanine increased superior mesenteric blood flow, pancreatic blood flow, gallbladder pressure, duodenal motility, pancreatic enzyme output, and pancreatic and intestinal O_2 consumption. Intravenous cholecystokinin produced similar effects. The vasodilator effect of this peptide might therefore be secondary to an increased tissue demand for oxygen.

The distributions of vascular effects produced by glucagon and secretin in the cat were very similar (123). Both increased superior mesenteric flow and had little or no effect on femoral or renal flow. Hepatic arterial flow was reduced by both agents. The structures of these two peptides closely resemble each other and it might be profitable to examine structure-activity relationships of fragments of these molecules.

Miscellaneous factors: Perfusion of the lumen of the proximal jejunum with hypertonic glucose solution increased its blood flow but the effect was entirely local and no change in flow occurred in nonperfused jejunal areas (153). Mechanical stimulation of the jejunal mucosa also increased jejunal flow in cats with a latency of 20–30 sec and a duration of 10–15 min (154). The response was unaltered by splanchnic nerve section, vagotomy, atropine, or ganglionic blocking agents. The latency and duration suggest the release of a vasodilator material and it would be of interest to determine whether blood flow in other areas was altered.

The relationship between intestinal motor activity and blood flow is complex (155). The ultimate response represents an integration of the effects of (a) active contraction of the intestinal smooth muscle, (b) changes in passive tension secondary to changes in intraluminal pressure, (c) alteration in the composition of the extracellular fluid secondary to the metabolic changes associated with muscle contractions, and (d) direct effects on the intestinal vasculature of the agents inducing the motility change. The relative importance of each of these factors will of course vary in different circumstances.

Blood flow in the canine superior mesenteric artery increases and mesenteric vascular resistance decreases after eating (156, 157). The increased flow begins 5–15 min after presentation of food, reaches a maximum in 30–90 min, and returns to control levels in 3–7 hr (157). The mesenteric vasodilatation is blocked by atropine but not by bilateral thoracic vagotomy or by α- or β-adrenergic blockade. These observations are compatible with an atropine-sensitive release of vasodilator substances and when taken in conjunction with the observations of Fara et al (150), discussed above, it seems likely that cholecystokinin is involved. The association of atropine sensitivity and the failure of vagotomy to block the response suggests that intrinsic cholinergic mechanisms in the gut wall may participate in the release of the postprandial vasodilator agent or agents.

During exercise the percentage of the cardiac output distributed by the superior canine mesenteric artery declines. Mesenteric flow remains close to resting values, but arterial pressure rises and hence mesenteric resistance is increased. Exercise performed during digestion, 90 min after taking food, produced a smaller pressor response than in the fasting state and therefore a smaller increase in calculated vascular resistance (158).

KIDNEY

The distribution of nutrient blood flow in the kidney of the unanesthetized dog was found by an indicator fractionation method to be cortex 86%, outer medulla 11.6%, and inner medulla 2.5% (159). These results were remarkably similar to those obtained by other methods (e.g., 160). Carrière (161) found that norepinephrine produced a patchy reduction in cortical flow, the outer cortex being most severely affected. Medullary flow increased. These effects were blocked by phenoxybenzamine. The α-adrenotropic receptors thus appeared to be present mainly in the outer cortex and were absent from the inner medulla. Isoproterenol was without effect in this study, but others have obtained a small vasodilator response (40). Angiotensin reduced both cortical and medullary flow (162). The cortical constriction, like that induced by norepinephrine, was nonuniform. Some areas, particularly the subcapsular aglomerular area, were grossly constricted whereas other portions were relatively unaffected. The decreased medullary flow was presumably due to constriction of the vasa recta. Angiotensin also increased PAH extraction and promoted Na retention possibly because of diversion of blood flow to the longer-loop nephrons of the juxtamedullary zone. The effects of angiotensin however are dose dependent and larger doses can induce natriuresis which may be the result of prostaglandin release (163). These and many earlier studies, reviewed by Hatch (164), reflect the growing interest in intrarenal blood flow.

Studies of the cholinergic innervation of autotransplanted kidneys revealed that total degeneration was infrequent (20). Acetylcholinesterase-positive nerve fibers accompanied the renal, interlobar, arcuate, and interlobular arteries and the vasa recta. The source of these fibers was believed to be acetylcholinesterase-positive ganglion cells found at the renal hilum. These ganglion cells and their fibers may play a role in autoregulation. Stinson et al (165) have shown that lowering the renal perfusion pressure in unanesthetized dogs does not change total renal blood flow or its distribution, which indicates that resistance is reduced equally in cortex and medulla. After atropine, the decrease in resistance did not occur and blood flow was reduced, particularly in the juxtamedullary cortex and outer medulla. Similar findings were obtained after surgical denervation. MacFarlane (166) has observed that acetylcholine injected into the renal artery produced vasodilation in that kidney but reduced vascular filling in the contralateral kidney. Denervation of either kidney prevented the response. These results demonstrate the existence of a renorenal vasoconstrictor reflex which might function to maintain total renal blood flow constant despite blood flow changes in one kidney. It would be interesting to determine whether other vasodilators induce this response and whether renorenal vasodilator reflexes occur.

The mechanism of autoregulation continues to be the principal focus of renal circulatory research. Kiil, Kjekshus & Löyning (167) found autoregulation unimpaired by infusions of norepinephrine or angiotensin or by sympathetic nerve stimulation adequate to reduce renal flow by 50%. It was conjectured that vasoactive agents might act mainly on smooth muscle cells other than those participating in autoregulation. This investigation did not support the view that autoregulation is overpowered by increased sympathetic activity (168) or the hypothesis that angiotensin is responsible for autoregulation which still occurred after tachyphylaxis to angiotensin had developed.

There is an association between autoregulation, perfusion, and renal vascular responses (169). In denervated autoregulating kidneys, responsiveness to acetylcholine, norepinephrine, adenosine, and angiotensin was a function of renal perfusion pressure. In contrast, nonautoregulating kidneys failed to show such a relationship. It could not be determined whether the pressure-dependent responsiveness was the cause or the consequence of autoregulation. The results have interesting clinical implications: they suggest that hypertension may sensitize the renal resistance vessels to vasoconstrictor substances thus leading to an escalating increase in systemic pressure.

Several diuretics increase renal blood flow and impair autoregulation (170) but the mechanism is unclear. The effects were probably not due to a direct action on vascular smooth muscle because similar changes were induced by raising ureteral pressure and because the onset and development of response were slow and paralleled the increase in urine flow. Chlorothiazide and chlormerodrin both increased renal vascular resistance but only chlormerodrin depressed autoregulation. Ethacrynic acid, chlormerodrin, furosemide, and mannitol all depressed renal vasoconstrictor responses, but this effectiveness did not parallel their ability to inhibit autoregulation. Thus, the effect of diuretics on autoregulation cannot be ascribed to natriuresis, to renal vasodilatation, or to their ability to affect renal vascular responsiveness.

The possibility that adenosine or 5′-adenosine monophosphate (5′-AMP) may be normal mediators of both autoregulation and renin secretion has been raised (171). Infusions of adenosine and 5′-AMP in anesthetized salt-depleted dogs initially reduced renal flow, but in the steady state flow was unchanged or slightly increased. Afferent arteriolar resistance increased, efferent resistance decreased. Adenosine triphosphate and cyclic AMP increased renal blood flow with no change in afferent resistance and a decrease in efferent resistance. All these agents decreased glomerular filtration rate, filtration fraction, Na excretion, and renal venous renin activity. It was suggested that adenosine or 5′-AMP might be released by a raised perfusion pressure and so account for autoregulation, although it was recognized that there was no direct evidence for the release of these compounds and that the data cited might not be relevant to states other than salt depletion.

Changes in Na balance have a profound effect on the renal circulation in man (172). Flow rate increased and there was evidence of increased cortical and reduced juxtamedullary perfusion when the daily intake of NaCl was 200 meq/day. On the other hand, NaCl restriction to 10 meq/day decreased total and cortical flow rates, but increased juxtamedullary flow. Patterns occur similar to those associated with high Na intake after diuretics and saline loading, and patterns resembling those of Na restriction are found in congestive cardiac failure and hemorrhage. Thus changes in intrarenal distribution of blood flow seem to be important in Na handling.

Elevation of ureteral pressure during mild saline diuresis increased total renal blood flow (173). Outer cortical flow increased whereas flow in the juxtamedullary zone was unchanged. On the other hand, increased ureteral pressure diminished total and cortical renal blood flow during copious mannitol-induced diuresis. Mannitol relaxed isolated renal arterial strips. The renal circulatory changes following ureteral occlusion therefore selectively involve the renal cortex and are probably secondary to increased tissue pressure. During mild saline diuresis, the afferent arterioles may dilate in response to the reduction in transmural pressure. On the other hand, mannitol dilates these vessels and the effect of increased tissue pressure is then to reduce flow.

The effect of intra-arterial infusions of varying osmolarity on renal vascular resistance was investigated by Gazitua et al. (174). Hypertonic dextrose produced a sustained reduction of renal vascular resistance with no 'overshoot' when the infusion terminated. Hypertonic NaCl and urea produced poorly sustained decreases in resistance, and a significant rise in resistance occurred when the infusions stopped. Isosmotic solutions of urea, but not of dextrose or NaCl, increased resistance as did hypotonic solutions of all three substances. It was considered that the sustained dilatation produced by hyperosmotic dextrose was due to the relative impermeability of the cell membranes of vascular smooth muscle to this substance, whereas the waning response of urea and NaCl was due to the entry of these molecules into the cells with a consequent reduction of the osmotic gradient. This explanation receives support from similar observations on the effects of urea on the isolated portal vein (74). The possibility that other factors such as renin might be involved is not excluded by these experiments since changes in neither renal function nor renin secretion were measured.

Wexler & Kao (175) have used cross-perfusion methods in anesthetized dogs to show that a humoral mechanism was responsible for the reduced renal blood flow which occurred with exercise, but the precise factor or factors involved could not be determined. The relevance of this study to spontaneous exercise in conscious dogs is uncertain since renal blood flow may not change appreciably under these circumstances (176).

Several prostaglandins have been isolated from the renal medulla in recent years. Fujimoto & Lockett (177) have shown that intravenous prostaglandin E_1 in cats produces a fall in renal perfusion pressure and an increase in GFR, but no change in filtration fraction, natriuresis, or diuresis; renal lymph flow increased. Intravenous norepinephrine increased renal perfusion pressure, GFR, filtration fraction, and renal lymph flow and also produced natriuresis and diuresis. An increased concentration of a prostaglandin-like substance in the renal lymph was also observed. Complete α- and β-adrenergic blockade prevented the rise in perfusion pressure and filtration fraction produced by norepinephrine, but did not prevent the natriuresis, the diuresis, or the effects on renal lymph. The natriuretic and diuretic actions of norepinephrine therefore seem to be attributable to prostaglandin release.

The Brain

Regional cerebral blood flow continues to be actively studied by a number of methods. The rate of clearance of ^{133}Xe from the human brain was followed using multiple collimated external detectors (178). Perfusion of grey matter was low in the temporal region and high in the precentral area, and the white matter of the internal capsule was more highly perfused than white matter elsewhere. A relatively low perfusion of the temporal lobes has also been found in conscious dogs (179). The average perfusion of grey matter was approximately five times that of white matter, a value similar to that obtained by previous workers. However, autoradiographic methods in cats have shown that grey matter flow varies considerably, for example 74 ml/100 g/min in the olfactory cortex and 174 ml/100 g/min in the inferior colliculus (180).

The view that neural control of the cerebral circulation is of minor importance is being seriously challenged. An extensive adrenergic innervation has been observed in vessels of the pia, hypothalamus, pons, medulla, and basal ganglia but only rarely in the deep vessels of the cortex, cerebellum, and spinal cord and not at all in the choroid plexuses (181). Sympathetic stimulation reduced cerebral blood flow in anesthetized dogs by 30% despite a reduction in arterial O_2 tension and an increase in CO_2 tension (182). Sympathectomy increased blood flow and enhanced the dilator response to CO_2 in anesthetized baboons. Sympathetic stimulation reduced cerebral flow and its effect was greater at high flow rates. Section of the carotid sinus, vagus, and aortic nerves reduced the dilator effects of hypercapnia and hypoxia and stimulation of the central ends of the vagus and aortic nerves produced cerebral vasodilatation independently of changes in Pco_2. Vasodilator fibers were demonstrated in the seventh cranial nerve (183). Metabolic influences on the cerebral vessels may thus be modified by neural activity and the circulation of the brain may be altered reflexly. At least part of the afferent pathway lies in the vagus (possibly originating from baro- and chemoreceptors). Constrictor sympathetic efferents synapse in the superior cervical ganglion. Some dilator fibers travel in the facial nerve, but the pathway for the remainder is not known. Cholinergic nerve fibers have been demonstrated in cerebral arteries (21) and atropine, but not hexamethonium, abolished the dilatation of rabbit pial arteries following a reduction in pressure (184). A local neural mechanism rather than a true reflex may therefore be involved in this response and the question arises whether nerve endings can sense changes in the metabolic demands of the cortex and react appropriately.

The papers presented at the international symposium on cerebral blood flow held in Mainz in 1969 have now been published (185). Although much of the symposium was devoted to clinical matters, several papers of physiological interest should be mentioned. Kanzow & Dieckhoff (186) showed that 40% of the resistance of the cortical circulation was situated between the aorta and arterioles of 30–40 μ diameter. They suggested, therefore, that more than 50% of the blood flow resistance of the cerebral cortex was not enclosed in cerebral tissue and concluded that this part of the resistance could not be adjusted by a direct influence of metabolites. This conclusion has yet to be supported by direct evidence. There was active discussion as to whether the mechanism of cerebral flow autoregulation is myogenic or metabolic. The former hypothesis was favored by Ekström-Jodal et al (187) who found that autoregulation did not occur in response to a reduction of perfusion pressure produced by raising the venous pressure, but did occur when equivalent or greater reductions were achieved by decreasing arterial pressure. The fact that autoregulation is impaired by changing from pulsatile to nonpulsatile perfusion pressure while a constant mean pressure is maintained was also held to support the myogenic hypothesis (188). However, the metabolic theory remains attractive because of the usual close correlation between the extracellular pH of the brain and cerebral blood flow and the observation that changes in cerebral venous pH and lactate/pyruvate ratio could be detected when cerebrospinal fluid pressure was raised in an autoregulating preparation in which blood flow remained constant (189). The influence of extracellular pH has been directly shown in an elegant study in which solutions of varying acid and base content were applied by a microinjection technique to the vicinity of pial arterioles of 30–100 μ diam. It was suggested that extracellular pH changes might act through an effect on membrane potential or a Ca pump (190).

Considerable variation in the sensitivity of flow to changing CO_2 levels occurs in different parts of the brain and appears to be directly related to their perfusion rates (191). Sensitivity was highest in the prosencephalon and lowest in the thoracic cord (3.05 as compared to 0.54 ml/100 g/min per mm Hg rise in arterial P_{CO_2}). Variations in CO_2 sensitivity have also been found in the spinal cord of goats (192). A role for adenosine in the control of the cerebral vascular resistance seems to have been excluded since it has negligible effects on cerebrovascular conductance (193). Tissue osmolality also appears unimportant since intracarotid injections of hyperosmolar dextrose yielded only a small increase in cerebral flow. On the other hand, hyperosmolar solutions of KCl, NaCl, and LiCl had a pronounced dilator effect preceded by a brief period of constriction (194).

CONCLUDING REMARKS

The last year has seen little change in our basic concepts of the regional circulation. Much patient work has unearthed a multitude of interesting new facts but, as Bülbring (6) has remarked in another context, although much has been observed, little is known. The key questions of how blood flow is linked to function and how neural and local factors interact are unanswered for many of the vascular beds. A commendable trend has been the increasing number of experiments in which regional distribution of blood flow within an organ is measured as well as total flow. More studies than ever before are also being carried out on unanesthetized animals. Future work is likely to be greatly facilitated by recent advances in the catheter electromagnetic flowmeter which has now been so reduced in size that it can be introduced percutaneously and yet will permit flow to be measured in any vessel (195). Such devices used in association with isotope clearance methods may greatly expand our knowledge of circulatory physiology in man as well as in animals.

LITERATURE CITED

1. Wiederhelm, L. A. 1971. Circulation: microcirculation. *Ann. Rev. Physiol.* 33:

2. Somlyo, A. P., Somlyo, A. V. 1968. Vascular smooth muscle. I. Normal structure, pathology, biochemistry, and biophysics. *Pharmacol. Rev.* 20:197–272

3. Somlyo, A. P., Somlyo, A. V. 1970. Vascular smooth muscle. II. Pharmacology of normal and hypertensive vessels. *Pharmacol. Rev.* 22: 249–353

4. Various authors. Vasomotion and electrophysiology of smooth muscle in *The Pulmonary Circulation and Interstitial Space*, ed. A. P. Fishman, H. H. Hecht, 127–88. Chicago: Univ. Chicago Press. 432 pp.

5. Bevan, J. A., Furchgott, R. F., Maxwell, R. A., Somlyo, A. P., Eds. 1970. *Physiology and Pharmacology of Vascular Neuroeffector Systems*. Basel: Karger

6. Bülbring, E., Brading, A. F., Jones, A. W., Tomita, T., Eds. 1970. *Smooth Muscle*. London: Arnold, 676 pp.

7. Verity, M. A., Bevan, J. A. Fine structural study of the terminal effector plexus, neuromuscular and intermuscular relationships in the pulmonary artery. *J. Anat.* 103: 49–63

8. Bevan, J. A., Nedergaard, O. A., Osher, J. V., Su, C., Torok, J., Verity, M. A. 1970. On the mechanism of neurotramuscular transmission in blood vessels. *Proc. 4th Int. Congr. Pharmacol.* Vol. 11. Basel: Schwabe

9. Schenk, E. A., El Badawi, A. 1968. Dual innervation of arteries and arterioles. *Z. Zellforsch. Mikrosk. Anat.* 91:170–77

10. Lever, J. D., Graham, J. D. P., Irvine, G., Chick, W. J. 1965. The vesiculated axons in relation to arteriolar smooth muscle in the pancreas. A fine structural and quantitative study. *J. Anat.* 99: 299–313

11. Lever, J. D., Ahmed, M., Irvine, G. 1965. Neuromuscular and intercellular relationships in the coronary arterioles. A morphological and quantitative study by light and electron microscopy. *J. Anat.* 99: 829–40

12. Fillenz, M. 1970. The innervation of the cat spleen. *Proc. Roy. Soc. B* 174:459–68

13. Rhodin, J. A. G., 1967. The ultrastructure of mammalian arterioles and precapillary sphincters. *J. Ultrastruct. Res.* 18:181–223

14. Ungvary, G., Donath, T. 1969. On the monoaminergic innervation of the liver. *Acta Anat.* 72:446–59

15. Mayer, H. E., Abboud, F. M., Ballard, D. R., Eckstein, J. W. 1968. Catecholamines in arteries and veins of the foreleg of dog. *Circ. Res.* 23:653–81

16. Jacobowitz, D. 1965. Histochemical studies of the autonomic innervation of the gut. *J. Pharmacol. Exp. Ther.* 149:358–64

17. Rhodin, J. A. 1968. Ultrastructure of mammalian venous capillaries, venules and small collecting veins. *J. Ultrastruct. Res.* 25:452–500

18. Johansson, B., Ljung, B. 1970. The neuroeffector system of a propagating vascular smooth muscle. *Physiology and Pharmacology of Vascular Neuroeffector Mechanisms*. See Ref. 5

19. Bell, C. 1968. Dual vasoconstrictor and vasodilator innervation of the uterine arterial supply in the guinea pig. *Circ. Res.* 23:279–89

20. Weitsen, H. A., Norwell, J. E. 1969. Cholinergic innervation of the autotransplanted canine kidney. *Circ. Res.* 25:535–41

21. Iwayama, T., Furness, J. B., Burnstock, G. 1970. Dual adrenergic and cholinergic innervation of the cerebral arteries of the rat: An ultrastructural study. *Circ. Res.* 26:635–646

22. Bolme, P., Fuxe, K. 1970. Adrenergic and cholinergic nerve terminals in skeletal muscle vessels. *Acta Physiol. Scand.* 78:52–59

23. Bolme, P., Novotny, J., Uvnäs, B., Wright, P. G. 1970. Species distribution of sympathetic cholinergic vasodilator nerves in skeletal muscle. *Acta Physiol. Scand.* 78: 60–4

24. Bell, C. 1969. Indirect cholinergic vasomotor control of intestinal blood flow in the domestic chicken. *J. Physiol.* 205:317–28

25. Bell, C. 1969. Fine structural localization of acetylcholinesterase at a

cholinergic vasodilator nerve-arterial smooth muscle synapse. *Circ. Res.* 24 :61–70

26. Ikeda, M. 1970. Adrenergic innervation of the ductus arteriosus of the fetal lamb. *Experientia* 26 :525–26

27. Silva, D. G., Ikeda, M. 1971. Ultrastructural and acetylcholinesterase studies on the innervation of the ductus arteriosus, pulmonary trunk and aorta of the fetal lamb. *J. Ultrastruct. Res.* In press

28. Moran, W. C. 1970. Beta adrenergic blockade: an historical review and evaluation. *Cardiovascular beta-adrenergic responses,* ed. A. A. Kattus, G. Ross, V. E. Hall, 1–20. Los Angeles: Univ. Calif. Press. 284 pp.

29. Viveros, D. H., Garlick, D. G., Renkin, E. M. 1968. Sympathetic beta adrenergic vasodilatation in skeletal muscle of the dog. *Am. J. Physiol.* 215 :1218–25

30. Greenway, C. V., Lawson, A. E. 1969. Beta-adrenergic receptors in the hepatic arterial bed of the anesthetized cat. *Can. J. Physiol. Pharmacol.* 47 :415–20

31. Greenway, C. V., Lawson, A. E., Stark, R. D. 1968. Vascular responses of the spleen to nerve stimulation during normal and reduced blood flow. *J. Physiol. London* 194 :421–33

32. Gerová, M., Gero, J. 1968. The effect of prolonged sympathetic stimulation on conduit vessel diameter. *Experientia* 24 :1134–35

33. Burks, T. F., Cooper, T. 1967. Enhancement of peripheral alpha-receptor stimulation by blockade of "silent" beta receptors. *Circ. Res.* 21 :703–15

34. Celander, O. 1954. The range of control exercised by the "sympathicoadrenal system". *Acta Physiol. Scand.* 32 : *Suppl. 116,* 1–132

35. Greenway, C. V., Lawson, A. V. 1966. The effects of adrenaline and noradrenaline on venous return and regional blood flows with special reference to intestinal blood flow. *J. Physiol. London* 186 : 579–95

36. Ross, G. 1967. Effects of epinephrine and norepinephrine on the mesenteric circulation of the cat. *Am. J. Physiol.* 212 :1037–42

37. Pitt, B., Elliot, E. C., Gregg, D. E. 1967. Adrenergic receptor activity in the coronary arteries of the unanesthetized dog. *Circ. Res.* 21: 75–86

38. Ross, G. 1967. Effects of catecholamines on splenic blood flow in the cat. *Am. J. Physiol.* 213 :1079–83

39. Ross, G., Kurrasch, M. 1969. Adrenergic responses of the hepatic circulation. *Am. J. Physiol.* 1380–85

40. Mark, A. L., Eckstein, J. W., Abboud, F. M., Wendling, M. G. 1969. Renal vascular responses to isoproterenol. *Am. J. Physiol.* 217 :764–67

41. Lands, A. M., Arnold, A., McAuliff, J. P., Luduena, F. B., Brown, T. G. 1967. Differentiation of receptor systems activated by sympathomimetic amines. *Nature* 214 :597–98

42. Levy, B., Wilkenfeld, B. E. 1969. An analysis of selective beta receptor blockade. *Eur. J. Pharmacol.* 5 : 227–33

43. Dunlop, D., Shanks, R. G. 1968. Selective blockade of adrenoceptive beta receptors in the heart. *Brit. J. Pharmacol.* 32 :201–18

44. Bevan, J. A. 1969. Some structural considerations of the reactivity of vascular smooth muscle. *Microvasc. Res.* 1 :329–34

45. Belleau, B. 1967. Stereochemistry of adrenergic receptors: newer concepts on the molecular mechanism of action of catecholamines and antiadrenergic drugs at the receptor level. *Ann. NY Acad. Sci.* 139 :580–605

46. Bloom, B. M., Goldman, I. M. 1966. The nature of the catecholamine-adenine mononucleotide interactions in adrenergic mechanisms. *Advan. Drug Res.* 3 :121–69

47. Robison, G. A., Butcher, R. W., Sutherland, E. W. 1967. Adenyl cyclase as an adrenergic receptor. *Ann. NY Acad. Sci.* 139 :703–23

48. Bolme, P., Novotny, J. 1969. Conditional reflex activation of the sympathetic cholinergic vasodilator nerves in the dog. *Acta Physiol. Scand.* 77 :58–67

49. Bolme, P., Edwall, L. 1970. The disappearance of Xe[133] and I[125] from skeletal muscle of the anesthetized dog during sympathetic cholinergic vasodilatation. *Acta Physiol. Scand.* 78 :28–38

50. Djojosugito, A. M., Folkow, B.,

Lisander, B., Sparks, H. 1968. Mechanism of escape of skeletal muscle resistance vessels from influence of sympathetic cholinergic vasodilator fiber activity. *Acta Physiol. Scand.* 72 :148–56

51. Bolme, P., Novotny, J. 1969. Oxygen uptake of skeletal muscle in the anesthetized dog during sympathetic vasodilatation. *Acta Physiol. Scand.* 77 :333–42

52. Mauskopf, J. M., Gray, S. D., Renkin, E. M. 1969. Transient and persistent components of sympathetic cholinergic vasodilatation. *Am. J. Physiol.* 216 :92–97

53. Folkow, B., Haeger, K., Uvnäs, B. 1948. Cholinergic vasodilator nerves in the sympathetic outflow to the muscles of the hind limbs of the cat. *Acta Physiol. Scand.* 15 :401–11

54. Schenk, E. A., Honig, C. R. 1970. Ganglion cells in skeletal muscle arterioles: Role in sympathetic vasodilation. *Fed. Proc.* 29 :613 Abstr.

55. Tobia, A. J., Adams, M. D., Miya, T. S., Bousquet, W. F. 1969. Histamine and reflex vasodilatation in the rat. *Life Sci.* 8: Part 1, 745–50

56. Heitz, D. C., Shaffer, R. A., Brody, M. J. 1970. Active vasodilatation evoked by stimulation of sinus nerves in the conscious dog. *Am. J. Physiol.* 218 :1296–300

57. Altura, B. M., Zweifach, B. W. 1965. Antihistamines and vascular reactivity. *Am. J. Physiol.* 209 :545–49

58. Mellander, S., Johansson, B. 1968. Control of resistance, exchange and capacitance functions in the peripheral circulation. *Pharmacol. Rev.* 20 :117–96

59. Sonnenschein, R. R., White, F. N. 1968. Systemic circulation: local control. *Ann. Rev. Physiol.* 30: 147–70

60. Campbell, G. 1970. Autonomic nervous supply to effector tissues. See Ref. 6, 451–95

61. Donald, D. E., Ferguson, D. A. 1970. A study of the sympathetic vasoconstrictor nerves to the vessels of the dog hind limb. *Circ. Res.* 26 :171–84

62. Honig, C. R., Frierson, J. L., Patterson, J. L. 1970. Comparison of neural controls of resistance and capillary density in resting muscle. *Am. J. Physiol.* 218 :937–42

63. Johansson, B., Lundgren, O., Mellander, S. 1964. Reflex influence of "somatic pressor and depressor afferents" on resistance and capacitance vessels and on transcapillary fluid exchange. *Acta Physiol. Scand.* 62 :280–86

64. Gerová, M., Gero, J. 1969. Range of the sympathetic control of the dog femoral artery. *Circ. Res.* 24 :349–59

65. Abdel-Sayed, W. A., Abboud, F. M., Ballard, D. R. 1970. Contribution of venous resistance to total vascular resistance in skeletal muscle. *Am. J. Physiol.* 218 :1291–95

66. Fuxe, K., Sedvall, G. 1965. The distribution of adrenergic nerve fibers to the blood vessels in skeletal muscle. *Acta Physiol. Scand.* 64: 75–86

67. Hilton, S. M., Jeffries, M. G., Vrbova, G. 1970. Functional specialization of the vascular bed of soleus. *J. Physiol. London* 206 :543–63

68. Hudlická, O. 1969. Resting and postcontraction blood flow in slow and fast muscles of the chick during development. *Microvasc. Res.* 1: 390–402

69. Reis, D. J., Moorhead, D., Wooten, G. F. 1969. Differential regulation of blood flow to red and white muscle in sleep and defense behavior. *Am. J. Physiol.* 217 :541–46

70. Rodbard, S., Ed. 1971. *Local Regulation of Blood Flow. Suppl. 1. Circ. Res.* 28. In press

71. Rodbard, S. 1971. Capillary control of blood flow and fluid exchange. See Ref. 70

72. Duling, B. R., Berne, R. M. 1970. Propagated vasodilatation in the microcirculation of the hamster cheek pouch. *Circ. Res.* 26 :163–70

73. Mellander, S., Lundvall, J. 1971. The role of tissue hyperosmolality in exercise hyperemia. See Ref. 70.

74. Arvill, A., Johansson, B., Jonsson, O. 1969. Effects of hyperosmolarity on the volume of vascular smooth muscle cells and the relation between cell volume and muscle activity. *Acta Physiol. Scand.* 75: 484–95

75. Overbeck, H. W., Grega, G. J. 1970. Response of the limb vascular bed in man to intra-arterial infusions

of hypertonic dextrose or hypertonic sodium chloride solutions. *Circ. Res.* 26:717–32

76. Scott, J. B., Radawski, D. 1971. Role of hyperosmolarity in the genesis of active and reactive hyperemia. See Ref. 70

77. Stainsby, W. N., Barclay, J. K. 1971. Effect of infusions of osmotically active substances on muscle blood flow and systemic blood pressure. See Ref. 70

78. Skinner, N. S., Jr., Costin, J. C. 1971. Interactions between oxygen, potassium and osmolality in the regulation of skeletal muscle blood flow. See Ref. 70

79. Duling, B. R., Berne, R. M. 1971. Longitudinal gradients in periarteriolar oxygen tension: a possible mechanism for the participation of oxygen in local regulation of blood flow. See Ref. 70

80. Reich, T., Tuckman, J., Naftchi, N. E., Jacobson, J. H. 1970. Effect of normo- and hyperbaric oxygenation on resting and postexercise calf blood flow. *J. Appl. Physiol.* 28:275–78

81. Bond, R. F., Blackard, R. F., Taxis, J. A. 1969. Evidence against oxygen being the primary factor governing autoregulation. *Am. J. Physiol.* 216:788–93

82. Kontos, H. A., Richardson, D. W., Raper, A. J., Patterson, J. L. 1970. Contribution of hypercapnia and hypoxia to the vasodilator response to ischemia. *Clin. Sci.* In press

83. Hilton, S. M. 1971. A new candidate for mediator of functional vasodilatation in skeletal muscle. See Ref. 70

84. Donald, D. E., Rowlands, D. J., Ferguson, D. A. 1970. Similarity of blood flow in the normal and the sympathectomized dog hind limb during graded exercise. *Circ. Res.* 26:185–99

85. Mosley, J. G. 1969. A reduction in some vasodilator responses in freestanding man. *Cardiovasc. Res.* 3:14–21

86. Lewis, G. P., Matthews, J. 1970. The mechanism of functional vasodilatation in rabbit epigastric adipose tissue. *J. Physiol. London* 207:15–30

87. Ballard, K., Rosell, S. 1969. The unresponsiveness of lipid metabolism in canine mesenteric adipose tissue

to biogenic amines and to sympathetic nerve stimulation. *Acta Physiol. Scand.* 77:442–48

88. Rosell, S. 1969. Nervous and pharmacological regulation of vascular reactions in adipose tissue. *Drugs Affecting Lipid Metabolism,* ed. W. L. Holmes, L. A. Carlson, R. Paoletti, 25–34. New York: Plenum

89. Goodman, H. M. 1970. Regulation of lipid metabolism. *Physiologist* 13:75–84

90. Mayerle, J. A., Havel, R. J. 1969. Nutritional effects of blood flow in adipose tissue of unanesthetized rats. *Am. J. Physiol.* 217:1694–98

91. Kovach, A. G. B. et al 1970. Blood flow, oxygen consumption and free fatty acid release in subcutaneous adipose tissue during hemorrhagic shock in control and phenoxybenzamine-treated dogs. *Circ. Res.* 26:733–42

92. Brück, K., Wünnenberg, B. 1965. Untersuchungen über die Bedeutung des multilokulären Fettgewebes für die Thermogenese des neugeborenen Meerschweinchens. *Pflügers Arch.* 283:1–16

93. Smith, R. E., Horwitz, B. A. 1969. Brown fat and thermogenesis. *Physiol. Rev.* 49:330–425

94. Rolewicz, T. F., Whitmore, L., Zimmerman, B. G. 1969. Transmitter release and responses of arteries and veins during nerve stimulation. *Am. J. Physiol.* 217:1459–63

95. Rolewicz, T. F., Gisslen, J. L., Zimmerman, B. G. 1970. Uptake of norepinephrine-³H by cutaneous arteries and veins of the dog. *Am. J. Physiol.* 219:62–67

96. Abdel-Sayed, W. A., Abboud, F. M., Calvelo, M. G. 1970. Effect of local cooling on responsiveness of muscular and cutaneous vessels. *Am. J. Physiol.* In press

97. Vanhoutte, P. M., Shepherd, J. T. 1969. Activity and thermosensitivity of canine cutaneous veins after inhibition of monoamine oxidase and catechol-O-methyl transferase. *Circ. Res.* 25:607–16

98. Webb-Reploe, M. M. 1969. Cutaneous venoconstrictor response to local cooling in the dog: Unexplained by inhibition of neuronal re-uptake of norepinephrine. *Circ. Res.* 24:607–16

99. Vanhoutte, P. M., Shepherd, J. T.

1970. Effect of temperature on re-activity of isolated cutaneous veins of the dog. *Am. J. Physiol.* 218: 187–90

100. Zelis, R., Mason, D. T., Braunwald, E. 1969. Partition of blood flow to the cutaneous and muscular beds of the forearm at rest and during leg exercise in normal subjects and in patients with heart failure. *Circ. Res.* 24:799–806

101. Ballard, D. R., Abboud, F. M., Mayer, H. E. 1971. Release of a humoral vasodilator substance during neurogenic vasodilatation. *Am. J. Physiol.* In press

102. Brody, M. J., Shaffer, R. A. 1970. Distribution of vasodilator nerves in the canine hind limb. *Am. J. Physiol.* 218:470–74

103. Beck, L., Pollard, A. A., Kayaalp, S., Weiner, L. M. 1966. Sustained dilatation elicited by sympathetic nerve stimulation. *Fed. Proc.* 25: 1596–1606

104. Zimmerman, B. G. 1968. Comparison of sympathetic vasodilator innervation of the hind limb of the dog and cat. *Am. J. Physiol.* 214:62–66

105. Jansson, G., Lundgren, O., Martinson, J. 1970. Neurohormonal control of gastric blood flow. *Gastroenterology* 58:425–28

106. Jansson, G. 1969. Vasovagal reflex relaxation of the stomach of the cat. *Acta Physiol. Scand.* 75:245–52

107. Cowley, D. J., Code, C. F. 1970. Effects of secretory inhibitors on mucosal blood flow in nonsecreting stomach of conscious dogs. *Am. J. Physiol.* 218:270–74

108. Jacobson, E. D., Linford, R. H., Grossman, M. I. 1966. Gastric secretion in relation to mucosal blood flow studied by a clearance technique. *J. Clin. Invest.* 45:1–13

109. Delaney, J. P., Grim, E. 1965. Experimentally induced variations in canine gastric blood flow and its distribution. *Am. J. Physiol.* 208: 353–58

110. Buchin, R. F., Edlich, R. F. 1969. Quantitation of gastric arteriovenous blood flow by the microsphere clearance technique. *Arch. Surg. Chicago* 99:579–81

111. Shoemaker, C. P., Powers, S. R., Jr. 1966. The absence of large functional arteriovenous shunts in the stomach of the anesthetized dog. *Surgery* 60:118–26

112. Delaney, J. P., Grim, E. 1964. Canine gastric blood flow and its distribution. *Am. J. Physiol.* 207:1195–202

113. Aune, S., Semb, L. S. 1969. The effect of secretin and pancreozymin on pancreatic blood flow in the conscious and anesthetized dog. *Acta Physiol. Scand.* 76:406–14

114. Goodhead, B., Himal, H. S., Zanbilowicz, J. 1970. Relationship between pancreatic secretion and pancreatic blood flow. *Gut* 11:62–68

115. Hickson, J. C. D. 1970. The secretory and vascular response to nervous and hormonal stimulation in the pancreas of the pig. *J. Physiol. London* 206:299–322

116. Uden, R. 1969. Effect of secretin in celiac and superior mesenteric angiography. *Acta Radiol. Diagn.* 8:497–513

117. Greenway, C. V., Stark, R. D. 1969. Vascular responses of the spleen to rapid hemorrhage in the anesthetized cat. *J. Physiol. London* 204:169–80

118. Lutz, J., Heinrich, H., Peiper, U., Bauereisen, E. 1969. Autoregulation und veno-vasomotorische Reaktion im Milzkreislauf. *Pflügers Arch.* 313:271–88

119. Greenway, C. V., Stark, R. D. 1970. The vascular responses of the spleen to intravenous infusions of catecholamines, angiotensin and vasopressin in the anesthetized cat. *Brit. J. Pharmacol.* 38:583–92

120. Takeuchi, J. et al 1969. Autoregulation and interaction between two vascular systems in dog liver. *J. Appl. Physiol.* 27:77–82

121. Wangensteen, S. L., Ludewig, R. M., Madden, J. J. 1970. Augmentation of hepatic blood flow by acetylcholine. *Am. J. Surg.* 119:510–14

122. Greenway, C. V., Stark, R. D., Lautt, W. W. 1969. Capacitance responses and fluid exchange in the cat liver during stimulation of the hepatic nerves. *Circ. Res.* 25:277–84

123. Ross, G. 1970. Regional circulatory effects of pancreatic glucagon. *Brit. J. Pharmacol.* 38:735–42

124. Shoemaker, W. C., Van Itallie, T. B., Walker, W. F. 1959. Measurement of hepatic glucose output and hepatic blood flow in response to glucagon. *Am. J. Physiol.* 196: 315–18

125. Ross, G. 1970. Cardiovascular effects of secretin. *Am. J. Physiol.* 218: 1166–70

126. Goodhead, B. 1969. Distribution of blood flow in various selected areas of small and large intestine in the dog. *Am. J. Physiol.* 217:835–37

127. Silva, D. G., Ross, G., Osborne, L. W. 1971. Adrenergic innervation of the ileum of the cat. *Am. J. Physiol.* In press

128. Baumgarten, H. G. 1967. Uber die Verteilung von Catecholaminen im Darm des Menschen. *Z. Zellforsch. Mikrosk. Anat.* 83:133–46

129. Genest, J., Simard, S., Rosenthal, J., Boucher, R. 1969. Norepinephrine and renin content in arterial tissue from different vascular beds. *Can. J. Physiol. Pharmacol.* 47:87–91

130. Richardson, D. R., Johnson, P. C. 1969. Comparison of autoregulatory escape and autoregulation in the intestinal vascular bed. *Am. J. Physiol.* 217:586–90

131. Ross, G. 1970. Effects of catecholamines on splanchnic blood flow before and after beta adrenergic blockade. See Ref. 36

132. Wallentin, I. 1966. Studies on intestinal circulation. *Acta Physiol. Scand.* 71: *Suppl. 279* 445–57

133. Jacobson, E. D. Mesenteric autoregulatory escape. See Ref. 70

134. Spanner, R. 1932. Neue Befunden über die Blutwege der Darmwand und ihre funktionelle bedeutung. *Morphol. Jahrb.* 69:394–454

135. Delaney, J. P. 1969. Arteriovenous anastomotic blood flow in the mesenteric organs. *Am. J. Physiol.* 216:1556–61

136. Baker, R., Mendel, D. 1967. Some observations on "autoregulatory escape" in cat intestine. *J. Physiol. London* 190:229–40

137. Duling, B. R., Berne, R. M. 1968. Microiontophoretic application of vasoactive agents to the microcirculation of the hamster cheek pouch. *Microvasc. Res.* 1:158–73

138. Shehadeh, Z., Price, W. E., Jacobson, E. D. 1969. Effects of vasoactive agents on intestinal blood flow and motility. *Am. J. Physiol.* 216:386–92

139. Ross, G., Brown, A. W. 1967. Cardiovascular effects of dopamine in the anesthetized cat. *Am. J. Physiol.* 212:823–28

140. Steckel, R. J., Ross, G., Grollman,

J. H. 1968. A potent drug combination for producing constriction of the superior mesenteric artery and its branches. *Radiology* 91: 579–81

141. McNeill, J. H., Barnes, R. V., Davis, R. S., Hook, J. B. 1969. The effect of vasodilator drugs on the noradrenaline constrictor response in the isolated mesenteric artery. *Can. J. Physiol. Pharmacol.* 47: 663–70

142. Weiner, R., Kaley, G. 1969. Influence of prostaglandin E_1 on the terminal vascular bed. *Am. J. Physiol.* 217: 563–66

143. Baez, S. 1969. Antagonistic effects of histamine and beta histine on the vasoconstrictor actions of catecholamines in mesentery microvessels. *5th Eur. Conf. Microcirc.*, No. 10, 340–48. Basel: Karger

144. Malik, K. U., Ling, G. M. 1969. Modification by acetylcholine of the response of rat mesenteric arteries to sympathetic stimulation. *Circ. Res.* 25:1–9

145. Ehinger, B., Falck, B., Sporrong, B. 1970. Possible axo-axonal synapses between peripheral adrenergic and cholinergic nerve terminals.. *Z. Zellforsch. Mikrosk. Anat.* 107: 508–21

146. Goldberg, L. I., McNay, J. L. 1970. The cardiovascular and renal actions of dopamine: The question of a specific dopamine receptor. See Ref. 36

147. Yeh, B. K., McNay, J. L., Goldberg, L. I. 1969. Attenuation of dopamine renal and mesenteric vasodilatation by haloperidol. Evidence for a specific dopamine receptor. *J. Pharmacol. Exp. Ther.* 168: 303–9

148. Hultén, L. 1969. Extrinsic nervous control of colonic motility and blood flow. *Acta Physiol. Scand. Suppl. 335*

149. Said, S. I., Mutt, V. 1970. Potent peripheral and splanchnic vasodilator peptide from normal gut. *Nature* 225:863–64

150. Fara, J. W., Rubinstein, E. H., Sonnenschein, R. R. 1969. Visceral and behavioural responses to intraduodenal fat. *Science* 166:110–11

151. Thomas, J. E., Crider, J. O. 1946. The secretion of pancreatic juice in the presence of atropine or hyoscyamine in chronic fistula

dogs. *J. Pharmacol. Exp. Ther.* 87 : 81–89

152. Fara, J. W., Rubinstein, E. H., Sonnenschein, R. R. 1970. The specificity and role of cholecystokinin in the mesenteric vasodilatation induced by intraduodenal fat. *Physiologist* 13:193

153. Van Heerden, P. D., Wagner, H. N., Jr., Kaihara, S. 1968. Intestinal blood flow during perfusion of the jejunum with hypertonic glucose in dogs. *Am. J. Physiol.* 215:30–33

154. Biber, B., Jodal, M., Lundgren, O., Svanvik, J. 1970. Intestinal vasodilatation after mechanical stimulation of the jejunal mucosa. *Experientia* 26:263

155. Jacobson, E. D., Brobmann, G. A., Brecher, G. A. 1970. Intestinal motor activity and blood flow. *Gastroenterology* 58:575–81

156. Fronek, K., Stahlgren, L. H. 1968. Systemic and regional hemodynamic changes during food intake and digestion in nonanesthetized dogs. *Circ. Res.* 23:687–92

157. Vatner, S. F., Franklin, D., Van Citters, R. L. 1970. Mesenteric vasoactivity associated with eating and digestion in the conscious dog. *Am. J. Physiol.* 219:170–74

158. Fronek, K., Fronek, A. 1970. Combined effect of exercise and digestion on hemodynamics in conscious dogs. *Am. J. Physiol.* 218:555–59

159. Steiner, S. H., King, R. D. 1970. Nutrient renal blood flow and its distribution in the unanesthetized dog. *J. Surg. Res.* 10:133–46

160. Kramer, K., Thurau, K., Deetjen, P. 1960. Hemodynamik des Nierenmarks. *Pflügers Arch.* 270:251–69

161. Carrière, S. 1969. Effect of norepinephrine, isoproterenol and adrenergic blockers upon the intrarenal distribution of blood flow. *Can. J. Physiol. Pharmacol.* 47:199–208

162. Carrière, S., Friborg, J. 1969. Intrarenal blood flow and PAH extraction during angiotensin infusion. *Am. J. Physiol.* 217:1708–15

163. McGiff, J. C., Crowshaw, K., Terragno, N. A., Lonigro, A. J. 1970. Release of a prostaglandin-like substance into renal venous blood in response to angiotensin II. *Suppl. No. 1. Circ. Res.* 26–27:I-121–30

164. Hatch, F. E., Johnson, J. G. 1969.

Intrarenal blood flow. *Ann. Rev. Med.* 20:395–408

165. Stinson, J. M. et al 1969. Reflex cholinergic vasodilatation during renal artery constriction in the unanesthetized dog. *Am. J. Physiol.* 217:239–46

166. MacFarlane, M. D. 1970. A renorenal vasoconstrictor reflex induced by acetylcholine. *Am. J. Physiol.* 218:851–56

167. Kiil, F., Kjekshus, J., Löyning, E. 1969. Renal autoregulation during infusion of noradrenaline, angiotensin and acetylcholine. *Acta Physiol. Scand.* 76:10–23

168. Folkow, B., Langston, J. B. 1964. The interrelationship of some factors influencing renal blood flow autoregulation. *Acta Physiol. Scand.* 61:165–76

169. McNay, J. L., Kishimoto, T. 1969. Association between autoregulation and pressure dependency of renal vascular responsiveness in dogs. *Circ. Res.* 24:599–605

170. Brody, M. J., Hook, J. B., Blatt, A. H., Williamson, H. E. 1969. Effect of several diuretics on autoregulation of renal blood flow. *Arch. Int. Pharmacodyn. Ther.* 180:114–20

171. Tagawa, H., Vander, A. J. 1970. Effects of adenosine compounds on renal function and renin secretion in dogs. *Circ. Res.* 26:327–38

172. Hollenberg, N. K. et al 1970. Effect of sodium balance on intrarenal distribution of blood flow in normal man. *J. Appl. Physiol.* 28:312–17

173. Carlson, E. L., Sparks, H. V. 1970. Intrarenal distribution of blood flow during elevation of ureteral pressure in dogs. *Circ. Res.* 26:601–10

174. Gazitua, S., Scott, J. B., Chou, C. C., Haddy, J. 1969. Effect of osmolarity on canine renal vascular resistance. *Am. J. Physiol.* 217:1216–23

175. Wexler, I., Kao, F. F. 1970. Neural and humoral factors affecting renal blood flow during induced muscular work. *Am. J. Physiol.* 218:755–61

176. Van Citters, R. L., Franklin, D. L. 1969. Cardiovascular performance of Alaska sled dogs during exercise. *Circ. Res.* 24:33–43

177. Fujimoto, S., Lockett, M. F. 1970. The diuretic actions of prostaglan-

din E_1 and of noradrenaline, and the occurrence of a prostaglandin E_1-like substance in the renal lymph of cats. *J. Physiol. London* 208 :1–20

178. Wilkinson, I. M. S. et al 1969. Regional blood flow in the normal cerebral hemisphere. *J. Neurol. Neurosurg. Psychiat.* 32 :367–78

179. Roth, J. A., Greenfield, A. J., Kaihara, S. Wagner, H. N., Jr. 1970. Total and regional cerebral blood flow in unanesthetized dogs. *Am. J. Physiol.* 219 :96–101

180. Reivich, M., Johle, J., Sokoloff, L., Kety, S. S. 1969. Measurement of regional cerebral blood flow with antipyrine-^{141}C in awake cats. *J. Appl. Physiol.* 27 :296–300

181. Angelakos, E. T., Irvin, J. D., King, M. P. 1970. Adrenergic innervation of blood vessels in various regions of the central nervous system. *Fed. Proc.* 29 :416 *Abstr.*

182. D'Alecy, L. G., Feigl, E. O. 1970. Sympathetic cerebral vasoconstriction. *Fed. Proc.* 29 :520 *Abstr.*

183. James, I. M., Millar, R. A., Purves, M. J. 1969. Observations on the extrinsic neural control of cerebral blood flow in the baboon. *Circ. Res.* 25 :77–93

184. Mchedlishvili, G. I., Nikolaishvili, L. S. 1970. Evidence of a cholinergic nervous mechanism mediating the autoregulatory dilatation of the cerebral blood vessel. *Pflügers Arch.* 315 :27–37

185. Brock, M., Fieschi, C., Ingvar, D. H., Lassen, N. A., Schürmann, K., Eds. 1969. *Cerebral Blood Flow.* New York : Springer

186. Kanzow, E., Dieckhoff, D. 1969. See Ref. 185, 96–97

187. Ekström-Jodal, B., Haggendal, E., Nilsson, N. J., Norbäck, B. 1969. See Ref. 185, 89–93

188. Held, K., Gottstein, V., Niedermayer, W. 1969. See Ref. 185, 94–95

189. Kjällquist, A., Siesjo, B. K., Zwetnow, N. 1969. Effects of increased intracranial pressure on cerebral blood flow and on cerebrospinal fluid HCO_3, pH, lactate and pyruvate in dogs. *Acta Physiol. Scand.* 75 :345–52

190. Wahl, M., Deetjen, P., Thurau, K., Ingvar, D. H., Lassen, N. A. 1970. Micropuncture evaluation of the importance of perivascular pH for the arteriolar diameter on the brain surface. *Pflügers Arch.* 316 :152–63

191. Flohr, H. W., Brock, M., Christ, R., Heipertz, R., Pöll, W. 1969. See Ref. 185, 86–88

192. Smith, A. L., Pender, J. W., Alexander, S. C. 1969. Effects of Pco_2 on spinal cord blood flow. *Am. J. Physiol.* 216 :1158–63

193. Buyniski, J. P., Rapela, C. E. 1969. Cerebral and renal vascular smooth muscle responses to adenosine. *Am. J. Physiol.* 217 :1660–64

194. Rapela, C. E., Buyniski, J. P. 1969. See Ref. 185, 106–8

195. Kolin, A. 1970. An electromagnetic catheter blood flow meter of minimal lateral dimensions. *Proc. Nat. Acad. Sci.* 66 :53–56

HEART: EXCITATION AND CONTRACTION[1] 1068

EDWARD A. JOHNSON AND MELVYN LIEBERMAN

*Department of Physiology and Pharmacology, Duke University
Medical Center Durham, North Carolina*

INTRODUCTION

In preparing this review we have attempted to monitor and index the entire physiological literature concerning cardiac muscle within the 2 year period ending early July 1970 (ca 1500 references). Overwhelmed at this number of papers, we were very willing to obey one of the editors' instructions to be selective in our choice of papers for review, to confine ourselves to "critical description and evaluation of outstanding papers", and to direct our review to those areas in which we have particular interest. We have focused on one active and controversial area which we considered to be fundamental and about which we had thought most and had particular interest— voltage-clamp of cardiac muscle. We have tried to recognize and include relevant information in other areas.

In reviewing the literature we were impressed by the lack of a serious attempt to build up a realistic model of the experimental method and preparation. With the appropriate physical laws and mathematics, a rigorous, critical analysis could have been made which would have taken into consideration the reasonableness of the assumptions on which the presentation, analysis, and interpretation of the data were based. Although such disregard is not confined to the field of voltage-clamp, it exemplifies, we think, the consequences of it. Furthermore, the conclusions drawn from the data concern those fundamental properties of cardiac muscle on which our understanding of its electrical activity is based. The detail required to illustrate this need for more rigorous premeditation has made some parts of the review somewhat unusual in that they involve a lengthy discussion of a small number of papers.

VOLTAGE-CLAMP AND THE GENERATION OF THE CARDIAC ACTION POTENTIAL

We preface our discussion of the results of voltage-clamp experiments of cardiac muscle with our main conclusion; indeed it is the essence of our criticism and our explanation of much of the experimental results: in the interpretation of the currents recorded during voltage-clamp experiments, one must remember that currents occurring at different times and at different

[1] Supported in part by USPHS grant No. 3PO1HE12157 from the National Institutes of Health.

479

potentials may be due to currents occurring at different times in different places, the potential at these places being different from that at the place one chooses to record and control it.

General considerations.—The purpose of the voltage-clamp technique is to measure the current required to hold the potential across a prescribed area of cell membrane at a known value that is uniform with respect to distance and time. Ideally, the technique should enable, when necessary, the potential to be changed instantaneously, or at least at such a rate that the electrical properties, in particular the ionic permeabilities of the membrane, do not have time to change during the time required to establish the new potential. In this way, if the charge carriers can be identified (and the current carried by each measured), then the law that governs the movement of each charged carrier across the membrane at any instant in time, namely the *instantaneous current-voltage relationship*, for each charged carrier, can be determined. For example, the relationship for each of the charged carriers involved (e.g. Na and K ions) may be one of direct proportionality and follow the linear Ohm's law (e.g. the squid giant axon in normal seawater) (1), as in Equation 1. Or the relationship may be curved and obey the Goldman constant-field equation, e.g. Equation 2 for sodium ions, as in frog nerve (2),

$$I_{Na} = G_{Na}(V - V_{Na}); \qquad V_{Na} = \frac{RT}{F} \ln (Na)_o/(Na)_i \qquad 1.$$

$$I_{Na} = \frac{P_{Na}F^2V}{RT} \frac{[(Na)_o - (Na)_i \exp (FV/RT)]}{[(1 - \exp FV/RT)]} \qquad 2.$$

where I_{Na} is the current and V the transmembrane potential; $(Na)_o$ and $(Na)_i$ are the internal and external sodium ion concentrations respectively; and R, T, and F have their usual meaning. In both relationships, the value of the coefficients, G_{Na} and P_{Na} (the sodium ion conductance and permeability, respectively), though constant at any given moment, may change with time following changes in membrane potential. For this reason it is required that the membrane potential be changed to its new potential (and the current measured at the new potential) before these coefficients (or ionic concentrations) can change to new values. The main job then to be done with the technique is to determine, quantitatively as well as qualitatively, how the various coefficients or concentrations change with time following a change in membrane potential.

In our view, such an experimental feat has yet to be achieved for the membrane of cardiac muscle. The reasons for this are interlinked, and arise from the complexity of the membrane geometry of preparations of cardiac muscle that are available for study and the limitations of available techniques of voltage-clamp. The necessary temporal and spatial uniformity of transmembrane potential was ensured in the experiments of Hodgkin,

Huxley & Katz (3) in the squid giant axon by reducing to a negligible value the longitudinal cytoplasmic resistance of the axon over the region of membrane under study by inserting a silver wire along the axis of the axon. In this way, charge could flow along the axis cylinder with negligible voltage gradients, and the only *intracellular* voltage gradient of concern that remains is that associated with the radial spread of current through the sheath of cytoplasm that separates the silver wire from the cell membrane. This can lead to errors in the measurement of the true transmembrane potential which, however, can be corrected for with relative ease (3). Therefore, for the purpose of voltage-clamping one would ideally prefer to use a muscle fiber of dimensions and geometry similar to that of the squid giant axon.

METHODS

Definitions.—For the sake of generality and impartiality we have used the following names. We use the name command potential rather than membrane potential. In the two-microelectrode and single-sucrose-gap methods of voltage-clamp the command potential is the potential difference that is demanded between the tip of an intracellular microelectrode and either a distant electrode outside the preparation or an electrode in extracellular space within the preparation. In the double-sucrose-gap method the command potential is the potential difference that is demanded between the voltage pool and an electrode in the central nodal stream of Krebs or Ringer solution.

Apart from a surge of capacitive current associated with steps changes in command potential, at least two early transient components of ionic current have been reported to which we have given the names *primary* early transient current and *secondary* early transient current in place of the names used by the authors: sodium current, initial current or slow inward current, calcium current.

THE PREPARATION

Despite an extensive search of hearts (4–8) of vertebrates, a cardiac muscle fiber of a diameter larger than 10–15 μ has not been found (4, 5, 7) [excluding Purkinje fibers of hearts from large mammals which are unsuitable in other respects (5)]. Indeed, there is good reason to believe that, apart from nerve fibers whose function is to do little more than propagate action potentials, large cells usually have complex interdigitating invaginations of the surface membrane so that the equivalent circuit of the membrane impedance is much more complicated than that of a simple parallel combination of a resistance and a capacitance [e.g. frog skeletal muscle (9); crab muscle (10)].

Mammalian cardiac muscle is composed of a population of muscle fibers, around 10 μ in diameter and of relatively uncertain but short length, which are closely apposed in the region of the intercalated disc. Indeed, the sarcolemma of apposed cardiac muscle fibers in these regions frequently fuse together so that separation of the cells is at present impossible. Although single cardiac muscle cells can be isolated intact in tissue culture (11–15), their small size (1–2 μ thick and of varying but small size in the other dimensions) necessitates the development of new and as yet unavailable techniques of voltage-clamp. Since we are restricted, at present, to preparations of cardiac muscle of natural origin, the preparations to which the voltage-clamp has been applied have contained a number of muscle fibers. For example, in preparations of trabeculae of ventricular muscle from the sheep and dog where the overall diameter was said to be less than 0.7 mm (16–18) and 0.6 mm (19), the number of fibers must have been of the order of 1000: if a value for the extracellular space of 25% of the whole muscle volume and an average diameter of individual muscle fibers of 10–15 μ is assumed for a trabecula of diameter 0.5 mm (neglecting any collagenous sheath), the number of fibers would be around 800–1900. And for preparations of frog atrial trabecula and atrial strips that were reported to be 100 μ in diameter (20) and 300 μ (21) respectively, similar calculations using 3 μ (7) as the average diameter of frog fibers give a number of around 800 and 7500 respectively. In Purkinje strands of the ungulate, the number of fibers is much smaller, not because the overall diameter of the preparation is smaller, indeed it is comparable to those described above, but because the fibers are much larger in diameter (around 50 μ) and furthermore, they are wrapped up in a fairly thick collagenous sheath (5).

The multifiber nature of the preparations clearly presents a number of difficulties, their exact nature being dependent on the technique of voltage-clamp used. In the ungulate Purkinje strand the thick collagenous sheath causes the closest excitable membrane to be a rather long distance from the outside free surface of the preparation so that difficulties might be expected in applying the double-sucrose-gap technique to this preparation. This may explain our failure to find any report of the application of such technique to this otherwise popular preparation of cardiac muscle. The technique that has been used with this preparation is to isolate electrically a short segment between two closely spaced ligatures, cuts or crushes, approx. 1–2 mm apart, allowing the severed or crushed ends to "heal over" and then to apply the two-microelectrode technique of voltage-clamp (22–27).

With all other preparations, e.g. guinea pig (28), dog (16–18), and sheep (19) ventricular muscle bundles, and frog atrial trabecula (20, 29, 30) or strips (21, 31), the single or double-sucrose-gap technique has been used in an attempt to restrict and define the area of membrane. With either technique, a clear-cut interface between sucrose and test solutions can only be expected for the sarcolemma of the fibers facing the free surface of the preparation, for the formation of such an interface about deeper fibers must largely be blurred by the effects of the diffusional intermixing of the two solutions. For example, using the double-sucrose-gap technique, the formation of a well-defined "node" about deeper fibers of a preparation must be a matter of fancy and not of reasonable expectation. In view of this, one must, we think, examine with grave suspicion the results obtained with this technique, particularly with preparations containing hundreds if not thousands of fibers. In other words, if an experimental result can be explained on the basis of inadequate control of membrane potential with regard to position or time, in this circumstance, this explanation rather than any other should be considered the more likely.

In the frog atrial trabecular preparation used by Rougier, Vassort & Stampfli (20) and others (29, 30), the frog atrial strip as used by Brown & Noble (21, 31), and the Purkinje strand from hearts of animals of the size of the dog and larger (e.g. sheep and goat) as used by Noble & Tsien (25–27) and others (22–24, 32, 33), there are addditional morphological features other than the multifiber nature of the preparation that might well cause more problems. In contrast, in preparations of mammalian ventricular muscle as used by Beeler & Reuter (16–18, 34, 35), Mascher & Peper (19), and Ochi (28), and, in particular, strands from the peripheral Purkinje network of hearts of mammals the size of the cat and rabbit or smaller (5, 6, 8) the morphology is relatively simple. Except where the individual fibers are forming junctional complexes with one another, the cells of mammalian ventricular muscle are relatively far apart (around 1 μ or greater) as well as being relatively small in diameter (approx. 10 μ).

In addition, the short length (around 5 μ) and wide diameter (2000 Å) of the transverse tubules in mammalian ventricular muscle (5, 8) and the total absence of such a transverse tubular system in the fibers of the Purkinje system (5, 6, 8) mean that little if any sarcolemma is in series with a significant external electrical resistance. This welcome feature is, however, not possessed by similar Purkinje bundles from hearts of animals *greater* in size than the cat and rabbit, e.g. goat and sheep. The fibers within such strands, although larger in diameter (around 50 μ) than those in strands from smaller hearts, are tightly packed (around 300 Å wide extracellular space) so that large areas of presumably excitable membrane are in series with an appreciable resistance (5). For example, in the sheep and goat Purkinje strands the clefts between the fibers are so long and narrow that for a specific membrane resistance of say 1000 ohms cm² or less, the transmembrane potential of the membrane in these clefts cannot, theoretically, be driven to anywhere near the same potential as that of the free sarcolemma, even in steady state (5). Furthermore, there is reason to believe that the sarcolemma contained in such clefts is similar to that of the free peripheral sarcolemma, for the sarcoplasmic reticulum forms couplings with the inner surface of the sarcolemma that are identical to those it forms with the undersurface of the peripheral scarcolemma (5) and such couplings are believed to be the morphological site of one step of excitation-contraction coupling (5). To make matters even worse, the bundle can split into daughter bundles which reunite to form a single bundle further along the strand (5).

In ventricular and atrial muscle of the frog and chicken hearts (7) the individual fibers (around 3 μ in diameter) are grouped into tightly packed bundles, aroud 10–20 μ in overall diameter. Since the bundles are smaller, the clefts between the fibers, although as narrow as those in Purkinje bundles of the sheep and goat hearts, are shorter, so that the resistive isolation of some of the sarcolemma is not as drastic. However, the fibers are much smaller in diameter so that for the same specific membrane resistance and resistivity of the cytoplasm the length constant in one-dimensional cable theory is correspondingly reduced. Thus, as will be clear from later discussion, with the double-sucrose-gap technique, a given width of central node with frog cardiac muscle [as in the experiments of Rougier et al (20, 29) and others (30)] will be approximately equivalent to a node wider by a factor of $(15/3) = 5$ for a strand preparation containing fibers 15 μ in diameter.

The larger overall diameter (300 μ) of the frog atrial strip preparation used by Brown & Noble (21, 31) further increases the practically obtainable width of the central node by a factor of three. This almost eliminates any theoretical possibility of improvement over the single sucrose gap: a node say 300 μ wide for a fiber 3 μ in diameter. Furthermore, we wonder to what extent changes in ionic concentrations in extracellular space in the midst of the enormous population of fibers that are contained in this preparation contributed to the slowly changing currents obtainable by these authors with this preparation.

The Technique

The two-microelectrode technique.—Theoretical analysis of the possible variation of potential about a source of current in a preparation of complex geometry is particularly difficult when the current source approaches a point, as for a microelectrode. In this situation, the variation in potential in intracellular space, as well as in the true transmembrane potential, depends on the geometry of the preparation seen from the source. To include all important aspects of current spread would require a three-dimensional analysis of the spread of current, since about a point source the current must flow in all directions to reach all the membrane in the preparation. Voltage-clamp experiments that employ a point source of current have, as a consequence, additional problems. A detailed discussion of and a theoretical analysis of the electrical fields associated with the three-dimensional spread of current about a point source within cells of varying idealized geometries have been made elsewhere (10, 36, 37). Added to this complexity is the one discussed above, namely that the sheep and goat Purkinje bundles in which this form of current source has been used in voltage-clamp experiments are more complex morphologically than other preparations. These factors, together with the inordinate length of the preparation of 1–2 mm, compared to the resting dc length constant, in our view, puts this combination of voltage-clamp method and preparation in first place as the most unsanitary experimental setup that has been made available.

In light of this, it is remarkable that reports of experiments using this setup (22–24, 32, 33) did not discuss the results in terms of such complicating factors. The attempts of Dudel & Rüdel (22) and others (24, 26) to express the magnitude of the controlling current in terms of A/cm^2 of membrane exemplify the general lack of awareness of such factors. Furthermore, not only is the complex morphology of the preparation oversimplified, but the nonuniformity of membrane potential control that must occur, at least at some times, in a preparation of such length and with such deep narrow clefts between fibers is completely disregarded. The values that Dudel & Rüdel (22) gave of the membrane area range from .001 to .005 cm^2. Unfortunately, they gave no details of the method of calculating "membrane area" other than what is contained in the statement "estimated by their total membrane capacity their surface areas were between 0.005 and 0.001 cm^2." For a preparation 2 mm long, if it is assumed, unrealistically, that this current flowed uniformly through a simple cylinder of that length, then the radius of their simple cylinder would range from 8–40 μ, a range that is somewhat lower than that for the radius of a bundle of Purkinje fibers and more like that of single fiber. They did not state the value of the specific membrane capacitance which they would have needed to make their calculation, but one suspects it was the value of 12 $\mu F/cm^2$ and this probably would account for the small value obtained for the radius in the above calculation.

For bundles of sheep Purkinje fibers, the equivalent circuit of the membrane impedance for small displacements of transmembrane potential is more complicated than that of a simple capacitance in parallel with a resistance (38, 39). As a first approximation, the membrane in the preparation was considered by Fozzard (38) to behave as though approximately 80% of the membrane capacitance were in series with an appreciable resistance. The equivalent circuit that he used for the membrane impedance is shown in Figure 1A. This circuit contains the *minimum* number of circuit elements that are required to describe the observed impedance. This is not the only circuit containing the minimum number of elements for there are three other (so-called canonical) forms as pointed out by Freygang & Trautwein (39). However, with regard to the physical interpretation of the equivalent circuit of the membrane impedance, one is not necessarily restricted to these four canonical forms; in fact circuits with an additional element have exactly the same impedance. For example, the form (R_m') which contains an additional element, Figure 1B, and is identical in electrical behavior to that of Figure 1A, represents, we think, a more realistic representation, bearing in mind the known morphology of the preparation. In this circuit, R_m', C_m' and R_m^*, C_m^* represent membrane with identical properties with and without, respectively, a series resistance. Electronmicroscopic images show that a considerable portion of the fiber membrane is located in deep narrow clefts (around 200–300 Å in width) (5). It is not

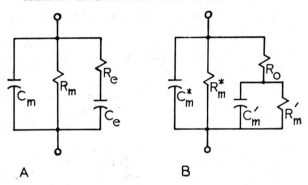

A   B

FIGURE 1. A. Equivalent circuit used to describe the membrane impedance of sheep and goat Purkinje strands by Fozzard (38). B. Modified version of the equivalent circuit of A that has one more than the minimum number of elements (R_m'); has the identical impedance to A. In B, R_m^* and C_m^* represent excitable membrane of the fibers which face the outside free surface of the preparation. R_m' and C_m' represent the lumped behavior of the membrane distributed down deep (approx. 50 μ) narrow (200–300 Å) clefts between fibers and R_o the distributed resistance of the material filling the clefts.

surprising then that the membrane in the preparation, as a first approximation, behaves electrically as in Figure 1B, where R_o represents resistance presented by the material in the narrow clefts.

A more detailed analysis and discussion of the physical significance of the passive electrical properties of Purkinje strands from sheep heart has recently been made by Freygang & Trautwein (39). Measurements were made of the phase angle of the characteristic admittance, as well as the longitudinal impedance, both as functions of frequency. It was found that the longitudinal impedance of the bundle was not simply resistive but that part of the longitudinal resistance was in parallel with a capacitance. This longitudinally oriented capacity had a time constant of 60–70 μsec, which they suggested represents the connections between cells both radially and longitudinally. It is clear to us that one cannot neglect these clefts as regions in which the ionic concentrations may vary and where the membrane in them can act as current generators and pathways for current.

In this latter regard, we were disappointed to find that McAllister (40) had taken the equivalent circuit (Figure 1A) proposed by Fozzard (38) at its face value and had considered that all the active membrane was represented by the element R_m in Figure 1A. The result is that McAllister's analysis considered, in our view, the unrealistic case where the entire excitable membrane is in parallel with a combination of a fixed resistor in series with a pure capacitance of obscure origin, morphologically. That is to say the entire excitable membrane, which was made to behave according to the Noble formulation for the membrane of sheep and goat Purkinje fibers (41), was free of a resistance in series with it. McAllister showed that even in this simplified situation, there is a danger that capacitive transient currents recorded during voltage-clamp experiments may be confused with currents arising through rapid changes in active membrane conductance. Furthermore, he computed the results one would get from ramp voltage-clamp experiments of the kind reported in the earlier cardiac muscle voltage-clamp literature. He showed that it was not possible to reconstruct the actual membrane behavior from these results.

We think there is a need for further theoretical analysis to aid in understanding and interpreting the results to be expected from our imperfect attempts at voltage-clamp. We would like to see a theoretical analysis of a system more closely approaching what might be considered a more realistic model described by the equivalent circuit of Figure 1B, where R_m' and R_m^* are both made to obey the Noble formulation (41). Better still would be an analysis of the distributed case, namely, a finite cylinder of membrane obeying the Noble formulation with current injected at one end and the voltage measured at the other.

Noble & Tsien (25–27) and Hauswirth, Noble & Tsien (23, 24) used essentially the same preparation and technique (sheep Purkinje fibers and the two-microelectrode technique) and confined their studies to very slowly changing currents with time constants of the order of a second, of which they identified three separate time-dependent outward currents. If we add their results to those of other authors using essentially the same preparation and setup, we are faced with a remarkably complicated system of voltage and time-dependent membrane permeabilities. Thus we have a sodium current inactivated by two processes, one fast (approx. 1 msec) and one slow (approx. 50 msec) (33); a Ca current (Reuter 33); five outward currents: a chloride current, two pure K currents, I_{K_1} and I_{K_2}, and two mixed currents, I_{X_1} plus I_{X_2} (26); and a possible unspecified current activated at large depolarizations (26). We find the evidence for these conclusions unconvincing and are reminded once again of the complex geometry of this preparation. The disturbing question arises as to what results should be attributed to the membrane itself and what to the complex geometry of the preparation, with its narrow clefts in which the ionic concentrations can change as the result of current flow, and where it might be difficult to flush out Na ions completely. Furthermore, as pointed out previously (5) for clefts of the dimensions found in the preparation, the displacement in transmembrane potential of the membrane lining these clefts will deviate, even in *steady state*, seriously from that across the free surface membrane.

An example which illustrates some of the reasons for our doubts and the difficulties of evaluating results obtained with this preparation and method is afforded by the papers of Reuter (33) and Peper & Trautwein (32). Both groups studied the behavior of early current transients in the sheep Purkinje strand preparation following depolarizing and repolarizing steps in command potential. Currents recorded during depolarizing steps to -20 mV and beyond consisted, initially, of short bursts of positive and negative current which were attributed to capacitive and ionic (sodium) origins, respectively. Thereafter, a relatively slow increasing component of positive (outward) current developed which reached a maximum in about 20 msec, thereafter declining to reach a quasisteady-state level in about 50–100 msec. Peper & Trautwein (32) called this current "positive dynamic current" and Reuter "initial outward current" (33). When the command potential was stepped back to the holding or resting potential, a tail of negative inward current occurred lasting 50 msec or so, which Peper & Trautwein called "negative dynamic current". Here we will call these two currents the positive and negative transient currents. Reuter's studies (33) of these currents led him to conclude that the positive transient was a chloride current since it disappeared in chloride-free media. The negative transient was more complex: he deemed it to have both Na and Ca current components; one component disappeared in Na-free media and another component of somewhat slower kinetics was still observable in such media and was labeled a Ca current. We do not completely understand his experiments that were designed to analyze the behavior of this latter current and consequently we cannot comment on their interpretation.

However, Peper & Trautwein (32) also observed that the positive transient disappeared in chloride-free media but did not attribute it to chloride ions since the negative transient current also disappeared in this medium! Their additional findlngs regarding the positive and negative transients made the origin of these currents even more puzzling. Their experiment was to make a series of measurements of the positive transient (20 msec after the start of a depolarizing step in command potential) and of the negative transient (5 msec after the start of a short repolarizing step) for both steps of varying magnitude. Both measurements, especially the latter, included an unknown amount of capacitive as well as ionic current. The series of measurements was made with the depolarizing followed by repolarizing steps repeated at two different regular rates, 0.5 sec^{-1} and 5 sec^{-1}. At 5 sec^{-1} no positive and negative transients (of the kind referred to here) were seen, the mechanism for their generation being presumably inactivated. At 0.5 sec^{-1} they were quite noticeable. The magnitudes of the positive and negative transients were arbitrarily defined as the difference in the currents measured at the above times at the two different rates.

As the magnitude of the depolarizing and repolarizing step was varied, a kind of current-voltage relationship for the positive and for the negative transient was obtained. Removing the extracellular chloride abolished both currents and replacing the extracellular chloride by nitrate enhanced the amplitudes of both currents. Reducing extracellular Na reduced the amplitude of the current component between the resting potential and -30 mV but left unaffected the current-voltage relationships in the potential range of -30 mV and more positive. None of the above maneuvers affected the membrane potential at which the currents changed sign (around -30 mV). The authors discussed a variety of explanations. One was that the positive and negative transients involve a transient increase in a nonspecific leak conductance, triggered by depolarization (they having observed that the potential recorded by a microelectrode driven into extruded myoplasm was -20 to -40 mV). Another explanation which they considered was that these currents were generated by changes in a sodium conductance, not blocked by tetrodotoxin, and a K (or chloride) conductance. They also considered the possibility of accumulation of K in the vicnity of the membrane but pointed out that this could not account for all of their findings.

Which of all of these and Reuter's proposed mechanisms are involved in the generation of the action potential of the sheep Purkinje strand is a question we doubt will be resolved soon, at least not before similar questions have been answered for preparations of simpler geometry that are more applicable to better methods of voltage-clamp.

The sucrose gap.—In a single or double-sucrose-gap method deionized isotonic aqueous solution of sucrose is used to replace the extracellular fluid, in an attempt to form an insulating cuff about the fibers. [The sucrose solution used by Beeler & Reuter (16), for some reason which they did not reveal, contained in addition to sucrose, 5 mM of tris chloride and 5 mM of glucose.]

Two main problems occur with this use of sucrose: 1. hyperpolarization of the membrane in the node of the double sucrose gap and 2. a slow increase in internal longitudinal resistance of the fibers in the sucrose gap, presumably due to leaching out of internal K ions into the sucrose solution. The hyperpolarization has been shown to be due to local circuit current driven through the membrane in the node by the liquid junction potential between the sucrose and test (Krebs solution) in the nodal stream

(42). The hyperpolarization is largely eliminated by reducing the area of the junction between the sucrose and test liquids. The use of rubber partitions by Rougier et al (20, 29) and others (16, 19, 43) was a convenient way of achieving this. Diaphragms also can be used to restrict the motion of the preparation and keep a stable interface between the test and sucrose solutions. However, the diaphragms cannot prevent the intermixing of solutions about the fibers within the bundle.

Methods of voltage-clamp which employ a single or double sucrose gap avoid the problems associated with a point source of current since current is in effect injected into all the fibers of the preparation. Because the source is more distributed, the spatial nonuniformity of potential within the preparation is largely determined by its geometry and size. The preparations to which the single and double-sucrose-gap methods of voltage-clamp have been applied are the frog atrial strips (21, 23), frog atrial trabeculae (20, 29, 30), and sheep and dog ventricular trabeculae [presumably composed entirely of ventricular fibers (16–19)]. As a first approximation, the geometry of these preparations can be considered as being composed of short cylindrical cells (diameter approx. 10–15 μ for mammalian ventricular muscle, 3 μ for frog atrial muscle) of uncertain length (approx. 100 μ in mammals) that are arranged into long columns which extend the length of the preparation. Each preparation, depending on its overall diameter, will contain a differing number of such columns aligned parallel to the longitudinal axis of the preparation. The frequency and distribution of low-resistance connections between cells, end-to-end in individual columns and side-to-side between cells in adjacent columns, is supposed to be sufficiently extensive so that if current is injected through the membrane of all fibers in the current pool of a sucrose-gapped preparation, current will uniformly reach all fibers in the test compartment or nodal region. For the purpose of analysis of current spread, we can treat the preparation as a bundle of continuous identical cylindrical fibers and hence need consider only one such cylinder having a current source of uniform density filling its cross sectional area at one end. In order to make this assumption we must also assume that there is a well-defined and uniform border between the sucrose and test solutions about all the fibers.

Figures 2A and B show the setup for the single sucrose gap and for the double sucrose gap respectively. The position of the intracellular voltage recording microelectrode in Figure 2A is important, since this affects the electrical properties of the effective feedback path of the control amplifier. With the microelectrode close to the left-hand end of the fiber, i.e. just as it leaves the sucrose gap, the behavior of the system is much simpler to analyze theoretically (44) and, one suspects, much more stable than with the electrode towards the other end of the fiber. In this situation, delays are introduced into the feedback loop by the distributed RC cable properties of the fiber, which makes the system much more unstable and difficult to analyze. The latter situation of course also applies to the double sucrose gap where current is injected between the current and nodal pools and enters the nodal region at its left-hand border. The voltage is measured between the voltage pool and the nodal pool and presumably is an average of the internal potential of the fibers at the right-hand border of the node. The drawings are roughly to scale; Figure 2B represents a single column of cells of the frog atrial trabeculae preparation used by Rougier et al (20) where the central node was stated to be approx. 100 μ and the diameter of the individual fibers is approx. 3 μ (7). Figure 2A represents a single column of cells, 1 mm long, of the sheep and dog ventricular trabeculae, the diameter of the individual fibers being approx. 15 μ.

The single sucrose gap.—From one-dimensional cable theory we can calculate the

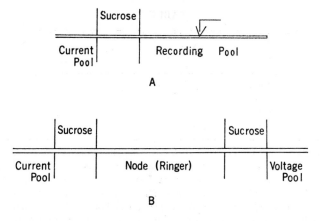

FIGURES 2A and B. Diagrams of A a single column of mammalian ventricular cells in the single sucrose gap and B a single column of muscle cells of the frog atrial trabecula (20) in the double sucrose gap. The length and diameter of the fiber in the recording pool in A and in the central node in B are drawn approximately to scale in each figure. The current pool in A and the current and voltage pools in B contain an isotonic K salt solution or some physiological solution such as Ringer or Krebs solution. In both A and B controlling current completes its circuit between an electrode in the current pool and one in the recording pool in A and the central node in B.

intracellular potential V (with respect to the outside of the fiber), at a point at the right-hand end of the fiber and compare it with that, V_0, close to the site of injection of current at the left-hand end of the fiber as it enters the recording pool.

Table 1 gives the value V at the right-hand end of the preparation in the recording pool as a percentage of that at the left-hand end, for various values of the specific membrane resistance R_m and for a length L of the preparation of 1 mm, typical of lengths of the ventricular trabeculae preparations that were used (16–19, 28). Beeler & Reuter (16), discussing the question of nonuniformity of potential control in their experiments, cited the value of 1–1.5 mm for λ, this being the estimated value reported by Kamiyama & Matsuda (45). Disregarding the question whether this value of 1–1.5 mm for λ is a reasonable one to apply to this preparation at all times, this value, nevertheless, hardly justifies an assurance of uniform potential control. Theoretically, this value would give a variation of potential from one end of the preparation to the other in the recording pool of 19–35%. It is thus surprising and puzzling to discover that Beeler & Reuter (16) found that "provided the fiber piece was 1 mm or shorter the voltage control along the fiber bundle was maintained within a range of less than 2 mV" and that Morad & Trautwein (46) found that "the voltage traces were practically identical even when the recordings were obtained from the two far ends of the muscle" approx. 1 mm apart.

Since in neither case was a value of the percentage variation given, let us assume it was 5%. If this were the case, λ would have to be approximately 3.08 mm for a preparation 1 mm long, i.e. R_m would have to be approximately 36 kΩ cm^2 (a and R_i having the values cited in the caption to Table 1). This might be realized if the membrane potential were driven to a steep region of its current-voltage relationship where the mem-

TABLE 1.

$V(L)$ $(\%V_0)$	R_m (Ωcm^2)	λ (mm)	Frequency at which $Z_c = R_m$ (Hz)
27%	1000	.5	80
65%	4000	1	20
89%	16000	2	5
95%	38000	3.08	2.1

$V(L)$ is the calculated potential at the right-hand end of the fiber in the recording pool expressed as a percentage of that at the left-hand end (see Figures 2A and B) derived from the equation $V(L) = V_0$ sech L/λ where L is the length of the fiber, $\lambda = (R_m a / 2R_i)^{1/2}$ and a is the fiber radius. R_m = specific membrane resistance, Ωcm^2; Z_c = frequency at which capacitive reactance of 1 cm^2 of membrane equals the value of R_m. Specific membrane capacitance assumed to be 2 μFcm^{-2}, fiber diameter = 15 μ, volume resistivity of cytoplasm $R_i = 150$ Ωcm, length preparation, $L = 1$ mm.

brane slope resistance could perhaps attain this value; however, this condition we think can hardly be considered to serve as a general case. Nevertheless, even if one were to claim this to be so, these calculations still are only for the case of steady-state potential displacements. The effects of the membrane capacitance in limiting the speed of control in preparations of cardiac muscle can be shown by calculating the frequencies of applied current for which the reactance of the membrane capacitance equals the values of the membrane resistance given in Table 1. The probable value of the specific membrane capacitance has a lower reasonable limit of $1\mu Fcm^{-2}$. Although a value of around 12 μFcm^{-2} (47) is cited in the earlier literature for cardiac muscle, this value is the capacitance calculated in terms of the area of surface membrane of a simple cylinder equal in diameter to the overall diameter of the bundle of Purkinje fibers in which this estimate of cardiac membrane capacitance was made. Hence this procedure grossly underestimates the area of membrane involved and thus overestimates the capacitance per unit area of membrane. Indeed, recent calculations of specific membrane capacitance of dog papillary muscle arrive at a value of close to 1 μFcm^{-2} (0.6–0.76 μFcm^{-2}). (48, 49). We will assume a value of 2.0 μFcm^{-2} which is close to the value of 2.24 ± 0.14 μFcm^{-2} calculated for the surface sarcolemma of skeletal muscle where fewer assumptions are made about the membrane geometry (50). It can be seen from Table 1 that 2 μFcm^{-2} has a reactance of 36 kΩ at approx. 2Hz! Thus, neglecting current flow through the membrane resistance, a 5% or greater variation in transmembrane potential between the two ends of the preparation would be expected for sinusoidal variations in controlling current of 2 Hz or greater.[2] It is clear then that it would be foolish to hope for a satisfactory spatial and temporal control in a preparation of this size. We do not think that these theoretical considerations can be ignored, nor do we think that one can take refuge in the fact that, for example, a certain reproducible current waveform is recorded for step changes in command potential. This merely means that the particular current waveform is required to cause the voltage at the

[2] The equivalent rise-time t_r (10–90% limits) is given by $t_r = 0.35 f_{3db}$ where f_{3db} in this instance is the frequency at which the capacitive reactance is equal to the resistance. A rise-time equivalent to a $f_{3db} = 2$ Hz is 175 msec.

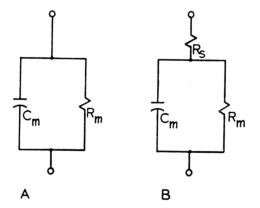

A   B

FIGURE 3. A. Equivalent circuit used to describe the impedance of the membrane of the ideal case. B. One form of the equivalent circuit used to describe the passive electrical behavior of the preparation of Beeler & Reuter (16). For a step change in voltage V between the two terminals of circuit B there is associated a current i given by:

$$i = \frac{V}{R_s + R_m}\left[1 + \frac{R_m}{R_s}\exp\left(-t/\tau\right)\right],$$

where

$$\tau = \frac{C_m R_s R_m}{R_s + R_m}$$

tip of the voltage microelectrode to change in the manner recorded. It does not mean that the current can be interpreted as being that current which is required to cause the voltage across a prescribed area of membrane to change in a similar manner.

The equivalent circuit of the membrane in the ideal preparation behaves like a resistor in parallel with a capacitance (Figure 3A). For small hyperpolarizing and depolarizing step changes in command potential, V, the controlling current waveform, $I(t)$, should consist of a large brief transient surge of charging current (Dirac delta function) coincident with and followed by a steady current given by V/R_m. Considering the effects of the size and morphology, as well as the voltage-clamp methods for the different preparations, it is not surprising to find that the current waveform as recorded deviated considerably from this ideal.

Beeler & Reuter (16), using the single-sucrose-gap method and mammalian ventricular trabeculae, made a remarkably revealing finding in that for a 10 mV step in command potential, the current record showed no rapid initial spike of capacitive current but a step change followed by an exponential decay with a time constant of about 1 msec.

We shall now consider in some detail their analysis of this finding and its bearing on the spatial and temporal homogeneity of potential control in their preparation. Our discussion should provide a good deal of insight into the problems encountered with this voltage-clamp setup and preparation, which is essentially identical to that used by other authors (16–19, 28). In their analysis of this waveform they assumed the equivalent circuit for their preparation as shown in Figure 3B, where a resistance R_s is in series with all the membrane capacitance (C_m). They make the statement that $\tau_c = R_s C_m$, where τ_c is a time constant of decay of the charging current. This is true only if the value of R_m tends to infinity; otherwise $\tau_c = C_m R_m R_s / (R_m + R_s)$. From their Figure 2 (16), showing the waveform of the charging current, it is clear that the current did not decline to zero at long times, which would have been the case if the value of R_m tended to infinity, but declined to a quite sizable steady-state value. Inspection of their Figure 2 (16) shows that the current had an initial value of around 22.7 μA (equal to V/R_s) which declined towards an estimated steady-state value of 8 μA [equal to $V/(R_m + R_s)$]. These two current values determine R_s and R_m which, together with a value of 1.0 msec for τ, we find gives a good fit to the waveform. The value of C_m given by $\tau_c (R_m + R_s)/R_m R_s$ for this case we calculate to be 3.5 μF whereas the value of τ_c given by $R_s C_m$, the expression used by Beeler et al (16), gives a value of 2.27 μF. We obtain a value of 400 Ω for R_s for the data of their Figure 2 (16). The latter value is close to the range of 550–600 Ω for three preparations reported by Beeler et al (16).

The approximate area of membrane in their preparations can be calculated to be around 1 cm² , assuming an extracellular space of 25% of the total volume of the preparation, an overall diameter of the preparation of say 0.6 mm (stated max = 0.7 mm) and a fiber diameter of 10 μ. This is close to the figure arrived at on unstated assumptions by the authors (16). The preparation therefore had a staggering figure of 550–600 Ω in series with every square centimeter of membrane which, for example, in their Figure 2 (16) had a value of around 1000 Ω in the resting state. That is to say, R_s was comparable with or larger than the likely values that R_m would have been in the experiments. We will return to the significance of this finding later in the following discussion.

These authors (16) continued with the investigation of possible limitations in the uniformity of membrane potential control in their experiments by placing two microelectrodes intracellularly 0.5 mm apart along the length of the preparation in the recording pool (the experimental setup utilized a single sucrose gap and a length of preparation in the recording pool of 1 mm, the overall diameter of the preparation stated to be <0.7 mm). The potential differences between these two intracellular electrodes was recorded while the potential difference between one of these electrodes (which was used as the controlling electrode) and a third electrode in the fluid bathing the preparation was driven in a stepwise fashion by the controlling system. The deviation in potential between the two intracellular electrodes was small except for the initial 10 msec or so after the start and the end of the step where it was considerable ($\sim$5 mV for a 10 mV step).

The potential differences between both internal electrodes and the electrode in the extracellular fluid were compared during voltage-clamp steps and the authors stated that "provided that the bundle was less than 1 mm or shorter the voltage control along the fiber bundle was maintained within a range of less than 2 mV" (16). We have expressed our surprise at this finding earlier, in view of the geometrical considerations, but perhaps the surprise is diminished somewhat when it is recalled that the electrode in the extracellular fluid was a distant electrode external to the preparation. When the authors measured the potential differences between an intracellular electrode and one in the extracellular space within the fiber bundle, this potential difference differed markedly from the controlled potential (intracellular potential with respect to a distant extracellular electrode) during the occurrence of large inward currents. The authors (16) in referring to their illustration (Figure 2) stated, however, that the two potentials returned to agreement at the end of the rapid inward current and remained in agreement throughout all smaller and slower currents which were observed in these preparations.

This finding is difficult to reconcile with their equivalent circuit given in our Figure 3B, which they have shown represents the electrical behavior of the preparation at other times, e.g. during a small step change in clamp potential referred to above. The contradiction becomes clearer when one considers in their equivalent circuit the probable physical origin of the resistance R_s. In discussing this question they referred to the histological finding of deep narrow clefts of extracellular space between Purkinje fibers. However, these clefts are only found in Purkinje fibers from hearts of mammals the size of the dog and larger (5) and certainly do not occur between fibers of the ventricular myocardium of which their preparation is composed (5). The authors ended their discussion with a reference to a suggestion that was made to them by Dr. Silvio Weidmann concerning the physiological origin of R_s which they did not pursue but which we think is the most likely cause of the high extracellular resistance R_s.

Dr. Weidmann suggested that the diffusion of sucrose from the middle compartment along the extracellular pathways might contribute to the high resistivity in the extracellular space within the preparation. If we draw the preparation to scale, a short cylindrical bundle of up to 0.7 mm in diameter, projecting out of a sucrose cuff into test solution for a distance of only 1 mm, the situation becomes clear. Unless one assumes, for sucrose, an anisotropic diffusion coefficient (which, by the way, one suspects would be greater along the long axis of the preparation than at right angles), then sucrose must diffuse at least as far along the long axis of the preparation in the recording pool as it does into the depths of the preparation in the sucrose-filled compartment. Indeed one would be hard to put stop it. As far as we are concerned this is sufficient evidence to place R_s physically apart from the membrane structure and in extracellular space.

We have then the following contradiction. The authors have shown convincingly in one group of experiments that the preparation behaved as though there were a fixed resistance R_s, in series with the membrane capacitance. That is to say the preparation behaved as the circuit in Figure 3B, where the combination of R_m in parallel with C_m represents the membrane of the preparation and, in our view, R_s represents the resistance of extracellular fluid polluted with sucrose. On the other hand, in another group of experiments, differences in potential between two electrodes in extracellular space, namely one within the extracellular space in the preparation and one outside the preparation, were found to be insignificant (except for large currents in response to depolarizing steps in command potential), which implies that little or no resistance was presented by extracellular space. In other words, in one group of experiments currents were associated with voltage drops in extracellular space, represented by voltage drops across R_s in the circuit of Figure 3B, whereas in another group of experiments such currents were not associated with voltage drops across R_s. We will try to reconcile this apparent contradiction later.

The importance of R_s becomes impressive when one compares its measured value of around 600 Ω with the values of the membrane slope resistance obtained from their current-voltage plots (16, 17). The "steady-state" outward current-voltage relationship (Figure 7 of Ref. 16) shows a slope resistance as low as 1500 Ω in which case R_s is hardly negligible in comparison. However, inspection of the current-voltage relationships for their slow inward current (17) shows slope resistances which range as low as 2.2–4.0 kΩ, again not sufficiently large compared with 600 Ω for R_s to be neglected.

Let us turn to Beeler & Reuter's analysis (16) of their equivalent circuit in the form shown in Figure 4B. They concluded from this analysis that "when the sodium

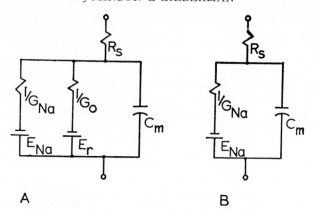

$$A \qquad\qquad\qquad B$$

FIGURE 4. A. Equivalent circuit used to describe the electrical behavior of the mammalian myocardial preparation in the single sucrose gap which contains an additional conductance G_o and battery E_r to those in the circuit of B. G_o represents the combined conductance of the membrane, and E_r the equilibrium potential, to ions other than Na. R_s is a resistance in series with the membrane which is represented by the capacitance C_m in parallel with the resistance(s) $1/G_{Na}$ and $1/G_o$ in A and $1/G_{Na}$ in B.

conductance is significantly smaller than the series conductance $(1/R_s)$, the actual membrane potential will be approximately equal to the clamp potential as desired." Their analysis is prefaced by the remark "that for the potentials and time of primary interests the other conductances can be neglected with respect to the sodium conductance" and hence they wrote that the total current I_m was given by their Equation 2 which is given below

$$I_m = (E_m - E_{Na})G_{Na} + C_m(dE_m/dt) \quad \text{(Equation 2 p. 185 of Ref. 1)}$$

and

$$I_m = (E_c - E_m)G_s \quad \text{(Equation 1 p. 185 of Ref. 1)}$$

where I_m is the true transmembrane potential, i.e. the potential across C_m and E_c is the command potential, i.e. the potential between the two terminals of the circuit of Figure 4A or B and $G_s = 1/R_s$. Combining Equations 1 and 2, they obtained

$$dE_m/dt = 1/C_m(E_cG_s + E_{Na}G_{Na} - E_m(G_s + G_{Na})) \quad \text{(Equation 3 p. 185 of Ref. 1)}$$

The steady-state value of E_m was obtained by setting the left-hand side of Equation 3 equal to zero, hence

$$E_{m_\infty} = \frac{G_s E_c + G_{Na} E_{Na}}{G_s + G_{Na}} \quad \text{(Equation 10 p. 186 of Ref. 1)}$$

In their analysis Beeler & Reuter also state that "if the sodium conductance is significantly smaller than the series conductance" $(1/R_s)$, their Equation 3 simplified to Equation 9.

$$dE_m/dt = (E_c - E_m)G_s/C_m \quad \text{(Equation 9 p. 186 of Ref. 1)}$$

in which case $E_{m_\infty} = E_c$. If by "significantly" is meant "very much smaller than," then this is true, but if for example $G_s = 2G_{Na}$ then $E_{m_\infty} \neq E_c$ but $E_{m_\infty} = 2/3(E_c + 0.5E_{Na})$. That is to say, for example, when $E_c = 0$, E_{m_∞} is in fact in error by $E_{Na}/3$. Their neglect of G_{Na} in this part of their analysis might perhaps be appropriate for situations at long times after the start of the depolarizing step in command potential. However, one cannot in this case continue to neglect other membrane conductances, i.e. they must retract their initial statement that conductances other than G_{Na} can be neglected. Indeed, we must include these other conductances since the current at long times for small steps in clamp potential was not neglible: these currents include their secondary slow inward current and the steady-state currents. Thus we revise their Equation 2 to give

$$I_m = G_{Na}(E_m - E_{Na}) + G_0(E_m - E_r) + \frac{C_m dE_m}{dt} \qquad 3.$$

where G_0 represents the sum total conductance of the membrane to participating ions other than sodium, and E_r represents their effective combined electrical driving force (see Figure 4a). The steady-state value of E_m is given by

$$E_{m_\infty} = \frac{G_{Na}E_{Na} + G_0E_r + G_sE_c}{G_{Na} + G_0 + G_s} \qquad 4.$$

and when G_{Na} is very much less than G_s then

$$E_{m_\infty} = \frac{G_0E_r + G_sE_c}{G_0 + G_s} \qquad 5.$$

so that it is clear that E_m is never equal to E_c (except for the trivial case where $E_c = E_r$). With the assumption that the sum of these other conductances, G_0, is ten times less than that of the series conductance, $1/R_s$, then $E_{m_\infty} = .91E_c + .091\ E_r$. That is to say the steady-state true transmembrane potential deviates by 9% from the command potential. Now if we insert for G_0 in Equation 5 the maximum values for the chord conductances obtainable from their current-voltage plots of (i) so-called "steady-state" current, (ii) peak primary early transient, and (iii) secondary early transient (secondary slow) current, and taking a value of 550 Ω for R_s (the middle value of their range of 500–600 Ω), we get the following results. From the "steady-state" current-voltage relationship of their Figure 7 (16), the curve has a maximum slope of ∼1460 Ω, which gives a value for the steady-state true transmembrane potential of 73% of the command potential.

For the curve representing the peak early primary transient current-voltage relations, the minimum recorded resistance there is ∼900 Ω, which, together with the given value of 49.5 mV for the equilibrium potential for this current, results in a value for the steady-state true transmembrane potential of 65% of the command potential. The secondary early transient current has a variety of minimum chord resistances of between 2.2 and 4.0 kΩ. These values, together with the value of 60 mV, assumed by the authors as the equilibrium potential for this current, give a true transmembrane potential of ∼80 and 88% of the command potential respectively. Thus, even assuming that the entire preparation was described by the lumped circuit of Figure 4A or B (which is indeed quite unrealistic considering the geometry of the preparation), there would be serious deviation between the measured and controlled value of the membrane potential and the true transmembrane potential in all circumstances of interest. One could go on to include the effects of the capacitive reactance of the membrane; we have already demonstrated this to be by no means insignificant when considering the effects of the size of the preparation.

In their final remarks (16) they stated that "the clamp loses control of the membrane only when the membrane conductances become significantly large with respect to the series conductance" ($1/R_s$). This is misleading if not erroneous. If by loss of control one means that the command potential E_c differs from the true transmembrane potential E_{m_∞} by greater than 10%, then their final statement that "tests on the data for both the second inward current and the outward current have indicated that all conductances and time parameters are within the criteria outlined above" (16) is, as related to our analysis of the data provided by their reports, incorrect.

Finally, we return to the apparent contradiction between the conclusion to be drawn from the experimental results and the above analysis, that there was a significant resistance in series with the membrane, and their finding that (except during the time course of the primary early transient current) the difference in potential between an electrode situated in the extracellular space of the preparation and one outside the preparation was insignificant. In an attempt to reconcile this contradiction, we suggest that the electrode in extracellular space was, in effect, not located at the junction of R_m and R_s in Figure 3B or 4A or B, but somewhere near the outside end of R_s. In this circumstance, the potential recorded there (except for very large currents) would not have been noticeably different from that at a distant reference point in extracellular space (signified by the upper input terminal to the network of Figure 3B or 4A or B). These large currents referred to above must, therefore, have been very much larger than those that occurred at all other times, since the latter produced no noticeable potential differences between this relatively superficial point in extracellular space in the preparation and the external reference electrode. An inspection of their current-voltage relationships shows, however, that the peak values of the primary early transient current (labeled I_{Na} in their current-voltage plots) were not all that much greater than the peak values of the slow secondary current and were not far off the values of the steady-state outward currents for large depolarizations. This appears to introduce another contradiction, for their experiments with the extracellular electrodes indicated that the primary early transient currents were very much larger than those at other times, whereas the current-voltage relationships indicated otherwise.

A final reconciliation lies, we think, in the possibility that although the total current flowing into the preparation was about the same in circumstances where significant changes in extracellular potential occur and in circumstances where none occur, membrane current density in certain regions might have differed quite markedly. Because of gross inhomogeneity of the spatial control of membrane potential, especially during regenerative changes in sodium conductance (which might have occurred during the primary early transient), the current density through the membrane of fibers lying in the shortest pathway between the voltage and current electrodes might have been very much higher at these than at other times. Thus an electrode in extracellular space, close to the intracellular voltage electrode, would have recorded larger potential changes corresponding to the higher current densities. Clearly then if this explanation is correct, their experimental observations related to potential changes in extracellular space are misleading and should be discounted. The equivalent circuit of Figure 3B (or its other forms 4A and B) should therefore be taken as a first approximation to the actual electrical behavior of the preparation and the consequences discussed above should be recognized.

Mascher & Peper (19) used a preparation of ventricular muscle from the sheep which is similar in size (1 mm long in the test compartment and an overall diameter of <0.6 mm) and morphology to that from the dog used by the preceding authors. However, Mascher & Peper (19), whose method is cited by Ochi (28), did not investigate the limitations of the clamp method nor did they mention findings comparable to those found by Beeler & Reuter (16), although the method was almost identical. They did, however, discuss the question of the uniformity of membrane potential control. They quoted the remarkable finding of Morad & Trautwein (46) that during a steady-state displacement in command potential no essential difference in the membrane potential of superficial fibers was observed and they concluded that the transmembrane potential in their preparation followed the applied voltage step with no appreciable delay. They discussed the membrane potential of membrane in possible extracellular clefts between cells or in the transverse tubular system. The transverse tubules, wherever they have been found in cardiac muscle, because of their large diameter and short length (5 μ or so) should present no problem for control, at least comparable in magnitude to the problems arising from the size of the preparation.

Although there are no narrow clefts of extracellular space in ventricular trabeculae, comparable with those that occur in bundles of Purkinje fibers from hearts of the size of the dog and larger, it does not follow that there is no significant resistance to the flow of controlling current presented by extracellular space. In fact, the preceding discussions regarding the dog ventricular trabeculae suggest that an important resistance, whatever the origin, does reside in extracellular space. Finally, the authors (19) stated what amounts to their general belief (unsupported in our view) that when the Na current was small "the membrane should be properly clamped even in deeply located cells of the preparation and the observed inward current should not be falsified by incomplete clamping of sodium spikes."

The double sucrose gap.—A conclusion to be drawn from the previous discussion is the need to reduce the membrane length in the preparation to be controlled. This is the main benefit that can accrue from the use of the double-sucrose-gap method. Provided the overall diameter is small, the length of preparation in the test pool (the central node) can be reduced by perhaps an order of magnitude from that obtainable with the single-sucrose-gapped preparation. Although the degree of spatial and temporal homogeneity of potential control (i.e. L/λ) is improved correspondingly, it may not be satisfactory.

Nevertheless, noticeable improvements in spatial and temporal control can, we think, be seen in the peak early transient current-voltage relationships obtained from these preparations (see later). A reasonable lower value for the width of the central node that can be achieved between the two sucrose-gap streams, at the free surface of the preparation, might be taken to be equal to the overall diameter of the preparation. This neglects the process of formation of the node about the fibers within the preparation which renders this low value quite unreasonable. This is unfortunate for one would like to achieve, as a rough rule of thumb, a node width about equal to the diameter of the individual fibers—seemingly unattainable with the preparations of cardiac muscle presently available. Furthermore, with the frog atrial trabecula in the double sucrose gap, the benefits accruing from a reduction in the length of the central node are partially offset by the unfortunate smaller average diameter of the individual fibers (i.e. a decrease in λ, all other properties being the same). It is for this reason that these tiny trabeculae with their thinner individual fibers are not as desirable as trabeculae of equivalent overall diameter from the mammalian ventricle.

THE EARLY TRANSIENT CURRENTS

The current waveform usually associated with a step change in command potential initially consists of two components one capacitive and the other resistive (comprising two or more ionic species). Both the separation of the ionic from the capacitive transient and the separation of one particular ionic from other contributing ionic currents are frought with difficulties and are particularly complicated in voltage-clamp experiments of cardiac muscle. Separation of the capacitive and the ionic current components of the current transient following a step change in the command potential can be circumvented by waiting for the capacitive component to die away. This, however, usually means that one must relinquish any attempt to follow changes in ionic currents that take a comparable time course. If one wishes to measure ionic current before the capacitive transient has died away, the established method is to record the current waveforms for command potential steps of magnitudes equal to those for the depolarizing steps but in the hyperpolarizing direction. For small steps, the initial transients are usually symmetrical in form and of equal magnitude. The record usually consists of a sudden, rapidly rising surge of current that declines, afterwards, less rapidly and in a manner that varies with the method and preparation.

Where the transient component decays exponentially with a time constant that is identical for small depolarizing and for all hyperpolarizing transients, the assumption is then made that the initial magnitude of the current and the time constant of its decay for larger depolarizing steps is the same as for its hyperpolarizing counterpart. It is a simple but tedious procedure to subtract the hyperpolarizing transient (with change in sign) from the total current transient for the step of equal magnitude in the depolarizing direction. None of the reports of voltage-clamp of cardiac muscle that we have reviewed have carried out such a procedure. Some of the authors have waited until the current that was believed to be of capacitive origin died away (21, 23–27, 31). Beeler & Reuter (16–18) made no clear attempt to separate ionic from capacitive components during the early transient currents (see below) but for the tails of current following repolarizing steps in command potential, they stated (17) that measurements of these tails were corrected for capacitive current. Inexplicably, no details of the method were given. Others made no attempt to separate the capacitive from resistive (ionic) currents and measured total ("global") clamp currents (20, 29, 30). Dudel & Rüdel (22) assumed that when they read the peak of the primary early transient a negligible capacitive current existed. They plotted the difference between the peak absolute value of the early primary transient and the current at some later time (tens of milliseconds later) and attributed the difference to one ionic current.

Beeler et al (16) used a somewhat similar but more complicated procedure. For small depolarizations the peak early ionic current was estimated as a difference between the beginning and the maximum value of the sharp downward and inward going deflection of the current trace. In this case, an indeterminant amount of capacitive and ionic current was subtracted from the total (peak) early current transient. For larger depolarizing steps they modified the procedure since in the records there was no early peak (other than the initial capacitive) in the current transient; the current waveform monotonically declined from an initial maximum to a later ("steady-state") minimum in two phases, a rapid one inflecting with a somewhat slower one. The early transient current in these cases was estimated as the difference between the point of inflection and the "steady-state" level. The values of current obtained by these two methods were then plotted on the same graph as ionic and of one kind (I_{Na}). This method not only resulted in an unknown amount of capacitive current left in the measurement but, as with the method of Dudel & Rüdel (22), involved the unjustified assumption for some or all depolarizing steps that other ionic currents at the time they made their measurement of the early transient current were identical to those some hundreds of milliseconds later.

In systems where these currents are clearly separable into their capacitive and ionic components, the usual procedure is to plot the absolute peak value of the early ionic transient as a function of membrane potential. Having shown that this transient is carried largely by one ion species, its value is estimated by a procedure which requires the assumption that at some other time or experimental condition, little if any of the recorded current is carried by the ion in question, and that the current carried by all other ions has not suffered any significant change as a consequence. The difference, then, between the currents measured in each circumstance is plotted to construct a true, peak ionic current-voltage relationship, the zero current intercept with the voltage axis being the true "reversal" or "equilibrium" potential for the ion in question.

Primary early transient current-voltage relationships.—Disregarding all doubts as to the purity of this current as measured in the previously described ways, investigators who have considered this current have found it abolished by tetrodotoxin [1.5×10^{-5} g/ml in mammalian ventricular muscle (16); $1 - 5 \times 10^{-7}$ g/ml in frog atrial trabecula (20)] and diminished by reducing the Na ion concentration in the bathing media (16, 19, 20). They have shown it to have many of the qualities exhibited by the early transient current that occurs in the squid giant axon and the frog node of Ranvier which had previously been shown to be carried by Na ions (16, 20, 22). The magnitude of this early transient current varies with the membrane potential: the peak value it reaches during a sudden change in command potential (to a given constant value) has been shown to be a sigmoidal function of the value of the command holding potential or resting potential prior to the sudden change (16, 22). Furthermore, this relationship varies with the concentration of Ca ions in the bathing media in a manner similar to that of squid axon membrane (16, 22, 51). These findings have led to the consensus that this primary early current transient is carried by sodium ions flowing down their electrochemical gradient as a result of changes in the membrane properties that arise from changes in the membrane potential, and that these changes can be described by the same general formulation devised by Hodgkin & Huxley (1) for the squid axon.

There are, however, several curious differences in this relationship as

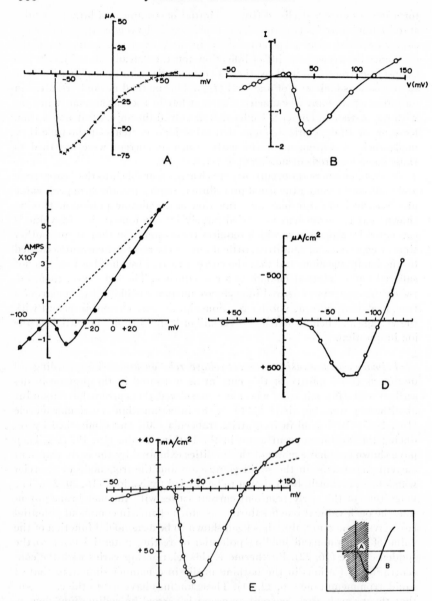

FIGURE 5A, B, C. Plots of the peak value of the primary early transient current as a function of the value of a step change in command potential. A. Dog ventricular trabecula and the single sucrose gap, redrawn from Beeler & Reuter (16); B. Frog atrial trabecula and double sucrose gap, redrawn from Rougier et al (20); C. Rabbit *P* strand (4) in the double sucrose gap (Dr. Leslie Harrington, personal communication). In B the potentials are displacements of potential with respect to the holding obtained from different preparations as well as kinds and species of cardiac muscle. Figures 5A–E show various current-voltage relationships for the primary early transient current obtained from A. dog ventricular trabecula (16), B. frog atrial trabecula (20), C. rabbit Purkinje trabecula (52), D. squid giant axon (3), and E. frog node of Ranvier (53, 54).

These differences, we think, can be accounted for by differences in the degree of spatial and temporal control of the membrane potential. Two features of the figures are to be noted, the curvature of the region of each current-voltage relationship indicated by B and the steepness in the region indicated by A in the insert to Figure 5.

It has been carefully established in the case of the squid and frog nerve, where the current is carried by Na ions, that a true difference in membrane properties is reflected in a difference in the relationship in region B. [(See Figures 5D and E) (3, 53).] In these preparations, the experimental conditions insured good spatial and temporal uniformity of membrane potential control and it was established that the difference in the current-voltage relationships originated from a difference between the *instantaneous* current-voltage relationships for the two membranes. As mentioned previously, the instantaneous current-voltage relationship for Na ions in the squid axon (in normal seawater) is linear and for the frog nerve, curved[3] with proportionality constants G_{Na} (Equation 1) and P_{Na} (Equation 2) respectively. For large depolarizations, the peak value of membrane conductance or permeability to Na ions approaches a maximum, so that in effect G_{Na} or P_{Na} becomes independent of the membrane potential. A plot of the peak Na current as a function of the membrane potential then becomes almost identical with that of the instantaneous current-voltage relationship determined, for example, at the peak of a Na conductance or permeability change during a large depolarizing step. We point out, in parenthesis, that for a current-voltage relationship to win the title of "instantaneous", the currents in it must at least have been determined within a time after the change in membrane potential that was insufficient for the membrane properties to change. We recognize that this time may vary from a few microseconds to seconds depending on the rapidity with which the particular property under study

---

potential: −ve, hyperpolarizing; +ve, depolarizing. For details of current measurement in A and C see text. Currents given in C are absolute values. D and E. Plots of the peak value of the single early transient current as a function of membrane potential; in D the squid giant axon, redrawn from (3) and in E the frog node of Ranvier, redrawn from (53). In D and E the potentials are displacements of transmembrane potential from the holding potential (N.B., in D −ve, depolarizing and +ve, hyperpolarizing; in E *vice versa*). The insert in the lower right-hand corner of the Figure defines regions of primary interest in the plots, namely, the negative slope region of the current-voltage curve in the shaded area A and the steep positive region of the curve in the unshaded area B.

[3] Note that the curvature becomes noticeable only for membrane potentials more positive than E_{Na}.

changes, and hence the title may be more or less achievable, but we do urge everyone to try.

There is, however, another explanation for nonlinearity in the peak early current transient-voltage relationship in region B of those of Figures 5A and B. Indeed, it is one which must be eliminated before alternatives such as that described above for frog nerve are considered. This explanation is based on the known properties of the Na-carrying system in squid and frog nerve membrane. As the magnitude of a depolarizing step in membrane potential is increased, both the rate at which the Na conductance or permeability turns on, and the rate at which it turns off, increase so that the peak of the conductance or permeability change occurs sooner following the start of the depolarizing step. For this reason, the peak of the surge of Na current moves more and more into the early outward capacitive transient as the magnitude of the depolarizing step is increased. By the time this transient has diminished and an inward transient becomes perceptible, more and more of the conductance (permeability) has been inactivated. This is particularly likely where spatial nonuniformity in membrane potential occurs so that the peak conductance (permeability) change during a given depolarizing step occurs at different times throughout the preparation. Close to the site of current injection, the resultant changes in transmembrane potential are, at least transiently, greater than those at more distant sites (see discussion of single sucrose gap).

This explanation is supported by the finding that in a preparation in which there must be, on geometrical grounds, better temporal and spatial control of potential, this curvature in the peak early current transient-voltage curve, though still present, is less marked (see Figure 5B). Furthermore, the negative slope region is less steep, in the case of Figure 5B compared with Figure 5A. This steepness of the negative slope region can be a sensitive index of the spatial uniformity of the control of membrane potential—it covers the region over which the membrane conductance or permeability changes markedly with membrane potential and hence where control is most difficult. The first sign of inadequate control that shows up in the current-voltage relationship is a steepening of this region, so that it is only possible to obtain one or two data points at its positive and negative current extremes. The satisfactory appearance of this region in the current-voltage curve of Figure 5B is, however, more apparent than real: indeed we were made suspicious of this, in that the degree of temporal and spatial control required to obtain this number of data points was somewhat surprising considering the morphology of the preparation from which they were obtained, the frog atrial trabecula (7). This preparation was a bundle, approx. 100 μ in overall diameter, whose individual fibers are approximately 3 μ in diameter and where the node was cited as approximately 100 μ or at least 30 or more times wider than the diameter of the individual fibers (20).

This is much wider than that found necessary for adequate control of single nerve fiber preparations. It is, therefore, not surprising to find that the authors were not able to obtain, in the negative slope region of the current-voltage characteristic, early primary transient waveforms that were free of notches on the falling phase. These notches were sometimes seen in voltage-clamp records of nerve membrane and are appropriately referred to by Cole (55) as "abominable notches". They have been shown in this case to reflect incipient oscillatory behavior and loss of spatial control of membrane potential, the turn on and turn off of sodium conductance in the nodal membrane becoming temporarily fragmented. With larger depolarizing steps, the fragmentation might be expected to diminish, so that the several peaks of inward current which have become displaced in time, progressively coalesce (as was observed) to give an apparently smoothly increasing first initial peak (whose peak value is plotted) (20). One should, however, point out that the absence of notches cannot be taken alone as evidence of adequate spatial control of potential. Indeed the appearance of them in the records of Rougier et al (20) is in our view an indication of a decided improvement of such control over that obtained with the single-sucrose-gap preparation.

With improvement of the experimental technique, e.g. by using a preparation which contained fibers of larger individual diameter, one might under favorable circumstances expect to obtain records free of "abominable notches". Furthermore, if the improvements in size were not too great, it might be expected that the steepness of the negative slope region would reappear (which indeed is the case, as reported by L. Harrington in a personal communication). That this does not reflect a return to the situation responsible for Figure 5B is indicated by the other index of clamp quality, namely the steepness and linearity of the current-voltage relationship in region B of Figure 5C compared with Figure 5B.

Differences, then, in the general shape of the early primary transient current-voltage relationship obtained by different groups with different preparations are attributable to differing degrees of inadequacies of temporal and spatial control of membrane potential. Until proved otherwise, such an explanation is, we think, more likely than one involving differences in membrane properties.

Such differences in shape should not, however, have affected the determination of the equilibrium or reversal potential for the ion species (assuming it to be one ion species) responsible for the early primary transient current, provided that the current values plotted were ionic and comprised solely of the ion in question. In this case, the equilibrium potential is given by the intercept of the current-voltage curve with the voltage axis. However, the separation of the current responsible for the early transient current from other ionic currents is not a simple matter.

One method is to plot the peak value of the early ionic transient (having corrected for any capacitive component) as a function of the command potential. The reversal potential is then evaluated by linearly extrapolating the current-voltage relationship for hyperpolarizing steps in command potential so as to intercept the peak early current-voltage curve for large depolarizations as illustrated in Figure 5 C, D. A second method is to determine the instantaneous current-voltage relationship for the membrane at the holding potential and find the intercept of this curve with the peak early current-voltage curve as in the first method. Both methods assume that the only change in permeability or conductance, if any, between the start of the step change in command potential and the time at which the value of the peak early transient is measured involves only one ion species.

Furthermore, it is assumed that the conductance or permeability to this ion is negligible for at least a short time after the change in command potential. The first method assumes that the membrane current-voltage relationship for the membrane during this short time is a linear extrapolation of the current-voltage relationship in the hyperpolarizing direction. The second method makes no such assumption.

Other methods might employ the fact that the early ionic current transient is abolished by tetrodotoxin. For example, the procedure might be to plot the peak early transient current-voltage relationship in the absence of tetrodotoxin, at the same time noting the differing times at which the current was measured in the various current records. The tissue would be then exposed to tetrodotoxin and the same series of command potential steps repeated. The current is measured at the identical time at which the currents were measured in the absence of tetrodotoxin. This is similar to a method used by Rougier et al (20), and is one which has the advantage of removing both capacitive (providing they are of a simple variety) and other ionic currents insensitive to tetrodotoxin. Furthermore, the method makes no assumption about the current-voltage relationship of the membrane for other ions flowing during the early current transient; it does, however, assume that tetrodotoxin specifically abolishes the current responsible for the early current transient and leaves all other currents unaffected.

However, the alternative procedures used by Beeler & Reuter (16) make the different, and we think questionable, assumption that the current-voltage relationship for ions other than the ion responsible for the primary early transient is given by the quasisteady-state current-voltage relationship for the preparation some 100 msec or so after the start of step changes in command potential. This relationship is very nonlinear (indeed it exhibits a negative slope region, which they attribute to the flow of Ca ions). They make the sweeping assumption that this nonlinear relationship is identical to the *instantaneous* current-voltage relationship for the preparation at the holding potential. The values of the peak of the primary early transient current naturally depend very greatly on the form of this steady-state current-voltage relationship and hence the value of the equilibrium potential that they so obtained. Furthermore, by this assumption one eliminates any consideration of the effects of experimental maneuvers on the true instantaneous current-voltage relationship, or that current-voltage relationship that exists for other ions at the peak of the early primary transient.

In the experiments of Dudel & Rüdel (22), the early primary transient was attributed to Na ions and its peak value was determined as the difference between the maximum inward current and the "steady-state" inward current at some unspecified later time—indicated by the statement "as seen at the end of the current trace in Figure 1"; this appears to be about 40 msec after the beginning of the command step. Dudel & Rüdel's paper (22) is outstanding in that it is the only one that we have come across that concerned itself with the kinetics of the turn on and turn off of the early primary transient current. In our view, it is unfortunate that they chose as a preparation a 2 mm long segment of a sheep Purkinje strand and the two-microelectrode method of voltage-clamp discussed above. They found that cooling the preparation to 4–5°C caused it to become depolarized and inexcitable, but when they hyperpolarized the preparation momentarily, anode-break excitations occurred regularly, even at this temperature. Similarly, hyperpolarization of the membrane momentarily to about −100 mV, followed by a depolarization to say −20 mV, resulted in an early transient current that reached a peak in about 10 msec. The time course, slow compared with that at normal body temperature of 37°C, encouraged the authors to use the preparation to analyze some of the kinetics of this current which they evaluate as described above and attributed to sodium ions. Shortly after the temperature of the preparation was reduced, the early currents were slowed but the command potential at which the peak value of the primary initial transient changed sign had a positive value, whereas after 10 min to 1 hr, this potential fell to zero.

This suggested to them that a Na pump was arrested at the low temperatures and time was required for the intracellular Na ion concentration to rise and hence the "reversal" potential to fall to zero. Furthermore, shortly after cooling to low temperatures, some early transient current could be obtained for depolarizing steps from conditioning prepotentials of −60 mV. Later, such current could only be obtained if the conditioning prepotential was greater than −100 mV. All of these changes were quite reversible on rewarming the preparation. The authors went on to examine the dependency of the magnitude of the early current transient on the duration of the conditioning prepotential and made the remarkable finding that for the magnitude of this current to be maximal the prepotential must be held at a value of −180 mV for 1 sec or at −110 mV for 10 sec. This is interpreted and analyzed in terms of the model of the Na-carrying system formulated by Hodgkin & Huxley (1) for the squid axon.

The authors point out that the curve relating the degree of inactivation of the Na-carrying system and the transmembrane potential in nerve is remarkably constant: changes in temperature do not alter the form but merely shift the curve along the voltage axis. However, in their experiments in the sheep Purkinje strand, the relationship was less steep at low temperatures compared with that at higher: the range from nearly maximum to minimum inactivation occurred over a range of membrane potentials of 100 mV compared with the smaller range of around 40 mV for nerve. This strange effect led them to suggest that some change in the basic structure of the Purkinje fiber membrane occurred in this temperature range. One wonders if the development of the need of a larger conditioning prepotential after prolonged cooling accompanied the shift in the potential at which the early current transient reversed sign. In other words, the question is: was one or were both of these effects functions of temperature and time? For example, the effect on the magnitude of the prepotential might have been an instantaneous function of temperature, whereas that on the "reversal" potential required time to occur.

Their lack of comment in this regard would seem to suggest that both effects required time to develop following the drop in temperature. If this were the case, then before one postulates a temperature and time-dependent differential change in the relationships between α_h and β_h (the rate constants governing the variable h in the Hodgkin-Huxley formulation) (1) and the membrane potential, one should exclude the alternative explanation that changes occurred in the ionic concentrations in the deep and narrow clefts separating the fibers in this preparation. The maintenance of a constant extracellular ionic composition in this space must depend very much on active membrane ion transport between the interior of the cell and the clefts.

Secondary early transient current.—This is a current transient that follows the primary early transient and has a slower time course. It is seen in various forms by many authors and is distinguished from the primary transient by its persistence after the early primary one has been reduced or abolished by various experimental maneuvers, e.g. exposure to tetrodotoxin, a depolarizing conditioning prepotential, or a reduction in the Na concentration in the bathing media. In addition, after the early primary transient current has been abolished by one or other of these procedures, the secondary transient, exposed or emphasized as a result (and by definition immune to these procedures), is reduced or abolished by a number of additional maneuvers, namely, reduction of the calcium concentration in the bathing media (17, 19, 28), greater depolarizing prepotentials than those required to eliminate the primary transient (16–19, 28), and exposure of the preparation to Mn ions (28, 29) (an ion said to block a calcium-sensitive current).

Features of the behavior of this secondary transient differ somewhat in different reports, but the consensus is that this current is at least partially carried by Ca ions flowing down their electrochemical gradient. This important conclusion has gained wide acceptance as apparently the likeliest to be drawn from the published experimental results. Although it is reasonable to conclude from Ca flux experiments (56, 57) that Ca ions do flow into the cell on excitation, it is open to considerable question whether this flux carries any significant current and whether this current is responsible for the secondary early transient currents seen in the various published reports under consideration.

We think there are alternative explanations for the results purported to substantiate such a notion and that these stem from inadequacies in the spatial and temporal control of membrane potential. We have gained the impression in reading the reports of this secondary early transient current that the notion of a Ca current preceded the final experimental findings presented in support of it. Be that as it may, it is not our purpose here to discredit such a notion but to point out alternative explanations which we think must take priority before such results, as presented, are attributed to Ca or any other ionic or nonionic current, however appealing. Since we are offering alternative explanations of experimental results, we will consider these results as presented by each group of authors.

Beeler & Reuter (16–18) describe two components in their current records. One which we have called the primary early transient current (discussed in the preceding section) is followed by a slower secondary component which we have called the secondary early transient. They reported (16) that within a few minutes, the "sodium current" (i.e. primary early transient) was abolished by tetrodotoxin but do not say whether the secondary component is affected. However, in the immediately following paper (17), in referring to these experiments, the authors stated that "tetrodotoxin (1.5×10^{-5} g/ml), in a concentration which greatly reduced or abolished I_{Na}" (the early primary transient) "had no effect on the slow inward current" (secondary early transient). Nevertheless, one wonders about the later effects of tetrodotoxin on the secondary transient particularly in view of the fact that the authors make no use of tetrodotoxin in separating the primary from the secondary transient. Nor do they separate the two on the basis of one being abolished by removing Na ions from the bathing media while the other is not. In fact, they found an inconsistent reduction in amplitude of the secondary transient after withdrawal of sodium from the bathing media.

One wonders whether such inconsistency is not due to some difficulty in interpretation, particularly when they make the remark that the primary transient was always rapidly abolished whereas the secondary transient persisted until "the preparation started to deteriorate after 20–40 minutes" in such solutions. Considering the size of their preparation (0.6 mm diameter) one questions whether this time is sufficient to remove all extracellular Na, especially about the deeper-lying fibers, and especially in view of the continual pollution of extracellular space by the effluxing internal Na ions. Needless to say, the authors do not consider this effect of extracellular sodium to be the consequence of a specific contribution of Na ions to the secondary transient current but rather it is thought "to be due to an accumulation of internal calcium in the fibers in the absence of (Na)$_o$."

Be that as it may, the method that they finally use to distinguish between the primary current ascribed solely to Na ions and the secondary transient current purportedly carried by Ca ions is on the basis of the following experiments. They changed the command potential in two steps: the first step, V_1, was of varying magnitude and constant duration (300 msec) and the second step, V_2, was always to -40 mV, a potential where they found the primary early transient to be large for *single* steps. They showed that the magnitude of the primary transient in the constant second step to -40 mV was a sigmoidal function of the conditioning prepotential step V_1, and that this relationship was shifted to more positive potentials the higher the external Ca concentration. This is a finding reminiscent of the relationship between the peak Na current and holding potential measured in similarly designed experiments in the squid axon (51, 58). They found that the peak value of the primary transient in the second voltage step, V_2, was completely abolished if the prepotential (V_1) were more positive than -45 mV, the slower secondary transient remaining. From this finding, it was concluded that the system responsible for causing a transient change in membrane Na permeability or conductance throughout the entire preparation (i.e. in practice that part of the preparation to which controlling current gains access) is completely inactivated. In other words, if the command potential is changed to -45 mV, all transient currents that are recorded following subsequent sudden changes in command potential are automatically non-Na in origin. Let us examine this conclusion.

As a first approximation, let us consider their preparation to be made up of two areas of membrane, one bordering the shortest pathway from the current source to the tip of the voltage microelectrode and one representative of the rest of the preparation, i.e. membrane more distant from these electrodes. Now, the displacement in internal potential along and about the route between the current source and the voltage electrode will at least equal and more than likely exceed in magnitude and speed the displacement in potential at the voltage electrode. Elsewhere, the change in internal potential must be less at all times and slower. It is clear that in response to a sudden medium-sized depolarizing step in command potential the membrane along this direct route would exhibit a rapid change in Na conductance (or permeability) which would be reflected in a rapid flux of controlling current —the early primary transient. The more distant membrane where the internal potential change was slower and smaller would give rise to a corresponding slower and smaller change in Na conductance and hence in controlling current (secondary early transient).[4] If this were the case, then their findings with the double-step experiment have another explanation. The transient current in both steps in command potential would then be Na current and hence the primary and secondary transients would be carried by the same ion, Na.

An experiment which they believe supported the idea that the two inward currents were not carried by the same ion was one in which the time course of the change in the early transient current was followed as a preparation was immersed in Na-free solution. Shortly after the bathing fluid was

[4] In this regard the findings of Neher & Lux (59) in their voltage-clamp study of the *Helix pomatia* neuronal membrane are of interest. They nicely demonstrate the complication introduced into the current waveform by current from membrane distal to the point of voltage control.

changed to Na-free solution, at which time the extracellular Na about the more superficial membrane of the preparation (around the voltage electrode) might be expected to be reduced, the magnitude of the peak of the primary early transient in the depolarizing step to −45 mV was reduced, and in a larger depolarizing step to −26 mV changed sign, becoming positive. A secondary early transient current of negative sign, however, appeared in a further depolarizing step to −20 mV, which, to the authors, clearly pointed to the appearance of a different current. In our view, the reduction in Na concentration in the bathing media would be expected to affect the magnitude of the early primary transient, considered here to originate from more superficial membrane, more than that of the secondary early transient which originated from deeper-lying membranes. The relative time course of the two currents would not be expected to be different, in identical voltage steps, in Na-containing and Na-free solutions, so that the existence of the two currents would become more noticeable. They would in effect appear to have different "reversal potentials", the extracellular Na ion concentration about one system of membranes (the more superficial) being changed, whereas that about the other (the deeper-lying one) remained relatively unchanged. The results of their experiment have, for us, the more likely explanation of being the consequence of temporal and spatial variation in membrane potential throughout the preparation and of variations in ionic composition in extracellular space. Indeed, the explanation that they proffer, appealing though it is, is only permitted if one is driven to it by the clear demonstration that such inhomogeneity did not occur.

Having not considered these possibilities and therefore deciding the current was of non-Na origin, Beeler & Reuter (17) then looked for the responsible ion, and on the basis of the results of their experiments they decided it was Ca. However, their analysis of this current is based on the assumption that all currents following changes in command potential from a holding potential of −40 mV are of non-Na origin. They claim that the secondary transient currents in depolarizing steps from this potential are of Ca origin since these currents are decreased in magnitude by decreases in Ca concentration in the bathing media. However, this is in accord with what one would expect if this current was a Na current which originated from distant membrane as apposed to membrane along the direct route from the current source to voltage electrode.

It is clear from their results (16) of the effects of changes in Ca concentration in the bathing media on the plot of the magnitude of the primary early transient (which they attribute to Na ions) versus the holding potential, that the holding potential of −40 mV was *more* than sufficient to eliminate this primary transient at other than the largest value of external calcium concentration used in these experiments. Therefore, using such a holding potential at lower Ca concentrations, one would begin to partially inactivate the more distant membrane from which the secondary early transient arises. The currents from this partially inactivated membrane in subsequent larger depolarizing steps would thus be less than if the experiment were done at a higher Ca concentration, for in this case little or none of the distant membrane would have been inactivated at the holding potential of −40 mV.

This explanation is in keeping with the effects of changes in Ca concentration on the plots of the maximum inward or the minimum outward current that occurred during depolarizing steps in command potential from −40 mV (the secondary transient current) observed by Beeler & Reuter (17). They found that the magnitude of this secondary transient and the slope of the current-voltage relationship for large depolarizations were increased with increased Ca concentrations. This increase in slope is nicely explained as simply due to a reduction in the degree of inactivation of the Na-carrying mechanism at the holding potential with increasing extracellular Ca. This effect of Ca on the membrane conductance underlying the secondary transient current is somewhat unexpected if that current were a Ca current. One would then have to presume that changing extracellular Ca had an effect (for example, on membrane properties) additional to the single expected effect of extracellular Ca on the electrical driving force for that ion.

One must also remember that the currents in their current-voltage plots are total currents. They do not distinguish between, for example, leakage current or currents carried by ions other than those responsible for the secondary transient. As a result, changes in the total current-voltage relationship produced by changes in Ca concentration in the bathing media have a variety of explanations. For example, they noted that "the threshold for initiation of this current" (the secondary transient) was shifted to more negative potentials when the calcium concentration was increased. Presumably, the authors meant by this "threshold", the voltage at which the current-voltage plot in the negative slope region crossed the voltage axis. A shift of this crossover point in the negative potential direction could be accounted for by a decrease in the leakage conductance or membrane conductance at the holding potential. This reminds us once again of the absence from their current-voltage relationships (16–18, 34, 35), as well as those of other authors (19, 22, 28), of current values for hyperpolarizing step changes in command potential from the resting or holding potential. This missing feature of these relationships requires an explanation, particularly since the form of this part of the relationship would help in assessing the reasonableness of assumptions regarding the form of the instantaneous current-voltage curve for the resting membrane in the depolarizing direction.

Having concluded that following steps in command potential at a holding potential of −40 mV, the secondary inward current transient was a Ca current transient, the authors then performed experiments designed to follow the time course of these currents at different membrane potentials (17). The results of these experiments are quite compatible with the behavior of a Na current except for the strange finding that their current turns off (inactivates) more slowly, the greater the size of the depolarizing step; this

is the inverse of the behavior of the Na conductance in the squid giant axon
(58) or the Na permeability in frog node of Ranvier (53). This anomalous
behavior might indicate anomalous membrane properties but one should
exclude the possibility that it is due to a system of membrane which behaves
"normally" as in nerve.

However, for small depolarizations, only the membrane in the vicinity
of the pathway between the current and voltage electrodes is activated, the
Na conductance there being rapidly activated and inactivated. For bigger
depolarizing steps in command potential, the currents originate from increasingly larger and more and more distant areas of membrane rather than
from the same membrane subjected to greater depolarizations. Thus larger
depolarizations can involve larger areas of membrane subjected to relatively
small depolarizations, in which case the rate of turn on and turn off of the
observed currents might not appear to increase with increasing depolarizing
steps in command potential. In any case this observed behavior of the
secondary transient current needs careful confirmation and reexamination.

The rate of exponential decline of the secondary current transient following a repolarizing step in command potential initiated at a fixed time following a fixed depolarizing step increased with increasing negativity of the
repolarizing step. This finding is quite compatible with similar behavior of
the Na conductance in the squid giant axon (the relationship between the
rate constant β_m of the Hodgkin-Huxley formulation and the membrane
potential describes this behavior). Whereas the result discussed above for
the turn off of this secondary current *during* depolarizing steps of varying
magnitude is totally anomalous to the behavior of β_h, the rate of turn off of
the Na conductance during depolarizing steps in membrane potential is
greater the greater the magnitude of the depolarizing step in potential.

Dudel & Rüdel (22), in their studies of the strand of Purkinje fibers of
the sheep, describe a single early current transient in normal Na media which
they attributed entirely to Na ions. This transient decayed with two time
constants, one being 2 to 3 times slower than the other, and the time constant of decay of the slower component was dependent on the prepotential
or holding potential. However, these currents were measured at very low
temperatures, 4–5°C, and extrapolation of trends which they observed at
20°C suggested to them that both components would be inactivated by the
time the crest of the action potential at 37°C was completed. They compared their slow component with that of Rougier et al (29) obtained in the
frog atrial trabecula but they pointed out that in that tissue it is 10–20
times slower than the faster component whereas in their experiments it was
only 2–3 times slower. Although they said that similar records (presumably
of a primary and secondary early transient current) were obtained by
Mascher & Peper (19), and Reuter & Beeler (16–18), these were orders of
magnitude slower than those obtained in the cooled Purkinje fiber, let alone
that fiber at 37°C.

We suggest that the similarity is more apparent than real and wonder if what Dudel & Rüdel (22) in fact achieved was the separation of the Na current components that might be expected from the two areas of membrane in the sheep Purkinje strand—one which is more rapidly depolarizable and activatable at more negative command potentials and one which is relatively inaccessible in the deep clefts between fibers. As they pointed out, Fozzard (38) has shown that a considerable fraction of the membrane capacitance is in series with a resistance. Rather than choose what we think is a bizarre idea, namely that this resistance is membrane resistance, we consider it as that of the extracellular fluid in the clefts. Then there is a system of two areas of excitable membrane, one relatively free of, and one in series with, a resistance. Intuitively this seems a likely origin for the two time constants of decay of their early current transient.

Mascher & Peper (19) have examined, in trabeculae of sheep ventricular muscle, the behavior of two components of controlling current to which we can give our names of primary and secondary early transient currents. The characteristic features of these currents were very similar to those of the currents recorded from dog ventricular trabecula by Beeler & Reuter (16, 17), except that the time course of Mascher & Peper's currents was somewhat slower. The early currents recorded by them following depolarizing steps in command potential began with a sudden jump in current followed by a monotonically decaying component lasting some 100 msec. Because of the relatively large peak value of this current at a command potential which the authors considered reasonably close to the expected value of the Na equilibrium potential for this preparation (+36 mV), they concluded that this current could not be carried solely by Na ions. This might have been a reasonable interpretation of this result, had they good reason to believe that the majority of the membrane in the preparation (accessible to the controlling current) had a transmembrane potential equal to this value of command potential. Considering the size of the fibers and of the preparation, the membrane capacitance of not less than $1-2 \mu F \ cm^{-2}$, and a membrane resistance of less than 800 Ωcm^2, this is to us an entirely unjustifible assumption.[5] Nevertheless, they considered the following findings further supported their interpretation.

One experiment was designed on the assumption that if the command potential was set to a holding potential of -25 mV the "Na-carrying sysstem" could be considered as entirely inactivated. When this was done, they observed that subsequent large depolarizing steps in command potential triggered an early secondary-type inward transient which reached a maximum after a delay of 100–200 msec, the delay being shorter the larger the depolarization. An "abominable notch" (55) appeared in one of their records (in the step to +3 mV). Similar early current waveforms were obtained

---

[5] From considerations discussed under single sucrose gap the area of membrane in the preparation is probably around 1 cm^2. They report that a holding current at around 10 μA was required to hyperpolarize the preparation from -62 to -70 mV. The membrane resistance therefore comes out to be around 800 Ωcm^2.

if the preparation was exposed to Na-free solution. The early primary type of transient currents which were initially maximal, and which dominated the records in normal Na solution, were lost, as they were in the preceding experiments when the holding potential was -25 mV. Again, the currents consisted of a slow-rising secondary-type transient that reached a delayed peak at approximately 100–200 msec after the start of the depolarizing step in command potential. The "abominable notches" were even more frequently seen in these current records.

As in similar experiments of Beeler & Reuter (16–18), the experimental maneuver was such as to place a majority of membrane giving rise to such controlling current at a more distant location from the current-to-voltage electrode pathway. Their holding potential of -25 mV would be expected to inactivate membrane in the more immediate vicinity of this pathway. Similarly, the exposure of the tissue to zero Na should be expected to affect membrane in the neighborhood of this pathway, since much of it would be expected to be situated in the more superficial fibers, one of which presumably contains the voltage-sensing electrode. The membrane current sources are thus driven away from the voltage electrode to be turned on by larger depolarizing steps, albeit more slowly than those occurring in membrane close to the current-to-voltage electrode pathway.

Rougier et al (20, 29) who used the double-sucrose-gapped frog atrial trabecula, also observed two components of the early transient current. The tissue was exposed to tetrodotoxin, and to Mn-containing Ringer with or without Na present (Na replaced by choline chloride). The authors concluded that the early primary transient was carried by Na ions and the secondary component was carried by Na *and* Ca ions in normal bathing media (29). Disregarding for the moment the results obtained with Mn, the finding that the secondary early transient could only be abolished by removing both Na and Ca ions from the bathing media and not by removing either one of the two is quite compatible with the notion that this current was carried by Na ions, particularly if one considers the following possibilities. The sucrose solution must have polluted the extracellular space about some of the fibers which were accessible to the controlling current and hence the concentration of tetrodotoxin there must have been less than elsewhere. In addition, the membrane of these fibers, surrounded by some sucrose, would be in series with a resistance that could be comparable to the resistance of the cell membrane, at least when the membrane current density is high. Thus the transmembrane potential of these fibers would be less than that of the recorded potential (see the discussion of the single sucrose gap).

Further, it might be difficult to achieve a zero Na ion concentration in the external media about the membrane in the narrow spaces separating the fibers of the tightly packed bundles which characterize this preparation. The effluxing of intracellular Na might keep the concentration in these spaces nonzero for a much longer time than might be expected from simple diffusion of sodium out of these spaces. One might therefore conclude from this latter possibility that removing the Na ions from the bathing media might dramatically reduce Na currents originating from the more superficial and accessible fiber membranes exposed to extracellular fluid which was relatively unpolluted by sucrose solution. This membrane, in our view, would give rise to the early primary transient, and the secondary transient could originate from the remainder of the membrane less accessible to controlling current. The additional effect of reducing the Ca concentration in the bathing media and its effect in activating the Na-carrying system could then be sufficient to reduce Na current in areas where the extracellular Na was incompletely removed. In other words, we suspect that the secondary early transient in these experiments is a Na current. The question whether this, together with the primary transient, is evidence for a Na permeability change which inactivates in two phases cannot be answered until the possibility of spatial inhomogeneity of membrane potential control has been eliminated.

Our interpretation of the results these authors obtained with Mn (29) was made difficult because we are unsure of the effects of $MnCl_2$ (1–2 mM) on the ionic permeabilities of the membrane. Although the authors cited the use of Mn by others as an inhibitor of Ca permeability, we know of no convincing direct evidence in support of such an action. Evidence for a different action of Mn was obtained by Ochi (28) in voltage-clamp experiments of guinea pig papillary and trabecula muscles using the single-sucrose-gap method. The same comments that we have made earlier regarding this method and the results obtained using it apply here too. His study was largely concerned with the properties of a slow inward current, in our terminology a secondary early transient current, which he defined as that transient current obtained in depolarizing steps from a holding potential of −40 mV. He found that Mn decreased the steady-state outward current and had a stabilizing action such that it seemed to shift the curves relating the parameters of activation and inactivation of his secondary early transient current along the potential axis to more positive potentials.

This is reminiscent of the action of increased Ca on the same parameters for the Na conductance of nerve (51). In other words, on exposure to Mn the disappearance of a secondary early transient current from a current obtained for a given depolarizing step simply meant that activation of such a current now required a greater depolarization. The secondary transient was not abolished by Mn in the way that, for example, tetrodotoxin eliminates the change in Na conductance. His results are compatible with his secondary early transient being entirely attributable to sodium ions. If Mn acts on a Na-carrying mechanism in a similar manner to Ca, then we can account for his otherwise strange result that, when the secondary early transient was rendered almost undiscernible by exposure to a medium free of Na and Ca, the secondary early transient *reappeared* when Mn (5 mM) was then added.

Ochi felt that this stabilizing action of Mn could not explain all of his results, particularly the following. The current-voltage relationships obtained in Ca-free, Mn-containing, solution on the one hand and a Ca-free solution with Mn on the other crossed the voltage axis at different potentials. This shift in the point of intersection of the two curves he described as a shift in the "reversal potential" for the secondary inward current. This is not the case, since these were not pure single current-voltage relationships but were a combination of at least that current responsible for the secondary inward transient and, for example, a steady-state outward current. It is clear from his current-voltage plots and his holding current values that there was a change in the outward current-voltage relationship and the shift he observed could be accounted for by a change in this current and not in the true reversal potential(s) for the current(s) responsible for the secondary early transient. Returning to the experiments of Rougier et al (29), one wonders then whether the secondary slow current is a pure Na current and the effect of Mn might have been due to a shift in the activation of this (Na) current outside the range of positive potentials used in their experiments.

In conclusion we suspect that, in fact, during a depolarizing step in membrane potential there is a transient inward Na current that rises to a peak within a time equal to the duration of the depolarizing phase of an action potential and that this declines in two phases, that is to say inactivates at two different rates. The differing evidence for two such components of inward current (albeit in this circumstance one Na and the other all or in part Ca) appearing in the voltage-clamp reports reviewed here are, in our opinion, inconclusive. Except for the experimental findings with the frog trabecula, the results put forward in support of such a notion are more than likely the consequence of inadequate spatial and temporal control of the transmembrane potential of membrane to which the controlling current gains access. In the case of the frog trabecula, the recorded current waveforms strongly suggest a biphasically decaying early inward transient membrane current. However, to what extent the waveform also reflects inhomogeneities of the kind we discuss can only await the results obtained from improved preparations and techniques for voltage-clamp. Finally, from the experimental evidence that we have reviewed here, one could not be driven but could only jump to the conclusion that Ca ions play a significant role as charge carriers in the generation of the cardiac action potential.

Action potentials and ions.—Electrophysiological techniques other than voltage-clamp have been used in attempts to investigate the possible contribution of Ca ions to the depolarizing current in cardiac cell membranes. Few, if any, of the studies have been able to extend our present understanding of the mechanisms fundamentally responsible for the long duration of the cardiac action potential. Alterations of external Ca concentration have been shown to affect principally the initial part of the plateau phase in the ventricular muscle (trabeculae carnae) of the dog without affecting the maximum plateau potential (60). Although this effect was augmented by reducing external sodium concentration, the obtained responses were less noticeable than those from frog (61) and guinea pig (62). In the presence of Mn (0.5–5.0 mM), transmembrane potentials recorded from rabbit atrial muscle exhibited a suppressed early plateau phase resulting in a decreased action-potential duration (63–65). The plateau phase was gradually restored when the solution containing Mn was replaced by a double strength Ca solution (63). The authors concluded that suppression of the plateau phase induced by Mn was due to an interference with Ca permeability.

Carmeliet & Vereecke (65) studied the effects of epinephrine on the plateau phase of the cow Purkinje strand and showed that epinephrine (10^{-5} M) increased the amplitude and duration of the plateau. Although arguments were presented for an increased inward Ca current under the influence of epinephrine, they were not able to rule out the contribution of a slow inward Na current or a decrease in K conductance (66).

Data obtained from the barnacle muscle fiber indicated that different species of divalent cations bind competitively at the same membrane sites with different dissociation constants according to the following order: $Mn^{++} > Ni^{++} > Ca^{++} > Mg^{++}$, Sr^{++} (67). The results obtained from electrophysiological studies of myocardial cells with Ni (68), Sr (69), and Mn (63–65) had a different order of effectiveness in affecting the duration of the action potential.

Paes de Carvalho et al (70) have employed the technique of phase-plane display of action potential upstrokes in an attempt to support the hypothesis that the cardiac action potential is composed of two distinct and physiologically separable components which occur sequentially and which may propagate independently. In our view their findings do not allow them to come to the conclusion that the action potential is generated by two *independent* mechanisms. Furthermore, the usefulness of phase-plane analysis is questionable in view of the unknown complex geometry of preparations of cardiac muscle and the assumptions necessitated by the use of one-dimensional cable theory. Attempts to use this method (71) with action potentials from frog ventricle and cultured chick heart cells were not helpful and seemed to give no more, if not less, information than assuming a constant conduction velocity for the action potential and taking the second derivative of voltage with respect to time.

Ion flux techniques are not as yet adequately developed to obtain good time resolution of ion movements during an action potential from an identifiable fiber of known dimensions and cell population. Lamb & McGuigan (72) have explained their phasic efflux measurements of Na, Ca, and K in beating frog ventricles in terms of mechanical artifacts. Whereas the latter investigators observed a decreased K efflux during contraction, Polimeni & Vassalle (73) noted a marked increase in K efflux. Quantitatively, the percentage change in K efflux with stimulation was less from cat papillary muscle than that from dog Purkinje fibers. The authors suggested that part of the K efflux might be retained in the transverse tubular system of ventricular muscle fibers and taken up again between beats. However, this explanation seems unlikely since the transverse tubules in ventricular muscle are wide (approx. 2000 Å) and short, 5–10 μ in length. Furthermore, on the contrary, the structure of dog Purkinje strands would favor such a retention and reuptake of K. The individual fibers form tightly packed bundles which are separated by narrow twisting extracellular clefts (200–300 Å) (5).

Niedergerke et al (74, 75) have developed a new method for directly determining ^{45}Ca flux (error factor about 0.1%) in the perfused frog heart. Resting influx for Ca was .004 pmole/cm² sec and increased to 0.13 pmole/cm² sec for the extra influx per heart beat, in contrast to 1.0 pmole/cm² per action potential reported for frog ventricle by Lamb & Lindsay (76). These fluxes correspond to currents of 1.3×10^{-8} A/cm² and 1.4×10^{-7} A/cm² respectively. The currents are exceedingly small and furthermore for them to produce any significant change in membrane potential all other currents must be correspondingly small, for example, one would have to presume that there is severe anomalous rectification in the potassium channels. Tetrodotoxin (2.5×10^{-7} g/ml) did not influence ^{45}Ca flux of resting frog ventricles (75) and since during the period of rest following stimulation the concentration of ^{45}Ca in the bathing media increased to values above that present in the perfusion fluid, the release was attributable to a net efflux of ^{45}Ca.

These findings are somewhat different from those obtained by Reuter & Seitz (77) for guinea pig atria and Lamb (78) for frog ventricle in which a decrease in Ca efflux was reported in the absence of Na. The latter results were interpreted in terms of a modified exchange diffusion mechanism responsible for Ca extrusion (77). Epinephrine has been shown to increase the amplitude and duration of the plateau (65) and increase twitch tension in low extracellular Ca (76). Flux studies have shown that epinephrine markedly reduces Ca influx (76). Conflicting results have been obtained with regard to the effects of epinephrine on Ca efflux: in one study it increased a component of Ca efflux (78) whereas in another (76) it decreased Ca efflux. Concentrations of Mn that reduced the action potential amplitude and duration (63) depressed (by 60%) the uptake of ^{45}Ca concomitant with an 8–10% reduction in contractile tension (79). This negative inotropic effect of Mn on guinea pig atrium was counteracted by increasing extracellular Ca (80). That Mn also diminished the positive inotropic effect of epinephrine (most significantly at low Ca concentrations) resulted in the tentative conclusion that this inotropic effect was due, in part, to an increase of Ca influx during excitation.

Voltage-clamp findings, to date, provide in our view unconvincing evidence of Ca acting as a significant charge carrier in the generation of the cardiac action potential. Ca currents calculated from the flux data would appear to be too small to account for the secondary transient currents, attributed to Ca, which are observed in voltage-clamp experiments. We are prevented from reaching a definitive conclusion on this point because, unfortunately, although the flux values are expressed in terms of an estimated membrane area the secondary currents are not.

To the two possible roles of Ca influx during an action potential, namely (a) as a charge carrier in the generation of the action potential and (b) as the activator of contraction, must be added a third, a possible role in the events initiating the changes in membrane ionic permeability. In regard to this third role, the study of Baker, Hodgkin & Ridgway (81) using the luminescence emitted from aequorin in the presence of Ca enabled them to show the occurrence of two phases of Ca entry during an action potential in the squid giant axon. An early transient phase reached a peak and was almost completed before the rise in Na conductance had reached its peak; both were abolished by tetrodotoxin and neither was affected by tetraethylammonium ion. This early transient phase was followed by a slowly rising phase that was seen to accompany the rise in K conductance. This slow phase was unaffected by tetrodotoxin or tetraethylammonium ion. The latter finding was not surprising to us since this ion did not appear to influence the opening or closing of K channels in squid axon (82), but rather to block the outward movement of K ions through them leaving the inward movement unaffected.

MEMBRANE POTENTIAL AND CONTRACTION

The wide variation in the kinds of experiments and methods, as well as uncertainties as to the degree of spatial and temporal control of membrane potential that were achieved with the preparations, makes the task of comparison and evaluation particularly difficult and restricts somewhat the possible conclusions one can draw from them. Some authors used a form of voltage-clamp, with which in some cases (18, 83, 84) and at some times (46) the tension was recorded as a function of step changes in command potential, voltage feedback being derived from an intracellular microelectrode. At other times, the tissue was stimulated with the control system "open-loop" and the subsequent action potential foreshortened by closing the loop with the command potential set at a value equal to the resting potential (46). It is not unlikely that these two procedures might have resulted in an entirely different magnitude and time course of change in internal potential throughout these large preparations (see voltage-clamp and the generation of the action potential) (85–88). Others made no attempt to control the membrane potential, but used constant currents which in some cases or at some times varied from sub- to superthreshold in magnitude (with reference to depolarizing current) and from continuous to intermittent in duration, being applied as pulses during the action potential or as longer pulses to the resting membrane.

All groups of workers except one (83) (who used the two-microelectrode method of voltage-clamp) have used the single-sucrose-gap or separation-chamber method (86, 87) to restrict the pathway of current injected into the preparation. Where a sucrose gap was used, the walls of the gap were formed from either stretched rubber diaphragms (18, 85, 88) or lucite partitions and vaseline seals (46) (for discussion see single sucrose gap). Some form of snare or tight grasping by the rubber diaphragm was used to restrict the motion of the muscle at the point where it entered the test or recording pool. This must have been somewhat short of complete strangulation, which would surely immobilize the preparation but would prevent polarizing current from flowing down the inside of the fibers to reach the membrane of fibers within the test or recording pool.

Not enough attention seems to have been directed to ensuring that the tension recorded by the force transducer attached to the free end of the preparation in the recording pool is only produced by that part of the preparation that is in that pool. The importance of this is illustrated nicely when methods employing some form of voltage-clamp are used (29, 46, 83, 84). When a depolarizing step in clamp potential is applied, such that the transmembrane potential within the vicinity of the voltage electrode is driven into a region where regenerative changes in membrane Na ion permeability occur, the following currents should flow. At first current will be directed in through the membrane of fibers in the current pool to flow out through the membrane of fibers in the recording pool, so depolarizing the fibers there (and hyperpolarizing fibers in the current pool). The subsequent regenerative inward currents induced in the fibers in the recording pool will result in a rapid transient reversal of the above currents, with, as a result, a rapid transient depolarization and perhaps contraction of the muscle in the current pool. Finally, repolarization at the end of the depolarizing step in command potential will result in a surge of current directed inwards in the recording pool and outwards in the current pool causing depolarization there and repolarization in the recording pool. One wonders to what extent this latter effect contributes to the after-contractions that were recorded following the termination of large depolarizing steps in command potential. Such contractions received little comment. Some authors (84) have attributed them to a surge of Ca current due to the persistence of an increased permeability to this ion induced by the preceding depolarization.

The effects of changes in membrane potential induced in these various ways on the contraction of cardiac muscle have been studied in three morphologically different kinds of cardiac muscle: first, mammalian ventricular muscle in the form of trabeculae or papillary muscles [dog (18, 46), sheep (46, 84, 88), cat (46, 85), rabbit (85), guinea pig (85), rhesus monkey (85), calf (84, 88)]; secondly, ungulate Purkinje strands (83); and finally, frog ventricular muscle (85–87).

Nevertheless, the results of these experiments have revealed some intriguing effects of applied current or membrane potential or both on cardiac contractility. For example, hyperpolarizing and depolarizing current applied during an action potential of frog ventricular muscle affected the twitch in response to that action potential, whereas in mammalian cardiac muscle the main effects of the applied current were on the twitch in response to the *following* action potential; effects on the twitch in response to the modified action potential were minimal.

In frog, application of a depolarizing current pulse during the action potential prolonged the duration (time to peak tension) of the associated twitch and as a consequence increased the peak tension (85–87); the rate of rise of tension was relatively unaffected (86, 87). The magnitude of this effect in subsequent action potentials during which an identical pulse was applied was much the same. Furthermore, the twitch in response to the action potential immediately following the cessation of current pulses showed no change in twitch tension from normal. Similarly, the application of a hyperpolarizing current pulse during an action potential caused a depression of peak tension (largely as a result of a decrease in time to peak tension) (85–87), an effect which again, as for the depolarizing current pulses, was confined to the twitch in response to that action potential.

In contrast, in mammalian cardiac muscle almost no effect was observed on the waveform of the twitch in response to the first action potential occurring during (moderate) current flow; the potentiation in response to depolarizing current and the depression in response to hyperpolarizing current were almost entirely delayed to the second beat (increasing somewhat with third and subsequent eight or so beats). Furthermore, the potentiation and depression of subsequent beats were largely the result of an increase in the rate of tension development rather than in the time to peak tension or duration of the twitch: the changes in the waveform of the twitch were rather like those that would occur if one varied the gain or magnification of the recording system, the various waveforms being essentially the same with the tension scaled. The slight depression or potentiation seen in the peak tension of the twitch in response to the first action potential modified by current was different, being qualitatively similar to but much smaller than those described above for frog ventricular muscle.

The period in the normal cardiac cycle during which the muscle is sensitive in this way to the application of moderate currents appeared to be restricted, being confined to the time of rising tension development (85–88). In the mammal this time was approximately 200–300 msec after the upstroke of the action potential (88). Similarly in voltage-clamp experiments, prolongation of depolarizing steps in command potential beyond 200–400 msec caused no further increase in peak tension (46).

Cutting short the duration of a normal action potential, either by the use of some form of voltage-clamp or the application of appropriately timed hyperpolarizing current pulses, gave somewhat different results depending on the preparation. In the frog, progressive shortening of the action potential produced at first a reduction in peak twitch tension as a result of a reduction in the time to peak tension, the rate of rise of tension remaining unchanged. Further foreshortening of the action potential also reduced the rate of rise of tension (87). In the Purkinje strand preparation, with the two-micro-electrode voltage-clamp technique (83), a depolarizing step in command potential lasting 20 msec and longer was sufficient to cause a maximum contraction of the preparation. No twitch was produced by voltage steps to -20 or 0 mV for less than about 4 msec. On the other hand in the cat, dog, and sheep trabeculae (46), reducing the duration of the action potential (in this case its unmodified length was 550 msec) to approximately 200 msec had no effect on the peak twitch tension in response to that action potential. Further reduction and duration of the action potential caused a progressive decrease in peak tension, at first the result of a reduction in time to peak, and then for durations of 50 msec or less the reduction in peak tension was largely the result of a decrease in rate of rise of tension, the time to peak tension remaining constant. We wonder to what degree these results (46, 83) were complicated by the temporal-spatial variations in membrane potential in the preparation (for discussion see single sucrose gap).

Larger, superthreshold depolarizing currents in mammalian ventricular muscle caused an initial twitchlike response which, however, relaxed more or less incompletely. Thereafter the tension rose again to reach a peak in 2–3 sec (46, 88) from which it declined to reach a steady-state tension that was maintained for the duration of the current (88). A sufficiently long current (2.7 sec) of just superthreshold magnitude caused the maximum potentiation of a subsequent contraction in response to a normal action potential (88). Further depolarizing currents of greater magnitude were associated with greater contracture-like responses, as described above, but did not cause any greater potentiation of the twitch in response to the subsequent action potential. A similar kind of response to large depolarizing current pulses was seen in the frog muscle (86); however, these were not associated with any changes in the tension generated during the twitch in response to a following normal action potential. In mammalian ventricular muscle, the "potentiated state" produced by superthreshold depolarizing (and reduced by hyper-polarizing) pulses as described above persisted for a considerable length of time after such currents were stopped if the muscle was left quiescent (88). After approximately 40 sec the potentiation then declined exponentially with a half-life averaging around 100 sec (88). If the preparations were stimulated, however, the "potentiation" disappeared progressively within approximately six beats, the rate of disappearance being largely independent of the interval between these beats (1–10 sec).

These and other features of the effects of applied current are reminiscent of the effects of changes in the rate and pattern of beat on the peak tension developed in a contraction, as exemplified by postextrasystolic potentiation, positive and negative staircase, and the inotropy caused by paired-pacing.

However, the relationship between not only the force of contraction but also the shape of the action potential and the rate and pattern of beat can be quite complex (89, 90); the fact that certain qualitative features of each relationship are very similar may be misleading. For example, that part of the relationship between the shape of an action potential and the rate and pattern of beat which is qualitatively similar to the relationship for the force of contraction was unaffected by changes in extracellular Ca concentration (91) whereas the latter was changed quite markedly (90, 91).

The results of the various experiments have led to a good deal of speculation as to their cause. Beeler & Reuter (18), in their studies of the relation between membrane potential and contraction, attempted to demonstrate that their secondary transient current (see voltage-clamp and generation of the action potential), which they believed to be carried by Ca, filled intracellular stores with Ca from which Ca was released by an unknown mechanism. In their view, however, this current directly activated contraction in Na-free media. Needless to say, the same criticisms of their interpretation of the secondary transient current, as detailed in the section on voltage-clamp, still apply and these conclusions then must be viewed in that light. Wood, Heppner & Wiedmann (88), on the basis of their experiments with mammalian ventricular muscle, speculated extensively on the possible role of the translocation of calcium ions to and fro from hypothetical binding sites on the inner surface of the sarcolemma and transverse tubules and the sarcoplasmic reticulum. Kawata et al (87) concluded that there were at least two different sources for activator calcium in frog ventricular muscle. Antoni et al (85) postulated that in mammalian ventricular muscle, the potentiation that was produced by an action potential and which was delayed to the twitch in response to the next action potential is caused by an influx of Ca during the first action potential. This Ca was prevented in some way from reaching the contractile protein (they suggested larger distances) but determined the Ca level in intracellular stores.

In our view, these experiments demonstrate an interesting and puzzling relationship between membrane potential and contraction in cardiac muscle which needs a good deal more investigation. Cleaner clamps, experiments involving sudden changes in extracellular ionic concentration, and a good Ca marker for electronmicroscopy would help. In previous studies of the relationship between the force of contraction and the rate and pattern of stimulation the shape of the action potential has been an uncontrollable variable (90). It would be interesting to reexamine certain features of this relationship with the "action potential" an independent variable (provided of course that sufficient spatial and temporal uniformity of membrane potential control throughout the preparation could be ensured).

With regard to the differences between the frog and mammalian cardiac muscle, Antoni et al (85) pointed out that the sarcoplasmic reticulum in the frog cardiac muscle is only poorly developed. However, it is noteworthy that the frog ventricular muscle does not appear to have any "couplings"; a coupling is a close association of a portion of the sarcoplasmic reticulum with the inner surface of sarcolemma either in the form of transverse tubular membrane (interior coupling or triad, dyad) or in the form of peripheral sarcolemma as in peripheral couplings (5). Uncertainty as to the complete absence of couplings is relatively unimportant, since the relevant fact (in the present view of the role of the coupling in excitation-contraction coupling) is the frequency of occurrence of couplings compared to the number of sarcomeres. In mammalian ventricular muscle, couplings are easily found and occur with a frequency of at least one per sarcomere. In frog ventricular muscle, couplings must therefore occur with relative infrequency, if at all, for them to have escaped detection (7) and as a consequence they can be considered as effectively absent in this muscle. On the other hand, although the sarcoplasmic reticulum is poorly developed compared to that in mammalian cardiac muscle (7), it is present and until one knows how much is required to be functionally effective its presence cannot be neglected.

From the structure-function point of view, it would be interesting to compare the contractile behavior of frog ventricular muscle with that of the chicken, since both are very similar in structure (absence of a transverse tubular system, small fibers, packed into bundles 10–20 μ in overall diameter) and in internal fine structure of the sarcomere, except for one outstanding difference: peripheral couplings occur in chicken heart fibers whereas they have escaped detection in the frog (7).

Calcium and contraction.—The role of Ca as the final activator of the contractile system under physiological conditions is universally accepted (92). Langer's review (57) incorporated an attempt to correlate the ionic movements associated with myocardial contractility and a hypothesis of the excitation-contraction process was presented which was based essentially on Niedergerke's model of Na-Ca competition for membrane sites (93, 94). Brady's review of 1964 (95) presented an intriguing concept of the roles of calcium in the generation of the action potential and in contraction. Antoni & Rotmann (96) examined the negative inotropic mechanism of acetylcholine in isolated frog ventricular strips and noted a consistent correlation between action potential duration and contraction amplitude which was unaffected by changes in stimulation frequency (3–60 beats/min) or external Ca concentration (0.5–8.0 mM). However, the presence of acetylcholine did not decrease peak tension when the preparation was activated by repetitive tetanic stimuli or by KCl-induced contracture. The results were suggestive of a dual source or mechanism of release of calcium for the maintenance of contractility under these experimental conditions. Orkand (97) studied the changes in peak tension caused by changes in extracellular Na and Ca ions and was careful to minimize the effects of changes in the action potential duration. The magnitude and time course of "facilitation" of contraction were studied following repetitive stimulation at low stimulus frequencies (3–12 beats/min). His findings were interpreted using Niedergerke's model (93, 94) and supported the hypothesis that facilitation may result from the accumulation of Ca within a cellular compartment whereas the decay of facilitation would reflect the time course of restoration of bound calcium to its low resting value.

In a subsequent report (98), repetitive stimulation of frog ventricle strips bathed in low Ca produced a decrease followed by an increase in successive tension responses unaccompanied by corresponding changes in the duration of the action potential. The slow facilitation following prolonged stimulation was unexplainable in terms of his model and the conclusion was that it resulted from changes in excitation-contraction coupling. Sands & Winegrad (99) demonstrated an increase in Ca content of frog ventricle as a function of contraction rate (2–20 beats/min), 0.2 $\mu M/g$ wet wt, per beat. This finding supported their hypothesis that an influx of calcium during the action potential could be responsible for treppe. Hadju (100) offered evidence for attributing treppe (Bowditch staircase) to the movement of Ca from extracellular stores and rest potentiation (Woodworth staircase) from bound cellular stores. Hadju's remarkable finding that guinea pig atria exhibited the Woodworth staircase, whereas the ventricle did not, suggests the need for a more detailed comparative analysis of the force-frequency relationships.

Furthermore, the force-frequency curve for guinea pig atrium after treatment with ryanoine (1 ug/ml) was similar to the ones seen for frog heart and guinea pig ventricle. The lack of a ryanodine effect on the latter two preparations clearly points to the need for correlative ultrastructural studies. Somewhat puzzling were the tension measurements from guinea pig atria reported by Little & Sleator (101). The force-frequency relationships which they obtained were markedly different from those reported by Hadju (100). Little & Sleator suggested that the additional Ca involved in larger contractions at higher frequencies came from an increase in calcium from intracellular stores.

Haacke et al (102) have related the increased force of contraction with increasing rate of stimulation to changes in ^{45}Ca flux in the guinea pig left atrium. Within a frequency range of 20–320 beats/min, total Ca remained unchanged although there was a tendency for ^{45}Ca uptake to increase at higher frequencies. He was not able to relate the increased force of contraction to changes in ^{45}Ca flux per stimulus, since calculations of the amount of Ca entering the cell during one excitation significantly decreased as the frequency was increased from 20/min (2.5×10^{-7} M Ca) to 320/min (6×10^{-8} M Ca). This frequency potentiation was therefore attributed to a high end diastolic level of cellular Ca possibly related to the ratio of Ca efflux and the amount of Ca entering the cell per beat. Mainwood & Lee (103) reported that electrical reexcitation of rat papillary muscle after a short interval (50–80 msec) resulted in normal action potentials unassociated with any significant mechanical response. This electrical-mechanical un-coupling was attributed to the recovery cycle of the contraction coupling mechanism that was responsible for restoring the fraction of intracellular-bound Ca that was released with each action potential.

In summary, it is clear that the results of force-frequency studies have resulted in the development of a multitude of possible explanations for the movement of Ca in relation to the electrical activity and mechanical re-sponse. The details of the coupling mechanism remain largely speculative.

The development and maintenance of tension in the absence of propa-gated electrical activity (contracture) is another means of gaining insight into the electrical-mechanical coupling events in muscular contraction. Graham & Lamb (104) reported that epinephrine (10^{-6} g/ml) reduced the tension developed in contractures of the frog ventricle produced by excess KCl, removal of Na or alternating current, though it increased the normal twitch tension. At low rates of stimulation, the time course of development of the two epinephrine effects became dissimilar: the contracture tension declined more quickly at 15/min than the twitch tension increased. The time course of the inotropic effect of epinephrine was shown to be dependent on the number of beats at a low $(Ca)_o/(Na)_o^2$ ratio but was dependent on time at high values of the ratio. The time course of the effect on the twitch when changing from 0.5 to 2 mM Ca depended on the number of previous twitches rather than the elapsed time. A tentative mechanism for the action of epinephrine in frog's heart considered the twitch tension to be propor-tional to the Ca held in a local store from which it was released in a con-traction whereas the contracture was proportional to the membrane perme-ability to Ca during the action potential. Hence, the effect on the contracture suggested that epinephrine decreased the Ca permeability but increased the Ca storage capacity of the cell. The location and existence of an intracellular Ca storage and release site that was activated by changes in membrane potential in the frog heart remains to be shown. Hence, whether its capacity could increase in the presence of epinephrine is speculation on speculation.

Bozler & Baker (105) demonstrated that epinephrine (5.5×10^{-6} M) produced relaxation of contractures induced by high Ca, low K-Ringer in frog ventricular strips; however, the opposite effect was seen in high K-Ringer. An attempt to relate the changes in tension to changes in membrane potential did not agree with the results of an earlier study (104). The effect of acetylcholine (5.5×10^{-6} M) on contractures was opposite and antagonistic to that of epinephrine. Acetylcholine was also capable of rapidly relaxing a contracture induced by Ringer solution after washing in Ca-free solutions. These effects of acetylcholine were attributed to changes in Ca permeability though evidence for this supposition is lacking.

Potassium chloride-induced contractures were obtained in cat ventricu-lar muscle by Morad (106) only after depletion of catecholamine stores, and these contractures were abolished by the subsequent addition of epinephrine (1 μg/ml). The experimental data were put forward in support of the hypothesis that earlier difficulties in producing contractures in mammalian myocardium could be attributed to the release of endogenous amounts of catecholamines by increased KCl. Scholz (107, 108) induced KCl contractures in isolated preparations of mammalian cardiac muscle without reserpine pretreatment and although he obtained tensions greater than those reported previously (106), it was not possible to relate the size of the contracture to that of the twitch. At any given K concentration, the amplitude of the contractures depended on the ratio $(Ca)_o/(Na)_o^2$, however, the response was most pronounced when K was high, especially in guinea pig and call ventricular muscle (108). The differences between the mechanical response of atrial and ventricular preparations were tentatively explained by differences in the ultrastructure of the tissue.

CARDIAC MUSCLE TISSUE CULTURE

In view of the discussion in the previous sections, it has become clear to us that definitive progress in the areas concerned with the generation of the cardiac action potential and excitation-contraction coupling would be greatly accelerated and clarified if one could obtain a preparation of cardiac muscle that was more suitable than those presently available. A survey of the ultrastructure of cardiac muscle from a variety of animals has failed to uncover a naturally occurring preparation of cardiac muscle that approached, satisfactorily, the ideal of a single long cylindrical cell (4). In this regard, perhaps the field of tissue culture offers a possible solution. With the development of new tissue and cell culture techniques, it is now possible to develop and sustain a "synthetic" preparation of cardiac muscle (11–15).

However, it is important that although electrophysiologic studies of cultured heart cells are generally prefaced by the statement "many of the electrophysiological properties of cultured embryonic heart cells are similar to those of cells in intact adult hearts" (109), we are still faced with the enigmatic findings that "membrane potentials of cultured chick heart cells are insensitive to acetylcholine, nicotine, catecholamines, serotonin, cholinergic and adrenergic blocking agents, histamine, and aconitine" (110) as well as diphenylhydantoin (110), tetrodotoxin (111), 15 mM Ca (112), 4 mM Mn (112), and 24 mM K (109) in the bathing media. Unfortunately, in all the studies from Sperelakis' laboratory, the Ringers solution bathing the cells during experimentation was, at least, pH 8.0 and of questionable ionic composition and osmolarity since "hypertonicity produced by evaporation was compensated for by addition of a few drops of distilled water every hour or so to maintain a constant volume" (109). Nevertheless, the use of cultured heart cells for electrophysiological studies should not be precluded, but extreme precautions should be taken to ensure an optimum physiological environment for the cells. Perhaps then the cells might behave like cells of intact adult hearts.

In their electrophysiological studies, DeHaan & Gottlieb (113) attributed their technical success in impaling isolated single cells (8 out of 96 attempts) to the use of "ultrafine electrodes and culture conditions favoring growth and membrane synthesis". Cells in "electrical contact" with neighbors were considered to be "protected from inevitable damage by the penetrating electrode, by a flow of ions or other substances from connected cells across low impedance intercellular junctions" (113) and for this reason the frequency of successful impalements was high. It would be interesting to see whether the methodological improvements would make the preparation useful in physiological studies.

Nakanishi & Takeda (114) recorded from cultured chick embryonic heart cells and reported that acetylcholine (10^{-5} g/ml) produced hyperpolarization and shortening of the action potential and a decrease in the rate of the slow diastolic depolarization in cultured atrial cells whereas cultured ventricular cells were generally insensitive. The findings perhaps shed light on the negative findings of Sperelakis et al (109–112): the tissue culture preparation was a mixed population of cells and they might very well have impaled only ventricular cells.

Two groups of investigators (115, 116) have recently demonstrated that alterations in extracellular Ca do indeed alter the electrical and mechanical activity of cultured embryonic chick heart cells in a manner analogous to the intact heart. Langer et al (117) employed a new technique to study Ca exchange in cultured rat cardiac cells. The preparation is described as a single layer of cells which have been grown on the surface of a slide composed of glass scintillator material. Although there is some doubt about the purity of the cell type present on the slide (cells of muscular and nonmuscular origin) and whether the cell layer(s) remained functionally intact and contractile during exposure to the serum-free labeling and washout solutions, the technique provided a sensitivity and time resolution which have previously not been obtainable in functioning cardiac muscle. It is interesting that whereas Langer et al (117) consider their results indicative of a two-component tissue compartment for Ca, earlier Na and K flux studies of cultured heart cells by Burrows & Lamb (118) offered evidence that most of the Na and K in the cells was present in a single compartment. Since a preparation of cultured heart cells similar to that used by Langer lacks an interstitial space as well as a developed sarcoplasmic retciulum and tubular network (119), the origin of the two compartments is somewhat puzzling unless one fraction of Ca is membrane bound and the other in the cytoplasmic pool.

In a combined electrophysiologic and morphologic study, Hyde et al (120) studied the properties of various types of cell junctions in cultured rat cardiac "myoblasts" and in association with "fibroblasts". Electrotonic coupling was found between heterotypic cells (myoblasts and fibroblasts); however, nexuses were found only at myoblast-myoblast junctions which suggests that electrotonic coupling may occur through junctional structures other than the nexus. The specific membrane resistance of completely isolated myoblasts was estimated to be approximately 60 Ωcm^2 (resting potential, 30–40 mV) (121). Assuming that tissue culture preparations of confluent fibroblasts and myoblasts behaved electrically as a thin plane cell, fits of theoretical plots to measured plots of membrane voltage as a function of distance from the site of current injection gave values for the specific membrane resistance of 15–20 $k\Omega cm^2$ for confluent myoblasts and approximately 3 $k\Omega cm^2$ for confluent fibroblasts. A lower effective resistance of the junctional structures between myoblasts was postulated as a result of finding that R_i was 419 Ωcm in "pure" myoblast cultures as opposed to 4134 Ωcm in "pure" fibroblast cultures. Inputs of voltage-current plots from cultured myoblasts were linear (no rectification) with slopes approximately 1 $M\Omega$.

These results differ significantly from those of Sperelakis (122, 123) and the question is open as to whether these differences might be attributed to differences in the preparations. It is unfortunate that no photomicrographic or electronmicrographic study has been reported of the cultures used in the electrophysiological studies of Sperelakis and thus morphologic comparisons are impossible. An unusual finding of Hyde et al (120) is the presence of action potentials in so-called "fibroblasts". The variation in definition ascribed to the various names for cells in culture creates a good deal of confusion in the literature as to the true nature of the cell, for example, myoblasts, fibroblasts, differentiating cardiac cell, dedifferentiating cardiac cell, quiescent myoblast, or beating fibroblast. Synchronous beating of myocardial cells interconnected by inactive cells has recently been reported by Goshima (124, 125) and was interpreted as electrotonic transmission through the inactive cell. The evidence for this was the observation of slowly rising (100 msec) low-voltage (7 mV) "mediating" potentials from the inactive "non-myogenic" cells. The question arises as to whether the microelectrode was truly intracellular since such potentials could have been due to mechanical movement artifact of the microelectrode resting against the cell membrane.

There have been several recent reports demonstrating the feasibility of preparing "intact isolated cells" from adult rat heart (126, 127) and adult mouse heart (128). The physiologic value of these preparations remains to be demonstrated for although they are contractile (127, 128) and have a normally appearing ultrastructure (126), the reported response to changes in Ca, for example, was physiologically abnormal. Normal Ca levels inhibited contractions of cells from rat heart (127) and contractions of mouse heart (128) were maintained in the absence of extracellular Ca and Na. To what extent the necessarily severe procedures for tissue dissociation of these adult hearts contributed to these and other unusual findings must await further study and evaluation of this new approach for preparing isolated adult heart cells.

ACKNOWLEDGMENTS

We wish to thank Dr. L. Harrington for her detailed constructive criticism of the manuscript. We also wish to thank Mrs. A. Oakeley, Miss D. McClure, and Miss M. Beath for their technical, secretarial, and bibliographic assistance, respectively.

LITERATURE CITED

1. Hodgkin, A. L.. Huxley, A. F. 1952. *J. Physiol. London* 117:500–44
2. Dodge, F. A., Frankenhaeuser, B. 1959. *J. Physiol. London* 148:188–200
3. Hodgkin, A. L., Huxley, A. F., Katz, B. 1952. *J. Physiol. London* 116:424–48
4. Johnson, E. A., Sommer, J. R. 1967. *J. Cell Biol.* 33:103–29
5. Sommer, J. R., Johnson, E. A. 1968. *J. Cell Biol.* 36:497–526
6. Sommer, J. R., Johnson, E. A. 1968. *J. Cell Biol.* 37:570–74
7. Sommer, J. R., Johnson, E. A. 1969. *Z. Zellforsch.* 98:437–68
8. Sommer, J. R., Johnson, E. A. 1970. *Am. J. Cardiol.* 25:184–94
9. Falk, G., Fatt, P. 1964. *Proc. Roy. Soc. London B* 160:69–123
10. Eisenberg, R. S. 1967. *J. Gen. Physiol.* 50:1785–806
11. Harary, I., Farley, B. 1963. *Exp. Cell Res.* 29:451–65
12. Lehmkuhl, D., Sperelakis, N. 1963. *Am. J. Physiol.* 205:1213–20
13. Lieberman, M. 1967. *Circ. Res.* 21:879–88
14. DeHaan, R. L. 1967. *Develop. Biol.* 16:216–49
15. Halle, W., Wollenberger, A. 1970. *Am. J. Cardiol.* 25:292–99
16. Beeler, G. W., Jr., Reuter, H. 1970. *J. Physiol. London* 207:165–90
17. Beeler, G. W., Jr., Reuter, H. 1970. *J. Physiol. London* 207:191–209
18. Beeler, G. W., Jr., Reuter, H. 1970. *J. Physiol. London* 207:211–29
19. Mascher, D., Peper, K. 1969. *Pflügers Arch.* 307:190–203
20. Rougier, O., Vassort, G., Stämpfli, R. 1968. *Pflügers Arch.* 301:91–108
21. Brown, H. F., Noble, S. J. 1969 *J. Physiol. London* 204:717–36
22. Dudel, J., Rüdel, J. 1970. *Pflügers Arch.* 315:136–58
23. Hauswirth, O., Noble, D., Tsien, R. W. 1968. *Science* 162:916–17
24. Hauswirth, O., Noble, D., Tsien, R. W. 1969. *J. Physiol. London* 200:255–65
25. Noble, D., Tsien, R. W. 1968. *J. Physiol. London* 195:185–214
26. Noble, D., Tsien, R. W. 1969. *J. Physiol. London* 200:205–31
27. Noble, D., Tsien, R. W. 1969. *J. Physiol. London* 200:233–54
28. Ochi, R. 1970. *Pflügers Arch.* 316:81–94
29. Rougier, O., Vassort, G., Garnier, D., Gargouïl, Y. M., Coraboeuf, E. 1969. *Pflügers Arch.* 308:91–110
30. Vassort, G. et al 1969. *Pflügers Arch.* 309:70–81
31. Brown, H. F., Noble, S. J. 1969. *J. Physiol. London* 204:737–47
32. Peper, K., Trautwein, W. 1968. *Pflügers Arch.* 303:108–23
33. Reuter, H. 1968. *J. Physiol. London* 197:233–53
34. Reuter, H., Beeler, G. W. 1969. *Science* 162:397–99
35. Reuter, H., Beeler, G. W. 1969. *Science* 162:399–401
36. Eisenberg, R. S., Engel, E. 1970. *J. Gen. Physiol.* 55:736–57
37. Eisenberg, R. S., Johnson, E. A. 1970. *Progr. Biophys. Mol. Biol.* 20:1–65
38. Fozzard, H. A. 1966. *J. Physiol. London* 182:255–67
39. Freygang, W. H., Trautwein, W. 1970. *J. Gen. Physiol.* 55:524–47
40. McAllister, R. E., 1968. *Biophysical J.* 8:951–64
41. Noble, D. 1962. *J. Physiol. London* 160:317–52
42. Blaustein, M. P., Goldman, D. E. 1966. *Biophys. J.* 6:453–70
43. Berger, W., Barr, L. 1969. *J. Appl. Physiol.* 26:378–82
44. Rall, W. 1969. *Biophys. J.* 9:1483–508
45. Kamiyama, A., Matsuda, K. 1966. *Jap. J. Physiol.* 16:407–20
46. Morad, M., Trautwein, W. 1968. *Pflügers Arch.* 299:66–82
47. Weidmann, S. 1952. *J. Physiol. London* 118:348–60
48. Sakamoto, Y. 1969. *J. Gen. Physiol.* 54:765–81
49. Sakamoto, Y., Goto, M. 1970. *Jap. J. Physiol.* 20:30–41
50. Gage, P. W., Eisenberg, R. S. 1969. *J. Gen. Physiol.* 53:265–78
51. Frankenhaeuser, B., Hodgkin, A. L. 1957. *J. Physiol. London* 137:218–44
52. Harrington, L., Johnson, E. A. 1969. *Physiologist* 12:248
53. Dodge, F. A., Frankenhaeuser, B. 1958. *J. Physiol. London* 143:76–90
54. Nonner, W. 1969. *Pflügers Arch.* 309:176–92
55. Cole, K. C. 1968. *Membranes, Ions and Impulses*, 325–54. Berkeley: Univ. of California Press. 569 pp.
56. Winegrad, S., Shanes, A. M. 1962. *J. Gen. Physiol.* 45:371–94

57. Langer, G. A. 1968. *Physiol. Rev.* 48: 708–57
58. Hodgkin, A. L., Huxley, A. F. 1952. *J. Physiol. London* 116:497–506
59. Neher, E., Lux, H. D. 1969. *Pflügers Arch.* 311:272–77
60. Matsubara, I., Matsuda, K. 1969. *Jap. J. Physiol.* 19:814–23
61. Niedergerke, R., Orkand, R. K. 1966. *J. Physiol. London* 184:291–311
62. Coraboeuf, E., Vassort, G. 1968. *J. Electrocardiol.* 1:19–30
63. Yanaga, T., Holland, W. C. 1969. *Am. J. Physiol.* 217:1280–85
64. Yanaga, T., Holland, W. C. 1970. *J. Pharmacol. Exp. Therap.* 171:20–25
65. Carmeliet, E., Vereecke, J. 1969. *Pflügers Arch.* 313:300–15
66. Hauswirth, O., McAllister, R. E., Noble, D., Tsien, R. W. 1969. *J. Physiol. London* 204:126–28P
67. Hagiwara, S., Kunitaro, T. 1967. *J. Gen. Physiol.* 50:583–601
68. Babskii, E. B., Donskikh, E. A. 1968. *Dokl. Akad. Nauk SSSR* 178:248–51
69. Carmeliet, E., Van Bogaert, P. P. 1969. *Arch. Int. Physiol. Biochem.* 77: 134–35
70. Paes de Carvalho, A., Hoffman, B. F., De Paula Carvalho, M. 1969. *J. Gen. Physiol.* 54:607–35
71. Sperelakis, N., Shumaker, H. K. 1968. *J. Electrocardiol.* 1:31–42
72. Lamb, J. F., McGuigan, J. A. S. 1968. *J. Physiol. London* 195:283–316
73. Polimeni, P. I., Vassalle, M. 1970. *Am. J. Physiol.* 218:1381–88
74. Niedergerke, R., Page, S. 1969. *Pflügers Arch.* 306:354–56
75. Niedergerke, R., Page, S., Talbot, M. S. 1969. *Pflügers Arch.* 306:357–60
76. Lamb, J. F., Lindsay, R. 1968. *J. Physiol. London* 196:49–50P
77. Reuter, H., Seitz, N. 1968. *J. Physiol. London* 195:451–70
78. Lamb, J. F. 1969. *J. Physiol. London* 202:85–87P
79. Sabatini-Smith, S., Holland, W. C. 1969. *Am. J. Physiol.* 216:244–48
80. Meinertz, T., Scholz, H. 1969. *Arch. Pharmakol.* 265:131–48
81. Baker, P. F., Hodgkin, A. L., Ridgway, E. B. 1970. *J. Physiol. London* 208:80–82P
82. Armstrong, C. M. 1966. *J. Gen. Physiol.* 50:491–503
83. Fozzard, H. A., Hellam, D. C. 1968. *Nature* 218:688–89
84. McGuigan, J. A. S. 1968. *Helv. Physiol. Acta* 26:CR 362-CR363
85. Antoni, H., Jacob, R., Kaufmann, R. 1969. *Pflügers Arch.* 306:33–57
86. Goto, M., Brooks, C. McC. 1970. *Am. J. Physiol.* 218:1038–45
87. Kawata, H., Shibata, J., Goto, M. 1969. *Jap. J. Physiol.* 19:492–508
88. Wood, E. H., Heppner, R. L., Weidmann, S. 1969. *Circ. Res.* 24:409–45
89. Gibbs, C. L., Johnson, E. A., Tille, J. 1963. *Biophys. J.* 3:433–58
90. Johnson, E. A., Kuohung, P. W. 1968. *Math. Biosci.* 3:65–89
91. Gibbs, C. L. 1964. *Aust. J. Exp. Biol.* 42:116–32
92. Ebashi, S., Endo, M. 1968. *Progr. Biophys. Mol. Biol.* 18:123–83
93. Niedergerke, R. 1963. *J. Physiol. London* 167:515–50
94. Niedergerke, R. 1963. *J. Physiol. London* 167:551–80
95. Brady, A. J. 1964. *Ann. Rev. Physiol.* 26:341–56
96. Antoni, H., Rotmann, M. 1968. *Pflügers Arch.* 300:67–86
97. Orkand, R. K. 1968. *J. Physiol. London* 196:311–25
98. Brown, A. M., Orkand, R. K. 1968. *J. Physiol. London* 197:295–304
99. Sands, S. D., Winegrad, S. 1970. *Am. J. Physiol.* 218:908–10
100. Hajdu, S. 1969. *Am. J. Physiol.* 216: 206–14
101. Little, G. R., Sleator, W. W. 1969. *J. Gen. Physiol.* 54:494–511
102. Haacke, H., Lullmann, H., van Zwieten, P. A. 1970. *Pflügers Arch.* 314 (2):113–23
103. Mainwood, G. W., Lee, S. L. 1970. *Science* 166:396–97
104. Graham, J. A., Lamb, J. F. 1968. *J. Physiol. London* 197:479–509
105. Bozler, E., Baker, H. R. 1970. *Am. J. Physiol.* 218:1795–800
106. Morad, M. 1969. *Science.* 166:505–6
107. Scholz, H. 1969. *Pflügers Arch.* 308: 315–32
108. Scholz, A. H. 1969. *Pflügers Arch.* 311: 63–81
109. Pappano, A. J., Sperelakis, N. 1969. *Exp. Cell Res.* 54:58–68
110. Sperelakis, N., Henn, F. A. 1970. *Am. J. Physiol.* 218:1224–27
111. Sperelakis, N., Lehmkuhl, D. 1965. *Am. J. Physiol.* 209:693–98
112. Pappano, A. J., Sperelakis, N. 1969. *Am. J. Physiol.* 217:615–24
113. De Haan, R. L., Gottlieb, S. H. 1968. *J. Gen. Physiol.* 52:643–65
114. Nakanishi, H., Takeda, H. 1969 *Jap.*

J. Pharmacol. 19:543–50

115. Ozaki, S. 1969. *Jap. J. Physiol.* 19: 632–40

116. Kaufmann, R., Tritthart, H., Rodenroth, S., Rost, B. 1969. *Pflügers Arch.* 311:25–49

117. Langer, G. A., Sato, E., Seraydarian, M. 1969. *Circ. Res.* 24:589–97

118. Burrows, R., Lamb, J. F. 1962. *J. Physiol. London* 162:510–31

119. Cedergren, B., Harary, I. 1964. *J. Ultrastruct. Res.* 11:428–42

120. Hyde, A. et al 1969. *Progr. Brain Res.* 31:283–311

121. Girardier, L., Hyde, A., Matter, A., Blondel, B. *J. Physiol. Paris* 59: 410–11

122. Sperelakis, N., Lehmkuhl, D. 1964. *J. Gen. Physiol.* 47:895–927

123. Sperelakis, N. 1967. In *Electrophysiology and Ultrastructure of the Heart*, ed. T. Sano, V. Mizuhira, K. Matsuda, 81–108. Tokyo: Bunkodo Co. Ltd. 267 pp.

124. Goshima, K. 1969. *Exp. Cell Res.* 58: 420–26

125. Goshima, K., Tonomura, Y. 1969. *Exp. Cell Res.* 56:387–92

126. Berry, N. M., Friend, D. S., Scheuer, J. 1970. *Circ. Res.* 26:679–87

127. Vahouny, G. V., Wei, R., Starkweather, R., Davis, C. 1970. *Science* 167:1616–18

128. Bloom, S. 1970. *Science* 167:1727–29

FEEDING: NEURAL CONTROL OF INTAKE[1]   1069

Bartley G. Hoebel

Department of Psychology, Princeton University, Princeton, N.J.

The year 1969–1970 was one of the most fruitful in the realm of feeding systems. New developments included aphagia produced without finickiness, glucose deprivation receptors revealed in the lateral hypothalamus, recovery of feeding shown to match ontogenetic development, electrically elicited feeding changed into drinking, hypothalamic aversion related to satiety, and α- and β-adrenergic feeding separated in function. Selected topics such as these will be reviewed in some depth. For the rest, the following reviews will be helpful.

The field up to early 1966 is covered magnificently in the *Handbook of Physiology* volume on *Control of Food and Water Intake* (1). The other indispensable source is the New York Academy of Sciences volume on *Regulation of Food and Water Intake* (2). A more integrated treatment of the field appears in shorter reviews (3–7).

Three reviews on feeding will appear at about the same time as this one. Finger & Mook (8) discuss regulation of blood glucose, meals, and body weight. Epstein (9) treats the lateral hypothalamic syndrome and Le Magnen (10) emphasizes studies of internal stimuli that determine intake patterns. The present review can therefore best serve by bringing together a variety of studies on brain integration of feeding behavior.

Hyperphagia Following Ventromedial Lesions

A child who lived 6 years after removal of a medial hypothalamic tumor displayed impairments in satiety, thirst, and temperature regulation, and was occasionally savage in addition to having metabolic problems from a pituitary disorder (11). In another very similar case a woman with a neoplasm in the same brain region had outbursts of violence that could only be stopped by feeding. She consumed 10,000 calories per day even after correction of metabolic and hormonal difficulties (12). A syndrome clearly related to this can be produced experimentally in other animals. Almost all of the detailed analysis has been done with laboratory rats.

[1] This work was supported by the United States Public Health Service grant MH08493, National Science Foundation grant GB4586, and the Nutrition Foundation. Literature search was facilitated by the new journal, *International Neuroscience Abstracts,* and by the UCLA Brain Information Service supported by contract NIH-70-2063.

Lesions of the ventromedial hypothalamus can cause overeating which leads to obesity. Doubling of body weight is not uncommon in rats; however, the amount of weight gain depends on starting weight. The animal may even lose weight to reach its stable, obese level if initially it is excessively fat. Thus the lesion does not necessarily cause hyperphagia; it causes a shift upward in the weight level at which an animal will stabilize its food intake (13). Ventromedial lesions also cause a change in metabolism, perhaps related to oxygen consumption or activity level, which leads to a slight weight gain even if food intake is matched to that of an unlesioned control animal (14).

Lesions and the irritation question.—Reynolds (15) and later Rabin & Smith (16) reported failure to obtain obesity following ventromedial hypothalamic electrocauterization by radiofrequency current. The lack of obesity was tentatively attributed to a lack of iron deposits from the electrode and thus a lack of irritation to the neighboring lateral hypothalamic feeding system. On the other hand, several investigators (17–19) repeatedly obtained hyperphagia and obesity with radiofrequency lesions. Reynolds suggested that in such instances iron deposits from cauterized blood cells may contribute to hyperphagia. Dahl & Ursin (20) agreed but emphasized that accurate neural destruction must accompany irritation in order to obtain obesity. Reynolds (21) confirmed earlier reports (9, 17) that temporary ventromedial deactivation with procaine injections causes a transient immediate hyperphagia. He agreed that this region can inhibit feeding, but maintained that some other brain region must be able to take over the inhibitory function when the ventromedial region is destroyed and obesity fails to develop.

Cox, Kakolewski & Valenstein (22) suggested that the crucial question was not irritation, but sex, since females became obese relative to their controls, while males gained relatively little or nothing even though slightly hyperphagic. Analyzing this further, Balagura & Devenport (23) found that soon after lesions, female rats given small pellets take bigger and more frequent meals, whereas lesioned males increase meal frequency, but not size. Research seeking sex-linked differences between males and females became particularly relevant. Valenstein and his group proposed that differences in gonadal atrophy might be responsible (22). Wade & Zucker (24) presented evidence that estrogen in the female activates the ventromedial hypothalamus, thereby inhibiting eating unless the ventromedial satiety system is blocked by growth hormone as in prepuberty. Pfaff (25) used hypophysectomized and gonadectomized rats to gain experimental control of rats' hormone functions and found that growth hormone increased food intake in males, but not in females, while prolactin did the opposite. Ventromedial lesions decreased growth hormone and increased prolactin; this could tentatively account for lesser hypothalamic hyperphagia in males than females. On the other hand, recent reports show a lack of growth (26) or an increase in growth (27) after hypothalamic lesions and thus call for further study of hypothalamic factors that release or inhibit growth hormone.

Finger & Mook (8) and Gold (28) suggest that in the Cox, Kakowleski & Valenstein study the failure of male rats to become dramatically hyperphagic may have been due in part to the use of powdered laboratory diet instead of a more palatable diet of pellets or oily chow which the lesioned rats prefer (29). The importance of this factor is shown clearly in the dietary study of lesioned male and female rats tabulated in Stevenson's article (19). Both types of lesions produced weight gains in males and females with a high carbohydrate diet, but not in lesioned males on a high protein diet unless saccharin was added.

The search for neural sites crucial to satiety continued. Partly as an outgrowth of the irritability issue, a number of devices were perfected for producing nonirritative or highly localized brain lesions. For electrolytic lesions, electrodes made of inert metal alloys such as platinum-iridium have clear advantages over those made of alloys which produce deposits during electrolysis. Several researchers successfully produced hyperphagia with knife cuts between the lateral and medial hypothalamus. Sclafani & Grossman (30) and Albert & Storlien (31) used a wire knife that pops out of the end of a guide tube; it can be implanted permanently so the cut can be enlarged at any time. Gold (32) used a knife made from a sliver of razor blade. He found that the fibers which must be cut are in a 1 mm long area at the anterior, lateral edge of the ventromedial nuclei. Cuts in this region produced the obesity syndrome without damaging the ventromedial nuclei themselves. Cuts of the same length further posterior were ineffective.

Ellison (33) describes a wire knife for making subcortical islands. An implanted guide shaft is used with a wire shaped like the foot crank on a bicycle; one end of the wire is turned causing the other end to sweep around inside the brain. Isolation of the ventromedial hypothalamus from the rest of the brain did not produce hyperphagia when the island included most of the lateral hypothalamus as well. Although the level of obesity can be increased by enlarging a small, electrolytic lesion (17), if the lesion or cut becomes extended too far laterally it loses its effectiveness (33, 30).

In summary, irritation to the lateral hypothalamic feeding system does not account for hypothalamic hyperphagia, but may contribute to hyperphagia in some cases, particularly if steel electrodes are used. Inert metal should be used for making electrical lesions. When ventromedial lesions are made in the least irritating manner, an increase in the level of weight regulation can still be guaranteed if the locus of neural destruction is well placed, bilaterally symmetrical, and not too small nor so large as to unnecessarily damage the feeding system or the pituitary axis, and if the food is very palatable and easily obtainable. Sex is not a crucial factor when knife cuts are used. With other techniques the above criteria are easier to meet with females than with males, perhaps because of a loss of estrogenic inhibition of feeding in the females.

Functionally produced changes in ventromedial tissue.—Gold thioglucose injections in mice produce the hyperphagia syndrome (34). Arees & Mayer

(35, 36) used nerve terminal degeneration and electronmicroscopy to link the syndrome to ventromedial and arcuate nucleus neurons with direct fiber connections to the lateral hypothalamus. The effect of gold thioglucose is insulin dependent (37). The lack of insulin in diabetic mice protects them from gold thioglucose lesions, and insulin injections immediately restore their susceptibility. Quite clearly insulin level gates the uptake of glucose in cells, contributing to satiety and weight control. Genetically obese mice, especially aged ones, develop unusually small lesions from gold thioglucose. Baile, Herrero & Mayer (38) suggest that old, obese mice have impairments in glucose utilization and insulin sensitivity. Inheritance of this defect could be a major cause of spontaneous hyperphagia and obesity.

Pfaff (39) reasoned that if satiety is produced by activity in normal ventromedial cells, this might be reflected in the cells' morphological characteristics. Histological comparison of unusually well-fed rats and underfed rats revealed that the nucleoli of ventromedial neurons, not others, were significantly enlarged in the well-fed animals. A diet of chow, chocolate, lettuce, oranges, and Swiss cheese apparently stimulated the development of satiety neurons. Discussion of the specific physiological stimuli which act to produce satiety via the ventromedial hypothalamus will be combined with discussion of the lateral hypothalamic syndrome.

THE LATERAL HYPOTHALAMIC SYNDROME UPDATED

Lateral hypothalamic lesions produce a syndrome of behavioral deficits in feeding and drinking followed by specific stages in recovery (9, 40). Few experimental phenomena in the history of brain function have led to such a fruitful analytical model. Stage 1 is aphagia and adipsia (no eating or drinking) ; stage 2 is anorexia and adipsia (intake of wet, palatable food without regulation) ; stage 3 is dehydration aphagia and adipsia (regulation of dry food intake if hydrated or given sweet liquids to drink) ; and stage 4 is recovery (the animal regulates its body weight on dry food and water). Recently there have been some important revelations leading to refinements in this model.

Osmotic, volemic, and salivary controls.—Epstein (9) reviews the evidence that a lesioned animal in the "recovered" stage does not recover its ability to drink in response to hyperosmotic stimulation nor to hypovolemia. All the drinking the animal does in stage 4 is immediately contiguous with eating, known as prandial or mealtime drinking (41). Even in the normal, unoperated rat, most water intake is prandial, thereby preventing thirst before it can be engendered (42) ; however, the normal rat can also regulate fluid intake by drinking extra amounts in response to intracellular osmotic stimuli, extracellular blood volume stimuli, or mouth dryness. The lesioned rat drinks only in response to mouth dryness incurred through eating. Prandial drinking is augmented by desalivation, abolished by concurrent injections of water into the mouth, and unaffected by water injected into the stomach; therefore prandial drinking in the lesioned rat is a byproduct of hunger, not a response to thirst (43). The lesioned rat might be said to "eat the water" flavored with food instead of drinking it.

Glucostatic and aminostatic control.—The rat with lateral hypothalamic lesions also suffers an irrevocable loss of response to glucose deprivation (44). This can be a lethal deficit to lesioned rats given insulin. They die of hypoglycemia instead of responding by eating as normal rats do. Glucose utilization, not blood sugar level, is the critical stimulus, as shown by dosing rats with unmetabolizable glucose, 2-deoxy-D-glucose, known as 2DG (45). By entering into competition with natural glucose, 2DG produces a "metabolic paradox"; decreased utilization from 2DG is coupled with high blood sugar. Blood glucose increases from the animal's behavioral and reflexual efforts to satisfy the blocked "glucoprivic" receptors. In the intact animal the glucoprivic response includes not only feeding behavior, but also direct, reflexive control of gastric acid secretion via the vagus (46), indirect control of insulin release, and an influence on growth hormone and corticosteroid release (47). Epstein (9) points out that initiation of feeding by glucoprivic receptors is not essential for commonplace feeding or body weight regulation in the overall multifactor scheme. It is only through specific tests with lesioned animals that the "recovered" rat's potentially fatal flaw is revealed.

Rats with ventromedial lesions still eat in response to insulin (44); therefore the information from the glucoprivic receptors is processed mainly in the lateral region. Nevertheless, recording from single cells in the rat's ventromedial hypothalamus revealed a 20% decrease in firing rate of some units in animals given a small dose of 2DG (48), and at the same time, some neurons in the lateral region increased firing by a comparable percentage. Not enough 2DG was used to affect recording sites in other parts of the brain, which suggests that the lateral and ventromedial hypothalamic cells were especially sensitive to glucose utilization. Decreased medial activity under the influence of 2DG could be due either to inhibition from the lateral hypothalamic glucoprivic receptors or to a different ventromedial type of receptor that directly signals satiety instead of deprivation.

Le Magnen (10, 49) has compiled evidence that the ventromedial region is critical for lipostatic control of meal size. One of the monitored stimuli, he suggests, could be insulin released at the onset of lipogenesis after feeding. Insulin might act by facilitating glucose transport into ventromedial glucose utilization receptors for satiety. These would be the receptors destroyed by gold thioglucose in insulin-rich mice (37). Ventromedial glucoreceptors are presumably also involved in insulin and epinephrine release, lipogenesis and lipolysis. Le Magnen hypothesizes that destruction of these receptors might impair fat mobilization and thereby require a rat to eat at short intervals all day long as well as all night in accordance with its short-term satiety signals. His article gives a comprehensive review of this material.

Steffens (50) has extensive and interesting evidence correlating levels of blood sugar, insulin, and also free fatty acids with meal initiation and termination in unrestrained rats. He suggests that excess available glucose is necessary to suppress feeding in ventromedial lesioned rats. Brown & Melzack (51) confirmed earlier studies showing that intravenous glucose infusion increases ventromedial, and decreases lateral, hypothalamic multi-unit activity. As a more direct demonstration, iontophoretic application of glucose, but not hypertonic saline, increased firing of some ventromedial cells, which suggests a glucose satiation receptor (52). Both increases and decreases were seen with lateral units. The decrease with glucose could be the response of a neuron connected to a glucoprivic receptor. Neurons responding positively to both glucose and hypertonic sodium chloride would be suited for osmoreception. There is no doubt, however, that glucostatic and osmotic control are separate. Yin, Hamilton & Brobeck (53) found that intravenous injections of water did not ameliorate satiety following an intragastric load of glucose.

Glucostatic receptors in the liver project to the brain. Russek and his colleagues (54) measured shifts in glucose differences between the hepatic vein and portal circulation. In cats and dogs they find positive correlations between inferred glucose uptake in the liver and anorexia. Niijima (55) recorded neural activity in the vagus nerve signaling glucose content in the portal venous blood, and stimulation of the vagus elicited feeding in cats (56). Somewhere there may also be a receptor sensitive to an amino acid or some correlate of it. Rozin (57) reports that rats can regulate their protein intake.

Motor activity, lipostatic and thermostatic controls.—The next question is whether there are neurons damaged by lateral lesions which are crucial to motor functions. Animals in stage 4 eat normally in response to food deprivation, caloric dilution of the diet, or a hot or cold environment (44). Even in stage 2 or 3 when the animals are extremely finicky about food, they do eat some things; therefore the question of inability to eat has arisen with regard to the more severe stages of the lateral syndrome. Morrison (58) suggests that when eating fails to occur it is the result of a deficit in motor coordination. Given that lateral lesions impair salivation (41), it is reasonable to suspect an impairment in licking or chewing. Observation of aphagic rats, however, creates the impression of active rejection of food, such as wiping food out of the mouth. Balagura, Wilcox & Coscina (59) find that the degree of motor difficulty is not well related to the degree of aphagia seen with lesions of various placement. Epstein (9) reviews this and other evidence that suggests an immediate dislike for the taste of food, over and above motor disability. The most recent indication of a primary motivational impairment following lateral hypothalamic lesions is in the Powley & Keesey (60) study in which rats were starved to a low weight level before being lesioned. The underweight animals usually ate a few hours after the lesion instead of refusing food for 3 days like rats lesioned at normal weights. Thus we can infer that if motor disorganization was at all responsible for aphagia, it occurred only in the first few hours out of 3 days of self-starvation.

Powley & Keesey (60) noted that body weight is chronically lowered after lateral hypothalamic lesions. Although low, it is perfectly stable, suggesting regulation of food intake according to some stimulus correlated with body weight. They suggest that initiation of eating after lateral lesions should not be interpreted as recovery, but simply as body weight regulation at a low weight level. This interpretation parallels the earlier conclusion that Hoebel & Teitelbaum (13) drew from studies of feeding and weight regulation in rats with ventromedial lesions. Just as the ventromedial rat is not necessarily hyperphagic if preoperatively obese, the lateral rat is not necessarily aphagic if preoperatively lean. Thus both the ventromedial and lateral lesioned rats regulate their weight, but at abnormal levels. Possibly some of the rats which die of medial or lateral lesions are attempting to regulate at lethally low or lethally high levels. In either case, weight control is not a function which recovers.

In spite of 20 years of searching, no one yet has managed to specify the stimulus which is correlated with body weight and serves such an important role in the control of food intake. Hervey (61) suggests that glucostatic or thermostatic signals are too transient to serve this long-term function, so he, like many before him, emphasizes a lipostatic mechanism. He suggests that the long-sought stimulus is a steroid or some other product which would be produced at a known rate within the body and degraded at a known rate, and which would be partitioned in a fixed ratio between lipid and aqueous phases of the body constituents. If these conditions were met, then the stimulus would act as a signal of fat stores. The fatter the animal, the greater the dilution of this trace substance, and the less it would appear in the aqueous phase represented by the blood supply. The amount of tracer in the blood could be measured in the hypothalamus. Collier (62) reviews evidence that body weight loss accurately reflects long-term conservation of the ratio of calories to body mass, or to the mass of body parts such as the liver. This in turn, is related to cellular parameters such as DNA content and cell size, either of which might release a tracer that controls feeding. The possibility that lipogenesis releases insulin has already been mentioned in the section on glucostasis (49). Steffens (63) is investigating the possible role of free fatty acids.

Grossman (64) reviews his own and other studies of temperature regulation in relation to feeding. Spector, Brobeck & Hamilton (65) found a striking positive correlation between preoptic temperature and feeding behavior. Warming this area increased feeding while reflexively decreasing core temperature. A high environmental temperature could override the effect. Within the hypothalamus, Traylor & Blackburn (66) find a positive correlation between ventromedial electroencephalographic activity and body temperature. Lateral hypothalamic activity varied reciprocally. Stevenson (19) mentions that some rats with ventromedial hypothalamic lesions failed to reduce their food intake appropriately in the heat. They will respond to escape heat, and the heavier they get the more aversive does heat become (67). None of these studies claimed to identify a causal relation between temperature at any one locus and feeding, although correlations between them are abundant.

Just as ventromedial lesions appear to affect feeding in proportion to the amount of sensitive tissue destroyed, so also the decrease in body weight following lateral lesions appears to be related to the size of the lesion (60). It follows from the dual nature of the hypothalamic systems that lesions which impinge on both the lateral and the medial type of functions should have mixed effects (9, 60). Ellison has found a way to separate the mixture.

Two new variants of the lateral hypothalamic syndrome.—Ellison's (33) technique for making a hypothalamic island has revealed two new feeding syndromes in the cat (68) and rat (69). In the first syndrome the animal is irrevocably aphagic and starves to death in spite of being maintained by eye dropper for over 100 days and being offered the most palatable diets. But the animal is not finicky; it will passively swallow food put in it mouth. This pattern was observed when the cut decommissioned all hypothalamic areas as far lateral as the internal capsule (69). The result is in striking contrast to the abhorrence of food shown by rats with ordinary lateral, or lateral plus ventromedial, lesions. To feed the familiar aphagic rat requires an intragastric tube instead of an eye dropper.

Unlike the ordinary lesion techniques, the hypothalamic island guarantees that the entire medial region is incapable of sending neural information to the rest of the brain. Thus the new self-starvation syndrome appears to be the result of complete loss of both approach and aversion tendencies. The perpetual aphagia is not due to motor loss. The rats would chew food viciously in response to the pain of tail pinching, but would never voluntarily ingest food to prevent death by starvation.

In the other new syndrome (69) the animal passively accepts food almost immediately after the hypothalamus is disconnected and then recovers voluntary nibbling of wet mash within just a few days, sustained eating in about 10 days, and weight maintenance within a week or two. This is remarkably fast considering the immense size of the lesions. Apparently a thin, outer edge of lateral hypothalamic tissue was left intact. The functions of this tissue could not be compromised in any way by the medial inhibitory tissue which had been isolated. This could explain why these animals enter recovery stage 4 very soon after the cut is made; the animals were left with enough of the feeding system to evidence approach without signs of aversion.

According to Ellison's interpretation, the syndrome observed after the common lateral lesions made with electrodes is the result not only of damage to the feeding system which only causes aphagia, but also of disinhibition of the medial inhibitory system which produces finickiness and the standard 4-stage syndrome. This proposal implies that the medial system can act in the absence of lateral tissue through its own output to an intact integrative system elsewhere in the brain.

Taste, olfactory, and gastric factors.—Snowdon (70) has proposed a peripheral model which accounts for several aspects of the control of feeding. In rats fed ad libitum, intragastric feeding to bypass nerves to and from the mouth shortened meal durations. Vagotomy to eliminate nerves to and from the stomach increased gastric emptying time and shortened intermeal intervals. Thus oral factors sustain a meal, and stomach emptying determines when the animal will eat again. This fits Le Magnen's (10) observation that the size of a given meal is well correlated with the onset, but not the size, of the next meal.

The amount consumed in a meal is controlled not only by the postabsorptive factors already discussed, but also by orogastric "preregulation" of energy balance before food is actually absorbed. Nicolaïdis (71) and Wyrwicka (72) review demonstrations of very rapid systemic changes induced by tastes, odors, and gastric factors. For example the mere presence of a sweet substance in the mouth can cause a rapid elevation of blood glucose level in fasted rats (71). Most of these effects are mediated neurally and are modulated by the animal's internal state. Recordings of electrical activity show clearly that taste and olfactory information project to the diencephalic feeding system (73–75), specifically including both the lateral and ventromedial hypothalamus.

Mook (76) contributes much behavioral evidence of the interaction of mouth factors and postingestional mechanisms, using rats with an esophageal fistula and an intragastric tube. Jordan (77) reviews and extends similar studies in humans with oral or intragastric tubes. In summarizing, Mook points out that systemic changes do not seem to act on peripheral receptors directly, but act instead by way of the central nervous system. For a recent experiment on this issue focusing on specific hunger for salt, see the Quartermain, Wolf & Keselica (78) report of loss of salt preference during hyponatremia after lateral, but not medial, hypothalamic damage. As an example of a different kind, Wade & Zucker (79) find modulation of taste by sex hormones and suggest this is a function of medial, not lateral, receptivity to estrogen (80). There is also a wealth of information on peripheral-central interactions in other kinds of animals, insects in particular, which cannot be covered in the present review; however, there is much to learn from these investigations (1).

Taste stimuli bear a specialized, innate relationship to gastric upset in the rat. Rozin (81) reviews studies of long-lasting bait-shyness after a single exposure to poisoning. His latest results clearly implicate the nervous system in spanning the time interval between tasting a food and onset of sickness from apomorphine a half hour later. Roth, Teitelbaum & Schwartz (82) report that aversions could no longer be learned in this way after lateral hypothalamic lesions. The ability to associate taste and sickness was lost. The effect is not due to a loss of taste ability; the animals show increased sensitivity to tastes, even after just a unilateral lesion (83). In Di Cara's (84) results, rats that had been tube fed after lateral lesions would not accept free milk when it was offered unless they had been given experience with milk before the lesion. Thus they do not lose memory in this case; to the contrary they depend on the established preferences.

Some preferences are learned through a process that is the opposite of bait-shyness. If a rat is ill, with a thiamine deficiency for example, it will prefer novel diets, will sample them, and will learn to eat the ones that alleviate the illness. Rozin (85) explains that this process accounts for some kinds of behavior formerly attributed to specific hungers. Even some of the most basic preferences such as for sweetness may have a component that is learned during the animal's development in addition to built-in approach to sugar. Mook & Blass (86) find that ventromedial lesioned obese rats show essentially normal taste-aversion functions for sucrose; they point out that even though the satiety mechanism is damaged, postingestive factors can counteract sweetness.

Apparently the reinforcing property of taste is one, if not the primary, recovery factor after lateral hypothalamic lesions. Lesioned rats with the most severe deficits will die rather than ingest food; if sustained by artificial feeding, then weeks or months later, too long to be just a matter of weight loss, they gradually begin to eat again. Such recovery is not well explained by changes in motor ability, glucostasis, weight, thirst, or any of the other factors we have discussed which recover either very rapidly or not at all. The nature of gradual recovery of feeding can be understood by analogy with the same stages in the behavioral development of feeding (7). Teitelbaum, Cheng & Rozin (87) conclude from their results that neural recovery after lateral hypothalamic lesions parallels ontogenetic development of the nervous system. Both may involve the same process of encephalization. Recovery is theoretically re-encephalization. Rosner (88) reviews this and other contributions to the study of recovery of brain function.

Recall that the results with hypothalamic islands suggested that some rats with no medial hypothalamic output had no negative reaction to taste and recovered quickly (69). The intermediate case, gradual recovery after partial lesions, would therefore seem to be a gradual shift in the animal's interpretation, presumably cortical, of the new mixture of lateral and medial, positive and negative, inputs. The emphasis is put on taste because we know most about its behavioral effects as Pfaffmann's review bears witness (89); however, the learning of interpretion of gastric inputs, a process

Snowdon (90) is bringing to light, might well be involved. A technique is needed for measuring neural correlates of reward and aversion in the feeding system. Self-controlled stimulation of the hypothalamus through implanted electrodes may suffice.

REWARD AND AVERSION SYSTEMS FOR FEEDING

A model for neural control of homeostatic behavior.—A rat with an electrode implanted in the lateral hypothalamus can be trained to turn electric current on, to self-stimulate, or to turn the current off, escaping or avoiding stimulation. Hoebel (17) has proposed a theory that the lateral hypothalamus generates a combination of reward and aversion which shifts along a continuum depending on the animal's homeostatic balance. This was shown by feeding rats liquid diets intragastrically or intravenously to determine the effects of short-term changes in energy balance on lateral hypothalamic self-stimulation and stimulation escape. Hypertonic solutions of glucose or saline injected intragastrically halved self-stimulation rate and doubled stimulation escape. Caloric, osmotic, and gastric distention effects on self-stimulation were each demonstrated independently. To study long-term effects, animals were made obese by combining stimulation-elicited feeding with self-stimulation, in a program that caused self-induced hyperphagia leading to increased body weight. As the rats became obese a shift from reward to aversion occurred progressively until self-stimulation was decreased to a third of its initial level and escape rate tripled. Both effects were reversible; when the food was digested about 2 hr after the meal in the short-term experiment, or when body weight was allowed to return to normal in the long-term experiment, then the animals resumed their normal rapid self-stimulation rate and slow escape rate (91).

As a generalization, it appears that when energy is low, then feeding reward is high, and the animal displays a good appetite; when energy is in balance, the same hypothalamic stimulation is less rewarding and more aversive, and the animal is satiated; when there is an energy surfeit, hypothalamic stimulation becomes predominantly aversive and the animal has a cloyed palate. Thus behavioral regulation of homeostatic balance from the animal's point of view may be regulation of rewards and aversions similar to those elicited by hypothalamic stimulation. Corresponding theories have been offered for copulation reward (17, 92) and drinking reward (93, 94). All are outgrowths of Olds' pioneering studies.

A conceptual paradox resolved.—A number of objections have been raised to the basic notion that reinforcement produced by brain stimulation has effects like those elicited by conventional reinforcers such as food. More important to this paper, questions have been raised for the model just outlined which goes further and attaches to lateral hypothalamic reinforcement the specific reinforcing properties of food.

Because self-stimulation and stimulus-bound eating are often obtained from the same electrode, some authors have objected to the feeding-reward analysis on the grounds that it is illogical to suppose that an animal would work to obtain a stimulus that makes it hungry (15, 95). This view has its roots in the idea that homeostatic behavior is a matter of avoiding discomfort, for example eating to stop hunger pangs. One solution is to postulate two systems which interact, one for reward and another for hunger. Ball (95) suggests that a train of lateral hypothalamic stimulation excites first one and then the other. A second resolution of the paradox requires looking at the problem in a different way. Many natural stimuli are rewarding *and* elicit eating, notably stimuli associated with the beginning of any meal. Appetite-whetting tastes and smells have the same properties as lateral hypothalamic stimulation; they are rewarding and they elicit eating. The emphasis here is on appetite whetting rather than on hunger pangs, on positive feedback rather than negative, on drive induction rather than drive reduction. If this emphasis is correct, then appetite-whetting stimuli should potentiate self-stimulation as well as food intake.

Coons & Cruce (96) demonstrated that rats press faster for self-stimulation if they can eat a little food simultaneously. Similarly, the odor of peppermint accelerated self-stimulation of the olfactory bulb (97). Studies of this type have been reviewed by Mendelson (98) and Mogenson & Kaplinsky (94). With an indwelling tube in the roof of a rat's mouth, Hoebel (99) found that sucrose dripped onto the tongue during self-stimulation not only increased self-stimulation, but also decreased stimulation escape. As a control, water applied to the tongue was ineffective. These studies were interpreted as evidence that neural input from taste receptors can augment the reward of self-stimulation and thus serve as an incentive to self-stimulate, just as they are an incentive to eat. Decrease in escape behavior was interpreted as an amelioration of aversion by Hoebel and as an inhibition of excess arousal by Mendelson (100). Theoretical discussions of incentive, drive, and arousal that draw on this work are available (101–106).

The feeding-reward interpretation of elicited eating and self-stimulation led Olds (107) to seek and find a possible site for hunger aversion. In the dorsal medial hypothalamus, stimulation again elicited eating, but predominantly caused aversion. This site may, therefore, have to do with the rewards of eating to escape the aversive sensations of starvation.

Rapid extinction.—Kent & Grossman (108) compile the evidence comparing brain reward and conventional rewards with regard to several schedules of reinforcement. This issue centers around unusually rapid extinction of brain-reinforced behavior after stimulation is terminated. These authors suggest that the aversive component of lateral hypothalamic stimulation causes both rapid extinction and the necessity for priming some animals with free stimulation to get self-stimulation started. The mixture of aversive and reward components during hypothalamic stimulation brings the animal into a conflict situation which well accounts for its behavior. This view is particularly interesting in the light of the proposal that the aversive component is related to satiety, for if correct, it means that the rat's responding for mixed reward and punishment from a single electrode may reflect normal behavior of an animal in conflict over whether or not to eat. The rewards of feeding are pitted against the aversions. Thus observed variations in the predominance of reward or aversion produced by different electrode placements (108) may be comparable to variations obtained with a single electrode when food intake or obesity is varied (91).

The priming problem.—Priming refers to the use of hypothalamic stimulation as an incentive for more hypothalamic stimulation. Gallistel (109) has studied the effects of priming on performance in a maze. He finds, for one thing, that a dozen priming trains delivered as long as 15 min before entering the maze can improve performance. Thus the rat remembers the free stimulation for 15 min and works to get more of the same. The problem, as far as neural control of feeding is concerned, is that any reward electrode could prime performance for stimulation through any other reward electrode. This demonstrates anew an interaction among self-stimulation sites, and raises questions on the specificity of the relation between self-stimulation and feeding. Gallistel does not claim that lateral hypothalamic stimulation is unrelated to feeding rewards; he does point out that self-stimulation at any given site may excite a general or multifunctional reward system.

Specificity of the feeding-reward system.—Evidence that physiological changes related to feeding have an effect on lateral hypothalamic stimulation that is not common to all stimulation sites has been reviewed (17). These studies, which measured self-stimulation rate at two electrodes in the same rat, show that it is possible to depress lateral hypothalamic self-stimulation by intragastric feeding without affecting septal self-stimulation, or to affect posterior hypothalamic self-stimulation with castration or androgen injections without similar effects on lateral hypothalamic self-stimulation (92). This specificity with some electrodes occurs although some others are affected by both feeding and sex hormones. There is little understanding of the process by which the animal's attention is channeled so that self-stimulation behavior primarily reflects just one of the many underlying systems which must be excited by a large electrode. Nonetheless, the consistent, logical, and physiologically specific changes which occur in self-stimulation and escape strongly suggest that this paradigm provides a model for normal brain function through which physiological changes are translated into instrumental behavior (91).

Disinhibition of reward.—Ventromedial hypothalamic lesions that disinhibit feeding also disinhibit lateral hypothalamic self-stimulation. There is a greater disinhibition of self-stimulation in the lateral hypothalamus than other tested sites (17). The reward and aversion which relate to feeding are inversely related to each other. Ferguson & Keesey (110) have confirmed that ventromedial lesions increase self-stimulation, but contrary to expectations, self-stimulation rate did not remain elevated in the subsequent days after the lesion even though the rats were allowed to eat no more food than controls; these rats subsequently developed hyperphagia when allowed to eat ad libitum. They interpret their result as calling for modification in the feeding-reward hypothesis. Either the increase in self-stimulation immediately after self-stimulation is an artifact of increased generalized activity, as they suggest, in which case the feeding-reward hypothesis is not firm; or else the failure of self-stimulation to remain increased is an artifact of inactivity or hormonal changes occurring in the long run after ventromedial lesions, in which case the hypothesis is still sound. Two available bits of evidence favor the latter. First, it is well known that activity is curtailed in the long-term after ventromedial lesions. Second, if bar pressing for stimulation increases after lesions as an activity artifact, then bar pressing for stimulation escape should increase too, but it does not. Stimulation escape decreases immediately (111). Whether escape is depressed permanently or only transiently is unknown.

Specificity and Plasticity in Hypothalamic Function

Intense interest focused on the phenomenon of electrically elicited feeding and drinking when Valenstein, Cox & Kakolewski (112) questioned the accepted interpretation of these classic observations. It is probably safe to say that Hess's interpretation was generally accepted: "specific autonomic functions are correlated with certain circumscribed regions of the diencephalon. In no case, however, is a sharp delineation possible. On the contrary there is overlapping and intermingling of various systems; and areas representing related functions may even form characteristic 'aggregations'" (113). Laboratory lore held that the study of elicited feeding began with the art of placing electrodes so as to hit an aggregation of feeding nerves, as opposed to nerves for drinking, gnawing, running, or other behavior patterns.

Plasticity of elicited eating.—Then Valenstein's group found that a site where stimulation always elicited feeding could be altered to elicit drinking too by stimulation in the absence of food. By the reverse procedure a drinking site could become a site for eliciting eating by removing water during a few nights of automatic stimulation. This led to their recent article reviewing many experiments and proposing that hypothalamic stimulation excites the substrate for a "group of responses related to a common state", in short, a mood (114). According to this hypothesis the behavior an animal displays, for example feeding, is not a simple manifestation of hunger, appetite, or even reinforcement associated specifically with eating, but rather a manifestation of the reinforcement triggered by less specific consummatory motor actions. For example, when a rat eating food pellets during hypothalamic stimulation prefers to drink water or gnaw the dish instead of eating the same food ground to a powder, this would be interpreted as an instance of behavior reinforced by feedback consumatory motor acts, not by the appetite-satisfying properties of food. Whether the animal feeds, drinks, or gnaws is thought to depend on the state of the individual animal and its species' typical characteristics.

Other investigators have confirmed the new behavior-shift phenomena, but see it somewhat differently. Wise (115) reported that multiple elicited behaviors could be demonstrated immediately by removing the food or the water, whichever the animal initially consumed, and then raising the current. Switching then becomes a matter of shifting thresholds for multiple underlying systems which could be quite separate and fixed in their functions. Valenstein, Cox & Kakolewski (116) emphasized that only with removal of the initially preferred object was the new behavior acquired. Milgram (117) went a step further, however, by showing that even without removing the preferred object, if testing was repeated daily, behavior would usually shift from either elicited feeding or elicited drinking to both elicited feeding and drinking. For example, rats that religiously ate during stimulation gradually converted to drinking as well. Thus the elicited behaviors can change spontaneously.

Inflexibility of elicited eating.—On the one hand, hypothalamic stimulation was displaying plasticity unprecedented in the previous 30 years of research on the subject; on the other hand, experiments were showing that elicited eating reflected many aspects of normal hunger. Taste preferences during hypothalamic stimulation were normal (118, 119), and electrically elicited feeding could be programed to produce overeating to the point of marked obesity (120). This was interpreted as evidence for overwhelming hunger. Similarly Hoebel & Thompson (91) programed hypothalamic stimulation in a way that locked the animal in a cycle of voluntarily pressing a lever which delivered both food and stimulation, the latter both rewarded them and made them eat. The result was self-induced obesity. If the animals had switched to drinking water, then the excess intake during stimulation would be excreted right away as Mogenson & Stevenson (121) found in experiments with only water present. But with both food and water available these animals did not learn to drink exclusively, instead the elicited behavior was so inflexible that they grew fat by eating three times their normal daily intake. If the current was too strong, the animals would be pushed to the limit and some would eat to death.

These two sets of studies represent one of those cases in the history of science when a technique was pushed to its limits in two opposite directions at the same time. In one situation, stimulated animals are as likely to drink water or gnaw on a dish as they are to eat food, in the other situations animals behave so rigidly that they will not stop eating even though it kills them. Does stimulation elicit a consumatory mood or specific appetite?

Stabilization and specific control.—Even though a rat that eats or drinks during stimulation gradually begins to do both with practice, the relative proportions of eating and drinking will gradually stabilize (117). Using this technique to provide a predictable baseline of behavior, Devor, Wise, Milgram & Hoebel (122) found that food intake inhibited elicited eating but not drinking, whereas water intake inhibited elicited drinking but not eating. In this experiment, elicited behaviors are neither undirected nor rigid results of stimulation; food and water intake exert specific and homeostatically appropriate control. Valenstein & Cox (123) report that deprivation conditions during initial training do not reliably determine whether an animal will initially display eating, drinking or both. The Devor et al (122) experiment shows that rats known to do both in established proportion will shift the proportion in ways logically predictable from ingestion of food or water.

The question boils down to whether the same nerves modulate both feeding and drinking. Neurochemical studies point to separate feeding and drinking systems within the hypothalamus. Fisher (124) has tried to shift cholinergically induced drinking to eating, but reports it has not happened. Identification of an additional system for hypothalamic mood is still a moot point.

Some of the reports of electrically elicited feeding in association with other appetitive behaviors include investigatory behavior (125), stalking attack (126–128), mouse killing (125, 129, 130), food carrying and hoarding (100, 131–133), gnawing (114, 122, 125, 132), running (134), salivation (113), and grooming, not to mention heat loss and heat gain reactions, respiratory responses, and changes in random activity. Roberts, Steinberg & Means' (125) study of many of these behaviors in the opossum is no longer new, but their interpretation must be mentioned. It is an outgrowth of MacDonnell & Flynn's (135) classic demonstration in cats that biting reflexes produced on contact are facilitated by stimulation of the hypothalamic attack zone as a function of stimulation intensity. It is suggested that hypothalamic stimulation facilitates separate, extrahypothalamic sensory and motor mechanisms for various response elements. Glickman & Schiff (136) theorize that facilitation of the motor mechanisms for consumatory acts is the essence of reinforcement. White, Wayner & Cott (137) recently suggested that motor excitement elicits behavior which is manifest according to the available environmental stimuli, which brings us back to the question of a general, as opposed to a specific, theory of hypothalamic function.

NEUROCHEMISTRY OF FEEDING

Proposals for α- and β-adrenergic systems.—Chemical stimulation of the brain through double cannulas has made evident that norepinephrine is a neurotransmitter in a hypothalamic feeding system and acetylcholine in a drinking system (138–142). The intriguing aspect of the several pharmacological techniques for manipulating brain function is their ability to selectively influence integrated behavior patterns and thereby provide some hope of untangling the Gordian knot in the hypothalamus. New chapters in the mystery of brain function are being written on the basis of classical pharmacology of the peripheral nervous system as adapted to the study of brain control of motivated behavior.

This year the plot has thickened. Leibowitz (143, 144) and Margules (145–148) have elaborated important differences between α- and β-adrenergic feeding subsystems in the hypothalamus. The α and β classification refers to established effects of chemicals on two types of peripheral adrenergic receptors (149). Let us start with the Leibowitz model because it is easier to explain. Any relation of this α and β model to the models based on lateral and medial, excitatory and inhibitory, and reward and aversion distinctions already discussed is strictly not a coincidence. Leibowitz suggests that α- and β-adrenergic systems act antagonistically, that the α "hunger" system elicits feeding and the β "satiety" system suppresses it. The evidence, in brief, is that fluid injection of α stimulants (norepinephrine and metaraminol) into the midlateral (perifornical) hypothalamic region initiated feeding in rats fed ad libitum. This confirmed the studies by Slangen & Miller (150), Booth (151), and their forerunners; a β agonist (isoproterenol) injected through the same cannula suppressed the natural tendency to eat in food-deprived rats. Epinephrine, which has both α and β actions peripherally, elicited feeding at low doses (presumably the α effect), and suppressed feeding at high doses (the β effect). Elicitation of eating was blocked only by an α antagonist (phentolamine), whereas elicitation of satiety was blocked by a β antagonist (propranolol). Finally, the appetite-killing properties of the β agonist were potentiated by the α antagonist, producing supersatiety that is predictable assuming that the rat treated this way has both an excited β "satiety" system and a blocked α "hunger" system. Evidently the α- and β-adrenergic synapses for the two systems come together in the midhypothalamic region in such a way that both the hunger and satiety can be controlled by chemicals from a single cannula.

By using cannulas further medial, Leibowitz obtained more purely α hunger effects; and further lateral, more purely β satiety effects. It is as if synapses for the two systems were fairly well separated in far-lateral and medial regions, but anatomically intermingled in the middle region. She suggests that the α terminations inhibit the medial hypothalamus, thereby disinhibiting feeding neurons. The β satiety terminations in the lateral hypothalamus inhibit feeding neurons (144).

Although this model is delightfully simple and fits in beautifully with the major postulates of related models of feeding mechanisms, it has been challenged by conflicting data from its inception. The types of problems raised, familiar from lesion studies, center on paradoxical signs of finickiness and the rat's unwillingness to meet work requirements. Margules has conducted tests with milk of varying sweetness instead of standard food pellets such as Leibowitz used. He finds some results similar to those described above and some quite different. The α agonist norepinephrine, instead of eliciting milk consumption, suppressed it. The α blocker phentolamine produced the feeding-suppression effect reported by Leibowitz if and only if the milk was quinine-adulterated to make it somewhat bitter, which suggests that pellets are acting as a relatively unpalatable food. Given sweet milk, rats overeat instead of undereat in response to the same drug. Thus the effect of α blockade is directly analogous to finickiness after ventromedial lesions (147). The β system seems to work in reverse: the β agonist isoproterenol suppressed intake of bitter milk but not sweet milk which suggests that the bad taste was heightened. On the other hand, the β blocker (LB-46) produced rapid intake of even bitter milk although the animals actually ingested less of it, which suggests a diminished taste selectivity combined with a heightened physiological satiety effect. Thus the β blockade caused the opposite of ventromedial hypothalamic lesions, less finickiness, and undereating (148).

In this scheme the β system is seen as a satiety system in agreement with the Leibowitz model, but for Margules the β system suppresses feeding in response to unattractive tastes as opposed to interoceptive satiety cues. Although Margules' model is somewhat counterintuitive, its great advantage is that it begins to cope with the problem of homeostasis versus hedonism at the neurochemical level and may lead to some badly needed understanding of hypothalamic control of finicky behavior.

Margules' neurochemical theory is quite like the model by Jacobs & Sharma (152) which makes the counterintuitive seem logical through experiments suggesting that hungry rats eat primarily for taste, as opposed to calories, because of a potentiated tendency to approach and consume sweet foods. It would follow that the α satiety system of Margules underlies feeding for calories in the ad libitum fed rat close to homeostatic energy balance, whereas the β taste selectivity system might underlie the behavior of starved rats with feeding patterns governed more by palatability factors.

The appetite-depressing action of amphetamine has been interpreted to fit both the Leibowitz α hunger : β satiety theory and the Margules α satiety : β taste selectivity theory. Margules cites evidence that amphetamine releases norepinephrine and would thereby be expected to indirectly excite the α-adrenergic receptors signaling internal satiety.

Leibowitz (153) proposes the intriguing theory that amphetamine does not act as an anorectic by releasing norepinephrine, since in her scheme norepinephrine elicits eating instead of causing anorexia. Amphetamine acts instead, she suggests, as a β agonist which gives it satiety-inducing properties. This is shown by blocking intrahypothalamic amphetamine anorexia with a β blocker and enhancing it with an α blocker (153). To a lesser degree amphetamines may act as an α agonist too, since intrahypothalamic amphetamine actually elicits a little eating in satiated rats if the rats' β system is blocked. To my knowledge this is the first report of amphetamine causing eating.

Margules may counter with the same argument he used to explain the feeding seen with norepinephrine (147). He suggests that small fluid doses of norepinephrine are only sufficient to activate a membrane pump that causes reuptake of norepinephrine from the synaptic gap, thus giving a reverse effect. To see the real α-adrenergic effect stand out, one must inundate the area with concentrated solutions, as from dissolving crystals, in order to get some of the exogenous α agonist into the gap to cause satiety. Perhaps the 0.1 μmole of amphetamine which Leibowitz injected into the hypothalamus was merely enough to trigger the uptake pump and cause the reverse effect. The argument for reverse effects with small doses is far-fetched, but not entirely theoretical. If norepinephrine release were sufficient to produce synaptic activation leading to eating, then, Margules argues, one should see rebound anorexia resulting from transient inhibition of norepinephrine synthesis comparable to endproduct inhibition as observed in peripheral noradrenergic synapses. The available evidence suggests there is no rebound anorexia after small norepinephrine doses, but there is rebound appetite after a large norepinephrine dose (145).

Coons & Quartermain (154) have yet another interpretation. They find that small fluid doses of norepinephrine elicit a small amount of eating as everyone agrees, but that the rats will not work by bar pressing for this food. This agrees with the finding that rats eating in response to norepinephrine have less tolerance for quinine in their mash (155) or milk (147). Instead of suggesting that norepinephrine stimulates a system for finicky eating, they suggest that norepinephrine overwhelms a feeding system by analogy with the finickiness and motivational depression seen after ventromedial hypothalamic lesions. The small dose of norepinephrine may be too much, they suggest, not too little as Margules proposes. However, a norepinephrine-induced block seems unlikely given the 14 logical ways Leibowitz has manipulated adrenergic feeding with various combinations of α and β agonists and antagonists.

Oomura and his colleagues (156) have tested the smallest possible dose of norepinephrine, too small to elicit behavior, but quite revealing nonetheless. Electrophoretic application of norepinephrine in the rat's lateral hypothalamus increased, never decreased, the activity of single units. Acetylcholine initiated activity in many of these same neurons. In the ventromedial region, norepinephrine increased some units and decreased others. This indicates at least two norepinephrine-sensitive systems; thus any of the procedures for inundating the area with norepinephrine from a cannula are going to elicit behavior that is a resultant of the two influences. If norepinephrine has only α-adrenergic effects, this suggests two or more kinds of α-adrenergic sensitive units, at least one of which also responds positively to acetylcholine and negatively to atropine. Given multiple α-adrenergic systems in the same region, it is quite possible that underlying the opposite interpretations of norepinephrine effects by Leibowitz and Margules are opposing systems. Both could be α-adrenergic, with one or the other favored depending on the dose, exact cannula location, diet offered, or deprivation state.

On the horizon there is also a glimmer of a possibility of dopaminergic (157) and cholinergic feeding systems (158, 159).

Another approach to chemical treatment of the feeding system lies through the ventricular fluids. Myers & Yakshi (160) found that intraventricular injection of several catecholamines including norepinephrine elicited hyperthermia and consumption of Noyes pellets, but not water. The β-adrenergic agonist, isoproterenol, produced only the hyperthermia in this study, but elicited eating in another (161). When adrenergic stimulation was applied directly to the lateral hypothalamus, drinking was obtained more often than eating (162). This unusual report may just reflect prandial drinking, or it may mean that rats sometimes drink as a nonspecific response to an adrenergic arousal or general reward system. This dual feeding-drinking effect of adrenergic stimulation is like effects in monkeys that both eat and drink in response to adrenergic hypothalamic stimulation (163). Unlike the rat, in monkeys cholinomimetic drugs in the lateral hypothalamus block drinking as well as eating. This nicely fits Stein's adrenergic approach and cholinergic suppression model (164). Since the model designed for the rat fits the monkey even better, it is not yet entirely clear whether the rat and monkey are really built with different neurotransmitters or whether we have simply not explored them enough to find all the similarities. The rat even has brain sites where stimulation with a given drug has opposite effects on drinking, depending on the deprivation state (165). Studies in other species will surely run into these reversals, which may be more a function of stimulation site, dose, and feeding schedule than actual species differences.

Routtenberg (166) has expressed concern that direct chemical treatment of the brain can be misleading because of chemical spread, particularly into the ventricular fluids (166). However, Myers (163) has made a satiated monkey eat by perfusing its lateral hypothalamus with cerebrospinal fluid collected from a hungry monkey. Injecting the same fluid into the recipient's ventricles was not effective. In addition, the intrahypothalamic chemical injections studies cited have used control sites. In many cases, moving a cannula 1 mm changes the behavioral effect entirely, even when the move places the cannula closer to the ventricle. Apparently the drugs are broken down, or so diluted, by the time they spread a millimeter, that the concentration is ineffective. Although behavior is the real test, it is reassuring to know that recent measurements of spread by histochemical fluorescence (167) or radioactive label (168) also demonstrate that chemicals do not usually get more than about half a millimeter beyond the cannula.

Neurochemistry of stimulation-induced feeding, reward, and aversion.— Stein (164, 169) has recently summarized work on the pharmacology of the reward system, which he identifies with the medial forebrain bundle, and the aversion or "punishment" system, which is part of the periventricular system including the medial hypothalamus. Lateral hypothalamic stimulation caused a time-locked release of tagged norepinephrine in the medial forebrain bundle anterior to the stimulation electrode, but not at control sites in the thalamus or cortex (170). Thus norepinephrine was released from synapses activated by stimulating the reward system, or at least in some neural system stemming from the lateral hypothalamus. That a reward system itself is indeed noradrenergic is shown by an enhancement of self-stimulation following drugs which inhibit adrenergic catabolism (iproniazid) or which block norepinephrine uptake (cocaine, imipramine). A decrease in self-stimulation behavior followed injection of adrenergic biosynthesis inhibitors (α-methyl-p-tyrosine), or depleters (reserpine), or blockers (chlorpromazine). Self-stimulation depressed by inhibition of its biosynthesis could be restored by injection of norepinephrine, but not dopamine or serotonin (169).

The aversion system is apparently not adrenergic. In the experiment with tagged norepinephrine, stimulation at escape sites produced no change or a decrease in norepinephrine release. Margules & Stein (171) give us some fresh clues to the chemical nature of this aversion system. First they cite evidence that minor tranquilizers, "antianxiety" drugs like meprobamate, ethanol, or oxazepam, disinhibited feeding behavior that had been suppressed either by shock, aversive brain stimulation, bitter taste, or simply by food withdrawal; thus these drugs had a generalized effect on suppressed behavior. Evidently this class of tranquilizers acts in part via the ventromedial hypothalamus because the action can be duplicated with bilateral mechanical damage or cholinergic blockade of the ventromedial region. The authors suggest that generalized punishment is served by ventromedial cholinergic synapses that excite a system which inhibits behavior. This agrees with Carlton's (172) general cholinergic behavior inhibition theory and the extensive evidence from a study by Olds & Domino (173) for cholinergic inhibition of self-stimulation.

Next, Margules & Stein (171) find that ventromedial damage disinhibits both bar pressing for milk and free consumption of the milk, whereas cholinergic blockade of the ventromedial region with atropine disinhibits bar pressing but not free consumption. This is an interesting dissociation of bar pressing as rewarded by the act itself from bar pressing as rewarded by food.

There is some question whether the rats simply became too active, too aroused to eat; however, the effect is reminiscent of the effects of systemic amphetamine which produces the same seemingly irrational behavior of bar pressing for food but not eating it (174). Apparently we must grant to the act of bar pressing an unidentified reward that may have something to do with some other motivated behavior, with muscular exercise as seen in wheel running (134) or with secondary reinforcing effects associated with the act of pressing (174). If the cholinergic system for suppression of general operant behavior does not suppress free feeding, then presumably it is one of the adrenergic satiety systems which does so. This implies that the adrenergic self-stimulation system which is inhibited by the cholinergic suppression system (169, 174) might not be the reward system for free feeding. It also follows that if one asks whether the ventromedial hypothalamus is a center for affective reactions, satiety, or both (175), the answer is, both.

Pharmacological studies of stimulation escape and stimulation-elicited eating help to clarify the dissociation of a general reward system and feeding reward. Systemic amphetamine increased lateral hypothalamic self-stimulation while decreasing matched responses for water (176), and decreasing the tendency to eat during stimulation (177). These results appeared inconsistent with the feeding-reward hypothesis discussed earlier, until it was shown that systemic injection of two other drugs which depress appetite, propadrine (phenylpropanolamine) (178) and epinephrine (179), decreases both elicited eating and self-stimulation. Propadrine is classified as an α agonist that causes anorexia but with less CNS excitation than amphetamine (149). Perhaps anorexia without exhilaration explains this drug's ability to decrease self-stimulation in concert with free feeding and elicited feeding. The decrease in self-stimulation is apparently not a general mood depression nor just motor inactivity because, during the same tests, elicited drinking was unaffected and stimulation escape increased (178). The drug apparently causes a shift from hypothalamic reward to aversion.

Propadrine injected directly into the lateral hypothalamus again decreased the elicited eating, but not drinking, in rats that initially did both. Thus direct hypothalamic treatment with this drug is sufficient for a selective anorectic effect (178).

Electrical recordings from the hypothalamus of rats under the systemic influence of amphetamine or a new nonexcitant anorectic drug, fenfluramine, variously suggest a primary action of increased ventromedial activity (180, 181) or decreased lateral hypothalamic activity (182). These authors review older lesion studies which bear on the issue.

RELATIONS WITH OTHER BRAIN AREAS

Functional neuroanatomy of feeding is still largely a welter of loose threads relating one brain area to some one or two others. Overall models for arousal, reward, and memory have been put forward. The parts of each of these theories most applicable to feeding behavior will be mentioned. For background the reader may want to refer to surveys by Grossman (183), Morgane (184), or Robinson & Mishkin (185) and the neuroanatomical presentation by Nauta & Haymaker (186).

Medial forebrain bundle, frontal cortex, and amygdala.—Stein (164) reviews neuroanatomical degeneration and fluorescent staining studies which trace an adrenergic system ascending from midbrain to the frontal and limbic cortex via the medial forebrain bundle. According to his hypothesis, these adrenergic terminations inhibit neurons which suppress behavior by cholinergic activation of punishment systems in the medial thalamus and ventromedial hypothalamus. At least some of the ventromedial hypothalamic neurons with cholinergic endings are thought to come from suppressor areas in the amygdala. Thus the adrenergic reward system releases approach movements, presumably including instrumental responses for food, that are otherwise held in check.

The amygdala apparently inhibits behavior such as feeding in response to a broad class of punishments, not just satiety. Stein & Wise (169) summarize Margules' early work and its extensions showing that feeding suppressed by foot shock was disinhibited by amygdalar damage, or injection of norepinephrine or epinephrine, but not sodium chloride, or dopamine. This effect matches the effect of lesioning or cholinergic blockade of the ventromedial hypothalamus, and suggests a pathway that is inhibited in the amygdala by adrenergic synapses and that ends with cholinergic inhibitory synapses in the ventromedial hypothalamus. The generality of behavior suppression by this pathway does not necessarily imply lack of specific suppression as well. Grossman (183) found that adrenergic amygdala stimulation increased responding on a food lever but not on a water lever, so the effect is not just nonspecific activation. The adrenergic system for behavior disinhibition is clearly distinguished from the reticular formation arousal mechanism which is thought to elicit arousal directly, not just by inhibiting a cholinergic suppressor system. If anything, the reticular system excites a cholinergic suppressor system as part of a negative feedback loop (188).

Grossman (138) reviews the finding that adrenergic stimulation of the amygdala augments food intake only if the rat is already somewhat hungry. This suggested that the amygdala mediates intake, but that initiation of behavior depends on activity elsewhere, perhaps in the lateral hypothalamus. In the amygdala, cholinergic stimulation, which augmented drinking in thirsty rats, tended to inhibit food intake; thus the amygdala, like the hypothalamus, manifests a reciprocal relationship between feeding and drinking. Presumably this is neurally mediated reciprocal inhibition, although Singer & Montgomery (187) suggest that synaptic release of a neurohumor may directly block adjacent, antagonistic systems (187).

Ventromedial single-unit discharges evoked by amygdalar stimulation

were decreased by iontophoretic application of γ-aminobutyric acid
(GABA) at the recording site (156). Hebb (189) reviews the evidence that
GABA is an inhibitory transmitter. There are two known pathways from
the amygdala to the ventromedial hypothalamus with distinctive electrophysiological characteristics, the stria terminalis and the amygdalafugal pathway (190–193). Murphy (193) has tentatively identified interneurons
which can be excited by stimulating either the lateral edge of the ventromedial nucleus or the paths from the amygdala and which will then inhibit
firing of large amplitude spikes from other ventromedial cells. Heimer &
Nauta (194) depict stria terminalis fibers terminating around the ventromedial hypothalamic nucleus. These possibly mediate the effects Murphy recorded. White (195) has related the stria terminalis pathway to suppression
of feeding by eliminating amygdalar elicited suppression of food intake
with stria terminalis knife cuts or ventromedial hypothalamic lesions.

Neurophysiological or neuroanatomical evidence for a direct lateral to
medial hypothalamic pathway is lacking (193). Therefore lateral, or at least
far-lateral, hypothalamic inhibition of its neighbor perhaps must travel by
way of the amygdala. Such a path might carry rebound inhibition of feeding after lateral hypothalamic stimulation (196). A pathway directly from
the medial to lateral hypothalamus has been seen histologically (35, 197).

Fonberg (198) reviews stimulation and lesion studies of the amygdala
including new results with dogs. Lesions of the dorsomedial amygdala produced effects like lateral hypothalamic lesions, and medial amygdala lesions
matched ventromedial hypothalamic lesions. Changes in food preferences
after orbitofrontal lesions in monkeys were similar to changes after amygdala lesions (199).

The hippocampus, septal region, and hypothalamus.—The dorsolateral
hippocampus is another site where stimulation elicits feeding, but the eating
is very different from that during stimulation of the lateral hypothalamus or
amygdala. Hippocampal eating occurs exclusively on the rebound immediately after the current goes off (200). The same site yields self-stimulation.
Milgram (200) has hypothesized that the hippocampus inhibits lateral hypothalamic activity and that rebound excitation of the lateral hypothalamic
system accounts for rebound eating. In recent observations supporting this
view, hypothalamic lesions which produced temporary aphagia also temporarily eliminated hippocampal induced feeding and self-stimulation (Server,
Milgram & Hoebel, unpublished). This implies that the reward for hippocampal self-stimulation may also be a poststimulation, rebound phenomenon.

Keesey & Powley (201) disinhibited hypothalamic self-stimulation with
septal lesions. Perhaps they were interrupting a pathway from the hippocampus. This and older suggestions of hippocampal-septal-hypothalamic
pathways are reviewed. Most of the literature on the septal area associates

it with drinking. Two separable septal systems may mediate acceptance and rejection of palatable and unpalatable fluids (202). Lorens & Kondo (203) describe septal lesioned rats which bar pressed for unusual amounts of food, but ate normal quantities ad libitum. This could mean some interplay between the septal region and the medial hypothalamic operant-inhibitory mechanism of Margules & Stein (171). Cuts thought to interrupt the corticohypothalamic tract prevented hippocampal induced increases in ventromedial multiunit activity (204).

Milgram (205) reported hippocampal rebound eating would not shift to drinking, even though he tried all of the tricks which have been successful in shifting feeding elicited from the lateral hypothalamus. He suggests that whatever it is about lateral hypothalamic organization that produces the shifts from one elicited behavior to more than one, it appears to be lacking in hippocampal organization. One intriguing possibility is that the hippocampus acts to inhibit the hypothalamic feeding system specifically, so that the rebound effect reflects an increase in activity solely in a specific feeding system. In other words, hippocampal stimulation may be a way of influencing hypothalamic feeding fibers without influencing drinking fibers, whereas an electrode in the lateral hypothalamus stimulates both because the systems are so close together there. Milgram reviews evidence suggesting that hippocampal feeding neurons are in the dorsolateral region, whereas drinking is located more dorsomedially. If correct, this anatomical separation of feeding and drinking systems should prove very useful in the future.

If the hippocampus inhibits feeding as indicated by rebound feeding, then lesions should disinhibit feeding. Grossman (206) compiles studies which indicate that this is the case. Hippocampal hyperphagia and obesity, however, seem to disappear with time.

Komisaruk (207) cites studies of the hippocampal theta rhythm and its possible relationship to learning, arousal, motivation and memory. He has an intriguing theory. He notes that sniffing, vibrissa twitching, chewing, licking, grooming, heart beat, theta rhythm, and hippocampal multiunit firing are at times synchronized, which suggests a single limbic pacemaker for stereotyped motor movements. Perhaps the rhythmic hippocampal output goes to the hypothalamus where it is channeled by interoceptive and exteroceptive signals into the homeostatically appropriate behavior sequence, such as feeding (207).

Frontal cortex, midbrain, and peripheral input.—Campbell & Lynch (188) have traced a behavioral arousal system from the reticular formation to the frontal cortex and back. In parallel with known neurophysiological effects, they propose that the reticular activation of behavior is suppressed by negative feedback from the frontal cortex. As evidence, food deprivation or systemic amphetamine produced increases in wheel running or stabilime-

ter activity that were magnified beyond all normal bounds for about a
month after surgical interruption of cortical suppression (208). The same
ablation impaired bar pressing for food during deprivation. Thus, while cortical ablation unbridles reactivity to reticular stimulants, it also depresses
the urge to eat. This suggested to the authors that hunger and amphetamine
might have their arousal effect in common through an action on the reticular formation, but influence food intake by a separate action. Sterman (209)
suggests on the basis of EEG observations that feeding may be one of a
variety of behaviors that succumbs to drowsiness after a meal. Although
this is probably true, it should not be taken to imply that satiety and drowsiness are mediated by the same underlying system as shown by the disassoci-
ation of feeding and reactivity in Campbell & Lynch's study.

Lynch (210) has disassociated two motor activity systems: one for the
arousal system mentioned earlier projecting diffusely from the frontal cortex caudally via the thalamus, and another controlling wheel-running behavior that courses downward through the medial forebrain bundle to the
hypothalamus and midbrain. Evidence is cited that the running system is
particularly sensitive to internal variables such as those which control feeding and thus may participate in locomotion dictated by homeostatic needs.

Peripheral inputs are treated in a forthcoming volume (211). Scott (73)
has demonstrated that olfactory stimuli can activate single units in the lateral hypothalamus. This was confirmed recently by Miller, Mogenson &
Stavraky (75) who report that olfactory or septal stimulation increased
some hypothalamic units and decreased others, whereas sciatic nerve stimulation only excited hypothalamic neurons. These authors are developing a
theory that septal influence over integrative neurons in the lateral hypothalamus depends on the baseline state of these neurons as determined by peripheral input. It has been suggested that the globus pallidus plays a motor
inhibitory role in a similar sensory gating scheme mediated through fibers
descending to the lateral hypothalamus and midbrain (212).

The ventromedial hypothalamus also projects to the mesencephalon, apparently via the bundle of Schutz (213). The many influences descending to
the midbrain are reflected in lesion studies showing aphagia (214) and hyperphagia (215, 216) following mesencephalic damage. Small lesions at
self-stimulation sites in the midbrain caused degeneration which Routtenberg (217) traced into the extrapyramidal system near the red nucleus.

Neural recordings from the midbrain identified single-unit responses
correlated with specific behavioral repertoires (218). Phillips (219) found
neurons which discriminated between three different tones that signaled
forthcoming food, water, or neither. If the animal was food deprived then
the neuron's anticipatory response to food was enhanced. Olds, Mink &
Best (220) chart a number of limbic areas where single units show an increase, a decrease, or both during anticipation of reward. Changes in firing

rate were largest in the hippocampus (221). Such observations led Olds (107) to speculate that the medial forebrain bundle carries integrated information about rewarding events forward to the neuronal grids of the hippocampus where it is temporarily stored as a memory of behavior associated with reinforcement. Perhaps this relates to the way that behavior and other sources of stimulation associated with the rewards or aversiveness of food are registered in short-term memory to call out a trace of the reward or aversion when similar situations occur in the future.

LITERATURE CITED

1. Code, C. F., Ed. 1967. Control of food and water intake. *Handbook of Physiology*, Sec. 6, *Alimentary Canal*, Vol. 1. Washington, D.C: Am. Physiol. Soc.

2. Morgane, P. J., Ed. 1969. Neural regulation of food and water intake. *Ann. N.Y. Acad. Sci.* 157: Art. 2, 531–1216

3. Stevenson, J. A. F. 1969. Neural control of food and water intake. *The Hypothalamus*, ed. W. Haymaker, E. Anderson, W. J. H. Nauta, 524–621. Springfield, Ill: Thomas. 805 pp.

4. Mayer, J., Thomas, D. W. 1967. Regulation of food intake and obesity. *Science* 156:328–37

5. Morgane, P. J., Jacobs, H. L. 1969. Hunger and satiety. *World Rev. Nutr. Dietet.* 10:100–213

6. Grossman, S. P. 1968. Hypothalamic and limbic influences on food intake. *Fed. Proc.* 27:1349–60

7. Teitelbaum, P. 1967. The biology of drive. *The Neurosciences, A Study Program*, ed. G. C. Quarton, T. Melnichuk, F. O. Schmitt, 557–66. New York: Rockefeller Univ. Press. 962 pp.

8. Finger, F. W., Mook, D. G. 1970. Basic drives. *Ann. Rev. Psychol.* In press

9. Epstein, A. N. 1971. The lateral hypothalamic syndrome: its implications for the physiological psychology of hunger and thirst. *Progr. Physiol. Psychol.* In press

10. Le Magnen, J. 1971. Advances in studies on the physiological control and regulation of food intake. *Progr. Physiol. Psychol.* In press

11. Killeffer, F. A., Stern, W. E. 1970. Chronic effects of hypothalamic injury—report of a case of near total hypothalamic destruction resulting from removal of a craniopharyngioma. *Arch. Neurol.* 22: 419–29

12. Reeves, A. G., Plum, F. 1969. Hyperphagia, rage and dementia accompanying a ventromedial hypothalamic neoplasm. *Arch. Neurol.* 20: 616–24

13. Hoebel, B. G., Teitelbaum, P. 1966. Weight regulation in normal and hypothalamic hyperphagic rats. *J. Comp. Physiol. Psychol.* 61:189–93

14. Han, P. W. 1968. Energy metabolism of tube-fed hypophysectomized rats bearing hypothalamic lesions. *Am. J. Physiol.* 215:1343–50

15. Reynolds, R. W. 1965. An irritative hypothesis concerning the hypothalamic regulation of food intake. *Psychol. Rev.* 72:105–16

16. Rabin, B. M., Smith, C. J. 1968. Behavioral comparison of the effectiveness of irritative and non-irritative lesions in producing hypothalamic hyperphagia. *Physiol. Behav.* 3:417–20

17. Hoebel, B. G. 1969. Feeding and self-stimulation. *Ann. N.Y. Acad. Sci.* 157:Art. 2, 758–77

18. Herrero, S. 1969. Radio-frequency-current and direct-current lesions in the ventromedial hypothalamus. *Am. J. Physiol.* 217:403–10

19. Stevenson, J. A. F. 1969. Mechanisms in the control of food and water intake. *Ann. N.Y. Acad. Sci.* 157: Art. 2, 1069–83

20. Dahl, E., Ursin, H. 1969. Obesity produced by iron and tissue destruction in the ventromedial hypothalamus. *Physiol. Behav.* 4:315–17

21. Reynolds, R. W., Simpson, C. W. 1969. Chronic infusion studies on the hypothalamic regulation of food intake. *Ann. N.Y. Acad. Sci.* 157:Art. 2, 755–57

22. Cox, V. C., Kakolewski, J. W., Valenstein, E. S. 1969. Ventromedial hypothalamic lesions and changes in body weight and food consumption in male and female rats. *J. Comp. Physiol. Psychol.* 67:320–26

23. Balagura, S., Devenport, L. D. 1970. Feeding patterns of normal and ventromedial hypothalamic lesioned male and female rats. *J. Comp. Physiol. Psychol.* 71:357–64

24. Wade, G. N., Zucker, I. 1970. Development of hormonal control over food intake and body weight in female rats. *J. Comp. Physiol. Psychol.* 70:213–20

25. Pfaff, D. W. 1969. Sex differences in food intake changes following pituitary growth hormone or pro-

lactin injections. *Proc. 77th Ann. Conv. Am. Psychol. Assoc.*, 211–12

26. O'Brien, C. P., Bach, L. M. N. 1970. Observations concerning hypothalamic control of growth. *Am. J. Physiol.* 218:226–30

27. Critchlow, V. et al 1970. Obesity and increased growth following isolation of medial-basal hypothalamus. *Fed. Proc.* 29:377

28. Gold, R. M. 1970. Hypothalamic hyperphagia: males get just as fat as females. *J. Comp. Physiol. Psychol.* 71:347–56

29. Carlisle, H. J., Stellar, E. 1969. Caloric regulation and food preference in normal hyperphagic and aphagic rats. *J. Comp. Physiol. Psychol.* 69:107–14

30. Sclafani, A., Grossman, S. P. 1969. Hyperphagia produced by knife cuts between the medial and lateral hypothalamus in the rat. *Physiol. Behav.* 4:533–37

31. Albert, D. J., Storlien, L. H. 1969. Hyperphagia in rats with cuts between the ventromedial and lateral hypothalamus. *Science* 165:599–600

32. Gold, R. M. 1970. Hypothalamic hyperphagia produced by parasagittal knife cuts. *Physiol. Behav.* 5:23–25

33. Ellison, G. D. 1968. Appetite behavior in rats after circumsection of the hypothalamus. *Physiol. Behav.* 3:221–26

34. de Ruiter, L. 1969. Ethological and neurological aspects of the regulation of food intake. *Ann. N.Y. Acad. Sci.* 157:Art. 2, 1204–14

35. Mayer, J., Arees, E. A. 1968. Ventromedial glucoreceptor system. *Fed. Proc.* 27:1345–48

36. Arees, E. A., Mayer, J. 1970. Electron miscropic study of goldthioglucose (GTG)-induced lesions in hypothalamus. *Fed. Proc.* 29:290

37. Debons, A. F., Krimsky, I., From, A., Cloutier, R. J. 1969. Rapid effects of insulin on the hypothalamic satiety center. *Am. J. Physiol.* 217:1114–18

38. Baile, C. A., Herrera, M. G., Mayer, J. 1970. Ventromedial hypothalamus and hyperphagia in hyperglycemic obese mice. *Am. J. Physiol.* 218:857–63

39. Pfaff, D. W. 1969. Histological differences between ventromedial hypothalamic neurons of well fed and underfed rats. *Nature* 223:77–78

40. Teitelbaum, P. 1969. Stages of recovery and development of lateral hypothalamic control of food and water intake. *Ann. N.Y. Acad. Sci.* 157:Art. 2, 849–60

41. Kissileff, H. R., Epstein, A. N. 1969. Exaggerated prandial drinking in "recovered lateral" rat without saliva. *J. Comp. Physiol. Psychol.* 67:301–8

42. Fitzsimons, J. T., Le Magnen, J. 1969. Eating as a regulatory control of drinking in the rat. *J. Comp. Physiol. Psychol.* 67:273–83

43. Kissileff, H. R. 1969. Oropharyngeal control of prandial drinking. *J. Comp. Physiol. Psychol.* 67:309–19

44. Epstein, A. N., Teitelbaum, P. 1967. Specific loss of the hypoglycemic control of feeding in recovered lateral rats. *Am. J. Physiol.* 213:1159–67

45. Smith, G. P., Epstein, A. N. 1969. Increased feeding in response to decreased glucose utilization in the rat and monkey. *Am. J. Physiol.* 217:1083–87

46. Colin-Jones, D. G., Himsworth, R. L. 1970. The location of the chemoreceptor controlling gastric acid secretion during hypoglycaemia. *J. Physiol. London* 206:397–409

47. Smith, G. P., Root, A. W. 1969. Effect of feeding on hormonal responses to 2-deoxy-D-glucose in conscious monkeys. *Endocrinology* 85:963–66

48. Desiraju, T., Banerjee, M. G., Anand, B. K. 1968. Activity of single neurons in the hypothalamic feeding centers: effect of 2-deoxy-D-glucose. *Physiol. Behav.* 3:757–60

49. Le Magnen, J. 1969. Peripheral and systemic actions of food in the caloric regulation of intake. *Ann. N.Y. Acad. Sci.* 157:Art. 2, 1126–57

50. Steffens, A. B. 1969. The influence of insulin injections and infusions on eating and blood glucose level in the rat. *Physiol. Behav.* 4:823–28

51. Brown, K. A., Melzack, R. 1969. Effects of glucose on multi-unit activity in the hypothalamus. *Exp. Neurol.* 24:363–73

52. Oomura, Y., Ono, T., Ooyama, H., Wayner, M. J. 1969. Glucose and osmosensitive neurons of the rat hypothalamus. *Nature* 222 :282–84

53. Yin, T. H., Hamilton, C. L., Brobeck, J. R. 1970. Food intake of rats given hypertonic solutions by gavage and water intravenously. *Proc. Soc. Exp. Biol. Med.* 133 : 83–85

54. Rodriquez-Zendejas, A. M., Vega, C., Soto-Mora, L. M., Russek, M. 1968. Some effects of intraperitoneal glucose and of intraportal glucose and adrenaline. *Physiol. Behav.* 3 :259–64

55. Niijima, A. 1969. Afferent impulse discharges from glucoreceptors in the liver of the guinea pig. *Ann. N.Y. Acad. Sci.* 157 :Art. 2, 690–700

56. Penaloza-Rojas, J. H., Mera, B. B., Garfias, C. K. 1968. The effect of vagal stimulation on food intake. *Proc. Int. Union Physiol. Sci.* 7 : 342

57. Rozin, P. 1968. Are carbohydrates and protein intakes separately regulated? *J. Comp. Physiol. Psychol.* 65 :23–29

58. Morrison, S. D. 1968. The relationship of energy expenditure and spontaneous activity to the aphagia of rats with lesions in the lateral hypothalamus. *J. Physiol. London* 197 :325–42

59. Balagura, S., Wilcox, R. H., Coscina, D. V. 1969. The effect of diencephalic lesions on food intake and motor activity. *Physiol. Behav.* 4 : 629–33

60. Powley, T. L., Keesey, R. E. 1970. Relationship of body weight to the lateral hypothalamic feeding syndrome. *J. Comp. Physiol. Psychol.* 70 :25–36

61. Hervey, G. R. 1969. Regulation of energy balance. *Nature* 222 :629–31

62. Collier, G. 1969. Body weight loss as a measure of motivation in hunger and thirst. *Ann. N.Y. Acad. Sci.* 157 :Art. 2, 594–609

63. Steffens, A. B. 1969. Blood glucose and FFA levels in relation to the meal pattern in the normal rat and the ventromedial hypothalamic lesioned rat. *Physiol. Behav.* 4 : 215–25

64. Grossman, S. P. 1968. Hypothalamic and limbic influences on food intake. *Fed. Proc.* 27 :1349–60

65. Spector, N. H., Brobeck, J. R., Hamilton, C. L. 1968. Feeding and core temperature in albino rats : changes induced by preoptic heating and cooling. *Science* 161 : 286–88

66. Traylor, R. A., Blackburn, J. G. 1969. Effects of temperature on the electrical activity of the hypothalamic feeding centers. *Exp. Neurol.* 23 : 91–101

67. Lipton, J. M. 1969. Effects of high fat diets on caloric intake, body weight, and heat-escape responses in normal and hyperphagic rats. *J. Comp. Physiol. Psychol.* 68 :507–15

68. Ellison, G., Flynn, J. P. 1968. Organized aggressive behavior in cats after surgical isolation of the hypothalamus. *Arch. Ital. Biol.* 106 :1–20

69. Ellison, G. D., Sorenson, C. A., Jacobs, B. L. 1970. Two feeding syndromes following surgical isolation of the hypothalamus in rats. *J. Comp. Physiol. Psychol.* 70 :173–88

70. Snowdon, C. T. 1970. Gastrointestinal sensory and motor control of food intake. *J. Comp. Physiol. Psychol.* 71 :68–76

71. Nicolaïdis, S. 1969. Early systemic responses to orogastric stimulation in the regulation of food and water balance : functional and electrophysiological data. *Ann. N.Y. Acad. Sci.* 157 :Art. 2, 1176–200

72. Wyrwicka, W. 1969. Sensory regulation of food intake. *Physiol. Behav.* 4 :853–58

73. Scott, J. W. 1970. Characteristics of responses of lateral hypothalamic neurons to olfactory stimulation in rat. *Anat. Rec.* 166 :375

74. Campbell, J. F., Bindra, D., Krebs, H., Ferenchak, R. P. 1969. Responses of single units of the hypothalamic ventromedial nucleus to environmental stimuli. *Physiol. Behav.* 4 :183–87

75. Miller, J. J., Mogenson, G. J., Stavraky, G. W. 1970. Effects of stimulation of the septum, sciatic nerve, and olfactory bulb on lateral hypothalamic neurons. *Fed. Proc.* 29 :837

76. Mook, D. G. 1969. Some determinants

of preference and aversion in the rat. *Ann. N.Y. Acad. Sci.* 157: Art. 2, 1158–75

77. Jordan, H. A. 1969. Voluntary intragastric feeding: oral and gastric contributions to food intake and hunger in man. *J. Comp. Physiol. Psychol.* 68:498–506

78. Quartermain, D., Wolf, G., Keselica, J. 1969. Relation between medial hypothalamic damage and impairments in regulation of sodium. *Physiol. Behav.* 4:101–4

79. Wade, G. N., Zucker, I. 1970. Hormonal modulation of responsiveness to an aversive taste stimulus in rats. *Physiol. Behav.* 5:269–73

80. Wade, G. N., Zucker, I. 1970. Modulation of food intake and locomotor activity in female rats by diencephalic hormone implants. *J. Comp. Physiol. Psychol.* 72:328–36

81. Rozin, P. 1969. Central or peripheral mediation of learning with long CS-US intervals in the feeding system. *J. Comp. Physiol. Psychol.* 67:421–29

82. Roth, S. R., Teitelbaum, P., Schwartz, M. 1969. *Absence of learned poison aversion in recovered lateral hypothalamic rats.* Presented at Psychon. Soc. Meet.

83. Wampler, R. S., Shulman, E., Machinton, S. 1970. *Regulatory deficits in rats following unilateral lesions of the lateral hypothalamus.* Presented at Eastern Psychol. Assoc. Meet.

84. Di Cara, L. U. 1970. Role of postoperative feeding experience in recovery from lateral hypothalamic damage. *J. Comp. Physiol. Psychol.* 72:60–65

85. Rozin, P. 1969. Adaptive food sampling patterns in vitamin deficient rats. *J. Comp. Physiol. Psychol.* 69:126–32

86. Mook, D. G., Blass, E. M. 1970. Specific hungers in hyperphagic rats. *Psychon. Sci.* 19:34–35

87. Teitelbaum, P., Cheng, M.-F., Rozin, P. 1969. Development of feeding parallels its recovery after hypothalamic damage. *J. Comp. Physiol. Psychol.* 67:430–41

88. Rosner, B. S. 1970. Brain functions. *Ann. Rev. Psychol.* 21:555–94

89. Pfaffmann, C. 1969. Taste preference and reinforcement. *Reinforcement and Behavior,* ed. J. T. Tapp, 215–41. New York and London: Academic. 429 pp.

90. Snowdon, C. T. 1969. Motivation and the control of meal parameters with oral and intragastric feeding. *J. Comp. Physiol. Psychol.* 69:91–100

91. Hoebel, B. G., Thompson, R. D. 1969. Aversion to lateral hypothalamic stimulation caused by intragastric feeding or obesity. *J. Comp. Physiol. Psychol.* 68:536–43

92. Caggiula, A. R. 1970. Analysis of the copulation-reward properties of posterior hypothalamic stimulation in male rats. *J. Comp. Physiol. Psychol.* 70:399–412

93. Mogenson, G. J. 1969. General and specific reinforcement systems for drinking behavior. *Ann. N.Y. Acad. Sci.* 157:Art. 2, 779–93

94. Mogenson, G. J., Kaplinski, M. 1970. Brain self-stimulation and mechanisms of reinforcement. *Learn. Motivat.* 1:186–98

95. Ball, G. G. 1969. Separation of electrical self-stimulation and electrically elicited eating in the hypothalamus. *Commun. Behav. Biol.* 3, 5–10

96. Coons, E. E., Cruce, J. A. F. 1968. Lateral hypothalamus: food current intensity in maintaining self-stimulation. *Science,* 159, 1117–1119

97. Phillips, A. G. 1969. *Facilitation of olfactory bulb self-stimulation by odour.* Presented at Eastern Psychol. Assoc. Meet.

98. Mendelson, J. 1970. Self-induced drinking in rats: the qualitative identity of drive and reward systems in the lateral hypothalamus. *Physiol. Behav.* 5:925–30

99. Hoebel, B. G. 1969. *Taste and hypothalamic reinforcement.* Presented at Psychon. Soc. Meet.

100. Mendelson, J. 1969. Lateral hypothalamic stimulation: inhibition of aversive effects by feeding, drinking, and gnawing. *Science* 166: 1431–33

101. Bindra, D. 1968. Neuropsychological interpretations of the effects of drive and incentive-motivation on general activity and instrumental behavior. *Psychol. Rev.* 75:1–22

102. Valenstein, E. S., Ed. 1968. Biology of drives. *Neurosci. Res. Progr. Bull.* 6:1–111

103. Campbell, B. A., Misanin, J. R. 1969.

Basic drives. *Ann. Rev. Psychol.* 20 :57–84

104. Trowill, J. A., Panksepp, J., Gandelman, R. 1969. An incentive model of rewarding brain stimulation. *Psychol. Rev.* 76 :264–81

105. Appley, M. H. 1970. Derived motives. *Ann. Rev. Psychol.* 21 :485–518

106. Oatley, K. 1970. Brain mechanisms and motivation. *Nature* 225 :797–801

107. Olds, J. 1969. Central nervous system and the reinforcement of behavior. *Am. Psychol.* 24 :114–32

108. Kent, E., Grossman, S. P. 1969. Evidence for a conflict interpretation of anomalous effects of rewarding brain stimulation. *J. Comp. Physiol. Psychol.* 69 :381–90

109. Gallistel, C. R. 1969. Self-stimulation : failure of pretrial stimulation to affect rats' electrode preference. *J. Comp. Physiol. Psychol.* 69 :722–29

110. Ferguson, N. B. L., Keesey, R. E. Comparison of ventromedial hypothalamic lesion effects upon feeding and lateral hypothalamic self-stimulation in the female rat. In press

111. Hoebel, B. G. 1969. *Hypothalamic and sensory control of hypothalamic aversion.* Presented at 3rd Int. Conf. Regulation of Food and Water Intake

112. Valenstein, E. S., Cox, V. C., Kakolewski, J. W. 1968. Modification of motivated behavior elicited by electrical stimulation of the hypothalamus. *Science* 159 : 1119–21

113. Hess, W. R. 1957. *Functional Organization of the Diencephalon,* ed. J. R. Hughes. New York : Grune & Stratton. 180 pp.

114. Valenstein, E. S., Cox, V. C., Kakolewski, J. W. 1970. Reexamination of the role of the hypothalamus in motivation. *Psychol. Rev.* 77 :16–31

115. Wise, R. A. 1968. Hypothalamic motivational systems : fixed or plastic neural circuits ? *Science* 62 : 377–79

116. Valenstein, E. S., Cox, V. C., Kakolewski, J. W. 1969. The hypothalamus and motivated behavior. *Reinforcement and Behavior,* ed. J. T. Tapp, 242–87. New York and London : Academic. 429 pp.

117. Milgram, N. W., Devor, M., Server, A. C. 1971. Spontaneous changes in behaviors induced by electrical stimulation of the lateral hypothalamus in rats. *J. Comp. Physiol. Psychol.* In press

118. Tenen, S. S., Miller, N. E. 1964. Strength of electrical stimulation of lateral hypothalamus, food deprivation, and tolerance for quinine in food. *J. Comp. Physiol. Psychol.* 58 :55–62

119. Perera, T. B., Glusman, M. 1968. Conditioned suppression and reinforcement of eating induced by hypothalamic stimulation. *J. Comp. Physiol. Psychol.* 66 :185–88

120. Steinbaum, E. A., Miller, N. E. 1965. Obesity from eating elicited by daily stimulation of hypothalamus. *Am. J. Physiol.* 208 :1–5

121. Mogenson, G. J., Stevenson, J. A. F. 1967. Drinking induced by electrical stimulation of the lateral hypothalamus. *Exp. Neurol.* 17 :119–27

122. Devor, M., Wise, R. A., Milgram, N. W., Hoebel, B. G. 1970. Physiological control of hypothalamically elicited feeding and drinking. *J. Comp. Physiol. Psychol.* 73 :226–32

123. Valenstein, E. S., Cox, V. C. 1970. Influence of hunger, thirst, and previous experience in the test chamber on stimulus-bound eating and drinking. *J. Comp. Physiol. Psychol.* 70 :189–99

124. Fisher, A. 1970. *Behavioral and anatomical specificity of the effects of drug injection into the limbic system and hypothalamus.* Presented at Winter Conf. Brain Res.

125. Roberts, W. W., Steinberg, M. L., Means, L. W. 1967. Hypothalamic mechanisms for sexual, aggressive, and other motivational behaviors in the opossum, *Didelphis virginiana. J. Comp. Physiol. Psychol.* 64 :1–15

126. Hutchinson, R. R., Renfrew, J. W. 1966. Stalking attack and eating behaviors elicited from the same sites in the hypothalamus. *J. Comp. Physiol. Psychol.* 61 :360–67

127. Vanegas, H., Seigel, A. Q., Chi, C. C., Flynn, J. P. 1969. Hypothalamic stimulation in cat—aggressive vs. alimentary behavior. *Acta Cient. Venez.* 20 :127

128. Bergquist, E. H. 1970. Output path-

ways of hypothalamic mechanisms for sexual, aggressive and other motivated behaviors in opossum. *J. Comp. Physiol. Psychol.* 70: 389–98

129. King, M. B., Hoebel, B. G. 1968. Killing elicited by brain stimulation in rats. *Commun. Behav. Biol. A* 2:173–77

130. Vergnes, M., Karli, P. 1969. Effets de la stimulation de l'hypothalamus latéral, de l'amygdale et de l'hippocampe sur le comportement d'agression interspecifique rat-souris. *Physiol. Behav.* 4:889–94

131. Phillips, A. G., Cox, V. C., Kakolewski, J. W., Valenstein, E. S. 1969. Object-carrying by rats: an approach to the behavior produced by brain stimulation. *Science* 166: 903–5

132. Roberts, W. W., Carey, J. R. 1965. Rewarding effect of performance of gnawing aroused by hypothalamic stimulation in the rat. *J. Comp. Physiol. Psychol.* 59:317–24

133. Herberg, L. J., Blundell, J. E. 1967. Lateral hypothalamus—hoarding behavior elicited by electrical stimulation. *Science* 155:349–50

134. Rosenquist, A. R., Hoebel, B. G. 1968. Wheel running elicited by electrical stimulation of the brain. *Physiol. Behav.* 3:563–66

135. MacDonnell, M. F., Flynn, J. P. 1966. Control of sensory fields by stimulation of hypothalamus. *Science* 152:1406–8

136. Glickman, S. E., Schiff, B. B. 1967. A biological theory of reinforcement. *Psychol. Rev.* 74:81–109

137. White, S. D., Wayner, M. J., Cott, A. 1970. Effects of intensity, water deprivation, prior water injection and palatability on drinking evoked by lateral hypothalamic electric stimulation. *Physiol. Behav.* 5:611–19

138. Grossman, S. P. 1969. A neuropharmacological analysis of hypothalamic and extrahypothalamic mechanisms concerned with the regulation of food and water intake. *Ann. N.Y. Acad. Sci.* 157: Art. 2, 902–17

139. Fisher, A. E. 1969. The role of limbic structures in the central regulation of feeding and drinking behavior. *Ann. N.Y. Acad. Sci.* 157:Art. 2, 894–901

140. Soulairac, A. 1969. The adrenergic and cholinergic control of food and water intake. *Ann. N.Y. Acad. Sci.* 157:Art. 2, 934–61

141. Myers, R. D. 1969. Chemical mechanisms in the hypothalamus mediating eating and drinking in the monkey. *Ann. N.Y. Acad. Sci.* 157:Art. 2, 918–31

142. Montgomery, R. B., Singer, G., Purcell, A. T., Narbeth, J., Bolt, A. G. 1969. Central control of hunger in the rat. *Nature* 223:1278–79

143. Leibowitz, S. 1970. A hypothalamic beta-adrenergic "satiety" system antagonizes an alpha-adrenergic "hunger" system in the rat. *Nature* 226:963–64

144. Leibowitz, S. 1970. Reciprocal hunger-regulating circuits involving α- and β-receptors located respectively in the ventromedial and lateral hypothalamus. *Proc. Nat. Acad. Sci.* 67:1063–70

145. Margules, D. L. 1969. Noradrenergic synapses for the suppression of feeding behavior. *Life Sci.* 8:693–704

146. Margules, D. L. 1970. Alpha- and beta-adrenergic receptors in perifornical hypothalamus for the suppression of feeding behavior by satiety and taste. *Fed. Proc.* 29: 485

147. Margules, D. L. 1970. Alpha-adrenergic receptors in hypothalamus for the suppression of feeding behavior by satiety. *J. Comp. Physiol. Psychol.* 73:1–12

148. Margules, D. L. 1970. Beta-adrenergic receptors in hypothalamus for learned and unlearned taste-aversions. *J. Comp. Physiol. Psychol.* 73:13–21

149. Goodman, L. S., Gilman, A., Eds. 1965. *The Pharmacological Basis of Therapeutics,* 478–86. New York: Macmillan. 3rd ed. 1785 pp.

150. Slangen, J. L., Miller, N. E. 1969. Pharmacological tests for the function of hypothalamic norepinephrine in eating behavior. *Physiol. Behav.* 4:543–52

151. Booth, D. A. 1968. Mechanism of action of norepinephrine in eliciting an eating response on injection into the rat hypothalamus. *J. Pharmacol. Exp. Therap.* 160: 336–48

152. Jacobs, H. L., Sharma, K. N. 1969.

Taste versus calories: sensory and metabolic signals in the control of food intake. *Ann. N.Y. Acad. Sci.* 157:Art. 2, 1084–111

153. Leibowitz, S. 1970. Amphetamine's anorexic versus hunger-inducing effects mediated respectively by hypothalamic beta- versus alpha-adrenergic receptors. *Proc. 78th Ann. Conv. Am. Psychol. Assoc.* 813–14

154. Coons, E. E., Quartermain, D. 1970. Motivational depression associated with norepinephrine-induced eating from the hypothalamus: resemblance to the ventromedial hyperphagic syndrome. *Physiol. Behav.* 5:687–92

155. Booth, D. A., Quartermain, D. 1965. Taste sensitivity of eating elicited by chemical stimulation of rat hypothalamus. *Psychon. Sci.* 3:525–26

156. Oomura, Y., Ooyama, H., Tamamoto, T., Ono, T., Kobayashi, N. 1969. Behavior of hypothalamic unit activity during electrophoretic application of drugs. *Ann. N.Y. Acad. Sci.* 157:Art. 2, 642–65

157. Taylor, K. M., Snyder, S. H. 1970. Amphetamine: differentiation by *d* and *l* isomers of behavior involving brain norepinephrine or dopamine. *Science* 168:1487–89

158. Halboth, P. H. 1969. Temporal summation of hypothalamically-elicited eating: a behavioral measure of synaptic facilitation assessed by drugs. *Sci. Eng.* 30:405

159. Smith, D. E. 1969. *Running controlled with lateral hypothalamic injections of cholinergic drugs.* Presented at Psychon. Soc. Meet.

160. Myers, R. D., Yakshi, T. L. 1968. Feeding and temperature responses in the unrestrained rat after injections of cholinergic and aminergic substances into the cerebral ventricles. *Physiol. Behav.* 3:917–28

161. Antunes-Rodriques, J., McCann, S. M. 1970. Water, sodium chloride, and food intake induced by injections of cholinergic and adrenergic drugs into third ventricle of rat brain. *Proc. Soc. Exp. Biol. Med.* 133:1464–70

162. Myers, R. D., Sharpe, L. G. 1968. Chemical activation of ingestive and other hypothalamic regulatory mechanisms. *Physiol. Behav.* 3:987–95

163. Myers, R. D. 1969. Chemical mechanisms in the hypothalamus mediating eating and drinking in the monkey. *Ann. N.Y. Acad. Sci.* 157:Art. 2, 918–33

164. Stein, L. 1969. Chemistry of purposive behavior. *Reinforcement and Behavior,* ed. J. T. Tapp, 329–52. New York and London: Academic. 429 pp.

165. Hutchinson, R. R., Renfrew, J. W. 1967. Modification of eating and drinking—interactions between chemical agent, deprivation state, and site of stimulation. *J. Comp. Physiol. Psychol.* 63:408–16

166. Routtenberg, A. 1967. Drinking induced by carbachol: thirst circuit or ventricular modification? *Science* 157:838–39

167. Routtenberg, A., Bondareff, W. 1969. Reply to Montgomery, R. B., Singer, G. Histochemical fluorescence as an index of spread of centrally applied neurochemicals. *Science* 165:1032

168. Grossman, S. P. 1969. Intracranial drug implants: an autoradiographic analysis. *Science* 166:1410–12

169. Stein, L., Wise, C. D. 1970. Mechanism of the facilitating effects of amphetamine on behavior. *Psychotomimetic Drugs,* ed. D. H. Efron, 123–49. New York: Raven

170. Stein, L., Wise, C. D. 1969. Release of norepinephrine from hypothalamus and amygdala by rewarding medial forebrain bundle stimulation and amphetamine. *J. Comp. Physiol. Psychol.* 67:189–98

171. Margules, D. L., Stein, L. 1969. Cholinergic synapses in the ventromedial hypothalamus for the suppression of operant behavior by punishment and satiety. *J. Comp. Physiol. Psychol.* 67:327–35

172. Carlton, P. 1969. Brain-acetylcholine and inhibition. *Reinforcement and Behavior,* ed. J. T. Tapp, 288–325. New York and London: Academic. 429 pp.

173. Olds, M. E., Domino, E. F. 1969. Comparison of muscarinic and nicotinic cholinergic agonists on self-stimulation behavior. *J. Pharmacol. Exp. Therap.* 166:189–204

174. Hill, R. T. Facilitation of conditioned reinforcement as a mechanism of psychomotor stimulation. *International Symposium on Amphetamines and Related Compounds,* ed. F.

Costa, S. Garattini. New York: Raven. In press

175. Grossman, S. P. 1966. The VMH: a center for affective reactions, satiety, or both? *Physiol. Behav.* 1:1–10

176. Mogenson, G. J. 1969. Effects of drugs on the preference between electrical stimulation of the lateral hypothalamus and water. *Psychon. Sci.* 17:13–14

177. Stark, P., Totty, C. W. 1967. Effects of amphetamines on eating elicited by hypothalamic stimulation. *J. Pharmacol. Exp. Therap.* 158: 272–78

178. Hoebel, B. G., Smith, D. E., Hendler, N. H. 1969. *Hypothalamic control of locomotor activity: evidence for adrenergic and cholinergic influences.* Presented at Am. Psychol. Assoc. meetings

179. Mogenson, G. J., Russek, M., Stevenson, J. A. F. 1969. The effect of adrenaline on bar-pressing for food and for self-stimulation. *Physiol. Behav.* 4:91–94

180. Foxwell, M. H., Funderburk, W. H., Ward, J. W. 1969. Studies on the site of action of a new anorectic agent, fenfluramine. *J. Pharmacol. Exp. Therap.* 165:60–70

181. Krebs, H., Bindra, D., Campbell, J. F. 1969. Effects of amphetamine on neuronal activity in the hypothalamus. *Physiol. Behav.* 4:685–91

182. Reiter, L. 1970. Effects of amphetamine on lateral hypothalamic activity in response to amygdaloid stimulation. *Fed. Proc.* 29:383

183. Grossman, S. P. 1968. The physiological basis of specific and nonspecific motivational processes. *Nebraska Symp. Motivation,* 1–46

184. Morgane, P. J. The function of the limbic and rhinic forebrain-limbic midbrain systems and reticular formation in the regulation of food and water intake. 1969. *Ann. N.Y. Acad. Sci.* 157:Art. 2, 806–48

185. Robinson, B. W., Mishkin, M. 1968. Alimentary responses to forebrain stimulation in monkeys. *Exp. Brain Res.* 4:330–66

186. Nauta, W. J. H., Haymaker, W. 1969. Hypothalamic nuclei and fiber connections. *The Hypothalamus,* ed. W. Haymaker, E. Anderson, W. J. H. Nauta, 136–209.

Springfield, Ill.: Thomas. 805 pp.

187. Singer, G., Montgomery, R. B. 1968. Neurohumoral interaction in the rat amygdala after central chemical stimulation. *Science* 160:1017–18

188. Campbell, B. A., Lynch, G. 1969. Cortical modulation of spontaneous activity during hunger and thirst. *J. Comp. Physiol. Psychol.* 67:15–22

189. Hebb, C. 1970. CNS at the cellular level: identity of transmitter agents. *Ann. Rev. Physiol.* 32: 165–92

190. Gloor, P., Murphy, J. T., Dreifuss, J. J. 1969. Electrophysiological studies of amygdalo-hypothalamic connections. *Ann. N.Y. Acad. Sci.* 157:Art. 2, 629–39

191. Sherwood, N. M. 1969. Relation of the amygdala and the hypothalamus during development and sexual maturation in the rat. *Sci. Eng.* 30:1338

192. Chi, C. C. 1970. Afferent connections to ventromedial nucleus of hypothalamus in rat. *Brain Res.* 17: 439–45

193. Murphy, J. T., Renaud, L. P. 1969. Mechanisms of inhibition in the ventromedial nucleus of the hypothalamus. *J. Neurophysiol.* 32:85–101

194. Heimer, L., Nauta, W. J. H. 1969. The hypothalamic distribution of the stria terminalis in the rat. *Brain Res.* 13:284–97

195. White, N. M. 1969. Relationship between amygdala and hypothalamus in the control of eating behavior. *Physiol. Behav.* 4:199–205

196. Cox, V. C., Kakolewski, J. W., Valenstein, E. S. 1969. Inhibition of eating and drinking following hypothalamic stimulation in the rat. *J. Comp. Physiol. Psychol.* 68:530–35

197. Sutin, J., Eager, R. P. 1969. Fiber degeneration following lesions in the hypothalamic ventromedial nucleus. *Ann. N.Y. Acad. Sci.* 157: Art. 2, 610–28

198. Fonberg, E. 1969. The role of the hypothalamus and amygdala in food intake, alimentary motivation and emotional reactions. *Acta Biol. Exp.* 29:335–58

199. Ursin, H., Rosvold, H. E., Vest, B. 1969. Food preferences in brain lesioned monkeys. *Physiol. Behav.* 4:609–12

200. Milgram, N. W. 1969. Effect of hippocampal stimulation on feeding in the rat. *Physiol. Behav.* 4 :665–70

201. Keesey, R. E., Powley, T. L. 1968. Enhanced lateral hypothalamic reward sensitivity following septal lesions in the rat. *Physiol. Behav.* 3 :557–62

202. Donovick, P. J., Burright, R. G., Zuromski, E. 1970. Localization of quinine aversion within the septum, habenula, and interpeduncular nucleus of the rat. *J. Comp. Physiol. Psychol.* 71 :376–83

203. Lorens, S. A., Kondo, C. Y. 1969. Effects of septal lesions on food and water intake and operant responding for food. *Physiol. Behav.* 4 :729–32

204. Johnson, J., Gallo, R. V., Kalra, S. P., Whitmoyer, D. I. 1970. Effect of electrochemical stimulation of ventral hippocampus (VHPC) on electrical activity in rat hypothalamus. *Anat. Rec.* 166 :325

205. Milgram, N. W. 1969. Motivational specificity of dorso-lateral hippocampal stimulation. *Commun. Behav. Biol.* 4 :1–5

206. Grossman, S. P. 1967. *A Textbook of Physiological Psychology*. New York: Wiley. 932 pp.

207. Komisaruk, B. R. 1970. Synchrony between limbic system theta activity and rhythmical behavior in rats. *J. Comp. Physiol. Psychol.* 70 :482–92

208. Lynch, G. S., Ballantine, P., Campbell, B. A. 1969. Potentiation of behavioral arousal after cortical damage and subsequent recovery. *Exp. Neurol.* 23 :195–206

209. Sterman, M. B. 1969. Electrophysiological correlates and neural substrates of alimentary behavior in the cat. *Ann. N.Y. Acad. Sci.* 157 : Art. 2, 723–39

210. Lynch, G. S. 1970. Separable forebrain systems controlling different manifestations of spontaneous activity. *J. Comp. Physiol. Psychol.* 70 :48–59

211. Pfaffmann, C., Ed. 1969. *Olfaction and Taste*: Proc. 3rd Int. Symp. New York: Rockefeller Univ. Press

212. Travis, R. P., Jr., Hooten, T. F., Sparks, D. L. 1968. Single unit activity related to behavior motivated by food reward. *Physiol. Behav.* 3 :309–18

213. Arees, E. A., Mayer, J. 1968. The bundle of Schutz and its relation to the regulation of food intake. *Experientia* 24 :1220–21

214. Blatt, B., Lyon, M. 1968. The interrelationship of forebrain and midbrain structures involved in feeding behavior. *Acta Neurol. Scand.* 44 :576–95

215. Randall, W., Lasko, V. 1968. Body weight and food intake rhythms and their relationship to the behavior of cats with brain stem lesions. *Psychon. Sci.* 11 :33–34

216. Skultety, F. M. 1969. Alterations of caloric intake in cats following lesions of the hypothalamus and midbrain. *Ann. N.Y. Acad. Sci.* 157 :Art. 2, 861–74

217. Routtenberg, A. 1969. Brainstem pathways of reward. *J. Comp. Physiol. Psychol.* 68 :22–30

218. Komisaruk, B. R., Olds, J. 1968. Neuronal correlates of behavior in freely moving rats. *Science* 161 : 810–13

219. Phillips, M. I. 1969. Unit activity : motivation-dependent responses from midbrain neurons. *Science* 165 :1269–71

220. Olds, J., Mink, W. D., Best, P. J. 1969. Single unit patterns during anticipatory behavior. *Electroencephalog. Clin. Neurophysiol.* 26 : 144–58

221. Olds, J., Hirano, T. 1969. Conditioned responses of hippocampal and other neurons. *Electroencephalog. Clin. Neurophysiol.* 26 :159–66

COMPARATIVE PHYSIOLOGY: GAS EXCHANGE AND CIRCULATION IN FISHES[1]

KJELL JOHANSEN[2]

Department of Zoology, University of Washington, Seattle, Washington

INTRODUCTION

Knowledge about the comparative physiology of respiratory and circulatory processes, particularly with reference to the vertebrate animal, has accumulated at an unprecedented rate during the last decade. The advancement of knowledge has sprung from physiological laboratories in zoology and biology departments, and involvement of physiologists in medical schools has progressively become important. This trend has placed cardiorespiratory physiology of invertebrates and lower vertebrates in proper context with general and mammalian physiology, and the resulting synthesis and integration of information have emphasized important common principles governing circulation and respiratory gas exchange.

The present review surveys gas exchange and circulation in fishes. Emphasis is on aquatic forms, but the special problems of transition to airbreathing are discussed in the context of airbreathing fishes.

Problems of gas exchange and internal gas transport in waterbreathing vertebrates have been analyzed in theory and presented graphically by Rahn and others (129, 170, 238, 260). The graphic representation of the exchange process in a Po_2-Pco_2 diagram was first introduced for fishes by Willmer (331) and was developed further and used by Rahn to set the limitations of aquatic gas exchange (238).

Recently, Jones et al (170) in a theoretical paper offered graphic representations relating the ventilation-perfusion ratio in fish to the level of arterial blood oxygen saturation. Assuming constant O_2 uptake, they described the determinants of the ventilation-perfusion ratio in terms of the O_2-Hb affinity of the blood, the O_2 content of blood and water passing to and from the exchange surfaces, and the average Po_2 gradient across the exchange surfaces. Their graphic representation aids in the prediction of adjustments to hypoxia and exercise.

On theoretical grounds Taylor et al (318) developed a computer model

---

[1] This review was written while the author was supported by NSF grant GB 1766 and NIH grant HE 12174.

[2] Established Investigator of The American Heart Association.

simulating some aspects of the cardiovascular and respiratory dynamics and feedback control mechanisms in a salmonid fish.

The quantification of aquatic gas exchange has progressed sufficiently to permit proper comparisons with aerial gas exchange and has stimulated interest in gas exchange and circulation in transitional bimodal breathers such as airbreathing fishes and amphibians. Several recent reviews concern phylogeny of vertebrate gas exchange, evolution of the lung, and the double circulation in a four-chambered heart (60, 114, 118, 147, 155, 161, 167, 190, 237, 260).

FUNCTIONAL ANATOMY OF GAS EXCHANGERS IN FISHES

The gross morphology of fish gills has been described by several authors (40–42, 85, 119, 124, 173, 207, 301, 302).

Variable data exist on gill surface area in fishes and the adaptability of surface area to ecological conditions and behavior. Gill surface area in a large number of marine teleosts showed that active fishes have a gill area per gram body weight up to 10 times that of sluggish species (85, 119, 124). Steen & Berg (301) substantiated this trend but observed that the total lamellar area varies less with varying demands for gas exchange than the coarseness (permeability) and the thickness of the tissue separating water and blood. Gill surface area in the hemoglobin-free Antarctic fish (*Chaenocephalus*) is not larger than that of other species living under similar conditions (301). However, the low lamellar frequency in this fish (inverse of distance between lamella) results in less resistance to water flow than in fishes with comparable surface area of the gills (119).

An increased gill surface area in active fishes seems to be produced mainly by more and longer filaments rather than increased areas of the secondary lamella (119). An enlargement of the gill area appears to be effected with little or no increase in the resistance to water flow.

Only recently has the relationship between body size and gill surface area been systematically worked out (124, 207). Gill area was shown to be related to body weight by the power of 0.85–0.90. Within a species a tendency prevails for larger gill areas in smaller fish calculated on a body weight basis.

Three species of *Thunnus* represented by numerous specimens ranging in weight from 1–40 kg showed a slope of the regression line for the total gill area against body weight ($A=AW^b$) of 0.85 for all three species. This relationship is closely similar to 0.89 which expresses the regression between O_2 consumption and body weight for a larger number of teleosts (207). Lungs of lower as well as higher vertebrates similarly show that the number and size of the alveoli and overall pulmonary surface area are related to the O_2 uptake of the species (320, 321). Even in the few cases where body size and metabolic rate bear an unusual relationship, the pulmonary surface area can be predicted from O_2 consumption rates and not from body size

(321). Recently, gill structure has been analyzed in the context of diffusion exchange for several species of Japanese freshwater fishes (316).

Fast-swimming pelagic teleosts have been shown to have the largest gill areas on record (207). Other structural adaptations to high swimming speeds in many pelagic fishes are most interesting (206). The primary modifications may involve a calcified flattened gill ray offering the filaments more substantial and rigid support (137). Secondly, these fishes may show both filamentous (324) and lamellar fusions which help to prevent lamellar deformation and collapse at high swimming speeds. Muir & Kendall (206) conclude that these modifications add strength and support to the exceptionally large gill surfaces and allow muscular control of the water passage through the tips of the filaments during passive or "ram" ventilation at great speed (see later discussion on ventilation).

The bowfin (*Amia calva*), a freshwater fish with both habits and a habitat vastly different from those of the marine fishes, has independently arrived at lamellar fusion (27). It has been surmised that this aids the fish in its habitat of O_2-deficient stagnant and turbid water, and prevents collapse of the gills during aerial respiration (160, 206, 218).

An analysis has been made of gill structure in relation to activity habits and exposure to O_2 deficiency in a tropical freshwater habitat (171). Forty-five out of 50 species studied were distinguished by a very short blood-to-water pathway, less than 1 μ. Typically, the ratio of the distance between adjacent lamellae to lamellar width was smaller than in fishes from normoxic water. The resulting reduction in the water-to-blood diffusion distance has an obvious adaptive value for fish in O_2-deficient water. The total thickness of the barrier structures in secondary lamellae is less in active than in sluggish forms and is smaller in fishes from O_2-deficient habitats than from normoxic waters (123, 301). The smallest total thickness of the diffusion path is 0.5 μ reported for the goldfish (*Carrassius carrassius*) (284). Fishes with accessory airbreathing organs showed a marked reduction in gill surface area and increased coarseness of the gill epithelium (63, 152, 164).

Structural adaptations for airbreathing in fishes are extremely diverse, although most types have developed as derivatives of the mouth, pharynx, or upper intestinal tract. Several reviews and recent papers have treated the morphology of airbreathing organs in fishes (46, 52, 166, 208–210, 279) and their fine structure and analysis of the air-to-blood diffusion distance have been reported on (56, 125, 126, 176, 284, 285). In the lungfishes, in which the air bladder is a lung homologous with the tetrapod lung, we find an amazingly short air-to-blood distance, which in the African lungfish (*Protopterus*) can be as short as 0.5 μ. Structural measures for surface expansion and efficient ventilation of the lungfish lung are, however, far less efficient than in most terrestrial vertebrates (152).

The fine structure of fish gills, particularly teleosts, has been reported on by several recent authors (123, 124, 133, 219, 220, 252, 284, 285) and structural characteristics have been correlated with the physiological factors determining the diffusion capacity of the fish gills.

The water-to-blood pathway in the secondary lamellae typically consists of one or two layers of flattened epithelial cells, a basement membrane and a thin cytoplasmic sheet lining the blood lacunae. Where a two-layered epithelium exists, lymphoid spaces have been observed between the two cell layers (125, 133).

The secondary lamellae show numerous projections of microvilli from the epithelial surface both in elasmobranchs and teleosts, (133). Specialized mucus cells are also common in the epithelium of secondary lamellae. It has been surmised that the microvilli function as anchors for the mucus film covering the gills. The mucus film may prevent water loss without hindering gas exchange (133, 217), although experimental evidence in support of this important contention is lacking.

Other specialized cells in the gill epithelium include the so-called chloride cells, which play an important role in the ionic and osmotic exchange of gills.

The cytoplasmic lining of the blood channels is derived from flangelike extensions of specialized pillar cells numerously distributed within the blood lacunae. These cells act as spacers in such a way that the perikarya of the cells prevent both collapse and overdistention of the endothelial surfaces of the lamellae (220).

Typically, the nuclei of epithelial cells are located immediately over the cell bodies of the pillar cells. Such concentration of the denser cellular components shortens the diffusion pathway between water and blood (123, 220, 302).

A striking feature of the specialized pillar cells is the presence of collagenous fibrils and discrete filaments running parallel to these. The filaments resemble myofilaments of smooth muscle from typical artery or gut, and the view has been advanced that the pillar cells may be contractile (123, 220) and may thus actively alter the dimension of the blood space in the gills. The resulting change in the ratio of surface to volume of the blood channels is of obvious importance to diffusion. This possibility takes on importance in the light of the findings that blood may flow through the secondary lamellae by alternate paths, either respiratory or nonrespiratory (254, 302). Blood flow through a gill filament can hence take three routes from the afferent to the efferent filament artery: 1. through the lacunar blood space of the secondary lamellae (respiratory flow), 2. through the central compartment, or 3. through the marginal filament vessels (nonrespiratory flow).

Since the entire cardiac output in most fishes perfuses the gills, an active control of the respiratory and nonrespiratory perfusion of the filaments becomes extremely important. Direct evidence for an active role of the pillar cells in distributing blood in the lamellae is lacking, although it is known that acetylcholine (Ach) and epinephrine (E) alter flow through the central compartment (302). Newstead (220) reported that the regions of the afferent and efferent arterial walls are not specialized for control of blood flow to the respiratory surfaces and surmised that flow distribution in the filament depends on active alteration of the cross-sectional area of the blood lacunae themselves, a viewpoint already advanced in 1901 (232). Species differences may be present since distinct circular muscle arrangement has been observed where the lamellar blood channel separates from the afferent filament artery in *Amia* and in *Squalus* (101, 133). Since nerve fibers appear to be absent from the secondary lamellae, the control of contractile filaments in pillar cells must be proven to be by an aneural mechanism if the foregoing hypothesis is to be generally accepted (133, 220).

Countercurrent exchange in gills.—It has long been known that the structural organization of teleost gills permits an increased efficiency in gas exchange due to the countercurrent arrangement of water and blood flow (50, 104, 130, 282, 302). Experimental proof of a countercurrent exchange rests with the presence of arterial O_2 tension exceeding O_2 tension of mixed expired water (95, 302). The possibility of perfusion shunts in gills as well as deadspace ventilation and variable diffusion barriers will tend to reduce or completely mask such a negative Po_2 gradient between expired water and arterial blood.

The operation of countercurrent exchange in elasmobranch gills has been denied (262) or questioned on anatomical grounds, because the extensive interbranchial septa will prevent a free and direct discharge of expired water. The finding by Piiper & Schumann (228) of negative arterial blood-expired water Po_2 gradients in sharks is, however, incompatible with concurrent gas exchange, and they suggest a multicapillary exchange model similar to that earlier suggested for mammalian placental gas exchange (200). This suggestion has recently been countered by findings of very large negative Po_2 gradients between expired water and arterial blood yielding an efficiency exceeding that possible with the multicapillary theory (95, 100). A recent analysis by Grigg (92, 95) reveals that the highest attainable efficiency in gas exchange in a multicapillary system under ideal conditions will allow the arterial Po_2 to match the mean of the inspired and expired Po_2. His data showed that arterial O_2 tensions commonly exceeded that maximum value, thus indicating a functional countercurrent exchange. The accessibility of truly mixed samples of exhaled water is crucial to the documentation of countercurrent exchange. The difficulty involved in obtaining truly mixed samples of exhaled water in fish is considerable and has been discussed in detail (53).

The lampreys among the cyclostome fishes represent an interesting case because their respiratory current is tidal, with water entering and leaving the branchial chambers through the same openings. Contrary to expectations from anatomical evidence, a countercurrent exchange may be in operation in lampreys during a slow inspiratory phase whereas the subsequent very active expiratory phase expels water so rapidly that there is little loss of the O_2 gained during the inspiratory phase (162). This interesting possibility needs further experimental verification.

A few fishes display a most remarkable use of countercurrent exchange in regulating their body temperature. Mako (*Isurus oxyrhynchus*) and Porbeagle (*Lamna nassus*) sharks have highly developed countercurrent heat exchangers in the vascular supply to the great swimming muscles. These countercurrent exchangers act as thermal barriers which prevent heat from being carried off by the blood stream and lost to the water in the gills (44). This mechanism allows the swimming muscles to remain at temperatures up to 10°C higher than ambient water, a fact which greatly increases the power of the swimming muscles. The bluefin tuna (*Thunnus thynnus*) possesses similar vascular retes, allowing the fish to undertake long seasonal migrations in fluctuating water temperatures. In a beautiful study, Carey & Teal (45) showed that the muscle mass varied only 5°C over a 10°–30°C range of water temperature.

The role of countercurrent exchange and multiplication in the concentrating mechanism of the teleost swimbladder has been under study for decades and has recently been convincingly worked out by Steen et al (69, 303, 304).

VENTILATION

Mechanics of breathing.—The mechanics of ventilation in fishes has been the subject of many earlier reviews (9, 329, 330, 334), but investigations reviewed before the 1950s were based upon direct visual observations and were mainly concerned with functional anatomy of the skeletal and muscular components of the breathing apparatus. New physiological techniques such as high-sensitivity electromanometers and electromyographical techniques often associated with direct measurements of water velocity and flow have greatly accelerated progress. In particular, G. M. Hughes and collaborators at Bristol, England have pioneered the experimental approaches to studies of fish ventilation (15, 115–117, 121, 127–130, 276).

The gills and muscular apparatus for water ventilation in the primitive cyclostome fishes differ markedly from those in other fishes. The specialized branchial basket and the pouchlike gills with ducts communicating with the buccal cavity and the exterior through a single (in myxinoids) opening or multiple (in lampreys) openings require entirely different mechanisms for water propulsion from those in other fishes. Functional accounts of the branchial apparatus in the lampreys (10, 54, 258) emphasize the unique situation that arises when these fish have their heads embedded in their prey, while feeding parasitically. A bidirectional (tidal) form of ventilation must then prevail with an active expulsion of water from the muscular gill pouches, with relaxation and elastic rebound of these causing water to be inhaled through the same external openings. The myxinoid gills and respiratory tracts are different from those in lampreys in that water enters a single nasal opening (nostril) and a peculiar scroll-like velum situated in a long pharynx propels water in a unidirectional passage through the pouchlike gills (83, 169, 311). The muscular gill pouches and their ducts have been demonstrated with X-ray techniques to actively participate in the propulsion of water (156).

Ventilation in elasmobranch and teleost fishes involves a double pumping mechanism with a positive pressure buccal (orobranchial) force pump and a parabranchial (opercular in teleosts) suctional pump drawing water over the gills. The mechanics of this double pumping mechanism and the resistance and water flow pattern at the finer channels of the gills (gill sieve) have been studied in detail (92, 93, 115, 116, 128, 129, 276).

The relative importance of the two pumps in the double pumping action varies between species (116). Also the duration of the inspiratory and expiratory phases can be actively modified in many fishes by alternating the configuration and size of the inhalant and exhalant openings (116, 330).

An interesting adaptation in ventilatory pattern has been reported in pleuronectid fishes. When flatfish are resting partly burrowed on the bottom, although they ventilate the gills on both sides, they expel the water only from the upper opercular opening (336) due to the presence of a ventral channel connecting the two opercular cavities. This adaption in pleuronectid fishes is not present in all flattened benthic forms, since many species of rays and skates (elasmobranchs) have the exhalant gill openings on the ventral side.

Gill resistance is actively controlled by specialized muscles which adjust the degree of deadspace ventilation (29, 226). The coordinated activity of the exceedingly complex system of muscles which operate the double action ventilation pump in fishes has been studied with electromyographical techniques in both elasmobranchs and teleosts (11–13, 15, 122). Several investigations have stimulated interest in the possibility of proporioceptive feedback from the respiratory as well as the motor musculature to the respiratory center (11, 12, 14, 117, 265, 269, 275).

Early in this century, Darbishire (51) described an altered waterflow pattern when elasmobranch fishes went from rest to exercise. Whereas water primarily enters the spiracles and escapes the anterior-most gill splits during rest, onset of swimming causes a large portion of water to enter the mouth and escape through the posterior gill slits. The change has recently been correlated with simultaneous changes in the distribution of blood flow through the gills (273).

Active swimming exerts an influence on ventilation in fish not only by its effect on the relative distribution of water across the gills, but also and most significantly by slowing down or turning off active ventilatory movements when the fishes reach a certain swimming speed. Such dependence on passive or "ram" ventilation for irrigation of the gills is most important in pelagic fishes, particularly larger species among both sharks and teleosts, and some rely solely on their swimming speed for ventilation (115, 131, 206, 327). The spiracles and many of the branchial pumping muscles have regressed or have become lost in these fishes.

The energy cost of ventilation in a waterbreather is very high because of the large ventilation volume necessitated by the low O_2 concentration in water, and the high density and viscosity of water. Few studies have addressed the important problem of energy cost of breathing in fish. At normal ventilation values in teleosts cost of breathing was estimated at 30% of the total O_2 uptake, increasing to more than 50% when ventilation was trebled (287). On the basis of these values, however, the fish will obviously face an upper limit beyond which further increase in ventilation is not only inefficient energetically, but impossible to accomplish. Corresponding changes for an airbreather (human) would maximally increase the O_2 cost of breathing 2–10% of total O_2 uptake (78), although extreme hyperventilation may drive O_2 cost to 34% of total (201). The quoted figures on O_2 cost of breathing in fish refer to the only recent experimental account, and more work is greatly needed since theoretical considerations suggest the reported values to be excessive. Shelton (293) has calculated (112, 278) that the breathing muscles in fish consume 10–15% of the resting O_2 uptake. Since increased O_2 demand in fishes is largely caused by activity, it seems of high adaptive value that ventilation powered by the activity of the swimming muscles has selectively been developed. Another advantage of passive ventilation may be related to a steady flow pattern at the gas exchange surfaces during continuous swimming. Interestingly, some fishes swim at such great speed (tunas and other pelagic teleost) that the amount and velocity of water diverted across the respiratory surfaces must be controlled by the gape of the mouth and opercula.

Studies of mechanics of breathing in fishes have recently been expanded to include airbreathing fishes, notably the lungfishes (31, 88, 198). The double pumping action in typical fishes with a buccal force pump and an opercular suction pump is essentially maintained in the waterbreathing of lungfishes (31, 198) and in amphibians (328, 329). The involvement of a buccal force pump for filling the lung has been described for the Australian (88, 165), African (143, 198), and South American lungfishes (31). A description of inhalation and exhalation in *Lepidosiren* (31) and a careful study of breathing in *Protopterus* involving recording of pressure gradients, electromyographic analysis, and X-ray cinematography have recently been published (198). Airbreathing in *Protopterus* is derived from a series of basically aquatic breathing cycles modified to serve a specific step in the airbreathing process. No rib movement or aspirating mechanism for filling the lung akin to that in reptiles or higher vertebrates is represented in airbreathing fishes or amphibians (198). McMahon (198) presents a most important discussion on the evolution of the mechanics of aerial respiration in the vertebrates, emphasizing the role of the buccal force pump as the main ventilatory mechanisms in purely aquatic as well as transitional bimodal breathers among fishes and amphibians.

Central hemodynamics.—This section will review the hemodynamics of venous return, cardiac ejection, and circulation through gas exchangers such as gills and accessory airbreathing organs in fishes. More complete appraisals of fish hemodynamics have recently been published (244, 272).

An understanding of factors affecting venous return and filling of the heart is essential to assess cardiac output regulation. The literature offers few and scattered references to central venous blood pressures in fishes (30, 38, 97, 154, 203, 268, 309), and only one paper reports on direct measurement of blood flow in a central vein (159). Conditions in elasmobranchs are by far the best known and have been thoroughly reviewed in two recent papers (30, 271).

On the basis of finding of a subambient intrapericardial pressure it was proposed early that the elasmobranch heart exerts some form of aspiratory or sucking effect aiding the return of venous blood (281). This idea has been contested since it was first proposed, but recent studies have proved its correctness (97, 148, 271, 312, 313). A *vis à fronte*, or sucking, effect in the fish heart is most notable in cyclostomes and chondrichthyan fishes, but is also present in teleosts (203) and lungfishes (159). Structurally, the genesis of cardiac suction in elasmobranchs rests with the presence of a semirigid pericardium supported by cartilage and surrounding muscle (148, 271). In teleosts the pericardium is less rigid but supported by fibrous septae (216). Chondrostean fishes such as the sturgeon (*Acipencer*) and the spoonbill (*Polyodon*) have a very rigid pericardium and a prevailing subambient intrapericardial pressure (98).

The reduction in cardiac volume during ventricular ejection results in a pressure drop inside the rigid pericardium. This downsurge in pressure is transmitted to the atrium and sinus venosus whereby an attraction for venous blood results from the steepening of the pressure gradients along the venous channels (30, 47, 148, 271, 312, 313). In sharks the intrapericardial pressure fluctuates between -2.2 cm H_2O and -5.6 cm H_2O (271). Pericardial tamponade by injection of saline into the pericardial space promptly abolishes the subambient pressure and causes a drastic drop in arterial pressure due to the reduced venous return (148, 313). Aspiration of pericardial fluid augments the suctional attraction by lowering central venous pressure (271). Partial obstruction of venous return by compression increases the amplitude of the subambient pericardial pressure (Holst 1969, quoted by Satchell 113). An increased heart rate accentuates the negativity of the intrapericardial pressure, while bradycardia conversely reduces it. It is significant that an increased heart rate causes a further decrease in intrapericardial pressure which in turn increases venous return during the decreased diastolic filling time (148). Respiratory movements also contribute to the level of subambient pressure (312). No satisfactory explanation has been offered for the genesis of the prevailing level of subambient pressure. If the intrapericardial pressure is raised by injecting iso-osmolar fluid into the pericardium it gradually returns to a lower mean value. The early findings that pericardial lymph has a lower osmolarity than blood plasma (296) suggest that osmotic forces may be involved in setting up the subambient pressure.

In the African lungfish ventricular systole caused the vena cava pressure to drop from about $+2.0$ cm H_2O to -0.5 cm H_2O with a concurrent large increase in vena cava flow (159).

Satchell (272) has pointed out that the usefulness of cardiac suction in elasmobranchs is related to the large capacious reservoir function of the cardinal sinuses and the uncollapsible venous channels connecting these with more peripheral veins. Birch et al (30) in an excellent study describe the structure and function of venous return in the Port Jackson shark *Heterodontus portusjacksonii.* The central ends of the uncollapsible trunk veins exhibited fluctuating subambient pressure transmitted from the pericardium. The lateral cutaneous and abdominal veins possess valves where they connect with the ducts of Cuvier. In the postpelvic trunk intercostal arteries and veins are also valved (268) and these aid crucially by allowing the swimming movements of the tail to transfer blood directionally from the dorsal aorta to the caudal vein. Chondrichtyan fishes also show prominent sphincters where the hepatic veins enter the sinus venosus. These sphincters may be of particular significance in the presence of subambient pressures in the sinus venosus and a suctional effect on venous blood. Under such circumstances a sphincteric release of hepatic blood flow allows adjustments of the volume and transit time of blood in the liver and may permit rapid mobilization of blood stored in the liver at times when an increase in cardiac output is needed (154).

Venous valves have also been described in teleosts (62). No physiological study has reported on their significance; but there can be little doubt that swimming movements will exert an important influence in augmenting venous return.

Atrial filling in fishes and in elasmobranchs in particular is greatly aided by the subambient pressure surrounding it (167, 242). An active contraction of the sinus venosus discernible as a V wave in the electrocardiogram (221) does not cause a detectable pressure rise in the atrium of elasmobranchs (272, 313). The atrium is, however, large and extremely compliant, a factor which, combined with the subambient surrounding pressure in the pericardium, may contribute to the absence of a measured pressure pulse. In teleosts a distinct pressure pulse results from sinus venosus contraction (307). The sinoatrial valve typical of lower vertebrates but absent in the higher vertebrates allows the atrium to play a very significant role in cardiac contraction by becoming the principal determinant of ventricular filling and ventricular end diastolic volume (147). Only during atrial contraction is atrial pressure higher than ventricular pressure, which makes atrial contraction the exclusive ventricular filling agent (272, 313).

The interesting double pumping action of the fish heart functioning simultaneously as a pressure and suction pump in a reciprocal manner by which the atrial and ventricular contractions assist the filling of each other merits further study, particularly with reference to the energetics of cardiac pumping.

The elasmobranch and dipnoan hearts differ from the teleost heart by having a cone-shaped chamber invested by cardiac muscle and elastic tissue intervening between the ventricle and the ventral aorta. This chamber, the bulbus cordis (conus arteriosus), houses a variable number of valves. Ventricular contraction is followed by contraction of this segment of the heart detectable as a wave in the electrocardiogram (319) and a pressure pulse in the ventral aortic pressure record (97, 147). In teleosts the bulbus cordis is replaced by a swelling at the base of the heart (bulbus arteriosus), composed of arterial smooth muscle and elastic tissue. The bulbus cordis segment of the vertebrate heart is distinctly present embryologically in all vertebrates. Its transformation in higher vertebrates is related to the formation of the right ventricular outflow tract and its valves (196).

The bulbus cordis (elasmobranchs and dipnoans), as well as the bulbus arteriosus (teleosts), has an important role in extending blood flow in the ventral aorta by elastic recoil (147, 159, 274). An active and variable contribution to the cardiac ejectate from bulbar contraction has also been demonstrated (97, 153).

Recently, it has also been contended that the muscular conus in elasmobranchs is important in effecting valve closure since the conal segment is surrounded by the negative intrapericardial pressure (274). Paralyzing the conal musculature markedly increased the retrograde surge of blood in the ventral aorta during diastole (274).

Peak ejection velocities range upwards to 20 cm/sec in elasmobranchs and deceleration of flow in the ventral aorta is very slow due to the bulbus segment (153). Normally there is no period of reversed flow in the ventral aorta (274). Analysis on a teleost (ling cod) (242) discloses that 29% or more of ventral aortic blood flow, depending on heart rate, can be attributed to elastic rebound of the bulbus arteriosus. The importance of the bulbus segment for cardiac outflow in the lungfishes has also been analyzed recently (159). In lungfishes, as well as in amphibians, the bulbus cordis and its modified valves are important for the selective passage of O_2-rich and O_2-deficient blood through the heart (148, 155, 157, 158).

Cardiac output and its regulation.—The introduction of direct techniques for blood flow measurement in fish (97, 145, 153, 159, 166, 242) and refinement in methods for sampling of arterial and venous blood in unrestrained animals (73, 298), for use in calculation of blood flow by the Fick principle, have in recent years remedied an almost total lack of information about cardiac output and its regulation in fishes. But information has not accumulated enough to allow many generalizations. The balance of evidence suggests that stroke volume adjustments to exercise and hypoxic stress play a greater role than heart rate changes in modifying cardiac output (74, 145). Results from trout (309, 310) show a fourfold increase in stroke volume and only a 15% increase in heart rate associated with moderate swimming. Other workers have found significant changes in heart rate associated with exercise (74, 315), but the resulting influence on cardiac output remains speculative since blood flow was not measured simultaneously.

Why heart rate changes per se are relatively ineffective in increasing the cardiac output may relate to the specialized mechanisms for venous return in fish. An increased temperature of the water will for instance increase the heart rate markedly (96, 180, 182). This response must be looked upon as a direct effect of temperature on the pacemaker potential and not as an integrated adjustment of the cardiovascular system to an increased output. Temperature has little effect on stroke volume in the teleost *Ophiodon elongatus* (307). Recent studies on elasmobranchs have shown a heart rate increase with temperature and a concomitant decrease in stroke volume in the quiescent fish, whereas initiation of swimming movements caused a prompt rise in stroke volume and cardiac output with no further change in heart rate (151).

The hypothesis that stroke volume adjustments for increased cardiac outputs are more important than heart rate changes receives no valid challenge from a number of studies of isolated hearts, artificially perfused with blood or saline. Such studies obviously ignore the integrity and multiple feedback control in an intact cardiovascular system. Typically, both Jensen (142) working with isolated lamprey and trout hearts and Bennion & Randall (24) working with isolated salmon hearts reported an increase in rate as well as force of contraction when venous return was augmented; yet in intact salmon or trout during exercise or hypoxic stress calling for an increased cardiac output, an almost exclusive stroke volume compensation was recorded (242, 244, 247). Stroke volume could be increased in isolated hearts by almost 40% by adding catecholamines to the perfusate in concentrations like those actually measured in resting and active trout (214, 242).

In elasmobranchs minor changes in cardiac output have been observed with short swimming periods, whereas the postexercise recovery period could show a significant cardiac output increase, mainly from stroke volume changes.

Studies of airbreathing fishes have demonstrated marked cardiac output increases associated with airbreaths as well as with exercise (159, 166).

Resting values for cardiac output in fishes have been measured by the Fick principle, by dye dilution, or by direct blood velocity measurements to range from about 10–40 ml/kg min (19, 38, 43, 74, 81, 100, 145, 159, 186, 212, 261).

An artificial alteration of blood O_2 capacity, induced by graded experimental anemia in trout, showed a compensatory increase in cardiac output, primarily through stroke volume increase (43). A less pronounced trend in the same direction was apparent from studies on a natural population of carp

(74). Extended to the hemoglobin-free Antarctic icefish *Chaenocephalus,* this reasoning would imply an exceptionally important role of cardiac output in gas transport (107). A recent survey of ventilation-perfusion control in all vertebrate classes (190) reveals a tendency for the ratio of cardaic output to O_2 uptake to increase from purely water- to airbreathers in apparent relationship to the circulating hemoglobin levels. The question naturally emerges, what level of hematocrit and oxygen capacity is optimal for the energy budget of a fish? With respiratory and systemic capillary beds largely in direct series, high hematocrits would tend to increase the viscosity and hence the overall vascular resistance excessively. Conversely, as shown by the studies cited above, low hematocrits and O_2 capacities will tax the heart with a necessary compensation in cardiac output. Studies addressing the question of cardiac work and cardiac index relative to a changing O_2 capacity in fish should be rewarding.

The literature is almost blank with reference to values for cardiac work in fishes. One recent study (74) of the carp reports 950 g/cm/min per kg or, computed as fraction of the total aerobic energy production assuming a 20% efficiency of the cardiac muscle, about 5% of the resting energy production supports cardiac work.

Regulation of heart rate.—The innervation and reflex control of heart rate in fishes continues to be controversial. The heart of hagfishes, the most primitive of vertebrates, has been thought to lack cardiac regulatory nerves altogether (67, 86, 139), leaving all heart rate changes to be elicited by a direct hormonal effect on the heart muscle (8, 67) or an intrinsic effect of stretch on the rate of change of the pacemaker potential and hence on heart rate (140, 144).

A high content of catecholamine-containing granules has been reported in specific cells in the hagfish heart (8, 35, 65, 110) and the claim has been made that a biochemical factor named eptatretin, with a positive chronotropic and inotropic effect, is produced directly in the hagfish heart (141). The absence of cardiac innervation has been refuted (110) by the finding of a system of ganglion cells with nerve fibers distributed along both epi- and endocardium in hagfish. The myocardial nerve fibers are similar although less extensive than those in teleost and amphibian hearts. No proof exists that this innervation plays a regulatory role, and pharmacological studies showing near-insensitivity of the hagfish heart to Ach and E (67) justify the view that the hagfish heart is not reflexly regulated. Catecholamines show a possible chronotropic effect on the hagfish heart if endogenous catecholamines have been depleted by treatment with reserpine (35).

It merits considerable interest that the lamprey heart differs from other vertebrate hearts by possessing a cholinergic vagus innervation which is cardioacceleratory (8, 142, 225).

Jensen (142) in a study of the lamprey and trout reemphasizes the presence and importance of a stretch-induced rate-controlling mechanism in the myocardium (34, 146, 172, 322). Such a mechanism takes on a considerable importance in phylogenetic perspective as the most important mechanism for rate change of the functionally aneural hagfish heart. The mechanism persists in lampreys (142), teleosts (24, 142), amphibians (322), reptiles (77), birds (16), and mammals (34, 79, 80, 158), but its importance in normal heart rate control is unknown. A possible increased importance of an intrinsic stretch control of heart rate was hypothesized for the hibernating mammal at low temperatures when cardiac innervation is temperature blocked (158). Note that the direct effect of filling pressure (stretch) on the pacemaker prepotentials in mammalian hearts has been much studied recently (102). Results of these studies conflict: both a positive effect (55) and no effect (82) of stretch on isolated pacemaker tissue have been reported.

The elasmobranch heart is supplied by two branches from the vagus, both cholinergic and inhibitory to the heart. Considerable interest relates to a pair of symmetrically placed bodies of chromaffin tissue located dorsally above the posterior cardinal sinus close to where the venous backflow is discharged into the heart (sinus venosus). The chromaffin tissue is innervated by fibers from adjacent sympathetic ganglia (338) and bioassay of the tissue reveals a high content of catecholamines (294). Satchell (272), in his recent valuable monograph on circulation in fish, alludes to the strategic location of the chromaffin tissue and its probable significance in bringing liberated catecholamines directly to the myocardium. The distribution of chromaffin tissue in teleost fishes has also recently been reviewed (215). Chromaffin cells of fishes are generally held to be homologous with the cells of the mammalian adrenal medulla.

Current views on the innervation and reflex control of the teleost heart are similarly not in general agreement. Teleost fishes conform to the general vertebrate scheme and show inhibitory vagal (cholinergic) innervation (183, 255) densely distributed to the sinoauricular and atrial regions and sparsely or not at all to the ventricular myocardium.

The prevailing viewpoint that vagal nerve fibers are the only cardiac efferents in fish (47, 48, 182, 240) has repeatedly been challenged recently, on the basis of ultrastructural and biochemical studies (66, 71, 84, 335). The presence of many granular vesicles in axons is conjectured as evidence of adrenergic innervation. Supporting evidence is taken from the demonstration of catecholamines in nerves of trout (71) or in the heart muscle itself (65). The presence of adrenergic receptors in teleost hearts has also been backed by experimental evidence (66). A positive chronotropic and inotropic effect on the fish heart from injected catecholamines (249) has been taken as evidence for adrenergic innervation, since those biogenic amines have been demonstrated in cardiac tissue from several species of fishes. Substantiation of this view awaits further information on the source of production of the catecholamines and their site of storage (35).

Physiological and pharmacological studies on heart rate control in intact fish are numerous, but results again conflict. Cardioacceleration as a result of lessened vagal tone has been a general finding (153, 249, 255), although the level of resting vagal tonus appears to vary in different species. Surprisingly, normally active fish like the salmonids have been reported to have no resting vagal tone in contrast to the less active cyprinoid fishes (242). This situation leaves the salmonid fish with no neural cardioaccelerating mechanism, except during hypoxia when the vagal tone is increased (247). Fishes in this respect are in contrast to higher vertebrates which generally show a correlation between active habits and a high level of resting vagal tone.

The balance of evidence for and against an excitatory adrenergic innervation to the fish heart has recently been decidedly shifted in favor of a double innervation typical of tetrapod vertebrates. The paper by Gannon & Burnstock (71) contains the most recent positive evidence, although data on the normal role of excitatory innervation of the fish heart are still lacking.

In addition to the histochemical evidence cited above, stimulation at low frequency of the cut peripheral vagus or the area of the duct of Cuvier where the vagal efferents run, produced a purely excitatory response (71). Stimulation at higher frequency and longer pulse duration caused the negative chronotropic and inotropic effect reported so generally. However, stimulation after treatment with atropine revealed an excitatory response which could be blocked by bretylium, guanethidine, or pronethalol. Administration of norepinephrine (NE) or epinephrine (E) mimicked the excitatory responses to nerve stimulation. These effects have been reported blocked by β-adrenergic blocking agents in the plaice (66), although other authors (249) failed to confirm this in the salmon, which leaves the question of the general presence of β-adrenergic receptors in the fish heart. Swimming released vagal tonus completely in trout (245) whereas atropinization of continuously swimming elasmobranchs (dogfish) gave a 30% cardioacceleration (153). Reflex cardioacceleration in fishes has also been alleged by Russian investigators to depend on the number of nerve elements involved in a vagal stimulation, since a weak stimulation of different gill branches of the vagus gave an increased heart rate, whereas a stronger stimulus resulted in bradycardia (263). These results were corroborated by constant repetitive stimulation and progressive transection of fibers in the nerve stimulated (178). The viewpoint of the Russian workers is inconsistent with the well-documented presence of tonic inhibitory vagal effect in many species of fish. In the light of the recent strong evidence of an adrenergic excitatory component to the fish heart (71) the earlier results can be better explained by the vagus mediating both an excitatory and an inhibitory innervation.

The response of the fish heart in vivo to catecholamines appears to depend on temperature and dose level. Bradycardia following low dose levels of E disappears after atropine blockade of vagal efferents, and is thus attributed to a reflex cholinergic inhibition elicited by a blood pressure increase from the E injection (240, 249).

Afferent fibers innervating cardiac receptors in fish distributed to the atrium and ventricle have been reported (182), but other workers have been unable to detect afferent nerve activity in cardiac branches of the vagus.

Heart rate in fishes has long been known to be extremely labile and every conceivable change in environmental physical factors such as temperature, light, mechanical vibrations, gas composition of the water, or handling of the fishes will alter heart rate markedly (28, 185, 179, 224, 290). These reponses, often transient and adaptive to the stimulus, probably express no primary adjustment in cardiac performance to the altered situation, but rather are the result of an unspecific change in vagal tone.

Circulation through the gas exchanger.—The structure of a gill filament allows three discrete perfusion routes through a gill filament: 1. The respiratory route through the secondary lamellae. 2. A direct shunt between the afferent and efferent filament arteries at the distal filament margin. 3. A nonrespiratory shunt through a central compartment (filamental sinus) of the filament body. On ultrastructural evidence, controlled resistance changes and consequent alteration of gill perfusion were surmised to rest on the state of contraction or elongation of the lamellar pillar cells, channeling blood mainly through the lamellae, either along a direct channel along the lamellar periphery (high degree of shunting) or through the main lamellar body (low degree of shunting). Other workers contend that effective control of blood distribution through the gill also depends on smooth muscle elements in the arterial walls of the filamental arteries and the arterial channels leading from these to the lamellar lacunae and central sinuses (101, 253). Early pharmacological evidence revealed that gill resistance is lowered when adrenaline is added to the perfusate in gill perfusions (174, 177). These early findings were extended by perfusion of excised gills under constant pressure: NE had stronger dilatory effects than E, while Ach and 5-HT both increased the overall vascular resistance to perfusion (223). Steen & Kruysse (302) studied excised individual gill filaments from eels on a microscope slide and observed the pattern of fluid movement when gentle pressure was applied to the cover of the preparation. When Ach was added to the solution bathing the filament, the resistance of the vascular paths altered so that flow preference was through the nonrespiratory path. Conversely when E was added, flow preference was through the respiratory lamellar portion. Richards & Fromm (253) repeated these experiments under more controlled conditions using perfusion under constant pressure and confirmed the earlier findings. The effect of atropine suggested some level of cholinergic constrictor tonus on overall gill resistance, but they conclude that blood flow through the teleost gill is primarily under adrenergic control.

In vivo assessment of changes in vascular resistance and flow distribution in gills is far more complicated. The serial arrangement of the branchial (gill) and the systemic vascular beds requires that dorsal as well as ventral aortic blood pressure and central venous pressure be monitored. Blood pressures at any point will also depend upon the energy released by cardiac contraction and the resultant flow. The relative flow distribution postbranchially will depend on vasomotor changes in sections of the parallel arrangement of postbranchial beds. This is highly important to consider in lungfishes and amphibians which have the systemic and pulmonary vascular beds in a parallel arrangement. Few investigators take proper cognizance of these problems, and changes in dorsal aortic pressure are often presumptuously attributed to specific changes in vascular resistance. In vivo studies of blood pressure, preferably coupled with flow measurements, should be combined with in vitro perfusions of isolated vascular beds (e.g. branchial vascular bed) at in and outflow pressures similar to those existing in vivo, if conclusive statements about vasomotor control mechanisms are to be made (168, 251).

The thesis that administration of E favors lamellar respiratory circulation has been deduced from an increase in O_2 tension of arterial blood (302). The importance of shunting inside the gills has been related to control not only of gas exchange (302) but of ionic exchange, water exchange, and exchange of metabolic products (18, 59, 194).

Responses to injection of catecholamines and other vasoactive agents take on importance in the context of changes in the circulating levels of these substances in response to activity and altered ambient conditions. Thus, the level of circulating catecholamines in the trout increased during swimming (214). In a survey of pharmacological effects on isolated arterial strips from lower vertebrates it was concluded that there is an increasing development of adrenergic compared to cholinergic nervous control of the larger arteries in vertebrate evolution (39, 175). The same authors detected a progressive increase in the sensitivity of the arterial smooth muscle to E and NE from fishes to mammals (39). They observed that the α and β adrenotropic blockers phenoxybenzamine, pentholamine, and pronethalol had little effect on the response of trout and eel ventral aorta strips to catecholamines.

In free-swimming salmon the normal increase in blood pressure associated with swimming activity (309) or intravenous injection of E was blocked after pretreatment with phenoxybenzamine, an α-adrenergic receptor blocking agent (249). Although these experiments do not conclusively localize the site of the α-adrenergic receptors, their presence is surmised both in the gills and in the systemic circulation.

Reite (251) has presented by far the most comprehensive study of the response of vascular smooth muscle to biogenic amines in fishes. He studied more than 14 representative species of cyclostome fishes, chondrichtyan fishes, and teleosts in addition to the African lungfish and *Polypterus senegalus*. The vascular response of various biogenic amines and their blocking agents were used to dissociate between specific and nonspecific actions in vivo and in controlled perfusion experiments. Normal tissue levels of some of the amines were also determined.

E and NE acquired receptor specificity in the jawless hagfishes, and gave the typical dichotomous response on fish by dilating the gill vessels and constricting the overall systemic vascular beds. Histamine and 5-HT seemed to reflect unspecific actions on adrenergic receptor mechanisms. Effects in chondrichtyan fishes were slight, but in teleosts specific stimulatory actions were produced from both histamine and 5-HT. In teleosts the branchial area first acquires specificity of response to 5-HT, while in lungfish specific vasoconstriction to both 5-HT and histamine is fully developed for branchial, pulmonary, and systemic beds. Reite's (251) work demonstrates that both inhibitory and stimulatory vascular reactions to E and NE in fish can be explained according to the general concept of adrenergic α and β receptors as introduced by Ahlquist (4).

In an evolutionary context the lungfishes occupy a crucial position as the most primitive example of a true pulmonary circulation in parallel with systemic beds, both in series with a branchial circulation which has discrete and large calibered vascular bypasses (152, 168). Regional distribution in this system is more complicated than that in the teleost fish. A recent study on intact as well as perfused vascular beds of the African lungfish demonstrated that Ach, histamine, and 5-HT increased branchial as well as pulmonary and systemic vascular resistances (168). The branchial vessels showed the highest sensitivity to Ach. The Australian lungfish, which unlike the African lungfish has efficient gills and depends predominantly on aquatic breathing, showed a striking sensitivity to Ach in that 2 μg injected intravenously caused an almost complete transient cessation of branchial flow with dorsal aortic pressure reduced to almost zero (165). E and NE caused increased resistance in pulmonary and systemic blood vessels in *Protopterus,* in distinction to a dilatory effect on the branchial vessels. β-Adrenergic receptors were thought to be present in the postbranchial section of the arterial system. No conclusive evidence of a cholinergic vasoconstrictor tonus to the primitive pulmonary vessels was produced, but atropinization suggested that endogenously released Ach may be important for normal control of pulmonary blood flow. The finding that pulmonary blood flow may spontaneously double without an overall increase in postbranchial flow suggests the presence of potent vasomotor mechanisms in the lung, particularly since such flow changes were associated with an increased use of the lung in air-breathing (159).

Arterial blood pressure.—There is a paucity of blood pressure measurement in fishes: records from unrestrained freeswimming fishes in particular are almost totally lacking. Salmonid fishes have been most studied and show average ventral aortic blood pressures ranging from 35 to 60 mm Hg in resting fish with a 30–40% pressure drop across the gills to the dorsal aorta

(111, 248, 299, 306, 309). Earlier studies have reported higher and lower values, but these were done on restrained fishes, usually excited or weak from exhaustion or trauma (87, 103, 259). Blood pressures in elasmobranchs tend to be lower than those recorded from the salmonid fishes studied (97, 153, 314). The few airbreathing fishes studied also show generally lower pressures (159).

Large species differences related to behaviour and environmental factors are to be expected in arterial blood pressure.

Of more general interest are comparisons of blood pressure gradients along the vascular circuits and how these are modified by various stimuli. A number of authors have reviewed or reported on blood pressure gradients across the branchial vascular bed in fishes (97, 167, 267, 306).

One is impressed with relatively modest drops in blood pressure across gills. The pressure usually drops by less than one third of the average pressure prevailing in the ventral aorta. Catecholamines and exercise cause a decrease in gill vessel resistance (267). The lessened resistance brings about a reduced ratio of ventral to dorsal aortic blood pressure and the amount of O_2 transferred from water to blood can increase as much as fivefold in trout (111). With nonrespiratory and respiratory perfusion paths in gills arranged in parallel, the relative resistance of the nonrespiratory shunts must normally exceed that in the respiratory lamellae. The claim of a usefulness of the shunts in lessening the cardiac work during times of reduced needs for gas exchange (302) hence becomes questionable.

Changes in vascular resistance of entire gill units may also be altered according to the distribution of the respiratory water flow. One recent study analyzes this possibility in skates (273) and suggests a number of important problems for future study. Studies on ionic exchange rates in gills also indicate large changes in gill vascular resistance (18, 194).

The relationships of the capacitance and compliance of the arterial systems afferent and efferent to the gills in relation to overall gill resistance and pattern of gill blood flow have been reviewed by Satchell (272). The relative shortening of diastole causing the slow deceleration of ventral aortic flow in fishes is limited by the necessity for coronary perfusion possible only during ventricular diastole (274, 272, 317). Because of the conspicuous elasticity of the bulbus segment of the fish heart, however, ventral aortic outflow can continue during part of the ventricular diastole.

Many of the airbreathing fishes, e.g. the African lungfish, have discrete anatomical shunts in the gill vasculature enabling blood to be shunted past the gills. These shunts are represented by large calibered vessels (3rd and 4th aortic arches). When aquatic breathing prevails, a definite but small pressure gradient prevails across the gills indicating at least partial constriction of the gills. When, however, the fish assumes more frequent airbreathing or when the fish is totally air-exposed, the pressure gradient across the gill vasculature is all but abolished, which indicates that blood is diverted through the nonrespiratory large calibered shunts (159). Fishes in general show a conspicuous increase in vascular resistance of gills when air-exposed. This is due to collapse of the gills and lack of these low-resistance perfusion shunts of lungfishes.

The presence of a pressor-depressor mechanism for regulation of blood pressure by reflex alteration of heart rate and peripheral vascular resistance has been looked for in fishes (270). In elasmobranchs (136, 193) and teleosts (204) an elevation of the arterial blood pressure caused a slowing of the heart. With the heart beating normally, bursts of nervous activity synchronous with cardiac systole were recorded from the pretrematic branches of all five true branchial nerves and in the posttrematic branches of the first four branchial nerves. Lutz & Wyman (193) had earlier forecasted such a baroreceptor mechanism in fish similar to the baroreceptors in the carotid sinus and aortic arch region of mammals.

Elevation of arterial pressure by E injection caused blood pressure increase and attendant bradycardia in a salmonid fish (*Onchorynchus*). The bradycardia could be prevented after pretreatment with atropine, which also caused a larger and more sustained blood pressure increase to E (306). A cardiac vagal tonus was surmised to result from the normal resting level of arterial blood pressure.

Spontaneous reflexly released pressor responses have been observed in lungfishes (159). Artificial and spontaneous lung inflations caused a blood pressure increase in *Protopterus*, while aspiration of gas from the lung elicited a prompt blood pressure drop.

An increase in the prebranchial (ventral aortic) pressure in *Neoceratodus* had no effect on blood pressure while a pressure increase by infusion of blood or saline postbranchially (pulmonary artery) caused a conspicuous lowering of both pre- and postbranchial pressures (165). The lungfish studies showed no heart rate responses to the infusions and thus prompt the suggestion that the vasomotor effector component of the baroreceptor reflex can be dissociated from the cardiac component.

The definite location of baroreceptors in fish and a verification and extension of the early studies of Irving et al (136) are still lacking.

External gas exchange.—The mandatory relationship between Po_2 and Pco_2 of the expired medium reflects in the waterbreather the large differences in solubility of these gases. A high ventilation is needed to satisfy O_2 requirements in waterbreathers because of the low O_2 content in water. The maximum attainable expired Pco_2 values characteristically become very low (19, 58, 59, 112, 160, 186, 188, 189, 199, 228, 245, 260, 261, 309, 310). The small inspired Pco_2 gradient in waterbreathers is minimized still further by the carbonate-bicarbonate buffering of some of the metabolically produced CO_2 (59) and also because expired water may be increased in excess base due to an ion exchange particularly of NH_4^+/Na^+ and HCO_3^-/Cl^- ions (59, 72, 194). Unlike O_2 solubility curves of water, the CO_2 solubility may show a curvilinear phase at very low Pco_2 values, provided the carbonate content of the water and its pH are high (59, 229). High concentrations of carbonic anhydrase in the gill tissues and erythrocytes of fish have also been alleged to play a role in maintaining low circulating Pco_2 levels since administration of carbonic anhydrase inhibitors substantially increases arterial Pco_2 (261).

The terms ventilatory and circulatory convection requirement have recently been introduced (60). These are expressed by the ratios of the volume of water, air, or blood moved per unit time, to the amount of gas transferred or eliminated via the gas exchanger. The authors discuss how the values of these ratios vary with ambient conditions as well as with factors such as temperature, activity, and food availability, all decisive for the demand for oxygen. Their extensive survey of aquatic and terrestrial animals emphasizes the much higher convection requirement of the ambient medium for waterbreathers. Blood convection requirements are, as a rule, lower than ambient medium convection due to the higher O_2-carrying capacity of blood than air or water. Notable exceptions occur at low O_2 capacities in anemic organisms (43) and in the hemoglobin-free icefishes (60, 107, 190).

When O_2 flow of ventilatory and circulatory convection is related to O_2 uptake the differences between water- and airbreathers are minimized (190). The term effectiveness in gas exchange, defined as the ratio of actual to maximum possible gas exchange, was introduced by Hughes & Shelton (130) and has been extensively used in recent papers (100, 117, 160, 170, 230, 245). The transfer factor for O_2 is defined as the ratio of gas volume taken up (or eliminated) to the mean partial pressure difference between water and blood (170, 230, 245).

Efficiency in aquatic gas exchange has traditionally been expressed by the percent extraction of O_2 from the ventilatory water current. Values ranging from 10% in trout (310) to the remarkably high value of 92% in the triggerfish (*Balistes capriscus*) (120) have been reported. Extraction varies inversely with ventilation but not in a regular fashion, depending upon concurrent variations in deadspace ventilation, perfusion shunts, level of O_2 uptake, and other factors altering the water to blood Po_2 gradient (19, 100, 170, 230, 243, 245). O_2 extraction in resting dogfish *Squalus suckleyi* varied between 20–50% at normal ventilation perfusion ratios, but could exceed 80% at very low V/Q ratios (100).

High values of O_2 extraction depend also on an effective countercurrent exchange. In a recent theoretical paper Hills & Hughes (109) offer a dimensional analysis of O_2 transfer in fish gills that supports the concept that laminar water flow exists between the secondary lamellae. This may be an important reason why the resistance afforded by convective transfer of gas (O_2) may be as high as 90% of the total diffusion resistance (109). Their analysis also bears out that a countercurrent exchange is the more probable.

Randall et al (245) calculated that the percent effectiveness of O_2 uptake by blood in rainbow trout approached 100% whereas effectiveness in removing O_2 from water ranged between 1–30%. Effectiveness in CO_2 removal from blood at the gills is very high, but the high CO_2 capacity of water and the high ventilation values in fishes bring about a low relative effectiveness in CO_2 uptake by the water.

Studies of gas exchange in sharks (100, 230) correspond well with each other and with the trout (245), particularly in view of differences in respiratory properties of blood and resting ventilation values.

Moderate exercise causes little change in effectiveness of gas exchange, while exposure to hypoxic water caused a marked decrease in effectiveness of O_2 uptake by blood, but affected O_2 removal from water much less (237, 245). Reduced effectiveness of O_2 uptake by blood during hypoxia is most likely a corollary to reduced arterial and/or venous O_2 content due to lower loading tensions and maintained arteriovenous differences if O_2 uptake is assumed unchanged. Comparisons of fishes with differing O_2-Hb affinity should verify this hypothesis. It would also be most interesting to study effectiveness in O_2 removal from water in fishes depending on passive or ram ventilation in moving water since the metabolic cost of ventilation would be reduced.

In calculation of effectiveness in CO_2 uptake by water and CO_2 removal from blood, one must carefully consider the chemical dissociation of carbonic acid and the CO_2 content of inspired water. Similarly, the nonlinearity of the CO_2 dissociation curve in water, the degree of blood oxygenation, and ion exchange or bicarbonate excretion which could alter the buffering qualities of expired water are important factors. (229) The importance of relating calculated values for effectiveness in gas exchange to values for ventilation and ventilation-perfusion ratios has also been discussed (100).

The transfer factor for O_2 is higher in trout than for the elasmobranchs studied (100, 229, 245), a difference likely to be related to differences in total and effective exchange areas as well as to the levels of O_2 uptake. Piiper & Baumgarten-Schumann (229) offer valuable comments about the complexity of factors influencing gas exchange in fish and the limitations in the use of calculated expressions.

Arterial Po_2 in fish inhabiting well-aerated water are generally high and commonly exceed values required to completely saturate the blood (310) (243). There are exceptions to such high arterializations, certainly among fishes inhabiting O_2-deficient waters, although these generally seem adapted to the O_2-poor environment by high O_2-Hb affinities (331) but also fishes in well-aerated water may show arterial saturations as low as 50%, as in resting eels (302). It has been argued that increased arterial saturation during exercise would meet the needed increase in arteriovenous O_2 difference in a more economical way than by lowering of the venous O_2 saturation only, since the ventilatory cost of maintaining high arterial saturations is so high in fish (74, 302).

Information on tissue gas tensions in fishes is almost totally lacking. The gas pocket technique (227, 236, 325) used on mammals indicates that pocket tensions are closely similar to those in venous blood draining the tissue.

A recent study using the gas pocket technique for tissue gas tension determination in trout and carp (76) shows that O_2 tensions lie slightly higher than in mixed venous blood, while the CO_2 tensions also were higher than in mixed venous blood. The high gas exchange ratios for the gas pockets are not readily explained unless ascribed to possible acidification and CO_2 release from blood by lactic acid or other metabolites (325). When tissue tensions were measured in this way for trout experiencing a cyclic fluctuation in ambient O_2 tension, the tissue values closely paralleled the mixed venous values. Tissue O_2 tensions in the carp were appreciably lower and less fluctuating than in trout, a fact ascribed to the much higher O_2-Hb affinity in carp which leaves the arterial and hence venous O_2 tensions largely unaffected by ambient O_2 tension unless this falls appreciably below what is needed to saturate the hemoglobin (76).

Venous O_2 tensions naturally vary more, reflecting differences in O_2-Hb affinity, cardiac output, and O_2 consumption levels. Many fishes retain a considerable venous O_2 reservoir and can draw from it during increased activity or during hypoxic stress. The adaptability of respiratory properties of blood to temperature and other ambient factors, as well as changes attending the transition from waterbreathing to airbreathing, has been reviewed many times (94, 152, 195, 243, 250, 331).

With blood O_2 concentration far exceeding those in water it is to be expected that ventilation-perfusion ratios in fish are very high compared to those in airbreathers. Values reported range from 9 in the shark *Scyliorhinus* (19) to as high as 70 in trout (245). The remarkably high ratio in trout is caused by exceptionally high ventilation values accompanied by a low O_2 extraction from water. In the dogfish *Squalus suckleyi* the effectiveness of O_2 removal from water decreased with increasing ventilation-perfusion ratios (100).

Jones et al (170) in a theoretical paper have calculated values for the ventilation-perfusion ratio for 95% arterial saturation in several species of fish when inspired O_2 tension, venous O_2 tension, and the average water-to-blood O_2 tension gradient were assumed to remain unchanged. Their analysis shows that a high O_2-Hb affinity correlates with a low ventilation-perfusion ratio for 95% saturation. The potentially most important adjustment for maintenance of arterial O_2 saturation during hypoxia was reasoned to be a lowering of the water-to-blood Po_2 gradient, a change actually observed in trout (112). Among other compensatory measures to hypoxia, an increased ventilation and an increased utilization of circulating O_2 by reduction in venous Po_2 have also been reported (112, 186).

Exercise in teleosts induces increases in ventilation, perfusion, and the transfer factor for O_2 proportional to the increase in overall O_2 uptake (310).

Studies of O_2 uptake and its variations with activity and ambient conditions continue to produce numerous papers, and comprehensive reviews on the subject have been published recently (243). The classification of animals as respiratory dependent or independent based on whether they reduce or maintain their O_2 uptake in the face of reduced ambient O_2 availability is ill defined and controversial (70).

Oxygen uptake varies with size, age, sex, season, and temperature (20, 21, 23, 89, 90, 106, 211, 239, 332), with qualities of the ambient environment including O_2 deficiency (17, 22, 64, 108, 131, 132, 197, 278), and with activity levels (37, 295, 310). Brett has excellently reviewed the various factors affecting respiratory metabolism in salmon (36).

Acclimation of metabolic rate to changing ambient conditions has also been extensively studied (138, 235, 256, 257, 286). Oxygen uptake rates at changing ambient conditions, particularly hypoxia, have been reported for airbreathing fishes (88, 159, 188, 199).

Many recent papers have contributed to the important problem of acid-base balance and how it is affected by temperature and salinity in the ambient water (229, 236). The very low circulating Pco_2 values in water-breathers correlate with low bicarbonate values and a low general buffering capacity (5, 114, 186, 187, 189, 231, 233). Lenfant & Johansen (186), working on the Pacific dogfish, observed that the CO_2 dissociation curves for whole blood and separated plasma differed little in actual shape, although the plasma curve showed lower CO_2 content at corresponding tensions. They proposed that dogfish blood shows a minor chloride shift component in mobilization of bicarbonate buffering; and they credited plasma proteins with most of the buffering capacity, a hypothesis they relate to the absence of a Haldane effect. This contention has been countered by several more recent studies (5, 6, 233). Albers & Pleschka (5) found that human blood diluted to the same red cell volume as dogfish blood displayed the same relationship between pH, Pco_2, and total CO_2 content as did dogfish blood. They dismiss the possibility that dogfish blood differs qualitatively in its buffer characteristics from mammalian blood. Further support for this was gained from studies showing a chloride shift from red cells to plasma when dogfish blood was exposed to increasing CO_2 (6, 49). The contention of a basic similarity in the buffering properties of hemoglobin in fish and mammals calls for a Bohr and Haldane effect. Contrary to earlier findings (61, 185) showing no Bohr shift in elasmobranch blood, Pleschka et al (233) demonstrated a Bohr shift and suggest that earlier negative studies may have been methodically deficient. However, these workers were unable to demonstrate any Haldane shift. Meanwhile, indirect evidence (49, 261) has demonstrated a large net loss of HCO_3^- from the blood being arterialized in the gills. A reverse change restoring HCO_3^- is indicated as a corollary to the O_2 unloading in the tissues. The presence of a marked Pasteur effect in elasmobranch red cells when exposed to 100% N_2 makes it experimentally difficult to demonstrate a Haldane effect. The excellent and careful study of Cross et al (49) deals with the acid-base characteristics in general of aquatic gas exchangers. Characteristically, the CO_2 titration curve shows a steep slope at low arterial P_{CO_2} which in fact is also demonstrated in mammalian blood at low P_{CO_2}. The authors conclude that vertebrates are similar in the chemical pattern of blood and body buffers, but that these buffers are relatively most effective at low concentrations of H_2CO_3, whereas the higher P_{CO_2} associated with airbreathing will largely titrate the buffers and produce smaller amounts of bicarbonate. The waterbreather can hence maintain a relatively stable extracellular pH over a severalfold increase in P_{CO_2}, whereas small P_{CO_2} changes in airbreathers produce much more marked changes in pH. Remember that the relative concentrations of most buffering compounds are much higher in the airbreathers. Cross et al (49) also offer interesting data on the direct elimination of H^+ across the gills and its implications in acid-base regulation.

The important problems of acid-base balance during exercise in fish have been studied in elasmobranchs (231, 261). Anaerobic glycolysis assessed by lactate analysis increases during and following severe exercise in fish as it does in other vertebrates (32, 33, 105, 231, 261, 308). Five minutes exercise in trout causes an 80% depletion of muscle glycogen, a 3.5-fold increase in muscle lactate, and a 10-fold increase in blood lactate. Blood lactate continued to increase in the recovery period after hard exercise (308). A comparison of the concentration change of lactate with bound H^+ revealed that they initially increased at a similar rate, while later the lactate increase greatly exceeded that of bound H^+. This implies that the buffering requirements are much less than could be expected from the high lactate concentrations, because H^+ either are effectively buffered in the tissues or are excreted across the gills and kidneys. The retention of lactate is important for further energy-yielding oxidation (231). A slow disappearance of lactate from fish blood has frequently been commented on (261, 308) and was expressed as no measurable arteriovenous difference in lactate across the gills even when lactate was administered in high doses (213).

Gas exchange in airbreathing fishes.—Airbreathing fishes are bimodal breathers with gills and/or skin functioning in aquatic gas exchange and a specialized organ variously structured and developed for direct aerial gas exchange (25, 152).

Airbreathing organs in fishes characteristically show very low gas exchange ratios and function primarily in O_2 absorption (75, 152, 160, 166, 188). Conversely, the gills, although often in much reduced form (63), and the skin are the principal sites for CO_2 elimination and these consequently show high gas exchange ratios (75, 114, 160, 188). In the electric eel, having all but totally lost its gills, 80% of the CO_2 elimination is effected via the skin.

The importance of the skin as a gas exchanger, and particularly its role in CO_2 elimination and acid-base balance in transitional bimodal breathers, has recently been discussed in particular detail (25, 114, 236) and placed in proper context with the role of the skin in amphibian and reptilian gas exchange.

Practically no work has been done on the profound and unique state of estivation seen in many airbreathing fishes. A marked reduction in general level of O_2 uptake and metabolism has been reported (297). A recent study involving short-term induction of estivation in the African lungfish (181) suggests that O_2 lack triggers the phenomenal reduction in metabolism earlier observed by Smith (297) when his animals were deprived of food or air-exposed. Lahiri et al (181) also offer data on anaerobic metabolism in the African lungfish during short-term hypoxia, and they compare the reduced metabolism and switch to anaerobiosis, coupled with bradycardia and peripheral circulatory redistribution, to the general reflexly released syndrome seen in habitually diving vertebrates upon submersion (7, 283) or in fishes upon air exposure (149, 185, 289).

The relative importance of airbreathing in total O_2 uptake varies in different species and may play no role in well-aerated water (25, 149, 189), but plays an increasingly important role in O_2-deficient or hypercarbic water such as shown for *Neoceratodus* (189) and *Polypterus senegalus* (1–3). Increased activity also intensifies airbreathing efforts (2, 88, 159). Aquatic and aerial gas exchange have been studied in relation to temperature and gas composition of the ambient water in *Amia calva,* a primitive airbreathing fish (160). With increasing temperature the rate of O_2 depletion from the airbladder and the rate of airbreathing increase progressively. Whereas at 10° no O_2 was taken from the air, at 30°C three times as much O_2 was taken from air as from water, while aquatic gas exchange continued to be the principal means of CO_2 elimination.

Some airbreathing fishes like the electric eel *Electrophorus electricus* are obligate airbreathers and succumb if denied access to air even if in well-aerated water (68, 75, 166). During ontogenetic development many airbreathing fishes change from pure waterbreathers during larval or juvenile stages to obligate airbreathers when adult. This interesting change in both the structure and physiology of the gas exchange organs has been studied for the African lungfish (199) and would be a valuable target for study in several other species.

Airbreathing fishes are predominantly freshwater and mostly tropical, but a few intertidal species of teleosts have developed interesting airbreathing habits (323). Tidal volumes and ventilation patterns in the bimodal breathing practice of airbreathing fishes have been studied only for a few species (68, 143).

Internal gas transport studied by blood sampling from unrestrained air-breathing fishes is understandably difficult technically and has only been reported for a few species (75, 149, 160, 165, 166, 181, 189).

The data presented in these papers suggest complex mechanisms adjusting the blood flow rates and shunt patterns in the vascular networks connecting the gas exchangers with the systemic vascular beds. In *Protopterus* (164), the electric eel (166), and the bowfin *Amia calva* (160) there are increases of cardiac output and of the fraction of the cardiac output perfusing the aerial gas exchanger associated with each breath. The act of breathing, possibly the mechanical distention of the airbreathing organ, and the quality of gas inside the airbreathing organ seem to be decisive for the perfusion changes (160, 166).

Garey & Rahn (75) working with the electric eel have recently emphasized the necessity of allowing sufficient time for recovery from the surgical implantation of catheters in airbreathing fishes, since plasma bicarbonate and pH levels are greatly distorted from a combined respiratory and metabolic acidosis within the first day after the operation. They claim that meaningful study of acid-base equilibrium must await 2 days recovery before blood sampling.

Acid-base balance in airbreathing fishes is faced with special problems since adoption of airbreathing for relief of aquatic O_2 deficiency caused a retention of CO_2 due to the reduced ventilation rate in airbreathers and the bidirectional airflow to the accessory airbreathing organs (114, 152). Increased dependence on airbreathing is hence associated with increased circulating P_{CO_2} levels, which call for increased buffering capacity. A good correlation exists between the level of bicarbonate and the preponderance of airbreathing (114, 152, 166, 189).

Control of breathing.—Regulation of breathing in fishes has been excellently reviewed recently (117, 293). Several studies and a recent review have discussed factors involved in the regulation of breathing in airbreathing fishes (26, 68, 152, 160, 166, 300). In teleosts the medullary region possesses the capacity to initiate and coordinate rhythmic breathing movements. The more exact location of the respiratory center has been studied by transections and ablations (291, 292) as well as from recordings of electrical activity in the brain (14, 134, 292, 326, 333). A wide area of the medulla is credited with functioning as generator of respiratory rhythmicity. Electrical rhythmic activity is, of course, also detectable in the motoneurons innervating the musculature used in respiratory pumping (326). The available evidence suggests that the respiratory neurons are widespread and that their activity depends upon afferent influx from proprioceptive or chemo-receptor stimulation (14, 293, 337). The generator function of the respiratory neurons seems independent of mechanoreceptor feedback according to experiments with neuromuscular blocking agents, but the actual frequency of the electrical activity shows variable influence from proprioceptive feedback (14, 265, 275, 288, 326). The exact nature and importance of secondary influences upon respiratory neurons remain largely speculative (293). As for the generation of normal breathing rhythm, it has been suggested (292) that the interaction between widely dispersed respiratory neurons takes the form of alternating and reciprocally inhibiting discharges between groups of neurons.

A proprioceptive feedback mechanism on the respiratory rhythmicity in sharks has long been contended (191, 192, 222, 270, 275). An inhibitory role of pharyngeal mechanoreceptors is indicated by an accelerated breathing rate following transection of the nerves innervating the respiratory pumping muscles.

A proprioceptive effect on branchial respiratory rhythm has been described for the South American and African lungfish (163, 164). Slight mechanical agitation of the water by gently tapping the outside aquarium wall caused a marked increase in breathing rate.

The transition from active ventilation powered by branchial muscles to passive ram ventilation as swimming speed increases has naturally stimulated speculation that a proprioceptive feedback exists between the swimming muscles and the respiratory center. While we await conclusive experimental proof of such feedback links, a fascinating study on the sucking fish *Remora remora* has indicated that proprioception from the swimming muscles may not be, or may at least not be the only feedback loop involved in transition from active to passive ventilation (205). *Remora* pumps water by active respiratory movements when in still water but when attached to an object in a water current, the active respiration gradually diminishes as the water speed increases, reaching a point when active respiration ceases altogether. This transition is totally independent of motor activity since the fish remains quietly attached by his dorsal sucking organ. The impingement of water against the head or buccal surfaces may stimulate mechanoreceptors to induce the inhibition of active respiration.

Respiration and chemoreceptor function.—The role of chemoreception in respiration feedback control must differ in aerial and aquatic breathers. The airbreather normally occupies an environment where no sudden changes in ambient gas composition occur. The stability of internal conditions important to respiration hence mostly depends on a correction of misalignments originating internally. The bidirectional airway and internal location of the gas exchanger will also shield the internal environment against external changes. The waterbreather faces an entirely different situation because the aquatic environment can be relatively unstable in its gas composition, pH, and temperature, and the intimate diffusion contact in the gills and the unidirectional passage of ventilated water will cause external instability to quickly manifest itself internally. If, for instance, a fish enters severely hypoxic water with resulting internal hypoxemia, an increased breathing effort may further aggravate the hypoxemia. It might better serve homeostasis if the fish attempted to relocate to water of higher O_2 content. A differential chemoreceptive control system is hence called for which allows a distinction between changes occurring externally or internally (152).

An increased ventilation volume in response to hypoxic water is reported for the majority of teleost fishes examined (see Shelton 293 for extensive references). It has also long been contended that fishes show preference reactions to external gradients in gas composition linked with an ability to detect water gas tensions by external chemoreceptors (135). Similarly, external Pco_2 and pH changes will cause prompt escape reactions (135, 234, 280). Whether such escape responses caused by incipient suffocation are directive or nondirective is not decided (152). However, many fishes living in hypoxic water show a clear chemotaxis for the more O_2-rich surface layers (46, 150).

A comparison of airbreathing fishes in their response to external hypoxia is interesting. Species like the Australian lungfish which depends almost entirely on aquatic breathing show a conspicuous ventilatory increase in hypoxic water (165), whereas obligate airbreathing fishes like *Protopterus* or the electric eel *Electrophorus* show no ventilatory response whatsoever to hypoxic water (68, 164, 166). However, in their juvenile stages when gillbreathing is important, these species show an increased ventilation in hypoxic water (143, 199). Studies are needed to determine whether the lack of sensitivity to hypoxic water in adult obligate airbreathing fish is due to the reduced gills and poor diffusion contact between water and the internal environment or to a specific specialization of the chemoreceptors. Note that hypercarbic water ($Pco_2 > 10$ mm Hg) causes a depression of branchial breathing in airbreathing fishes. In aquatic fishes hypercarbic water is reported to cause increased gill ventilation (240, 278), although higher concentrations have a depressive effect. Airbreathing fishes show a conspicuous, prompt increase in airbreathing when exposed to air (26, 164).

It has been argued that an increased ventilation in response to increased CO_2 in the water can do little to reduce the already very small Pco_2 gradient between blood and water in fishes (293), and if hypercarbia in the water is not associated with O_2-deficient water the increased ventilation becomes superfluous for providing O_2 (246).

It has been suggested that the CO_2 response is coupled primarily to increased internal levels in the tissues or venous blood, offering appropriate signals about metabolic changes (293). The presence of bloodborne CO_2 or pH detectors on the venous side is countered at least for the Australian lungfish by the demonstration that increased venous P_{CO_2} from artificial deposition of a high CO_2 level in the lung evoked no ventilatory response at all, whereas exposure to increased CO_2 in the water promptly elicited a response. This observation speaks for the presence of CO_2 sensors located externally or in the efferent (postbranchial) circulation. The high CO_2 concentrations on the venous side from deposition of CO_2 in the lung were completely eliminated from the blood during passage through the gills.

Although it has been definitely established that chemical stimuli reflexly influence breathing in fishes, the location, structure, and sensory mechanism of the chemoreceptors are very poorly understood. A study on trout has described alleged chemoreceptors in the buccal cavity and on the gills (57). Laurent (183, 184) in the most direct studies of chemoreceptor function in fishes, to date, recorded electrical discharges from a branch of the glosso-pharyngeal nerve innervating the pseudobranch. He worked with an isolated perfused pseudobranch preparation from the tench and demonstrated an altered electrical discharge to changes in O_2 and CO_2 concentrations.

Experiments with nerve sectioning and the fact that not all fishes possess a pseudobranch make it clear that receptors sensitive to lack of O_2 exist outside areas innervated by the vagus and glossopharyngeus (130, 293). In a recent study on *Protopterus*, Lahiri et al (181) claim to have demonstrated chemoreceptors responsive to O_2 lack. They demonstrated an exponential relationship between arterial P_{O_2} and the frequency of airbreathing and pointed out the similarity to mammalian conditions. Hyperoxic breathing decreased the frequency of airbreathing, which indicates as had been shown earlier on both waterbreathing and airbreathing fishes (166) that breathing is at least partly maintained by a hypoxic drive. In a theoretical analysis Jones et al (170) also predicted an equilibrium position to be reached on a curve relating arterial O_2 tension to the ventilation-perfusion ratio when the rate of change of chemoreceptor firing signifies the presence of a maximum economically attainable arterial tension.

Using serial injections of hypoxic blood and cyanide into afferent gill arteries on *Protopterus*, Lahiri et al (181) demonstrated that ventilatory stimulation was elicited from the anterior and posterior gill arches with a more pronounced effect from the anterior arches. Bilateral nerve sectioning markedly decreased the response to hypoxemia and abolished the ventilatory response to cyanide. Another study on *Protopterus* (164) offered evidence that intravenous or external administration of nicotine to the water elicits an increase in both air- and waterbreathing.

In addition to an arterial or external location of chemoreceptors in fish, the theoretical paper by Taylor et al (318) suggests a venous location for chemoreceptors in fish. Speaking for such a location is the rationale that some product of metabolism is a natural and easily detectable stimulus if the sensor screens the mixed venous blood. Speaking against it is the lack of direct contact with ambient conditions, and the sensitivity needed would be high since venous O_2 tensions fall on the steepest portion of the O_2 Hb dissociation curve. Such venous receptors would also encroach on the usefulness of a venous O_2 reserve.

A coupling of the control of aquatic and aerial breathing in bimodal breathers has been demonstrated for both lungfishes and the bowfin *Amia clava* (160, 164).

LITERATURE CITED

1. Abdel Magid, A. M. 1966. Breathing and function of the spiracles in *Polypterus senegalus. Anim. Behav.* 14 :530–33

2. Abdel Magid, A. M. 1967. Respiration of air by the primitive fish *Polypterus senegalus. Nature* 215 :1096–97

3. Abdel Magid, A. M., Vokac, Z., Nasr El Din Ahmed. 1970. Respiratory function of the swim-bladders of the primitive fish, *Polypterus senegalus. J. Exp. Biol.* 52 :27–37

4. Ahlquist, R. P. 1948. A study of adrenotropic receptors. *Am. J. Physiol.* 153 :586–600

5. Albers, C., Pleschka, K. 1967. Effect of temperature on CO_2 transport in elasmobranch blood. *Resp. Physiol.* 2 :261–73

6. Albers, C., Pleschka, K., Spaich, P. 1969. Chloride distribution between red blood cells and plasma in the dogfish (*Scyliorhinus canicula*). *Resp. Physiol.* 7 :295–99

7. Andersen, H. T. 1966. Physiological adaptation in diving vertebrates. *Physiol. Rev.* 46 :212–43

8. Augustinsson, K. B., Fänge, R., Johnels, A., Östlund, E., 1956. Histological, physiological, and biochemical studies on the heart of two cyclostomes, Hagfish (*Myxine*) and Lamprey (*Lampetra*). *J. Physiol. London* 131 :257–76

9. Baglioni, S. 1910. Zur vergleichende Physiologie der Atembewegungen der Wirbeltiere. *J. Fische. Ergeb. Physiol.* 9 :90–137

10. Balabai, P. P. 1935. Zur Morphologischen Characteristik des präbranchialen Teiles des visceralen Apparates bei den Petromizonten. *Trav. Morphol. Animaux Kiev* 1 : 131–68

11. Ballintijn, C. M. 1968. Muscle coordination of the respiratory pump of the carp (*Cyprinus carpio* L.). *J. Exp. Biol.* 50 :569–91

12. Ballintijn, C. M. 1968. Movement pattern and efficiency of the respiratory pump of the carp (*Cyprinus carpio* L.). *J. Exp. Biol.* 50 : 593–613

13. Ballintijn, C. M. 1969. Functional anatomy and movement co-ordination of the respiratory pump of the carp (*Cyprinus carpio* L.). *J. Exp. Biol.* 50 :547–67

14. Ballintijn, C. M. 1969. The influence of proprioception upon respiratory neurones in the medulla oblongata of fishes. *Acta Physiol. Pharmacol. Neer.* 15 :25–6

15. Ballintijn, C. M., Hughes, G. M. 1965. The muscular basis of the respiratory pumps in the trout. *J. Exp. Biol.* 43 :349–62

16. Barry, A. 1950. The effect of epinephrine on the myocardium of the embryonic chick. *Circulation* 1 :1362–68

17. Basu, S. P. 1959. Active respiration of fish in relation to ambient concentrations of oxygen and carbon dioxide. *J. Fish. Res. Bd. Can.* 16 :175–212

18. Baumgarten, D., Randall, D. J., Malyusz, J. 1970. Gas exchange versus ion exchange across the gills of fish. In preparation

19. Baumgarten-Schumann, D., Piiper, J. 1968. Gas exchange in the gills of resting unanesthetized dogfish, *Scyliorhinus. Resp. Physiol.* 5 : 317–25

20. Beamish, F. W. H. 1964. Respiration of fishes with special emphasis on standard oxygen consumption. II. Influence of weight and temperature on respiration of several species. *Can. J. Zool.* 42 :189–94

21. Beamish, F. W. H. 1964. Respiration of fishes with special emphasis on standard oxygen consumption. III. Influence of oxygen. *Can. J. Zool.* 42 :355–66

22. Beamish, F. W. H. 1964. Respiration of fishes with special emphasis on standard oxygen consumption. IV. Influence of carbon dioxide and oxygen. *Can. J. Zool.* 42 :847–56

23. Beamish, F. W. H., Mookherjii, P. S. 1964. Respiration of fishes with special emphasis on standard oxygen consumption. I. Influence of weight and temperature on respiration of gold fish. *Can. J. Zool.* 42 :161–75

24. Bennion, G. R., Randall, D. J. 1969. Starling's law and the control of the isolated, perfused trout heart. In preparation

25. Berg, T., Steen, J. B. 1965. Physio-

logical mechanisms for aerial respiration in the eel. *Comp. Biochem. Physiol.* 15:469–84

26. Berg, T., Steen, J. B. Regulation of ventilation in eels exposed to air. *Comp. Biochem. Physiol.* 18:511–16

27. Bevelander, G. 1934. The gills of *Amia calva* specialized for respiration in an oxygen deficient habitat. *Copeia* 3:123–27

28. Bianki, V. L., Vinnitskii, A. M. 1965. Cardiac conditioned reflexes in cerebellectomized fish. *Dokl. Akad. Nauk SSSR.* 164:674–77

29. Bijtel, H. J. 1949. The structure and the mechanism of movement of the gill filaments in teleostei. *Arch. Neer. Zool.* 8:267–87

30. Birch, M. P., Carre, C. G., Satchell, G. H. 1969. Venous return in the trunk of the Port Jackson Shark, *Heterodontus portusjacksoni. J. Zool.* 159:31–49

31. Bishop, I. R., Foxon, G. E. H. 1968. The mechanism of breathing in the South American lungfish, *Lepidosiren paradoxa;* a radiological study. *J. Zool.* 154:263–71

32. Black, E. C. 1957. Alterations in the blood level of lactic acid in certain salmonoid fishes following muscular activity. II. Lake Trout, *Salvelinus namayeush. J. Fish. Res. Bd. Can.* 14(4):645–49

33. Black, E. C., Chiu, W.-G., Forbes, F. D., Hanslip, A. 1959. Changes in pH, carbonate, and lactate of the blood of yearling Kamloops trout, *Salmo gairdneri,* during and following severe muscular activity. *J. Fish. Res. Bd. Can.* 16(4):391–402

34. Blinks, J. R. 1956. Positive chronotropic effect of increasing right atrial pressure in the isolated mammalian heart. *Am. J. Physiol.* 186:299–303

35. Bloom, G., Östlund, E., von Euler, U. S., Lishajko, F., Ritzen, M., Adams-Ray, J. 1961. Studies on catecholamine-containing granules of specific cells in cyclostome hearts. *Acta Physiol. Scand.* 53: Suppl. 185, 1–34

36. Brett, J. R. 1962. Some considerations in the study of respiratory metabolism in fish, particularly salmon. *J. Fish. Res. Bd. Can.* 19(6):1025–38

37. Brett, J. R. 1964. The respiratory metabolism and swimming performance of young sockeye salmon. *J. Fish Res. Bd. Can.* 21:1183–226

38. Burger, J. W., Bradley, S. E. 1951. The general form of the circulation in the dogfish *Squalus acanthias. J. Cell. Comp. Physiol.* 37:389–402

39. Burnstock, G., Kirby, S. 1970. Absence of inhibitory effects of catecholamines on lower vertebrate arterial strip preparations. *J. Pharm. Pharmacol.* In press

40. Byczkowski-Smyk, W. 1957. The respiratory surface of the gills in teleosts. Part I: The respiratory surface of the gills in the flounder, *Pleuronectes platessa,* and perch, *Perca fluviatilis. Zool. Pol.* 8:91–111

41. Byczkowski-Smyk, W. 1958. The respiratory surface of the gills in teleosts. Part II: The respiratory surface of the gills in the eel (*Anguilla anguilla* L.), the loach (*Misgurnus fossilis* L.) and the perchlike (*Lucioperca lucioperca* L.). *Acta Biol. Cracov.* 1:83–97

42. Byczkowski-Smyk, W. 1959. The respiratory surface of the gills in teleosts. Part III: The respiratory surface of the gills in the tench (*Tinca tinca* L.), the silver bream (*Blicca bjoerkna* L.) and the chondrostoma (*Chondrostoma nosus* L.). *Acta Biol. Cracov.* 2:73–88

43. Cameron, J. N., Davis, J. C. 1970. Gas exchange in rainbow trout (*Salmo gairdneri). J. Fish. Res. Bd. Can.* 27:1069–85

44. Carey, F. G., Teal, J. M. 1969. Mako and Porbeagle: Warmbodied sharks. *Comp. Biochem. Physiol.* 28:199–204

45. Carey, F. G., Teal, J. M. 1969. Regulation of body temperature by the bluefin tuna. *Comp. Biochem. Physiol.* 28:205–13

46. Carter, G. S., Beadle, L. C. 1931. The fauna of the swamps of the Paraguayan Chaco in relation to its environment. II. Respiratory adaptations in the fishes. *J. Linn. Soc. London Zool.* 37:327–66

47. Couteaux, R., Laurent, P. 1957. Étude au microscope éléctronique du coeur de l'Anguille: observations sur la structure du tissu musculaire de l'oreillette et son

innervation. *C. R. Acad. Sci.* 245 : 2097–100

48. Couteaux, R., Laurent, P. 1958. Observations au microscope éléctronique sur l'innervation cardiaque des téléosteens. *Bull. Assoc. Anat. Paris* 98 :230

49. Cross, C. E., Packer, B. S., Linta, J. M., Murdaugh, H. V., Robin, E. D. 1969. H+ buffering and excretion in response to acute hypercapnia in the dogfish, *Squalus acanthias. Am. J. Physiol.* 216 : 440–52

50. Dam, L. van. 1938. *On the utilization of oxygen and regulation of breathing in some aquatic animals.* Dissertation. Groningen

51. Darbishire, A. D. 1907. On the direction of the aqueous current in the spiracle of the dogfish ; together with some observations on the respiratory mechanism in other elasmobranch fishes. *J. Linn. Soc. London Zool.* 30 :36–94

52. Das, B. K. 1940. Nature and causes of evolution and adaptation of the air-breathing fishes. *Proc. 27th Indian Sci. Congr.* No. 2, 215–60

53. Davis, J. C., Watters, K. 1970. Evaluation of several methods for sampling water expired by fish. *J. Fish. Res. Bd. Can.* 27 :1627–35

54. Dawson, J. 1905. The breathing and feeding mechanism of the lampreys. *Biol. Bull.* 9 :1–21, 91–111

55. Deck, K. A. 1964. Dehnungseffekte am spontanschlagenden, isoliertem Sinusknoten. *Pfluegers Arch.* 280 : 120–30

56. DeGroodt, M., Lagasse, A., Sebruyns, M. 1960. Elektronenmikroskopische morphologie der lungenalveolen des *Protopterus* und *Amblystoma. Proc. 4th Int. Conf. Electron Microscopy.* 1 :418–21. Berlin : Springer

57. de Kock, L. L. 1963. A histological study of the head region of two salmonids with special reference to pressor and chemoreceptors. *Acta Anat.* 55 :39–50

58. Dejours, P. 1966. Respiratory gas exchange of aquatic animals during confinement. *J. Physiol. London* 186 :126–27P

59. Dejours, P., Armand, J., Verriest, G. 1968. Carbon dioxide dissociation curves of water and gas exchange of waterbreathers. *Resp. Physiol.* 5 :23–33

60. Dejours, P., Garey, W. F., Rahn, H. 1970. Comparison of ventilatory and circulatory flow rates between animals in various physiological conditions. *Resp. Physiol.* 9 :108–117

61. Dill, D. B., Edwards, H. T., Florkin, M. 1932. Properties of the blood of the skate (*Raia oscillata*). *Biol. Bull.* 62 :23–36

62. Dornesco, G. T., Santa, V. 1963. La structure des aortes et des vaisseaux de la carpe (*Cyprinus Carpio* L.). *Anat. Anz.* 113 :136–45

63. Dubale, M. S. 1951. A comparative study of the extent of gill surface in some representative Indian fishes, etc. *J. Univ. Bombay* 19 : 90–101

64. Erichson, Jones, J. R. 1952. The reactions of fish to water of low oxygen concentration. *J. Exp. Biol.* 29 :403–15

65. von Euler, U. S. 1953. Presence of catecholamines in visceral organs of fish and invertebrates. *Acta Physiol. Scand.* 28 :297–305

66. Falck, B., Mecklenburg, C. von, Myhrberg, H., Persson, H. 1966. Studies on adrenergic and cholinergic receptors in the isolated hearts of *Lampetra fluviatilis* (Cyclostomata) and *Pleuronectes platessa* (Teleostei). *Acta Physiol. Scand.* 68 :64–71

67. Fänge, R., Östlund, E. 1954. The effects of adrenaline, noradrenaline, tyramine and other drugs on the isolated heart from marine vertebrates and a cephalopod (*Eledone cirrosa*). *Acta Zool. Stockholm* 37 : 289–305

68. Farber, J., Rahn, H. 1970. Gas exchange between air and water and the ventilation pattern in the electric eel. *Resp. Physiol.* 9 :151–61

69. Forster, R. E., Steen, J. B. 1969. The rate of the Root shift of eel red cells and hemoglobin solution. *J. Physiol.* 204 :259–82

70. Fry, F. E. J. 1957. The aquatic respiration of fish. *Physiology of fishes.* ed. M. E. Brown, I :1–63. New York : Academic

71. Gannon, J., Burnstock, G. 1969. Excitatory adrenergic innervation of the fish heart. *Comp. Biochem. Physiol.* 29 :765–73

72. Garcia Romeu, F., Motais, R. 1966. Mise en évidence d'échanges Na⁺/NH₄⁺ chez l'angiulle d'eau douce. *Comp. Biochem. Physiol.* 17 :1201–4

73. Garey, W. F. 1969. Sampling blood from freely swimming fish. *J. Appl. Physiol.* 27 :756–57

74. Garey, W. F. 1970. Cardiac output of the carp (*Cyprinus carpio*). *Comp. Biochem. Physiol.* 33 :181–89

75. Garey, W. F., Rahn, H. 1970. Normal arterial gas tensions and pH and the breathing frequency of the electric eel. *Resp. Physiol.* 9 : 141–50

76. Garey, W. F., Rahn, H. 1970. Gas tensions in tissues of trout and carp exposed to diurnal changes in oxygen tension of the water. *J. Exp. Biol.* 52 :575–82

77. Gaskell, W. H. 1880. On the tonicity of the heart and blood vessels. *J. Physiol. London* 3 :48–75

78. Glauser, S. C., Glauser, E. M., Busy, B. F. 1967. Gas density and the work of breathing. *Resp. Physiol.* 2 :344–50

79. Goetz, K. L. 1964. Effect of pressure changes within the right heart upon the heart rate in dogs. *Circulation* 30 :*Suppl. 3*, 85

80. Goetz, K. L. 1965. Effect of increased pressure within a right heart cul-de-sac on heart rate in dogs. *Am. J. Physiol.* 209 :507–12

81. Goldstein, L., Forster, R. P., Fanelli, G. M. 1964. Gill blood flow and ammonia excretion in the marine teleost, *Myxocephalus scorpius*. *Comp. Biochem. Physiol.* 12 :489–99

82. Golenhofen, K., Lippross, H. 1969. Mechanische Koppelungswirkungen der Atmung auf den Herzschlag. *Pfluegers Arch.* 309 :156–59

83. Goodrich, E. S. 1930. *Studies on the structure and development of vertebrates.* London : MacMillan

84. Govyrin, V. A., Leont'eva, G. R. 1965. Distribution of catecholamines in vertebrate myocardium. *Zh. Evol. Biokhim. Fiziol.* 1(1) : 38–44

85. Gray, E. I. 1954. Comparative study of the gill area of marine fishes. *Biol. Bull.* 107 :219–25

86. Greene, C. W. 1902. Contributions to the physiology of the California hagfish, *Polistotrema stouti*. II. The anatomy and physiology of the absence of regulative nerves for the systemic heart. *Am. J. Physiol.* 6 :318–24

87. Green, G. W. 1904. Physiological studies of the chinook salmon. *Bull. U.S. Fish. Bur.* 24 :431–56

88. Grigg, G. C. 1965. Studies of the Queensland lungfish *Neoceratodus forsteri* (Krefft). I. Anatomy, histology and functioning of the lung. *Aust. J. Zool.* 13 :243–53

89. Grigg, G. C. 1965. Studies on the Queensland lungfish *Neoceratodus forsteri* (Krefft). II. Thermal acclimation. *Aust. J. Zool.* 13 :407–11

90. Grigg, G. C. 1969. Temperature induced changes in the oxygen. Equilibrium curve of the blood of the brown bullhead, *Ictalurus nebulosus. Comp. Biochem. Physiol.* 29 : 1203–23

91. Grigg, G. C. 1969. The failure of oxygen transport in a fish at low levels of ambient oxygen. *Comp. Biochem. Physiol.* 29 :1253–57

92. Grigg, G. C. 1970. Water flow through the gills of Port Jackson sharks. *J. Exp. Biol.* 52 :565–68

93. Grigg, G. C. 1970. Use of the first gill slits for water intake in a shark. *J. Exp. Biol.* 52 :569–74

94. Grigg, G. C. 1971. Respiratory function of the blood. In *Chemical Zoology.* VIII. *Pisces*, ed. M. Florkin, B. T. Scheer. New York : Academic

95. Grigg, G. C., Read, J. 1970. Gill function in an elasmobranch. *Resp. Physiol.* In press

96. Grodzinski, Z. 1955. Tetno. odcinkow izolowanego serca zaradkow troci. Salmo trutta. *Folia Biol.* 3 :65–82

97. Hanson, D. 1967. *Cardiovascular dynamics and aspects of gas exchange in chondrichtyes.* PhD thesis. Univ. of Wash. 178 pp.

98. Hanson, D. 1970. Personal communication

99. Hanson, D., Martin, A. W. 1967. Counter current exchange in gills of dogfish. *Fed. Proc.* 26 :442

100. Hanson, D., Johansen, K. 1970. Relationship of gill ventilation and perfusion in dogfish. *Squalus suckleyi. J. Fish. Res. Bd. Can.* 27 : 551–64

101. Hanson, D., Johansen, K. 1971. Control of branchial circulation in the bowfin, *Amia calva.* In preparation

102. Harris, W. S., Morton, M. J. 1968. A cardiac intrinsic mechanism that relates heart rate to filling pressure. *Circulation* 38 :Suppl. 6, 95

103. Hart, J. S. 1945. The circulation and respiratory tolerance of some Florida fresh water fishes. *Proc. Fla. Acad. Sci.* 7 :221–46

104. Hazelhoff, E. H., Evenhuis, H. H. 1952. Importance of the counter current principle for oxygen uptake in fishes. *Nature* 169 :77

105. Heath, A. G., Pritchard, A. W. 1965. Effects of severe hypoxia on carbohydrate energy stores and metabolism in two species of fresh water fish. *Physiol. Zool.* 38 :325–34

106. Hemmingsen, E. A., Douglas, E. L., Grigg, G. C. 1969. Oxygen consumption in an antarctic hemoglobin free fish, *Pagetopsis Macropterus*, and in three species of *Notothenia. Comp. Biochem. Physiol.* 29 :467–70

107. Hemmingsen, E. A., Douglas, E. L. 1970. Respiratory characteristics of the hemoglobin free fish, *Chaenocephalus aceratus. Comp. Biochem. Physiol.* 33 :733–44

108. Heusner, A., Kayser, C., Marx, C., Stussi, T., Harmelin, M. L. 1963. Relation entre le poids et la consommation d'oxygene. II. Etude intraspecifique chez le poissons. *C.R. Soc. Biol.* 157 :654–57

109. Hills, B. A., Hughes, G. M. 1970. A dimensional analysis of oxygen transfer in the fish gill. *Resp. Physiol.* 9 :126–40

110. Hirsch, E. F., Jellinek, M., Cooper, T. 1964. Innervation of the systematic heart of the California hagfish. *Circ. Res.* 14 :212–17

111. Holeton, G. F., Randall, D. J. 1967. Changes in blood pressure in the rainbow trout during hypoxia. *J. Exp. Biol.* 46 :297–305

112. Holeton, G. F., Randall, D. J. 1967. The effect of hypoxia upon the partial pressure of gases in the blood and water afferent and efferent to the gills of rainbow trout. *J. Exp. Biol.* 46 :317–27

113. Holst, R. 1969. Unpublished

114. Howell, B. J. 1970. Acid-base balance in the transition from water breathing to air breathing. *Fed. Proc.* 29 :1130–34

115. Hughes, G. M. 1960. The mechanism of gill ventilation in the dogfish and skate. *J. Exp. Biol.* 37 :11–27

116. Hughes, G. M. 1960. A comparative study of gill ventilation in marine teleosts. *J. Exp. Biol.* 37 :28–45

117. Hughes, G. M. 1964. Fish respiratory homeostasis. *Symp. Soc. Exp. Biol.* 18 :81–107

118. Hughes, G. M. 1966. Evolution between air and water. *Development of the Lung. Ciba Found. Symp.*, 64–80. London : Churchill

119. Hughes, G. M. 1966. The dimensions of fish gills in relation to their function. *J. Exp. Biol.* 45 :177–95

120. Hughes, G. M. 1967. Experiments on the respiration of the trigger fish (*Balistes capriscus*). *Experientia* 23 :1077

121. Hughes, G. M. 1970. A comparative approach to fish respiration. *Experientia* 26 :113–22

122. Hughes, G. M., Ballintijn, C. M. 1965. The muscular basis of the respiratory pumps in the dogfish (*Scilliorhynus canicula*). *J. Exp. Biol.* 43 :363–83

123. Hughes, G. M., Grimstone, A. V. 1965. The fine structure of the secondary lamellae of the gills of *Gadus pollachius. Quart. J. Microsc. Sci.* 106 :343–53

124. Hughes, G. M., Morgan, M. 1970. The structure and respiratory function of fish gills. *Biol. Rev.* In press

125. Hughes, G. M., Munshi, J. S. D. 1968. Fine structure of the respiratory surface of an air-breathing fish, the climbing perch *Anabas testudineus* (Bloch). *Nature* 219 :1382–84

126. Hughes, G. M., Munshi, J. S. D. 1970. Fine structure of the respiratory epithelia of some Indian air-breathing fishes. In preparation

127. Hughes, G. M., Roberts, J. D. 1970. A study of the effect of temperature changes on the respiratory pumps of the rainbow trout. *J. Exp. Biol.* 52 :177–92

128. Hughes, G. M., Shelton, G. 1957. Pressure changes during the respiratory movements of teleostan fishes. *Nature* 179 :225

129. Hughes, G. M., Shelton, G. 1958. The mechanism of gill ventilation in three fresh water teleosts. *J. Exp. Biol.* 35 :807–23

130. Hughes, G. M., Shelton, G. 1962. Respiratory mechanism and their nervous control in fish. *Advan.*

Comp. Physiol. Biochem. 1:275–364

131. Hughes, G. M., Umezawa, S. I. 1968. Oxygen consumption and gill water flow in the dogfish Scyliorhinus canicula L. J. Exp. Biol. 49:557–64

132. Hughes, G. M., Umezawa, S. I. 1968. On the respiration of the dragonet Callionymus lyra. J. Exp. Biol. 49:565–82

133. Hughes, G. M., Wright, D. E. 1970. A comparative study of the ultrastructure of the water-blood pathway in the secondary lamellae of the Teleost and Elasmobranch fishes—Benthic Forms. Z. Zellforsch. Mikrosk. Anat. 104:478–93

134. Hukuhara, T., Okada, H. 1956. On the automaticity of the respiratory centers of the catfish and the crucian carp. Jap. J. Physiol. 6:313–20

135. Høglund, L. B. 1966. The reactions of fish in concentration gradients. A comparative study based on Fluvarium experiments with special reference to oxygen, acidity, carbon dioxide, and sulphite waste liquor. (SWL). Rep. No. 43 Inst. Freshwater Res. Fish Bd. 1–147

136. Irving, L., Solandt, D. V., Solandt, O. M. 1935. Nerve impulses from branchial pressure receptors in the dogfish. J. Physiol. London 84:187–90

137. Iwai, T., Nakamura, I. 1964. Branchial skeleton of the bluefin tuna, with special reference to the gill rays. Bull. Misaki Mar. Biol. Inst. Kyoto Univ. 6:21–5

138. Jankowsky. 1966. The effect of adaptation temperature on the metabolic level of the eel, Anguilla vulgaris L. Helgoländer Wiss. Meeresunters. 13:402–7

139. Jensen, D. 1958. Some observations on cardiac automation in certain animals. J. Gen. Physiol. 42:289–302

140. Jensen, D. 1961. Cardioregulation in an aneural heart. Comp. Biochem. Physiol. 2:181–201

141. Jensen, D. 1963. Eptatretin: a potent cardioactive agent from the branchial heart of the Pacific hagfish Eptatretus stoutii. Comp. Biochem. Physiol. 10:129–51

142. Jensen, D. 1969. Intrinsic cardiac rate regulation in the sea lamprey, Petromyzon marinus and rainbow trout, Salmo gairdneri. Comp. Biochem. Physiol. 30:685–90

143. Jesse, M. J., Shub, C., Fishman, A. P. 1968. Lung and gill ventilation of the African lungfish. Resp. Physiol. 3:267, 287

144. Johansen, K. 1960. Circulation in the hagfish, Myxine glutinosa L. Biol. Bull. Mar. Biol. Lab. Woods Hole Mass. 118:289–95

145. Johansen, K. 1962. Cardiac output and pulsatile aortic flow in the teleost, Gadus morhua. Comp. Biochem. Physiol. 7:169–74

146. Johansen, K. 1963. The cardiovascular system of Myxine glutinosa. The Biology of Myxine, ed. A. Brodal, R. Fänge, 289–316. Oslo: Universitets Forlaget

147. Johansen, K. 1965. Cardiovascular dynamics in fishes, amphibians, and reptiles. Ann. N.Y. Acad. Sci. 127:414–42

148. Johansen, K. 1965. Dynamics of venous return in elosmobranch fishes. Hvalradets. Skr. No. 48:94–100

149. Johansen, K. 1966. Airbreathing in the teleost Symbranchus marmoratus. Comp. Biochem. Physiol. 18:383–95

150. Johansen, K. 1968. Airbreathing fishes. Sci. Am. 219:102–11

151. Johansen, K. 1970. Unpublished observations

152. Johansen, K. 1970. Airbreathing in fishes. In Physiology of Fishes IV, ed. W. S. Hoar, J. D. Randall. New York and London: Academic. In press

153. Johansen, K., Franklin, D. L., Van Citters, R. L. 1966. Aortic blood flow in free-swimming elasmobranchs. Comp. Biochem. Physiol. 19:151–60

154. Johansen, K., Hanson, D. 1967. Hepatic vein sphincters in elasmobranchs and their significance in controlling hepatic blood flow. J. Exp. Biol. 46:195–203

155. Johansen, K., Hanson, D. 1968. Functional anatomy of the hearts of lungfishes and amphibians. Am. Zool. 8:191–210

156. Johansen, K., Hol, R. 1960. A cineradiographic study of respiration in Myxine glutinosa L. J. Exp. Biol. 37:474–80

157. Johansen, K., Hol, R. 1968. A radiological study of the central circulation in the lungfish, Protopterus

aethiopicus. *J. Morphol.* 126 :333–48

158. Johansen, K., Krog, J., Reite, O. B. 1964. Autonomic nervous influence on the heart of the hypothermic hibernator. *Finn. Acad. Sci. A. IV :245–55*

159. Johansen, K., Lenfant, C., Hanson, D. 1968. Cardiovascular dynamics in the lungfishes. *Z. Vergl. Physiol.* 59 :157–86

160. Johansen, K., Hanson, D., Lenfant, C. 1970. Respiration in a primitive air breather, *Amia calva. Resp. Physiol.* 9 :162–74

161. Johansen, K., Lenfant, C., Hanson, D. 1970. Phylogenetic development of pulmonary circulation. *Fed. Proc.* 29 :1135–40

162. Johansen, K., Lenfant, C., Hanson, D. 1971. Gas exchange in the lamprey, *Entosphenus tridentatus.* In preparation

163. Johansen, K., Lenfant, C. 1967. Respiratory function in the South American lungfish. *J. Exp. Biol.* 46 :205–18

164. Johansen, K., Lenfant, C. 1968. Respiration in the African lungfish, *Protopterus aethiopicus.* II. Control of breathing. *J. Exp. Biol.* 49 :453–68

165. Johansen, K., Lenfant, C., Grigg, G. C. 1967. Respiratory control in the lungfish *Neoceratodus forsteri* (Krefft). *Comp. Biochem. Physiol.* 20 :835–54

166. Johansen, K., Lenfant, C., Schmidt-Nielsen, K., Petersen, J. A. 1968. Gas exchange and control of breathing in the electric eel, *Electrophorus electricus. Z. Vergl. Physiol.* 61 :137–63

167. Johansen, K., Martin, A. W. 1965. Comparative aspects of cardiovascular function in vertebrates. *Handbook of Physiology,* Sec. 2. *Circulation* 3 :2583–614, ed. W. F. Hamilton, Washington, D.C : Am. Physiol. Soc.

168. Johansen, K., Reite, O. B. 1967. Effects of acetylcholine and biogenic amines on pulmonary smooth muscle in the African lungfish, *Protopterus aethiopicus. Acta Physiol. Scand.* 74 :465–71

169. Johansen, K., Strahan, R. 1963. The respiratory system of *Myxine glutinosa. The Biology of Myxine Glutinosa,* 352–77. Oslo Univ. Press

170. Jones, D. R., Randall, D. J., Jarman, G. M. 1970. A graphical analysis of oxygen transfer in fish. *Resp. Physiol.*

171. Junqueira, L. C., Steen, J. B., Tinoce, R. M. 1967. The respiratory area of the fishes of teleosts from Rio Negro and Rio Branco area. Research Papers from the *Alpha Helix* Amazon Expedition, pp. B20–1

172. Keatinge, W. R. 1959. The effects of increased filling pressure on rhythmicity and atrioventricular conduction in isolated hearts. *J. Physiol. London* 149 :193–208

173. Kempton, R. T. 1969. Morphological features of functional significance in the gills of the spiny dogfish, *Squalus acanthias. Biol. Bull.* 136 : 226–40

174. Keys, A., Bateman, J. 1932. Branchial response to adrenaline and pitressin in the eel. *Biol. Bull.* 63 : 327–36

175. Kirby, S., Burnstock, G. 1969. Comparative pharmacological studies of isolated spiral strips of large arteries from lower vertebrates. *Comp. Biochem. Physiol.* 28 :307–9

176. Klika, E., Lelek, A. 1967. A contribution to the study of the lungs of the *Protopterus annectens* and *Polypterus senegalensis. Folia Morphol.* 15 :168–75

177. Krawkow, N. P. 1913. Über die Wirkung von Giften auf die Gefässe isolierten Fischkiemen. *Pfluegers Arch.* 151 :583–603

178. Kulaev, B. S. 1958. The nervous regulation of cardiac rhythm in fish. II. The vagus nerve of fish. An efferent path of double reflex influences on the cardiac rhythm. *Bull. Exp. Biol. Med. USSR* 45 : 398–402

179. Labat, R. 1966. *Electrocardiologie chez les poissons téléostéens influence de quelques facteurs écologiques.* Thésis. Univ. Toulouse

180. Labat, R., Raynaud, P., Serfaty, A. 1961. Réactions cardiaques et variations de masse sanguine chez les téléostéens. *Comp. Biochem. Physiol.* 4 :75–80

181. Lahiri, S., Szidon, J. P., Fishman, A. P. 1970. Potential respiratory and circulatory adjustments to hypoxia in the African lungfish. *Fed. Proc.* 29 :1141–48

182. Laurent, P. 1962. Contribution à l'étude morphologique et physiologique de l'innervation du coeur des téléostéens. *Arch. Anat. Microsc. Morphol. Exp.* 51:337–458

183. Laurent, P. 1967. Le pseudobranchie des Téléostéens: preuves éléctrophysiologique de ses fonctions, chemoréceptrice et baroréceptrice. *C.R. Acad. Sci.* 264:1879–82

184. Laurent, P., Rouseau, J. P. 1969. Actions de la PO_2 sur l'activité nerveuse afferente provenant de la pseudobranchie d'un Téléostéens. *J. Physiol. Paris* 61:145

185. Leivestad, H., Andersen, H. T., Scholander, P. F. 1957. Physiological response to air exposure in the codfish. *Science* 126:505

186. Lenfant, C., Johansen, K. 1966. Respiratory function in the elasmobranch *Squalus suckleyi. Resp. Physiol.* 1:13–29

187. Lenfant, C., Johansen, K. 1967. Respiratory adaptations in selected amphibians. *Resp. Physiol.* 2:247–60

188. Lenfant, C., Johansen, K. 1968. Respiration in the African lungfish. I. Respiratory properties of blood and normal patterns of breathing and gas exchange. *J. Exp. Biol.* 49:437–52

189. Lenfant, C., Johansen, K., Grigg, G. C. 1967. Respiratory properties of blood and pattern of gas exchange in the lungfish, *Neoceratodus forsteri* (Krefft). *Comp. Biochem. Physiol.* 20:835–54

190. Lenfant, C., Johansen, K., Hanson, D. 1970. Bimodal gas exchange and ventilation-perfusion relationship in lower vertebrates. *Fed. Proc.* 29:1124–29

191. Lutz, B. R. 1930. Reflex cardiac and respiratory inhibition in the elasmobranch *Scyllium canicula. Biol. Bull.* 59:170–78

192. Lutz, B. R. 1930. Respiratory rhythm in the elasmobranch, *Scyllium canicula. Biol. Bull.* 59:179–86

193. Lutz, B. R., Wyman, L. C. 1932. Reflex cardiac inhibition of branchio-vascular origin in the elasmobranch *Squalus acanthias. Biol. Bull.* 62:10–16

194. Maetz, J., Garcia Romeu, F. 1964. The mechanism of sodium and chloride uptake by the gills of a fresh water fish, *Carassius auratus.* II. Evidence for NH_4^+/Na^+ and HCO_3^-/Cl^- exchanges. *J. Gen. Physiol.* 47:1209–27

195. Manwell, C. 1960. Comparative Physiology: Blood pigments. *Ann. Rev. Physiol.* 22:191–244

196. March, H. W., Ross, J. K., Lower, R. R. 1962. Observations on the behavior of the right ventricular outflow tract, with reference to its developmental origins. *Am. J. Med.* 32:835–45

197. Marvin, D. E., Heath, A. G. 1968. Cardiac and respiratory responses to gradual hypoxia in three ecologically distinct species of freshwater fish. *Comp. Biochem. Physiol.* 27:349–55

198. McMahon, B. R. 1969. A functional analysis of the aquatic and aerial respiratory movements of an African lungfish, *Protopterus aethiopicus,* with reference to the evolution of the lung-ventilation mechanism in vertebrates. *J. Exp. Biol.* 51:407–30

199. McMahon, B. R. 1970. The relative efficiency of gaseous exchange across the lungs and gills of an African lungfish, *Protopterus aethiopicus. J. Exp. Biol.* 52:1–15

200. Metcalfe, J., Bartels, H., Moll, W. 1967. Gas exchange in the pregnant uterus. *Physiol. Rev.* 47:782–838

201. Milic-Emili, G., Petit, J. M. 1960. Mechanical efficiency of breathing. *J. Appl. Physiol.* 15:359–62

202. Millen, J. E., Murdaugh, H. V., Hearn, D. C., Robin, E. D. 1966. Measurement of gill water flow in *Squalus acanthias* using dye-dilution technique. *Am. J. Physiol.* 211:11–14

203. Mott, J. C. 1950. Radiological observations on the cardiovascular system in *Anguilla anguilla. J. Exp. Biol.* 27:324–33

204. Mott, J. C. 1951. Some factors affecting the blood circulation in the common eel (*Anguilla anguilla*). *J. Physiol. London* 114:387–98

205. Muir, B. S., Buckley, R. M. 1967. Gill ventilation in *Remora remora. Copeia* 1:581–86

206. Muir, B. S., Kendall, J. I. 1968. Structural modifications in the gills of tunas and some other oceanic fishes. *Copeia* 2:388–98

207. Muir, B. S., Hughes, G. M. 1969.

Gill dimensions for three species of tunny. *J. Exp. Biol.* 51:271–85

208. Munshi, J. S. D. 1961. The accessory respiratory organs of *Clarias batrachus* (Linn.). *J. Morphol.* 109: 115–40

209. Munshi, J. S. D. 1962. On the accessory respiratory organs of *Ophiocephalus punctatus.* (Bloch) and *Ophiocephalus striatus* (Bloch). *J. Linn. Soc. London Zool.* 44: 616–24

210. Munshi, J. S. D. 1968. The accessory respiratory organs of *Anabas testudineus* (Bloch) (Anabantidae, Pisces). *Proc. Linn. Soc. London* 179:107–26

211. Munz, F. W., Morris, R. W. 1965. Metabolic rate of the hagfish, *Eptatretus stoutii* (Lockinton) 1878. *Comp. Biochem. Physiol.* 16(1):1–6

212. Murdaugh, H. V., Robin, E. D., Millen, J. E., Drewery, W. I. 1965. Cardiac output determinations by the dye dilution method in *Squalus acanthias. Am. J. Physiol.* 209: 723–26

213. Murdaugh, H. V., Robin, E. D. 1967. Acid base metabolism in the dogfish shark. In *Sharks, skates and rays,* ed. P. W. Gilbert, R. F. Mathewson, D. P. Rall, 249–64. Baltimore: Johns Hopkins Univ. Press

214. Nakano, T., Tomlinson, N. 1967. Cathecolamine and carbohydrate concentrations in rainbow trout (*Salmo gairdneri*) in relation to physical disturbance. *J. Fish. Res. Bd. Can.* 24:1701–15

215. Nandi, J. 1962. The structure of the interrenal gland in teleost fishes. *Univ. Calif. Publ. Zool.* 65:129–212

216. Nawar, G. 1955. On the anatomy of *Clarias lazera.* III. The vascular system. *J. Morphol.* 97:179–214

217. Negus, V. E. 1963. The function of mucus. *Acta Oto-Laryngol.* 56: 204–14

218. Neill, W. T. 1950. An estivating bowfin. *Copeia,* 240

219. Newstead, J. D. 1965. Fine structure of respiratory lamellae of teleost gills. *Anat. Rec.* 15:393

220. Newstead, J. D. 1967. Fine structure of the respiratory lamellae of telestean gills. *Z. Zellforsch. Mikrosk. Anat.* 79:396–428

221. Oets, J. 1950. Electrocardiograms of fishes. *Physiol. Comp. Oecol.* 2: 181–86

222. Ogden, E. 1945. Respiratory flow in *Mustelus. Am. J. Physiol.* 145: 134–39

223. Østlund, E., Fange, R. 1962. Vasodilatation by adrenaline and noradrenaline and the effects of some other substances on perfused fish gills. *Comp. Biochem. Physiol.* 5: 307–8

224. Otis, L. S., Cerf, J. A., Thomas, G. J. 1957. Conditioned inhibition of respiration and heart rate in the goldfish. *Science* 126:263–64

225. Otorii, T. 1953. Pharmacology of the heart of *Entosphenus japonicus. Acta Med. Biol. Niigata* 1:51–59

226. Pasztor, V. M., Kleerekoper, H. 1962. The role of the gill filament musculature in teleosts. *Can. J. Zool.* 40:785–802

227. Piiper, J. 1965. Physiological equilibria of gas cavities in the body. *Handbook of Physiology.* Sec. 3. *Respiration* II:1205–18, ed. W. O. Fenn, H. Rahn. Washington, D.C: *Am. Physiol. Soc.*

228. Piiper, J., Schumann, D. 1967. Efficiency of oxygen exchange in the gills of the dogfish, *Scyliorhinus stellaris. Resp. Physiol.* 2: 135–48

229. Piiper, J., Baumgarten-Schumann, D. 1968. Transport of O_2 and CO_2 by water and blood in gas exchange of the dogfish (*Scyliorhinus stellaris*). *Resp. Physiol.* 5:326–37

230. Piiper, J., Baumgarten-Schumann, D. 1968. Effectiveness of O_2 and CO_2 exchange in the gills of the dogfish (*Scyliorhinus stellaris*). *Resp. Physiol.* 5:338–49

231. Piiper, J., Baumgarten, D. 1969. Blood lactate and acid-base balance in the elasmobranch *Scyliorhinus stellaris* after exhausting activity. *Pubbl. Sta. Zool. Napoli* 37:84–94

232. Plehn, M. 1901. Zum feineren Bau der Fischkeime. *Zool. Anz.* 24: 439–43

233. Pleschka, K., Albers, C., Spaich, P. 1970. Interaction between CO_2 transport and O_2 transport in the blood of the dogfish *Scyliorhinus canicula. Resp. Physiol.* 9:118–25

234. Powers, E. B., Clark, R. T. 1942. Control of normal breathing in fishes by receptors located in the regions of the gills, and innervated

by the IXth and Xth cranial nerves. *Am. J. Physiol.* 138 :104–7

235. Prosser, C. L., Precht, H., Jankowsky, H.-D. 1965. Nervous control of metabolism during temperature acclimation of fish. *Naturwissenschaften* 52 :168–69

236. Rahn, H. 1957. Gasometric method for measurement of tissue oxygen tension. *Fed. Proc.* 16 :685–88

237. Rahn, H. 1966. Gas transport from the external environment to the cell. *Development of the Lung. Ciba Found. Symp.,* 3–23

238. Rahn, H. 1966. Aquate gas exchange. Theory. *Resp. Physiol.* 1 :1–12

239. Ralph, R., Everson, J. 1968. The respiratory metabolism of some antarctic fish. *Comp. Biochem. Physiol.* 27 :299–307

240. Randall, D. J. 1966. The nervous control of cardiac activity in the tench (*Tinca tinca*) and the goldfish (*Carassius auratus*). *Physiol. Zool.* 39 :185–92

242. Randall, D. J. 1968. Functional morphology of the heart in fishes. *Am. Zool.* 8 :179–89

243. Randall, D. J. 1970. *Gas exchange in fishes. Physiology of Fishes.* ed. W. S. Hoar, J. D. Randall, Vol. 4 :253–92. New York & London : Academic. In press

244. Randall, D. J. 1970. *Circulation in fishes.* See Ref. 243, 133–72

245. Randall, D. J., Holeton, G. F., Stevens, E. D. 1967. The exchange of oxygen and carbon dioxide across the gills of rainbow trout. *J. Exp. Biol.* 46 :339–48

246. Randall, D. J., Shelton, G. 1963. The effects of changes in environmental gas concentrations on the breathing and heart rate of a teleost fish. *Comp. Biochem. Physiol.* 9 :229–39

247. Randall, D. J., Smith, J. C. 1967. The regulation of cardiac activity in fish in a hypoxic environment. *Physiol. Zool.* 40 :104–13

248. Randall, D. J., Smith, L. S., Brett, J. R. 1965. Dorsal aortic blood pressure recorded from rainbow trout (*Salmo gairdneri*). *Can. J. Zool.* 43 :863–77

249. Randall, D. J., Stevens, E. D. 1967. The role of adrenergic receptors in cardiovascular changes associated with exercise in salmon. *Comp. Biochem. Physiol.* 21 :415–24

250. Redfield, A. C. 1933. The evolution of the respiratory function of the blood. *Quart. Rev. Biol.* 8 :31–57

251. Reite, O. B. 1969. The evolution of vascular smooth muscle responses to histamine and 5-hydroxytryptamine. I. Occurrence of stimulatory actions in fish. *Acta Physiol. Scand.* 15 :221–39

252. Rhodin, J. A. G. 1964. Structure of the gills of the marine fish pollack (*Pollachius virens*). *Anat. Rec.* 148 :420

253. Richards, B. D., Fromm, P. O. 1969. Patterns of blood flow through filaments and lamellae of isolated-perfused rainbow trout (*Salmo gairdneri*) gills. *Comp. Biochem. Physiol.* 29 :1063–70

254. Riess, J. A. 1881. Der Bau der Keimenblätter bei den Knochenfischen. *Arch. Naturgesch.* 47 :518–50

255. Ripplinger, J. 1950. Le coeur des poissons. Son innervation extrinséque. Ses centres automatiques. *Ann. Sci. Univ. Besançon Zool. Physiol.* (2) 5 :45–57

256. Roberts, J. L. 1964. Metabolic responses of freshwater sunfish to seasonal photoperiods and temperatures. *Helgolaender Wiss. Meeresunters.* 9 :459–73

257. Roberts, J. L. 1966. Systemic versus cellular acclimation to temperature by poikilotherms. *Helgolaender Wiss. Meeresunters.* 14 :451–65

258. Roberts, T. D. M. 1950. The respiratory movements of the lamprey (*Lampetra fluiratilis*) *Proc. Roy. Soc. Edinburgh B* 64 :235–51

259. Robertson, O. H., Krupp, M. A., Thompson, N., Thomas, S. F., Hane, S. 1966. Blood pressure and heart weight in immature and spawning pacific salmon. *Am. J. Physiol.* 256 :957–64

260. Robin, E. D., Murdaugh, H. V. 1966. Quantitative aspects of vertebrate gas exchange. *Development of the Lung. Ciba Found. Symp.,* 85–98. London : Churchill

261. Robin, E. D., Murdaugh, H. V., Millen, J. E. 1966. Acid-base fluid and electrolyte metabolism in the elasmobranch. III. Oxygen, CO_2, bicarbonate, and lactate exchange across the gill. *J. Cell. Physiol.* 67 :93–100

262. Robin, E. D., Murdaugh, H. V. 1967. Gill gas exchange in the elasmo-

branch, *Squalus acanthias.* See Ref. 213, 221–47

263. Rodinov, I. M. 1959. The reflex regulation of the activity of the heart in fishes. I. Reflex action on the heart from stimulation of the afferent fibres of the mesentery and intestine. *Bull. Exp. Biol. Med. USSR* 47 :653–56

264. Root, R. W. 1931. The respiratory function of the blood of marine fishes. *Biol. Bull.* 61 :427–56

265. Satchell, G. H. 1959. Respiratory reflexes in the dogfish. *J. Exp. Biol.* 36 :62–71

266. Satchell, G. H. 1961. The response of the dogfish to anoxia. *J. Exp. Biol.* 38 :531–43

267. Satchell, G. H. 1962. Intrinsic vasomotion in the dogfish gill. *J. Exp. Biol.* 39 :503–12

268. Satchell, G. H. 1965. Blood flow through the caudal vein of elasmobranch fish. *Aust. J. Sci.* 27 : 240–41

269. Satchell, G. H. 1968. A neurological basis for the co-ordination of swimming with respiration in fish. *Comp. Biochem. Physiol.* 27 :835–41

270. Satchell, G. H. 1968. The genesis of certain cardiac arrhythmias in fish. *J. Exp. Biol.* 49 :129–41

271. Satchell, G. H. 1970. A functional appraisal of the fish heart. *Fed. Proc.* 29 :1120–23

272. Satchell, G. H. 1971. *Circulation in fishes.* Cambridge. In press

273. Satchell, G. H., Hanson, D., Johansen, K. 1970. Differential blood flow through the afferent branchial arteries of the skate, *Raja rhina. J. Exp. Biol.* 52 :721–76

274. Satchell, G. H., Jones, M. P. 1967. The function of the conus arteriosus in the Port Jackson shark, *Heterodontus portusjacksoni. J. Exp. Biol.* 46 :373–82

275. Satchell, G. H., Way, H. K. 1962. Pharyngeal proprioceptors in the dogfish *Squalus acanthias. J. Exp. Biol.* 39 :243–50

276. Saunders, R. L. 1961. The irrigation of the gills in fishes. I. Studies of the mechanism of branchial irrigation. *Can. J. Zool.* 39 :637–53

278. Saunders, R. L. 1962. The irrigation of gills in fishes. II. Efficiency of oxygen uptake in relation to respiratory flow, activity and concen-

trations of oxygen and carbon dioxide. *Can. J. Zool.* 40 :817–62

279. Saxena, B. B. 1963. A review on ecological studies and their importance in the physiology of air-breathing fishes. *Ichthyologica* 2 : 116–28

280. Scharrer, E., Smith, S. W., Palay, S. L. 1947. Chemical sense and taste in the fishes, *Prionotus* and *Trichogaster. J. Comp. Physiol.* 86 :183–98

281. Schoenlein, K., Willem, V. 1895. Beobachtungen über Blutkreislauf und Respiration bei einigen Fischen. *Z. Biol.* 32 :511–47

282. Scholander, P. F. 1958. Counter current exchange. A principle in Biology. *Hvalrådets Skr.* 44 :24

283. Scholander, P. F. 1964. *Handbook of Physiology. Adaptation to the environment,* 729. Washington, D.C : Am. Physiol. Soc.

284. Schulz, H. 1960. Die submikroskopische Morphologie des Kiemenepithels. *Proc. 4th Int. Conf. Electron Microsc.* 2 :421–26

285. Schulz, H. 1962. Some remarks on the submicroscopic anatomy and pathology of the blood-air pathways in the lung. *Pulmonary Structure and Function,* ed. A. V. S. deReuck, M. O'Connor, 205–14. London : Churchill

286. Schultze, D. 1965. Beiträge zur Temperatureadaption des Aales (*Anguilla vulgaris* L.). 2. *Z. Wiss. Zool.* 172 :104–33

287. Schumann, D., Piiper, J. 1966. Der Sauerstoffbedarf der Atmung bei Fischen nach Messungen an der narkotisierten Schleie (*Tinca tinca*). *Pfluegers Arch.* 288 :15–26

288. Serbenyuk, Ts. V. 1965. The importance of afferentation in the development of rhythmic activity of the respiratory centre in fish. *Essays on Physiological Evolution,* ed. J. W. S. Pringle, 262–71. Oxford : Pergamon

289. Serfaty, A., Raynaud, P. 1957. Reflex aerocardiaque chez la truite de rivière (*Salmo trutta* L.). *J. Physiol. Pathol. Gen.* 49 :378–81

290. Serfaty, A., Labat, R. 1961. Euryhalinité et frequence cardiaques chez les téléostéens. *Comp. Biochem. Physiol.* 3 :218–22

291. Shelton, G. 1959. The respiratory centre in the tench (*Tinca tinca*

L.). I. The effects of brain transection on respiration. *J. Exp. Biol.* 36 :191–202

292. Shelton, G. 1961. The respiratory centre in the tench (*Tinca Tinca*). II. Respiratory neuronal activity in the medulla oblongata. *J. Exp. Biol.* 38 :79–92

293. Shelton, G. 1970. The regulation of breathing. See Ref. 243, Vol. 4

294. Shepherd, D. M., West, G. B., Erspamer, V. 1953. Chromaffin bodies of various species of dogfish. *Nature* 112 :509

295. Smit, H. 1965. Some experiments on the oxygen consumption of goldfish (*Carassius Auratus* L.), in relation to swimming speed. *Can. J. Zool.* 43 :623–33

296. Smith, H. W. 1929. The composition of the body fluids of elasmobranchs. *J. Biol. Chem.* 81 :407–19

297. Smith, H. W. 1930. Metabolism of the lungfish, *Protopterus aethiopicus*. *J. Biol. Chem.* 88 :97–130

298. Smith, L. S., Bell, G. R. 1964. A technique for prolonged blood sampling in free swimming salmon. *J. Fish. Res. Bd. Can.* 21 :711–17

299. Smith, L. S., Brett, J. R., Davis, J. C. 1967. Cardiovascular dynamics in swimming adult Sockeye salmon. *J. Fish. Res. Bd. Can.* 24 : 1775–90

300. Spurway, H., Haldane, J. B. S. 1963. The regulation of breathing in a fish *Anabas testudineaus*. In *The Regulation of Human Respiration*, ed. D. J. C. Cunningham, B. B. Lloyd, 431–34. Oxford : Blackwell

301. Steen, J. B., Berg, T. 1966. The gills of two species of haemoglobin free fishes compared to those of other teleosts—with a note on severe anemia in an eel. *Comp. Biochem. Physiol.* 12 :127–42

302. Steen, J. B., Kruysse, A. 1964. The respiratory function of teleostean gills. *Comp. Biochem. Physiol.* 12 : 127–42

303. Steen, J. B. 1963. The physiology of the swimbladder in the eel, *Anguilla vulgaris*. III. The mechanism of gas secretion. *Acta Physiol. Scand.* 59 :221–41

304. Steen, J. B. 1970. The swimbladder as a hydrostatic Organ. In *Physiology of Fishes* IV, ed. W. H. Hoar, J. D. Randall. New York and London : Academic. In press

305. Stevens, E. D. 1968. The effect of exercise on the distribution of blood to various organs in rainbow trout. *Comp. Biochem. Physiol.* 25 : 615–2ʳ

306. Stevens, E. D. 1968. *Cardiovascular dynamics during swimming in Fish, particularly rainbow trout (Salmo gairdneri)*. PhD thesis. Univ. Brit. Columbia. 154 pp.

307. Stevens, E. D., Bennion. 1968. Unpublished observations

308. Stevens, E. D., Black, E. C. 1966. The effect of intermittent exercise on carbohydrate metabolism in rainbow trout, (*Salmo gairdneri*). *J. Fish. Res. Bd. Can.* 23 :471–85

309. Stevens, E. D., Randall, D. J. 1967. Changes in blood pressure, heart rate, and breathing rate during moderate swimming activity in rainbow trout. *J. Exp. Biol.* 46 : 307–15

310. Stevens, E. D., Randall, D. J. 1967. Changes in gas concentrations in blood and water during moderate swimming activity in rainbow trout. *J. Exp. Biol.* 46 :329–37

311. Strahan, R. 1958. The velum and the respiratory current of myxine. *Acta Zool.* 39 :227–40

312. Sudak, F. N. 1965. Some factors contributing to the development of subatmospheric pressure in the heart chambers and pericardial cavity of *Mustelus canis* (Mitchill). *Comp. Biochem. Physiol.* 15 :199–215

313. Sudak, F. N. 1965. Intrapericardial and intracardiac pressures and the events of the cardiac cycle in *Mustelus canis* (Mitchill). *Comp. Biochem. Physiol.* 14 :689–705

314. Sudak, F. N., Wilber, C. G. 1960. Cardiovascular responses to hemorrhage in the dogfish. *Biol. Bull.* 119 :342

315. Sutterlin, A. M. 1969. Effects of exercise on cardiac and ventilation frequency in three species of freshwater teleosts. *Physiol. Zool.* 42 : 36–52

316. Suzuki, N. 1969. Gill structure and its function on gas exchange in fresh water fishes. *Physiol. Ecol.* 15 :79–100

317. Taylor, M. G. 1964. Wave travel in arteries and the design of the cardiovascular system. *Pulsatile*

Blood Flow, ed. E. O. Attinger. New York: McGraw

318. Taylor, W., Houston, A. H., Horgan, J. D. 1968. Development of a computer model simulating some aspects of the cardiovascular-respiratory dynamics of the salmonid fish. *J. Exp. Biol.* 49:477–93

319. Tebecis, A. K. 1967. A study of electrograms recorded from the conus arteriosus of an elasmobranch heart. *Aust. J. Biol. Sci.* 20:843–46

320. Tenney, S. M., Remmers, J. E. 1966. Alveolar dimensions in the lungs of animals raised at high altitude. *J. Appl. Physiol.* 21:1328–30

321. Tenney, S. M., Tenney, J. B. 1970. Quantitative morphology of cold-blooded lungs: *Amphibia* and *Reptilia. Resp. Physiol.* 9:197–215

322. Tiitso, M. 1937. Chronotrope Wirkungen der Spannungsänderungen des rechten Vorhofes. *Pfluegers Arch.* 238:738

323. Todd, E. S., Ebeling, A. W. 1966. Aerial respiration in the longjaw mudsucker *Gillichtys mirabilis. Biol. Bull.* 130:265–88

324. Trois, E. F. 1883. Osservazioni sull' intima struttura delle branchie del *Xiphias gladius. Atti Ist. Sci. Venezia,* 1882–83 1:773–85

325. Van Liew, H. D. 1968. Oxygen and carbon dioxide tensions in tissue and blood of normal and acidotic rats. *J. Appl. Physiol.* 25:575–80

326. von Baumgarten, R., Salmoiraghi, G. C. 1962. Respiratory neurons in the goldfish. *Arch. Ital. Biol.* 100:31–47

327. von Wahlert, G. 1964. Passive respiration in sharks. *Naturwissen-schaften* 51:297

328. Willem, V. 1920. Observation sur la respiration des Amphibiens. *Bull. Cl. Sci. Acad. Roy. Belg.* 6:298–314

329. Willem, V. 1929. Les manoeuvres respiratoires chez les poissons et les amphibiens. *Bull. Cl. Sci. Acad. Roy. Belg.* 15:1–194

330. Willem, V. 1947. Les manoeuvres respiratoires chez les poissons teleosteens. *Bull. Mus. Roy. Hist. Natur. Belg.* 23:1–15

331. Willmer, E. N. 1934. Some observations on the respiration of certain tropical fresh water fish. *J. Exp. Biol.* 11:283–306

332. Wohlschlag, D. E. 1962. Antarctic fish growth and metabolic differences related to sex. *Ecology* 43:589–97

333. Woldring, S., Dirken, M. N. J. 1951. Unit activity in the medulla oblongata of fishes. *J. Exp. Biol.* 28:218–20

334. Woskoboinikoff, M. M. 1932. Der Apparat der Kiemenatmung bei den Fischen. *Zool. Jahrb.* (Abt. 2). 55:315–488

335. Yamauchi, A., Burnstock, G. 1968. An electron microscopic study on the innervation of the trout heart. *J. Comp. Neurol.* 132:567–88

336. Yazdani, G. M., Alexander, R. McN. 1967. Respiratory currents of flat-fish. *Nature* 213:96–97

337. Young, S. 1969. The activity of respiratory neurons in fish observed with chronically implanted electrodes. *J. Physiol. London* 200:85P

338. Young, J. Z. 1933. The autonomic nervous system of Selachians. *Quart. J. Microsc. Sci.* 75:571–624

SOME RELATED ARTICLES APPEARING IN OTHER *ANNUAL REVIEWS*

From the *Annual Review of Biochemistry,* Volume 40 (1971)

DeLange, Robert J., and Smith, Emil L. Histones: Structure and Function

Hess, G. P., and Rupley, John A. Structure and Function of Proteins

Holzer, Helmut, and Duntze, Wolfgang. Metabolic Regulation by Chemical Modification of Enzymes

Jost, Jean-Pierre, and Rickenberg, H. V. Cyclic AMP

Lucas-Lenard, Jean, and Lipmann, Fritz. Protein Biosynthesis

Molinoff, Perry B., and Axelrod, Julius. Biochemistry of Catecholamines

Shooter, E. M., and Einstein, Elizabeth Roboz. Proteins of the Nervous System

Stöffel, Wilhelm. Sphingolipids

Sussman, Arthur J., and Gilvarg, Charles. Peptide Transport and Metabolism in Bacteria

van Dam, Karel, and Meyer, Alfred J. Oxidation and Energy Conservation by Mitochondria

From the *Annual Review of Fluid Mechanics,* Volume 3 (1971)

Fung, Y. C., and Zweifach, B. W. Microcirculation: Mechanics of Blood Flow in Capillaries

Jaffrin, M. Y., and Shapiro, A. H. Peristaltic Pumping

Rivlin, R. S., and Sawyers, K. N. Nonlinear Continuum Mechanics of Viscoelastic Fluids

From the *Annual Review of Medicine,* Volume 22 (1971)

DePasquale, N. P., and Burch, G. E. Papillary Muscle Dysfunction in Coronary (Ischemic) Heart Disease

Dreizen, Paul. Structure and Function of the Myofibrillar Contractile Proteins

Gray, Gary M. Intestinal Digestion and Maldigestion of Dietary Carbohydrates

Mills, John A., and Cooperband, Sidney R. Lymphocyte Physiology

Rubenstein, Arthur H., and Steiner, Donald F. Proinsulin

From the *Annual Review of Pharmacology,* Volume 11 (1971)

Bassett, Arthur L., and Hoffman, Brian F. Antiarrythmic Drugs: Electrophysiological Actions

Hurwitz, Leon, and Suria, Amin. The Link Between Agonist Action and Response in Smooth Muscle

Izquierdo, Iván, and Izquierdo, Juan A. Effects of Drugs on Deep Brain Centers

Kellie, A. E. The Pharmacology of Estrogens

Landon, Erwin J., and Forte, Leonard R. Cellular Mechanisms in Renal Pharmacology

AUTHOR INDEX

615

SUBJECT INDEX

CUMULATIVE INDEXES

VOLUMES 29 - 33

INDEX OF CONTRIBUTING AUTHORS

INDEX OF CHAPTER TITLES

VOLUMES 29-33

COMPARATIVE PHYSIOLOGY